Vassar Coll.
Dept. of Mathematics

$\int f(x)\,dx$ — antiderivative of f

$\int_a^b f(x)\,dx = \int_a^b f$ — integral of f over interval $[a, b]$

$N_\delta(x_0)$ — δ-neighborhood of $x_0 = \{x \mid x_0 - \delta < x < x_0 + \delta\}$

$N_\delta^*(x_0)$ — deleted-δ neighborhood of x_0

$N_\delta^+(x_0)$ — right δ-neighborhood of $x_0 = \{x \mid x_0 < x < x_0 + \delta\}$

$N_\delta^-(x_0)$ — left δ-neighborhood of x_0

X' — set of cluster points of set X

$\bar{X}$ — closure of set X ($= X \cup X'$)

$\mathscr{I}(X)$ — interior of set X

$\mathscr{B}(X)$ — boundary of set X

$\mathbf{i}, \mathbf{j}, \mathbf{k}$ — unit vectors in direction of x, y, z-axes, respectively

$|\mathbf{v}|$ — length or magnitude of vector $\mathbf{v}$

$\mathbf{a} \cdot \mathbf{b}$ — inner (scalar) product of vectors $\mathbf{a}$ and $\mathbf{b}$

$\mathbf{a} \times \mathbf{b}$ — vector product of vectors $\mathbf{a}$ and $\mathbf{b}$

$\mathbf{T}$ — unit tangent vector

$\mathbf{N}$ — unit normal vector

$\mathbf{B}$ — unit binormal vector

$\nabla f(\mathbf{x}_0)$ — gradient vector of f at $\mathbf{x}_0$

$D_\mathbf{u} f(\mathbf{x}_0)$ — directional derivative of f in direction of vector $\mathbf{u}$ at point $\mathbf{x}_0$

Formulas From Elementary Geometry

Circle of radius r:
circumference $= 2\pi$
area $= \pi r^2$

Sphere of radius r:
surface area $= 4\pi r^2$
volume $= \dfrac{4\pi}{3} r^3$

Right Circular Cylinder, radius r, height h:
lateral (curved) area $= 2\pi rh$
total area $= 2\pi rh + 2\pi r^2$
volume $= \pi r^2 h$

Cone, radius r, height h:
lateral (curved) area $= \pi r \sqrt{r^2 + h^2}$
volume $= \dfrac{\pi}{3} r^2 h$

Calculus with **Analytic Geometry**

William K. Smith *New College, Sarasota, Florida*

Calculus

with **Analytic**

Geometry

THE MACMILLAN COMPANY

COLLIER-MACMILLAN LIMITED, LONDON

First Printing

Library of Congress catalog card number: 69–10293

THE MACMILLAN COMPANY
COLLIER-MACMILLAN CANADA, LTD., TORONTO, ONTARIO

Printed in the United States of America

TO JULIE

Preface

One of the major purposes of this book is a successful wedding of intuition and rigor. It is this aim which has largely dictated both the organization and point of view of the early chapters. Thus, the field and order properties of the real numbers are introduced in Chapter 1, but the Axiom of Continuity does not appear until the beginning of Chapter 3 when it can be made dramatically evident that an intuitively reasonable calculus *demands* this completeness property of the number system. Similarly, a careful discussion of limits is postponed until after both the derivative and integral have been studied intuitively, thereby exposing some of the real limitations imposed by lack of knowledge of limits. Even so, after this partial setting of the stage, the definition of limit of a function is introduced in a progressive fashion which serves to indicate why the more "obvious" formulations are, in fact, not satisfactory. In this way it is hoped that this most fundamental—and most difficult—of the concepts peculiar to calculus will be made more comprehensible to a larger proportion of students than is usually deemed possible.

A second aim is to encourage—indeed, to help *produce*—a gradual increase in the mathematical sophistication of the student. Toward this end, the writing in the early chapters makes relatively few demands on the reader, the main assumptions being a reasonable knowledge of algebra (the "college algebra" of a few years ago) and of elementary geometry. It is the intention, however, that with the increase in the page and chapter numbers there will also be an increase in the contribution made by the reader. Of course, if this rather elusive hope were perfectly realized the student would *notice* no increase in the level of difficulty; but this ideal would be very difficult to achieve.

A further objective of this work is a close $(2\varepsilon$, say) approximation to a true integration of analytic geometry with calculus. Thus in Chapter 1 only the most fundamental ideas of analytic geometry are introduced; subsequently, calculus techniques are used in the study of geometry and, conversely, many of the early applications of the calculus concepts are to geometric problems.

  With regard to analytic geometry, it should be noted that the conic section curves are defined and studied first in terms of polar coordinates and then translated to rectangular coordinates for further study.

  It would perhaps be foolhardy to claim for a beginning calculus text that the proof of every theorem is included—and we make no such claim. However, an unusually large number of proofs are included, either in the usual way in the body of the text, or by means of fairly complete outlines in the exercises. This latter device enables the instructor to omit the proof completely, or to assign the appropriate exercise or series of exercises to everyone, or to make such an assignment only to the better students as an honors challenge. The major exception to the claim about the inclusion of proofs is for some of the theorems on multiple integrals in Chapter 14. On the other hand, the theoretical discussion of the integral (in Chapter 9) is exceptionally complete and detailed.

  It would be highly desirable from the instructor's point of view if a calculus course could begin with calculus itself—with, in other words, Chapter 2. In even a small class, unfortunately, there is often a wide range of mathematical backgrounds and usually some attention must be paid to pre-calculus material. It is hoped that the different topics of Chapter 1 will satisfy such demands. It is fairly clear that a wide range of choices is available between—and including— the two extremes of taking up *all* of Chapter 1, or of omitting it entirely. The only mild warning necessary about this latter alternative concerns the aforementioned treatment of the real number field and the fact that the definition of a function is *not* in terms of a set of ordered pairs.

  It is our intention that much of the beginning discussion of limits in Chapter 3 —certainly at least the first third of that chapter—be comprehensible to the student without benefit of or need for the instructor. Thus, it has been my practice in teaching from preliminary versions of the manuscript, to assign the reading of Chapter 3 during the time the class discussion is focused on Chapter 2. Such assignment can appropriately be made after the section on theorems for calculating derivatives has been studied in class.

  Similarly, the first section of Chapter 6 *should* be largely in the nature of review. It is included for this purpose and also, in part, to establish a common basis for the study of the calculus properties of the trigonometric functions. Consequently, it may be possible largely to omit this section or (as I have usually done) to assign it to be read, without class discussion, prior to taking up in class the remainder of Chapter 6.

  It should be pointed out that, if time or the tastes of the instructor so dictate, the material on hyperbolic functions (Sections 7.5 and 7.6) can easily be omitted.

  Also, if the orientation and level of difficulty of the course suggest it, some of the theoretical discussion of the integral (in Sections 9.1 and 9.2) can be omitted.

  Along these same lines, it should be mentioned that the study of infinite series could, if one so desires, quite appropriately be moved forward. In particular, it would be suitable to take up this chapter any time after the study of the transcendental functions (Chapters 6 and 7).

Any work of this sort is shaped by a large number of people: one's teachers, one's colleagues, and—a group often overlooked, but in my case certainly as influential as those already mentioned—one's students over the years. In particular, I owe a large word of thanks to my recent New College students who have been obliging and responsive guinea pigs—and characteristically critical.

In addition, several reviewers of early versions of the manuscript made a large number of valuable suggestions which have been incorporated in subsequent revisions.

It is a pleasure, too, to acknowledge the considerable help and unbounded cooperative spirit of Macmillan editors HARRY R. CONN and A. H. McLEOD.

I am also indebted to New College for assistance in a number of ways during the periods of writing and revising the manuscript.

Sarasota, Florida   W. K. S.

Contents

Chapter **3** Limits and Continuity

Chapter **4** Basic Theory of Differential Calculus

Chapter **5** Applications of the Derivative

Chapter **6** Trigonometric Functions

Chapter 7 The Logarithm and Exponential Functions

Chapter 8 Techniques of Integration

Chapter 9 The Integral, Theory and Developments

Chapter 10 Polar Coordinates and Conic Sections

Chapter 11 Vectors and Parametric Equations

Chapter 12   Geometry and Vectors in Three Space

Chapter 13   Partial Derivatives

Chapter 14   Multiple Integration

Contents

Chapter 15 Taylor's Theorem, Sequences, and Series

Chapter 16 Differential Equations

Chapter 1 Fundamental Notions: Sets, Numbers, Functions, and Graphs

1.1 Introduction

There are some considerations which suggest that a study of calculus should begin with a derivative, or possibly a definite integral. The temptation to "get right on with it" is very strong, but it must be resisted, as must be the temptation to jump into deep water before one can swim. After all, both derivatives and integrals involve functions and are concerned with numbers; therefore it is wise for us to have a clear understanding of the meaning of function, and of the properties of the particular system of numbers with which we shall be working. Further, we shall see that derivatives and integrals are both dependent upon the rather deep concept of limit of a function—dependent to such an extent that no real comprehension of calculus is possible without a corresponding comprehension of limits.

These arguments suggest, then, that one should postpone the questions, "What is a derivative?" and "What is an integral?", until a careful study has been made of all the necessary foundational ideas: numbers, functions, and limits. Logically, there is absolutely no quibbling with this plan. But, pedagogically, it does have some drawbacks. First, the curiosity of the student should not be ignored: if he is supposed to be studying calculus, how long must be wait before he gets into ideas which are peculiar to calculus? Second, some of the important facts about limits simply do not have much point or meaning when limits are studied in the abstract, whereas these same facts make very good sense when they are associated with a derivative.

We shall, therefore, attempt a compromise. Since one cannot build on nothing, we lay the essential foundations in this chapter: the field and order properties of

1

the real-number system; definition and preliminary discussion of functions; and elementary analytic geometry, including graphs of functions in general and the linear function in particular. In Chapter 2 an attempt will be made to develop some of the ideas of calculus in terms of the equipment provided in this chapter. This can be, of necessity, only very partially successful, but along with the introduction of the nature of derivative and integral and the suggestion of some of their applications, we can quite clearly emphasize the need to lay a deeper foundation than that provided in Chapter 1. It will be the purpose of Chapter 3 to provide these further fundamental concepts: the axiom of continuity for the real numbers, and definitions and theorems of limits and continuity.

1.2 Sets

Our first aim in this chapter is to study the essential properties of the real-number system (to be denoted, throughout this work, by the symbol **R**) upon which calculus is based. It will be convenient, however, to introduce first a few of the notations of set theory, and this we do in the present section.

We shall define a set intuitively as a collection of objects, usually called elements. Sets may be described in different ways: (i) If the number of elements is not too large, one can simply list the elements; for example,

$$A = \{1, 2, 3, 4\}, \quad \text{or} \quad B = \{a, b, c, d, e\}.$$

(ii) When listing is impracticable, a set may be defined by a property which characterizes the elements of the set; this is achieved by the following notational device:

$$C = \{x \in \mathbf{R} \mid 0 < x < 1\}.$$

The verbalization of the preceding equation is "C equals the set of *all* x in **R** satisfying the condition that (or, such that) x is greater than 0 and less than 1." This set is also known as the *open* interval—end points excluded—between 0 and 1, and will sometimes be indicated by $C = (0, 1)$. Some writers prefer to use a colon where we have used the vertical bar. Thus, they would describe a set as

$$D = \{x \in \mathbf{R} : 0 \le x \le 1\},$$

verbalized as "D equals the set of *all* x in **R** such that x is greater than or equal to 0 and less than or equal to 1." This set is the *closed*—end points included—interval between 0 and 1 and is also symbolized as $D = [0, 1]$.

To indicate that x is an element of a set X we write $x \in X$. Thus, in the preceding examples

$$2 \in A, \quad d \in B, \quad 0 \in D.$$

Note that 0 is not in C; we describe this by $0 \notin C$.

Different verbal descriptions may characterize the same set of elements (x is the father of our country, or x was the first president of the United States); thus

$$\{x \in \mathbf{R} \mid x^2 > 1\} \quad \text{and} \quad \{x \in \mathbf{R} \mid \text{ either } \quad x < -1 \quad \text{ or } \quad x > 1\}$$

will be seen to determine the same set.

In general, equality of sets is defined in terms of elements, not the verbal description. To say that two sets A and B are equal means that they contain precisely the same elements. This can be described more succinctly by using "$\Rightarrow$" to mean "implies" and "$\Leftrightarrow$" to mean "implies and is implied by," or "necessary and sufficient condition for," or "if and only if," or "is logically equivalent to":

$$A = B \Leftrightarrow \begin{cases} \text{(i)} & x \in A \Rightarrow x \in B, \quad \text{and} \\ \text{(ii)} & y \in B \Rightarrow y \in A. \end{cases}$$

If we know only that condition (i) holds, that is, if $x \in A \Rightarrow x \in B$, then we say that A is a *subset* of B, symbolized as $A \subset B$. Notice that always $A \subset A$. If it should happen that $A \subset B$, but $A \neq B$, i.e., there is an element in B which is not in A, then A is said to be a *proper subset* of B. In the examples given earlier C is a proper subset of D, since $x \in C \Rightarrow x \in D$ and $0 \in D$, but $0 \notin C$; similarly $1 \in D$, but $1 \notin C$.

Equality of sets can thus be described in terms of the subset relation:

$$A = B \Leftrightarrow \begin{cases} \text{(i)} & A \subset B, \quad \text{and} \\ \text{(ii)} & B \subset A. \end{cases}$$

This provides an important and useful way of proving that two sets are equal: show that each is a subset of the other.

In addition to the two *relations* ($=$ and $\subset$) between sets, there are several *operations* which will be useful to us.

1. The *union* of the sets A and B is the set of all elements in either A or B:

$$A \cup B = \{x \mid x \in A \quad \text{or} \quad x \in B\}.$$

2. The *intersection* of the sets A and B is the set of all elements in both A and B:

$$A \cap B = \{x \mid x \in A \quad \text{and} \quad x \in B\}.$$

3. The *cartesian product* of the sets A and B is the set of all ordered pairs consisting of first element from A and second element from B:

$$A \times B = \{(a, b) \mid a \in A \quad \text{and} \quad b \in B\}.$$

In order not to have to make exceptions, we define the *empty set* $\varnothing$ to be the set with no elements. In this way if two sets A and B have no elements in common (i.e., they are *disjoint*) we have $A \cap B = \varnothing$, a *set*.

Thus, if

$$A = \{1, 2, 3, 4\}, \qquad B = \{3, 4, 5\}, \qquad C = \{a, b\},$$

then

$$A \cup B = \{1, 2, 3, 4, 5\},$$
$$A \cap B = \{3, 4,\}$$
$$A \cup C = \{1, 2, 3, 4, a, b\},$$

$A \cap C = \emptyset$,

$A \times C = \{(1, a), (1, b), (2, a), (2, b), (3, a), (3, b), (4, a), (4, b)\}$,

$C \times C = \{(a, a), (a, b), (b, a), (b, b)\}$.

As will be shown in the following exercises, the binary operations $\cup$ and $\cap$ are associative (and commutative). It is possible, therefore to generalize them unambiguously. Now, a different look at the definition of union discloses that an element is in the union of A and B precisely if it is in at least one of A and B. Then, if we have a collection of sets $A_1, A_2, \ldots, A_n$, we define

$$\bigcup_{i=1}^{n} A_i = \{x \mid x \text{ is in at least one of } A_1, \ldots, A_n\}.$$

Similarly,

$$\bigcap_{i=1}^{n} A_i = \{x \mid x \text{ is in every one of } A_1, \ldots, A_n\}.$$

The fact is that both of these definitions can be extended, in a natural way, to nonfinite collections of sets.

The cartesian product, also defined as a binary operation, is neither commutative nor, in the strictest sense, associative. Nevertheless, it also lends itself to generalization. If $A_1, A_2, \ldots, A_n$ are sets, then

$$A_1 \times A_2 \times \cdots \times A_n = \{(a_1, a_2, \ldots, a_n) \mid a_i \in A_i\},$$

where $(a_1, a_2, \ldots, a_n)$ stands for an ordered n-tuple.

EXERCISES

1. Let $A = \{1, 2, 3, 4\}$, $B = \{3, 4, 5, 6, 7\}$, $C = \{1, 3, 5, 7, 8\}$. Find:

(a) $A \cup B$.
(b) $A \cup C$.
(c) $B \cup C$.
(d) $A \cap B$.
(e) $A \cap C$.
(f) $B \cap C$.

(g) $(A \cup B) \cup C$.
(h) $A \cap (B \cap C)$.
(i) $A \cap (B \cup C)$.
(j) $(A \cap B) \cup (A \cap C)$.
(k) $A \cup (B \cap C)$.
(l) $(A \cup B) \cap (A \cup C)$.

2. Let $A = \{x \mid 0 < x < 2\}$, $B = \{x \mid 1 < x < 5\}$, $C = \{x \mid 4 \leq x \leq 10\}$, where x stands for a real number. Find:

(a) $A \cup B$.
(b) $A \cup C$.
(c) $B \cup C$.
(d) $A \cap B$.

(e) $A \cap C$.
(f) $B \cap C$.
(g) $A \cup B \cup C$.
(h) $A \cap B \cap C$.

3. Let $A = \{x \in \mathbf{R} \mid 3 < x < 5\}$, $B = \{x \in \mathbf{R} \mid 3.5 < x < 4.5\}$, $C = \{x \in \mathbf{R} \mid 3.9 < x < 4.1\}$, $D = \{x \in \mathbf{R} \mid 3.99 < x < 4.01\}$, and $E = \{x \in \mathbf{R} \mid 3.999 < x < 4.001\}$. $\mathbf{R}$ means the set of real numbers. Find:

(a) $A \cap B$.   (b) $C \cap E$.   (c) $B \cap C \cap D$.
(d) $A \cup C \cup E$.   (e) $A \cap B \cap C \cap D \cap E$.

4. Identify differently each of the following sets. In every case $x \in \mathbf{R}$, i.e., x stands for a real number.

   (a) $A = \{x \mid x^2 = 4\}$.
   (b) $B = \{x \mid x = \sqrt{4}\}$.
      (Answer $B = \{2\}$)
   (c) $C = \{x \mid x = x\}$.
   (d) $D = \{x \mid (x-3)(x+7)(x-11) = 0\}$.

   (e) $E = \{x \mid x = \sqrt{-7}\}$.
   (Answer $E = \varnothing$)
   (f) $F = \{x \mid x = x^2\}$.
   (g) $G = \{x \mid 2x + 3 = 15\}$.
   (h) $H = \{x \mid x \neq x\}$.

5. Refer to the sets in Exercise 1. Verify that

   (a) $(A \cap B) \subset A$. (b) $(A \cap B) \subset B$. (c) $A \subset (A \cup B)$.
   (d) $B \subset (A \cup B)$. (e) $A \cap B = B \cap A$.

6. Same as Exercise 5, only use the sets in Exercise 2.

7. Let $A = (1, 3) = \{x \mid 1 < x < 3\}$, $B = [3, 5] = \{x \mid 3 \leq x \leq 5\}$, and $C = (5, 6) = \{x \mid 5 < x < 6\}$.

   (a) Find $A \cup B$. What symbol might be used for this kind of interval?

   (b) Find $B \cup C$. Suggest a symbol. (Answer $[3, 6)$.)

   (c) Find $A \cap B$.

8. (a) If $A \subset B$, what can be said about $A \cap B$? About $A \cup B$?

   (b) If $A \cap B = A$, what can be said about A and B?

   (c) If $A \cup B = B$, what can be said about A and B?

9. If $A \cup B = A \cup C$, does $B = C$? Find an example to support your answer.

10. If $A \cap B = A \cap C$, does $B = C$? Find an example to support your answer.

11. (a) What can be said about $A \cup (B \cup C)$ and $(A \cup B) \cup C$?

    (b) Is $A \cup B \cup C$ meaningful?

12. We consider $\{2\}$ and 2. (A set with one element is called a *singleton*.)

    (a) Is $2 \in \{2\}$?
    (b) Is $2 \subset \{2\}$?
    (c) Is $\{2\} \in 2$?
    (d) Is $2 = \{2\}$?
    (e) Is $\{2\} \subset 2$?
    (f) Is $\{2\} \subset \{2\}$?

13. If A and B are intervals in $\mathbf{R}$, is $A \cap B$ an interval? What about $A \cup B$? (One way to handle this question is to consider the various possible cases. (Also, examine Exercises 3 and 7.)

14. Let B be any set. Prove that $\varnothing \subset B$. [*Hint.* Suppose $\varnothing$ is not a subset of B. Use the definition of the relation $A \subset B$ and find a contradiction.]

15. Let $A = \{1, 2\}$, $B = \{x, y, z\}$, then

(a) Find $A \times B$.

(b) Find $B \times A$. Does $A \times B = B \times A$?

(c) Find $A \times A$ and $B \times B$.

(d) Suppose A has five elements and B has seven elements. How many elements are there in $A \times B$? In $B \times A$?

(e) Let A be as above. Find $A \times \varnothing$.

(f) Suppose $A \times B = \varnothing$. What can be said about A and B?

(g) Let $\mathbf{R}$ = the set of real numbers. What is the geometric interpretation of $\mathbf{R} \times \mathbf{R}$? Notice that

$$\mathbf{R} \times \mathbf{R} = \{(x, y) \mid x \in \mathbf{R}, y \in \mathbf{R}\}.$$

1.3   Fields

In this section we consider some of the basic algebraic properties of the real number system $\mathbf{R}$. Much of this material may be familiar to the reader, but what may not be clearly known is the logical relationships among these properties. Perhaps the healthiest (and, to be sure, most difficult) attitude for the student to assume is that of complete ignorance—to attempt, in other words, to see this material as new mathematics. This suggestion does not apply to those already familiar with fields.

We first mention explicitly the properties with which we want the relation of "equality" to be endowed. In general, the letters a, b, c, ..., of the first three axioms below can represent any mathematical objects (e.g., the sets in Section 1.2), but our immediate interpretation of them will be as numbers.

Assertion 1. *The relation of equality* ($=$) *between elements of a set will have the following properties:*

$$E_1. \quad a = a \text{ (reflexive)}$$
$$E_2. \quad a = b \Rightarrow b = a \text{ (symmetric)}$$
$$E_3. \quad \left.\begin{array}{c} a = b \\ b = c \end{array}\right\} \Rightarrow a = c \text{ (transitive)}.$$

If the set has defined on it operations of addition and multiplication, we further assume

$$E_4. \quad \left.\begin{array}{c} a = b \\ c = d \end{array}\right\} \Rightarrow \left\{\begin{array}{c} a + c = b + d \\ ac = bd. \end{array}\right.$$

A few remarks are in order about these familiar properties. Frequently, students forget that an equal sign can be read in both directions, as E_2 guarantees.

For example, if asked what $\sin 2x$ equals, they may be able to reply quickly $2 \sin x \cos x$; but if the question is turned around, it may go unanswered. Axiom E_3 can, by means of mathematical induction (see Section 1.5), be extended to an arbitrary (finite) number of elements. These axioms enable one to deduce the principle of substitution, whereby either one of two equal elements may be substituted for the other. Finally, we observe that the axioms do not define equality. Usually in mathematics equality is understood to mean strict identity.

In working with a set of numbers we like to be assured that we will be able to carry out the usual arithmetic operations. One set of assumptions which is minimal for most of elementary algebra is the set given in Definition 1. These guarantee, for example, the possibility of solving linear equations.

Definition 1. *A field F is a set of at least two elements with two operations, addition and multiplication, satisfying the following properties (in these axioms a, b, and c stand for arbitrary elements of F):*

A_1	$a + b \in F$	*(closure)*	M_1	$ab \in F$
A_2	$a + b = b + a$	*(commutativity)*	M_2	$ab = ba$
A_3	$a + (b + c) = (a + b) + c$	*(associativity)*	M_3	$a(bc) = (ab)c$
A_4	*there exists* $0 \in F$ *such that*	*(identity)*	M_4	*there exists* $1 \in F$,
	$a + 0 = a$, *all* $a \in F$			$1 \neq 0$, *such that*
				$a \cdot 1 = a$, *all* $a \in F$
A_5	*for every* $a \in F$ *there exists*	*(inverse)*	M_5	*for every* $a \in F$,
	$-a \in F$ *such that* $a + (-a)$			$a \neq 0$ *there exists*
	$= 0$			$a^{-1} \in F$ *such that*
				$a \cdot a^{-1} = 1$

$$D. \quad a(b + c) = ab = ac \quad \text{(distributivity)}.$$

Notice that Axiom D is the only axiom which involves both addition and multiplication. Notice also that four of the axioms use the phrase "there exists"; because this is a widely used phrase in mathematics, it is convenient to have a special symbol for it. The standard one is $\exists$: there exist(s). Similarly, the phrase "for every," or "for all," occurs very often and is conveniently symbolized by $\forall$. With these symbols we can write A_5 as

$$A_5. \quad \forall a \in F \Rightarrow \exists (-a) \in F \quad \text{such that} \quad a + (-a) = 0.$$

In verbalizing this, it is useful to read "$\Rightarrow$" as "it is true that."

Many of the familiar properties of elementary algebra are consequences of Definition 1. As illustrations we state a few and prove fewer, leaving others for exercises.

Theorem 1. (Cancellation Law for Addition).

$$a + c = b + c \Rightarrow a = b.$$

Proof.

$a + c = b + c$	(Hypothesis)
$\exists (-c)$	(A_5)
$-c = -c$	(E_1)
$(a + c) + (-c) = (b + c) + (-c)$	(E_4)
$a + (c + (-c)) = b + (c + (-c))$	(A_3)
$a + 0 = b + 0$	(A_5)
$a = b.$	(A_4) ∎

Theorem 2. (*Cancellation Law for Multiplication*).

$$\left.\begin{array}{r} ac = bc \\ c \neq 0 \end{array}\right\} \Rightarrow a = b.$$

Theorem 3. (*Uniqueness of the Additive Inverse*). The additive inverse $(-a)$ is unique.

Proof. Suppose $\exists b \in F$ such that

$$a + b = 0.$$

Since, by A_5,

$$a + (-a) = 0,$$

E_2 and E_3 enable us to write $a + b = a + (-a)$, which A_2 allows us to change to $b + a = (-a) + a$, from which, by Theorem 1, we conclude that $b = -a$. ∎

Theorem 4. (*Uniqueness of the Multiplicative Inverse*). The multiplicative inverse a^{-1} is unique.

Theorem 5. $\forall a \in F \Rightarrow a \cdot 0 = 0.$

Proof. Let $a \in F$ be arbitrary. Then

$a + 0 = a$	(A_4)
$= a \cdot 1$	(M_4)
$= a(1 + 0)$	(A_4)
$= a \cdot 1 + a \cdot 0$	(D)
$= a + a \cdot 0$	(M_4)

Thus, by E_2 and A_2,

$$a \cdot 0 + a = 0 + a,$$

whence, by Theorem 1, $a \cdot 0 = 0$. ∎

The next theorem is the basis for an important equation-solving technique (see Exercise 10).

Theorem 6. $ab = 0 \Rightarrow$ *either* $a = 0$, *or* $b = 0$, *or both.*

Proof. Suppose $ab = 0$ and $b \neq 0$. We show $a = 0$. Since $b \neq 0$, by M_5, b^{-1} exists, and by E_1,

$$b^{-1} = b^{-1}.$$

Then

$$
\begin{aligned}
(ab)b^{-1} &= 0 \cdot b^{-1} &&(\text{E}_4) \\
a(bb^{-1}) &= 0 &&(\text{M}_3, \text{M}_2, \text{ and Theorem 5}) \\
a \cdot 1 &= 0 &&(\text{M}_5) \\
a &= 0 &&(\text{M}_3). \quad \blacksquare
\end{aligned}
$$

We remark that subtraction and division, except by 0, are always possible in a field. To see this we *define*

$$b - a = b + (-a)$$

and

$$b \div a = b/a = b\left(\frac{1}{a}\right) = b(a^{-1}).$$

Then Axioms A_5 and M_5 guarantee that $b - a$ and b/a always exist, provided that $a \neq 0$ in the case of b/a.

To support our earlier assertion that much of elementary algebra is a consequence of the field axioms, we state the following omnibus theorem.

Theorem 7. *The field axioms imply the following for a, b, c, d arbitrary elements of F:*

1. $(-a)b = -(ab)$
2. $a(-b) = -(ab)$
3. $(-a)(-b) = ab$
4. $-(-a) = a$
5. $-a = (-1)a$
6. $-(b + c) = (-b) + (-c)$
7. $a - (-b) = a + b$
8. $a - (b + c) = a + (-b) + (-c)$
9. $a - (b - c) = a + (-b) + c$
10. $a(b - c) = ab - ac$
11. $a = b \Rightarrow a - c = b - c$
12. $1/(1/a) = a$
13. $(a/c) \pm (b/c) = (a \pm b)/c$
14. $\left.\begin{array}{l} a = b \\ c \neq 0 \end{array}\right\} \Rightarrow a/c = b/c$
15. $a(b/c) = (ab)/c$
16. $(1/c)(1/d) = 1/(cd) \quad (cd \neq 0)$
17. $(ac)/(bc) = a/b \quad (bc \neq 0)$
18. $(a/b)(c/d) = (ac)/(bd)$
19. $(a/b)/(c/d) = (a/b) \cdot (d/c) = (ad)/(bc)$
20. $a/b = c/d \Leftrightarrow ad = bc \quad (bd \neq 0)$
21. $(a/b) \pm (c/d) = (ad \pm bc)/bd$
22. $(-a)/b = -(a/b) = a/(-b)$
23. $(-a)/(-b) = a/b$
24. $(a/b)/c = a/bc$.

Proof. It would be pointless to take time to prove all parts of this theorem. We give proofs of a few.

2. The assertion is that $a(-b)$ is the *unique* additive inverse of ab. We prove this by showing that $a(-b) + ab = 0$. Thus

$$
\begin{aligned}
a(-b) + ab &= a((-b) + b) &&(\text{D}) \\
&= a(0) &&(\text{A}_2 \text{ and A}_5) \\
&= 0. &&(\text{Theorem 5}).
\end{aligned}
$$

It follows that $a(-b) = -(ab)$.

10. We use the definition of $b - c$ as $b + (-c)$. Then

$$
\begin{aligned}
a(b - c) &= a(b + (-c)) \\
&= ab + a(-c) &&\text{(D)} \\
&= ab + (-ac) &&\text{(part 2 of this theorem)} \\
&= ab - ac &&\text{(def. of } b - c).
\end{aligned}
$$

16. Before proving this result we use E_2 and M_2 to write it in a different way:

$$(cd)^{-1} = d^{-1}c^{-1}$$

Verbally, this says that $d^{-1}c^{-1}$ is the unique multiplicative inverse of cd. We can prove this by showing that $(cd)(d^{-1}c^{-1}) = 1$. But

$$
\begin{aligned}
(cd)(d^{-1}c^{-1}) &= c(d\,d^{-1})c^{-1} &&(M_3) \\
&= c(1)c^{-1} &&(M_5) \\
&= c\,c^{-1} &&(M_4) \\
&= 1 &&(M_5).
\end{aligned}
$$

17. This result, simple as it is, is one of the most useful in algebra. It should be known in its verbal form: the numerator and denominator of a fraction can be multiplied by the same nonzero quantity without changing the value of the fraction. Here is the proof:

$$
\begin{aligned}
(ac)/(bc) &= (ac)\cdot(1/bc) = (ac)(bc)^{-1} &&\text{(def. of } m/n). \\
&= (ac)(c^{-1}b^{-1}) &&\text{(part 16)} \\
&= a(c\,c^{-1})b^{-1} &&(M_3) \\
&= a\cdot 1 \cdot b^{-1} &&(M_5) \\
&= a\,b^{-1} &&(M_4) \\
&= a/b &&\text{(def. of } a/b).
\end{aligned}
$$

We suggest that the reader work out proofs for a few more of the parts of this theorem. ∎

EXERCISES

1. Prove Theorem 2.

2. Prove Theorem 4.

3. Prove that the additive identity is unique. [*Hint.* Suppose $\exists x \in F$ such that $a + x = a$, all $a \in F$. Let $a = 0$; also axiom A_4 says that $0 + 0 = 0$. Use Theorem 1.]

4. Prove that the multiplicative identity is unique.

5. Prove parts 1, 3, 4, 6, 8, 13, 18, 20, and 21 of Theorem 7.

6. Find all solutions x of $a + x = b$.

7. Assuming $a \neq 0$, find all solutions x of $ax = b$.

8. Suppose $a = 0$.

   (a) Find all solutions x of $0 \cdot x = 0$.

   (b) Find all solutions x of $0 \cdot x = b$, where $b \neq 0$.

9. Discuss the implications of Exercise 8 with regard to division by 0.

10. (a) Apply Theorem 6 to the solution of $x^2 - 3x + 2 = 0$. [*Hint.* Since $x^2 - 3x$ $+ 2 = (x - 1)(x - 2)$, $x^2 - 3x + 2 = 0 \Rightarrow (x - 1)(x - 2) = 0 \Rightarrow x - 1 = 0$ or $x - 2 = 0$. Why?]

    (b) What is wrong with the following similar approach?
    To solve

    $$x^2 - x - 1 = 0,$$

    write

    $$x^2 - x = 1,$$

    or

    $$x(x - 1) = 1 \Rightarrow x = 1 \quad \text{or} \quad x - 1 = 1 \Rightarrow x = 1 \quad \text{or} \quad x = 2.$$

1.4 Ordered Fields

For several reasons the field axioms alone do not characterize the real numbers. For one thing, the axioms of Definition 1 do not give any basis for comparing the size of numbers: for being able to say that 1 is less than 2. The essential fact is that **R** is an ordered field, in the following sense.

Definition 2. *A field F is **ordered** $\Leftrightarrow$ there is a relation $<$ defined on F satisfying the following axioms:*

O_1. *For arbitrary $a, b \in F$ exactly one of the following holds:*

$$\left.\begin{array}{c} a < b \\ a = b \\ b < a \end{array}\right\} \quad \text{(law of the trichotomy)}$$

O_2. *For $a, b, c \in F$,*

$$\left.\begin{array}{c} a < b \\ b < c \end{array}\right\} \Rightarrow a < c \quad \text{(transitivity)}$$

O_3. *For $a, b, c \in F$,*

$$a < b \Rightarrow a + c < b + c.$$

O_4. *For $a, b \in F$,*

$$\left.\begin{array}{c} 0 < a \\ 0 < b \end{array}\right\} \Rightarrow 0 < ab.$$

Note: the symbol $\Leftrightarrow$ used in Definition 2 should be interpreted as "means by definition," or "is defined to mean." This is not a standard notation; some writers use "iff," an abbreviation for "if and only if," and some use "$\leftrightarrow$". We prefer to reserve "$\leftrightarrow$" for use in theorems, and yet we would like to emphasize the symmetry of the preceding statement, the possibility of using the definition in either direction. Both $\leftrightarrow$ and $\Leftrightarrow$ can be verbalized as "is logically equivalent to," but we use the latter to indicate that this equivalence is by fiat of definition.

The inequality symbol $<$ is usually verbalized as "is less than"; thus $a < b$ is read "a is less than b." If $a < b$ we might also write $b > a$ ("b is greater than a"). Also, $a \leq b$ is used to mean either $a < b$ or $a = b$; similarly, $b \geq a$ means either $b > a$ or $b = a$. If $a > 0$, we say a is *positive*; if $b < 0$, then b is *negative*.

Note that Axioms O_3 and O_4 of Definition 2 specify how $<$ is related to the operations of $+$ and $\cdot$, respectively.

We collect in the following theorem the essential facts about the order relation.

Theorem 8. *Let a, b, c, d, be elements of an ordered field F. Then the following are true.*

1. $a > 0 \Rightarrow -a < 0$.

2. $a < 0 \Rightarrow -a > 0$.

3. $1 > 0, -1 < 0$.

4. $\left.\begin{array}{l} a < b \\ c < d \end{array}\right\} \Rightarrow a + c < b + d.$

5. $\left.\begin{array}{l} a < b \\ c > 0 \end{array}\right\} \Rightarrow ac < bc.$

6. $\left.\begin{array}{l} a < b \\ c < 0 \end{array}\right\} \Rightarrow ac > bc.$

7. $a > 0 \Rightarrow \dfrac{1}{a} > 0.$

8. $a < 0 \Rightarrow \dfrac{1}{a} < 0.$

9. $a \neq 0 \Rightarrow a^2 > 0.$

Before turning to the proof, we remark that 5 and 6 together give the multiplicative analog of Axiom O_3. Also, if in 4, $c = 0$, then the effect is to make the big side bigger, leaving the small side unchanged. Or, if we take $d = 0$, the effect will be to make the small side smaller and leave the big side unchanged. Thus 4 provides a justification for either of these modifications in an inequality.

Proof. We give a few of the proofs, leaving the others as exercises.

2. If $a < 0$, then, by O_2, $a + (-a) < 0 + (-a)$, or $0 < -a$. The proof of 1 is similar.

3. First we note that $1 \neq 0$, by M_4 of Definition 1. Thus, by O_1, the law of the trichotomy, either $1 > 0$ or $1 < 0$. Suppose $1 < 0$. Then, by part 2 of this theorem, $-1 > 0$, and, by O_4,

$$\left.\begin{array}{l} -1 > 0 \\ -1 > 0 \end{array}\right\} \Rightarrow (-1)(-1) > 0.$$

But $(-1)(-1) = 1$. Thus, assuming $1 < 0$ leads to the contradictory statement $1 > 0$. The only remaining possibility is that $1 > 0$. By part 1 of this theorem, then $-1 < 0$.

4. By hypothesis and O_3,

$$a < b \Rightarrow a + c < b + c;$$

similarly,

$$c < d \Rightarrow c + b < d + b.$$

Now transitivity (O_2) leads to $a + c < b + d$.

5. First we note that by Exercise 3, $a < b \Rightarrow b - a > 0$. Then, using O_4 and the hypothesis that $c > 0$, we have

$$c(b - a) > 0, \qquad \text{or} \quad bc - ac > 0,$$

or, using Exercise 3 again, $ac < bc$.

7. Let $a > 0$ and suppose $\dfrac{1}{a} < 0$; then by 2 of this theorem, $-\dfrac{1}{a} > 0$. Now we use O_4:

$$-1 = a\left(-\frac{1}{a}\right) > 0,$$

which contradicts 3 of this theorem. It follows that $\dfrac{1}{a} > 0$.

9. If $a > 0$, then $a^2 = a \cdot a > 0$, by O_4. If $a < 0$, then $-a > 0$ and $a^2 = (-a)(-a) > 0$, again by O_4. ∎

We now assert that the field **R** of real numbers is an ordered field and has, therefore, all the properties of Theorem 8. For **R** we shall designate the set of positive numbers by $\mathbf{R}^+$ (and the set of negative numbers by $\mathbf{R}^-$).

It is frequently a matter of great importance to be able to solve an inequality which contains a letter representing an unspecified number. The result of solving will be a set of numbers, each of which makes the inequality statement valid when it is substituted throughout for the unknown. This set is called the *solution set*; it is understood that it will contain *all* the numbers which are solutions. We illustrate the process of solving inequalities with a few examples.

Example 1. Solve for x:

$$2x + 1 < 4 - x.$$

If we add $x - 1$ to both sides, we get

$$3x < 3.$$

Now multiplying both sides by $\frac{1}{3}$ (why is this possible?) we get

$$x < 1.$$

Strictly speaking, we are not finished. What we have done might be looked on as an exploratory process, the result of which suggests that $\{x \in \mathbf{R} \mid x < 1\}$ is the solution set. The correct completion of the process involves reversing the steps:

$$x < 1 \Rightarrow 3x < 3 \Rightarrow 2x + 1 < 4 - x.$$

A perhaps more sophisticated description of the two parts of this solution is that the first part, ending with $x < 1$, provides us with a *necessary condition* for elements to be in the solution set S—if x is a solution, *then $x < 1$*. In symbols, this means

$$S \subset \{x \in \mathbf{R} \mid x < 1\}.$$

Then the second part, the reversal of the steps, amounts to showing that this necessary condition is in fact a *sufficient condition*—if $x < 1$, *then x is a solution*, or

$$\{x \in \mathbf{R} \mid x < 1\} \subset S.$$

Together, then, the two parts show that

$$S = \{x \in \mathbf{R} \mid x < 1\}.$$

Customarily, however, it is the practice to do the first part and *then check that the steps used are reversible*.

Example 2. We find the solution set S for

$$x^2 < 4.$$

We have

$$x^2 < 4 \Rightarrow x^2 - 4 < 0 \Rightarrow (x + 2)(x - 2) < 0 \Rightarrow (x + 2)(x - 2) \in \mathbf{R}^-.$$

Now (see Exercise 5) the product of two numbers is in $\mathbf{R}^-$ exactly when one of the numbers is in $\mathbf{R}^+$ and the other is in $\mathbf{R}^-$. Thus, the last statement leads to either

$$\begin{cases} x + 2 < 0 \Rightarrow x < -2 \\ \text{and} \\ x - 2 > 0 \Rightarrow x > 2, \end{cases}$$

conditions which are incompatible (why?), or

$$\left. \begin{cases} x + 2 > 0 \Rightarrow x > -2 \\ \text{and} \\ x - 2 < 0 \Rightarrow x < 2 \end{cases} \right\} \Rightarrow -2 < x < 2.$$

Reversing the steps, then, gives

$$S = \{x \in \mathbf{R} \mid -2 < x < 2\}.$$

Example 3. We find S for $x^2 > 9$. We have

$$x^2 > 9 \Rightarrow x^2 - 9 > 0 \Rightarrow (x + 3)(x - 3) > 0.$$

Now the product of two numbers is positive if either both are positive or both are negative. The first of these leads to

$$\left.\begin{array}{c} x+3>0 \Rightarrow x>-3 \\ \text{and} \qquad \text{and} \\ x-3>0 \Rightarrow x>3 \end{array}\right\} \Rightarrow x>3$$

(the last $\Rightarrow$ follows from the fact that $3>-3$); whereas the second leads to

$$\left.\begin{array}{c} x+3<0 \Rightarrow x<-3 \\ \text{and} \qquad \text{and} \\ x-3<0 \Rightarrow x<3 \end{array}\right\} \Rightarrow x<-3.$$

since $-3<3$. Thus (you reverse the steps)

$$S=\{x \in \mathbf{R} \mid x<-3\} \cup \{x \in \mathbf{R} \mid x>3\}.$$

Example 4. We use a technique like that used in Example 1 to find S for $x^2+6<5x$. We have

$$x^2+6<5x \Rightarrow x^2-5x+6<0 \Rightarrow (x-2)(x-3)<0.$$

One of the two alternatives for this last statement is

$$x-2<0 \Rightarrow x<2$$
$$\text{and} \qquad \text{and}$$
$$x-3>0 \Rightarrow x>3.$$

But $x<2$ and $2<3 \Rightarrow x<3$, so these two conditions are incompatible. The other alternative is

$$\left.\begin{array}{c} x-2>0 \Rightarrow x>2 \\ \text{and} \qquad \text{and} \\ x-3<0 \Rightarrow x<3 \end{array}\right\} \Rightarrow 2<x<3.$$

Thus $S=\{x \mid 2<x<3\}$.

It is worth noting that not every field is ordered. For example, the *complex numbers*, the field which includes the number i with the property that $i^2=-1$, is not ordered. For, the defining property of i, just given, contradicts parts 9 and 3 of Theorem 8. As the assertions of Theorem 8 must hold for every ordered field, the field of complex numbers is not ordered.

There exist fields with only a finite number of elements, and these too are not ordered, by the following assertion.

Theorem 9. *Every ordered field has infinitely many elements.*

Proof. This will be an informal proof. We know, by item 3 of Theorem 8, that $0 < 1$. Now we use Axiom O_3—many times:

$$0 < 1 \overset{O_3}{\Rightarrow} 0 + 1 < 1 + 1, \quad \text{or} \quad 1 < 2;$$

$$1 < 2 \overset{O_3}{\Rightarrow} 1 + 1 < 2 + 1, \quad \text{or} \quad 2 < 3;$$

$$2 < 3 \overset{O_3}{\Rightarrow} 2 + 1 < 3 + 1, \quad \text{or} \quad 3 < 4;$$

$$\cdot \quad \cdot \quad \cdot$$

Continuing in this way we generate the set $\{1, 2, 3, \ldots\}$. By O_3, O_2, and O_1, no two numbers in the set can be equal. As the process can be continued indefinitely, there will be infinitely many numbers in the set, and hence in the field. ∎

Focusing attention on the ordered field **R**, we can say that the sets described formally below are all subsets of **R**.

Definition 3.

(a) *The set* **N** *of* **natural numbers**, *or* **positive integers**, *is the set generated in the proof of Theorem* 9:

$$\mathbf{N} = \{1, 2, 3, \ldots\}.$$

(b) *The set* **Z** *of* **all integers** *is the set*

$$\mathbf{Z} = (-\mathbf{N}) \cup \{0\} \cup \mathbf{N},$$

where $(-\mathbf{N}) = \{m \mid -m \in \mathbf{N}\}$ *is the set of* **negative integers**. *Thus*

$$\mathbf{Z} = \{\ldots, -3, -2, -1, 0, 1, 2, 3, \ldots\}.$$

(c) *The set* **Q** *of* **rational numbers** *is described by*

$$\mathbf{Q} = \left\{ \frac{m}{n} \,\middle|\, m \in \mathbf{Z}, n \in \mathbf{N} \right\}.$$

The name *rational numbers*, applied to **Q**, arises simply from the description of the numbers in **Q** as ratios of integers.

The fact is that **Q** is itself an ordered field (and, of course, $\mathbf{Q} \subset \mathbf{R}$). Now the only number properties we have introduced thus far are the field axioms of Definition 1 and the order axioms of Definition 2. Both **Q** and **R** satisfy these axioms and we have not indicated wherein **Q** and **R** differ. The prior mathematical experience of the reader should have provided him with the knowledge that **R** contains numbers (e.g., $\sqrt{2}$ and π) which are not in **Q**. This is indeed the case, and for the time being it is our intention to let the matter rest there. We shall return to the subject in Chapter 3 when we can meaningfully bring forward the axiom that distinguishes the field **R** from **Q** (and, in fact, from all other ordered fields). In the meantime we ask that the reader keep in mind the field and order axioms which help to describe the system **R**.

EXERCISES

1. Find the solution set S for each of the following:

(a) $3x - 2 < 10 - x$.

(b) $1 - x < 3x - 7$.

(c) $x^2 - 3x < 0$.

(d) $x^2 - 3x > 0$.

(e) $\dfrac{x-2}{x+4} > 0$. [*Hint.* Both numerator and denominator must be positive or both must be negative.]

(f) $x^2 - 10 < 3x$.

(g) $x^2 + 9x > -18$.

(h) $\dfrac{x}{x-1} < 0$.

(i) $(x-1)(x-2)(x-3) > 0$.

(j) $x^2 + x + 1 > 0$. [*Hint.*
$x^2 + x + 1 = (x^2 + x + \tfrac{1}{4}) + \tfrac{3}{4}$.]

(k) $2x^2 - 3 < x^2 - 5$.

(l) $\dfrac{x+3}{x-5} < 0$.

(m) $x^2 - x < 6$.

(n) $x^2 + 6x > -8$.

(o) $x^2 + 1 > x$.

(p) $x^2 + 2x + 2 < 0$.

(q) $x^2 + 5x > -7$.

(r) $x^3 > 1$.

2. Prove parts 1, 6, and 8 of Theorem 8.

3. Prove that in an ordered field $a < b \Leftrightarrow b - a > 0$.

4. This refers to the proof of Theorem 9. Show explicitly how axioms O_3, O_2, and O_1 imply the statement that "no two numbers in the set can be equal."

5. Let $a, b \in \mathbf{R}$. Prove

(a) $ab \in \mathbf{R}^+ \Leftrightarrow a \in \mathbf{R}^+$ and $b \in \mathbf{R}^+$, or $-a \in \mathbf{R}^+$ and $-b \in \mathbf{R}^+$.

(b) $ab \in \mathbf{R}^- \Leftrightarrow a \in \mathbf{R}^+$ and $b \in \mathbf{R}^-$, or $a \in \mathbf{R}^-$ and $b \in \mathbf{R}^+$.

6. Let $a, x \in F$, where F is an ordered field; further, suppose that $a > 0$. Prove

(a) $x^2 < a^2 \Leftrightarrow -a < x < a$.

(b) $x^2 > a^2 \Leftrightarrow x > a$ or $x < -a$.

7. Let F be an ordered field, let $a > 0$. Prove

(a) $a < 1 \Rightarrow a^2 < a$.

(b) $a > 1 \Rightarrow a^2 > a$.

8. Prove the following assertion:

$$0 \le h \le a \Rightarrow |\sqrt{a \pm h} - \sqrt{a}| \le \sqrt{h}.$$

9. Prove the following (Exercise 3 may be of help):

(a) $0 < a < b \Rightarrow \dfrac{1}{a} > \dfrac{1}{b} > 0$.

(b) $a < b < 0 \Rightarrow \dfrac{1}{b} < \dfrac{1}{a} < 0$.

10. In this exercise we give the skeleton of Euclid's proof that $\sqrt{2} \notin \mathbf{Q}$, i.e., that $\sqrt{2}$ is not expressible as the ratio of two integers. The exercise consists in providing the reasons for the implications. The argument is a contrapositive one. Thus we begin by assuming that there do exist integers p and q such that $p/q = \sqrt{2}$. We further assume that the fraction p/q is in lowest terms, i.e., that p and q have no common factors. Now let us see where these assumptions lead us.

$$\frac{p}{q} = \sqrt{2} \Rightarrow p^2 = 2q^2$$
$$\Rightarrow p^2 \text{ even} \quad (\text{why?})$$
$$\Rightarrow p \text{ even} \quad (\text{why?})$$
$$\Rightarrow p = 2r \quad (\text{why?})$$
$$\Rightarrow p^2 = 4r^2$$
$$\Rightarrow 4r^2 = 2q^2$$
$$\Rightarrow q^2 = 2r^2 \quad (\text{why?})$$
$$\Rightarrow q^2 \text{ even}$$
$$\Rightarrow q \text{ even} \quad (\text{why?})$$
$$\Rightarrow \text{a contradiction. What?}$$

Therefore, $\sqrt{2} \notin \mathbf{Q}$.

1.5   The Natural Numbers N and Mathematical Induction

In this section we focus attention on the subset $\mathbf{N}$ of the field $\mathbf{R}$, where $\mathbf{N}$ is the infinite set discussed in the preceding section,

$$\mathbf{N} = \{1, 2, 3, \ldots\}.$$

We could spend considerable time on the study of questions associated with $\mathbf{N}$—the branch of mathematics known as the theory of numbers is devoted largely to problems and theory involving numbers in $\mathbf{N}$—but that would take us too far off our path.

Our present purposes will be served by recalling how the set $\mathbf{N}$ was generated (in Section 1.4). We begin with the multiplicative identity 1, shown by part 3 of Theorem 8 to be in $\mathbf{R}^+$. It then follows from the order axioms that $2 = 1 + 1 > 1$, $3 = 1 + 2 > 2, \ldots$; in general, if n represents any number obtainable in this way, $n + 1 > n$. We then defined $\mathbf{N} \subset \mathbf{R}^+$ to be the set of all numbers generated by this process and showed that $\mathbf{N}$ is infinite; in particular, since $\mathbf{R}$ is ordered the process will continue to produce numbers different from those previously obtained.

It follows from this discussion of the way in which $\mathbf{N}$ is generated (i.e., $1 \in \mathbf{N}$ and $n \in \mathbf{N} \Rightarrow n + 1 \in \mathbf{N}$) that $\mathbf{N}$ possesses the following property.

Theorem 10. (*The Induction Principle*). *Let S be a subset of $\mathbf{N}$ with the following two properties:* (i) $1 \in S$, *and* (ii) $n \in S \Rightarrow n + 1 \in S$. *Then $S = \mathbf{N}$. In symbols,*

$$\left. \begin{array}{l} S \subset \mathbf{N} \\ \text{(i)} \quad 1 \in S \\ \text{(ii)} \quad n \in S \Rightarrow n + 1 \in S \end{array} \right\} \Rightarrow S = \mathbf{N}.$$

The very informal discussion preceding the statement of Theorem 10 does not constitute a proof of that theorem; the purpose of that discussion was to make the assertion of the theorem reasonable. For a formal definition of **N** and proof of Theorem 10, see Exercise 11.

Notice that properties (i) and (ii) of the hypothesis of Theorem 10 are clearly necessary conditions for a subset S to equal **N**. The force of the theorem is that it guarantees that these conditions, obviously necessary, are in fact sufficient.

The great utility of the induction principle rests with the observation that many important theorems in mathematics assert that some identity or relation is valid for all $n \in$ **N**. The proofs of such theorems can then be easily obtained by an application of Theorem 10 in the following way: let S be the subset of **N** for which the identity or relation is valid, and then show that S has the properties (i) and (ii) of Theorem 10. It follows then that $S =$ **N**, i.e., the identity or relation is valid for all $n \in$ **N**. We proceed to illustrate this technique of *proof by mathematical induction*.

Theorem 11. *The identity*

$$1 + 2 + 3 + \cdots + n = \tfrac{1}{2}n(n + 1) \tag{1}$$

*holds for all $n \in$ **N**.*

Proof. Before beginning the proof we remark that the sum $1 + 2 + \cdots + n$ can, and frequently will, be symbolized by using the Greek upper case sigma as follows:

$$\sum_{k=1}^{n} k = 1 + 2 + \cdots + n.$$

Similarly,

$$\sum_{k=1}^{n} k^2 = 1^2 + 2^2 + \cdots + n^2.$$

For the proof itself we let

$$S = \{n \in \mathbf{N} \,|\, \text{Eq. (1) is valid for } n\}.$$

Then we observe that S has property (i) of Theorem 10, since both sides of Eq. (1) reduce to the number 1 if $n = 1$. To show that S has property (ii) of Theorem 10 we assume that $n \in S$, i.e., that (1) holds for n, and show that it holds for $n + 1$, which is to say $n + 1 \in S$. Consider

$$\sum_{k=1}^{n+1} k = 1 + 2 + \cdots + n + (n + 1)$$

$$= \tfrac{1}{2}n(n + 1) + (n + 1) \qquad (\text{since } n \in S)$$

$$= \tfrac{1}{2}(n + 1)(n + 2)$$

$$= \tfrac{1}{2}(n + 1)(\overline{n + 1} + 1).$$

Thus S has property (ii), and so $S =$ **N**. ∎

There are several other theorems, related to Theorem 11, which we now give.

Theorem 12. *The identity*

$$\sum_{k=1}^{n} k^2 = 1^2 + 2^2 + \cdots + n^2 = \frac{n(n+1)(2n+1)}{6}$$

holds for all $n \in \mathbf{N}$.

The proof will be left as an exercise.

Theorem 13. *The identity*

$$\sum_{k=1}^{n} k^3 = \left[\frac{n(n+1)}{2}\right]^2 \qquad (2)$$

holds for all $n \in \mathbf{N}$.

Proof. Let $S = \{n \in \mathbf{N} \mid$ Eq. (2) holds for $n\}$. If we set $n = 1$, both sides of Eq. (2) reduce to 1, so S has property (i) of Theorem 10, i.e., $1 \in S$. To show that S has property (ii) of Theorem 10, we consider an $n \in S$ and show that $n + 1 \in S$. We look at

$$\sum_{k=1}^{n+1} k^3 = \underline{1^3 + 2^3 + \cdots + n^3} + (n+1)^3$$

$$= \left[\frac{n(n+1)}{2}\right]^2 + (n+1)^3 \qquad \text{(since } n \in S\text{)}$$

$$= \frac{(n+1)^2}{4}\left[n^2 + 4(n+1)\right]$$

$$= \frac{(n+1)^2}{4}(n+2)^2$$

$$= \left[\frac{(n+1)(\overline{n+1}+1)}{2}\right]^2.$$

Thus $n + 1 \in S$, S has property (ii) of Theorem 10, and so $S = \mathbf{N}$. ∎

Theorem 14. *The identity*

$$\sum_{k=1}^{n}(2k-1) = 1 + 3 + \cdots + (2n-1) = n^2 \qquad (3)$$

holds for all $n \in \mathbf{N}$.

Proof. Let $S = \{n \in \mathbf{N} \mid$ Eq. (3) is valid for $n\}$. Then it is easy to see that $1 \in S$, so S has property (i) of Theorem 10. Now suppose $n \in S$ and consider the sum of the first $n + 1$ odd integers:

$$\sum_{k=1}^{n+1}(2k-1) = \underline{1+3+\cdots+(2n-1)} + (2n+1)$$

$$= \underline{n^2} + (2n+1) \qquad \text{(since } n \in S)$$

$$= n^2 + 2n + 1$$

$$= (n+1)^2.$$

But this shows that $n + 1 \in S$; thus S, having properties (i) and (ii) of Theorem 10, is in fact equal to **N**. ∎

Occasionally one encounters a theorem of the same type as the preceding except that the smallest meaningful value of n is larger than 1. The same kind of proof can be used, with obvious modification, as we shall now illustrate.

Theorem 15. *Let $x > -1$, $x \neq 0$; then the inequality*

$$(1+x)^n > 1 + nx \tag{4}$$

holds for $n = 2, 3, 4, \ldots$, i.e., for $n \in \mathbf{N} - \{1\}$.

Proof. We let

$$S = \{n \in \mathbf{N} \mid n > 1 \quad \text{and (4) is valid for } n\}.$$

Our first step now will be to show that $2 \in S$. To this end consider

$$(1+x)^2 = 1 + 2x + x^2$$

$$> 1 + 2x,$$

since $x \neq 0 \Rightarrow x^2 > 0$. This last inequality is simply Eq. (4) with $n = 2$, so $2 \in S$. We next suppose we have an $n \in S$:

$$(1+x)^n > 1 + nx.$$

We now multiply both sides of this inequality by the positive number $1 + x$, thus preserving the inequality:

$$(1+x)^{n+1} > (1+nx)(1+x) = 1 + nx + x + nx^2,$$

or

$$(1+x)^{n+1} > 1 + (n+1)x + nx^2,$$

or

$$(1+x)^{n+1} > 1 + (n+1)x, \qquad \text{since} \quad nx^2 > 0.$$

We have shown that $n \in S \Rightarrow n + 1 \in S$. Thus $S = \{2, 3, 4, \ldots\}$. ∎

For our final illustration of proof by mathematical induction, we plan to prove the binomial theorem. In order, however, to do this we need a few preliminary results. The first concerns a few properties of the sigma notation for summation.

Lemma 1. *Let $S(i)$ and $T(i)$ be formulas such that for every $i \in \mathbf{N}$ $S(i)$ and $T(i)$ are numbers. Then*

$$\text{(i)}\quad \sum_{i=1}^{n}[S(i) + T(i)] = \sum_{i=1}^{n}S(i) + \sum_{i=1}^{n}T(i)$$

$$\text{(ii)}\quad \sum_{i=1}^{n}cS(i) = c\sum_{i=1}^{n}S(i), \qquad c \in \mathbf{R}.$$

$$\text{(iii)}\quad \sum_{i=1}^{n}c = nc.$$

Proof. The proofs of these three properties are quite simple; we look at (i):

$$\sum_{i=1}^{n}[S(i) + T(i)] = [S(1) + T(1)] + [S(2) + T(2)] + \cdots + [S(n) + T(n)]$$

$$= [S(1) + S(2) + \cdots + S(n)] + [T(1) + T(2) + \cdots T(n)]$$

$$= \sum_{i=1}^{n}S(i) + \sum_{i=1}^{n}T(i).$$

The proofs of (ii) and (iii) are similar and will be omitted. ∎

Still in pursuit of the binomial theorem, we give two more definitions:

Definition 4.
$$n! = 1 \cdot 2 \cdot \cdots \cdot n, \qquad \forall n \in \mathbf{N},$$
$$0! = 1.$$

The number $n!$ is called n factorial.

As an indication of why the possibly unexpected definition of 0! appears as it does, note that in general $n! = n(n-1)!$ Now try this relation with $n = 1$.

Definition 5. *For $n \in \mathbf{N}$ and for $k = 0, 1, \ldots, n$,*

$$\binom{n}{k} = \frac{n(n-1)\cdots(n-k+1)}{1 \cdot 2 \cdot 3 \cdot \cdots \cdot k} = \frac{n!}{k!(n-k)!}.$$

The numbers $\binom{n}{k}$, called the *binomial coefficients*, can be interpreted as the number of ways of selecting k things from n things. Note that for all n, $\binom{n}{0} = \binom{n}{n} = 1$; in particular, $\binom{n+1}{n+1} = \binom{n}{n} = 1$.

Lemma 2. *The binomial coefficients satisfy the following identities:*

$$\text{(i)}\quad \binom{n}{n-k} = \binom{n}{k}$$

$$\text{(ii)}\quad \binom{n}{k} + \binom{n}{k-1} = \binom{n+1}{k}.$$

Proof. We leave the proof of (i) as an exercise. For (ii) we use Definition 5:

$$\binom{n}{k} + \binom{n}{k-1} = \frac{n!}{k!(n-k)!} + \frac{n!}{(k-1)!(n-k+1)!}$$

$$= \frac{n!}{(k-1)!(n-k)!}\left[\frac{1}{k} + \frac{1}{n-k+1}\right]$$

$$= \frac{n!}{(k-1)!(n-k)!}\,\frac{n-k+1+k}{k(n+1-k)}$$

$$= \frac{(n+1)!}{k!(n+1-k)!}$$

$$= \binom{n+1}{k}. \quad \blacksquare$$

Theorem 16. (*Binomial Theorem*). *For every $n \in$ N and every a, $b \in$ R,*

$$(a+b)^n = \sum_{k=0}^{n} \binom{n}{k} a^{n-k} b^k. \tag{5}$$

Proof. As with other proofs which use mathematical induction, we let

$$S = \{n \in \text{N} \mid \text{Eq. (5) holds for } n\}.$$

To show that $1 \in S$ we look at the right side of Eq. (5) with $n = 1$:

$$\sum_{k=0}^{1} \binom{1}{k} a^{1-k} b^k = \binom{1}{0} a^1 b^0 + \binom{1}{1} a^0 b$$

$$= a + b,$$

since $\binom{1}{0} = \binom{1}{1} = a^0 = b^0 = 1$. Thus Eq. (5) holds for $n = 1$, i.e., $1 \in S$.

Next we consider an $n \in S$; this means

$$(a+b)^n = \sum_{k=0}^{n} \binom{n}{k} a^{n-k} b^k.$$

To show $n + 1 \in S$ we multiply both sides by $a + b$:

$$(a+b)^{n+1} = (a+b)\left(\sum_{k=0}^{n} \binom{n}{k} a^{n-k} b^k\right)$$

$$= \sum_{k=0}^{n} \binom{n}{k} a^{n+1-k} b^k + \sum_{k=0}^{n} \binom{n}{k} a^{n-k} b^{k+1}.$$

In the second term on the right we replace $k + 1$ by j; this means $k = j - 1$.

Thus

$$(a+b)^{n+1} = \sum_{k=0}^{n}\binom{n}{k}a^{n+1-k}b^k + \sum_{j=1}^{n+1}\binom{n}{j-1}a^{n+1-j}b^j$$

$$= \binom{n}{0}a^{n+1}b^0 + \sum_{k=1}^{n}\binom{n}{k}a^{n+1-k}b^k + \sum_{k=1}^{n}\binom{n}{k-1}a^{n+1-k}b^k$$

$$+ \binom{n}{n}b^{n+1}.$$

This step involved writing separately the first term of the first sigma and the last term of the second. In addition, the "dummy" index j in the second sigma was replaced by k. But now, combining the two sigma expressions into one, we have

$$(a+b)^{n+1} = \binom{n}{0}a^{n+1}b^0 + \left(\sum_{k=1}^{n}\left[\binom{n}{k}+\binom{n}{k-1}\right]a^{n+1-k}b^k\right) + \binom{n}{n}a^0 b^{n+1}$$

$$= \binom{n+1}{0}a^{n+1}b^0 + \sum_{k=1}^{n}\binom{n+1}{k}a^{n+1-k}b^k + \binom{n+1}{n+1}a^0 b^{n+1}$$

$$= \sum_{k=0}^{n+1}\binom{n+1}{k}a^{n+1-k}b^k.$$

In the transition from the first to the second of the preceding three lines, we have used, along with the result of Lemma 2, the facts that $\binom{n}{0} = \binom{n+1}{0} = \binom{n}{n} = \binom{n+1}{n+1} = 1$. But now we have shown that $n+1 \in S$, so, by Theorem 10, $S = \mathbf{N}$. ∎

EXERCISES

1. Use mathematical induction to prove that the following identities hold for all $n \in \mathbf{N}$.

(a) $\displaystyle\sum_{k=1}^{n} k^2 = 1^2 + 2^2 + \cdots + n^2 = \frac{n(n+1)(2n+1)}{6}$ (Theorem 12).

(b) $\displaystyle\sum_{k=1}^{n} 2k = n^2 + n$.

(c) $a_n = a_1 r^{n-1}$,   where $a_{k+1} = a_k r$.

(d) $1 \cdot 2 + 2 \cdot 3 + \cdots + n(n+1) = \dfrac{n(n+1)(n+2)}{3}$.

(e) $\dfrac{1}{1\cdot 3} + \dfrac{1}{3\cdot 5} + \cdots + \dfrac{1}{(2n-1)(2n+1)} = \dfrac{n}{2n+1}$.

(f) $\dfrac{1}{1\cdot 2} + \dfrac{1}{2\cdot 3} + \cdots + \dfrac{1}{n(n+1)} = \dfrac{n}{n+1}$.

2. Show that

(a) $(\tfrac{3}{2})^n > n$,   all $n \in \mathbf{N}$.   (b) $2^n > 2n+1$,   all $n \geq 3$.   (c) $2^n > n^2$,   all $n \geq 5$.

(d) $(\frac{3}{2})^n > n$,   all $n \geq 7$. Note that this inequality is also valid for $n = 1$; however, it is not hard to check that it fails to hold for $n = 2, 3, 4, 5, 6$. Does this contradict Theorem 10?

3. Prove (i) of Lemma 2, i.e., prove that

$$\binom{n}{n-k} = \binom{n}{k}, \qquad n \in \mathbf{N}, \quad k = 0, 1, \ldots, n.$$

4. Use the factorial form of $\binom{n}{k}$ to obtain another motivation for the definition $0! = 1$.

5. Interpret the identity (i) of Lemma 2 (see Exercise 3) in terms of number of selections.

6. Prove that

(a) $(a - b)^n = \sum_{k=0}^{n} (-1)^k \binom{n}{k} a^{n-k} b^k.$ (b) $(1 + x)^n = \sum_{k=0}^{n} \binom{n}{k} x^k.$

7. Show that

(a) $\sum_{k=0}^{n} \binom{n}{k} = 2^n.$ [*Hint.* Use Exercise 6(b).]   (c) $\sum_{k=1}^{n} k \binom{n}{k} = n 2^{n-1}, \quad n \geq 2.$

(b) $\sum_{k=0}^{n} (-1)^k \binom{n}{k} = 0.$ [*Hint.* Use Exercise 6(a).]   (d) $\sum_{k=1}^{n} (-1)^{k-1} k \binom{n}{k} = 0, \quad n \geq 2.$

8. Property (ii) of Lemma 2 provides the basis for constructing *Pascal's triangle*, the nth row of which gives the nth set of binomial coefficients. To illustrate we write this identity as

(ii) $\binom{n+1}{k} = \binom{n}{k-1} + \binom{n}{k}$

and write a few rows of the triangle in Table 1. Observe that the elements in row 5, say, are obtained by adding the two elements in row 4 as indicated by (ii). Complete Table 1 through $n = 9$.

TABLE 1

n \ k	0	1	2	3	4	5	6	7	8	9
0	1	—	—	—	—	—	—			
1	1	1	—	—	—	—	—			
2	1	2	1	—	—	—	—			
3	1	3	3	1	—	—	—			
4	1	4	6	4	1	—	—			
5	1	5	10	10	5	1				
6	1	6	15	20	15	6	1			
7										
8										
9										

9. Prove the telescoping property of the sigma notation:

$$\sum_{i=1}^{n} (c_i - c_{i-1}) = c_n - c_0.$$

10. Prove Theorem 14 by using Lemma 1 and Theorem 11.

11. In this exercise we give a formal definition of the set $\mathbf{N}$ of natural numbers and a proof of Theorem 10, the induction principle.

   (a) First a definition. A *successor set* in the ordered field $\mathbf{R}$ is a set S such that

      (i) $1 \in S$.
      (ii) $x \in S \Rightarrow x + 1 \in S$.

   Give at least two examples of successor sets in $\mathbf{R}$.

   (b) Prove that the intersection of any collection of successor sets is a successor set. In symbols;

   $$\left. \begin{array}{l} S_\alpha \text{ successor set, all } \alpha \\ S = \cap_\alpha S_\alpha \end{array} \right\} \Rightarrow S \text{ is a successor set.}$$

   [*Hint.* Show that S inherits properties (i) and (ii) from the S_α.]

   (c) Now another definition. The set $\mathbf{N}$ of *natural numbers* is the intersection of *all* successor sets in $\mathbf{R}$:

   $$\mathbf{N} = \cap S,$$

   where the intersection is taken over all successor sets of $\mathbf{R}$. By (b), $\mathbf{N}$ is a successor set. In fact, $\mathbf{N}$ is the smallest successor set in $\mathbf{R}$.

   (d) Prove Theorem 10. [*Hint.* The hypotheses say that $S \subset \mathbf{N}$ is a successor set. Use the definition of $\mathbf{N}$.]

1.6 Functions

The idea of function in mathematics grew out of formulas from geometry or physics such as

$$A = \pi r^2, \qquad s = 16t^2, \qquad F = ma, \qquad I = \frac{E}{R},$$

the central idea being that the formula provides a correspondence between *every* number in some set of numbers and another number (or, in some cases, several other numbers) from a second set of numbers. During the course of its evolution from the version just illustrated to the present one, some reshaping has taken place. For one thing, the alternative, mentioned parenthetically, of allowing more than one number to be the functional correspondent of a given number is now not allowed; thus, the formula $y = \pm \sqrt{x}$ does not now describe a function. For another thing, the sets involved need not be sets of numbers. And, for a third, the dependence of a function upon a formula has been dropped (although, to be sure, many of the functions with which we shall work in calculus will be defined in terms of a formula). Thus if we consider a set of people in a room, the correspondence between each person in the set and the integer which represents, to the nearest year, that person's age is an illustration of a function for which one of the basic sets is a set of people. Or, assuming the people of the preceding sentence are seated in chairs, we can cite as an example of a function the correspondence between each person and the chair in which he is sitting. In this example no numbers appear; and in neither of these last two examples is there a formula.

Suppose, for the sake of simplicity, the room mentioned in the example has only three people in it. Then the age function can be completely displayed as follows:

$$\{(\text{Eric, 31}), (\text{Fletcher, 38}), (\text{Gardner, 34})\}.$$

This scheme illustrates what is no doubt the most popular method of defining a function: a set of ordered pairs, no two of which have the same first element. This approach, which has been called the "static" definition, has much to recommend it, but we prefer to give an equivalent definition which serves to emphasize the role of a function in mapping from one set to another (the "dynamic" definition). Although we shall be concerned largely with functions which map a subset (perhaps all) of the real numbers into a subset of the real numbers, we give the definition in its general form.

Definition 6. *A **function** f consists of a set X, a set Y (which may equal X), and a rule which makes correspond to each element $x \in X$ exactly one element $f(x) \in Y$. The set X is called the **domain of f** and the subset of Y defined as*

$$f(X) = \{y \in Y \mid y = f(x), \quad \text{some } x \in X\}$$

*is called the **range of f**.*

The range of f is, in other words, the set of all *images* under the mapping (see following examples).

Functions may be described in various ways. For example, if $X = \{1, 2, 3, 4\}$, $Y = \{a, b, c, d, e,\}$ the rule might be given by Table 2, the element appearing in the $f(x)$ column being the image of the element opposite it in the x column. Thus $f(1) = a$, and so on. Note that $a = f(4)$ also, i.e., a is the image of both 1 and 4, an allowable occurrence. For this example the range $f(X) = \{a, b, c\}$, a proper subset of Y.

TABLE 2

x	$f(x)$
1	a
2	b
3	c
4	a

In the sequel, X and Y will often be subsets of the field $\mathbf{R}$ of real numbers, and in these cases the rule will usually be given by some formula or " recipe." Then the domain will be taken as the largest admissible subset of $\mathbf{R}$.

Example 5. If f is defined by $f(x) = x^2$, all real numbers are admissible, so the domain $X = \mathbf{R}$; but the range $f(x) = \{y \,|\, y \geq 0\}$ is the set of all nonnegative real numbers. In the sense of providing a mapping, this function maps all of $\mathbf{R}$ into the nonnegative part of $\mathbf{R}$.

Example 6. If f is defined by $f(x) = \sqrt{x}$, then the domain is $X = \{x \,|\, x \geq 0\}$. Also, the range is $f(X) = \{y \,|\, y \geq 0\}$, so that this function maps the nonnegative part of $\mathbf{R}$ into itself.

[*It is important to recall that, when working in the field* $\mathbf{R}$ *of real numbers,* $\sqrt{x}$ *exists if and only if* $x \geq 0$ *and in this case* $\sqrt{x} \geq 0$. *This latter point can be emphasized by remarking that* $\sqrt{x^2} = |x|$ (*see Example 8 for a brief discussion of the absolute value function*).]

Example 7. The formula for a function might be in more than one piece. For example, we might have

$$f(x) = \begin{cases} x, & \text{if } x < 0 \\ x^2, & \text{if } x \leq 0 \leq 1 \\ 1, & \text{if } x > 1 \end{cases}$$

For this function $X = \mathbf{R}$ and $f(X) = \{y \,|\, y \leq 1\}$.

Example 8. An important example of a function with a two-part formula is the *absolute value* function:

$$\begin{cases} f(x) = x, & \text{if } x \geq 0 \\ f(x) = -x, & \text{if } x < 0 \end{cases}.$$

It will be noted that the domain $X = \mathbf{R}$ and the range $f(X) = \{y \,|\, y \geq 0\}$. As our readers should know, this function has its special symbol, $f(x) = |x|$, verbalized as "the absolute value of x."

Because of the importance for our future work of the absolute value function, it will not be amiss to digress a bit by mentioning some of its properties.

Geometrically, the absolute value of x simply gives the distance, *without regard to direction*, that x is from 0. More generally, $|a - b|$ represents the distance between a and b, without regard to direction, i.e., without regard to which is the greater number (see Figure 1).

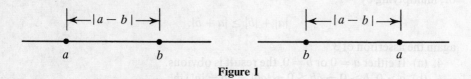

Figure 1

For the sake of convenience we collect in a theorem the useful properties of the absolute value function.

Theorem 17. *The absolute value function has the following properties (all letters represent numbers in* **R**).

1. $|-a| = |a|$.
2. $-|a| \le a \le |a|$.
3. $|a + b| \le |a| + |b|$.
4. $|ab| = |a| \cdot |b|$.
5. $b \neq 0 \Rightarrow \left|\dfrac{a}{b}\right| = \dfrac{|a|}{|b|}$.
6. $|a| = a \Leftrightarrow a \ge 0$.
7. $\{x \mid |x| < a, a > 0\} = \{x \mid -a < x < a\}$.
8. $\{x \mid |x| > a, a > 0\} = \{x \mid x < -a\} \cup \{x \mid x > a\}$.
9. $\{x \mid |x - a| < h\} = \{x \mid a - h < x < a + h\}$.

Proof. As we have done with some of the preceding multipart theorems, we will give the proof for a few of the preceding assertions, thus indicating the technique, and leave the proof of the remaining parts as exercises.

1. (a) If $a = 0$, the result is obviously true.
   (b) $a > 0 \Rightarrow -a < 0 \Rightarrow |-a| = -(-a) = a = |a|$.
   (c) $a < 0 \Rightarrow -a > 0 \Rightarrow |-a| = -a = |a|$.

2. (a) If $a = 0$, then $-|a| = a = |a|$.
   (b) If $a > 0$, then $-|a| < a = |a|$.
   (c) If $a < 0$, then $-|a| = a < |a|$.
In every case we can say $-|a| \le a \le |a|$.

3. Using the result of 2 for both a and b, we have

$$-|a| \le a \le |a|$$
$$-|b| \le b \le |b|.$$

Adding these inequalities (why is this legal?) gives

$$-(|a| + |b|) \le a + b \le |a| + |b|.$$

Now if $|a + b| = a + b$, then the right-hand inequality gives us the desired result; if $|a + b| = -(a + b)$, then $a + b = -|a + b|$, and the left-hand inequality gives

$$-(|a| + |b|) \leq -|a + b|,$$

or, multiplying by -1,

$$|a| + |b| \geq |a + b|,$$

again the assertion of 3.

    4. (a) If either $a = 0$ or $b = 0$, the result is obvious.

    (b) $a > 0, b > 0 \Rightarrow ab > 0 \Rightarrow |ab| = ab = |a| \cdot |b|$.

    (c) $a < 0, b < 0 \Rightarrow ab > 0 \Rightarrow |ab| = ab = (-a)(-b) = |a| |b|$.

    (d) $a > 0, b < 0 \Rightarrow ab < 0 \Rightarrow |ab| = -(ab) = a(-b) = |a| |b|$.

    (e) $a < 0, b > 0 \Rightarrow ab < 0 \Rightarrow |ab| = -(ab) = (-a)b = |a| |b|$.

    7. We let $A = \{x \mid |x| < a, a > 0\}$, $B = \{x \mid -a < x < a\}$. Our aim, to show $A = B$, will be accomplished by showing (i) $A \subset B$ and (ii) $B \subset A$. For (i) we let $x \in A$ and use assertion 2 of this theorem:

$$- |x| \leq x \leq |x|.$$

But since $x \in A$, $|x| < a$, from which follows $-|x| > -a$; putting together the three results just obtained gives

$$-a < -|x| \leq x \leq |x| < a.$$

Thus $x \in B$.

    For (ii) we consider $x \in B$; thus we know $-a < x < a$. Now

$$x \geq 0 \Rightarrow |x| = x < a,$$

whereas

$$x < 0 \Rightarrow |x| = -x.$$

But

$$x > -a \Rightarrow -x < a;$$

thus $x < 0 \Rightarrow |x| = -x < a$, so in every case $|x| < a$, and $x \in A$. Thus $A = B$. We leave the remaining parts of the proof as exercises. ∎

Example 9. As another example of a function with interesting properties we mention the greatest integer function

$$f(x) = [x],$$

where the symbol $[x]$ represents the largest integer less than or equal to x. Thus

$$[3] = 3, \qquad [3.2] = 3, \qquad [\pi] = 3, \qquad [-\tfrac{1}{2}] = -1, \quad \text{etc.}$$

The domain of this function is $\mathbf{R}$, the range is the set $\mathbf{Z}$ of all integers, and the function has the constant value n for $n \leq x < n + 1$.

Example 10. The greatest integer function of Example 9 has, as was just noted, the property of being constant on the intervals between the integers. We call attention now to the functions which are constant on all of **R**; for example, let

$$f : x \to 1, \quad \text{all } x \in \mathbf{R}.$$

In the sequel we shall indicate this function by the symbol **1**. More generally, we shall denote by **c** the function whose range is the singleton $\{c\}$; thus $\mathbf{c}(x) = c$, all $x \in \mathbf{R}$.

Example 11. Another function of a special nature that is worth special mention is the *identity function j*, defined by the formula

$$j(x) = x, \quad \text{all } x \in \mathbf{R}.$$

Obviously, the domain and range of j are both equal to **R**.

There are two classes of functions which will prove to be especially useful in our future work. The first of these is the set of *polynomial functions*. A *polynomial p* is a function defined by the formula

$$p(x) = a_0 x^n + a_1 x^{n-1} + a_2 x^{n-2} + \cdots + a_{n-1} x + a_n,$$

where $a_0\, a_1, \ldots, a_n \in \mathbf{R}$, and n is a nonnegative integer. If $a_0 \neq 0$, then p is a polynomial of *degree n*. Clearly the domain of every polynomial is **R**.

A *rational function* is the ratio of two polynomials:

$$r(x) = \frac{a_0 x^n + a_1 x^{n-1} + \cdots + a_{n-1}x + a_n}{b_0 x^m + b_1 x^{m-1} + \cdots + b_{m-1}x + b_m} = \frac{p(x)}{q(x)}.$$

The domain of a rational function is $\{x \,|\, q(x) \neq 0\}$.

Thus

$$p(x) = 4x^3 - 10x^2 + 7x + 3$$

is a polynomial of degree 3, and

$$r(x) = \frac{4x^3 - 10x^2 + 7x + 3}{x^2 - 6x + 8}$$

is a rational function with domain $= \{x \,|\, x \neq 2, 4\}$.

We next mention several conventions about notations for functions which we shall find useful. If the function f has domain X and range in the set Y we can indicate this by writing

$$f : X \to Y;$$

this is verbalized as "f maps X into Y." If it should happen that $Y = f(X)$, i.e., if every $y \in Y$ is an image of some $x \in X$, then f is called an *onto* mapping. We shall indicate this by writing

$$f : X \relbar\joinrel\twoheadrightarrow Y.$$

(This notation, however, is not standard.)

On the *point* (rather than set) level, we can use the preceding notation in the form

$$f : x \rightarrow f(x);$$

thus the function in Example 9 can be indicated by $f : x \rightarrow [x]$. Notice, by the way, that if we write $f : y \rightarrow [y]$, or $f : u \rightarrow [u]$, or $f : t \rightarrow [t]$, *we are in each case describing the same function*; in other words, the choice of letter to represent an element of X is quite irrelevant.

While on the subject of notation, we call attention to the fact that in defining the range of f we have used the symbol $f(X)$; strictly speaking, we are using f here as a *set function*, i.e., as a function which maps one *set* into another *set*. It would perhaps be in order to indicate this use by a distinguishing symbol on f; we shall hereafter use brackets for this purpose. Thus, if $A \subset X$, we can write

$$f[A] = \{y \in Y \mid y = f(x), \ x \in A\}.$$

Along the same lines, we may want to consider, for a subset $B \subset Y$, the set of all *pre-images*, a subset of X. We shall indicate this set in the following way (see Figure 2):

$$f^{-1}[B] = \{x \in X \mid f(x) \in B\}.$$

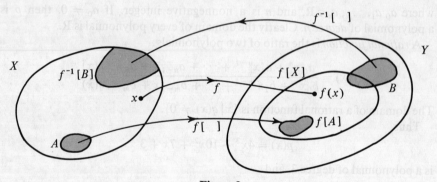

Figure 2

We have already mentioned (in the first example of this section) that it is consistent with the definition of a function to have $x_1, x_2 \in X, x_1 \neq x_2$, yet $f(x_1) = f(x_2)$; i.e., it may happen that different points of X map into the same point of Y. It is, however, important for some of our subsequent work that we give consideration to cases where this does *not* occur.

If it should happen that $f : X \rightarrow Y$ and if, for every pair of distinct points $x_1, x_2 \in X, f(x_1) \neq f(x_2)$, then f is said to be *one-to-one* (which we shall hereinafter abbreviate as 1-1).

Of the examples given earlier in this section, only the ones in Examples 6 and 11 are 1-1. (Why do the others fail to have this property?)

We next give a brief survey of the *algebra of functions*. As we did in defining a function, we shall make this survey as general as possible.

First of all we define *equality* for functions; this will mean *strict identity*, as equality does with sets.

Definition 7. *Let f and g be functions with domains X_f and X_g, respectively. Then $f = g$ means exactly that $X_f = X_g$ and, for every x in this common domain, $f(x) = g(x)$. Notice that this definition requires that $f[X_f] = g[X_g]$.*

Next we observe that in some cases we can define, in a natural way, arithmetic operations for functions. The possibility of introducing these operations depends upon the properties of the set Y. In particular, suppose that Y is a field of numbers, such as the field **R** of real numbers. Suppose further that

$$f : X_f \to Y$$
$$g : X_g \to Y$$

and that $X_f \cap X_g \neq \varnothing$, i.e., that X_f and X_g have points in common. If $x \in X_f \cap X_g$ then $f(x)$ and $g(x)$ are numbers in Y and can be added to give the number $f(x) + g(x)$ in Y (see Figure 3).

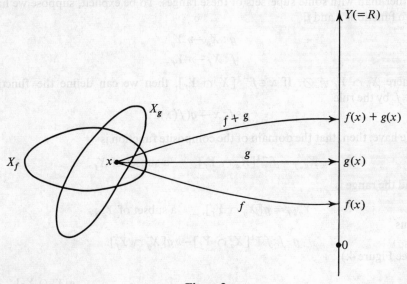

Figure 3

Since this is possible for every $x \in X_f \cap X_g$, it is natural to call the number $f(x) + g(x)$ the image of x under the mapping $f + g$; i.e.,

$$(f + g) : x \to f(x) + g(x).$$

In a similar way we can define $f - g$, fg, and $\dfrac{f}{g}$. The domains of $f + g$, $f - g$, and fg will all be $X_f \cap X_g$, whereas

$$X_{f/g} = X_f \cap \{x \in X_g \,|\, g(x) \neq 0\}.$$

For example, if $X_f = X_g = \mathbf{R}$, and if

$$f : x \rightarrow x + 1$$
$$g : x \rightarrow x^2 - 4,$$

then it can easily be verified that

$$f + g : x \rightarrow x^2 + x - 3, \qquad\qquad (X_{f+g} = \mathbf{R})$$

$$f - g : x \rightarrow -x^2 + x + 5, \qquad\qquad (X_{f-g} = \mathbf{R})$$

$$fg : x \rightarrow x^3 + x^2 - 4x - 4, \qquad (X_{fg} = \mathbf{R})$$

$$\frac{f}{g} : x \rightarrow \frac{x+1}{x^2 - 4} \qquad\qquad (X_{f/g} = \{x \in \mathbf{R} \,|\, x \neq \pm 2\}).$$

There is another important method of combining two functions g and f to get a third, known as the *composition of g and f*, and symbolized by $g \circ f$. The description we are about to give may at first seem a little complicated, but the operation *is* important and deserves careful study.

Our discussion will be simplified if we deal with the ranges of the functions rather than with some supersets of these ranges. To be explicit, suppose we have two functions g and f,

$$g : X_g \longrightarrow Y_g$$
$$f : X_f \longrightarrow Y_f,$$

where $X_g \cap Y_f \neq \varnothing$. If $x \in f^{-1}[X_g \cap Y_f]$, then we can define the function $g \circ f$ by the rule

$$g \circ f : x \rightarrow g(f(x)).$$

We have, then, that the domain of the composite function is

$$X_{g \circ f} = f^{-1}[X_g \cap Y_f], \qquad \text{a subset of } X_f,$$

and the range is

$$Y_{g \circ f} = g[X_g \cap Y_f], \qquad \text{a subset of } Y_g;$$

thus

$$g \circ f : f^{-1}[X_g \cap Y_f] \longrightarrow g[X_g \cap Y_f].$$

(See Figure 4.)

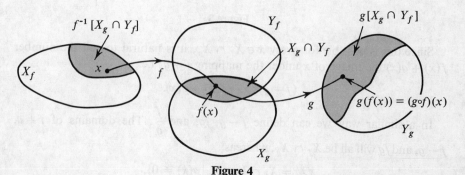

Figure 4

For example, let g be the square root function and let $f : x \to x^2 + 1$. Then

$$(g \circ f) : x \to g(f(x)) = \sqrt{f(x)} = \sqrt{x^2 + 1}.$$

Or, if g is the greatest integer function and f is the same as above,

$$(g \circ f) : x \to g(f(x)) = [f(x)] = [x^2 + 1].$$

It should be clear that in its most general formulation $g \circ f$ may exist and yet $f \circ g$ may not—in fact, it *will* not exist if $X_f \cap Y_g = \varnothing$. Moreover, even if $g \circ f$ and $f \circ g$ both exist they will usually not be equal. For the first of the two preceding examples we have, in fact,

$$(f \circ g) : x \to f(g(x)) = f(\sqrt{x}) = x + 1;$$

thus $g \circ f$ and $f \circ g$ both exist, but obviously $f \circ g \neq g \circ f$.

We conclude this section with a few remarks about some terminology for functions. If f is defined by a formula, such as $f(x) = x^3 \sqrt{x^2 + 1}$, it is frequently customary to refer to x as the *independent variable*. In the same way, if y is used to represent the functional values then y may be called the *dependent variable*. A *variable* is used here as a name for a generic symbol for the elements of a set. Thus, an independent variable is the generic symbol for a set which is the domain of a function; when a set is the range of a function we may refer to the generic symbol as the dependent variable.

EXERCISES

1. Find the domains of the functions with the following formulas. In each case the domain should be taken as a subset of **R**.

   (a) $f(x) = x^2 - 1$.

   (b) $f(x) = \dfrac{x^2 - 1}{x}$.

   (c) $f(x) = \dfrac{x^2 - 1}{x + 1}$.

   (d) $f(x) = \sqrt{x^2 - 1}$.

   (e) $f(x) = \dfrac{x}{x^2 - 1}$.

   (f) $f(x) = x^2 - 2x - 3$

   (g) $f(x) = \sqrt{x^2 - 2x - 3}$

   (h) $f(x) = \sqrt{1 - x^2}$

2. Let the function f be defined by $f(x) = 4 - x^2$, i.e., $f : x \to 4 - x^2$.

   (a) What is the domain of f?   (b) What is the range of f?

   (c) Note that $f(1) = 3$. Find another value of x which f maps into 3.

   (d) Find $\{x \mid 3 \leq f(x) \leq 4\}$.   (e) Find $\{x \mid 0 \leq f(x) \leq 3\}$.

3. Let $f : x \to x^2 - 2x - 8$.

   (a) Find the domain and range of f.

(b) Note that $f(0) = -8$. Find another value of x which f maps into -8, i.e., find another point in the inverse image of -8.

(c) Find $\{x \mid f(x) = 0\}$.   (d) Find $\{x \mid f(x) = -5\}$.

(e) Find $\{x \mid -5 < f(x) < 0\}$.   (f) Find $\{x \mid f(x) \geq 0\}$.

4. Let $f : x \to \dfrac{x-2}{x+4}$.

(a) Find the domain and range of f.   (b) Find $\{x \mid f(x) = 1\}$.

(c) Show that for every $y \neq 1$ there exists an x such that $f(x) = y$. [*Hint.* Set
$y = \dfrac{x-2}{x+4}$ and solve for x.]

(d) Find $\{x \mid -\frac{1}{2} < f(x < 0\}$.   (e) Find $\{x \mid 0 \leq f(x) < 1\}$.

5. Let the domain of the function f be denoted by X_f and let the domain of g be X_g. For each of the following pairs of functions, find $X_f \cap X_g$.

(a) $f : x \to 3x + 1, g : x \to \sqrt{x}$.

(b) f is defined by $f(x) = \dfrac{x^2 - 4}{x^2 - 9}$, g by $g(x) = \dfrac{5-x}{4-x^2}$.

(c) $f : x \to \sqrt{-x}, g : x \to x^{-1/2}$.

(d) $f : x \to \dfrac{x^2 - 1}{x^2 - 4}$, g is defined by $g(x) = -x$.

6. For each of the pairs of functions f and g of Exercise 5 find $f + g$, $f - g$, fg, and f/g. In each case give the domain.

7. Which of the functions in Exercise 5 are 1-1?

8. Given the following functions h, find functions g and f such that $h = g \circ f$:

(a) $h(x) = (x^2 + 1)^3$ (*One* answer: $f(x) = x^2 + 1$, $g(x) = x^3$.)
(b) $h(x) = x$.
(c) $h(x) = x^2$.
(d) $h(x) = 1$, i.e., $h = 1$.

9. For each pair f, g of the following functions write the formula for $f \circ g$ and $g \circ f$. In each case give the domain.

(a) $f(x) = \sqrt{x}, g(x) = x^2$.   (f) $f(x) = \dfrac{x^2 - 1}{x^2 + 1}, g(x) = \dfrac{x^2 + 1}{x^2 - 1}$.
(b) $f(x) = x^2 + 1, g(x) = \sqrt{x - 1}$.
(c) $f(x) = 3x + 2, g(x) = \frac{1}{3}(x - 2)$.   (g) $f(x) = x, g(x) = x^2 - 2$.
(d) $f(x) = \dfrac{1}{x}, g(x) = \dfrac{1}{x}$.   (h) $f(x) = x, g(x) = \dfrac{x^2 + 4}{x^2 - 7}$.
(e) $f(x) = -x^2 - 7, g(x) = \sqrt{x^2 + 4}$.   (i) $f(x) = x, g(x) = g(x)$.

10. Write a formula for each of the following functions:

(a) $j^2 + 1$ *Solution*: $(j^2 + 1)(x) = j^2(x) + 1(x)$
$$= j^2(x) + 1$$
$$= (j(x))(j(x)) + 1$$
$$= x^2 + 1.$$

(b) $2j + 3$ (c) $3j^2 + 4j + 5$ (d) $j^3 + 5j^2 - 3j + 7$.

11. Let f be a function with domain **R**. Determine the nature of each of the following functions:

(a) $f \circ j$ (f) $f \circ 1$

(b) $j \circ f$ (g) $0 \circ f$

(c) $f \cdot 1$ (h) $f \circ 0$

(d) $f + 0$ (i) $f \circ c$

(e) $1 \circ f$ (j) $c \circ f$.

12. Say which of the following pairs of functions are equal.

(a) $f: x \to \dfrac{x^2 + 1}{x^2 + 1}, g: x \to 1$.   (b) $f: x \to \dfrac{x + 1}{x + 1}, g: x \to 1$.

(c) $f(x) = \dfrac{x^3 + x}{x}, g(x) = x^2 + 1$.   (d) $f(x) = \sqrt{x^2}, g(x) = |x|$.

13. Prove that every linear function $f: x \to mx + b$, $m \neq 0$, is 1-1. [*Hint.* Suppose $f(x_1) = f(x_2)$.]

1.7   Graphs of Functions

In this section we begin the study of analytic geometry. In particular, we concern ourselves with the problem of learning as much as possible about the set of points in the plane determined by a function whose domain and range are subsets of **R**. As we shall see, it is possible to develop techniques for translating into geometric terms information about the function available from the rule which defines the functional correspondence. We will also become aware that the techniques provided by our present level of knowledge are somewhat limited, and we should see the need for more powerful tools, tools which will become available as we master the concepts of calculus.

We assume that the student is already familiar with the procedures used customarily in setting up first a coordinate system on a line (a one-dimensional space) and then extending these procedures to the development of a rectangular coordinate system for the plane (two-dimensional space). Thus, we omit these details and, instead, comment briefly on the basis for this procedure and some of the general consequences thereof.

Setting up a coordinate system on a line is possible because there exists a 1-1 correspondence between the numbers in **R** and the points on a straight line. This means, to be explicit, that every number corresponds to a point and every point is the correspondent of a number, and, moreover, that different numbers correspond to different points and conversely. There are, to be sure, many ways of setting up such a correspondence, and the choice of origin, of the positive direction, and of a unit of distance simply fixes on one of these. Once this has been done it is possible to travel freely between the field **R** and its geometric counterpart, the line—so freely, in fact, that we shall not resist the temptation to identify points and numbers, for example, to speak of the point -4 rather than to say "the point which corresponds to the number -4." A similar remark applies to the correspondence between the points in the plane and the ordered pairs of real numbers (elements of $\mathbf{R} \times \mathbf{R}$): we may speak of the point $(-4, 3)$, rather than of the point with coordinates $(-4, 3)$; or of the parabola $y = x^2$, rather than the parabola determined by the equation $y = x^2$.

Having a correspondence between pairs of numbers and points in the plane, we are led rather naturally to consider *sets* of pairs of numbers and the corresponding *sets* of points. For example, an equation involving x and y will determine a set of pairs of numbers, the pairs (x, y) which satisfy the equation, the *solution set of the equation* (which may be the empty set), to which will correspond a set of points. We will be interested in such sets, but our present concern will be with a particular case: that in which the equation involving x and y arises from a function.

Definition 8. *The* **graph** *of a function f with domain* $X \subset \mathbf{R}$ *is the set of points* (*determined by*)

$$G_f = \{(x, y) \mid y = f(x), x \in X\}.$$

Our primary concern in the remainder of this section will be to develop techniques enabling us to extract from the function rule geometric information about the graph of a function. We illustrate with examples from the preceding section.

Example 12. The function is defined by $f : x \to x^2$, so

$$G_f = \{(x, y) \mid y = x^2, \quad x \in \mathbf{R}\}.$$

One way of obtaining information about the graph of f is to use the rule for f to obtain specific points on the graph; thus, one can obtain a table such as Table 3.

TABLE 3

x	0	1	-1	2	-2	3	-3
y	0	1	1	4	4	9	9

From Table 3 we can plot the corresponding points and, hopefully, join them with a "reasonable" curve, as in Figure 5.

This technique (of calculating and then plotting points) is, however, crude.

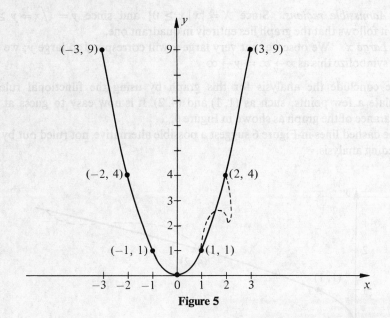

Figure 5

One is only guessing when connecting the adjacent pairs of points: the graph of this example might truly be represented by the dashed line between (1, 1) and (2, 4). A superior method is to look for information of the following sorts.

1. *Intersections with axes (intercepts).* Since the x-axis is characterized by the fact that $y = 0$, we can find the points of G_f which intersect the x-axis by setting $y = 0$ and finding those points of G_f which result; i.e., we look for the points (x, y) in

$$\{(x, y) \mid y = x^2, x \in \mathbf{R}\} \cap \{(x, y) \mid y = 0\}.$$

It is easy to see that the desired set is $\{(0, 0)\}$, the origin.

Similarly, the intersection of the graph and the y-axis is precisely the origin.

2. *Regions of the plane in which the graph may or may not lie.* Since in this example $y = x^2 \geq 0$, the graph must lie entirely in quadrants one and two.

3. *Behavior of y for numerically large x.* Since here $y = x^2$, it is evident that numerically large x will correspond to very large y.

These general results are in agreement with the sketch obtained earlier (Figure 5), although they still do not preclude the behavior suggested by the dashed lines; for this we must await the more powerful techniques of calculus.

Example 13. The function is defined by $f(x) = \sqrt{x}$, so

$$G_f = \{(x, y) \mid y = \sqrt{x}, x \geq 0\}.$$

1. *Intercepts.* Setting $x = 0$ gives $y = 0$ and setting $y = 0$ gives $x = 0$. Thus the origin is the only intercept.

2. *Admissible regions.* Since $X = \{x \mid x \geq 0\}$ and since $y = \sqrt{x} \Rightarrow y \geq 0$, it follows that the graph lies entirely in quadrant one.

3. *Large x.* We observe that very large x will correspond to large y; we can symbolize this as $x \to \infty \Rightarrow y \to \infty$.

We conclude the analysis for this graph by using the functional rule to calculate a few points, such as $(1, 1)$ and $(4, 2)$. It is now easy to guess at the appearance of the graph as shown in Figure 6.

The dashed lines in Figure 6 suggest a possible alternative, not ruled out by the preceding analysis.

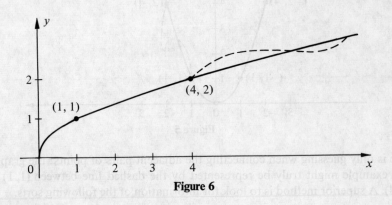

Figure 6

Example 14. We have $f(x) = |x|$, so

$$G_f = \{(x, y) \mid y = |x|, x \in \mathbf{R}\}.$$

1. Intercepts. $(0, 0)$.
2. Admissible regions. Quadrants one and two, since $|x| \geq 0$, all $x \in \mathbf{R}$.
3. Large x corresponds to large positive y ($x \to \pm\infty \Rightarrow y \to \infty$). The graph is shown in Figure 7.

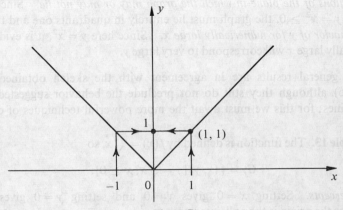

Figure 7

Example 15. For the greatest integer function f,

$$G_f = \{(x, y) \mid y = [x], x \in \mathbf{R}\}.$$

The special nature of this function suggests dispensing with the methods used in the earlier examples. As we noted in Section 1.6, the function has the constant value n for $n \le x < n + 1$; the graph is a series of horizontal line segments lying in quadrants one and three (see Figure 8).

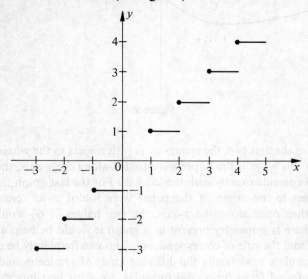

Figure 8

We consider one more illustration.

Example 16. Let f be defined by $f(x) = \dfrac{x}{1 + x^2}$.

Then

$$G_f = \left\{ (x, y) \mid y = \frac{x}{1 + x^2}, x \in \mathbf{R} \right\}.$$

We find the following:

1. Intercept: $(0, 0)$.
2. Admissible regions. Since $x < 0 \Rightarrow y < 0$ and $x \ge 0 \Rightarrow y \ge 0$, the graph lies in quadrants one and three.
3. Behavior of y for large x. Since, for $x > 1$, x^2 and hence $x^2 + 1$ is greater than x, $x > 1 \Rightarrow y < 1$. Moreover, calculation of y for very large values of x suggests that very large x will correspond to very small y.

The graph G_f is shown in Figure 9.

We conclude this section by calling attention to features of *symmetry* present in the graphs in Examples 12, 14, and 16 (Figures 5, 7, and 9, respectively).

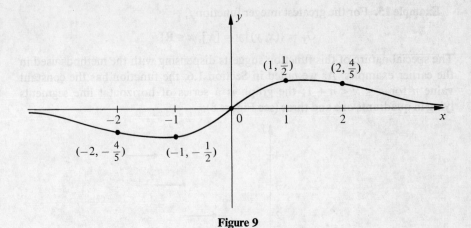

Figure 9

In the cases of the first two, the symmetry is with respect to the y-axis and can be described in this way: if the paper were folded along the y-axis, the right half of G_f would coincide exactly with the left half. For the last graph the symmetry is with respect to the origin: if the paper were folded twice, once along the y-axis and then once along the x-axis, the two halves of G_f would coincide. Clearly, if there is symmetry present in a graph it would be helpful to be able to detect it from the rule of correspondence. This can frequently be done, but in order to formulate analytically the different kinds of symmetry and show how they can be found from functional formulas, we must first introduce analytic descriptions of distance and direction and one or two other geometric concepts. This we do in the next section.

EXERCISES

1. Obtain as much information as possible about the graph of each of the following functions and sketch the graph.

(a) $f: x \to 2x - 1$.

(b) $f(x) = x^2 - 1$.

(c) $f(x) = (x - 1)^2$.

(d) $f: x \to -2x - 1$.

(e) $f(x) = x^4 - x^2$.

(f) $f: x \to 2x + 1$.

(g) $f(x) = \dfrac{1}{x^2}$.

(h) $f(x) = \dfrac{1}{(x - 2)^2}$.

(i) $f(x) = |x - 1|$.

(j) $f(x) = \dfrac{x}{|x|}$.

(k) $f(x) = x^3$.

(l) $f(x) = x^3 - x$.

(m) $f(x) = |2x - 1|$.

(n) $f(x) = \dfrac{1}{x^2 + 1}$.

(o) $f(x) = \dfrac{x^2}{x^2 + 1}$.

(p) $f(x) = (x + 2)(x - 3)$.

(q) $f(x) = |(x + 2)(x - 3)|$.

2. Sketch the graphs of the following functions. [*Hint.* In working with the greatest integer function it may occasionally be helpful to represent a number $x \in \mathbf{R}$ as $x = n_x + \theta_x$, where n_x is an integer and $0 \leq \theta_x < 1$; then $[x] = n_x$.]

(a) $f(x) = x + [x]$.   (b) $f(x) = x - [x]$.   (c) $f(x) = 1 + [x] - x$.
(d) $h(x) = $ minimum $(f(x), g(x))$, where $f(x) = 1 + [x] - x$, $g(x) = x - [x]$.
(e) $f(x) = [2x]$.   (f) $f(x) = [x + \frac{1}{2}]$.

3. Sketch the graph of each of the following functions:

(a) $f(x) = x$ (i.e., $f = j$).   (b) $f(x) = -x$.
(c) $f(x) = 2$ (i.e., $f = 2$).   (d) $f(x) = -1$.

4. Drawing on the crude intuitive description of symmetry given at the end of Section 1.7, decide which of the graphs in Exercise 1 are symmetric with respect to

(a) the y-axis.
(b) the origin.

5. Make a complete study of the graph of the *linear* function f defined by $f(x) = ax + b$, i.e., study the set

$$G_f = \{(x, y) \mid y = ax + b, x \in \mathbf{R}\}.$$

Suggestions:

1. Consider first $a = b = 0$.
2. Consider $a \neq 0$, $b = 0$. What is the distinction between $a > 0$ and $a < 0$?
3. Consider $a = 0$, $b \neq 0$. What is the geometric interpretation of b?
4. Consider $a \neq 0$, $b \neq 0$.

6. This refers to Exercise 5.

(a) Is the following true?
Given any two distinct points $P_1(x_1, y_1)$, $P_2(x_2, y_2)$ in the plane, there exist unique values of a and b such that the graph of $f(x) = ax + b$ contains P_1 and P_2.

(b) If true prove it. If not find a counterexample.

(c) If the assertion of (a) is not true, can it be modified so as to be true in the modified version?

1.8 More Analytic Geometry: Distance, Direction and Symmetry

In discussing the graphs of functions in the preceding section we saw that in some cases the graph may have a symmetry, knowledge of which would be useful in constructing the graph. When present, the different kinds of symmetry can frequently be detected from the functional formula; we shall, later in this section, indicate how this can be done. However, in order to formulate analytic definitions of symmetry—and, to be sure, for numerous other purposes—we need first to put in analytic terms the basic geometric concepts of *distance, direction* and *midpoint*.

We begin by considering these matters in the one-dimensional geometry of a straight line. If two points P_1 and P_2 on a line on which a coordinate system has been established have coordinates x_1 and x_2, respectively, then we *define* the distance between them as

$$\overline{P_1 P_2} = |x_2 - x_1|. \tag{6}$$

Since a line has only two possible directions, one of which in setting up the coordinate system has already been chosen as the positive direction, little need be said about direction in one-dimensional geometry. If we want to indicate direction in going from P_1 to P_2 we define the *directed distance* to be

$$\overrightarrow{P_1 P_2} = x_2 - x_1. \tag{7}$$

Then, by definition, the direction from P_1 to P_2 is the *positive* direction $\Leftrightarrow x_2 - x_1 > 0$; and the direction from P_1 to P_2 is the *negative* direction $\Leftrightarrow x_2 - x_1 < 0$.

The midpoint problem in one-dimensional geometry is also quickly solved. Given two points $P_1(x_1)$ and $P_2(x_2)$, it is desired to find the point $P_0(x_0)$ midway between them (see Figure 10). It is a simple matter, which we leave as an exercise, to show that

$$x_0 = \tfrac{1}{2}(x_1 + x_2). \tag{8}$$

Figure 10

We now move on to two-dimensional geometry and begin by reminding ourselves that in each of the three matters presently concerning us we have a line segment determined by two points P_1 and P_2 (see Figure 11).

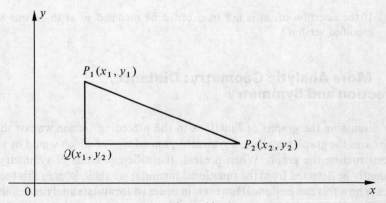

Figure 11

For distance we allow ourselves to be motivated by the Pythagorean Theorem.

Definition 9. *Given two points P_1 and P_2 in the plane with coordinates (x_1, y_1) and (x_2, y_2), respectively, the **distance** $\overline{P_1P_2}$ between them is given by*

$$\overline{P_1P_2} = \sqrt{(x_1 - x_2)^2 + (y_1 - y_2)^2}. \tag{9}$$

Notice that if $y_2 = y_1$, say, i.e., if the points are on the same horizontal line, then (9) reduces to (6):

$$\overline{P_1P_2} = \sqrt{(x_1 - x_2)^2} = |x_1 - x_2| = |x_2 - x_1|.$$

We postpone for the time being the matter of directed distance in the plane and turn to the subject of direction of the line segment determined by P_1 and P_2. This can, as it turns out, be treated in various ways (later we show how direction of a line segment can easily—and equivalently—be defined in terms of an angle), but the following is reasonably standard.

Definition 10. *Given two points $P_1(x_1, y_1)$ and $P_2(x_2, y_2)$, where $x_2 \neq x_1$, the **direction** between them will be measured by the **slope** m defined as*

$$m = \frac{y_2 - y_1}{x_2 - x_1}. \tag{10}$$

If $x_2 = x_1$, the slope is not defined.

Note that

$$\frac{y_1 - y_2}{x_1 - x_2} = \frac{y_2 - y_1}{x_2 - x_1},$$

so that the measure of slope is the same whether we consider the line segment as going from P_1 to P_2, or from P_2 to P_1.

We remark that if $P_3(x_3, y_3)$ is a third point on the segment determined by P_1 and P_2, the slope m can be calculated by using the coordinates of P_3 in place of those of either P_1 and P_2—in other words, the slope m is independent of the points on the line segment used to calculate it. Although this assertion is sometimes proven using simple properties of similar triangles from plane geometry, we do not intend to prove it. Instead we assert that the preceding result follows from the approach we are going to take toward the straight line: that the straight line is a *curve of constant direction*.

As an application of the assertion of the preceding paragraph we give an interpretation of the slope of a line segment.

Theorem 18. *The slope m of a line segment measures the change in y (the ordinate) which corresponds to an increase of one unit in x (the abscissa) (see Figure 12).*

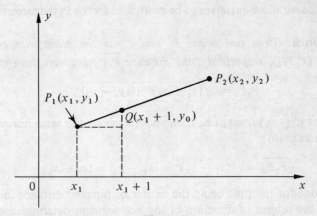

Figure 12

Proof. Suppose the segment with slope m is determined by points $P_1(x_1, y_1)$ and $P_2(x_2, y_2)$; we also assume that $x_2 - x_1 \geq 1$. Let Q be a point on the segment with abscissa $x_1 + 1$ and ordinate y_0. Then, using P_1 and Q to calculate the slope, we have

$$m = \frac{y_0 - y_1}{(x_1 + 1) - x_1} = y_0 - y_1,$$

which is the desired result. ∎

We now give the two-dimensional analog of the midpoint formula obtained earlier for one-dimensional geometry.

Theorem 19. *Let $P_1(x_1, y_1)$ and $P_2(x_2, y_2)$, distinct points, determine a line segment with slope* (see Figure 13). *If $P_0(x_0, y_0)$ is the midpoint of the segment then*

$$x_0 = \tfrac{1}{2}(x_1 + x_2), \quad y_0 = \tfrac{1}{2}(y_1 + y_2). \tag{11}$$

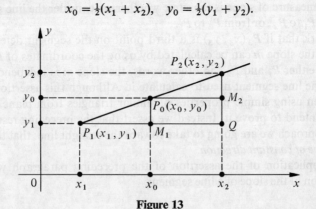

Figure 13

Proof. We make use of the result from plane geometry that corresponding sides of similar triangles are proportional. Using the triangles $P_1 M_1 P_0$ and

$P_1 Q P_2$, we have

$$\frac{\overline{P_1 M_1}}{\overline{P_1 Q}} = \frac{\overline{P_1 P_0}}{\overline{P_1 P_2}} = \frac{1}{2},$$

since P_0 is the midpoint of $P_1 P_2$. It follows that M_1 is the midpoint of $P_1 Q$. This, in turn, implies that the abscissa of M_1—and hence of P_0—is

$$x_0 = \tfrac{1}{2}(x_1 + x_2).$$

In a similar way, using triangles $P_0 M_2 P_2$ and $P_1 Q P_2$, we show that M_2 is the midpoint of $Q P_2$. Thus the ordinate of M_2—and hence of P_0—is

$$y_0 = \tfrac{1}{2}(y_1 + y_2). \quad \blacksquare$$

We point out that the problems of distance, direction, and midpoint with which we have just been concerned all were expressed in terms of a line segment determined by two points. We want now to extend the concept of slope to an entire line; this can be done very easily, since a line is a curve of *constant direction*.

Definition 11. *The slope of a line is the slope of any segment on that line.*

We next define two lines to be *parallel* to mean that they have the *same direction*. From this we immediately obtain the following result.

Theorem 20. *Two lines with slopes are parallel if and only if their slopes are equal.*

There is an analogous theorem concerning the arithmetical relation between slopes of perpendicular lines.

Theorem 21. *Let L_1 and L_2 be two lines with slopes m_1 and m_2, respectively. Then L_1 and L_2 are perpendicular if and only if $m_1 m_2 + 1 = 0$. In symbols,*

$$L_1 \perp L_2 \Leftrightarrow m_1 m_2 + 1 = 0.$$

Proof. Because of Theorem 20, we may consider lines through the origin (see Figure 14).

Suppose first that L_1 and L_2 are perpendicular. Take points $P_1(1, y_1)$ and $P_2(1, y_2)$ on L_1 and L_2, respectively. Then, by Theorem 18, $m_1 = y_1$ and $m_2 = y_2$. Now, we use the Pythagorean Theorem on the triangle $O P_1 P_2$:

$$\overline{P_1 P_2}^2 = \overline{OP_1}^2 + \overline{OP_2}^2,$$

or,

$$(y_1 - y_2)^2 = (1 + y_1^2) + (1 + y_2^2).$$

Upon squaring the left-hand side and simplifying the equation, we get

$$-2 y_1 y_2 = 2,$$

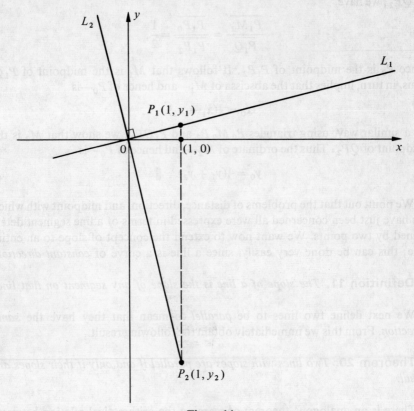

Figure 14

or

$$m_1 m_2 + 1 = 0,$$

since $y_1 = m_1$ and $y_2 = m_2$.

In order to prove the other half of the theorem, we can start with $m_1 m_2 + 1 = 0$, reverse the steps and use, finally, the *converse* of the Pythagorean Theorem. ∎

We can now discuss symmetry.

Definition 12.

(a) *Two points P_1 and P_2 are **symmetric with respect to a line** $L \Leftrightarrow L$ is the perpendicular bisector of the segment determined by P_1 and P_2.*

(b) *Two points P_1 and P_2 are **symmetric with respect to a point** $P_0 \Leftrightarrow P_0$ is the midpoint of the segment determined by P_1 and P_2.*

Definition 13. *A set S of points in the plane is **symmetric with respect to a line L** (point P_0) $\Leftrightarrow \forall P_1 \in S \Rightarrow \exists P_2 \in S$ such that P_1 and P_2 are symmetric with respect to the line L (point P_0).*

The essential part of Definition 13 is that the second point P_2 be *in* S.
We can now give conditions for symmetry with respect to coordinate axes and to the origin.

Lemma 3.
(a) $P_1(x_1, y_1)$ and $P_2(x_2, y_2)$ are symmetric with respect to the y-axis

$$\Leftrightarrow \begin{cases} x_2 = -x_1 \\ y_2 = y_1 \end{cases}.$$

(b) $P_1(x_1, y_1)$ and $P_2(x_2, y_2)$ are symmetric with respect to the x-axis

$$\Leftrightarrow \begin{cases} x_2 = x_1 \\ y_2 = -y_1 \end{cases}.$$

(c) $P_1(x_1, y_1)$ and $P_2(x_2, y_2)$ are symmetric with respect to the origin

$$\Leftrightarrow \begin{cases} x_2 = -x_1 \\ y_2 = -y_1 \end{cases}.$$

Proof. Exercise for student. ▌

Theorem 22. *A set S of points in the plane is symmetric with respect to the*

(a) *y-axis* $\Leftrightarrow (x, y) \in S \Rightarrow (-x, y) \in S$.
(b) *x-axis* $\Leftrightarrow (x, y) \in S \Rightarrow (x, -y) \in S$.
(c) *origin* $\Leftrightarrow (x, y) \in S \Rightarrow (-x, -y) \in S$.

Proof. Lemma 3. ▌

Corollary 1. *If a set S is symmetric with respect to both the x-axis and the y-axis, then S is symmetric with respect to the origin.*

In case the set S is the graph G_f of a function f, parts (a) and (c) of Theorem 22 can be put in the following form, since for points $(x, y) \in G_f, y = f(x)$.

Corollary 2. *The graph G_f of a function f is symmetric with respect to the*

(a) *y-axis* $\Leftrightarrow f(-x) = f(x)$.
(b) *origin* $\Leftrightarrow f(-x) = -f(x)$.

Note that the graph of a function cannot be symmetric with respect to the x-axis. (Why?)
Functions which have the properties specified in the preceding corollary are sufficiently important to have special names.

Definition 14. *Let f be a function with domain X which is symmetric with respect to the origin (i.e., $x \in X \Rightarrow -x \in X$). Then*

(a) *f is **even*** $\Leftrightarrow \forall x \in X \Rightarrow f(-x) = f(x)$.
(b) *f is **odd*** $\Leftrightarrow \forall x \in X \Rightarrow f(-x) = -f(x)$.

Thus, according to Definition 14 and Corollary 2, the graph of an even function is symmetric with respect to the y-axis, whereas the graph of an odd function is symmetric with respect to the origin. The names "even" and "odd" come from the fact that every polynomial function containing only even powers of x is even and every polynomial function containing only odd powers of x is odd. For example,

$$f : x \rightarrow 2x^6 + 5x^4 - x^2 + 7 \text{ is even}$$

and

$$g(x) = x^5 - 4x^3 + 7x$$

is odd. However, these polynomials are by no means the only examples of even and odd functions; for example, two of the trigometric functions are even and the other four are odd.

Symmetry with respect to the line which bisects the first and third quadrants is especially easy to detect. Although this sort of symmetry does not occur too often with graphs of functions we discuss it now, for it does show up in graphs of equations other than functional equations.

The line in question is characterized by the fact that for every point on it the ordinate is equal to the abscissa: in fact, a point $P(x, y)$ is on this line $\Leftrightarrow y = x$. From this it quickly follows that the slope of this line is 1.

Lemma 4. *Two points $P_1(x_1, y_1)$ and $P_2(x_2, y_2)$ are symmetric with respect to the line characterized by $y = x \Leftrightarrow \begin{cases} x_2 = y_1 \\ y_2 = x_1 \end{cases}$.*

Proof. We first prove the $\Rightarrow$ part of the theorem. We assume $P_1(x_1, y_1)$ and $P_2(x_2, y_2)$ are symmetric with respect to the line $y = x$ and attempt to express x_2 and y_2 in terms of x_1 and y_1 (see Figure 15).

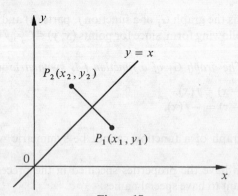

Figure 15

Since the slope of $y = x$ is 1, that of $P_1 P_2$ must be -1. Thus

$$\frac{y_2 - y_1}{x_2 - x_1} = -1$$

or

$$y_2 - y_1 = -x_2 + x_1,$$

which we write as

$$x_2 + y_2 = x_1 + y_1. \tag{12}$$

Next the midpoint of $P_1 P_2$ must lie on $y = x$, i.e., its two coordinates must be equal:

$$\tfrac{1}{2}(x_1 + x_2) = \tfrac{1}{2}(y_1 + y_2);$$

we write this equation as

$$x_2 - y_2 = -x_1 + y_1. \tag{13}$$

Solving Eqs. (12) and (13) simultaneously for x_2 and y_2 gives $x_2 = y_1$ and $y_2 = x_1$.

The proof of the $\Leftarrow$ part of the theorem is quite easy. Given two points $P_1(x_1, y_1)$ and $P_2(y_1, x_1)$, it is routine to show that the slope of the segment $\overline{P_1 P_2}$ is -1 and that the midpoint of the segment $\overline{P_1 P_2}$ is at $(\tfrac{1}{2}(x_1 + y_1), \tfrac{1}{2}(x_1 + y_1))$ on $y = x$. Thus, the line $y = x$ is the perpendicular bisector of the segment $\overline{P_1 P_2}$, and P_1 and P_2 are symmetric with respect to the line $y = x$. ∎

Theorem 23. *A set S of points in the plane is symmetric with respect to the line determined by $y = x \Leftrightarrow (x, y) \in S \Rightarrow (y, x) \in S$.*

Proof. Lemma 4. ∎

If the set S of Theorem 23 is the graph G of a function f, the condition of Theorem 23 takes an interesting form. For $(x, y) \in G \Rightarrow y = f(x)$; and if, as the condition for symmetry requires, $(y, x) \in G$, then $x = f(y)$. Substituting the first of these equations into the second gives

$$x = f(y) = f(f(x)) = (f \circ f)(x).$$

Thus the graph of a function f is symmetric with respect to $y = x \Leftrightarrow f \circ f = j$ (see Section 1.6). An example of such a function is the one for which $f(x) = \dfrac{1}{x}$.

Example 17. We illustrate some of the preceding ideas with a rather transparent example, the graph of the function f defined by

$$f(x) = \frac{1}{x^2 + 1}.$$

Thus

$$G = \left\{ (x, y) \mid y = \frac{1}{x^2 + 1} \right\}.$$

The following observations are available by inspection:

1. The domain of f is $\mathbf{R}$.
2. The y-intercept is $(0, 1)$. Since y cannot equal 0 there is no x-intercept.
3. $\forall x \Rightarrow y > 0$; thus the graph lies entirely above the x-axis.
4. f is an even function, so the graph is symmetric with respect to the y-axis.
5. Since, $\forall x \Rightarrow x^2 + 1 \geq 1$, it follows that for all x, $y \leq 1$. Combining this with 3, we have $0 < y \leq 1$, all $x \in \mathbf{R}$.
6. Clearly, numerically large x correspond to small y. A stronger statement can be made: the value of y can be made as close to zero as we please by taking $|x|$ suitably large. The geometric implication of this is that the graph approaches arbitrarily close to the x-axis for numerically large x. The x-axis is, in other words, a *horizontal asymptote* (definition to appear later).

Because of the symmetry referred to in 4, we can concentrate on the sketch of G for $x \geq 0$. The entire graph is then obtained by using the symmetry with respect to the y-axis (see Figure 16). The solid line shows G as it is; the dashed

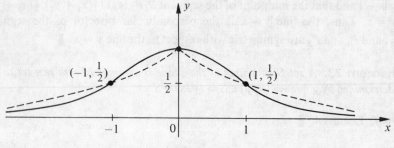

Figure 16

line indicates another possible version, not ruled out by the preceding analysis. We conclude this section with one more example.

Example 18. Let f be defined by

$$f(x) = \frac{1}{x^2 - 1}.$$

Thus

$$G = \left\{ (x, y) \mid y = \frac{1}{x^2 - 1} \right\}.$$

Observations analogous to those made in Example 17 are:

1. The domain of f is $X = \{x \mid x^2 \neq 1\} = \{x \mid x \neq \pm 1\}$.
2. The y-intercept is $(0, -1)$. There is no x-intercept.
3. $x^2 > 1 \Rightarrow y > 0$; $x^2 < 1 \Rightarrow y < 0$.
4. f is even, the graph is symmetric with respect to the y-axis.
5. For all $x \in X$, either $y > 0$ or $y \leq -1$. This fact is not transparent. Its proof appears in the exercises below.

6. The x-axis is a horizontal asymptote.
7. This function requires further study near the points where the denominator is zero. Because of the symmetry, we can focus attention on points near $x = 1$. Clearly, if x, and hence x^2, is near 1, then $x^2 - 1$ is near zero, so $y = \dfrac{1}{x^2 - 1}$ is large. In fact, we can make a stronger statement: we can make y as large as we please by taking x sufficiently close to 1. Geometrically, this is usually described by saying $x = 1$ is a *vertical asymptote*. We complete this discussion by pointing out that if x is close to 1 but $x > 1$, then $y > 0$, whereas if $x < 1$, but x is close to 1, then $y < 0$.

Utilizing the information obtained above enables us to obtain the sketch shown in Figure 17.

The dashed line in Figure 17 shows a possible variation, later to be found impossible by use of calculus. Note that the curve (singular) is in three separate pieces.

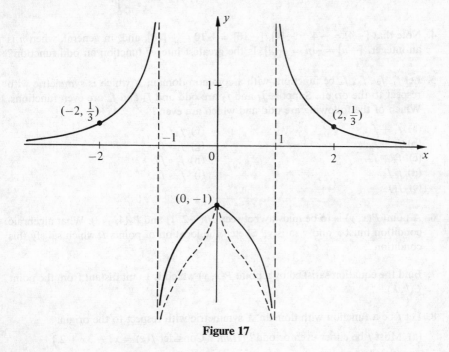

Figure 17

EXERCISES

1. Prove by two methods that each of the triangles with vertices A, B, C, is a right triangle.

(a) $A(-2, 1)$, $B(5, 4)$, $C(8, -3)$. Which is the right angle? Can you say anything about the other angles?

(b) $A(10, 11)$, $B(-3, 0)$, $C(-5, 5)$.

(c) $A(-5, -11)$, $B(4, 1)$, $C(7, -5)$.

2. For each of the triangles in Exercise 1 find the triangles whose vertices are the midpoints of the sides of triangle ABC. Are these midpoint triangles also right triangles?

3. Determine which of the following functions are even or odd. Carry out a geometric analysis and sketch the graph for each.

(a) $f(x) = x + |x|$.

(b) $f(x) = x|x|$.

(c) $f(x) = \dfrac{x}{|x|}$.

(d) $f(x) = \sqrt[3]{x}$.

(e) $f(x) = \dfrac{1}{x^2}$.

(f) $f(x) = \dfrac{x^2 - 1}{x^2 + 1}$.

(g) $f(x) = \dfrac{x^2 + 1}{x^2 - 1}$.

(h) $f(x) = x^4 - 4x^2$.

(i) $f(x) = x^3 - x$.

(j) $f(x) = \dfrac{x - 1}{x^2 + 1}$.

4. Note that $[-4] = -4 = -[4]$, $[-10] = -10 = -[10]$, and, in general, when n is an integer, $[-n] = -n = -[n]$. Is the greatest integer function an odd function?

5. Let f_1, f_2, f_3, f_4 be functions with a common domain X which is symmetric with respect to the origin. Suppose f_1 and f_3 are odd and f_2 and f_4 are even functions. Which of the following are odd and which are even?

(a) $f_1 + f_3$.

(b) $f_1 + f_2$.

(c) $f_2 + f_4$.

(d) $f_1 f_3$.

(e) $f_1 f_2$.

(f) $f_2 f_4$.

(g) $f_1 \circ f_2$.

(h) $f_1 \circ f_3$.

(i) $f_2 \circ f_4$.

6. A point $P(x, y)$ is to be midway between $P_1(-2, 1)$ and $P_2(4, -3)$. What algebraic condition must x and y satisfy? Sketch the location of points P which satisfy this condition.

7. Find the equation satisfied by a point $P(x, y)$ which is 1 unit distant from the point $C(h, k)$.

8. Let f be a function with domain X symmetric with respect to the origin.

(a) Must f be either even or odd? [*Hint.* Consider $f(x) = x^2 + 3x + 2$.]

(b) Note that we can write the formula for the function of the preceding hint as

$$f(x) = (x^2 + 2) + 3x$$
$$= f_1(x) + f_2(x),$$

where $f_1(x) = x^2 + 2$ is even and $f_2(x) = 3x$ is odd.

For a function f with domain symmetric with respect to the origin let

$$f_1(x) = \tfrac{1}{2}[f(x) + f(-x)]$$
$$f_2(x) = \tfrac{1}{2}[f(x) - f(-x)].$$

Show that

$$\text{(i) } f = f_1 + f_2$$
$$\text{(ii) } f_1 \text{ is even}$$
$$\text{(iii) } f_2 \text{ is odd.}$$

9. (a) Let $P_1(x_1, y_1)$ and $P_2(x_2, y_2)$ be symmetric with respect to the vertical line through $(a, 0)$ (i.e., the line characterized by the fact that every point on it has abscissa $x = a$). Show this is true $\Leftrightarrow \begin{cases} x_2 = 2a - x_1 \\ y_2 = y_1 \end{cases}$.

   (b) Show that the function f defined by $f(x) = (x - 1)^2$ is symmetric with respect to the vertical line $x = 1$.

10. See Example 18. Suppose $a > 0$. Sketch the graph of the function defined by

$$f(x) = \frac{1}{x^2 - a^2}$$

for a few values of a. In particular, investigate the behavior of the graph for small values of a and for very large values of a.

11. Prove Lemma 3.

12. Prove Assertion 5 in Example 18.
    [*Hint.* Solve the equation for x^2 in terms of y and argue from there.]

1.9   The Straight Line and Circle

In this section we consider the analytic representation of a few of the simpler and more common curves, including the straight line and the circle. Note that, whereas in Section 1.7 we began with the analytic entity, the functional formula, and sought to determine its geometric correspondent, the curve, we will be proceeding in the opposite direction in this section. Thus, starting with the geometric concept "straight line," we shall seek to determine the corresponding analytic entity, a functional equation.

As we have already indicated, we consider a *straight line* as a *curve of constant direction*, and we have defined two lines to be parallel if they have the same direction. Consequently, if we specify a direction, say $m = \frac{1}{2}$, we are specifying a set (frequently called in this connection a "family") of parallel lines. In order to determine a unique member of this family we need to impose a further condition, for example that the line go through the point $P_1(-2, 1)$ (see Figure 18).

Suppose now that $P(x, y)$ is any other point on the line through P_1 with slope $m = \frac{1}{2}$. We can use Definition 11 (for the slope) to obtain a condition which x and y must satisfy:

$$\frac{y - 1}{x - (-2)} = \frac{1}{2},$$

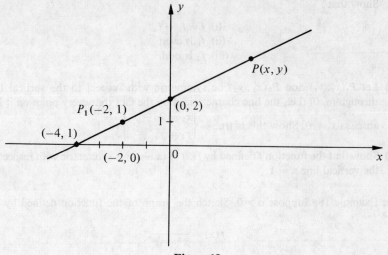

Figure 18

or

$$y - 1 = \tfrac{1}{2}(x + 2), \tag{14}$$

which can also be written as $y = \tfrac{1}{2}x + 2$.

Conversely, note that the coordinates of $P_1(-2, 1)$ satisfy (14), and that if (x, y) is any other pair which satisfies (14), one can divide by $x + 2$ to obtain the statement that the slope of the line determined by $P_1(-2, 1)$ and $P(x, y)$ is $\tfrac{1}{2}$. In other words, Eq. (14) is both necessary and sufficient that a point (x, y) lie on the line through P_1 with $m = \tfrac{1}{2}$.

It is a simple step to generalize the preceding example and assert that $P(x, y)$ is on the line through $P_1(x_1, y_1)$ with slope m if and only if x and y satisfy.

$$y - y_1 = m(x - x_1). \tag{15}$$

Equation (15) is called the *point-slope form* of the equation for the straight line.

If P_1 is the point $(0, b)$, the y-intercept of the line, then (15) takes the form

$$y - b = mx,$$

or

$$y = mx + b. \tag{16}$$

This is called the *slope-intercept form* of the equation for the straight line.

Of course the line could be determined by specifiying two points on the line, say $P_1(x_1, y_1)$ and $P_2(x_2, y_2)$, where $x_2 \neq x_1$. One can use this information to calculate the slope:

$$m = \frac{y_2 - y_1}{x_2 - x_1}.$$

Now Eq. (15) is applicable:

$$y - y_1 = \frac{y_2 - y_1}{x_2 - x_1}(x - x_1). \tag{17}$$

This is called the *two-point form* of the equation for the straight line. We shall mention other forms in later exercises.

The preceding discussion, dealing with lines with slope, of necessity does not apply to vertical lines; for the definition of slope requires of the two points that the abscissas be different. If we consider the line through two points with the same abscissas, say $P_1(3, -1)$ and $P_2(3, 5)$ we see that the line is vertical and that a point $P(x, y)$ is on this line $\Leftrightarrow x = 3$. Thus the equation $x = 3$ can be used as an exact and unambiguous description of the line (there is no restriction or requirement imposed on the ordinate y).

More generally, a vertical line with x-intercept a can be described by the equation $x = a$.

We can summarize the preceding discussion of straight lines as follows.

Theorem 24. *A set of points in the plane is a straight line $\Leftrightarrow$ the coordinates (x, y) of points in the set satisfy the equation*

$$Ax + By + C = 0, \tag{18}$$

where A and B are not both zero.

Proof. For the $\Rightarrow$ part of the proof we consider first a line with slope. Then the slope-intercept form $y = mx + b$ can be used to describe the line; but this equation can be written as

$$mx - y + b = 0,$$

which is in the form of (18) with $A = m$, $B = -1 \neq 0$, and $C = b$. If the line is vertical, its description is $x = a$, which can be written as

$$x - a = 0,$$

which is in the form of (18) with $A = 1 \neq 0$, $B = 0$, $C = -a$.

For the $\Leftarrow$ part of the proof we consider a set of points which satisfy (18). Suppose first that $B \neq 0$; then we can rewrite (18) as

$$y = \left(-\frac{A}{B}\right)x + \left(-\frac{C}{B}\right). \tag{19}$$

But this shows that the set of points is the line with slope $m = -\dfrac{A}{B}$ and y-intercept $b = -\dfrac{C}{B}$. Secondly, if $B = 0$, then we must have that $A \neq 0$, and Eq. (18) can be written as

$$x = -\frac{C}{A}; \tag{20}$$

this shows that the set of points is the vertical line which intersects the x-axis at $-\dfrac{C}{A}$. ∎

Example 19. Find the equation of the line through $P_1(3, -2)$ perpendicular to the line $4x + 2y - 1 = 0$.

We can write the equation of the given line as

$$y = -2x + \tfrac{1}{2}$$

to see that its slope is $m_1 = -2$. Thus the slope of the desired line is $m = \tfrac{1}{2}$. Using the point-slope form, we have the equation

$$y + 2 = \tfrac{1}{2}(x - 3),$$

or

$$y = \tfrac{1}{2}x - \tfrac{7}{2}, \qquad \text{or} \quad x - 2y - 7 = 0$$

(see Figure 19).

Example 20. Find the point of intersection of the two lines of Example 19. If (x_0, y_0) is the required point, then, using the two slope-intercept forms in

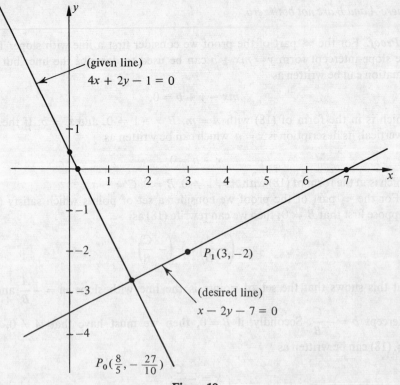

(given line)
$4x + 2y - 1 = 0$

$P_1(3, -2)$

(desired line)
$x - 2y - 7 = 0$

$P_0\left(\dfrac{8}{5}, -\dfrac{27}{10}\right)$

Figure 19

Example 19, x_0 and y_0 must satisfy

$$y_0 = -2x_0 + \tfrac{1}{2},$$

and

$$y_0 = \tfrac{1}{2}x_0 - \tfrac{7}{2}.$$

We can equate these values of y_0 and solve for x_0:

$$-2x_0 + \tfrac{1}{2} = \tfrac{1}{2}x_0 - \tfrac{7}{2}$$

or

$$-\tfrac{5}{2}x_0 = -\tfrac{8}{2},$$

so $x_0 = \tfrac{8}{5}$. Substituting this value into either of the slope-intercept forms gives $y_0 = -\tfrac{27}{10}$. Thus the point of intersection is $(\tfrac{8}{5}, -\tfrac{27}{10})$ (see Figure 19).

Example 21. Explain why the system of equations

$$\begin{cases} 2x + 3y = 4 \\ 6x + 9y = 10 \end{cases}$$

has no solution.

From the geometric point of view the first equation represents a line with slope $m_1 = -\tfrac{2}{3}$ and the second is a line with slope $m_2 = -\tfrac{6}{9} = -\tfrac{2}{3}$. Thus the two lines have the same direction and are either coincident (share all points) or do not intersect (share no points). The y-intercept of the first line is $b_1 = \tfrac{4}{3}$, whereas that of the second is $b_2 = \tfrac{10}{9} \neq b_1$. Consequently, the two lines are distinct and have *no* points in common:

$$\{(x, y) \mid 2x + 3y = 4\} \cap \{(x, y) \mid 6x + 9y = 10\} = \varnothing.$$

We turn now to another simple curve, the circle. Notice that the straight line and the circle can be given analogous definitions: a straight line is a set of points *equidirectional* from a given point, whereas a circle is a set of points *equidistant* from a given point.

If we take the given point, the center, as $C(h, k)$ and take the common distance, the radius, as r, and let $P(x, y)$ be a point on the circle, then Definition 9 tells us that x and y must satisfy

$$\sqrt{(x - h)^2 + (y - k)^2} = r,$$

or equivalently,

$$(x - h)^2 + (y - k)^2 = r^2. \tag{21}$$

Conversely, if a point (x, y) satisfies (21) it is obviously at a distance r from the point (h, k). Thus (21) provides an analytic representation of the circle.

As a special case, if the center is at the origin and the radius is $r = 1$, we have the *unit circle* $x^2 + y^2 = 1$.

As another specific example, if the center is at $(3, 2)$, and the radius is $r = 4$, we have

$$(x - 3)^2 + (y - 2)^2 = 4^2,$$

or

$$x^2 + y^2 - 6x - 4y - 3 = 0. \tag{22}$$

These circles are shown as $\mathscr{C}_1$ and $\mathscr{C}_2$, respectively, in Figure 20.

Notice that if a point (x, y) on $\mathscr{C}_2$ also lies on $\mathscr{C}_1$ then $x^2 + y^2 = 1$; if we replace $x^2 + y^2$ by 1 in (22) and simplify, we obtain

$$3x + 2y + 1 = 0,$$

a straight line. If $\mathscr{C}_1$ and $\mathscr{C}_2$ have points in common these must also lie on this line (see Figure 20).

In general, if we write Eq. (21) in a form analogous to that of Eq. (22), we have

$$x^2 + y^2 - 2hx - 2ky + h^2 + k^2 - r^2 = 0. \tag{23}$$

This is a second degree equation in x and y, but it is by no means the most general; this would look like

$$Ax^2 + Bxy + Cy^2 + Dx + Ey + F = 0, \tag{24}$$

where at least one of A, B, C is different from zero.

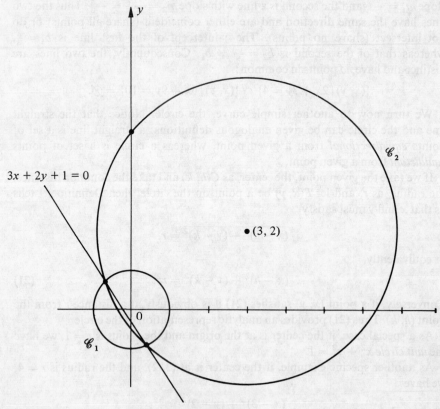

Figure 20

Necessary conditions on the coefficients of (24) for the resulting set of points to be a circle [for Eq. (24) to be in the form of (23)] are obviously

$$B = 0 \quad \text{and} \quad A = C \neq 0. \tag{25}$$

If the conditions in (25) are satisfied, the geometric features can be obtained by completing the squares in x and y. Consider, for example,

$$2x^2 + 2y^2 + 4x - 7y + 2 = 0. \tag{26}$$

We note that $A = C = 2$ and $B = 0$. Dividing by 2 and regrouping

$$(x^2 + 2x \quad) + (y^2 - \tfrac{7}{2}y \quad) = -1.$$

We now add 1 and $\tfrac{49}{16}$, respectively to the parenthetical expressions and the same numbers to the right side:

$$(x^2 + 2x + 1) + (y^2 - \tfrac{7}{2}y + \tfrac{49}{16}) = -1 + 1 + \tfrac{49}{16},$$

or

$$(x + 1)^2 + (y - \tfrac{7}{4})^2 = \tfrac{49}{16}.$$

Thus the original equation represents a circle with center at $(-1, \tfrac{7}{4})$ and radius $r = \tfrac{7}{4}$ (see Figure 21).

Note, however, that if the constant term (F) in Eq. (26) had been $> \tfrac{65}{8}$, for example, $F = 10$, then the same process would have converted (26) to

$$(x + 1)^2 + (y - \tfrac{7}{4})^2 = -\tfrac{15}{16}.$$

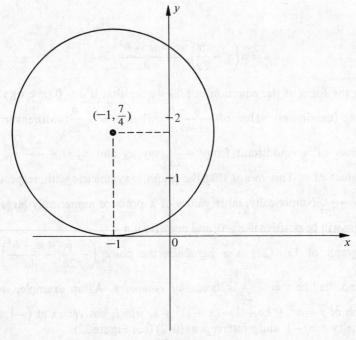

Figure 21

Clearly, the set of points (x, y) described by this equation is $\varnothing$. As a borderline case, if $F = \frac{65}{8}$, the resulting equation would be

$$(x + 1)^2 + (y - \tfrac{7}{4})^2 = 0,$$

an equation which is satisfied by the singleton $(\{(-1, \tfrac{7}{4})\}$. Thus we see that the conditions in (25) are necessary but not sufficient for an equation of type (24) to represent a circle.

We look at one further special case of Eq. (24) at this time. We can obtain what we want by choosing the following values for the coefficients in Eq. (24):

$$A = -a \neq 0, \qquad B = C = 0, \qquad D = -b, \qquad E = 1, \qquad F = -c.$$

This assignment gives us

$$y = ax^2 + bx + c, \qquad \text{where} \quad a \neq 0. \tag{27}$$

To obtain geometric information about the set of points determined by (27) we complete the square in x:

$$y = a\left(x^2 + \frac{b}{a}x \quad \right) + c$$

$$= a\left(x^2 + \frac{b}{a}x + \frac{b^2}{4a^2}\right) + c - \frac{b^2}{4a},$$

or

$$y = a\left(x + \frac{b}{2a}\right)^2 + \frac{4ac - b^2}{4a}. \tag{28}$$

From the form of the equation in (28) we see that if $a > 0$ $(a < 0)$ y has its minimum (maximum) value of $\dfrac{4ac - b^2}{4a}$ when $x = -\dfrac{b}{2a}$. Moreover, if we take values of x equidistant from $-\dfrac{b}{2a}$, say x_1 and $x_2 = -\dfrac{b}{a} - x_1$, we get equal values of y. This means that the graph is symmetric with respect to the line $x = -\dfrac{b}{2a}$. Numerically, large values of x produce numerically large values of y; these will be positive if $a > 0$, and negative if $a < 0$.

The graph of Eq. (27) is a *parabola*; the point $\left(-\dfrac{b}{2a}, \dfrac{4ac - b^2}{4a}\right)$ is its *vertex* and the line $x = -\dfrac{b}{2a}$ is its *axis of symmetry*. As an example, we show the graph of $y = x^2 + 2x + 2 = (x + 1)^2 + 1$, which has vertex at $(-1, 1)$, axis of symmetry $x = -1$, and y intercept at $(0, 2)$ (see Figure 22).

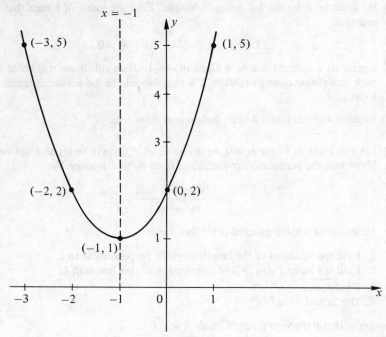

Figure 22

EXERCISES

1. Find the equations of the lines determined by the following conditions:

   (a) $m = -\frac{1}{3}$, $P_1(-6, 2)$.
   (b) $P_1(4, -3)$, $P_2(-5, 2)$.
   (c) x-intercept $(2, 0)$, y-intercept $(0, -4)$.
   (d) parallel to $2x - y + 4 = 0$, through $(-2, 5)$.
   (e) perpendicular to $2x - y + 4 = 0$, through $(3, 1)$.

2. Suppose $ab \neq 0$; if a line has x-intercept $(a, 0)$ and y-intercept $(0, b)$, show that its equation can be written in the *intercept-form*:

$$\frac{x}{a} + \frac{y}{b} = 1.$$

3. (a) Draw the graph of $Ax + 2y + 3 = 0$ for a few values of A. What do all graphs obtained in this way have in common?

   (b) Same as part (a), only for $4x + By + 3 = 0$.

   (c) Same as part (a), only for $4x + 2y + C = 0$.

4. Find the line with slope $m = -1$ which goes through the point of intersection of $3x - y - 1 = 0$ and $2x - 5y + 8 = 0$.

5. (a) Do Exercise 4 by the following technique: Find the value of t such that the equation

$$3x - y - 1 + t(2x - 5y + 8) = 0$$

represents a straight line with slope $m = -1$. Then substitute this value of t back into the preceding equation. The result should be the answer obtained for Exercise 4.

(b) Explain why the method described in part (a) works.

6. (a) Let $y = mx + b$, where $m \neq 0$, be a line L, let $P_1(x_1, y_1)$ be a point not on L. Show that the perpendicular distance d from P_1 to L is given by

$$d = \frac{|y_1 - mx_1 - b|}{\sqrt{m^2 + 1}}.$$

[*Hint.* One way to proceed is the following:

1. Find the equation of the line through P_1 perpendicular to L.
2. Find the point $P_2(x_2, y_2)$ of intersection of this line with L.
3. Find $\overline{P_1 P_2}$.
4. Dig in and have fun.]

(b) Show that the above formula holds if $m = 0$.

(c) What happens if P_1 is *on* L?

7. Describe geometrically the set of points

$$\{(x, y) \mid y < -2x + 3\}.$$

8. Describe analytically the set of points which lie above the line $y = x - 1$.

9. Graph the following equations:

(a) $|x - y| = 2$.
(b) $|x - y| \leq 2$.
(c) $|x| + |y| = 2$.
(d) $|x| - |y| = 2$.

(e) $[y - x] = 2$.
(f) $[y] = [x]$.
(g) $[y] - [x] = 2$.

10. Find the center and radius of each of the following circles:

(a) $x^2 + y^2 + 6x - 4y - 3 = 0$.
(b) $x^2 + y^2 - 8x + 2y + 17 = 0$.
(c) $2x^2 + 2y^2 - 4x + 6y - 5 = 0$.
(d) $3x^2 + 3y^2 - 12x + 15y + 16 = 0$.

11. Find the equation of the circle determined by

(a) $C(3, 4), r = 5$.
(b) Center $(-2, 4)$, tangent to the x-axis.
(c) Center $(-3, -2)$, tangent to $x + y = 2$.   [*Hint.* See Exercise 6(a).]

12. (a) Suppose we define the distance $\overline{P_1 P_2}^*$ between $P_1(x_1, y_1)$ and $P_2(x_2, y_2)$ as

$$\overline{P_1 P_2}^* = |x_1 - x_2| + |y_1 - y_2|.$$

Describe geometrically how $\overline{P_1 P_2}^*$ measures the distance between P_1 and P_2.

(b) What is the equation of the unit circle $(C(0, 0), r = 1)$ if the preceding definition of distance is used? Graph this unit circle.

13. Draw the graph of each of the following:

(a) $y = x^2 - 4x$.   (f) $y - 1 = \frac{1}{2}(x - 2)^2$.
(b) $y = x^2 - 4$.   (g) $y - 1 = -\frac{1}{2}(x - 2)^2$.
(c) $y = x^2 - 4x - 4$.   (h) $y = x^2 + x + 1$.
(d) $y = \frac{1}{4}x^2$.   (i) $y = |x^2 - 4x|$.
(e) $y = -\frac{1}{4}x^2 + 2$.

14. Draw each of the following on the same coordinate system:

$$y = 2x - x^2, \qquad 0 \leq x \leq 2$$
$$y = \sqrt{2x - x^2}, \qquad 0 \leq x \leq 2.$$

15. Draw each of the following pairs of curves on the same sketch:

(a) $y = x^2 + 2x + 3$, $y = x^2 - 2x + 3$.
(b) $y = x^2 + 2x + 3$, $y = x^2 + 2x - 3$.
(c) $y = x^2 + 2x + 3$, $y = \frac{1}{4}x^2 + 2x + 3$.

16. Refer to Exercise 15. Describe the geometric effect of changing a, b, or c in $y = ax^2 + bx + c$.

Chapter 2 Intuitive Introduction to Calculus

In this chapter we give an intuitive introduction to the basic ideas of calculus. What we shall find, however, is that the intuitive approach can be pushed only so far and then we encounter the need to master some deeper properties of the field of real numbers and of functions. We refer, in the case of **R**, to the Axiom of Continuity and some of its consequences, and, in the case of functions, to the concepts of limits and continuity. The next chapter will be devoted to a careful study of these ideas.

There is one point with regard to our procedure that bears special emphasis: Although we shall be drawing as much as possible on intuition, what we will be doing will be done correctly. Thus, the attitude of the student toward this material should *not* be that it need not be mastered and may be gone over only superficially because it will later be "done the right way." It is not a matter of doing something once "the easy way" and then a second time the "hard, right way." Our aim in taking this particular line is to point up the dependence of calculus on the Axiom of Continuity (thus indicating how inextricably calculus is rooted in the field of real numbers), and on those properties of functions centering on limits and continuity.

2.1 Three Problems

In this section we solve three problems which, in their initial formulation, may seem quite different. We shall find, however, that, when cast in a more general fashion, the problems and their solutions become strikingly similar, and the apparent differences become, from a mathematical point of view, quite superficial.

Problem 1. *Given a curve C and a point P on C, to find the line tangent to C at P.*

In approaching this problem we must first ask ourselves what we mean by a tangent line to a curve at a point. It is highly likely that our previous experience with this question has been limited to the case where the curve is a circle; from this special case we are led to such descriptions as "a tangent is a line which intersects the curve at one point only," or "a tangent is a line which intersects but does not cross the curve." Now both of these are correct characterizations of a tangent to a circle, but the special nature of the circle in this regard is clearly illustrated in Figure 1, where "reasonable" tangents have been drawn to the curve C at several points. The tangent at P_1 intersects C at P_3 and the tangent at P_2 crosses C at P_2. Clearly an approach to the concept of tangent different from those suggested by the case of a circle must be used.

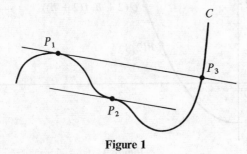

Figure 1

We advance the following argument. By a tangent is meant a straight line; one of the widely known facts about lines is that it takes *two* points to determine a line, and we are asking for a line at a *single* point of a curve. Of course, the behavior of the curve near the point must play a role, so we might be led to approximate the tangent at a point P on C by drawing the line through P and a nearby point Q (see Figure 2). If this seems to give a reasonable approximation, we could consider the line through P and a point Q_1 closer to P (than was Q); then we could try $\overline{PQ_2}$, $\overline{PQ_3}$, etc., where Q_2, Q_3, ..., are points on C which are taken closer, and closer to P. Perhaps there might be a uniquely determined line

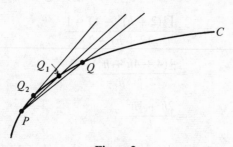

Figure 2

which is in some sense a limit of such a set of secant lines. If so, this should surely have the properties sought after in a tangent line.

We can put the whole matter in sharper focus by expressing the problem in analytic terms. To be explicit, suppose C is the graph of a function f; in fact, to be more explicit, suppose f is given by the formula $f(x) = \frac{1}{2}x^2 - 1$ and suppose the point is $P(2, 1)$ (see Figure 3).

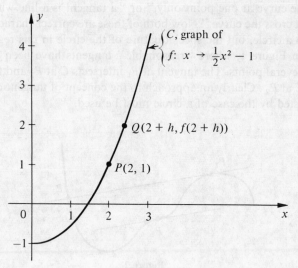

Figure 3

Since the tangent to C at P must go through P, we can use the point-slope form to write the equation of the desired line as

$$y - 1 = m(x - 2),$$

thus reducing (in this case) the original problem to that of the determination of the slope m. To follow the argument previously advanced, we consider a point Q "near" P. One way to achieve this is to take Q on C with abscissa $2 + h$, where h is understood to be small. Note that in Figure 3 h is taken as positive, but this is not necessary; if h were negative then Q would lie to the left of P. Thus the slope, m_{PQ}, of the secant line through P and Q, is given by

$$m_{PQ} = \frac{[\frac{1}{2}(2 + h)^2 - 1] - 1}{(2 + h) - 2}$$

$$= \frac{\frac{1}{2}(4 + 4h + h^2) - 2}{h}$$

$$= \frac{2h + \frac{1}{2}h^2}{h}$$

$$m_{PQ} = 2 + \frac{1}{2}h, \qquad \text{provided} \quad h \neq 0.$$

The restriction that $h \neq 0$, essential to the last algebraic step, is in fact in keeping with our choice of Q as a point different from P. Now, since the geometric statement "taking Q close to P" is equivalent to the analytic statement "taking h close to 0," the earlier question of finding a unique line which is the limit of secant lines as Q approaches P translates into the question of finding a unique number m which is the limit of the slopes m_{PQ} as h approaches 0. The standard symbols are

$$\lim_{h \to 0} (2 + \tfrac{1}{2}h) = m.$$

(This is read: the limit, as h approaches zero, of two plus one-half h equals m.) Intuitively it would seem that 2 is the likely candidate, i.e.,

$$\lim_{h \to 0} (2 + \tfrac{1}{2}h) = 2.$$

If we accept this statement, then the problem of finding the tangent line to C at $P(2, 1)$ is completely solved: the desired line is the one with equation $y - 1 = 2(x - 2)$. A careful drawing of the curve and the line obtained makes the result appear at least acceptable (see Figure 4).

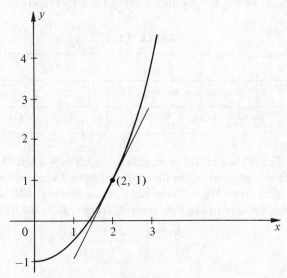

Figure 4

We conclude our discussion of this problem by putting in a general form the key expression: that for the slope of the tangent line. If we are considering the graph of a function f and seek the tangent line at $(a, f(a))$ then the preceding method produces as slope of the tangent, the number

$$m = \lim_{h \to 0} \frac{f(a + h) - f(a)}{h}. \tag{1}$$

We must, of course, keep in mind the fact that we have thus far interpreted the symbol "lim" only intuitively.

We consider now the second of the three problems mentioned at the beginning of this section.

Problem 2. *An object, or particle, is traveling along a straight line. If its directed distance from a specified point on the line is known at any time t, find a measure of the velocity of the particle.*

As was the case with Problem 1, we must agree on the meaning of the key word, in this instance "velocity." However, here we find it advisable to work with a specific example immediately. Suppose, then we focus attention on the case of a falling body.

If we assume an object falling from rest from a height great enough so that the distances which follow are meaningful and if we neglect the resistance of the air, then the distance s (in feet) traveled in t seconds is given approximately by

$$s = s(t) = 16t^2, \qquad t \geq 0.$$

(In Section 2.9 we derive this result.) In Table 2.1 we give, along with a few values of s and t, the differences Δs between consecutive values of s. Thus the kth entry in the Δs row is the distance travelled during the kth second.

TABLE 2.1

t	0	1	2	3	4	5	6
s	0	16	64	144	256	400	576
Δs		16	48	80	112	144	176

We observe that in the first two seconds the object falls a total of 64 ft, or an average of 32 ft/sec, whereas in the time interval (also 2 sec long) between $t = 4$ and $t = 6$ the object drops $576 - 256 = 320$ ft, or an average of 160 ft/sec. Thus if we define *average velocity* in the time interval from t_1 to t_2 sec $(t_1 < t_2)$ as

$$\left. \begin{array}{c} \text{average velocity} \\ [t_1, t_2] \end{array} \right\} = \frac{s(t_2) - s(t_1)}{t_2 - t_1},$$

then we have

$$\left. \begin{array}{c} \text{average velocity} \\ [0, 2] \end{array} \right\} = \frac{s(2) - s(0)}{2 - 0} = \frac{64 - 0}{2} = 32 \text{ ft/sec,}$$

$$\left. \begin{array}{c} \text{average velocity} \\ [2, 4] \end{array} \right\} = \frac{s(4) - s(2)}{4 - 2} = \frac{256 - 64}{2} = 96 \text{ ft/sec,}$$

and

$$\left. \begin{array}{c} \text{average velocity} \\ [2, 3] \end{array} \right\} = \frac{s(3) - s(2)}{3 - 2} = \frac{144 - 64}{1} = 80 \text{ ft/sec.}$$

We ask now if we can determine, in a reasonable way, a velocity, not averaged over an interval of time, but at an *instant* of time, say $t = 2$, an *instantaneous velocity*. (If the falling body carried a speedometer, then its reading at the end of 2 seconds of fall is what we seek.) We proceed in a fashion similar to that used in finding the slope of the tangent line. Thus in the interval from $t = 2$ sec to $t = 2 + h$ sec (we suppose temporarily that $h > 0$, if $h < 0$, an obvious modification in what follows will give the same final result) we have

$$
\begin{aligned}
\left.\begin{array}{c}\text{average velocity}\\ [2, 2 + h]\end{array}\right\} &= \frac{s(2 + h) - s(2)}{2 + h - 2} \\
&= \frac{16(2 + h)^2 - 64}{h} \\
&= \frac{64h + 16h^2}{h} \\
&= 64 + 16h \ \text{ft/sec},
\end{aligned}
$$

if $h \neq 0$.

It would seem reasonable to consider the instantaneous velocity at $t = 2$ seconds to be the limiting value, if we can agree upon one, of the preceding average velocity as "h approaches 0." But the obvious candidate for such a limiting value would seem to be 64. Thus we write

$$
v = v(2) = \lim_{h \to 0} (64 + 16h) = 64 \ \text{ft/sec}.
$$

More generally, if $a \geq 0$, we can find the instantaneous velocity at $t = a$ sec, by the same technique. For

$$
\begin{aligned}
\left.\begin{array}{c}\text{average velocity}\\ [a, a + h]\end{array}\right\} &= \frac{s(a + h) - s(a)}{a + h - a} = \frac{16(a + h)^2 - 16a^2}{h} \\
&= \frac{32ah + 16h^2}{h} \\
&= 32a + 16h \ \text{ft/sec}, \qquad \text{if } h \neq 0.
\end{aligned}
$$

Then

$$
v(a) = \lim_{h \to 0} (32a + 16h) = 32a \ \text{ft/sec},
$$

provided we agree that "the limit, as h approaches 0, of $32a + 16h$ is $32a$."

A further generalization is in order. Suppose an object is moving along a straight line in such a way that its distance s in feet from some fixed point at time t seconds is given by a function s, i.e., $s = s(t)$. Then we have

$$
\left.\begin{array}{c}\text{average velocity}\\ [a, a + h]\end{array}\right\} = \frac{s(a + h) - s(a)}{(a + h) - a} = \frac{s(a + h) - s(a)}{h},
$$

and the approach used above to instantaneous velocity would suggest that the velocity at $t = a$ seconds be given by

$$v(a) = \lim_{h \to 0} \frac{s(a + h) - s(a)}{h}. \tag{2}$$

This is, of course, the same as the expression obtained for the slope of the tangent to the graph of f at the point $(a, f(a))$.

Problem 3. (We shall state the problem in the course of the following discussion.)

We consider a possibly irregularly shaped rod or wire, say 10 cm long. We associate a one-dimensional coordinate system with the rod as indicated in Figure 5. For our purposes here we consider only the length of the rod from the

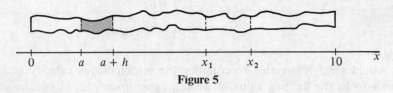

Figure 5

left end, ignoring other dimensions. It is possible, experimentally, to determine the mass (in grams, say) of the rod between the left end, $x = 0$, and any point $x \le 10$; i.e., we can consider given a mass function m with values $m(x)$, where $0 \le x \le 10$. Clearly, if $0 \le x_1 < x_2 \le 10$, $m(x_2) - m(x_1)$ represents the mass between the points x_1 and x_2 on the rod. If this number (of grams) is divided by the length $x_2 - x_1$, the resulting number (units: grams per centimeter) is called the *average density*:

$$\left. \begin{array}{c} \text{average density} \\ [x_1, x_2] \end{array} \right\} = \frac{m(x_2) - m(x_1)}{x_2 - x_1}.$$

We are interested in the possibility of defining a "pointwise" density for each value of x, $0 < x < 10$. In view of the discussion of the preceding two problems there should be no need to dwell on the task here. If $0 < a < 10$ and $h > 0$ such that $a + h < 10$, then

$$\left. \begin{array}{c} \text{average density} \\ [a, a + h] \end{array} \right\} = \frac{m(a + h) - m(a)}{(a + h) - a},$$

and, using the lower case Greek delta, δ, for density, we would have

$$\delta(a) = \lim_{h \to 0} \frac{m(a + h) - m(a)}{h} \tag{3}$$

provided it is possible to obtain a value for the limit.

Once again we suggest that this expression be compared with (1) and (2) obtained at the end of Problems 1 and 2, respectively. In the next section we will follow up on the ideas suggested by the problems of this section.

EXERCISES

1. Use the technique illustrated in the discussion of Problem 1 to find tangents to the graphs of the following functions at the points indicated. Make a sketch of the graph and the tangent found.

(a) $f: x \to x^2$, $(2, 4)$.
(b) $f: x \to x^2$, $(0, 0)$.
(c) $f: x \to x^2$, (a, a^2).
(d) $f(x) = 2x - 1$, $(2, 3)$.
(e) $f(x) = mx + b$, $(0, b)$.

(f) $f(x) = 4x - x^2$, $(2, 4)$.
(g) $f: x \to 3$, $(1, 3)$.
(h) $f(x) = |x|$, $(2, 2)$.
(i) $f(x) = |x|$, $(-2, 2)$.

2. Is our intuition always reliable? Does every curve have a tangent at every point? Sketch the graphs of the following functions and, without doing any calculations, say whether or not there is a tangent at the point with abscissa 0.

(a) $f(x) = x^3$.
(b) $f(x) = |x|$.

(c) $\begin{cases} f(x) = x + 1, & \text{if } x \leq 0. \\ f(x) = x, & \text{if } x > 0. \end{cases}$

(d) $\begin{cases} f(x) = -x, & \text{if } x < 0. \\ f(x) = x^2, & \text{if } x \geq 0. \end{cases}$

(e) $\begin{cases} f(x) = -x^2, & \text{if } x \leq 0 \\ f(x) = x^2, & \text{if } x > 0 \end{cases}$.

(f) $\begin{cases} f(x) = x^2, & \text{if } x < 0 \\ f(x) = x, & \text{if } x \geq 0 \end{cases}$.

3. Consider the following "pathological" function: f is defined by

$$\begin{cases} fx) = 0, & \text{if } x \text{ is rational} \\ f(x) = 1, & \text{if } x \text{ is irrational} \end{cases}.$$

(a) What would the graph of f look like?

(b) What can you say about the tangent to the graph of f at a point—*you* pick the point?

4. One way of thinking intuitively about the relation between the tangent line to and the direction of a curve is this: a person walking along the curve and looking straight ahead should be looking in the direction of the tangent line—*and this must be so independently of the sense with which he traverses the curve, i.e., independently of whether he is walking away from a fixed point on the curve or toward that same fixed point.* Use this criterion to say whether or not the graphs of the functions with formula given below have tangents at the origin,

(a) $f(x) = x^2$.

(b) $\begin{cases} f(x) = x^2 - x, & \text{if } x < 0 \\ f(x) = x^2 + x, & \text{if } x \geq 0 \end{cases}$.

5. (a) Use your intuition to assign numerical values to the following limits:

(i) $\lim_{h \to 0} (2 + h) = ?$

(ii) $\lim_{h \to 0} (3 + 5h) = ?$

(iii) $\lim_{h \to 0} \dfrac{1}{3(3 + h)} = ?$

(b) Same as part (a), but for the following:

(i) $\lim\limits_{h \to 0} \dfrac{2h + h^2}{h} = ?$ $\left[Hint: \quad \dfrac{2h + h^2}{h} = (2 + h)\dfrac{h}{h} \right]$

(ii) $\lim\limits_{h \to 0} \dfrac{3h + 5h^2}{h} = ?$

(iii) $\lim\limits_{h \to 0} \dfrac{h}{3h(3 + h)} = ?$

(c) What condition must be imposed on h so that the limits in (b) can be evaluated?

6. An object is thrown from a very high building in such a way that the distance s in feet it has fallen after t seconds is given by $s = 40t + 16t^2$.

(a) Find the average velocity during the first two seconds.

(b) Find the average velocity in the interval between $t = 2$ and $t = 4$ seconds.

(c) Use the methods of the text to find the instantaneous velocity at time $t = 2$.

(d) Find the instantaneous velocity at time $t = a$ seconds.

7. An object starts at the origin at $t = 0$ and travels to the right along the x-axis at the constant speed of 4 ft/sec.

(a) If s is the distance in feet the object is from the origin at the end of t seconds, write the relation between s and t.

(b) Use the method of the text to find the instantaneous velocity at time $t = 2$ seconds.

(c) Are you surprised at the result found at (b)?

8. Use your intuition to assign values to the following limits:

(a) $\lim\limits_{h \to 0} (4h + h^2)$.   (b) $\lim\limits_{h \to 0} (3 + \tfrac{1}{2}h)$.   (c) $\lim\limits_{h \to 2} (3 + \tfrac{1}{2}h)$.

(d) $\lim\limits_{h \to 1} \dfrac{h}{h}$.   (e) $\lim\limits_{h \to 0} \dfrac{h}{h}$.

9. A steel rod is 10 cm long. For $0 < a < 10$, find the value $\delta(a)$ of the density function if the mass function is

(a) $m(x) = x$, $0 \le x \le 10$.   (b) $m(x) = x^2$, $0 \le x \le 10$.

2.2 The Derivative

The common features of the three superficially different problems considered in the preceding section suggest that we indulge in some abstraction. This process will lead to the introduction of one of the two main concepts of calculus, the derivative.

It is fairly clear that in each of the problems discussed we were working with a function; more specifically, our interest centered on the ratio of the difference of two values of the function to the difference of their pre-images:

$$\frac{f(x_2) - f(x_1)}{x_2 - x_1} \quad \text{or} \quad \frac{f(x_0 + h) - f(x_0)}{(x_0 + h) - x_0}.$$

More than that, we asked if it were possible to attach a unique numerical value, a limiting value, to this ratio as one of the points in the domain "approached the other." When the limit sought exists the result is a number, but the examples considered suggest that this process could be carried out at many—perhaps all—points of the domain of the function. Thus we are led to make the following definition.

Definition 1. *Let f be a function. The **derivative** of f, or **derived function** f', is the function whose value at a point x_0 in the domain of f is given by*

$$f'(x_0) = \lim_{h \to 0} \frac{f(x_0 + h) - f(x_0)}{h}, \tag{4}$$

provided the limit exists.

We are guilty here of putting the cart before the horse, in view of the fact that we have so far given virtually no discussion of the limit concept upon which the derivative depends. As the following examples and subsequent discussion of this chapter will show, we can, if we do not get too ambitious, bypass the problem of limits temporarily and learn some useful facts about derivatives and their applications. At the same time we shall be getting a clearer idea of just what needs to be learned about limits when we do take them on (in Chapter 3).

We next comment on the basic nature of Definition 1. *An understanding of this simple point is absolutely essential to the comprehension of calculus.* The numerator on the right-hand side of (4) represents the *change* in the function between the points x_0 and $x_0 + h$ in its domain. Similarly, the denominator $[(x_0 + h) - x_0]$ represents the change in x. Thus the fraction represents a measure of the *average rate of change* of the function with respect to the change in the independent variable, the average being taken over the interval between x_0 and $x_0 + h$ (remember that h can be negative). The result of applying the limit operation is to give us a *measure of instantaneous rate of change of f with respect to x* at the point x_0. Thus the value of a derivative at a point can always be interpreted as a measure of rate of change of the function; the widespread applicability of rates of change suggests the importance of the derivative.

A few remarks about terminology and notation are in order. If a function has a derivative at a point x_0, i.e., if $f'(x_0)$ exists, then f is said to be *differentiable at x_0*. The process of finding the derivative of a function is spoken of as *differentiating*. Since differentiating can be thought of as an operation which takes us from a function f to the function f', the operation is frequently denoted by the symbol D. Thus, on the function level,

$$Df = f',$$

and on the point level,

$$Df(x_0) = f'(x_0).$$

Sometimes, when its use is indicated, a subscript is used with the D, and the operator may be used in the following way:

$$D_x x^2 = 2x,$$

or

$$D_t(16t^2) = 32t.$$

It is clear from Definition 1 that the domain of f' is a subset of the domain of f; thus if these domains are indicated by X_f and $X_{f'}$, then we always have

$$X_{f'} \subset X_f.$$

That $X_{f'}$ may be a proper subset of X_f will be illustrated in several of the subsequent examples; as these examples indicate, this result is not too unexpected. What is much less in accord with our intuition is the fact that functions exist which are, from one point of view, reasonably well behaved, and for which

$$X_f = \mathbf{R}, \qquad X_{f'} = \emptyset.$$

However, to give an example of one of these would be to get well beyond our present depth.

We now illustrate Definition 1 with a few examples. In all of these it will be necessary to make a decision about a limit statement. We shall do this unilaterally, but we now assert that all of these should be intuitively reasonable. With this blanket statement we intend to avoid, with each example, an appeal for agreement with the limit statement.

Example 1. Let f be defined by the formula $f(x) = x^3$. Since the domain $X_f = \mathbf{R}$ we attempt to find $f'(x_0)$ for a fixed but arbitrary point of $\mathbf{R}$. By Definition 1,

$$f'(x_0) = \lim_{h \to 0} \frac{f(x_0 + h) - f(x_0)}{h}$$

$$= \lim_{h \to 0} \frac{(x_0 + h)^3 - x_0^3}{h} = \lim_{h \to 0} \frac{x_0^3 + 3hx_0^2 + 3h^2 x_0 + h^3 - x_0^3}{h}$$

$$= \lim_{h \to 0} \frac{3hx_0^2 + 3h^2 x_0 + h^3}{h} \qquad \text{(assuming } h \neq 0)$$

$$= 3x_0^2.$$

Thus $Dx^3 = 3x^2$, or, equivalently, $D: x^3 \to 3x^2$.

Suppose we exploit this result a little. As no restriction seems to be imposed on x we conclude that $X_{f'} = X_f = \mathbf{R}$. Moreover, if we apply the derivative to the tangent problem, we see that at (0, 0) the slope of the tangent to *f* is zero, but at every other point of the graph the tangent has a positive slope. Thus, since $f'(-2) = 3(-2)^2 = 12$ (i.e., *f* is increasing 12 times as fast as is *x* at this point), the tangent line at $(-2, -8)$ has the equation

$$y + 8 = 12(x + 2).$$

or

$$y = 12x + 16.$$

The graph of *f* is shown in Figure 6.

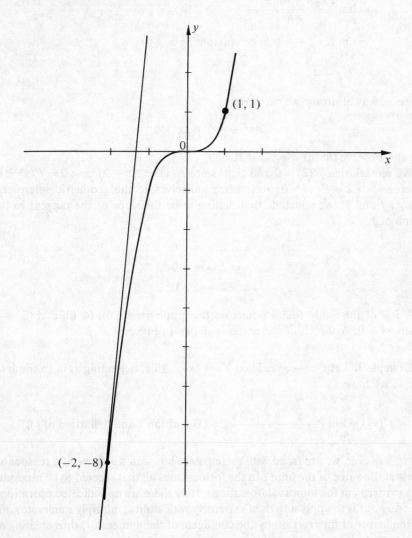

Figure 6

Example 2. Let f be the quadratic function defined by $f(x) = x^2 - 4x$. Then, if x_0 is an arbitrary but fixed point of $X_f = \mathbf{R}$, we have

$$f'(x_0) = \lim_{h \to 0} \frac{f(x_0 + h) - f(x_0)}{h} \qquad \text{(Definition 1)}$$

$$= \lim_{h \to 0} \frac{[(x_0 + h)^2 - 4(x_0 + h)] - [x_0^2 - 4x_0]}{h} \qquad \text{(definition of } f\text{)}$$

$$= \lim_{h \to 0} \frac{x_0^2 + 2x_0 h + h^2 - 4x_0 - 4h - x_0^2 + 4x_0}{h}$$

$$= \lim_{h \to 0} \frac{2x_0 h - 4h + h^2}{h}$$

$$= \lim_{h \to 0} (2x_0 - 4 + h) \qquad \text{(assuming } h \neq 0\text{)}$$

$$= 2x_0 - 4.$$

Since x_0 was arbitrary we can write

$$D(x^2 - 4x) = 2x - 4;$$

we also observe that $X_{f'} = X_f = \mathbf{R}$.

We remark that $f'(2) = 0$ and that, since $f'(x) = 2(x - 2)$, $x < 2 \Rightarrow f'(x) < 0$, whereas $x > 2 \Rightarrow f'(x) > 0$. Restricting ourselves to the geometric interpretation of f and f', we conclude that, letting m be the slope of the tangent to the graph of f,

$$x < 2 \Rightarrow m < 0$$
$$x = 2 \Rightarrow m = 0$$
$$x > 2 \Rightarrow m > 0.$$

A few of the easily found points on the graph are $(0, 0)$, $(4, 0)$, and $(2, -4)$ where $m = 0$. A sketch of the graph is shown in Figure 7.

Example 3. Let $f : x \to \sqrt{x}$. Then $X_f = \{x \mid x \geq 0\}$. Beginning as in Examples 1 and 2, we have

$$f'(x_0) = \lim_{h \to 0} \frac{\sqrt{x_0 + h} - \sqrt{x_0}}{h} \qquad \text{(Definition 1 and definition of } f\text{)}.$$

Now, however, we are faced with an impasse: how can we arrive at a reasonable guess at the value of the limit? In the former cases all that seemed to be necessary was to carry out the indicated operations. Here there are no indicated operations. The way out is to apply a trick of extremely wide utility: multiply numerator and denominator of the fraction by the conjugate of the numerator, thus creating an operation to be carried out. This gives

$$f'(x_0) = \lim_{h \to 0} \frac{\sqrt{x_0 + h} - \sqrt{x_0}}{h} \cdot \frac{\sqrt{x_0 + h} + \sqrt{x_0}}{\sqrt{x_0 + h} + \sqrt{x_0}}$$

$$= \lim_{h \to 0} \frac{x_0 + h - x_0}{h[\sqrt{x_0 + h} + \sqrt{x_0}]}$$

$$= \lim_{h \to 0} \frac{h}{h[\sqrt{x_0 + h} + \sqrt{x_0}]}$$

$$= \lim_{h \to 0} \frac{1}{\sqrt{x_0 + h} + \sqrt{x_0}} \qquad \text{(assuming } h \neq 0\text{)}.$$

We pause here to remark that the trick of rationalizing the numerator "freed" the h from the numerator, permitting the dividing out of the h from the numerator and denominator. We now assert that carrying out the limit operation leads to

$$f'(x_0) = \frac{1}{\sqrt{x_0} + \sqrt{x_0}} = \frac{1}{2\sqrt{x_0}},$$

because when h is close to zero $x_0 + h$ is close to x_0 and $\sqrt{x_0 + h}$ is close to $\sqrt{x_0}$. Expressed differently, this result says $D\sqrt{x} = \dfrac{1}{2\sqrt{x}}$.

We immediately notice that we must exclude zero from $X_{f'}$; thus $X_{f'} = \mathbf{R}^+$ is a proper subset of X_f. We can without difficulty make the following additional observations about the behavior of f': for all $x > 0$, $f'(x) > 0$; for x close to zero $f'(x)$ is very large; and, at the other extreme, for x large, $f'(x)$ is close to zero. Interpreted in terms of the tangent line, these statements say that the tangent to the graph of f always has a positive slope, the tangent is nearly vertical at points

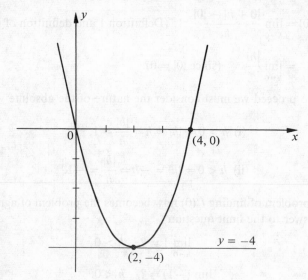

(4, 0)

$y = -4$

(2, −4)

Figure 7

on the graph near the origin, and the tangent is nearly horizontal at points on the graph with large abscissas. In particular, since $f(1) = 1, f'(1) = \frac{1}{2}$, the tangent at $(1, 1)$ is the line $y - 1 = \frac{1}{2}(x - 1)$, or $y = \frac{1}{2}x + \frac{1}{2}$ (see Figure 8).

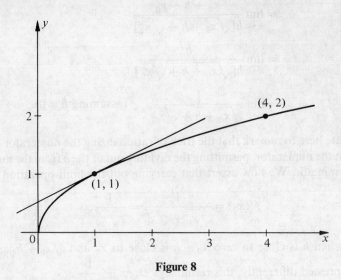

Figure 8

Example 4. Consider now the absolute value function $f : x \to |x|$. We plan to leave for the exercises the proofs of the assertions

$$x < 0 \Rightarrow f'(x) = -1$$
$$x > 0 \Rightarrow f'(x) = 1$$

and consider only $f'(0)$. Thus,

$$f'(0) = \lim_{h \to 0} \frac{|0 + h| - |0|}{h} \qquad \text{(Definition 1 and definition of } f)$$

$$= \lim_{h \to 0} \frac{|h|}{h} \qquad \text{(since } |0| = 0).$$

In order to proceed we must consider the nature of the absolute value:

$$\text{(i)} \ h > 0 \Rightarrow |h| = h \Rightarrow \frac{|h|}{h} = 1,$$

$$\text{(ii)} \ h < 0 \Rightarrow |h| = -h \Rightarrow \frac{|h|}{h} = -1.$$

Thus the problem of finding $f'(0)$ now becomes the problem of agreeing upon a unique answer to the limit question

$$\lim_{h \to 0} 1 = ?, \quad h > 0$$

$$\lim_{h \to 0} (-1) = ?, \quad h < 0.$$

The unilateral decision is that there is no unique answer, which is to say $f'(0)$ does not exist. See the graph of f in Figure 1.7. In general, we will find that $f'(x_0)$ fails to exist whenever the graph of f has a "corner" at $(x_0, f(x_0))$.

Example 5. As our final example of this section we consider the function $f : x \to \dfrac{1}{x}$. Clearly the domain $X_f = \{x \mid x \ne 0\}$. For the determination of f' we consider an arbitrary but fixed $x_0 \in X_f$. Then

$$
\begin{aligned}
f'(x_0) &= \lim_{h \to 0} \frac{\dfrac{1}{x_0 + h} - \dfrac{1}{x_0}}{h} \qquad \text{(Definition 1 and definition of } f) \\
&= \lim_{h \to 0} \frac{x_0 - (x_0 + h)}{h x_0 (x_0 + h)} \\
&= \lim_{h \to 0} \frac{-h}{h x_0 (x_0 + h)} \\
&= \lim_{h \to 0} \frac{-1}{x_0 (x_0 + h)} \\
&= \frac{-1}{x_0^2},
\end{aligned}
$$

since h close to $0 \Rightarrow x_0 + h$ close to x_0.

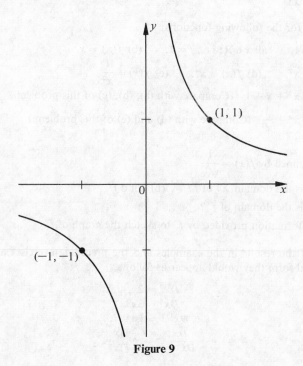

Figure 9

In different notation we have $D\left(\dfrac{1}{x}\right) = -\dfrac{1}{x^2}$. Notice that $X_{f'} = X_f$. Notice also that $x \in X_f \Rightarrow f'(x) < 0$; i.e., at every point of the graph of f there is a tangent line with negative slope. Since large (either positive or negative) values of x cause both $f(x)$ and $f'(x)$ to be close to zero, and since values of x close to zero are mapped by f into large (positive if x is positive, negative if x is negative) numbers, the graph of f is easily obtained as in Figure 9.

EXERCISES

1. Find $f'(x_0)$ for the functions defined as follows:

   (a) $f(x) = x^2$.   (b) $f(x) = 3x^2$.
   (c) $f(x) = -8x^2$.   (d) $f(x) = cx^2$.

2. If $f : x \to |x|$, find

   (a) $f'(2)$.   (b) $f'(-3)$.
   (c) $f'(x_0)$, where $x_0 > 0$. Assume h is chosen such that $x_0 + h > 0$.
   (d) $f'(x_0)$, where $x_0 < 0$. Assume h is chosen such that $x_0 + h < 0$.

3. Find the derivatives at the numbers indicated for the following functions:

   (a) $f(x) = x^2 + x + 1$, $a = 3$.   (b) $f(x) = x^3 - 1$, $a = 2$.
   (c) $f(x) = \dfrac{1}{x^2}$, $a = 4$.   (d) $f(x) = \sqrt{x - 1}$, $a = 5$.

4. Find $f'(a)$ for the following functions:

   (a) $f(x) = 1$,   all $x \in \mathbf{R}$; i.e., $f = 1$.   (b) $f(x) = x$.
   (c) $f(x) = x^2$.   (d) $f(x) = x^4$.   (e) $f(x) = \dfrac{1}{x^2}$.
   (f) $f(x) = x^2 + x + 1$ (Compare with (a), (b), (c) of this problem.)
   (g) $f(x) = x^4 + \dfrac{1}{x^2}$ (Compare with (d) and (e) of this problem.)

5. Let f be defined by $f(x) = \dfrac{1}{\sqrt{x}}$.

   (a) What is the domain X_f of f?   (b) Find f'.
   (c) What is the domain of f'?
   (d) Use information provided by f' to sketch the graph of f.

6. If some of the results in the examples and the preceding exercises are written in exponential form they would appear as follows:

$$Dx^2 = 2x,$$
$$Dx^3 = 3x^2,$$
$$Dx^{1/2} = \tfrac{1}{2}x^{-1/2},$$
$$Dx^{-1} = (-1)x^{-2},$$
$$Dx^{-1/2} = (-\tfrac{1}{2})x^{-3/2}.$$

(a) Do these suggest the presence of a pattern? If so, what is it?

(b) If you found an encouraging answer for part (a) try it out on a few other functions.

7. Let $f: t \rightarrow at^2 + bt + c$, where $a \neq 0$.

(a) Find f'. (b) Find $(f')'$.

(c) What interpretation can be given to $(f')'$?

2.3 Theorems for Calculating the Derivative

Before investigating a few applications of the derivative we attempt, for the sake of efficiency, to improve our procedures for finding the derivative.

We begin with two observations. First, the method used thus far in calculating f' for a function f is distressingly laborious. And second, there do seem to be certain patterns which one should be able to exploit in finding derivatives.

The fact is that before we are finished with our study of calculus we will have compiled a list of between 20 and 30 differentiation formulas, almost all of which should be learned as well as one learns the multiplication tables. However, our aim in this section will be to introduce only a few of the simpler, more essential results. Even so, our "proofs" of the few theorems below will of necessity be incomplete, because the assertions about derivatives involve limits, and we can only give complete and rigorous proofs of the theorems of this section after the limit concept is thoroughly developed. It is our hope that this arrangement will provide increased understanding of the discussion of limits (in Chapter 3).

We begin with derivatives for the constant and the identity functions. At the risk of belaboring the point, we state the formulas in several different, but equivalent, forms.

Theorem 1.

$$\begin{cases} (a_1) & Dc = 0. \\ (a_2) & D\mathbf{c} = \mathbf{0}. \\ (a_3) & c' = \mathbf{0}. \end{cases}$$

$$\begin{cases} (b_1) & Dx = 1. \\ (b_2) & j(x) = x \Rightarrow j'(x) = 1, \qquad \forall x \in \mathbf{R}. \\ (b_3) & Dj = \mathbf{1}. \\ (b_4) & j' = \mathbf{1}. \end{cases}$$

Before proving these two assertions we remark that the forms (a_1) and (b_1) are the more traditional ones, and they are the ones that are usually verbalized, e.g., in the case of (a_1): the derivative of a constant is zero. However, it should be borne in mind that the operation of differentiation is applied *to a function*. For that reason the other forms are more accurate.

Proof. Let $x_0 \in \mathbf{R}$ be fixed but arbitrary. Then

(a) $$\mathbf{c}'(x_0) = \lim_{h \to 0} \frac{\mathbf{c}(x_0 + h) - \mathbf{c}(x_0)}{h} \qquad \text{(Definition 1)}$$

$$= \lim_{h \to 0} \frac{c - c}{h} = \lim_{h \to 0} \frac{0}{h} = \lim_{h \to 0} 0$$

$$= 0.$$

Thus $D\mathbf{c} = \mathbf{0}$.

(b) We have, with x_0 as above,

$$j'(x_0) = \lim_{h \to 0} \frac{j(x_0 + h) - j(x_0)}{h} \qquad \text{(Definition 1)}$$

$$= \lim_{h \to 0} \frac{x_0 + h - x_0}{h} \qquad \text{(definition of } j)$$

$$= \lim_{h \to 0} \frac{h}{h}$$

$$= 1.$$

Thus $j' = 1$. ∎

We next show that, as an operator on functions, D is *linear*. This means, in symbols, that if f and g are differentiable functions and a and b are numbers, then $D(af + bg) = a(Df) + b(Dg)$. Actually, the result we state is in a slightly different—but equivalent—form. You will be asked in the exercises below to demonstrate the equivalence.

Theorem 2. *Let f and g be differentiable functions in some common domain X and let c be a number. Then*

$$\begin{cases} (a_1) & D(f + g) = Df + Dg \\ (a_2) & (f + g)' = f' + g' \end{cases}$$

$$\begin{cases} (b_1) & D(cf) = c(Df) \\ (b_2) & (cf)' = cf' \end{cases}$$

Proof. Let $x_0 \in X$ be arbitrary but fixed. Then

(a) $$(f + g)'(x_0) = \lim_{h \to 0} \frac{(f + g)(x_0 + h) - (f + g)(x_0)}{h} \qquad \text{(Definition 1)}$$

$$= \lim_{h \to 0} \frac{[f(x_0 + h) + g(x_0 + h)] - [f(x_0) + g(x_0)]}{h}$$

$$\text{(definition of } f + g)$$

$$= \lim_{h \to 0} \left[\frac{f(x_0 + h) - f(x_0)}{h} + \frac{g(x_0 + h) - g(x_0)}{h} \right]$$

$$= \lim_{h \to 0} \frac{f(x_0 + h) - f(x_0)}{h} + \lim_{h \to 0} \frac{g(x_0 + h) - g(x_0)}{h} \qquad (?)$$

$$= f'(x_0) + g'(x_0) \qquad \text{(Definition 1)}$$

$$= (f' + g')(x_0).$$

Thus $D(f + g) = Df + Dg$.

The step labeled "(?)" is essential to our result, but do we have a right to use it? It is a valid statement about limits which, loosely verbalized, can be described as "The limit of a sum is the sum of the limits." Its proof will appear in Chapter 3.

(b) We have, for $x_0 \in X$,

$$(cf)'(x_0) = \lim_{h \to 0} \frac{(cf)(x_0 + h) - (cf)(x_0)}{h} \qquad \text{(Definition 1)}$$

$$= \lim_{h \to 0} \frac{cf(x_0 + h) - cf(x_0)}{h} \qquad \text{(definition of } cf\text{)}$$

$$= \lim_{h \to 0} c \frac{f(x_0 + h) - f(x_0)}{h}$$

$$= c \lim_{h \to 0} \frac{f(x_0 + h) - f(x_0)}{h} \qquad (??)$$

$$= cf'(x_0) \qquad \text{(Definition 1)}$$

$$= (cf')(x_0).$$

Thus $D(cf) = c(Df)$, where c is a constant.

Again we have used, in the step (??), a valid but as yet unproved property of limits. The usual verbalization of the property is: "The limit of a constant times a function is the constant times the limit of the function." ∎

Corollary. *Let f and g be differentiable functions in some common domain X. Then*

$$D(f - g) = (Df) - (Dg)$$

or, alternatively,

$$(f - g)' = f' - g'.$$

Proof. Left as an exercise. ∎

Our next result is also of a general nature and concerns the derivative of a product. It would be nice if we could announce that, analogous to the result of Theorem 2a, "the derivative of a product is the product of the derivatives"; unfortunately, it does not come out that way.

Theorem 3. *Let f and g be functions differentiable in some common domain X. Then*

$$D(fg) = f(Dg) + g(Df)$$

or

$$(fg)' = fg' + gf'.$$

Proof. As our proof must be given on the point level, we begin by writing what we seek as our end result. It is, for arbitrary but fixed $x_0 \in X$,

$$(fg)'(x_0) = f(x_0)\, g'(x_0) + g(x_0)f'(x_0). \tag{5}$$

Making the usual start, then, we have

$$(fg)'(x_0) = \lim_{h \to 0} \frac{(fg)(x_0 + h) - (fg)(x_0)}{h} \qquad \text{(Definition 1)}$$

$$= \lim_{h \to 0} \frac{f(x_0 + h)g(x_0 + h) - f(x_0)g(x_0)}{h} \qquad \text{(definition of } fg\text{)}.$$

Now the question is: Where do we go from here? We have an expression which apparently inextricably interlinks the values of f and g. A glance at (5) shows we must somehow extract the values of f' and g'. This can be done by a trick which is frequently useful (see, for example, the proof in Chapter 3 of the very limit theorem for products used below): we add and subtract the same quantity to the expression on the right, thus changing its *form* but not its *value*.

$$(fg)'(x_0)$$

$$= \lim_{h \to 0} \frac{f(x_0 + h)g(x_0 + h) - f(x_0 + h)g(x_0) + f(x_0 + h)g(x_0) - f(x_0)g(x_0)}{h}$$

$$= \lim_{h \to 0} \left[f(x_0 + h)\frac{g(x_0 + h) - g(x_0)}{h} + g(x_0)\frac{f(x_0 + h) - f(x_0)}{h} \right]$$

$$= \lim_{h \to 0} \left[f(x_0 + h)\frac{g(x_0 + h) - g(x_0)}{h} \right] + \lim_{h \to 0} \left[g(x_0)\frac{f(x_0 + h) - f(x_0)}{h} \right] \tag{?}$$

$$= \lim_{h \to 0} \left[f(x_0 + h)\frac{g(x_0 + h) - g(x_0)}{h} \right] + g(x_0)\lim_{h \to 0}\frac{f(x_0 + h) - f(x_0)}{h} \tag{??}$$

$$= \lim_{h \to 0} \left[f(x_0 + h)\frac{g(x_0 + h) - g(x_0)}{h} \right] + g(x_0)f'(x_0) \qquad \text{(Definition 1)} \tag{6}$$

We pause to comment on what has been and what remains to be done. The steps above labeled (?) and (??) are identical to those discussed in the proof of Theorem 2. Comparing (6) to (5) we see that we have achieved half of our goal —the second term in (5); but we still have a limit on our hands. In fact, another look at both (5) and (6) suggests that we need the following:

$$\lim_{h \to 0} \left[f(x_0 + h) \frac{g(x_0 + h) - g(x_0)}{h} \right]$$

$$= \lim_{h \to 0} f(x_0 + h) \cdot \lim_{h \to 0} \frac{g(x_0 + h) - g(x_0)}{h} \qquad \text{(???)}$$

and

$$\lim_{h \to 0} f(x_0 + h) = f(x_0) \qquad \text{(????)}$$

If these steps are justifiable, then, using Definition 1, we can replace the first term on the right of (6) by

$$f(x_0)g'(x_0),$$

giving us the desired result (5).

Now the step indicated by (???) involves a third limit theorem: "The limit of a product is the product of the limits," which will be proved in Chapter 3. On the other hand, the step (????) seems quite acceptable, but it is equivalent to saying the function f is *continuous at* x_0†, a fact which will be shown, in Chapter 4, to follow from the hypothesis that $f'(x_0)$ exists. ∎

To give emphasis to the technique used in the proof of Theorem 3 we state and prove the following result. We can safely omit the detailed explanations given above, but references to limit operations (some of those already discussed plus one other) will be given in the same fashion as before.

Notice that the statement below is on the point level.

Theorem 4. *Let $f'(x_0)$ exist and suppose $f(x_0) \neq 0$. Then the function $\left(\dfrac{1}{f}\right)$ is differentiable at x_0 and*

$$\left(\frac{1}{f}\right)'(x_0) = \frac{-f'(x_0)}{(f(x_0))^2}.$$

Proof. We have

$$\left(\frac{1}{f}\right)'(x_0) = \lim_{h \to 0} \frac{\left(\frac{1}{f}\right)(x_0 + h) - \left(\frac{1}{f}\right)(x_0)}{h} \qquad \text{(Definition 1)}$$

$$= \lim_{h \to 0} \frac{\dfrac{1}{f(x_0 + h)} - \dfrac{1}{f(x_0)}}{h} \qquad \left(\text{definition of } \frac{1}{f}\right)$$

† As we shall see in Chapter 3, f is continuous at a point x_0 of its domain $\Leftrightarrow \lim\limits_{h \to 0} f(x_0 + h)$ $= f(x_0)$.

$$= \lim_{h \to 0} \frac{f(x_0) - f(x_0 + h)}{h f(x_0) f(x_0 + h)}$$

$$= \lim_{h \to 0} \left[\frac{-1}{f(x_0) f(x_0 + h)} \frac{f(x_0 + h) - f(x_0)}{h} \right]$$

$$= \left[\lim_{h \to 0} \frac{-1}{f(x_0) f(x_0 + h)} \right] \left[\lim_{h \to 0} \frac{f(x_0 + h) - f(x_0)}{h} \right] \quad \text{(???)}$$

$$= \left[\lim_{h \to 0} \frac{-1}{f(x_0) f(x_0 + h)} \right] f'(x_0) \quad \text{(Definition 1)}$$

$$= \frac{-f'(x_0)}{f(x_0)} \left[\lim_{h \to 0} \frac{1}{f(x_0 + h)} \right] \quad \text{(??)}$$

$$= \frac{-f'(x_0)}{f(x_0)} \frac{1}{\lim\limits_{h \to 0} f(x_0 + h)} \quad \text{(?????)}$$

$$= \frac{-f'(x_0)}{f(x_0)} \frac{1}{f(x_0)} \quad \text{(????)}$$

$$= \frac{-f'(x_0)}{(f(x_0))^2}.$$

The valid limit statement which covers the operation (?????) is the one with the slightly loose verbalization, "The limit of a quotient is the quotient of the limits." ∎

The next theorem is an immediate consequence of the preceding two results. Its proof will be left as an exercise.

Theorem 5. *Let f and g be functions differentiable in some common domain X. Let*

$$X_0 = \{ x \in X \mid g(x) \neq 0 \}.$$

Then on X_0 we have

$$\left(\frac{f}{g} \right)' = \frac{g f' - f g'}{g^2}, \quad \text{or} \quad D\left(\frac{f}{g} \right) = \frac{g(Df) - f(Dg)}{g^2},$$

i.e. for every $x \in X_0$,

$$\left(\frac{f}{g} \right)'(x) = \frac{g(x) f'(x) - f(x) g'(x)}{(g(x))^2}.$$

A verbalization of this complicated-looking result may make it easier to keep in mind. It says: "The derivative of a quotient is the denominator times the derivative of the numerator *minus* the numerator times the derivative of the denominator, all divided by the square of the denominator."

Our next result is an explicit one.

Theorem 6. *For all integers* $n \in \mathbf{Z}$

$$Dx^n = nx^{n-1}, \tag{7}$$

or

$$(j^n)' = nj^{n-1}.$$

If $n < 0$, *it is understood that* $x \neq 0$.

Proof. We consider three cases: (a) $n = 0$, (b) $n > 0$, (c) $n < 0$.

(a) The case $n = 0$ is covered by Theorem 1 (a): $D1 = 0$.

(b) For $n > 0$ we use mathematical induction. Thus let $S = \{n \in \mathbf{N} \mid$ assertion (7) is valid for $n\}$. We shall show that $S = \mathbf{N}$. In fact,

(i) $1 \in S$. This is covered by Theorem 1(b): $Dx = 1 = 1 \cdot x^0$.
Also,

(ii) $n \in S \Rightarrow n + 1 \in S$. We have

$$
\begin{aligned}
Dx^{n+1} &= D(x \cdot x^n) \\
&= x(Dx^n) + x^n(Dx) \quad \text{(Theorem 3)} \\
&= x(nx^{n-1}) + x^n \cdot 1 \quad (n \in S \text{ and Theorem 1(b))} \\
&= nx^n + x^n \\
&= (n + 1)x^n.
\end{aligned}
$$

Thus, by the induction principle (Theorem 1.10), $S = \mathbf{N}$.

(c) Now suppose n is negative. Let $n = -m$, where $m \in \mathbf{N}$. Then

$$
\begin{aligned}
Dx^n &= D(x^{-m}) \\
&= D\left(\frac{1}{x^m}\right) \quad \text{(definition of } x^{-m}) \\
&= \frac{-mx^{m-1}}{x^{2m}} \quad \text{(Theorem 4 and part (b) of this theorem)} \\
&= (-m)x^{-m-1} \\
&= nx^{n-1} \quad (n = -m). \quad \blacksquare
\end{aligned}
$$

Actually, the statement of Theorem 6 holds if n is allowed to be an arbitrary element of $\mathbf{R}$. The proof of this more general assertion will be given later (see Exercise 6, Section 4.3, p. 210). In the meantime we shall use it, for example, in such cases as

$$Dx^{1/2} = \tfrac{1}{2}x^{-1/2} = \frac{1}{2\sqrt{x}}, \qquad x > 0.$$

We do not want to put too many carts before our overworked intuitive horse, but for various reasons we mention the following differentiation facts about functions which will be discussed in full detail later. We include only the point level form.

Assertion.

$$(1) \quad D \sin x = \cos x, \qquad \forall x \in \mathbf{R}.$$

$$(2) \quad D \cos x = -\sin x, \qquad \forall x \in \mathbf{R}.$$

$$(3) \quad D \log x = \frac{1}{x}, \qquad x > 0.$$

$$(4) \quad De^x = e^x, \qquad \forall x \in \mathbf{R}.$$

It should be understood that in (1) and (2) of this assertion x is a number, and does not refer to degrees. You may think in terms of radians if you wish. In (3) the logarithm is the natural logarithm, i.e., to the base e.

We conclude this section with a few illustrations of the theorems. We remark first, however, that Theorem 2(a), which involves the derivative of a sum of two functions can be immediately extended, by mathematical induction, to the sum of n functions for all $n \in \mathbf{N}$.

Example 6.

$$
\begin{aligned}
D(3x^2 + 4x + 5) &= D(3x^2) + D(4x) + D(5) \qquad \text{Theorem 2(a))} \\
&= 3(Dx^2) + 4(Dx) + 0 \qquad \text{(Theorem 2(b) and} \\
&\qquad\qquad\qquad\qquad\qquad\qquad \text{Theorem 1(a))} \\
&= 3(2x) + 4(1) \qquad \text{Theorem (6)} \\
&= 6x + 4.
\end{aligned}
$$

In different symbols, if

$$f : x \rightarrow 3x^2 + 4x + 5,$$

then

$$f' : x \rightarrow 6x + 4.$$

Example 7. By a technique exactly similar to that used in Example 6, we can show that if p is a polynomial of degree $n \geq 1$, then p' is a polynomial of degree $n - 1$. Thus, let

$$p(x) = \sum_{k=0}^{n} c_k x^{n-k}, \qquad \text{where} \quad c_0 \neq 0, \qquad n \in \mathbf{N}.$$

Then

$$
\begin{aligned}
D(p(x)) &= D\left(\sum_{k=0}^{n} c_k x^{n-k} \right) \\
&= \sum_{k=0}^{n} D(c_k x^{n-k}) \qquad \text{(extension of Theorem 2(a))} \\
&= \sum_{k=0}^{n} c_k D x^{n-k} \qquad \text{(Theorem 2(b))} \\
&= \sum_{k=0}^{n} c_k (n-k) x^{n-k-1} \qquad \text{(Theorem 6)} \\
&= \sum_{k=0}^{n-1} c_k (n-k) x^{n-k-1},
\end{aligned}
$$

a polynomial of degree $n - 1$.

By means of the theorems of this section, any rational function can be differentiated at every point of its domain. The general statement is not too helpful; thus we illustrate with a few simple examples.

Example 8. If

$$f(x) = \frac{1}{x^4 + x^2 + 1},$$

then, by Theorem 4,

$$f'(x) = \frac{-(4x^3 + 2x)}{(x^4 + x^2 + 1)^2}.$$

Example 9. If $r(x) = \dfrac{2x + 1}{x^2 - 3x + 5}$, then by Theorems 5, 2, and 1,

$$r'(x) = \frac{(x^2 - 3x + 5)D(2x + 1) - (2x + 1)D(x^2 - 3x + 5)}{(x^2 - 3x + 5)^2}$$

$$= \frac{(x^2 - 3x + 5)(2) - (2x + 1)(2x - 3)}{(x^2 - 3x + 5)^2}$$

$$= \frac{-2x^2 - 2x + 13}{(x^2 - 3x + 5)^2}.$$

Example 10.

$$D(e^x \sin x) = e^x D(\sin x) + \sin x \, D(e^x)$$

$$= e^x \cos x + \sin x \cdot e^x$$

$$= e^x(\cos x + \sin x).$$

Example 11. If $f : x \to x \log x - x$, $x > 0$, then $f' : x \to x\left(\dfrac{1}{x}\right) + \log x(1) - 1 = \log x$.

E X E R C I S E S

1. Use the theorems of this section to find the derivatives of the functions defined by the following formulas.

   (a) $f(x) = 2x^3 - 7x^2 - 4x + 13$.

   (b) $f(x) = x^4 + 4x^3 - 8x^2 + 12x + 1$.

   (c) $f(x) = (x^2 + 1) \cos x$.

   (d) $f(x) = \dfrac{x^2 - 1}{x^2 + 1}$.

   (e) $f(x) = \dfrac{\sqrt{x}}{x^2 + x + 1}$.

   (f) $f(x) = \dfrac{1}{x^2 - 1}$.

   (g) $f(x) = 2 \sin x \cos x$.

   (h) $f(x) = \dfrac{1 - \sqrt{x}}{1 + \sqrt{x}}$.

   (i) $f(x) = \dfrac{x^2 - 4x + 6}{x^2 + x - 7}$.

   (j) $f(x) = \dfrac{\log x}{x}$.

   (k) $f(x) = x^2 + 3x - 4 + \dfrac{2}{x} - \dfrac{7}{x^2}$.

   (l) $f(x) = 2x^{5/2} + 3x^{3/2} - \sqrt{x}$.

2. The functions described below can be differentiated either by immediately applying the product formula (Theorem 3) or by first carrying out the indicated multiplication and then differentiating "term by term," i.e., using Theorem 2(a). Do each part both ways; this may give you an idea of which method you prefer.

(a) $f(x) = x(4 - x)$.
(b) $f(x) = (2x + 1)(x - 3)$.
(c) $f(x) = (x^2 + 4)(x^2 + 3x - 1)$.
(d) $f(x) = (x^3 - 2x^2 + 3x + 5)(2x^2 - 4x + 1)$.
(e) $f(x) = (x - 1)(x - 2)(x - 3)$.

3. Each of the following functions can be differentiated either by using the quotient formula (Theorem 5) or by changing the form as indicated in part (a). Use both methods for comparative purposes.

(a) $f(x) = \dfrac{x - 1}{x} = 1 - \dfrac{1}{x} = 1 - x^{-1}$.

(b) $f(x) = \dfrac{x^2 - 3x + 7}{x}$.

(c) $f(x) = \dfrac{1 - 4x - x^2}{x^2}$.

(d) $f(x) = \dfrac{(x - 3)(x + 2)}{x^3}$.

(e) $f(x) = \dfrac{x^2}{4} = \dfrac{1}{4}x^2$.

4. Prove that $Dx^n = nx^{n-1}$, where $n \in \mathbf{N}$, by using Definition 1 and the binomial theorem. What limit statements do you need to carry out the proof?

5. Prove the following assertion. The letters a, b, c stand for arbitrary real numbers and f and g represent differentiable functions.

$$D(cf) = c(Df)$$
and
$$D(f + g) = (Df) + (Dg)$$
$$\Leftrightarrow D(af + bg) = a(Df) + b(Dg).$$

6. Let r be an arbitrary rational function; thus r is defined by

$$r(x) = \frac{a_0 x^m + a_1 x^{m-1} + \cdots + a_m}{b_0 x^n + b_1 x^{n-1} + \cdots + b_n}, \qquad m, n \in \mathbf{N}.$$

Show that r' is also rational and that r and r' have the same domains.

7. Use mathematical induction to prove the extension of Theorem 2(a); i.e., prove that, if all functions involved are differentiable,

$$\forall n \in \mathbf{N} \Rightarrow \left(\sum_{k=1}^{n} f_k \right)' = \sum_{k=1}^{n} f_k'.$$

8. Prove the Corollary to Theorem 2; i.e., show that, if f and g are differentiable functions, then

$$D(f - g) = (Df) - (Dg).$$

9. Prove Theorem 5. $\left[\textit{Hint.} \quad \text{Write } \dfrac{f}{g} \text{ as } f\left(\dfrac{1}{g}\right) \text{ and use Theorems 3 and 4.} \right]$

10. For purposes of generalization it is preferable to write Theorem 3 in the form $(fg)' = f'g + fg'$.

    (a) Suppose f_1, f_2, and f_3 are differentiable functions. Apply Theorem 3 twice to show that

    $$(f_1 f_2 f_3)' = f_1' f_2 f_3 + f_1 f_2' f_3 + f_1 f_2 f_3'.$$

    (b) State and prove, by mathematical induction, the extension to n differentiable functions, for every $n \in \mathbb{N}$.

2.4 The Chain Rule

The theorems in the preceding section explain how the operation of differentiation is related to the arithmetic operations on functions: the derivative of a sum is the sum of the derivatives, the derivative of a product is the first factor times the derivative of the second plus the second times the derivative of the first, etc. However, in Chapter 1, when discussing ways of combining functions, we defined, in addition to the arithmetic combinations, one other, the *composition* of two functions: $(f \circ g)(x) = f(g(x))$. As we shall see time and time again in what follows, the rule for differentiating this function in terms of the component functions f and g is the most important single differentiation assertion in the calculus.

Theorem 7 (*The Chain Rule*). Suppose f and g are functions such that $F = f \circ g$ is defined at x_0; $F(x_0) = f(g(x_0))$. Suppose also that $f'(g(x_0))$ and $g'(x_0)$ exist. Then $F'(x_0)$ exists and

$$F'(x_0) = (f \circ g)'(x_0) = f'(g(x_0))g'(x_0). \tag{8}$$

Proof. By definition,

$$F'(x_0) = \lim_{h \to 0} \frac{F(x_0 + h) - F(x_0)}{h}$$

$$= \lim_{h \to 0} \frac{f(g(x_0 + h)) - f(g(x_0))}{h}.$$

In order to extricate the combinations we need for working toward the formula in (8) we perpetrate the following far from obvious manipulations. Let

$$u_0 = g(x_0)$$
$$u_0 + k = g(x_0 + h). \tag{9}$$

Then

$$F'(x_0) = \lim_{h \to 0} \frac{f(u_0 + k) - f(u_0)}{h}.$$

which begins to look like a derivative. But we need k, not h, in the denominator; we put it there:

$$F'(x_0) = \lim_{h \to 0} \frac{f(u_0 + k) - f(u_0)}{k} \cdot \frac{k}{h}.$$

Now we must worry about the factor $\frac{k}{h}$. A big improvement here is achieved by noticing that subtracting the first equation from the second in (9) gives

$$k = g(x_0 + h) - g(x_0).$$

With this the expression for $F'(x_0)$ becomes

$$F'(x_0) = \lim_{h \to 0} \frac{f(u_0 + k) - f(u_0)}{k} \frac{g(x_0 + h) - g(x_0)}{h}.$$

It is obvious that we should draw on the theorem about the limit of a product (it equals the product of the limits):

$$F'(x_0) = \lim_{h \to 0} \frac{f(u_0 + k) - f(u_0)}{k} \lim_{h \to 0} \frac{g(x_0 + h) - g(x_0)}{h}.$$

If only the h in the first limit expression were a k. We can obtain this *desideratum* by noting that

$$\lim_{h \to 0} k = \lim_{h \to 0} [g(x_0 + h) - g(x_0)] = 0.$$

The reason for this is that g is continuous at x_0, because $g'(x_0)$ exists, by hypothesis (see the end of the proof of Theorem 3, p. 87). Thus, because $\lim\limits_{h \to 0} k = 0$ (for a more complete discussion of this point see Section 4.3), we can write

$$F'(x_0) = \lim_{k \to 0} \frac{f(u_0 + k) - f(u_0)}{k} \lim_{h \to 0} \frac{g(x_0 + h) - g(x_0)}{h}$$

$$= f'(u_0)g'(x_0)$$

$$= f'(g(x_0))g'(x_0). \quad \blacksquare$$

Now that we have finished the proof, we must point out that there is a flaw in it. The possible difficulty occurs when we multiplied by $\frac{k}{k}$. For, by the definition in (9), k is the change in g from x_0 to $x_0 + h$, and this change *could be* zero —*would be* if, for example, g is a constant function. There are other, more serious, cases where $k = 0$. However, mostly $k \neq 0$. Better yet, the theorem is true in any case. This proof covers most of the cases encountered in elementary work. In Chapter 4 we shall give a correct proof. In the meantime, we can use the chain rule.

Example 12. Let $F(x) = (x^3 + 5)^{10}$. We could find $F'(x)$ by using the binomial theorem and then differentiating term by term. A superior method is to let

$f(u) = u^{10}$, $g(x) = x^3 + 5$. Then $F = f \circ g$, or $F(x) = f(g(x)) = f(x^3 + 5) = (x^3 + 5)^{10}$. By the chain rule,

$$F'(x) = 10(x^3 + 5)^9 (3x^2) = 30x^2(x^3 + 5)^9.$$

Example 13. If $F(x) = \sqrt{x^3 + 5} = (x^3 + 5)^{1/2}$ the binomial theorem could not be used; one would have to use the chain rule. As in Example 12, we have

$$F'(x) = \frac{1}{2}(x^3 + 5)^{-1/2}(3x^2) = \frac{3x^2}{2\sqrt{x^3 + 5}}.$$

Both of the preceding examples illustrate the following important special case of the chain rule.

Corollary. *If $g'(x_0)$ exists and $F(x) = (g(x))^n$, then, for all n,*

$$F'(x_0) = n(g(x_0))^{n-1} g'(x_0). \tag{10}$$

Proof. This follows immediately from (8) with $f(u) = u^n$. Then, by Theorem 6, $f'(u) = nu^{n-1}$ and, by (8),

$$F'(x_0) = f'(g(x_0))g'(x_0)$$
$$= n(g(x_0))^{n-1}g'(x_0). \quad \blacksquare$$

Example 14. Let $F(x) = \sin(4x^2 - 3x + 1)$. We can "decompose" F into $F = f \circ g$ by letting

$$g(x) = 4x^2 - 3x + 1, \qquad f(u) = \sin u.$$

Then

$$g'(x) = 8x - 3, f'(u) = \cos u,$$

and, by (8),

$$F'(x) = (\cos u)(8x - 3) = (8x - 3)\cos(4x^2 - 3x + 1).$$

Example 15. Let $F(x) = \sin^2 x$. Recall that $\sin^2 x = (\sin x)^2$. Thus $F = f \circ g$, where

$$g(x) = \sin x, \qquad f(u) = u^2.$$

Then

$$g'(x) = \cos x, \qquad f'(u) = 2u,$$

and (8) gives

$$F'(x) = (2u)\cos x = 2\sin x \cos x = \sin 2x.$$

EXERCISES

In numbers 1–10 find F' if F is defined by

1. $F(x) = (3x + 1)^7$.

2. $F(x) = (5x^4 - 2x^3 + 7x - 4)^8$.

3. $F(x) = \sin(5x^2 + 3)$.

4. $F(x) = \log(x^2 + 1)$.

5. $F(x) = \cos(2x^3 + 3)$.

6. $F(x) = \sqrt[3]{3x^2 + 7}$.

7. $F(x) = \sqrt[5]{3 - 4x^2}$.

8. $F(x) = e^{-x^2}$.

9. $F(x) = \sin^2 2x$.

10. $F(x) = \sin^3(2x^2 + 1)$.

11. Suppose $g(x) = c$, one of the possibilities mentioned in the confession of the flaw after the end of the proof of the chain rule.

(a) Find $F(x) = f(g(x))$.   (b) Find, directly, without using (8), $F'(x)$.

(c) Show that this agrees with the result given by using the chain rule.

2.5   Tangent and Velocity

It is worth recalling that the discussion in Section 2.1 of tangent line to a curve and instantaneous velocity associated with linear motion was from an intuitive point of view, serving largely to motivate the definition of derivative in Section 2.2. We are now in a much more favorable position for dealing with these concepts. Before giving the definition of tangent line, however, we investigate, by means of an example, one point which could prove slightly troublesome.

Example 16. We consider the "cube-root function", i.e., $f: x \to x^{1/3}$. We see immediately that its domain $X_f = \mathbf{R}$ and that $x < 0 \Rightarrow f(x) < 0$, $x > 0 \Rightarrow f(x) > 0$. Moreover, using Theorem 6, we find that

$$f'(x) = \frac{1}{3} x^{-2/3} = \frac{1}{3x^{2/3}}.$$

Thus $X_{f'} = \{x \mid x \neq 0\}$. If, as was suggested by the discussion of Section 2.1, we use the value of the derivative at a point as the slope of the tangent to the graph of f, then we see that for every x_0, $x_0 \neq 0$, the tangent at $(x_0, f(x_0))$ has a positive slope. For example, since $f'(1) = \frac{1}{3}$, the tangent at $(1, 1)$ should be the line with equation

$$y - 1 = \tfrac{1}{3}(x - 1).$$

The question with which we are now concerned is: What happens at the point $(0, 0)$, since $f'(0)$ is not defined? If one makes a careful sketch (see Figure 10)

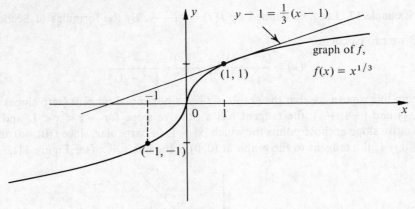

Figure 10

and if one observes the behavior of f' for numbers close to zero, he will have the very strong impression that the tangent at $(0, 0)$ should be the y-axis. Since vertical lines do not have slopes, we now realize that the use of the derivative as already suggested will fail to give us vertical tangent lines. If we continue to study this example we observe that the reason $f'(0)$ fails to exist is the presence of a zero in the denominator of its formula (whereas the numerator is not zero); in other words, $\dfrac{1}{f'}(0) = 0$. In general, the implication of this is that values of x near zero will produce very large values of $|f'(x)|$—i.e., nearly vertical tangent lines. We can use this property of the derivative to find vertical tangents.

Definition 2. *Let f be a function, let x_0 be in the domain of f, so that $(x_0, f(x_0))$ is a point on the graph $\mathscr{C}$ of f. If $f'(x_0)$ exists, then the **tangent** to $\mathscr{C}$ at $(x_0, f(x_0))$ is the line*

$$y - f(x_0) = f'(x_0)(x - x_0).$$

*If $f'(x_0)$ fails to exist, but $\left(\dfrac{1}{f'}\right)(x_0) = 0$, then the **tangent** to $\mathscr{C}$ at $(x_0, f(x_0))$ is the line $x = x_0$.*

It is true that this definition is in terms of a coordinate system. Although a good case could be made for a definition of tangent line which is independent of any coordinate system, the fact is that all of our work in calculus will be done in terms of a coordinate system, so we have not imposed any real restriction. Another point which should be mentioned is this. Frequently, we work with curves which are not graphs of functions (consider, as a simple example, the unit circle $x^2 + y^2 = 1$); it is usually possible in such cases to represent a portion of the curve on which our interest is focused as the graph of a suitably chosen function (thus $f(x) = \sqrt{1 - x^2}$ gives the upper half of the unit circle). Then Definition 2 applies.

We look at a few illustrations.

Example 17. Let f be defined by $f(x) = \dfrac{x}{x^2 + 1}$. By the formulas of Section 2.3 we can calculate

$$f'(x) = \frac{(x^2 + 1)1 - x(2x)}{(x^2 + 1)^2} = \frac{1 - x^2}{(x^2 + 1)^2}.$$

From this we can see that the graph of f has a horizontal tangent (zero slope) at $(1, \frac{1}{2})$ and $(-1, -\frac{1}{2})$, the tangent has a positive slope for $-1 < x < 1$, and a negative slope at those points for which $|x| > 1$. In particular, since $f(0) = 0$ and $f'(0) = 1$, the tangent to the graph at $(0, 0)$ is the line $y = x$ (see Figure 11).

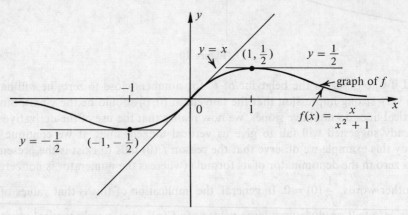

Figure 11

Example 18. Let $f : x \to x^{2/3}$. Then $f' : x \to \frac{2}{3} x^{-1/3} = \dfrac{2}{3\sqrt[3]{x}}$. We note that

$$\forall x \in \mathbf{R} \Rightarrow f(x) \geq 0,$$

$$x < 0 \Rightarrow f'(x) < 0,$$

$$x > 0 \Rightarrow f'(x) > 0,$$

and that $f'(0)$ does not exist. However, $\left(\dfrac{1}{f'}\right)(x) = \dfrac{3}{2}\sqrt[3]{x}$, so $\left(\dfrac{1}{f'}\right)(0) = 0$.

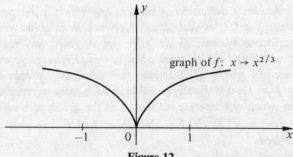

graph of $f : x \to x^{2/3}$

Figure 12

Thus, at those points on the graph to the left of the y-axis the tangent has a negative slope, to the right a positive slope, and at $(0, 0)$ the tangent is the y-axis ($x = 0$). The graph is shown in Figure 12.

We can also apply the abstract concept of derivative of a function to the physical problem of linear motion. To be specific, motivated by the discussion of Section 2.1, we now define instantaneous velocity as follows.

Definition 3. *Let a particle (object, body) be moving along a straight line on which a coordinate system has been established. If s is a function such that $s(t_0)$ represents the (directed) distance from the origin to the particle at time t_0, then the* **instantaneous velocity** *of the particle at time t_0 is defined to be*

$$v(t_0) = s'(t_0).$$

We illustrate the definition and bring out a few additional points in the following example.

Example 19. Suppose a particle is travelling along a line in such a way that its distance s from the origin at time t is given by the formula

$$s(t) = t^2 - 6t + 8 = (t - 2)(t - 4).$$

Suppose the unit of time is a second (sec) and that of distance is a centimeter (cm). Further, we shall consider that the motion starts at time $t = 0$; thus the domain of s is $\{t \mid t \geq 0\}$. By Definition 3, then, the instantaneous velocity is given by

$$v(t) = s'(t) = 2t - 6 = 2(t - 3) \text{ cm/sec.}$$

From this we see that

$$v(t) < 0, \qquad \text{for } 0 \leq t < 3,$$

$$v(3) = 0$$

$$v(t) > 0, \qquad \text{for } 3 < t.$$

Perhaps Table 2.2 and Figure 13 will help to convey the nature of the motion.

TABLE 2.2

t(sec)	$s(t)$(cm)	$v(t)$(cm/sec)
0	8	−6
1	3	−4
2	0	−2
3	−1	0
4	0	2
5	3	4
6	8	6
7	15	8

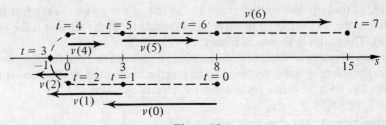

Figure 13

Thus the particle, starting at $s = 8$, moves to the left for the first three seconds, after which it changes direction (note that $v(3) = 0$) and moves toward the right (in the positive direction). We see, then, that the *sign of v* describes the *direction* of motion.

The fact is that velocity, like force, is usually considered to be a *vector*, i.e., to have both *magnitude* and *direction*. By a process of abstraction, vectors in physics can be represented mathematically by directed line segments. When the motion is one-dimensional there are only two possible directions, and these can be distinguished by means of sign. In Figure 13 we have indicated some of the velocity vectors with the initial point on the same vertical line as that which indicates the position at the time. Theoretically all of the lines and vectors of Figure 13 should be superimposed on the s-axis, but this presents obvious practical difficulties. Vectors in two and three dimensions will be studied in detail later.

Before leaving this example we bring out one further concept. We can approach it in two ways. First, we refer to Table 2.2 and observe the way in which the velocity changes with time: each increase of one second in t brings about an increase of 2 cm/sec in v. Thus the time rate of change of velocity seems to be constant at 2 (units?). From a second, more sophisticated, point of view, we recall that $v = s'$ is itself a function and, as such is subject to being operated on by differentiation. Since differentiation can always be interpreted as a measure of rate of change, v' would give the rate of change of velocity (with respect to time), or *acceleration*. Since in this example

$$v(t) = 2t - 6,$$

we have

$$v'(t) = 2 = a(t),$$

where $a = v'$. Thus the motion of this example has constant acceleration. It is an interesting fact, which we shall study later, that knowledge of the acceleration function and of values of v and s at some particular time t_0 (say $t_0 = 0$) is sufficient to characterize the motion completely.

We give a formal definition of acceleration.

Definition 4. *Under the conditions of Definition 3, the (instantaneous) acceleration of the particle at time t_0 is defined to be*

$$a(t_0) = v'(t_0).$$

We remark that acceleration, like velocity and force, is a vector. Its units would be velocity units per time unit; in the case of Example 19 this would be (cm/sec)/sec. It is customary, however, to write this as cm/sec^2, read: centimeters per second squared.

Note that, since v is the derivative of s, a is the derivative of a derivative. This is called the *second derivative* and denoted as follows:

[
$$a = v' = (s')'] = s'',$$
or
$$a = Dv = [D(Ds)] = D^2 s.$$

The third member, [ ], in each of these chains is not customarily used but is inserted here for the sake of explanation.

For an arbitrary function f the second derivative f'' is defined by $f'' = (f')' = Df'$ and the $(n + 1)$st derivative $f^{(n+1)}$ is defined by $f^{(n+1)} = (f^{(n)})' = Df^{(n)}$.

EXERCISES

1. Find the equations of the tangents at the points indicated.

   (a) $f: x \to x^2 - 8x + 15$, $(3, 0), (4, -1), (6, 3)$.
   (b) $f(x) = x^3 - 1$, $(0, -1), (2, 7)$.
   (c) $f(x) = \dfrac{x^2 - 1}{x^2 + 1}$, $(0, -1), (-1, 0)$.
   (d) $x^2 + y^2 = 4$, $(1, -\sqrt{3})$.
   (e) $y^2 = 4x$, $(4, -4)$.
   (f) $f(x) = \sin x$, $(0, 0), \left(\dfrac{\pi}{6}, \dfrac{1}{2}\right), \left(\dfrac{\pi}{2}, 1\right)$.
   (g) $f(x) = \sqrt{x}$, $(0, 0), (4, 2)$.
   (h) $f(x) = \log x$, $(1, 0)$.
   (i) $f(x) = \sqrt[3]{x} - 1$, $(8, 1), (0, -1)$.
   (j) $f(x) = x^{3/2}$, $(4, 8), (0, 0)$.

2. Consider the function f defined by $f(x) = \dfrac{1}{x}$.

   (a) Find f' (b) Observe that $\left(\dfrac{1}{f'}\right)(0) = 0$

   (c) What does this say about the tangent to the graph of f at the point where $x = 0$?

   (d) Observe that $0 \notin X_f$, the domain of f. Should there be a tangent at $x = 0$?

   (e) Is there a conflict with Definition 2? Why or why not?

3. Give a complete description of the linear motions for which the position functions are given by the following formulas. The domain of s in each case is $\{t \mid t \geq 0\}$. The description should include the velocity and acceleration functions, the initial

position, $s(0)$, initial velocity, $v(0)$, intervals when $v<0$ and when $v>0$ and a sketch.
Use seconds and centimeters for time and distance units, respectively.

(a) $s(t)=t^2-8t+7$ (b) $s(t)=t^2+t+1$ (c) $s(t)=\sin t$

(d) $s(t)=t^3-3t^2+3t$. Describe the motion for t near 1. Be sure to calculate $s(0)$, $s(1)$, $s(2)$.

(e) $\begin{Bmatrix}0\le t<3, s(t)=t^2+1\\3\le t, s(t)=37-t^3\end{Bmatrix}$.   What can be said about $v(3)$?
What might have happened to the particle at $t=3$?

(f) $s(t)=\dfrac{t}{t+1}$. How far will the particle travel if it goes on for all time ($0\le t<\infty$)?
Note the signs of v and of a for all $t\ge0$.

(g) $s(t)=\dfrac{t^2}{t+1}$. Between what numbers does $v(t)$ lie for all $t\ge0$?

4. If an object travels in a vertical straight line, for which the positive direction is upward, if only the force due to gravity is considered, and if the time and distance units are seconds and feet respectively, then its position function is given approximately by

$$s(t)=-16t^2+v_0t+s_0, t\ge0,$$

where v_0 and s_0 are constants.

(a) Calculate v and a.   (b) Interpret the numbers v_0 and s_0.

(c) If the object begins its journey by simply being dropped, what can be said about v_0?

(d) Suppose the object is thrown (or shot) vertically upward. What can be said about v_0?

(e) If one takes the positive direction on the line to be downward, how should the formula for s be changed?

5. For each of the following functions find f' and f''.

(a) $f:x\to ax^2+bx+c, a\ne0$.   (g) $f:x\to x^3-3x^2+3x-1$.
(b) $f(x)=\log x$.
(c) $f(x)=\sin x$.   (h) $f(x)=\dfrac{\sqrt{x}}{x-1}$.
(d) $f(x)=\cos x$.
(e) $f(x)=e^x$.
(f) $f(x)=x^3-6x^2+11x-6$.   (i) $f(x)=\dfrac{x}{x^2+1}$.

6. (a) Suppose $f:x\to ax^2+bx+c$. What can be said about f''? About $f'''=(f'')'$?

(b) Suppose $f(x)=ax^3+bx^2+cx+d$. Calculate f', f'', f''', and $(f''')'=f^{iv}$.

(c) Suppose $f(x)=c_0x^4+c_1x^3+c_2x^2+c_3x+c_4$. Calculate the first five derivatives of f.

(d) If f is a polynomial of degree n, what can be said about the nth and $(n+1)$st derivatives of f?

7. Consider $f(x) = x^3 - 3x^2$.

   (a) Calculate f' and f'' (b) Sketch the graph of f

   (c) Recall that $f'' = (f')'$ measures the rate of change of f'. Compare the sets $\{x \mid f''(x) < 0\}$ and $\{x \mid f''(x) > 0\}$ with the graph of f and try to obtain a geometric interpretation of f''.

8. (Newton's Method).   In this exercise we develop a technique, devised by Newton, for finding, approximately, a root of an equation or, alternatively, a zero of a function. [*Note about terminology*: If f is a function and x_0 is a point in the domain of f such that $f(x_0) = 0$, then x_0 is called a *zero* of f; the more familiar description is to call x_0 a *root* of the conditional equation obtained by setting f equal to zero.]

   The technique is an especially simple and natural one. Suppose we have an initial estimate x_0 of the zero of f. We find the tangent line to the graph of f at $(x_0, f(x_0))$ and take as the first approximation to the zero the point x_1 where the tangent line at $(x_0, f(x_0))$ crosses the x-axis.

   (a) Sketch the graph of a function f with a zero near the point x_0.

   (b) Assume $f'(x_0)$ exists, and find the equation of the tangent line to the curve at $(x_0, f(x_0))$. Show this line on your sketch.

   (c) Show that the x-intercept of this tangent line is

   $$x_1 = x_0 - \frac{f(x_0)}{f'(x_0)}.$$

   What must be assumed about $f'(x_0)$ to obtain this result?

   (d) Show that if the process is repeated, a second approximation is given by

   $$x_2 = x_1 - \frac{f(x_1)}{f'(x_1)}.$$

   (e) In general, having the nth approximation, one can find the $(n + 1)$st approximation as

   $$x_{n+1} = x_n - \frac{f(x_n)}{f'(x_n)}.$$

   Show this.
   It is fairly clear that one should be working in an interval where f' does not equal zero.

9. See Exercise 8.

   (a) Using $x_0 = 1$, show that a second approximation to the zero of $f(x) = x^3 + x - 1$, which lies between 0 and 1, is $x_2 = 0.686$.

   (b) Show that $f(x) = x^3 - 4x^2 + 1$ has a zero between 3 and 4. Using $x_0 = 4$, show that $x_1 = \dfrac{63}{16}$.

   (c) Notice that the function in part (b) has a zero between 0 and 1. Consider each of those numbers as candidates for x_0, then find x_1.

2.6 Monotonic Functions

Motivated by questions involving tangents and velocities, we have introduced the concept of derivative of a function, noting that it provides a measure of instantaneous rate of change of the function. We have developed a few elementary formulas for performing the operation of differentiation, and, in a modest way, we have applied the derivative to a few problems of analytic geometry and of linear motion. In this section we shall see how the derivative helps us describe the way in which a function changes.

It probably has already been observed that, when applying the derivative to curve-sketching, an inevitable awkwardness was present in saying, for example, that in a certain interval the tangent to the curve always had a positive slope. What is needed is greater precision. Now the fact is that with almost all of the functions of elementary calculus the following are true: (1) The domain is the union of intervals within each of which the function is monotonic (definitions appear shortly). (2) The derivative exists everywhere in the domain of the function except, at worst, at a set of isolated points. There should be a connection between the derivative and the monotonic behavior of the function. There is, and we shall indicate what it is, but, in the interests of the needed precision, we first give some definitions.

Definition 5. *Let I be an interval (open, closed, half-open, finite, or infinite). Let f be a function whose domain includes I. Then*

(i) *f is **increasing** on* $I \Leftrightarrow x_1, x_2 \in I,\ x_1 < x_2 \Rightarrow f(x_1) < f(x_2)$.
(ii) *f is **decreasing** on* $I \Leftrightarrow x_1, x_2 \in I,\ x_1 < x_2 \Rightarrow f(x_1) > f(x_2)$.

A concept closely related to those of Definition 5 is the following.

Definition 6. *Let I be an interval (as in Definition 5). Let f be a function whose domain includes I. Then*

(i) *f is **nondecreasing** on* $I \Leftrightarrow x_1, x_2 \in I,\ x_1 < x_2 \Rightarrow f(x_1) \leq f(x_2)$.
(ii) *f is **nonincreasing** on* $I \Leftrightarrow x_1, x_2 \in I,\ x_1 < x_2 \Rightarrow f(x_1) \geq f(x_2)$.

There is not complete agreement about the terminology of these definitions. Some writers use the term "increasing" where we have used "nondecreasing," calling "strictly increasing" those functions we have called "increasing." It is simply a matter of taste. Notice, however, that in the alternate terminology a constant function is both increasing and decreasing.

If, throughout an interval *I*, a function is nondecreasing or if throughout *I* it is nonincreasing, then the function is said to be *monotonic* on *I*.

The more or less anticipated connection between monotonic behavior of a function and behavior of its derivative is as follows.

Proposition 1. *A differentiable function is monotonic on an interval if and only if its derivative does not change sign on the interval. In symbols this takes the following form.*

f' exists on (a, b)

(i) f nondecreasing on $(a, b) \Leftrightarrow f'(x) \geq 0$, $\forall x \in (a, b)$.

(ii) f nonincreasing on $(a, b) \Leftrightarrow f'(x) \leq 0$, $\forall x \in (a, b)$.

We shall prove this proposition, in slightly modified form, in Chapter 4.

There is a second result, rather easily seen to be a corollary of Proposition 1, which is important in its own right. It characterizes, by means of the derivative, a function constant on an interval.

Proposition 2.

f' exists on (a, b)

f constant on $(a, b) \Leftrightarrow f'(x) = 0$, $\forall x \in (a, b)$.

Proof. We have

f constant $\Leftrightarrow f$ is both nondecreasing and nonincreasing $\Leftrightarrow$
$f'(x) \geq 0$ and $f'(x) \leq 0 \Leftrightarrow f'(x) = 0$. ∎

We will see later that Proposition 2 plays an important role in the discussion of antiderivatives.

Another application of the derivative to the behavior of functions is the relation, perhaps already observed, between points where the function has a maximum or minimum and points where the derivative is zero (i.e., the tangent line is horizontal). Because the words maximum and minimum, unqualified, can be misleading (see, for example, Figure 14, where $f(x_1)$, is maximum with

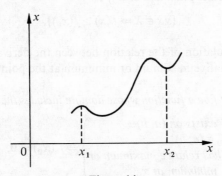

Figure 14

respect to nearby points, $f(x_2)$ is minimum with respect to nearby points and $f(x_1) < f(x_2)$), it will be appropriate to make a few definitions at this time.

Definition 7. *A **neighborhood** (abbreviated nbd.) of a point x_0 is the set*

$$N_\delta(x_0) = \{x \mid x_0 - \delta < x < x_0 + \delta\} = \{x \mid |x - x_0| < \delta\}.$$

*The number $\delta > 0$ is the **radius** of the neighborhood.*

Thus a nbd. of a point is simply an open interval centered at the point (see Figure 15). The requirement that a nbd. of x_0 be centered at x_0 is not essential (one *could* take a nbd. of x_0 to be any open interval containing x_0), but the minor disadvantage of having to center the nbd. at x_0 is probably offset by the advantage of being able to describe a nbd. in terms of a single number (δ).

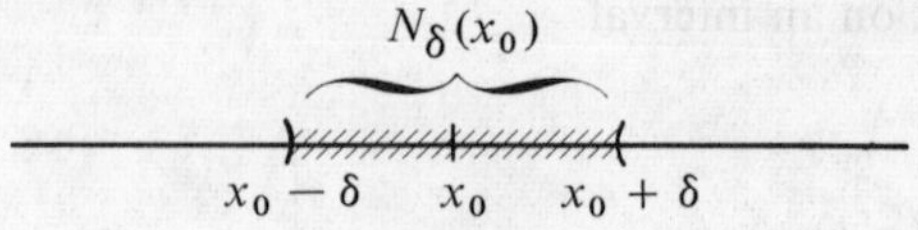

$$N_\delta(x_0)$$

$$x_0 - \delta \qquad x_0 \qquad x_0 + \delta$$

Figure 15

Definition 8. *Let f be a function and let x_0 be a point in the domain of f.*

(i) $\{f$ *has a* **relative maximum** *at $x_0\} \Leftrightarrow$*

$$\{\exists N(x_0) \text{ such that } \forall x \in N(x_0) \Rightarrow f(x) \leq f(x_0)\}.$$

(ii) $\{f$ *has a* **relative minimum** *at $x_0\} \Leftrightarrow$*

$$\{\exists N(x_0) \text{ such that } \forall x \in N(x_0) \Rightarrow f(x) \geq f(x_0)\}.$$

Definition 9. *Let f be a function and let X be the domain of f. Then*

(i) $\{f$ *has an* **absolute maximum** *at $x_0\} \Leftrightarrow$*

$$\{\forall x \in X \Rightarrow f(x) \leq f(x_0)\}.$$

(ii) $\{f$ *has an* **absolute minimum** *at $x_0\} \Leftrightarrow$*

$$\{\forall x \in X \Rightarrow f(x) \geq f(x_0)\}.$$

The correct formulation of the relation between the derivative at a point and the presence of a relative maximum or minimum at the point can now be given.

Theorem 8. *Let f be a function whose domain includes the interval (a, b). Then*

$$\left.\begin{array}{l} f' \text{ exists on } (a, b) \\ x_0 \in (a, b) \\ f \text{ has relative maximum or} \\ \text{minimum at } x_0 \end{array}\right\} \Rightarrow f'(x_0) = 0.$$

The proof will be given in Chapter 4.

A few remarks are in order about the information supplied by Theorem 8. Notice that this theorem does not enable one to distinguish between a relative maximum or a relative minimum—or, in fact, to distinguish either of the above from a point where the derivative is zero but which is neither relative maximum nor minimum. These distinctions can easily be made (as will be illustrated below) by studying the behavior of f' near x_0. Actually, there is much more to be said on the subject of maxima and minima, and it will be said later (see Section 5.5).

At the risk of overly tantalizing the reader we illustrate how some of the preceding unproved assertions can be used.

Example 20. Consider the function f defined by

$$f(x) = x^3 - 6x^2 + 9x.$$

We calculate

$$
\begin{aligned}
f'(x) &= 3x^2 - 12x + 9 \\
&= 3(x^2 - 4x + 3) \\
&= 3(x - 1)(x - 3).
\end{aligned}
$$

From this we see that

$$f'(1) = f'(3) = 0,$$

and that

$$x < 1 \Rightarrow f'(x) > 0,$$

$$1 < x < 3 \Rightarrow f'(x) < 0,$$

$$3 < x \Rightarrow f'(x) > 0.$$

Thus, by Proposition 1, f is increasing for $x < 1$ and for $x > 3$, decreasing for $1 < x < 3$. From this it is easy to see that at $x = 1$ and $x = 3$, where $f'(x) = 0$, f has a relative maximum and a relative minimum, respectively. It is now a simple matter to make a sketch of the graph (see Figure 16).

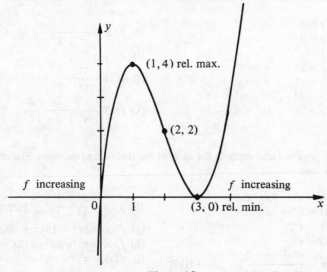

Figure 16

Example 21. Let $f: x \to x^3$. Then $f': x \to 3x^2$. From this we see that $f'(0) = 0$ and that $f'(x) \geq 0$ for all $x \in \mathbf{R}$. It follows, by Proposition 1, that f is an increasing function throughout its entire domain. Moreover, even though $f'(0) = 0$, the point $(0, 0)$ is neither relative maximum nor relative minimum (see Figure 17).

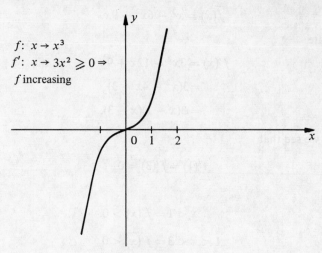

$f: x \to x^3$
$f': x \to 3x^2 \geqslant 0 \Rightarrow$
f increasing

Figure 17

EXERCISES

1. Find the intervals where each of the following functions is non-decreasing.

(a) $f(x) = x$.
(b) $f(x) = x^2$.
(c) $f(x) = x^3$.
(d) $f(x) = x^n$, n odd.
(e) $f(x) = x^n$, n even.
(f) $f(x) = x^3 - 3x^2 - 45x - 5$.
(g) $f(x) = 2x^3 + 3x^2 + 6x - 1$.

(h) $f: x \to \dfrac{1}{x^2 + 1}$.
(i) $f: x \to 3$.
(j) $f(x) = \dfrac{x^2 + 1}{x^2 - 1}$.
(k) $f(x) = \dfrac{x^2 - 3x + 2}{x^2 + x - 12}$.

2. Find all maxima and minima for each of the following functions. Sketch the graph in each case.

(a) $f(x) = x^2 - 4x - 8$.
(b) $f(x) = x^3 - 3x^2$.
(c) $f(x) = x^4$.
(d) $f(x) = x^5$.
(e) $f: x \to \dfrac{x^2 - 3x + 2}{x^2 + x - 12}$,   (see 1(k)).

(f) $f: x \to \dfrac{x^2 + 1}{x^2 - 1}$,   (see 1(j)).
(g) $f: x \to 2x^3 - 15x^2 - 300x$.
(h) $f: x \to x^3 - 6x^2 + 12x - 8$.
(i) $f(x) = x^{3/2}$.

3. Consider the absolute value function, $f(x) = |x|$, on the interval $(-1, 1)$. From properties of the absolute value we can assert that this function has a minimum (relative or absolute?) at $x = 0$.

   (a) Is it true that $f'(0) = 0$?

   (b) Does the answer to (a) contradict Theorem 8?

4. A rectangle, with sides of length x and y, has a perimeter of 60 inches.

   (a) Find an expression for the area A as a function f of x.

   (b) What is the domain of the function in (a)?

   (c) Find the maximum value of f.

   (d) Is the maximum found in (c) relative or absolute?

5. A rectangle with sides of length x and y has an area of 225 square inches. Show that the perimeter of the rectangle is least when the rectangle is a square.

6. A straight, flexible rod, 60 inches long, is bent at points equidistant from the two ends to form an open (three sided) rectangle. How far from the ends should the right-angle bends be made so that the area of the rectangle is maximum?

7. A particle traveling on the x-axis starts at time $t = 0$ and at time t is at the point

$$x = x(t) = \frac{1}{t+1}.$$

   (a) Find the velocity $v(t)$.

   (b) For what value of $t \geq 0$ is $v(t)$ a maximum?

   (c) Does $v'(t_0) = 0$ for the time of maximum velocity?

   (d) Do the results of (b) and (c) contradict the assertion of Theorem 8? Why?

8. Let f be the greatest integer function, $f(x) = [x]$.

   (a) Find $f'(1.5), f'(2.5)$.

   (b) Find $f'(2)$. Remember that in Definition 1, h may be negative.

   (c) Since f is constant on intervals, should it not be, by Proposition 2, that $f'(x_0) = 0$, for every $x_0 \in R$?

   (d) Does the result of (b) contradict Proposition 2? Why?

9. Consider the following functions to be defined on the open interval $(0, 1)$. Which have absolute maxima or minima there?

   (a) $f(x) = x^2$.
   (b) $f(x) = x$.
   (c) $f(x) = \sqrt{x - x^2}$. [*Hint.* Sketch the graph.]
   (d) $f(x) = (x - \frac{1}{2})^2$.

10. Answer Exercise 9 if the domain is defined to be the closed interval $[0, 1]$.

2.7 The Integral (Introduction)

In the next few sections we continue our intuitive introduction to the calculus by considering the definite integral, antiderivatives, and their interconnections.

Recall that our definition of the derivative was preceded by a discussion of three superficially different problems, one from geometry and two from physics, the solutions of all of which produced the same abstract mathematical formulation, thereby motivating us to introduce the concept of derivative of a function. Now a similar approach can be used in studying the integral, but in the interests of brevity we limit ourselves to the consideration of one geometric problem and one problem from physics.

Problem 1. *To find the area of a plane region part of whose boundary is a curve.*

To be specific suppose we consider a region such as that shown in Figure 18,

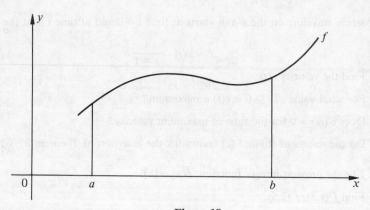

Figure 18

the boundary of which consists of a portion of the graph of a function f, the x-axis between $x = a$ and $x = b$, and the ordinates at a and b. We assume $f(x) \geq 0$ for $a \leq x \leq b$.

We assume known about areas that the area of a rectangle of height h and width w is hw, and we approach our problem by attempting to approximate the desired area. The first step, which will make good sense shortly, is to express the given area as a sum of smaller areas of the same sort. We do this by inserting $n - 1$ points between a and b, and erecting ordinates at these points (see Figure 19). Note that we call a and b also x_0 and x_n, respectively. The x_i need not be equally spaced.

Now for the approximation process: in each of the subintervals $[x_0, x_1]$, $[x_1, x_2], \ldots, [x_{n-1}, x_n]$ we pick, *quite arbitrarily*, a point $z_1, z_2, \ldots, z_n$, respec-

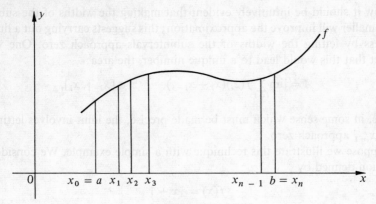

Figure 19

tively, and approximate the desired area by the sum of the areas of the n rectangles with heights

$$f(z_1), \qquad f(z_2), \ldots, f(z_n)$$

and widths

$$x_1 - x_0, \qquad x_2 - x_1, \ldots, x_n - x_{n-1},$$

respectively. Figure 20 shows a typical subinterval from Figure 19, enlarged.

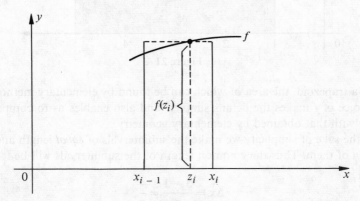

Figure 20

Thus, using $\approx$ to mean "is approximately equal to," we can write

$$A \approx \sum_{i=1}^{n} f(z_i)(x_i - x_{i-1}).$$

To point up what we have done, suppose we let A_i be the area under the curve and above the ith subinterval and let A_i' be the area of the ith rectangle. Then

$$A = \sum_{i=1}^{n} A_i \approx \sum_{i=1}^{n} A_i'.$$

Now it should be intuitively evident that making the widths of the subintervals smaller will improve the approximation; this suggests carrying out a limiting process by letting the widths of the subintervals approach zero. One would expect that this would lead to a unique number, the area:

$$A = \lim \sum_{i=1} f(z_i)(x_i - x_{i-1}), \qquad z_i \in [x_{i-1}, x_i],$$

where, in some sense which must be made precise, the limit involves letting the $x_i - x_{i-1}$ approach zero.

Suppose we illustrate this technique with a simple example. We consider the function defined by

$$f(x) = \tfrac{1}{4}x + 1$$

and we let $a = 1$ and $b = 5$ (see Figure 21). The figure involved is, to be sure,

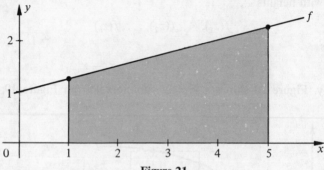

Figure 21

simply a trapezoid, the area of which can be found by elementary methods, but this choice of f makes the details simpler (and also enables us to compare our answer with that obtained by elementary geometry).

For the sake of simplicity we make the subintervals of *equal* length and agree to use n of them. Thus the common length of the subintervals will be

$$\Delta x = \frac{5-1}{n} = \frac{4}{n},$$

and the inserted points will be

$$x_i = 1 + i \cdot \Delta x = 1 + \frac{4i}{n}, \qquad i = 0, 1, 2, \ldots, n.$$

Finally, we choose $z_i = x_i$, i.e., we choose z_i to be the right endpoint of the ith subinterval (see Figure 22). Then

$$f(z_i) = f(x_i) = \frac{1}{4}x_i + 1 = \frac{1}{4}\left(1 + \frac{4i}{n}\right) + 1 = \frac{1}{4} + \frac{i}{n} + 1 = \frac{5}{4} + \frac{i}{n},$$

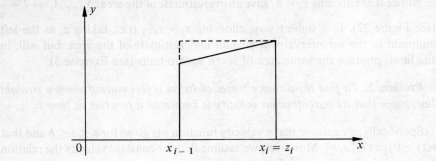

Figure 22

and

$$A'_i = f(z_i)(x_i - x_{i-1}) = \left(\frac{5}{4} + \frac{i}{n}\right)\frac{4}{n} = \frac{5}{n} + \frac{4}{n^2} i.$$

Thus the approximation to the desired area is given by

$$A \approx \sum_{i=1}^{n} A'_i = \sum_{i=1}^{n} \left(\frac{5}{n} + \frac{4}{n^2} i\right)$$

$$= \sum_{i=1}^{n} \frac{5}{n} + \sum_{i=1}^{n} \frac{4}{n^2} i$$

$$= \frac{5}{n} n + \frac{4}{n^2} \sum_{i=1}^{n} i$$

$$= 5 + \frac{4}{n^2} \cdot \frac{n(n+1)}{2}, \qquad \text{(Theorem 1.11)}$$

$$= 5 + 2 \frac{n+1}{n}$$

$$= 5 + 2 + \frac{2}{n}$$

$$= 7 + \frac{2}{n}.$$

Since the width of each subinterval is $\Delta x = \frac{4}{n}$, we can achieve the effect of letting these lengths approach zero by letting n get big beyond all bounds (symbolized as $n \to \infty$). But when this happens the term $\frac{2}{n}$ approaches zero, and the approximation $7 + \frac{2}{n}$ approaches the unique number 7:

$$A = \lim \sum_{i=1}^{n} A'_i = \lim \left(7 + \frac{2}{n}\right) = 7 \text{ square units.}$$

Notice that choosing $z_i = x_i$ gave an overestimate of the area: $\sum_{i=1}^{n} A_i' = 7 + \dfrac{2}{n}$
(see Figure 22). In a similar way, choosing $z_i = x_{i-1}$ (i.e., taking z_i as the left endpoint of the subinterval will give an underestimate of the area, but will, in the limit, produce the same area of seven square units (see Exercise 3).

Problem 2. *To find the distance travelled by an object moving along a straight line, given that its instantaneous velocity is known as a function of time t.*

Specifically, we assume that a velocity function v is given for $a \leq t \leq b$ and that $v(t) \geq 0$ for $t \in [a, b]$. Moreover, we assume that for constant velocity the relation between velocity, time and distance is that

$$\text{distance} = (\text{velocity}) \times (\text{time}).$$

Our approach is as follows: divide the interval $[a, b]$ into n subintervals by inserting $n - 1$ points $t_1, t_2, \ldots, t_{n-1}$, giving

$$a = t_0 < t_1 < t_2 < \cdots < t_{n-1} < t_n = b.$$

In each subinterval $[t_{i-1}, t_i]$ choose, quite arbitrarily, a point z_i and evaluate the velocity function v at z_i. Then, approximately, according to the preceding relation, the distance traveled in the ith subinterval is

$$v(z_i)(t_i - t_{i-1}),$$

and the total distance traveled is given by

$$s \approx \sum_{i=1}^{n} v(z_i)(t_i - t_{i-1}).$$

Once again one would expect, as the time intervals $t_i - t_{i-1}$ go to zero that the sum on the right will give us the desired value of s:

$$s = \lim \sum v(z_i)(t_i - t_{i-1}), \qquad z_i \in [t_{i-1}, t_i];$$

the limit, the meaning of which must be precisely defined, is taken as $t_i - t_{i-1}$ goes to zero.

For example, if $v(t) = \frac{1}{4}t + 1$, then the calculations of Problem 1 tell us that the object travels 7 distance units in the time interval from $t = 1$ to $t = 5$. This result seems less trivial than does that for Problem 1, for the velocity in this problem is not constant and we do not have a prior formula to fall back on as we did with the example in Problem 1.

We now use the suggestions of the preceding discussion to define an abstract operation on functions which leads to a number called the *definite integral*. Let f be a function defined on the interval $[a, b]$. We define a *partition* π of $[a, b]$ to be the set

$$\pi = \{a = x_0 < x_1 < x_2 < \cdots < x_{i-1} < x_i < \cdots < x_{n-1} < x_n = b\}.$$

Thus a partition π subdivides $[a, b]$ into n subintervals $[x_{i-1}, x_i]$. We denote $x_i - x_{i-1}$ by Δx_i:

$$\Delta x_i = x_i - x_{i-1},$$

and we define the *norm of the partition* by

$$|\pi| = \max \Delta x_i, \ i = 1, \ldots, n.$$

If, as may be the case, all Δx_i are equal, the partition is referred to as a *regular partition*. Finally, choose, quite arbitrarily, points $z_i \in [x_{i-1}, x_i]$.

Definition 10. *Let f be a function defined on $[a, b]$, let π be a partition of $[a, b]$, and let $z_i \in [x_{i-1}, x_i]$. Consider*

$$\sum_{i=1}^{n} f(z_i) \Delta x_i.$$

Suppose there is a number L such that

$$\lim_{|\pi| \to 0} \sum_{i=1}^{n} f(z_i) \Delta x_i = L.$$

*Then L is called the **definite integral of f over the interval** $[a, b]$, and is denoted by*

$$\int_a^b f = \int_a^b f(x) \, dx.$$

Of course, the sense of the limit must be made precise. This will be done later.

The endpoints a and b of the interval are called the *lower* and *upper limits* of the integral, respectively. If $\int_a^b f$ exists, then f is said to be *integrable on* $[a, b]$.

In the notation just introduced the result of the example discussed in Problem 1 would appear as

$$\int_1^5 \left(\frac{1}{4} x + 1 \right) dx = 7.$$

Moreover, the same function, interpreted as a velocity as in Problem 2 would lead to

$$\int_1^5 \left(\frac{1}{4} t + 1 \right) dt = 7.$$

Thus we see that the particular letter used in writing the integral is irrelevant. If $\int_a^b f$ exists, then

$$\int_a^b f = \int_a^b f(x) \, dx = \int_a^b f(t) \, dt = \int_a^b f(u) \, du, \quad \text{etc.}$$

We must next consider conditions under which the integral of f exists and methods of evaluating the integral. This latter project will lead us into consideration of some of the properties of the integral and to the *Fundamental Theorem of Calculus*.

EXERCISES

1. Use the technique illustrated in the example in Problem 1 to find

   (a) $\int_2^6 \left(1 - \frac{1}{2}x\right) dx$ Explain the sign.

   (b) $\int_0^4 \left(1 - \frac{1}{2}x\right) dx$ Explain this answer.

2. Find, using the same technique as for Exercise 1,

$$\int_0^4 x^2 \, dx.$$

   [*Hint.*   Use Theorem 1.12.]

3. This concerns the example in Problem 1.

   (a) Take $z_i = x_{i-1}$ (i..e, z_i = left endpoint of the subinterval). Show that

$$\sum_{i=1}^n A_i' = \sum_{i=1}^n f(z_i) \, \Delta x = \sum_{i=1}^n f(x_{i-1}) \, \Delta x = 7 - \frac{2}{n}.$$

   (b) Take z_i as the midpoint of each subinterval, i.e.,

$$z_i = \tfrac{1}{2}(x_{i-1} + x_i).$$

   (i) Show that $z_i = 1 - \dfrac{2}{n} + \dfrac{4}{n} i.$

   (ii) Show that

$$\sum_{i=1}^n A_i' = \sum_{i=1}^n f(z_i) \, \Delta x = 7.$$

   (iii) Draw a careful sketch.

4. Find $\int_0^b x^3 \, dx$, using the technique of the example in Problem 1. Also Theorem 1.13 may be helpful.

5. It is possible to show that, for $m, n \in N$,

$$\sum_{k=1}^n k^m = \frac{1}{m+1} n^{m+1} + c_m n^m + c_{m-1} n^{m-1} + \cdots.$$

   Use this fact to show that

$$\int_0^b x^m \, dx = \frac{b^{m+1}}{m+1}.$$

6. This is a continuation of Exercise 5. Let $f(x) = x^m$. The result of Exercise 5 can also be written as

$$\int_0^b t^m \, dt = \frac{b^{m+1}}{m+1},$$

or

$$\int_0^x t^m \, dt = \frac{x^{m+1}}{m+1} = F(x).$$

Show that $F'(x) = f(x)$.

7. This refers to Problem (*not* Exercise) 3 in Section 2.1. Suppose an irregular rod 10 cm long has a density function given by $\delta(x) = x^2$, $0 \le x \le 10$.

(a) Find the mass of the whole rod. [*Hint.* Use Exercise 6.]

(b) Find the mass of the left half of the rod ($0 \le x \le 5$).

(c) Find the mass of the right half.

(d) Do the results of (a), (b), (c) suggest a general property which ought to hold for integrals?

2.8 The Integral (Continuation)

In this section we continue our study of the integral, our purpose being an investigation of the basic properties of the integral and the development of a reasonably efficient method of evaluating an integral.

We begin, however, with a few remarks, partly about notation. The symbol $\int$, called the *integral sign*, is simply an elongated S, indicating that an integral is a kind of summing process. The inclusion of the apparently unnecessary "dx" in the symbol may seem strange at this time, but there is ample reason for carrying it along, as will become apparent later (there *are* times, however, when the "dx" is not needed and we shall not always use it). It is unfortunate that the term "limits" is applied to the endpoints a and b of the interval over which the function is integrated, but the usage is pretty well fixed.

A deeper remark concerns the relation between Problem 2 in Section 2.1 and Problem 2 in Section 2.7, and between Problem 3 in Section 2.1 and Exercise 7 at the end of Section 2.7. The two Problems 2 involve distance and velocity functions for linear motion and show that, whereas *differentiation* takes us from the distance function to the velocity function, *integration* (i.e., evaluating an integral) takes us from the velocity function to distance. Similarly, one goes from mass to density by differentiation and in the opposite direction by integration. Thus, the two processes seem to be *inverses* of each other. This will be made explicit later in this section. It is worth noting, however, that this interrelationship between the processes of differentiation and integration is more apparent from the physical than from the geometric examples.

Our first task now will be to give conditions which guarantee the existence of the integral. The following theorem will suffice for our present purposes, although it can be greatly strengthened—and will be later.

Theorem 9. *Let a function f be defined on* $[a, b]$. *For f to be integrable on* $[a, b]$ *it is sufficient that f be continuous on* $[a, b]$ *or that f be increasing on* $[a, b]$ *or that f be decreasing on* $[a, b]$. *In symbols,*

(i) *f continuous on* $[a, b] \Rightarrow \int_a^b f$ *exists.*

(ii) *f increasing on* $[a, b] \Rightarrow \int_a^b f$ *exists.*

(iii) *f decreasing on* $[a, b] \Rightarrow \int_a^b f$ *exists.*

Our failure in Section 2.7 to define precisely the limiting process used in the definition of the integral means that we cannot prove Theorem 9 at this time. The same is true of the next two theorems, but proofs of all of these theorems will be given later (see Chapter 9).

The next theorem we mention says that the integral has the linearity property (see Theorem 2).

Theorem 10. *Let f and g be integrable on* $[a, b]$ *and let* $c \in \mathbf{R}$. *Then*

(a) $\int_a^b (f + g) = \int_a^b f + \int_a^b g$

(b) $\int_a^b cf = c \int_a^b f$.

Verbally, Theorem 10 says that the sum of two integrable functions is integrable, and that the integral of a sum is the sum of the integrals (this can be extended, by mathematical induction, to the sum of any finite number of integrable functions), and that the product of a constant and an integrable function is an integrable function and the integral is the product of the constant and the integral of the function.

Part (a) of Theorem 10 says that the integral is additive with respect to functions; we next assert that the integral is additive with respect to *intervals* (see Figure 23).

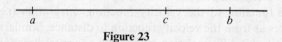

Figure 23

Theorem 11. *Let f be integrable on* $[a, b]$ *and let* $c \in (a, b)$. *Then*

$$\int_a^c f + \int_c^b f = \int_a^b f.$$

The fact is that Theorem 11 can be extended to the case where c lies *outside* the interval $[a, b]$, provided, of course that f is integrable on the intervals involved. To achieve this extension we first make a definition.

Definition 11. *Let f be a function which is integrable on $[a, b]$. Then*

(i) $\displaystyle\int_b^a f = -\int_a^b f$

(ii) $\displaystyle\int_a^a f = 0.$

It is now a simple matter to give the advertised extension of Theorem 11.

Theorem 12. *Let $a, b, c \in \mathbf{R}$ and let f be a function which is integrable on an interval which contains a, b, and c. Then*

$$\int_a^c f + \int_c^b f = \int_a^b f.$$

Proof. Exercise for student. ∎

Before embarking on our next major project, it may be wise to point out that although integrability is a property possessed by most of the functions one encounters in elementary mathematics, there do exist functions which are not integrable. Consider, for example, the function f defined on $[0, 1]$ by

$$\begin{cases} f(x) = 0, & x \text{ irrational} \\ f(x) = 1, & x \text{ rational} \end{cases}.$$

Now let π be any partition of $[0, 1]$, where the norm $|\pi|$ can be taken as small as one pleases. Then, by taking the z_i all irrational, one would have

$$\sum_{i=1}^{n} f(z_i)\,\Delta x_i = 0,$$

whereas, if the z_i are all rational numbers, then

$$\sum_{i=1}^{n} f(z_i)\,\Delta x_i = 1$$

(recall that $\Sigma \Delta x_i = 1$). In fact, by suitable choice of π (for arbitrarily small norm) and of the z_i, one could make $\Sigma f(z_i)\,\Delta x_i$ equal any preassigned number between 0 and 1. No reasonable definition of the limiting process of Definition 10 would allow this function to be integrable.

We now call attention to a fact which has been perfectly obvious all along: the value of an integral depends not only upon the function f but upon the interval $[a, b]$. We stress this fact now because we want to study this relationship in detail. Suppose we hold fixed one endpoint, a, say, of the interval and consider how the integral changes with the other endpoint. To be more explicit, suppose f

is *continuous*, hence integrable (see Theorem 9) on $[a, b]$ and suppose $x \in [a, b]$. We wish to study

$$\int_a^x f(t) \, dt.$$

(We remark that we use t here as the "variable of integration"—actually any letter other than x could be used. But x and t play different roles and should therefore not be represented by the same symbol.)

Since f is integrable on $[a, b]$, the integral above assigns to each $x \in [a, b]$ a unique number in **R**—in others words, it provides a mapping from $[a, b]$ to **R**, which is to say it represents a function with domain $[a, b]$. We shall call it F, and we observe that we know that $F(a) = 0$, by Definition 11:

$$F(x) = \int_a^x f(t) \, dt. \tag{11}$$

If we now concern ourselves with the way in which the integral changes with changes in the interval, then it would seem natural to study the derivative of F, since the derivative of a function always gives a measure of the rate of change of the function. The result has already been suggested in the discussion at the beginning of this section.

Theorem 13. *Let f be continuous on $[a, b]$ and, for $x \in [a, b]$, let F be defined as in (11). Then, for all $x \in [a, b]$, $F'(x)$ exists and*

$$F'(x) = f(x).$$

This theorem is sometimes referred to as the *First Fundamental Theorem of Calculus* because of the way it describes the relation between integration and differentiation. Its proof is within our grasp provided we assume a geometrically plausible result the proof of which we must defer. We state this result now and illustrate it in Figure 24.

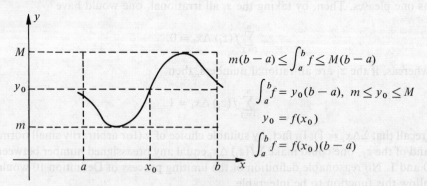

$$m(b - a) \le \int_a^b f \le M(b - a)$$

$$\int_a^b f = y_0(b - a), \quad m \le y_0 \le M$$

$$y_0 = f(x_0)$$

$$\int_a^b f = f(x_0)(b - a)$$

Figure 24

Theorem 14. (*The First Mean Value Theorem of Integral Calculus*). *Let f be continuous on $[a, b]$. Then there exists $x_0 \in [a, b]$ such that*

$$\int_a^b f = f(x_0)(b - a).$$

The reason for the name "mean value" applied to Theorem 14 will be more apparent if we write the last equation as

$$\frac{\int_a^b f}{b - a} = f(x_0), \qquad x_0 \in [a, b].$$

Now recall that, by its definition, the integral involves a sum $\sum_{i=1}^n f(z_i) \, \Delta x_i$, which can be thought of as the sum of the values of f at the z_i, *weighted* by the Δx_i. Thus the expression

$$\frac{\sum\limits_{i=1}^n f(z_i) \, \Delta x_i}{\sum\limits_{i=1}^n \Delta x_i}$$

is a *weighted average* or *weighted mean*. Then

$$\frac{\lim \sum\limits_{i=1}^n f(z_i) \, \Delta x_i}{\sum\limits_{i=1}^n \Delta x_i} = \frac{\int_a^b f(x) \, dx}{b - a}$$

gives an average value of f over $[a, b]$. The *Mean Value Theorem* says that when f is continuous on $[a, b]$ there is an $x_0 \in [a, b]$ at which f takes on its mean value.

Proof of Theorem 13. Our object is to find the derivative of the function F defined by

$$F(x) = \int_a^x f(t) \, dt.$$

Our only recourse is to the definition of the derivative; let x and $x + h$ be in $[a, b]$:

$$F'(x) = \lim_{h \to 0} \frac{F(x + h) - F(x)}{h}$$

$$= \lim_{h \to 0} \frac{1}{h} [F(x + h) - F(x)]$$

$$= \lim_{h \to 0} \frac{1}{h} \left[\int_a^{x+h} f(t) \, dt - \int_a^x f(t) \, dt \right] \qquad \text{(Definition of } F\text{)}$$

$$= \lim_{h \to 0} \frac{1}{h} \left[\int_x^{x+h} f(t) \, dt \right] \qquad \text{(Theorem 12)}$$

$$= \lim_{h \to 0} \frac{1}{h} [f(x_0)h] \qquad \text{(Theorem 14)}$$

where x_0 is between x and $x + h$ (see Figure 25).

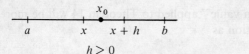

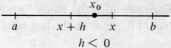

Figure 25

Thus we conclude that

$$F'(x) = \lim_{h \to 0} f(x_0),$$

where x_0 lies between x and $x + h$. It is a consequence of the continuity of the function f that $\lim_{h \to 0} f(x_0) = f(x)$. This gives the desired result:

$$F'(x) = f(x). \quad \blacksquare$$

What have we done? Using a continuous function f and an integral we have created a new function F whose derivative is f. Such a function F is called an *antiderivative* of f.

Definition 12. *Let f be a function. Any function F such that $F' = f$ is called an **antiderivative** of f. The symbol*

$$\int f(x)\, dx$$

*is used to represent an antiderivative of f. The process of finding an antiderivative is called **antidifferentiation**.*

We seem to have opened a new box of toys. Given a function f, does it always have an antiderivative? If so, is it unique, or might there be several? Suppose we look at some examples. Since

$$Dx^2 = 2x \quad \text{and} \quad D \sin x = \cos x,$$

we can conclude that $F(x) = x^2$ is an antiderivative of $f(x) = 2x$ and that $G(x) = \sin x$ is an antiderivative of $g(x) = \cos x$. But note that

$$D(x^2 + 1) = D(x^2 - 13) = D(x^2 + 147) = D(x^2 + c) = 2x,$$

where in the last parentheses c is any number. Thus $f(x) = 2x$ has many anti-derivatives: any function obtained by adding a constant to x^2. Similarly, we quickly see, since $Dc = 0$, that if F is a particular antiderivative of f, then $F + c$, where c is a constant, is another. But might there be other functions, of a different sort, which produce f upon differentiation? The following theorem guarantees a negative answer to this question.

Theorem 15. *Let F and G be functions such that for all $x \in [a, b]$ it is true that $F'(x) = G'(x)$. Then there exists a constant c such that $F(x) = G(x) + c$, for all $x \in [a, b]$.*

Proof. Let $H(x) = F(x) - G(x)$, $x \in [a, b]$. Then $H'(x) = F'(x) - G'(x) = 0$, $x \in [a, b]$, since $F'(x) = G'(x)$. Now by Proposition 2 in Section 2.6 (p. 105), $H(x)$ is constant on $[a, b]$, i.e., $F(x) = G(x) + c$ on $[a, b]$. ∎

We are now in a position to obtain the end result of this section.

Theorem 16. (*The Second Fundamental Theorem of Calculus*). *Let f be continuous on $[a, b]$ and let F be any antiderivative of f. Then*

$$\int_a^b f = F(b) - F(a).$$

Proof. Let $x \in [a, b]$ and let

$$G(x) = \int_a^x f(t)\, dt.$$

If F is any antiderivative of f, then, by Theorem 15, $F(x) = G(x) + c$. But we know that $G(a) = 0$, so, setting $x = a$, we can find the value of c:

$$F(a) = G(a) + c$$
$$= 0 + c.$$

Thus $c = F(a)$ and

$$G(x) = F(x) - F(a)$$

or

$$\int_a^x f(t)\, dt = F(x) - F(a).$$

In particular,

$$\int_a^b f(t)\, dt = F(b) - F(a). \quad ∎$$

With this theorem we have transferred the problem of finding an integral of f to that of finding an antiderivative of f. Thus, since, as we have already seen, $F(x) = x^2$ is an antiderivative of $f(x) = 2x$,

$$\int_a^b 2x\, dx = F(b) - F(a)$$
$$= b^2 - a^2.$$

It is customary to use the following notation to indicate this process:

$$\int_a^b (2x)\, dx = x^2 \Big|_a^b = b^2 - a^2.$$

More generally, if F is an antiderivative of f,

$$\int_a^b f = F(x) \Big|_a^b = F(b) - F(a).$$

As another example,

$$\int_0^\pi \cos x \, dx = \sin x \Big|_0^\pi = \sin \pi - \sin 0 = 0.$$

(Explain this result.)

It follows that, if we want to use the result of Theorem 16 to evaluate integrals, we must learn something about the process of antidifferentiation. We shall discuss this briefly in the next section.

EXERCISES

1. Find antiderivatives of the following functions:

(a) $f(x) = 1$, i.e., $f = 1$.   (f) $f(x) = x^n$.
(b) $f(x) = c$, i.e., $f = c$.   (g) $f(x) = cx^n$, $c \in \mathbf{R}$.
(c) $f(x) = x$, i.e., $f = j$.   (h) $f(x) = x + x^2$.
(d) $f(x) = x^2$.   (i) $f(x) = x^m + x^n$.
(e) $f(x) = x^3$.

2. Find the value of the following integrals:

(a) $\int_0^1 x \, dx$.   (e) $\int_a^b x^n \, dx$.

(b) $\int_0^2 x \, dx$.   (f) $\int_a^b (x + x^2) \, dx$.

(c) $\int_1^2 x \, dx$.   (g) $\int_a^b (x^2 + 2x + 4) \, dx$.

(d) $\int_0^b x^n \, dx$.

3. Use Theorem 16 to do Exercise 1 at the end of Section 2.7.

4. An object traveling along a straight line has velocity function

$$v(t) = t^2 + t + 1 \text{ cm/sec}.$$

How far does the object travel in the interval between 2 and 6 sec?

5. Find the area bounded by the graph of $f(x) = x^3$, the x-axis, and the line $x = 2$.

6. Find the area bounded by the curve of Exercise 5, the y-axis, and the line $y = 8$.

7. Find the area bounded by the graph of $f(x) = \cos x$, the y-axis, and the x-axis between 0 and $\dfrac{\pi}{2}$.

8. Prove Theorem 12.

9. Use Theorem 10 and mathematical induction to prove the following: for all $n = 2, 3, \ldots$, let $f_1, f_2, \ldots, f_n$ be integrable on $[a, b]$. Then $f = \sum_{i=1}^{n} f_i$ is integrable on $[a, b]$ and

$$\int_a^b f = \sum_{i=1}^{n} \int_a^b f_i.$$

10. A piece of wire 20 inches long has density function $\delta(x) = 3x^2 + 2x$, $0 \le x \le 20$.

(a) Find the mass of the wire.

(b) Find the mass of the wire between $x = 5$ and $x = 15$.

11. Let

$$f(1) = 8, \qquad f(2) = 10, \qquad f(3) = 4,$$
$$w_1 = 3, \qquad w_2 = 2, \qquad w_3 = 5.$$

(a) Find

$$\frac{\sum_{i=1}^{3} f(i)w_i}{\sum_{i=1}^{3} w_i} = \text{average}$$

(b) Is there an i among $\{1, 2, 3\}$ such that $f(i) = \text{average}$?

12. Let f be defined on $[0, 2]$ by

$$\begin{cases} f(x) = x, \ 0 \le x \le 1 \\ f(x) = 2, \ 1 \le x \le 2. \end{cases}$$

(a) Find $\int_0^2 f$. *Hint.* $\int_0^2 f = \int_0^1 f + \int_1^2 f$.]

(b) Does there exist $x_0 \in [0, 2]$ such that $\dfrac{\int_0^2 f}{2 - 0} = f(x_0)$? Compare with Theorem 14.

2.9 Antiderivatives

As we saw in the preceding section, the problem of evaluating an integral of a function f is transformed by Theorem 16 into the problem of finding an anti-derivative (or *primitive*, as it is sometimes called) of f. The general problem of finding a primitive function for a given function is an extensive one which we must postpone until later (see Chapter 8). However, it will be wise for us at this time to indicate a few properties of antiderivatives and to find the antideriva-tives of a few simple functions.

We first remark that the operation of finding antiderivatives is linear: to be specific, we have the following result.

Theorem 17.

(a) $\int [f(x) + g(x)] \, dx = \int f(x) \, dx + \int g(x) \, dx$ (12)

(b) $\int cf(x) \, dx = c \int f(x) \, dx.$ (13)

Proof. This theorem follows immediately from Theorem 2; we give the proof of part (a) only.

Suppose we let

$$\int f(x)\, dx = F(x), \qquad \int g(x)\, dx = G(x),$$

and

$$\int [f(x) + g(x)]\, dx = H(x).$$

Then, by definition of antiderivative,

$$F'(x) = f(x), \qquad G'(x) = g(x), \qquad H'(x) = f(x) + g(x);$$

moreover, by Theorem 2,

$$D\left[\int f(x)\, dx + \int g(x)\, dx\right] = D[F(x) + G(x)]$$

$$= DF(x) + DG(x)$$

$$= f(x) + g(x).$$

But this says that $\int f(x)\, dx + \int g(x)\, dx$ is an antiderivative of $f(x) + g(x)$, i.e., that

$$\int [f(x) + g(x)]\, dx = \int f(x)\, dx + \int g(x)\, dx. \quad \blacksquare$$

When it comes to primitives of particular functions, we note that *every* derivative statement can be immediately translated into an antiderivative statement. Thus, from $Dx^2 = 2x$, we get

$$\int 2x\, dx = x^2 + c,$$

and from $D \sin x = \cos x$, we get

$$\int \cos x\, dx = \sin x + c.$$

We list in a theorem a few of the antiderivatives immediately available to us. The proof of the assertions consists simply in checking that the derivative of the function on the right is equal to the function which appears behind the integral sign (the *integrand*).

Theorem 18.

(a) $\displaystyle \int x^n\, dx = \frac{x^{n+1}}{n+1} + c, \qquad n \neq -1.$

(b) $\displaystyle \int \sin x\, dx = -\cos x + c.$

(c) $\displaystyle \int \cos x\, dx = \sin x + c.$

(d) $\displaystyle \int e^x\, dx = e^x + c.$

From Theorem 17 and (a) of Theorem 18 it is possible to find the antiderivative of any polynomial function. For example (and in complete detail), we have

$$\int (2x^2 + 3x - 4)\, dx = \int 2x^2\, dx + \int 3x\, dx + \int (-4)\, dx$$

$$= 2 \int x^2\, dx + 3 \int x\, dx - 4 \int 1\, dx$$

$$= 2 \frac{x^3}{3} + 3 \frac{x^2}{2} - 4x + c.$$

One usually omits the two intermediate steps. Note that instead of writing a separate c for each term we lump all the constants together into c. Note also that

$$\int dx = \int 1 \cdot dx = \int x^0\, dx = x + c.$$

The process of finding antiderivatives for rational functions or for products of functions is more difficult than that for polynomial functions, largely because the derivatives of quotients and of products are not as simple as are the derivatives of sums.

As an example of the utility of antidifferentiation, suppose we are told that a curve at every point (x, y) has a tangent line with slope $m = -2x + 4$. If the curve is the graph of a function f, then we know that the slope of the tangent line is given by f', i.e.,

$$f'(x) = -2x + 4.$$

To find f we perform an antidifferentiation:

$$f(x) = -x^2 + 4x + c. \tag{14}$$

The fact is that Eq. (14) represents a *family* of congruent curves—different values of c give different members of the family. For instance, if we want the curve in the family which goes through the point $(2, 0)$, we can find the value of c determined by this condition:

$$0 = -4 + 8 + c,$$

or $c = -4$, so

$$f(x) = -x^2 + 4x - 4 = -(x - 2)^2.$$

The graph of this f is shown in Figure 26, along with the graph of the member for which $c = -5$;

$$f(x) = -x^2 + 4x - 5.$$

Example 22. Suppose we have an object moving on a vertical line subject only to the force of gravity. This means the acceleration is constant. If the positive direction is taken as upward, then the constant acceleration will be negative, say $-g$ ft/sec^2, i.e.,

$$a(t) = -g.$$

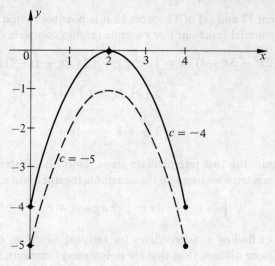

Figure 26

To find the velocity function we recall that $v'(t) = a(t)$, so v is an antiderivative of a; thus

$$v(t) = -gt + c_1. \tag{15}$$

Similarly, since $v(t) = s'(t)$, the distance function s is an antiderivative of v:

$$s(t) = -\tfrac{1}{2}gt^2 + c_1 t + c_2. \tag{16}$$

It is easy to discern the meaning of the constants of integration c_1 and c_2. For, setting $t = 0$ in (15) tells us that $c_1 = v(0)$; this is usually denoted by v_0 and is called the *initial velocity*. In a like manner we see that $c_2 = s(0) = s_0$, the *initial distance*. Thus, the equation of motion can be written

$$s(t) = -\tfrac{1}{2}gt^2 + v_0 t + s_0. \tag{17}$$

We consider one more example. It is known that the rate of decay of a radioactive substance is proportional to the amount present. Thus if $y(t)$ is the amount present at time t, then the rate of change of y is y' and the preceding sentence tells us that

$$y'(t) = -k^2 y(t), \tag{18}$$

where k is a constant which depends upon the substance. Note that $y(t) \geq 0$, and, since the amount *decreases* with time, $y'(t) < 0$. Thus the constant of proportionality should be negative; to guarantee this we write it as $-k^2$. Our present knowledge of the antidifferentiation process is inadequate to find the function y described in Eq. (18). The solution turns out to be

$$y(t) = y_0 \cdot e^{-k^2 t},$$

where y_0 is the amount of substance at time $t = 0$.

The preceding three examples are all illustrations of the solving of differential equations: equations which involve the derivative of an unknown function. Clearly, the solution of such equations is dependent upon an extensive knowledge of antidifferentiation—and frequently, as it turns out, upon some tricks.

EXERCISES

1. Find the following antiderivatives. In every case check your answer by differentiating.

(a) $\int (2x - 1) \, dx.$

(d) $\int (2x^4 - 4x^3 - x^2 + 6x + 4) \, dx.$

(b) $\int (x^2 + 3x - 1) \, dx.$

(e) $\int \dfrac{x^4 + 2}{x^2} \, dx. \left[Hint. \quad \dfrac{x^4 + 2}{x^2} = x^2 + \dfrac{2}{x^2}. \right]$

(c) $\int (3 \sin x + 2e^x) \, dx.$

(f) $\int \dfrac{x^5 + 3x^4 + 5x^3 - 2x + 7}{x^3} \, dx.$

2. (a) Can you discover two different methods for finding $\int (x + 1)^3 \, dx$? [*Hint.* Use the binomial theorem.]

(b) Do the two methods give the same result?

(c) If you *did* find two methods in part (a), try them on $\int (x^2 + 1)^3 \, dx$ and check the results obtained.

3. Find the antiderivatives. Check by differentiating.

(a) $\int \sqrt{x} \, dx.$

(d) $\int (x^{1/2} + x^{-1/2}) \, dx.$

(b) $\int \sqrt[3]{x} \, dx.$

(e) $\int \sqrt{x}(3x^2 - 4x + 7) \, dx.$

(c) $\int x^{2/3} \, dx.$

(f) $\int (2\sqrt{x} - 1)\left(4x - \dfrac{1}{\sqrt{x}}\right) dx.$

4. (a) Find the family $\mathscr{C}$ of curves for which at every point (x, y) the slope of the tangent line is $m = 3x^2 - 1$.

(b) Find the member of the family in (a) which goes through the origin.

(c) Prove or disprove about the family $\mathscr{C}$ of (a): For every point $P_0(x_0, y_0)$ of the plane there exists *exactly* one member of $\mathscr{C}$ which goes through P_0.

5. An object is traveling along a straight line. It starts from rest (i.e., $v_0 = 0$) at the origin, and at any instant t its acceleration is $a(t) = 2 - 6t$ ft/sec². Find the distance function s.

6. The tangent to a curve has the following property at every point (x, y):

$$x < 0 \Rightarrow m = 2x,$$
$$x > 0 \Rightarrow m = -3x^2.$$

(a) If the curve is the graph of a function f, find a formula for f, assuming $f(0) = 0$.

(b) Give an explicit formula for f, assuming that the curve is continuous (has no jump) at $x = 0$.

(c) Suppose the curve has a jump, of, say, one unit, at $x = 0$. Give a formula for f.

7. (a) Is the greatest integer function the derivative of a function; in other words, does

$$F(x) = \int [x]\, dx$$

   exist?

(b) If the answer to (a) is yes, can you draw the graph of F? Is the graph (if it exists) continuous or discontinuous?

8. Let $\mathscr{D}$ be the set of all differentiable functions on some set $X \subset \mathbf{R}$. We define a binary relation on $\mathscr{D}$ by saying F_1 and F_2 are *equivalent* (in symbols $F_1 \sim F_2$) $\Leftrightarrow F_1 = F_2$ + constant (which, by Assertion 2 in Section 2.6, is the same as saying that $F_1' = F_2'$).

(a) Prove that $\sim$ has the following properties:

   (i) $\forall F \in \mathscr{D} \Rightarrow F \sim F$ (reflexive property)
   (ii) $F_1 \sim F_2 \Rightarrow F_2 \sim F_1$ (symmetric property)
   (iii) $\left.\begin{array}{c} F_1 \sim F_2 \\ F_2 \sim F_3 \end{array}\right\} \Rightarrow F_1 \sim F_3$ (transitive property)

   [*Remark.* A relation on a set having the above three properties is called an *equivalence relation*. Can you think of other equivalence relations?]

(b) For an $F_0 \in \mathscr{D}$ define

$$\mathscr{F}_0 = \{F \in \mathscr{D} \mid F \sim F_0\}$$

Consider the set of all sets $\mathscr{F}$ obtainable in this way. Prove the following about these sets:

   (i) $\mathscr{D} = \cup \mathscr{F}$, i.e., every function $F \in \mathscr{D}$ is in one of the $\mathscr{F}$.
   (ii) $\mathscr{F}_1 \neq \mathscr{F}_2 \Rightarrow \mathscr{F}_1 \cap \mathscr{F}_2 = \varnothing$, i.e., any two distinct sets are disjoint.

   [*Remark.* The sets $\mathscr{F}$ are called *equivalence classes*. An equivalence relation on a set always divides the set into equivalence classes having the above two properties. This is usually described by saying an equivalence relation on a set induces a *partition* of the set.]
   The significance of this problem in terms of antiderivatives should be clear. Strictly, if $F' = f$, one should write

$$\int f(x)\, dx = \{F\},$$

the equivalence class containing F. The long-established procedure, however, is to write

$$\int f(x)\, dx = F + c,$$

where c is a constant.

9. Consider a function f which is differentiable on some set $X \subset \mathbf{R}$ and which has an antiderivative.

(a) Find $D\left(\int f(x)\, dx\right)$. (b) Find $\int D(f(x))\, dx$.

(c) Are the results in (a) and (b) the same? If not, how do they differ?

(d) Let $a, x \in X$. Find $D\left(\int_a^x f(t)\, dt\right)$. (e) Let $a, x \in X$. Find $\int_a^x D(f(t))\, dt$.

(f) Are the results in (d) and (e) the same? If not, how do they differ?

2.10 More on Integrals

Having available now a means of evaluating integrals we conclude our preliminary and intuitive introduction to calculus with a further discussion of some simple applications of the integral.

A. AREA. In order to help motivate the definition of the integral we considered the problem of finding the area of a plane region, part of whose boundary is a curve. This was done with some restrictions on the region (e.g., that it lie in the first or second quadrants); although at this time we cannot consider the problem in its most general form, we can relax somewhat the conditions imposed in Section 2.7.

We begin with an example.

Example 23. Consider the region of the plane bounded by the graph of $f : x \to 4x - x^2$ and the x-axis between $x = 0$ and $x = 4$ (see Figure 27). Our discussion in Section 2.7 would lead to the conclusion that the area A of this region is given by

$$A = \int_0^4 f(x)\, dx = \int_0^4 (4x - x^2)\, dx$$

$$= 2x^2 - \frac{1}{3}x^3 \Big|_0^4$$

$$= \left(32 - \frac{64}{3}\right) - 0$$

$$= \frac{32}{3} \text{ square units.}$$

Now suppose we consider the graph of $g = -f$, for $0 \le x \le 4$; i.e., $g(x) = x^2 - 4x$. On the one hand, the graph of g is the reflection in the x-axis of the graph of f (see Figure 28), so the area bounded by the graph of g and the x-axis should be the same as that bounded by the graph of f and the x-axis. And on the other hand, by (b) of Theorem 10, with $c = -1$,

$$\int_0^4 g(x)\, dx = \int_0^4 -f(x)\, dx = -\int_0^4 f(x)\, dx = -\frac{32}{3}.$$

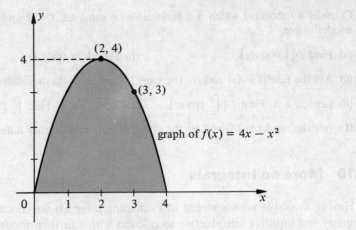

Figure 27

The fairly obvious—and correct—conclusion is that the location of this region below the x-axis causes the sign of the integral to be negative. (The reason for this is rather clear if one considers that when $f(x) < 0$ every term in the approximating sum

$$\sum_{i=1}^{n} f(z_i) \, \Delta x_i,$$

and hence the sum itself, will be negative.) Thus for a region such as in Figure 28 we have

$$A = - \int_0^4 g(x) \, dx = \int_0^4 [-g(x)] \, dx = \int_0^4 |g(x)| \, dx,$$

since, for $0 \le x \le 4$, $g(x) < 0$ and $|g(x)| = -g(x)$.

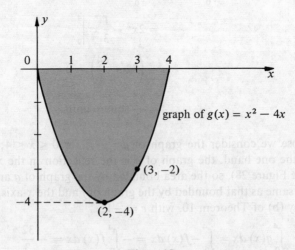

Figure 28

As another illustration of what we have just seen, consider the cosine function between $x = 0$ and $x = \pi$. Since $\int \cos x \, dx = \sin x$, the following integrals are easily obtained:

$$\int_0^{\pi/2} \cos x \, dx = 1, \qquad \int_{\pi/2}^{\pi} \cos x \, dx = -1, \qquad \int_0^{\pi} \cos x \, dx = 0.$$

Compare these values with the areas of the appropriate regions of the graph of the cosine function, as shown in Figure 29. Thus the measure of the area bounded by the graph of cos between 0 and π is not given by $\int_0^{\pi} \cos x \, dx$, but by

$$A = 1 + 1 = \int_0^{\pi/2} \cos x \, dx - \int_{\pi/2}^{\pi} \cos x \, dx = \int_0^{\pi/2} \cos x \, dx + \int_{\pi/2}^{\pi} (-\cos x) \, dx$$

$$= \int_0^{\pi/2} |\cos x| \, dx + \int_{\pi/2}^{\pi} |\cos x| \, dx$$

$$= \int_0^{\pi} |\cos x| \, dx,$$

since $0 < x < \dfrac{\pi}{2} \Rightarrow \cos x > 0$ and $\dfrac{\pi}{2} < x < \pi \Rightarrow \cos x < 0$.

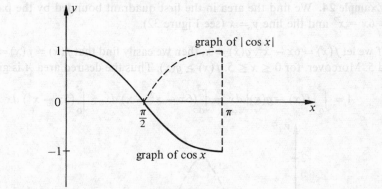

Figure 29

This indicates what is generally true: the area bounded by the graph of an integrable function f and the x-axis for $x \in [a, b]$ is given by

$$A = \int_a^b |f(x)| \, dx. \tag{19}$$

Thus, if f is defined by the formula

$$f(x) = x(x - 1)(x - 3) = x^3 - 4x^2 + 3x$$

then the area bounded by the graph of f and the x-axis for $0 \le x \le 3$ is given by

$$A = \int_0^3 |f(x)| \, dx = \int_0^3 |x^3 - 4x^2 + 3x| \, dx$$

$$= \int_0^1 (x^3 - 4x^2 + 3x) \, dx + \int_1^3 [-(x^3 - 4x^2 + 3x)] \, dx$$

$$= \frac{5}{12} + \frac{32}{12}$$

$$= \frac{37}{12}.$$

We leave it to the student to check the preceding values. Figure 30 shows a sketch of the graph of f.

In general, the area between two curves is measured as follows. See Figure 31.

Definition 13. *Let f and g be integrable on $[a, b]$. Then the **area** A bounded by their graphs and the lines $x = a$ and $x = b$ is*

$$A = \int_a^b |f(x) - g(x)| \, dx. \tag{20}$$

Note that if $g = 0$ (graph is the x-axis), then Eq. (20) reduces to (19).

Example 24. We find the area in the first quadrant bounded by the parabola $y = 6x - x^2$ and the line $y = x$ (see Figure 32).

If we let $f(x) = 6x - x^2$, $g(x) = x$, then we easily find that $f(x) = g(x) \Rightarrow x = 0$ and 5. Moreover, for $0 \leq x \leq 5$, $f(x) \geq g(x)$. Thus the desired area A is given by

$$A = \int_0^5 |f(x) - g(x)| \, dx = \int_0^5 (6x - x^2 - x) \, dx = \int_0^5 (5x - x^2) \, dx$$

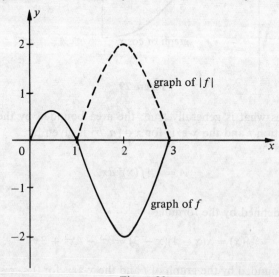

Figure 30

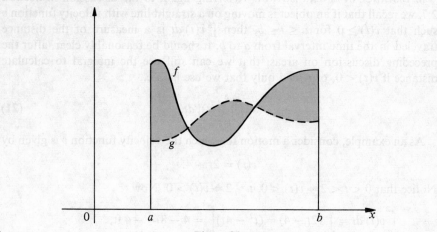

Figure 31

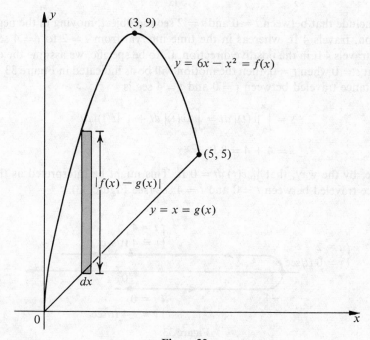

Figure 32

$$= \frac{5}{2} x^2 - \frac{1}{3} x^3 \Big|_0^5 = \frac{5^3}{2} - \frac{5^3}{3} = \frac{125}{6}$$

$$= 20\tfrac{5}{6} \text{ square units.}$$

In Figure 32 we show an "element of area," a rectangle with height $|f(x) - g(x)|$ and with base dx.

B. DISTANCE IN LINEAR MOTION. Referring again to the discussion in Section 2.7, we recall that if an object is moving on a straight line with velocity function v such that $v(t) \geq 0$ for $a \leq t \leq b$, then $\int_a^b v(t)\, dt$ is a measure of the distance traveled in the time interval from a to b. It should be reasonably clear, after the preceding discussion on areas, that we can still use the integral to calculate distance if $v(t) < 0$, provided only that we use $|v|$, i.e.,

$$s = \int_a^b |v(t)|\, dt. \tag{21}$$

As an example, consider a motion for which the velocity function v is given by

$$v(t) = 2t - 4.$$

Notice that $0 < t < 2 \Rightarrow v(t) < 0$, $t > 2 \Rightarrow v(t) > 0$. Now

$$\int_0^2 v(t)\, dt = \int_0^2 (2t - 4) = (t^2 - 4t)\Big|_0^2 = 4 - 8 = -4 \text{ ft},$$

$$\int_2^4 v(t)\, dt = \int_2^4 (2t - 4)\, dt = t^2 - 4t\Big|_2^4 = (16 - 16) - (4 - 8) = 4 \text{ ft}.$$

We conclude that between $t = 0$ and $t = 2$ sec the object, moving in the negative direction, travels 4 ft, whereas in the time interval from $t = 2$ to $t = 4$ sec the object travels 4 ft in the positive direction. If, to be specific, we assume the object starts at $s = 0$ when $t = 0$, then the motion will be as indicated in Figure 33. Thus the distance traveled between $t = 0$ and $t = 4$ sec is

$$s = \int_0^4 |v(t)|\, dt = \int_0^2 |v(t)|\, dt + \int_2^4 |v(t)|\, dt$$

$$= 4 + 4 = 8 \text{ ft}.$$

Note, by the way, that $\int_0^4 v(t)\, dt = 0$ ft. This might be interpreted as the *net* distance traveled between $t = 0$ and $t = 4$ sec (see Figure 33).

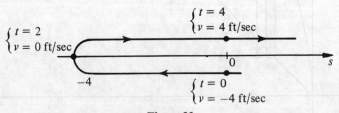

Figure 33

C. VOLUMES. We conclude this section by showing how, in certain special cases, an integral can be used to find the measure of volume of three-dimensional regions. The general discussion of volume must wait for generalization of the integral.

Suppose we have a region of space, such as that shown in Figure 34 (where we have taken $a = 0$), with the property that for every x between a and b the cross-

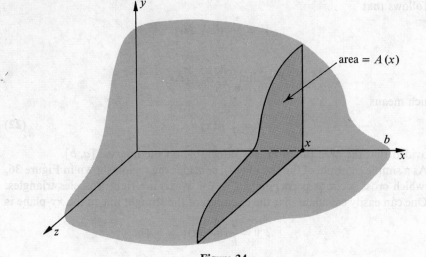

Figure 34

sectional area $A(x)$ of the region is known. We shall see that from an intuitive point of view, the definition of the integral (Definition 10) can be used to give us a measure of the volume of the region.

As we did in Section 2.7, we partition the interval $[a, b]$ into subintervals:

$$\pi = \{a = x_0 < x_1 < x_2 < \cdots < x_{i-1} < x_i < \cdots < x_{n-1} < x_n = b\}.$$

In each subinterval $[x_{i-1}, x_i]$, we select a point z_i, and consider the area function A at z_i: *approximately*, the volume of the region between x_{i-1} and x_i will be given by $A(z_i)\,\Delta x_i$, the product of the value of the area function at z_i, and the thickness Δx_i of this portion of the region. We illustrate this in Figure 35.

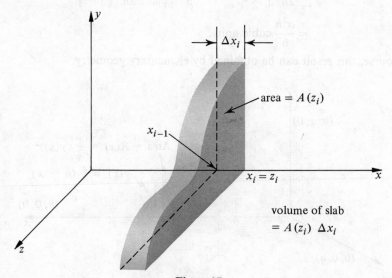

Figure 35

It follows that

$$V \approx \sum_{i=1}^{n} A(z_i) \, \Delta x_i,$$

or

$$V = \lim_{|\pi| \to 0} \sum_{i=1}^{n} A(z_i) \, \Delta x_i,$$

which means

$$V = \int_a^b A(x) \, dx, \qquad (22)$$

provided that the area function A is integrable on the interval $[a, b]$.

As a simple example of the use of (22), consider the region shown in Figure 36, of which cross sections perpendicular to the x-axis are right isosceles triangles. One can easily calculate that the equation of the straight line in the xy-plane is

$$y = \frac{a}{h} (h - x);$$

thus, since the triangular cross sections are isosceles,

$$A(x) = \frac{1}{2} y^2 = \frac{a^2}{2h^2} (h - x)^2.$$

By (22), then, we have

$$V = \int_0^h A(x) \, dx = \int_0^h \frac{a^2}{2h^2} (h - x)^2 \, dx$$

$$= \frac{a^2}{2h^2} \int_0^h (h^2 - 2hx + x^2) \, dx$$

$$= \frac{a^2}{2h^2} \left[h^2 x - hx^2 + \frac{1}{3} x^3 \right] \Big|_0^h = \frac{a^2}{2h^2} \left[\frac{1}{3} h^3 \right]$$

$$= \frac{a^2 h}{6} \text{ cubic units.}$$

Of course, this result can be obtained by elementary geometry.

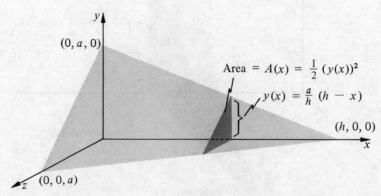

$$\text{Area} = A(x) = \frac{1}{2} (y(x))^2$$

$$y(x) = \frac{a}{h} (h - x)$$

Figure 36

A special case of (22) which leads to results not obtainable by elementary geometry occurs when the region is one of revolution: the region can be considered as obtained by revolving about a line (the x-axis, say) a plane region. To be specific, suppose we have a plane region $\mathscr{A}$ such as that shown in Figure 37.

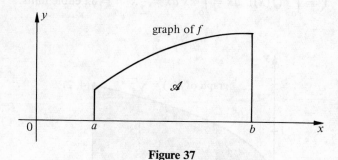

Figure 37

The upper boundary is the graph of a function f. If this region $\mathscr{A}$ is revolved about the x-axis, a three-dimensional region $\mathscr{V}$ will be generated, one fourth of which is shown in Figure 38.

In this case the cross-sectional area is circular, the radius being $f(x)$, so

$$A(x) = \pi(f(x))^2,$$

and (22) becomes

$$V = \pi \int_a^b (f(x))^2 \, dx. \tag{23}$$

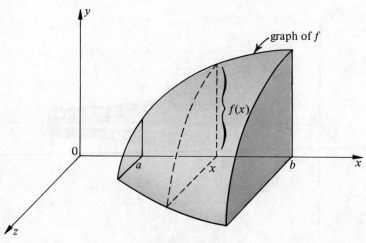

Figure 38

As an example, consider the region $\mathscr{A}$ shown in Figure 39. The upper boundary is the graph of $f : x \to \sqrt{x}, 0 \le x \le 4$.

By (23), the volume of the region obtained when $\mathscr{A}$ is revolved about the x-axis is

$$V = \int_0^4 \pi(f(x))^2 \, dx = \int_0^4 \pi x \, dx = \frac{\pi}{2} x^2 \bigg|_0^4 = 8\pi \text{ cubic units.}$$

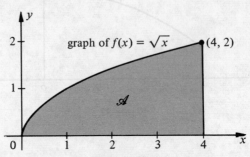

Figure 39

As a final example, let $f(x) = \dfrac{1}{x}$ for $1 \le x \le b$. The three-dimensional region $\mathscr{V}$ generated is shown in Figure 40. By (23) the volume V of $\mathscr{V}$ is

$$V = \pi \int_1^b \left(\frac{1}{x}\right)^2 \, dx = \pi \int_1^b x^{-2} \, dx = \pi \left[-\frac{1}{x} \right] \bigg|_1^b = \pi \left(-\frac{1}{b} + 1 \right)$$

$$V = \pi \left(1 - \frac{1}{b} \right).$$

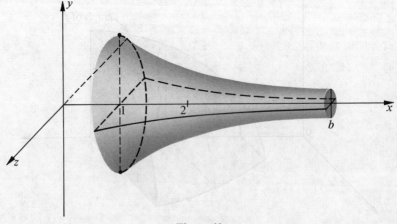

Figure 40

EXERCISES

1. Find the area bounded by the graphs of the following functions and the x-axis over the interval indicated. In each case make a sketch.

   (a) $f(x) = x^2 - 6x$, $[0, 6]$.
   (b) $f(x) = x^3 - 2x^2 - 8x$, $[-2, 4]$.
   (c) $f(x) = x^3$, $[0, 1]$.
   (d) $f(x) = x^n$, $[0, 1]$, $n \neq -1$.
   (e) $f(x) = (x + 3)(x - 1)(x - 8)$, $[-3, 8]$.
   (f) $f(x) = \sin x$, $[0, 2\pi]$.

2. Evaluate the following integrals. Interpret each result in terms of area.

   (a) $\displaystyle\int_{-1}^{1} (x - x^3)\, dx$.
   (b) $\displaystyle\int_{-2}^{6} (x^2 - 4x - 12)\, dx$.
   (c) $\displaystyle\int_{0}^{2\pi} \cos x\, dx$.
   (d) $\displaystyle\int_{-\pi/2}^{\pi/2} \sin x\, dx$.

3. Consider the answer to Exercise 1(d).

   (a) What happens to the area as $n \to \infty$ (i.e., as n gets big beyond all bounds)?

   (b) What happens to the graph of f as $n \to \infty$?

   (c) Note that for every n, $f(1) = 1$. Does this imply a contradiction of some sort?

4. Find the area bounded by each pair of curves.

   (a) $\begin{cases} y = 4x - x^2 \\ y = x^2 \end{cases}$.
   (d) $\begin{cases} y = 5 + 4x - x^2 \\ y = x - 5 \end{cases}$.
   (b) $\begin{cases} y = x^2 - 8x \\ y = -x \end{cases}$.
   (e) $\begin{cases} y = \frac{3}{2}x - \frac{1}{4}x^2 - \frac{5}{4} \\ y = x^2 - 6x + 5 \end{cases}$.
   (c) $\begin{cases} y = x^2 - 8x + 12 \\ y = x + 4 \end{cases}$.

5. For each of the following velocity functions find the distance traveled in the time interval indicated.

   (a) $v(t) = -16t^2$, $[0, 4]$.
   (b) $v(t) = -16t^2 - 8t$, $[0, 4]$.
   (c) $v(t) = -16t^2 + 8t$, $[0, 4]$.
   (d) $v(t) = -16t^2 + 8t + 8$, $[0, 4]$.
   (e) $v(t) = 2t - 8$, $[0, 10]$.
   (f) $v(t) = -\sin t$, $[0, 2\pi]$.

6. A homemade rocket starts from rest ($v_0 = 0$) at $t = 0$. Its acceleration at time t is $a(t) = 100 - t^2$ ft/sec^2. The rocket goes straight up and comes straight down.

   (a) How long is its trip?
   (d) How far does it travel?
   (b) How long is its trip up?
   (e) What is its velocity as it hits the ground?
   (c) What is its maximum height?

7. Draw the graph of f and of $|f|$ (on the same sketch) for the interval indicated.

   (a) $f(x) = \cos$, $[0, \pi]$.
   (b) $f(x) = x - x^2$, $[0, 2]$.
   (c) $f(x) = x^3 - x$, $[-1, 1]$.
   (d) $f(x) = (x + 4)(x - 2)(x - 6)$, $[-4, 6]$.

8. Find the volume of the region generated when each of the plane regions described below is revolved about the x-axis.

(a) $f(x) = \sqrt{1-x^2}$,　　$[-1, 1]$.　　　　　(d) $f(x) = x^3$,　　$[0, 1]$.

(b) $f(x) = mx$,　　$[0, h]$, $m > 0$.　　　　　(e) $f(x) = x^3 - 4x^2 + 3x$,　　$[0, 1]$.

(c) $f(x) = \dfrac{a}{h}(h - x)$,　　$[0, h]$.

9. (a) Is it true that $\left| \int_a^b f \right| = \int_a^b |f|$?

(b) If the answer to (a) is no, can you find a statement involving $\left| \int_a^b f \right|$ and $\int_a^b |f|$ which *is* true?

Chapter 3 Limits and Continuity

Our purpose in this chapter is to establish a firm foundation for the two concepts, limit of a function and continuity of a function. The fact is that all of calculus rests on the idea of limit, and it is essential to a clear comprehension of calculus that the deep—but not inaccessible—concept of limit be fully understood. This is not only a possible, but a reasonable goal, as we shall demonstrate.

As much as possible we shall try to draw on intuition in developing the theory; however, as the history of the subject amply shows, even some of the best intuitions have proven inadequate to the task of arriving at a sound theory of limits, and we shall occasionally find it necessary to produce an external force to turn the discussion in the proper direction.

Before considering the basic problem of assigning a precise meaning to the limit statement, we take time to complete the definition of $\mathbf{R}$, the field of real numbers.

3.1 The Axiom of Continuity

As we already know from the discussion in Chapter 1, $\mathbf{R}$ is an ordered field. But so is the set of rational numbers $\mathbf{Q}$. How do $\mathbf{Q}$ and $\mathbf{R}$ differ? And why is it the case, as we have already indicated, that in calculus we *must* work with $\mathbf{R}$? We proceed to answer these questions.

Suppose we begin with some examples, one involving derivatives, one an integral.

Example 1. We consider the behavior of the polynomial function f defined by

$$f(x) = 4x - x^3 = x(4 - x^2) = x(2 - x)(2 + x)$$

for $0 \leq x \leq 2$, *and with x restricted to the field $\mathbf{Q}$ of rational numbers.*
It is straightforward to observe that

$$f(0) = f(2) = 0, 0 < x < 2 \Rightarrow f(x) > 0,$$

and that

$$0 < x < 2 \Rightarrow f(x) \leq 2 \cdot 2 \cdot 4 = 16$$

(this inequality follows from the last form given for f). Thus, for $0 \leq x \leq 2$, the functional values $f(x)$ lie between 0 and 16, are equal to 0 at the endpoints of the interval, and are positive elsewhere. Moreover, if we calculate the derivative of f,

$$f'(x) = 4 - 3x^2 = 3(\tfrac{4}{3} - x^2),$$

we see that $f'(x)$—and the slope of the tangent to the curve—is positive for $x^2 < \tfrac{4}{3}$ and is negative for $x^2 > \tfrac{4}{3}$. Clearly the graph of f, for $x \in [0, 2]$, should appear as shown in Figure 1.

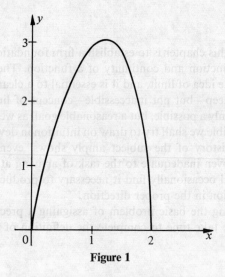

Figure 1

It is "obvious" that f must have a maximum value at some point x_0 between 0 and 2. But does it? Not if we restrict x to lie in $\mathbf{Q}$. For at the maximum, we would have $f'(x_0) = 0$; for the interval $[0, 2]$, f' has the value 0 only when $x_0^2 = \tfrac{4}{3}$, i.e., when $x_0 = \dfrac{2}{\sqrt{3}}$ *which is not a rational number.* Also

$$f(x_0) = f\left(\frac{2}{\sqrt{3}}\right) = \frac{2}{\sqrt{3}}\left(4 - \frac{4}{3}\right) = \frac{16}{3\sqrt{3}},$$

which is not a rational number.

By choosing $x \in \mathbf{Q}$, x close to $x_0 = \dfrac{2}{\sqrt{3}} \approx 1.155$, one can make $f(x)$ close to

$\dfrac{16}{3\sqrt{3}} \approx 3.079$, but when x is restricted to $\mathbf{Q}$, there is no maximum value of $f(x)$.

This can be described in the following way: for every choice of $x_1 \in [0, 2] \cap \mathbf{Q}$, it is possible to find $x_2 \in [0, 2] \cap \mathbf{Q}$ such that $f(x_2) > f(x_1)$. Thus the functional values are bounded above (by 4, in fact), but there is no maximum value if x is restricted to $\mathbf{Q}$—a highly unsatisfactory state of affairs.

Example 2. We now consider a simple area problem. We are concerned with the rational function f defined by

$$f(x) = \frac{1}{x}$$

for $x \in [1, 2]$. Notice that $f(1) = 1$, $f(2) = \frac{1}{2}$, and that the maximum value of f occurs when $x = 1$. Thus the graph of f for $x \in [1, 2]$ will be like that shown in Figure 2.

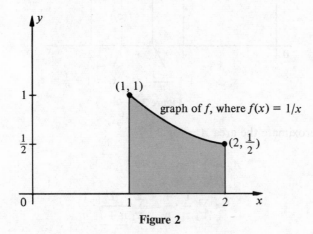

Figure 2

Intuitively it is "obvious" that the area bounded by the graph of f, the x-axis, and the vertical lines at $x = 1$ and $x = 2$ must exist and be less than one square unit. But, as we shall show in Chapter 7, this area would have the value $\log 2$, where the logarithm is the natural (base e) logarithm—and $\log 2 \notin \mathbf{Q}$. Thus, if we were attempting to do our calculus within the framework of the rational number system, the area described, which "obviously exists," would fail to have a numerical measure.

We can relate the difficulty here to that in the preceding example by going back to the definition of the integral. Suppose we consider a regular partition π of $[1, 2]$:

$$\pi = \{1 = x_0, x_1, x_2, \ldots, x_{n-1}, x_n = 2\},$$

where

$$\Delta x_i = x_i - x_{i-1} = \frac{1}{n}.$$

It is easy to see, then, that, for $i = 0, 1, 2, \ldots, n$,

$$x_i = 1 + \frac{i}{n}.$$

Suppose also that we choose $z_i = x_i$ for every $i = 1, \ldots, n$ (see Figure 3).

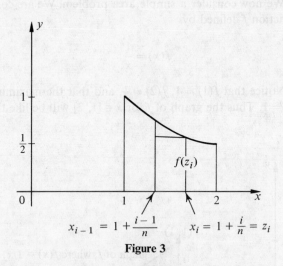

$$x_{i-1} = 1 + \frac{i-1}{n} \qquad\qquad x_i = 1 + \frac{i}{n} = z_i$$

Figure 3

We thus approximate the area $A = \log 2$ by

$$A_n = \sum_{i=1}^{n} f(z_i)\, \Delta x_i$$

$$= \sum_{i=1}^{n} \frac{1}{z_i} \cdot \frac{1}{n} = \sum_{i=1}^{n} \frac{1}{\dfrac{n+i}{n}} \cdot \frac{1}{n}$$

$$= \sum_{i=1}^{n} \frac{1}{n+i}.$$

We note the following about these approximations A_n:

(i) The choice of z_i causes every A_n to be an underestimate of A: $\forall n \Rightarrow A_n < A$.

(ii) The first few values of A_n are

$$A_1 = \frac{1}{2} = 0.50,$$

$$A_2 = \frac{1}{2+1} + \frac{1}{2+2} = \frac{1}{3} + \frac{1}{4} = \frac{7}{12} \approx 0.58,$$

$$A_3 = \frac{1}{4} + \frac{1}{5} + \frac{1}{6} = \frac{37}{60} \approx 0.62,$$

$$A_4 = \frac{1}{5} + \frac{1}{6} + \frac{1}{7} + \frac{1}{8} = \frac{533}{840} \approx 0.63.$$

(iii) The suggestion, given by looking at $A_1, \ldots, A_4$, that A_n increases with n is easily checked:

$$A_n = \sum_{i=1}^{n} \frac{1}{n+i} = \frac{1}{n+1} + \cdots + \frac{1}{2n},$$

$$A_{n+1} = \frac{1}{n+2} + \cdots + \frac{1}{2n} + \frac{1}{2n+1} + \frac{1}{2n+2};$$

thus

$$A_{n+1} - A_n = \frac{1}{2n+1} + \frac{1}{2n+2} - \frac{1}{n+1}$$

$$= \frac{1}{2n+1} - \frac{1}{2n+2} = \frac{1}{(2n+1)(2n+2)} > 0,$$

an inequality which holds for all $n \in \mathbf{N}$. Thus, for every $n \in \mathbf{N} \Rightarrow A_{n+1} > A_n$.

(iv) The A_n's are all less than 1. To see this, we write

$$A_n = \frac{1}{n+1} + \frac{1}{n+2} + \cdots + \frac{1}{2n}$$

$$\leq \frac{1}{n+1} + \frac{1}{n+1} + \cdots + \frac{1}{n+1} \qquad (n \text{ terms})$$

$$= \frac{n}{n+1} < 1.$$

(v) Finally we note that, by its definition, every A_n is a rational number.

To summarize, we have in this example a set of positive rational numbers,

$$A_n = \frac{1}{n+1} + \cdots + \frac{1}{2n-1} + \frac{1}{2n},$$

where, for every $n \in \mathbf{N}$, $A_n < A_{n+1}$ and $A_n < 1$. Moreover, these numbers are obtained as approximations (underestimates, in this case) for the measure of area which authorial omniscience says should be log 2. And log $2 \notin \mathbf{Q}$, this same omniscience says. The point is that the A_n can serve as rational approximations to the measure of the area under discussion, but that *the measure itself is not attainable as a number in* $\mathbf{Q}$.

It is because of this incompleteness that we must insist on working in $\mathbf{R}$ rather than in $\mathbf{Q}$. We now introduce the property that distinguishes between these two ordered fields. First we need several definitions.

Definition 1. *Let S be a nonempty set of numbers.*

(a) *The number B is an **upper bound** of $S \Leftrightarrow \forall x \in S \Rightarrow x \leq B$.*

(b) *The number b is a **lower bound** of $S \Leftrightarrow \forall x \in S \Rightarrow b \leq x$.*

Definition 2. *Let S be a nonempty set of numbers.*

(a) *The number k is the **least upper bound** of S (written k = lub S)* $\Leftrightarrow$
  (i) $x \in S \Rightarrow x \le k$,
  (ii) *for every $\varepsilon > 0$ there exists $x \in S$ such that $x > k - \varepsilon$.*
(b) *The number h is the **greatest lower bound** of S (written h = glb S)* $\Leftrightarrow$
  (i) $x \in S \Rightarrow h \le x$,
  (ii) *for every $\varepsilon > 0$ there exists $x \in S$ such that $x < h + \varepsilon$.*

In the case of lub S, statement (i) requires that k be *an* upper bound of S and statement (ii) requires that k be the *least* upper bound—for if (ii) did not hold then $k - \varepsilon$ would also be an upper bound, and smaller than k. Similar remarks apply to the glb S (see Figure 4).

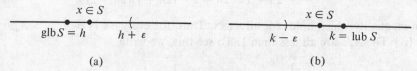

(a)   (b)

Figure 4

We remark that a nonempty set S may have both lub and glb, or one alone, or neither. For example, if $S = [0, 1) = \{x \mid 0 \le x < 1\}$, then lub $S = 1$, glb $S = 0$ (note that $0 \in S$, $1 \notin S$). If $S = \mathbf{R}^+ = \{x \mid x > 0\}$, then lub S does not exist, glb $S = 0$. If $S = \mathbf{R}^-$, then lub $S = 0$, glb S does not exist. If $S = \mathbf{R}$, neither lub S nor glb S exists. If S is finite, then lub S is simply the maximum element of S; but an infinite set, such as the interval $[0, 1)$, need not have a maximum.

The property possessed by $\mathbf{R}$—and not by $\mathbf{Q}$—that makes possible an intuitively reasonable calculus is the following.

Axiom of Continuity (*Completeness Axiom*). *Every nonempty set of numbers which is bounded above has a least upper bound. Also, every nonempty set of numbers which is bounded below has a greatest lower bound.*

This statement is twice as long as it need be, for the second half can be proved from the first (see Exercise 5).

Both Examples 1 and 2 provide evidence that the *Axiom of Continuity* does not hold for the field of rational numbers. Another example (the standard one) is the following. Let S be the set of positive rational numbers whose square is less than 2:

$$S = \{x \in \mathbf{Q} \mid x > 0 \quad \text{and} \quad x^2 < 2\}.$$

Then S is nonempty, for $1 \in S$, and S is bounded above, since 2 serves as an upper bound. But S has no least upper bound in $\mathbf{Q}$—for the number symbolized by $\sqrt{2}$ "should be" lub S, but $\sqrt{2} \notin \mathbf{Q}$.

Now we can describe the real number system $\mathbf{R}$.

Definition 3. *The **real number system** $\mathbf{R}$ is an ordered field which satisfies the Axiom of Continuity (the Completeness Axiom).*

Loosely speaking, the field of rational numbers has most of the essential properties—we can add, subtract, multiply, and divide in $\mathbf{Q}$, and we have an order relation—but there are too many gaps. Even the Greeks in classical times discovered this when they became concerned about measuring the diagonal of the unit square. The effect of requiring that the ordered field with which we work satisfy also the *Completeness Axiom* is to "fill in" the gaps, so that the numbers necessary for solving the problems of calculus are there. The "gap-filling" numbers are, of course, the irrational numbers. Geometrically, the effect of the *Axiom of Continuity* is to provide a 1–1 correspondence between the numbers in $\mathbf{R}$ and the points on a line.

EXERCISES

1. This refers to Example 2. Take a regular partition π as in the example, but choose each z_i to be the left end of the subinterval, i.e.,

$$z_i = x_{i-1} = 1 + \frac{i-1}{n} = \frac{n+i-1}{n}.$$

(Thus the approximating sums $B_n = \sum_{i=1}^{n} f(z_i)\, x_i$ will overestimate the area.) Show the following about the B_n obtained from this choice of z_i.

(a) $\forall n \in \mathbf{N} \Rightarrow B_n > B_{n+1}$. [*Hint.* Begin by finding a formula for B_n.]

(b) The B_n are bounded below by $\frac{1}{2}$ (it is *obvious* that 0 serves as a lower bound).

(c) $\forall n \in \mathbf{N} \Rightarrow B_n \in \mathbf{Q}$.

(d) $\forall n \in \mathbf{N} \Rightarrow B_n - A_n = \dfrac{1}{2n}$. This shows that the A_n and B_n tend to the same limit as n gets big beyond all bounds.

2. This refers to Exercise 1. Calculate B_4, use part (d) of Exercise 1 to obtain A_4, and thus get a squeeze on log 2. Further estimate log 2 by using the arithmetic mean of A_4 and B_4. Compare this with log $2 = 0.69$, to the nearest hundredth.

3. For each of the following subsets of $\mathbf{R}$ give lub S and glb S, if they exist:

(a) $S = \mathbf{N} = \{1, 2, 3, \ldots\}$.   (e) $S = [0, 2) \cup [3, 8)$.

(b) $S = [1, 2]$.   (f) $S = (-\mathbf{N}) = \{\ldots, -4, -3, -2, -1\}$.

(c) $S = (1, 2)$.   (g) $S = \mathbf{Z} = \{\ldots, -3, -2, -1, 0, 1, 2, 3, \ldots\}$.

(d) $S = [1, 2)$.   (h) $S = \{y \mid y = 4x - 4x^2, 0 \le x \le 4\}$.

(i) $S = \{y \mid y = 9x - x^3, 0 \le x \le 3\}$. What would be the answer if we restricted ourselves to the field $\mathbf{Q}$ of rational numbers?

4. Let S be a nonempty set of real numbers which is bounded above. Suppose

$$\text{lub } S = k_1,$$
$$\text{lub } S = k_2.$$

Show that $k_1 = k_2$, i.e., the least upper bound of a bounded set of real numbers is unique.

5. Let S be a nonempty set of numbers which is bounded below, i.e., $\exists b$ such that $\forall x \in S \Rightarrow b \leq x$. Use the first sentence in the statement of the *Axiom of Continuity* to prove that glb S exists. [*Hints.* (1) Define $(-S) = \{y \mid -y \in S\}$; (2) Prove $(-b)$ is an upper bound for $(-S)$; (3) Apply the first sentence in the *Axiom of Continuity* to obtain lub $(-S) = k$, say; and (4) Prove $(-k) = $ glb S.]

6. Assure yourself that the *Axiom of Continuity* does guarantee a maximum on $[0, 2]$ for the function of Example 1 and a measure for the area under the curve in Example 2—in other words, the two problems do have solutions if one works in **R**.

3.2 The First Version

We begin with a word about the form of the problem with which we shall be concerned. The definition of the derivative (Definition 2.1) involves consideration of

$$f'(x_0) = \lim_{h \to 0} \frac{f(x_0 + h) - f(x_0)}{h}; \tag{1}$$

with x_0 fixed, the preceding expression is a function of h, say

$$\varphi(h) = \frac{f(x_0 + h) - f(x_0)}{h}. \tag{2}$$

Then the derivative (1) can be written as

$$f'(x_0) = \lim_{h \to 0} \varphi(h). \tag{3}$$

We can describe (1) in a slightly different way by letting $x_0 + h = x$, so that $h = x - x_0$. With this change we have

$$f'(x_0) = \lim_{x \to x_0} \frac{f(x) - f(x_0)}{x - x_0},$$

or

$$f'(x_0) = \lim_{x \to x_0} g(x), \tag{4}$$

where

$$g(x) = \frac{f(x) - f(x_0)}{x - x_0}. \tag{5}$$

The point of these remarks is that the definition of a derivative involves consideration of a fairly special kind of limit. In order not to allow unnecessary notational difficulties enter into our discussion, we announce that we plan to take the cue provided by either (3) or (4) and restrict ourselves to the problem of assigning a precise meaning to

$$\lim_{x \to a} f(x) = L.$$

When this statement has been defined and its properties explored we will be able to apply it to special functions such as those occurring in (2) and (5).

As a point of departure, suppose we list the following examples of the limit statement:

Example 3. $\lim_{x \to 2} (x + 3) = 5$

Example 4. $\lim_{x \to 2} (2x + 1) = 5$

Example 5. $\lim_{h \to 0} (x^2 + 2hx + 5h^2) = x^2$

Example 6. $\lim_{h \to 0} \dfrac{h}{h} = 1$

Example 7. $\lim_{x \to 0} \dfrac{x^3 + 2x}{x} = 2$

Example 8. $\lim_{x \to 3} \dfrac{x^2 - 9}{3x - 9} = 2.$

A reasonably natural interpretation of some of these statements is the following.

(Example 3). If x is close to 2, then $x + 3$ is close to 5.
(Example 4). If x is close to 2, then $2x + 1$ is close to 5.
(Example 5). If h is close to 0, then $x^2 + 2hx + h^2$ is close to x^2.

These examples suggest the following definition of limit.

Definition (*First Version*). *The statement* $\lim_{x \to a} f(x) = L$ *means that if* x *is close to a then* $f(x)$ *is close to L.*

Suppose we examine this proposed definition to see to what extent it does what we want it to do. As we know, one of the elementary applications of a limit is to the finding of a tangent line to a curve at a point; and when the curve is " well behaved" we would expect that there should be just one tangent line at a point. The implication of this geometric *desideratum* is that the limit L of a function be unique. Other considerations also suggest that uniqueness is a desirable property. Does our First Version guarantee it? It would seem that it does not. For, could we not say about Example 3, that if x is close to 2 then $x + 3$ will be close to 5.003, or close to 4.999996, or close to many other numbers which are themselves close to 5? Thus our initial attempt at a definition is not wholly successful.

And there is another defect in the First Version. We shall indicate this by means of an example. We consider a set of functions $f_1, f_2, f_3, \ldots$, where the formulas are $f_n(x) = 10^n x + 1$, for $n = 1, 2, 3, \ldots$. We claim that *for every n it is natural to say*

$$\lim_{x \to 0} (10^n x + 1) = 1.$$

(This is so, as is provable from our final definition, see Exercise 5, page 163.) Suppose now we agree that $x_0 = 0.000001$ is close to 0. By our First Version it should follow that $f_n(x_0)$ is close to $L = 1$. We check this for a few values of n:

$$f_1(x_0) = 10 x_0 + 1 = 1.00001,$$

$$f_2(x_0) = 10^2 x_0 + 1 = 1.0001,$$

$$f_3(x_0) = 10^3 x_0 + 1 = 1.001,$$

$$f_4(x_0) = 10^4 x_0 + 1 = 1.01.$$

We probably would not rebel against the statement that these numbers are "close to 1." Nor would we likely object to saying that

$$f_5(x_0) = 10^5 x_0 + 1 = 1.1$$

and

$$f_6(x_0) = 10^6 x_0 + 1 = 2$$

are "close to 1." But if we continue in this way we soon find the corresponding statements not only unpalatable but downright unacceptable:

$$f_7(x_0) = 10^7 x_0 + 1 = 11,$$

$$f_8(x_0) = 10^8 x_0 + 1 = 101,$$

$$f_9(x_0) = 10^9 x_0 + 1 = 1001,$$

$$f_{10}(x_0) = 10^{10} x_0 + 1 = 10{,}001.$$

This should be enough to make our point. We may be willing to agree that 1.0001 is close to 1, but not that 10,001 is close to 1.

And yet we still insist that for *every n, $n = 1, 2, 3, \ldots$,*

$$\lim_{x \to 0} (10^n x + 1) = 1$$

is correct. (The graph of each of these functions is a straight line with y-intercept equal to 1.) *Can* we make $f_{10}(x) = 10^{10} x + 1$ "close to 1"? If we are still willing to agree that 1.0001 is close to 1, it is very easy to see that all we need do is choose $x_1 = 10^{-14}$: then

$$f_{10}(x_1) = 10^{10} \cdot 10^{-14} + 1 = 10^{-4} + 1 = 1.0001.$$

Or, if one demands that nothing larger than 1.00000001 can be called close to 1, then that one can be silenced by being presented with $x_2 = 10^{-18}$:

$$f_{10}(x_2) = 10^{10} \cdot 10^{-18} + 1 = 10^{-8} + 1 = 1.00000001.$$

Thus a careful examination of the nature of the defect discloses a remedy: instead of *starting* with an x "close to a," we begin by specifying *how close we want $f(x)$ to be to L,* and then inquiring whether or not an x satisfying this requirement can be found. We shall incorporate this in our next attempt at a definition.

EXERCISES

Use intuition, arithmetic calculations, or other suitable methods to determine the value of L for each of the following:

1. $\lim\limits_{x \to 3} (5x - 1)$.

2. $\lim\limits_{x \to -10} (7x + 4)$.

3. $\lim\limits_{x \to 0} (mx + b)$.

4. $\lim\limits_{x \to a} (mx + b)$.

5. $\lim\limits_{x \to 3} (2x^2 + 7x - 4)$.

6. $\lim\limits_{x \to 7} \dfrac{x^2 - 16}{x^2 - 5x + 4}$.

7. $\lim\limits_{x \to 4} \dfrac{x^2 - 16}{x^2 - 5x + 4}$.

8. $\lim\limits_{x \to 1} (px^2 + qx + r)$.

9. $\lim\limits_{x \to 4} \dfrac{x^2 - 9}{x^2 + x - 12}$.

10. $\lim\limits_{x \to 3} \dfrac{x^2 - 9}{x^2 + x - 12}$.

11. $\lim\limits_{x \to 1} \dfrac{x + 7}{6 - 2x}$.

12. $\lim\limits_{x \to 3} \dfrac{x + 7}{6 - 2x}$.

13. $\lim\limits_{x \to 1} \dfrac{x^2 + 3x - 10}{x^2 - 6x + 8}$.

14. $\lim\limits_{x \to 2} \dfrac{x^2 + 3x - 10}{x^2 - 6x + 8}$.

According to the First Version, can one use the given values of L for the following limit statements?

15. $\lim\limits_{x \to 2} (3x^2 - 1) = L$.

  (a) $L = 11.00000001$.
  (b) $L = 10.99999998$.
  (c) $L = 11.1$.
  (d) $L = 11$.

16. $\lim\limits_{x \to 1/2} \dfrac{2x - 1}{4 - 8x} = L$.

  (a) $L = 1$.
  (b) $L = -4$.
  (c) $L = -0.2499999$.
  (d) $L = -\frac{1}{4}$.
  (e) $L = 0$.
  (f) $L = -0.250006$.
  (g) $L = \infty$.

3.3   Second and Third Versions

We now use the suggestion obtained from the previous example.

Definition   *(Second Version). The statement* $\lim\limits_{x \to a} f(x) = L$ *means the numbers*
$f(x)$ *can be made to lie as close to L as we please by taking x close enough to a.*

This form does repair the second flaw we have discussed, but does it guarantee
uniqueness? Unfortunately, the answer must be in the negative, as the following
example shows.

We consider a function f with a two-part formula:

$$\begin{cases} f(x) = x + 1, & \text{if } x \text{ is rational} \\ f(x) = x + 3, & \text{if } x \text{ is irrational} \end{cases}.$$

Now if we assert that $\lim\limits_{x \to 0} f(x) = 1$, then we can certainly make the values of $f(x)$
lie as close to 1 as we please by taking x sufficiently close to 0, *provided we take*
rational values for x. Similarly, we could assert that $\lim\limits_{x \to 0} f(x) = 3$ and argue that
$f(x)$ can be made to lie as close to 3 as we please by taking x sufficiently close to
0, *provided we are allowed to use irrational x*.

We conclude that the Second Version does not produce the desired uniqueness.
But once again the illustrated difficulty suggests a way to remove it: what made
possible the double-valuedness of L in the preceding example was our insistence
that we be able to choose x in special ways. If we remove this possibility the
trouble presented by this example will go away. This we now do.

Definition   *(Third Version). The statement* $\lim\limits_{x \to a} f(x) = L$ *means that the*
numbers f(x) will lie as close to L as we please for all x sufficiently close to a.

A little reflection will show that, according to the Third Version, we can
no longer say for the function of the preceding example that $\lim\limits_{x \to 0} f(x) = 1$ or
$\lim\limits_{x \to 0} f(x) = 3$, or in fact, that $\lim\limits_{x \to 0} f(x) = L$, no matter what L we choose. Moreover,
the Third Version removes as candidates for L in Example 3 the numbers 5.003
and 4.999996 that were in the running before: only $L = 5$ remains.

Have we, then, achieved our aim? Again we cannot be content. For if our aim
is to obtain a *precise* definition, we must readily admit that a definition which
includes such phrases as "as close to L as we please" and "sufficiently close to
a" leaves something to be desired. We have already observed that the question
of when a number is to be considered close to 1 can be answered in various ways.

In order to sharpen the definition we make use of the concept of *neighborhood*
(nbd.) of a number, introduced in Definition 2.7. We repeat the definition.

Definition 4. *By a **nbd.** of a, $N(a)$, we mean an interval with its center at a. More precisely,*

$$N_\delta(a) = \{x \mid a - \delta < x < a + \delta\}.$$

Some examples of nbds. are

$$N_{0.1}(2) = \{x \mid 1.9 < x < 2.1\},$$
$$N_{0.1}(5) = \{y \mid 4.9 < y < 5.1\},$$
$$N_{0.01}(2) = \{x \mid 1.99 < x < 2.01\},$$
$$N_{00.1}(5) = \{y \mid 4.99 < y < 5.01\},$$

etc. (see Figure 5).

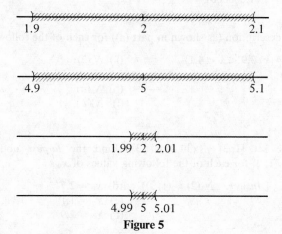

Figure 5

The purpose of the nbd., of course, is to put in slightly different form the idea of one number being close to another: that x is close to a will be expressed by saying that $x \in N(a)$. We shall see in the next section how this is used.

EXERCISES

1. Let the function f be defined by

$$\begin{cases} f(x) = x + 1, & x \le 0 \\ f(x) = x, & x > 0 \end{cases}.$$

Are the following limit statements justifiable according to the Second Version? If so, how?

(a) $\lim\limits_{x \to 0} f(x) = 1.$ (c) $\lim\limits_{x \to 2} f(x) = 2.$

(b) $\lim\limits_{x \to 0} f(x) = 4.$ (d) $\lim\limits_{x \to 0} f(x) = 0.$

2. Consider the function f

$$\left\{ \begin{aligned} &f: x \to \frac{|x|}{x}, \quad x \neq 0 \\ &f: 0 \to 2. \end{aligned} \right\}.$$

According to the Third Version, which of the following limit statements are valid?

(a) $\lim\limits_{x \to -1} f(x) = 1$ (f) $\lim\limits_{x \to 0} f(x) = 2$

(b) $\lim\limits_{x \to 0} f(x) = 1$ (g) $\lim\limits_{x \to 0} f(x) = 0$

(c) $\lim\limits_{x \to -1} f(x) = -1$ (h) $\lim\limits_{x \to 0} f(x) = 4$

(d) $\lim\limits_{x \to 0} f(x) = -1$ (i) $\lim\limits_{x \to 2} f(x) = 0.9999999.$

(e) $\lim\limits_{x \to -1} f(x) = -1.0000001$

3. Give the set description (as shown in part (a)) for each of the following nbds.

(a) $N_{0.1}(4) = \{x \mid 3.9 < x < 4.1\}$ (f) $N_{\varepsilon}(2)$
(b) $N_{0.001}(4)$ (g) $N_{1/3}(-1)$
(c) $N_{1/2}(0)$ (h) $N_{\delta}(a)$
(d) $N_1(0)$ (i) $N_{\varepsilon}(L).$
(e) $N_{\delta}(7)$

4. Consider the set $[1, 3) = \{x \mid 1 \leq x < 3\}$. Find the *largest* nbd. of x_0 such that $N(x_0) \subset [1, 3)$ for each of the following values of x_0.

(a) $x_0 = 2$ [*Answer.* $N_1(2) = (1, 3)$]   (d) $x_0 = 2.7$
(b) $x_0 = 2.2$ (e) $x_0 = 1.1$
(c) $x_0 = 1.3$ (f) $x_0 = 2.9.$

5. Given $N_{0.1}(2)$ and $N_{0.13}(2)$, find $N_{\delta}(2)$ such that $N_{\delta}(2) \subset N_{0.1}(2)$ and $N_{\delta}(2) \subset N_{0.13}(2)$.

6. Prove that

$$\delta_1 < \delta_2 \Rightarrow N_{\delta_1}(a) \subset N_{\delta_2}(a).$$

7. Prove that given $N_{\delta_1}(a)$ and $N_{\delta_2}(a)$ there exists $N_{\delta}(a)$ such that $N_{\delta}(a) \subset N_{\delta_1}(a)$ and $N_{\delta}(a) \subset N_{\delta_2}(a)$. What is the maximum value of δ that can be used?

3.4   The Fourth Version

We can now rephrase the current definition of limit as follows:

Definition   (*Fourth Version*). *The statement* $\lim\limits_{x \to a} f(x) = L$ *means that given any* $N_{\varepsilon}(L)$, *no matter how small* $\varepsilon > 0$ *is, we can find an* $N_{\delta}(a)$, $\delta > 0$, *such that* $x \in N_{\delta}(a) \Rightarrow f(x) \in N_{\varepsilon}(L).$

This simply says that no matter how close we want $f(x)$ to be to L (this is what the $N_\varepsilon(L)$ prescribes) we can get x close enough to a (this is what the $N_\delta(a)$ gives) to guarantee that $f(x)$ will be that close to L.

In general, the δ which determines the size of $N(a)$ depends upon ε: δ is a function of ε, it usually being the case that the smaller the value used for ε, the smaller must be the value of δ. We shall illustrate this shortly. It will sometimes be convenient to emphasize the dependence of δ upon ε, by writing δ_ε, so that the nbd. of a would be written $N_{\delta_\varepsilon}(a)$.

We first illustrate the use of the Fourth Version with the fairly transparent Example 3: $\lim_{x\to 2} (x + 3) = 5$. It is tempting to say that it is obvious that if x is in $N_{0.1}(2)$ then $x + 3$ is in $N_{0.1}(5)$. The statement is true, as Figure 6 is designed to show.

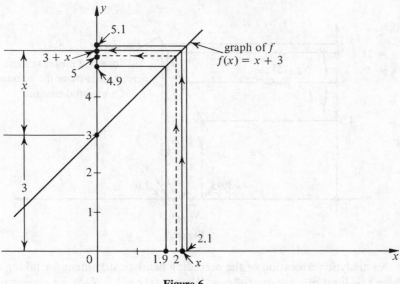

Figure 6

However, this is both a faulty and an incomplete application of the definition. A correct framing of the preceding statement is: if the ε- nbd. of 5 is prescribed by $\varepsilon = 0.1$ then we can take a 0.1 nbd. of 2; now we can confirm this choice by saying that if $x \in N_{0.1}(2)$, then $x + 3 \in N_{0.1}(5)$. The incompleteness stems from the requirement of the definition that we be able to find a suitable $N_\delta(a)$ for *every* $N_\varepsilon(5)$. In this case it is rather easy to see that if ε is used to define a nbd. of 5, then the same number (or a smaller one) could be used to define the required $N(2)$, i.e., we can take $\delta_\varepsilon = \varepsilon$, as the equivalence of the following inequalities shows:

$$2 - \varepsilon < x < 2 + \varepsilon \Leftrightarrow 5 - \varepsilon < x + 3 < 5 + \varepsilon.$$

It is not always as easy as this to find the required $N_\delta(a)$, but a look at Example

4 may give a better idea of the nature of the problem. The statement is $\lim_{x \to 2}(2x + 1) = 5$. Suppose we again pick $\varepsilon = 0.1$, so we have

$$N_{0.1}(5) = \{y \mid 4.9 < y < 5.1\}.$$

Now in Example 3 all we had to do to go from x to $f(x) = x + 3$ was to add 3 to x; but in the present case $f(x) = 2x + 1$, and a multiplication by 2 is involved. The effect of this is a *doubling* of distances, and if we want to guarantee that we end up at most 0.1 from 5, we have to start out at most $\frac{1}{2}$ of 0.1 from 2; i.e., we should use

$$N_{0.05}(2) = \{x \mid 1.95 < x < 2.05\}.$$

For then $2x$ will lie in the open interval from $2(1.95) = 3.9$ to $2(2.05) = 4.1$ and $y = 2x + 1$ will lie in the interval from $3.9 + 1 = 4.9$ to $4.1 + 1 = 5.1$, i.e., in the prescribed $N_{0.1}(5)$ (see Figure 7).

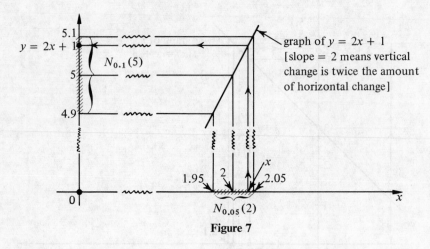

Figure 7

An analytic verification of the preceding heuristic argument for taking $\delta = \frac{1}{2}\varepsilon$ from this limit proceeds as follows. We want $2x + 1 \in N_\varepsilon(5)$, i.e., we want

$$5 - \varepsilon < 2x + 1 < 5 + \varepsilon,$$

or

$$4 - \varepsilon < 2x < 4 + \varepsilon,$$

so

$$2 - \tfrac{1}{2}\varepsilon < x < 2 + \tfrac{1}{2}\varepsilon.$$

The result of this exploratory development suggests taking $\delta = \frac{1}{2}\varepsilon$ (or, if one prefers, any smaller value of δ could be chosen; $\delta = \frac{1}{2}\varepsilon$ is the largest acceptable value of δ, but any smaller positive number could be used, e.g., $\delta = \frac{1}{100}\varepsilon$). The proof that this δ is satisfactory goes like this: assume x satisfies

$$2 - \delta < x < 2 + \delta,$$

or

$$2 - \tfrac{1}{2}\varepsilon < x < 2 + \tfrac{1}{2}\varepsilon \qquad \text{(choice of } \delta),$$

i.e.,

$$4 - \varepsilon < 2x < 4 + \varepsilon \qquad \text{(multiplying by 2),}$$

so

$$5 - \varepsilon < 2x + 1 < 5 + \varepsilon \qquad \text{(adding 1).}$$

It will be noted that the proof is simply a reversing of the steps of the exploratory development; it is usually not written out, but it must be verified that the steps of the exploration are reversible.

The problem of finding $N_{\delta_\varepsilon}(a)$ for a given $N_\varepsilon(L)$ *can* be fairly difficult.

EXERCISES

1. Apply the Fourth Version to $\lim_{x \to 6} (x + 1) = 7$. In particular, find $N_\delta(6)$ for each of the following nbds. of 7.

(a) $\varepsilon = 1$
(b) $\varepsilon = 0.1$
(c) $\varepsilon = 0.01$
(d) $\varepsilon = 0.000000000000000001 = 10^{-18}$
(e) $\varepsilon = \varepsilon$.

2. Same as Exercise 1, only for $\lim_{x \to 4} (2x + 3) = 11$.

3. Same as Exercise 1, only for $\lim_{x \to -1} (2x + 3) = 1$.

4. Same as Exercise 1, only for $\lim_{x \to 4} (\tfrac{1}{2}x + 5) = 7$.

5. Let $c > 0$. Using the Fourth Version, find a δ_ε for $\lim_{x \to 3} (cx + 2) = 3c + 2$, in case

(a) $\varepsilon = 0.1$
(b) $\varepsilon = 0.001$
(c) $\varepsilon = 10^{-9}$
(d) $\varepsilon = \varepsilon$.

6. Same as Exercise 5, only assume $c < 0$.

3.5 Final Version, or Success at Last

It would seem, then, that we have surely achieved our purpose and that the Fourth can be taken as the Final Version. Not so. For the Fourth Version does not enable us to deal with the limits in Examples 6, 7, and 8. Suppose we look first at Example 6:

$$\lim_{h \to 0} \frac{h}{h} = 1.$$

We begin with three observations:

(1) if $h \neq 0$, then $\frac{h}{h} = 1$;

(2) we can*not* have $h = 0$;

(3) this example looks artificial, but it is in fact a simple example of what must be faced up to with a derivative (namely, the "zero over zero" kind of limit).

Note that, excluding $h = 0$ from consideration, in any $N(0)$ we have $\frac{h}{h}$ equals

1—not only *is close to 1*, but *equals 1*. This is the reason we write $\lim_{h \to 0} \frac{h}{h} = 1$.

But we cannot apply the Fourth Version to this limit, because $0 \in N(0)$, whereas $0 \notin$ the domain of the function defined by $f(x) = \frac{x}{x}$. Once again the nature of the difficulty suggests a simple remedy: exclude 0 from $N(0)$. This may seem a little unexpected and arbitrary, but as we shall see, it is a device which works. We begin by modifying the definition of nbd. (see Figure 8).

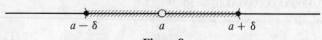

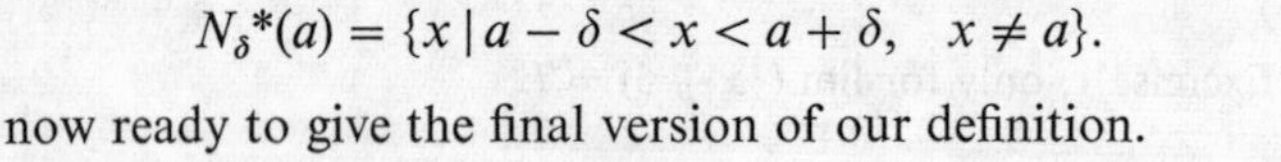

$$a - \delta \qquad\qquad a \qquad\qquad a + \delta$$

Figure 8

Definition 5. *By a **deleted nbd. of a**, $N_\delta{}^*(a)$, we mean exactly $N_\delta(a)$ with the number a deleted*; i.e.,

$$N_\delta{}^*(a) = \{x \mid a - \delta < x < a + \delta, \quad x \neq a\}.$$

We are now ready to give the final version of our definition.

Definition 6. (*Final Version*). *The statement* $\lim_{x \to a} f(x) = L \Leftrightarrow$ *for every $N_\varepsilon(L)$, no matter how small $\varepsilon > 0$ is, there exists an $N_\delta{}^*(a)$, $\delta > 0$, such that $x \in N_\delta{}^*(a) \Rightarrow f(x) \in N_\varepsilon(L)$.*

Note that a deleted nbd. of a is used, but that the nbd. of L still contains L. Suppose we apply the definition to Example 7:

$$\lim_{x \to 0} \frac{x^3 + 2x}{x} = \lim_{x \to 0} (x^2 + 2) \frac{x}{x}.$$

By rewriting the formula, as we just did, we isolate the source of difficulty (the possible 0 in the denominator); but now, since we are using *deleted* nbds. of $a = 0$, the factor $\frac{x}{x}$ is no longer troublesome: for every $x \in N_\delta{}^*(0)$ (no matter what $\delta > 0$

is used) $\dfrac{x}{x} = 1$. Thus, if $\varepsilon = 0.01$, i.e., if we choose $N_{0.01}(2) = \{y \mid 1.99 < y < 2.01\}$ then $\delta = 0.1$ can be used to define a deleted nbd. of 0, i.e., we can take

$$N_{0.1}^*(0) = \{x \mid -0.1 < x < 0.1, \quad x \neq 0\}.$$

For, if $x \in N_{0.1}^*(0)$, then $0 < x^2 < 0.01$ and $f(x) = (x^2 + 2)\dfrac{x}{x}$ satisfies the inequalities

$$2 < f(x) < 2.01,$$

i.e., $f(x) \in N_{0.01}(2)$.

In general, if ε is chosen such that $0 < \varepsilon < 1$, then it is not difficult to show that one can take $\delta_\varepsilon = \sqrt{\varepsilon}$, or any positive number less than $\sqrt{\varepsilon}$. In particular, since for $0 < \varepsilon < 1$ it is true that $\varepsilon < \sqrt{\varepsilon}$, one *could* take $\delta_\varepsilon = \varepsilon$, for the $N^*(0)$.

It is relatively easy to see now that Example 8 presents no difficulty. We write it as follows:

$$\lim_{x \to 3} \frac{x^2 - 9}{3x - 9} = \lim_{x \to 3} \frac{(x + 3)(x - 3)}{3(x - 3)} = \lim_{x \to 3} \left[\frac{1}{3}(x + 3)\right]\frac{x - 3}{x - 3}.$$

Since for *every* x in *every* deleted nbd. of 3 it is true that $\dfrac{x - 3}{x - 3} = 1$, we need only concern ourselves with $\frac{1}{3}(x + 3) = \frac{1}{3}x + 1$. As the following exploratory development shows, one can, for any $\varepsilon > 0$, take $\delta_\varepsilon = 3\varepsilon$ (or any smaller positive number): we want

$$2 - \varepsilon < \tfrac{1}{3}x + 1 < 2 + \varepsilon,$$

or, adding -1,

$$1 - \varepsilon < \tfrac{1}{3}x < 1 + \varepsilon,$$

or, multiplying by 3,

$$3 - 3\varepsilon < x < 3 + 3\varepsilon;$$

thus the suggestion is that $\delta_\varepsilon = 3\varepsilon$.

We end this section by writing the Final Version of our definition in an alternative form which is probably more widely used than the one we have already given. To this end we note that the nbds. we have used can be described in terms of absolute values as follows:

$$N_\varepsilon(L) = \{y \mid L - \varepsilon < y < L + \varepsilon\} = \{y \mid |y - L| < \varepsilon\}$$

and

$$N_\delta^*(a) = \{x \mid a - \delta < x < a + \delta, \quad x \neq a\} = \{x \mid 0 < |x - a| < \delta\}.$$

Thus we can formulate the limit definition in the following equivalent statement.

Definition 6a. (*Final Version, Alternative Form*). *The statement* $\lim\limits_{x \to a} f(x) = L \Leftrightarrow$ *for every* $\varepsilon > 0$, *no matter how small, there exists a* $\delta_\varepsilon > 0$, *such that for all* x *satisfying* $0 < |x - a| < \delta_\varepsilon$ *it is true that* $f(x)$ *satisfies* $|f(x) - L| < \varepsilon$.

This concludes our discussion of the definition of the concept of limit of a function. Either of the two forms given for the Final Version says precisely what we mean by the symbols $\lim\limits_{x \to a} f(x) = L$, no more and no less. The purpose of the discussion leading up to these definitions was to show why they were formulated as they were: why we do not start by saying "if x is close ..." and why a deleted nbd. of a is used.

E X E R C I S E S

1. Give the set description of the following deleted nbds.:

   (a) $N_1{}^*(2) = \{x \mid 1 < x < 2\} \cup \{x \mid 2 < x < 3\} = \{x \mid 1 < x < 3, x \neq 2\}$
   (b) $N^*_{0.01}(2)$.
   (c) $N^*_{0.001}(2)$.
   (d) $N^*_{0.1}(-1)$.
   (e) $N^*_{0.01}(0)$.
   (f) $N^*_{0.001}(-10)$.

2. Are the following limit statements valid according to Definition 6? (You need not find δ_ε.)

   (a) $\lim\limits_{x \to 2} (x^2 - 3) = 1$.

   (b) $\lim\limits_{x \to 2} (x^2 - 3) = 1.000001$.

   (c) $\lim\limits_{x \to 2} \dfrac{x - 1}{x - 1} = 1$.

   (d) $\lim\limits_{x \to 1} \dfrac{x - 1}{x - 1} = 1$.

   (e) $\lim\limits_{x \to 4} \dfrac{x^2 - 16}{x^2 - 5x + 4} = \dfrac{8}{3}$.

   (f) $\lim\limits_{x \to -4} \dfrac{x^2 - 16}{x^2 - 5x + 4} = 0$.

   (g) $\lim\limits_{x \to 1} \dfrac{2x - 1}{10 - 20x} = -\dfrac{1}{10}$.

   (h) $\lim\limits_{x \to \frac{1}{2}} \dfrac{2x - 1}{10 - 20x} = -\dfrac{1}{10}$.

3. Using the last example as a model, apply Definition 6 to find the following limits. In particular, find $N_\delta{}^*(a)$ for an arbitrary $N_\varepsilon(L)$.

   (a) $\lim\limits_{x \to 4} \dfrac{x^2 - 16}{6x - 24}$.

   (b) $\lim\limits_{x \to 4} \dfrac{x^2 - 16}{12 - 3x}$.

   (c) $\lim\limits_{x \to 4} \dfrac{8 - 2x}{x - 4}$.

   (d) $\lim\limits_{x \to 4} \dfrac{x^2 - x - 12}{5x - 20}$.

   (e) $\lim\limits_{x \to 1} \dfrac{x^2 - 3x + 2}{1 - x}$.

4. Give the value of L for each of the following limits and in each case say whether or not a deleted nbd. of a is necessary.

   (a) $\lim\limits_{x \to 4} (2x^2 - 3x + 7)$.

   (b) $\lim\limits_{x \to 3} \dfrac{x^2 + 3x - 4}{x^2 + x - 2}$.

(c) $\lim\limits_{x\to 1}\dfrac{x^2+3x-4}{x^2+x-2}$.

(d) $\lim\limits_{x\to 5}\dfrac{x^2+5x-36}{x^2-7x+12}$

(e) $\lim\limits_{x\to 4}\dfrac{x^2+5x-36}{x^2-7x+12}$.

(f) $\lim\limits_{x\to 2}\dfrac{2x-6}{5}$.

(g) $\lim\limits_{x\to 3}\dfrac{2x-6}{5}$.

(h) $\lim\limits_{x\to 3}\dfrac{2x-6}{21-7x}$.

5. Use Definition 6a to prove that, for all $a, b, m \in \mathbf{R}$, $\lim\limits_{x\to a}(mx+b) = ma + b$.

3.6 Limits Involving Infinity

In this section we make an adaptation of the definition arrived at in Section 3.5. Now, implicit in our previous discussion of $\lim\limits_{x\to a} f(x) = L$ was the assumption that both a and L were to be finite. Occasionally, it is convenient to admit some generalizations. Consider, for example,

Example 9.

$\lim\limits_{x\to\infty}\dfrac{1}{x} = 0$ (the symbol $x \to \infty$ should be read: "as x gets big beyond all bounds").

Example 10.

$\lim\limits_{x\to 0}\dfrac{1}{x^2} = \infty$ (the correct verbalization of this is: "$\dfrac{1}{x^2}$, as x tends to 0, gets big beyond all bounds").

Example 11.

$\lim\limits_{x\to\infty}(2x^2 + 3) = \infty$ ("as x gets big beyond all bounds $2x^2 + 3$ gets big beyond all bounds").

Example 12.

$\lim\limits_{x\to -\infty}\left(1 - \dfrac{2}{x-3}\right) = \lim\limits_{x\to -\infty}\dfrac{x-5}{x-3} = 1$ ("the limit of $1 - \dfrac{2}{x-3}$, as x gets big beyond all bounded negatively, is 1").

An exact and precise statement covering each of these cases can be made very simply after we have suitably defined certain nbds.

Definition 7. *A **nbd. of infinity** is the set of all numbers greater than some specified positive number. In symbols* (see Figure 9)

$$N_M(\infty) + \{x \mid x > M, M > 0\}.$$

A nbd. of minus infinity is the set of all numbers less than some specified negative number:

$$N_Q(-\infty) = \{x \mid x < Q, \ Q < 0\}.$$

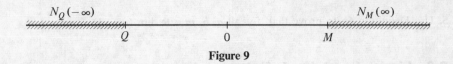

Figure 9

We now formulate the definitions for the statements which pertain to Examples 9–12. There are four more statements of these types (e.g., $\lim\limits_{x\to\infty} f(x) = -\infty$, etc.); the reader should have no difficulty in writing the statements and their definitions after seeing the definitions we are about to give.

Definition 8. $\lim\limits_{x\to\infty} f(x) = L \Leftrightarrow$ *for every* $N_\varepsilon(L)$, *no matter how small* ε *is, there exists an* $N_M(\infty)$ *such that* $x \in N_M(\infty) \Rightarrow f(x) \in N_\varepsilon(L)$.

Definition 9. $\lim\limits_{x\to a} f(x) = \infty \Leftrightarrow$ *for every* $N_M(\infty)$, *no matter how large* M *is, there exists an* $N_\delta^*(a)$ *such that* $x \in N_\delta^*(a) \Rightarrow f(x) \in N_M(\infty)$.

Definition 10. $\lim\limits_{x\to\infty} f(x) = \infty \Leftrightarrow$ *for every* $N_M(\infty)$, *no matter how large* M *is, there exists an* $N_K(\infty)$ *such that* $x \in N_K(\infty) \Rightarrow f(x) \in N_M(\infty)$.

Definition 11. $\lim\limits_{x\to -\infty} f(x) = L \Leftrightarrow$ *for every* $N_\varepsilon(L)$, *no matter how small* ε *is, there exists an* $N_Q(-\infty)$ *such that* $x \in N_Q(-\infty) \Rightarrow f(x) \in N_\varepsilon(L)$.

In Figures 10, 11, 12, and 13, we show the graphs of the functions for Examples 9–12, along with the nbds. used. Also, we give below the exploratory steps which lead to the determination of the sizes of the appropriate nbds. in the domains of the functions in these examples.

For Example 9:

$$\left.\begin{array}{c} \dfrac{1}{x} \in N_\varepsilon(0) \\[2mm] x > 0 \end{array}\right\} \Rightarrow \dfrac{1}{x} < \varepsilon \text{ or } x > \dfrac{1}{\varepsilon}.$$

$$\left[\text{\textit{Suggestion.} \quad Take } M_\varepsilon = \dfrac{1}{\varepsilon}.\right]$$

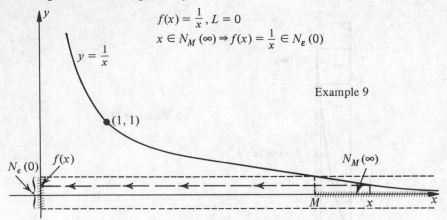

$$f(x) = \frac{1}{x}, L = 0$$
$$x \in N_M(\infty) \Rightarrow f(x) = \frac{1}{x} \in N_\varepsilon(0)$$

Example 9

Figure 10

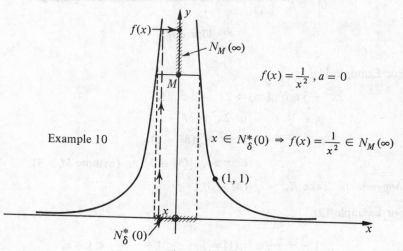

$$f(x) = \frac{1}{x^2}, a = 0$$

Example 10

$$x \in N_\delta^*(0) \Rightarrow f(x) = \frac{1}{x^2} \in N_M(\infty)$$

Figure 11

For Example 10:

$$\frac{1}{x^2} \in N_M(\infty) \Rightarrow \frac{1}{x^2} > M,$$

$$\text{or } x^2 < \frac{1}{M},$$

$$\text{or } \frac{-1}{\sqrt{M}} < x < \frac{1}{\sqrt{M}}, \qquad x \neq 0.$$

$$\left[\textit{Suggestion.} \quad \text{Take } \delta_M = \frac{1}{\sqrt{M}}. \right]$$

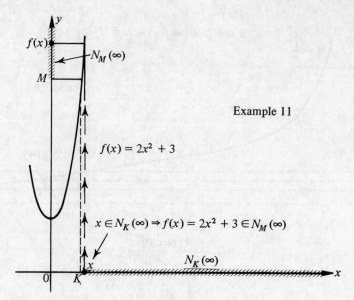

Figure 12

For Example 11:

$$2x^2 + 3 \in N_M(\infty) \Rightarrow 2x^2 + 3 > M,$$
$$\text{or } 2x^2 > M - 3,$$
$$\text{or } x^2 > \tfrac{1}{2}(M - 3),$$
$$\text{or } x > \sqrt{\tfrac{1}{2}(M - 3)} \qquad (\text{assume } M > 3).$$

[*Suggestion.*   Take $K_M = \sqrt{\tfrac{1}{2}(M - 3)}$.]

For Example 12:

$$1 - \frac{2}{x - 3} \in N_\varepsilon(1) \Rightarrow 1 - \varepsilon < 1 - \frac{2}{x - 3} < 1 + \varepsilon,$$

$$\text{or } -\varepsilon < -\frac{2}{x - 3} < \varepsilon$$

$$\text{or } -\frac{x - 3}{2} > \frac{1}{\varepsilon}$$

$$\text{or } x - 3 < \frac{-2}{\varepsilon}$$

$$\text{or } x < \frac{-2}{\varepsilon} + 3 \qquad (\text{assume } \varepsilon < \tfrac{2}{3}).$$

$$\left[\textit{Suggestion.} \quad \text{Take } Q_\varepsilon = \frac{-2}{\varepsilon} + 3. \right]$$

Of course, all of these are simply exploratory steps; the proof in each case that the suggestion obtained gives an acceptable nbd. involves checking that the steps used are reversible.

We conclude this section with an important remark about terminology. We have, in our preceding discussion, apparently given equal status to statements such as $\lim_{x \to a} f(x) = L$, where L is a finite number, and $\lim_{x \to a} f(x) = \infty$. It should be noted, however, that it is customary to say that *a limit exists* precisely when L is a finite number. Thus, the limits in Examples 10 and 11 do not exist, even though we have given, in Definitions 9 and 10, precise formulations for such statements as $\lim_{x \to a} f(x) = \infty$ and $\lim_{x \to \infty} f(x) = \infty$. To put the matter in another fashion, limits may fail to exist in a variety of ways (see the exercises below); several of these, such as the situations occurring in Definitions 9 and 10 are special enough and important enough to deserve special formulation. We have given these statements, but we should realize that the limits do not exist as finite numbers.

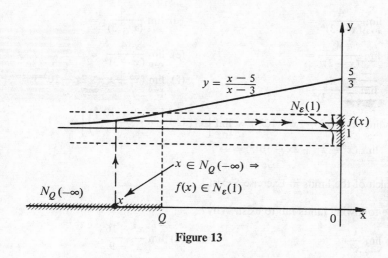

Figure 13

E X E R C I S E S

1. Give the set-theoretical description of the following nbds.:

(a) $N_{100}(\infty)$.

(b) $N_{10,000}(\infty)$.

(c) $N_{-2}(-\infty)$.

(d) $N_{-10,000,000}(-\infty)$.

2. (a) Find $N(\infty)$ such that $N(\infty) \subset N_{100}(\infty) \cap N_{1000}(\infty)$.

(b) Find $N(-\infty)$ such that $N(-\infty) \subset N_{-1000}(-\infty) \cap N_{-645}(-\infty)$.

3. Complete the following statements:

(a) $\lim\limits_{x \to 2} \dfrac{1}{(x-2)^2} =$

(b) $\lim\limits_{x \to \infty} \dfrac{1}{(x-2)^2} =$

(c) $\lim\limits_{x \to \infty} \dfrac{x^2 - 4x + 7}{3x^2 - 10x - 13} =$

(d) $\lim\limits_{x \to -\infty} \dfrac{x^2 - 4x + 7}{3x^2 - 10x - 13} =$

(e) $\lim\limits_{x \to 0} \dfrac{x^2 - 4x + 7}{3x^2 - 10x - 13} =$

(f) $\lim\limits_{x \to \infty} (2x - 1) =$

(g) $\lim\limits_{x \to -\infty} (2x - 1) =$

(h) $\lim\limits_{x \to \infty} \dfrac{2x - 1}{x} =$

(i) $\lim\limits_{x \to \infty} \dfrac{2x - 1}{x + 3} = \lim\limits_{x \to \infty} \left(2 - \dfrac{7}{x + 3}\right) =$

(j) $\lim\limits_{x \to \infty} (4x^2 - 3) =$

(k) $\lim\limits_{x \to -\infty} \dfrac{2x - 1}{x + 3} =$

4. Which of the limits in Exercise 3 exist?

5. Complete the following statements:

(a) $\lim\limits_{x \to 3} \dfrac{4}{(x-3)^4} =$

(b) $\lim\limits_{x \to \infty} \dfrac{4}{(x-3)^4} =$

(c) $\lim\limits_{x \to -\infty} \dfrac{4}{(x-3)^4} =$

(d) $\lim\limits_{x \to 4} \dfrac{4}{(x-3)^4} =$

(e) $\lim\limits_{x \to 0} \dfrac{4}{(x-3)^4} =$

(f) $\lim\limits_{x \to 0} (x^3 - x^2 + 2x - 10^{25}) =$

(g) $\lim\limits_{x \to \infty} (x^3 - x^2 + 2x - 10^{25}) = \lim\limits_{x \to \infty} \left[x^3 \left(1 - \dfrac{1}{x} + \dfrac{2}{x^2} - \dfrac{10^{25}}{x^3}\right)\right] =$

(h) $\lim\limits_{x \to -\infty} (x^3 - x^2 + 2x - 10^{25}) =$

6. Which of the limits in Exercise 5 exist?

7. The following limits fail to exist. Why?

(a) $\lim\limits_{x \to 0} \dfrac{1}{x^2}.$

(b) $\lim\limits_{x \to 3} \dfrac{2}{x - 3}.$

(c) $\lim\limits_{x \to \infty} (x^2 + 4).$

(d) $\lim\limits_{x \to 3} \dfrac{x^2 - 16}{x^2 - 9}.$

(e) $\lim\limits_{x \to -\infty} x^2.$

8. The following limits fail to exist. Why?

(a) $\lim\limits_{x \to 0} \dfrac{|x|}{x}.$

(b) $\lim\limits_{x \to 0} f(x)$, where f is defined by $\begin{cases} f(x) = x^2 + 7, & x \le 0 \\ f(x) = x - 4, & x > 0 \end{cases}.$

(c) $\lim\limits_{x \to 5} f(x)$, where $\begin{cases} f: x \to x + 8, & x \le 5 \\ f: x \to x^2 - 11.99999, & x > 5 \end{cases}.$

(d) $\lim\limits_{x \to -4} \dfrac{x^2 + 9}{x^2 - 16}.$

(e) $\lim\limits_{x \to \infty} \dfrac{x^3 + 2x^2 - 1}{x^2 - 4} = \lim\limits_{x \to \infty} \left(x + 2 + \dfrac{4x + 7}{x^2 - 4} \right).$

(f) $\lim\limits_{x \to -\infty} \dfrac{x^3 + 2x^2 - 1}{x^2 - 4}.$

9. Formulate definitions, analogous to Definitions 8–11, for the following statements:

   (a) $\lim\limits_{x \to a} f(x) = -\infty.$ (b) $\lim\limits_{x \to \infty} f(x) = -\infty.$

   (c) $\lim\limits_{x \to -\infty} f(x) = \infty.$ (d) $\lim\limits_{x \to -\infty} f(x) = -\infty.$

10. For which of the statements in Exercise 9 do the limits exist?

11. Verify that the exploratory steps for the determination of the nbds. in Examples 9–12 can all be reversed.

12. In the exploratory steps for Example 12 it is assumed, near the final step, that $\varepsilon < \frac{2}{3}$. Why?

13. This again refers to the exploratory steps for Example 12. In going from the second to the third step one part of the inequality is dropped. Why can this safely be done?

14. Prove that $M_1 > M_2 > 0 \Rightarrow N_{M_1}(\infty) \subset N_{M_2}(\infty)$. Thus prove that, given any two nbds. of ∞, there exists a nbd. of ∞ which is included in both of the given ones.

3.7 One-Sided Limits

Another variation on the limit theme has to do with "one-sided" limits; these can be illustrated by the following examples:

Example 13.

$$\lim\limits_{x \to 0^+} \dfrac{|x|}{x} = 1 \qquad \text{(See Figure 14)}$$

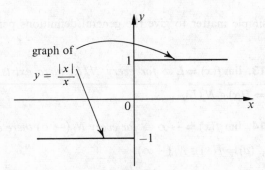

graph of

$y = \dfrac{|x|}{x}$

Figure 14

Example 14.

$$\lim_{x \to 0^-} \frac{|x|}{x} = -1 \qquad \text{(See Figure 14)}$$

Example 15.

$$\lim_{x \to 0^+} \frac{1}{x} = \infty$$

Example 16.

$$\lim_{x \to 0^-} \frac{1}{x} = -\infty$$

The notation $x \to a^+$ means that only values of x *greater than a* will be considered; similarly, $x \to a^-$ means that only values of x *less than a* will be considered.

It is easy to see that all that is required for a definition of the one-sided limits is another pair of nbd. definitions.

Definition 12. *By a **right δ-nbd.** of a we mean the set of numbers between a and a + δ, exclusive:*

$$N_\delta^+(a) = \{x \mid a < x < a + \delta\}.$$

*By a **left δ-nbd.** of a we mean the set of numbers between a − δ and a, exclusive (see Figure 15):*

$$N_\delta^-(a) = \{x \mid a - \delta < x < a\}.$$

Note that both $N_\delta^+(a)$ and $N_\delta^-(a)$ are deleted nbds.

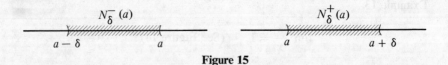

$$N_\delta^-(a) \qquad\qquad\qquad N_\delta^+(a)$$
$$\overline{\qquad\quad a - \delta \qquad\qquad a \qquad} \qquad \overline{\qquad a \qquad\qquad a + \delta \qquad}$$

Figure 15

Now it is a simple matter to give the general definitions pertaining to one-sided limits.

Definition 13. $\lim\limits_{x \to a^+} f(x) = L \Leftrightarrow$ *for every $N_\varepsilon(L)$ there exists an $N_\delta^+(a)$ such that $x \in N_\delta^+(a) \Rightarrow f(x) \in N_\varepsilon(L)$.*

Definition 14. $\lim\limits_{x \to a^-} f(x) = -\infty \Leftrightarrow$ *for every $N_Q(-\infty)$ there exists an $N_\delta^-(a)$ such that $x \in N_\delta^-(a) \Rightarrow f(x) \in N_Q(-\infty)$.*

Similar definitions can be given for the other one-sided limit statements.

Although we plan to discuss the limit theorems in detail later, it seems appropriate to mention at this time the following assertion.

Theorem 1.

$$\lim_{x\to a} f(x) = L \Leftrightarrow \lim_{x\to a+} f(x) = \lim_{x\to a-} f(x) = L.$$

The proof, which is very easy and which is left as an exercise, depends in part upon the following relation between nbds.:

$$N_\delta{}^*(a) = N_\delta{}^+(a) \cup N_\delta{}^-(a).$$

It is interesting to point out that we can tie up in one neat package the original limit definition and all the variations thereof, in the following manner.

Definition 15. *Let a stand for any finite number or "∞" or "$-\infty$" and let L stand for any finite number or "∞" or "$-\infty$"; then* $\lim\limits_{x\to a} f(x) = L \Leftrightarrow$ *for every N(L) there exists an N*(a) such that* $x \in N^*(a) \Rightarrow f(x) \in N(L)$. *The different interpretations, including the one-sided limits, are obtained simply by using the suitable nbds.*

EXERCISES

1. Give the set-theoretical description of each of the following nbds.:

(a) $N_{\overline{0.1}}(0)$.   (b) $N_{0.05}^+(2)$.   (c) $N_{0.01}^+(-8)$

(d) $N_{\overline{0.14}}(3)$.   (e) $N_{\overline{0.26}}(-5)$.   (f) $N_{0.017}^+(-0.01)$.

2. Complete the following statements:

(a) $\lim\limits_{x\to 0+} \dfrac{1}{x^3} =$

(b) $\lim\limits_{x\to 0-} \dfrac{1}{x^3} =$

(c) $\lim\limits_{x\to 0+} \dfrac{1}{x^2} =$

(d) $\lim\limits_{x\to 0-} \dfrac{1}{x^2} =$

(e) $\lim\limits_{x\to 4+} (2x-7) =$

(f) $\lim\limits_{x\to 4-} (2x-7) =$

(g) $\lim\limits_{x\to 0+} |x| =$

(h) $\lim\limits_{x\to 0+} f(x) =$,   where $\begin{cases} f: x \to x^2, \ x < 0 \\ f: x \to x+1, \ x \geq 0 \end{cases}$

(i) $\lim\limits_{x\to 0-} f(x) =$,   for the function of (h)

(j) $\lim\limits_{x\to 0-} f(x) =$,   where $\begin{cases} f: x \to 2x, \ x < 0 \\ f: x \to x^2 + 6, \ x \geq 0 \end{cases}$

(k) $\lim\limits_{x\to 0+} f(x) =$,   for the function of (j)

(l) $\lim\limits_{x\to 1+} \dfrac{|x-1|}{x-1} =$

3. Which of the limits in Exercise 2 exist?

4. Give definitions, analogous to Definitions 13 and 14 for the following statements:

(a) $\lim\limits_{x \to a^+} f(x) = \infty$.   (b) $\lim\limits_{x \to a^+} f(x) = -\infty$.

(c) $\lim\limits_{x \to a^-} f(x) = L$.   (d) $\lim\limits_{x \to a^-} f(x) = \infty$.

5. Which of the limits in Exercise 4 exist?

6. Prove the following:

(a) $N_\delta^-(a) \cap N_\delta^+(a) = \varnothing$.   (b) $N_\delta^-(a) \cup N_\delta^+(a) = N_\delta^*(a)$.

7. Give a complete proof of Theorem 1. The following remarks may be helpful.
   (1) There are *two* things to prove:

   (i) *if* $\lim\limits_{x \to a} f(x) = L$, then $\lim\limits_{x \to a^+} f(x) = \lim\limits_{x \to a^-} f(x) = L$;

   (ii) *if* $\lim\limits_{x \to a^+} f(x) = \lim\limits_{x \to a^-} f(x) = L$, then $\lim\limits_{x \to a} f(x) = L$.

   (2) For (i) we *know* there exists, for every $N_\varepsilon(L)$, an $N_\delta^*(a)$, all points of which map into $N_\varepsilon(L)$. Use the same δ, apply Exercise 6 and obtain $N_\delta^+(a)$ and $N_\delta^-(a)$, all points of which map into $N_\varepsilon(L)$.
   (3) For (ii) we *know* there exist $N_{\delta_1}^+(a)$ and $N_{\delta_2}^-(a)$, all points of which map into $N_\varepsilon(L)$. Thus, to satisfy Definition 6, pick $\delta =$ smaller of δ_1, δ_2. Then all points of $N_\delta^*(a)$ map into $N_\varepsilon(L)$. This can be done for every choice of $\varepsilon > 0$. Thus, $\lim\limits_{x \to a} f(x) = L$.

3.8   Cluster Points

We pause now to discuss a question which may have already occurred to the reader. We refer to the following: in considering $\lim\limits_{x \to a} f(x) = L$ we have encountered some examples (3 and 4) in which the number a is in the domain of f, and we have encountered some (6, 7, 8 and 13, among others) in which the number a is not in the domain of f. Thus, existence of the limit does not seem to depend upon whether or not $a \in X$ (where $X =$ domain of f), and the question arises: are there any conditions which a must satisfy in order that $\lim\limits_{x \to a} f(x) = L$ be meaningful? Suppose we look at an especially chosen case.

Example 17. Let f be defined as follows:

$$\left\{\begin{matrix} 0 < x < 1 \Rightarrow f(x) = x^2 \\ f(2) = 3 \\ 3 < x < 4 \Rightarrow f(x) = 4 - x \end{matrix}\right\}.$$

The graph of f is shown in Figure 16. Note that the domain X of f is

$$X = (0, 1) \cup \{2\} \cup (3, 4).$$

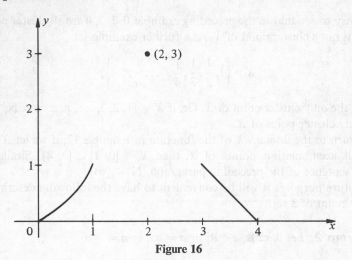

Figure 16

We claim that the following limit statements are obvious and correct:

$$\lim_{x \to 0^+} f(x) = 0,$$

$$0 < a < 1 \Rightarrow \lim_{x \to a} f(x) = a^2,$$

$$\lim_{x \to 1^-} f(x) = 1,$$

$$\lim_{x \to 3^+} f(x) = 1,$$

$$3 < a < 4 \Rightarrow \lim_{x \to a} f(x) = 4 - a,$$

$$\lim_{x \to 4^-} f(x) = 0.$$

Note, by the way, that $0, 1, 3, 4 \notin X$.

But what can be said about $\lim_{x \to 2} f(x)$? By Definition 6, if, for some choice of L, one claims $\lim_{x \to 2} f(x) = L$, then it must follow that for every $N_\varepsilon(L)$ there exists $N_\delta^*(2)$ such that $x \in N_\delta^*(2) \Rightarrow f(x) \in N_\varepsilon(L)$. However, if $0 < \delta \leq 1$ then $N_\delta^*(2) \cap X = \varnothing$; the result is that for $x \in N_\delta^*(2), f(x)$ is not defined, so it is not meaningful to say either that $f(x) \in N_\varepsilon(L)$ or $f(x) \notin N_\varepsilon(L)$—no matter what the choice of L.

The conclusion we reach from the preceding example is this: in order that $\lim_{x \to a} f(x) = L$ be meaningful it is *necessary* that *every* $N^*(a)$ contain at least one point of the domain X of f. This is described by saying that a is a *cluster point*, or *point of accumulation*, of X.

Definition 16. *Let X be a subset of $\mathbf{R}$, and let $a \in \mathbf{R}$, or $a = \infty$ or $a = -\infty$. Then a is a **cluster point** or point of accumulation of $X \Leftrightarrow \forall N^*(a) \Rightarrow \exists x \in N^*(a) \cap X$.*

It is easy to see that in the preceding example, 0, 1, 3, 4 are all cluster points of X, but 2 is not a cluster point of X. As a further example, let

$$X = \left\{ 1, \frac{1}{2}, \frac{1}{3}, \frac{1}{4}, \ldots, \frac{1}{n}, \ldots \right\};$$

then 0 is the only cluster point of X. Or, if $X = \{1, 2, 3, \ldots, n, \ldots\} = \mathbf{N}$, then ∞ is the only cluster point of X.

To return to the domain X of the function in Example 17, if we let X' be the set of all accumulation points of X, then $X' = [0, 1] \cup [3, 4]$. Similarly, by the last sentence of the preceding paragraph, $\mathbf{N}' = \{\infty\}$.

For future purposes it will be convenient to have the following description of a cluster point of a set.

Theorem 2. *Let $X \subset \mathbf{R}$, $a \in \mathbf{R}$, or $a = \infty$, or $a = -\infty$.*

$$a \text{ is a cluster point of } X \Leftrightarrow \begin{cases} \textit{every } N^*(a) \textit{ contains} \\ \textit{infinitely many points} \\ \textit{of } X. \end{cases}$$

Proof. Surely we can say that the implication $\Leftarrow$ is obvious, so we turn our attention to the $\Rightarrow$ assertion.

Suppose there exists $N^*(a)$ which does contain only a finite number of points of X:

$$N^*(a) \cap X = \{x_1, x_2, \ldots, x_n\}.$$

Let

$$\delta = \min \{|a - x_1|, |a - x_2|, \ldots, |a - x_n|\}.$$

Then $N_\delta^*(a) \cap X = \varnothing$, contrary to the hypothesis that a is a cluster point of X. ∎

It is clear that the nbd. of a in this theorem need not be deleted.

EXERCISES

1. For each set X given below describe the set X' of all cluster points of X.

(a) $X = (0, 1) = \{x \mid 0 < x < 1\}$. $(X' = [0, 1] = \{x \mid 0 \le x \le 1\})$.
(b) $X = [0, 1]$.
(c) $X = (1, 2) \cup [3, 4] \cup \{5\}$.
(d) $X = \{1, 2, 3, \ldots, 10^{25}\}$.
(e) $X = [2, 4] \cup (7, 10) \cup \{16\}$.
(f) $X = $ all rational numbers $(X' = \{-\infty\} \cup \mathbf{R} \cup \{\infty\})$.
(g) $X = \{x \mid x \ne -5\}$.
(h) $X = \mathbf{R} - \{1, 4\} = \{x \in \mathbf{R} \mid x \ne 1, x \ne 4\}$.
(i) $X = \{x \in \mathbf{R} \mid x^2 > 0\}$.

2. What is the set X' of cluster points for the domain X of each of the following functions:

(a) $f: x \to x^2 - 4.$ (Answer $X' = \{-\infty\} \cup \mathbf{R} \cup \{\infty\}$

(b) $f: x \to \dfrac{x+3}{x-2}.$

(c) $f: x \to \dfrac{x^2 - 11}{(x+2)(x-7)}.$

(d) $f: x \to \sqrt{1 - x^2}$

(e) $f: x \to \dfrac{1}{1 - x^2}.$

3. What can be said about $\lim\limits_{x \to 2} f(x)$ for the functions defined as follows:

(a) $\begin{cases} f(x) = x^2, & 0 \le x \le 1 \\ f(2) = 4 \end{cases}.$ (b) $f(x) = \dfrac{x^2 - 4}{x - 2}.$ (c) $f(x) = \dfrac{1}{(x-2)^2}.$

4. (a) Is it true that " ∞ " is a cluster point of the set $\{1, 2, 3, \ldots\}$? (Can you find $N_M(\infty)$ which contains only a finite number of points of $\{1, 2, 3, \ldots\}$?)

(b) Is it true that " ∞ " is the only cluster point of the set $\{1, 2, 3, \ldots\}$? (If there were another cluster point, what would it be?)

5. Let X be a subset of $\mathbf{R}$, let $\bar{X} = X \cup X'$. Find examples of sets $X \subset \mathbf{R}$ which satisfy the following.

(a) $X = X'.$
(b) $X \ne X'.$
(c) $X \subset X'.$
(d) $X' \subset X.$

(e) $X \not\subset X', X' \not\subset X.$
(f) $\bar{X} = X$ (such a set is called *closed*).
(g) $\bar{X} \ne X.$

6. This exercise concerns an important assertion about the existence of cluster points for a set:

Theorem (*Bolzano–Weierstrass*). *Every bounded infinite subset of $\mathbf{R}$ has at least one cluster point. In symbols,*

$$\left. \begin{array}{l} X \subset \mathbf{R} \\ X \text{ bounded} \\ X \text{ infinite} \end{array} \right\} \Rightarrow X \text{ has a cluster point } (X' \ne \varnothing).$$

Prove it.
Hints.
1. X bounded $\Rightarrow \exists [a, b]$ such that $X \subset [a, b]$.
2. Divide $[a, b]$ into two equal parts. Since X is infinite, *at least one* of these two intervals must contain infinitely many points of X. If both do, pick the left half; otherwise, pick the half that has infinitely many points of X. Rename the endpoints a_1 and b_1. Note that $b_1 - a_1 = \frac{1}{2}(b - a)$.

3. Divide $[a_1, b_1]$ into halves. Again, at least one half must contain infinitely many points of X. If just one does, pick it; if both do, pick the left half. Name the half picked $[a_2, b_2]$. Note that

$$b_2 - a_2 = \frac{1}{2}(b_1 - a_1) = \frac{1}{2^2}(b - a).$$

4. Proceed in this way. At step n obtain the interval $[a_n, b_n] \subset [a, b]$ such that $[a_n, b_n]$ contains infinitely many points of X and such that

$$b_n - a_n = \frac{1}{2^n}(b - a).$$

5. Note that $a \le a_1 \le a_2 \le \cdots \le a_n \le \cdots < b$. Thus the nonempty set $\{a_n\}$ is bounded above (by b) and has a least upper bound (why?) which we call x_0.
6. Note that $b \ge b_1 \ge b_2 \ge \cdots \ge b_n \ge \cdots > a$. Thus $\{b_n\}$ is bounded below (by a). Let $y_0 = \text{glb } b_n$. But $y_0 = x_0$, since

$$b_n - a_n = \frac{1}{2^n}(b-a) \to 0 \qquad \text{as } n \to \infty.$$

7. Show x_0 is a cluster point for X. Let $N_\delta(x_0)$ be *any* nbd. of x_0. Choose n_0 large enough so that $[a_{n_0}, b_{n_0}] \subset N_\delta(x_0)$. Then $[a_{n_0}, b_{n_0}]$ and thus $N_\delta(x_0)$ contain infinitely many points of X (See Figure 17).

[Note: The cluster point for X guaranteed by the Bolzano–Weierstress theorem need not be in X. Thus, if $X = \left\{ 1, \frac{1}{2}, \frac{1}{3} \ldots, \frac{1}{n}, \ldots \right\}$, then $x_0 = 0 \notin X$.]

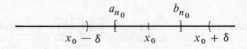

Figure 17

3.9 Continuity

We return now to the discussion of Section 3.5, more particularly to the distinction between the next-to-the-last and the last version of the limit definition.

The fact is that the Fourth Version, the version which did not use deleted nbds. of a, was satisfactory for Examples 3–5 but that the use of deleted nbds. was essential for Examples 6–8. The implication we intended to make was that for the sake of uniformity we would always use deleted nbds., even though there are cases where their use is not necessary.

Suppose we look at some examples in order to illustrate the points we want to make. The earlier Examples 7 and 3 will serve: however, for our present purposes we take them up in reverse order:

$$\text{(Example 7)} \quad \lim_{x \to 0} \frac{x^3 + 2x}{x} = 2,$$

$$\text{(Example 3)} \quad \lim_{x \to 2} (x + 3) = 5.$$

Now the reason a deleted nbd. of zero must be used in Example 7 is simply that zero is not in the domain of the function with recipe $f(x) = \dfrac{x^3 + 2x}{x}$ (however, zero is a cluster point of the domain and, as we have seen, the limit exists there); consequently, in talking about values of x close to zero it would not be meaningful to include zero itself. And, precisely because 2 is in the domain of the function defined by $f(x) = x + 3$ and because $f(2) = 5$ ($=L$)—for these reasons we *can* include 2 in the nbd. of 2, which is to say we do not have to resort to a deleted nbd.

Thus, in Example 3 we find occurring what in general terms may be described as follows: in considering $\lim_{x \to a} f(x) = L$ it may happen that

(i) a is in the domain of f,
(ii) $f(a) = L$.

Clearly, when $\lim_{x \to a} f(x) = L$ and when, in addition (i) and (ii) hold, we are not required to use deleted nbds. of a in considering the limit. When this occurs we say that the function f is *continuous at $x = a$*. This is said more precisely in either of the following equivalent definitions.

Definition 17(a). *The function f is **continuous at the point** $x = a$ in its domain* $\Leftrightarrow$

$$\lim_{x \to a} f(x) = f(a).$$

Definition 17(b). *The function f is **continuous at the point** $x = a$ in its domain* $\Leftrightarrow$ *for every $N_\varepsilon(f(a))$ there exists an $N_\delta(a)$ such that $x \in N_\delta(a) \Rightarrow f(x) \in N_\varepsilon(f(a))$.*

It should be evident that the two versions (a) and (b) *are* equivalent. Form (a) is obtained by combining the statement $\lim_{x \to a} f(x) = L$ with conditions (i) and (ii) mentioned before, namely, that a is in the domain of f and $L = f(a)$. Form (b) is obtained by applying Definition 6 to form (a); note that it says precisely what we had been saying earlier: we can use a nondeleted nbd. of a if and only if f is continuous at $x = a$.

It may happen that $\lim_{x \to a} f(x) = L$ and yet neither condition (i) nor (ii) holds, or it may happen that $\lim_{x \to a} f(x) = L$ and condition (i) holds but not (ii) (obviously we cannot have (ii) holding if (i) does not). In other words, a function may fail *in various ways* to be continuous at a point, even though the limit exists there.

For example, consider again

$$\text{(Example 7)} \quad \lim_{x \to 0} \frac{x^3 + 2x}{x} = 2;$$

the limit exists and is equal to 2, but 0 is not in the domain of f so both (i) and (ii) fail. But consider a function f with two-part formula as follows:

$$\left\{ \begin{aligned} f(x) &= \frac{x^2 + 3x}{x}, \quad x \neq 0 \\ f(0) &= 6 \end{aligned} \right\}.$$

Clearly the domain of f is **R**, so, in particular, 0 is in the domain and (i) holds. But, if we write the first part of the formula in the form

$$f(x) = (x + 3)\frac{x}{x}, \qquad x \neq 0,$$

we see that we can use a technique illustrated in Section 3.5 to show that $\lim_{x \to 0} f(x) = 3$; since the second part of the formula specifies that $f(0) = 6$, condition (ii) fails.

Thus, both of the preceding functions have limits at zero, but both fail to be continuous there, and in discussing the limits one would have to use deleted nbds. of 0.

Although continuity of a function f was defined as a property that may or may not hold at a *point* it can, of course, happen that a function is continuous at *every* point in some set in its domain, e.g., over some closed interval $[a, b] = \{x \mid a \leq x \leq b\}$. In this case it is customary to say that f is continuous *on* the interval $[a, b]$ or *over* the interval $[a, b]$.

It is appropriate at this time to mention an intuitive description of the concept of a function being continuous over a subset of its domain, where the subset is *connected*, or "all in one piece" (as, e.g., an interval). It is simply this: when two points are close together in the subset the corresponding two functional values will be close together.

But geometric intuition should not be relied upon too heavily in thinking about continuity. We call attention to the fact that this section on continuity is devoid of pictures—this was done more or less deliberately. It is true that the naive concept of the graph of a continuous function as an unbroken curve (without jumps) is *usually* safe. However, in order to keep the reader somewhat on guard we mention the following examples.

Consider first the "pathological" function f with two-part formula:

$$\left\{ \begin{aligned} f(x) &= 0, \text{ if } x \text{ is a rational number} \\ f(x) &= 1, \text{ if } x \text{ is an irrational number} \end{aligned} \right\}.$$

Any attempt to draw a graph of this function would result in what appears to be two unbroken straight lines: the x-axis and the line parallel to the x-axis and one unit above it. And yet we assert that this function *fails to be continuous at every* $x \in \mathbf{R}$. The proof, which we shall not give here, depends upon the fact that every nbd. of a rational number contains (infinitely many) irrational numbers and every nbd. of an irrational number contains (infinitely many) rational numbers.

As a second example, consider the function f defined by $f(x) = 1/x$. The graph is an equilateral hyperbola, lying in the first and third quadrants, and asymptotic to the coordinate axes. A quick glance at this curve would cause one to agree with the observation often made about this function: there is an infinite discontinuity at $x = 0$. But further consideration would force one to concur that this function *is continuous at every point in its domain*, for 0 is not in the domain of this function.

We conclude this discussion of continuity by showing a slightly different but occasionally extremely useful interpretation of the property. For this interpretation we need the intuitively obvious limit result:

$$\lim_{x \to a} x = a$$

(see Exercise 8). Using this simple statement and Definition 17(a), we have the following assertion, which we state as a theorem.

Theorem 3.

$$\left. \begin{array}{l} f \text{ is continuous at} \\ \text{the point } x = a \text{ in} \\ \text{its domain} \end{array} \right\} \Leftrightarrow \lim_{x \to a} f(x) = f(\lim_{x \to a} x).$$

Thus, if in the expression $\lim\limits_{x \to a} f(x)$ we consider that there are two operations involved: (1) the functional operation of mapping x into $f(x)$ and (2) the limit operation—then the theorem tells us that we may interchange the order of performing these operations if and only if the function f is continuous at a.

EXERCISES

1. Say whether or not a deleted nbd. of a is necessary in evaluating the following limits:

   (a) $\lim\limits_{x \to 4} (x^2 - 3x + 5)$.   (b) $\lim\limits_{x \to a} (x^2 - 3x + 5)$, *any* $a \in \mathbf{R}$.   (c) $\lim\limits_{x \to 0} |x|$.

   (d) $\lim\limits_{x \to 2} \dfrac{x^2 - 4}{x^2 - 3x + 2}$.   (e) $\lim\limits_{x \to 2} \dfrac{x^2 + 3x - 10}{x^2 - 4}$.

   (f) $\lim\limits_{x \to 2} f(x)$, where $\left\{ \begin{array}{l} f : x \to \dfrac{x^2 + 5x + 4}{x + 1}, \quad x \neq -1 \\ f : -1 \to 0 \end{array} \right\}$.

   (g) $\lim\limits_{x \to -1} f(x)$, same f as in part (f).

2. For each function in Exercise 1 find all points *in the domain* at which the function is not continuous.

3. Each of the following functions fails to be continuous at the value of a specified. Why?

(a) $\begin{cases} f : x \to \dfrac{|x|}{x}, & x \neq 0 \\ f : 0 \to 0 \\ a = 0 \end{cases}$.

(b) $\begin{cases} f(x) = \dfrac{x^2 + x - 6}{x - 2}, & x \neq 2 \\ f(2) = 0 \\ a = 2 \end{cases}$.

(c) $\begin{cases} f(x) = x, & x \leq 2 \\ f(x) = x + 1, & 2 < x \end{cases}$.
$a = 2$.

4. For each function given below 0 is not in the domain. Is it possible to define $f(0)$ so that f is continuous at 0? If so, what value should be assigned $f(0)$?

(a) $f(x) = \dfrac{1}{x}$.

(b) $f(x) = \dfrac{1}{x^2}$.

(c) $f(x) = 2^{-1/x^2}$.

(d) $f(x) = \dfrac{1}{1 - 2^{1/x}}$.

(e) $f(x) = \dfrac{1}{1 - 2^{1/x^2}}$.

5. For each function given below 0 is in the domain. Is f continuous at 0? If not, is it possible to modify the definition of f at 0 so that the modified f will be continuous at 0?

(a) $f(x) = x^2$.

(b) $\begin{cases} f(x) = \dfrac{1}{x^2}, & x \neq 0 \\ f(0) = 0 \end{cases}$.

(c) $\begin{cases} f(x) = x, & x \leq 0 \\ f(x) = x + 2, & x > 0 \end{cases}$.

(d) $\begin{cases} f(x) = \dfrac{x^2 + x}{x}, & x \neq 0 \\ f(0) = 2 \end{cases}$.

(e) $\begin{cases} f(x) = \dfrac{|x|}{x}, & x \neq 0 \\ f(0) = 0 \end{cases}$.

6. For each of the following functions find two points which are "close together" in the domain but whose functional values are not "close together."

(a) $\begin{cases} f : x \to x, & x < 0 \\ f : x \to x^2 + 1, & x \geq 0 \end{cases}$.

(b) $\begin{cases} f(x) = 1 - x, & x \leq 1 \\ f(x) = 2, & x > 1 \end{cases}$.

7. According to Definition 17 (either (a) or (b)), which of the following functions have points of discontinuity, i.e., points at which they fail to be continuous? For the ones which do, indicate these points.

(a) $f(x) = \dfrac{1}{x^2}$.

(b) $f(x) = \dfrac{2}{(x - 1)(x - 3)}$.

(Answer: No point of discontinuity in the domain.)

(c) $f(x) = (x - 1)(x - 3)$.

(d) $f(x) = \dfrac{|x|}{x}$.

(e) $\begin{cases} f(x) = \dfrac{x^2 - 4}{x - 2}, & x \neq 2 \\ f(2) = 0 \end{cases}$.

(f) $f(x) = \dfrac{x^2 - 4}{x - 2}$.

(g) $f(x) = \dfrac{x^3 + x}{x}$.

(h) $\begin{cases} f(x) = \dfrac{x^3 + x}{x}, & x \neq 0 \\ f(0) \end{cases}$.

8. Use Definition 6 or 6a to prove $\lim\limits_{x \to a} x = a$.

3.10 Theorems About Limits and Continuity

In this section we state and prove some of the important limit theorems, theorems which enable one to avoid the rather tedious use of either of the Definitions 6 or 6a. The procedure involved in using the theorems will be illustrated to obtain some results about continuous functions.

Before turning to the theorems we pause to make a comment about the nature of Definition 6. A correct understanding of the significance of this remark is essential to comprehending the details of the proofs which follow. The definition says that $\lim_{x \to a} f(x) = L$ means that for every $N_\varepsilon(L)$ it is possible to find $N_\delta^*(a)$ such that $x \in N_\delta^*(a) \Rightarrow f(x) \in N_\varepsilon(L)$. Now, when our aim is to *prove* valid a limit statement, then we must produce, for every possible $N_\varepsilon(L)$, a deleted nbd. of a, all the points of which map under f into $N_\varepsilon(L)$. On the other hand, if we have as *hypothesis* that $\lim_{x \to a} f(x) = L$, then we have available for our purposes the knowledge that there exists an $N_{\delta_\varepsilon}^*(a)$, all of whose points map into $N_\varepsilon(L)$, for *every* possible choice of $N_\varepsilon(L)$.

We begin by proving that Definition 6 does in fact guarantee the uniqueness mentioned in Section 3.2.

Theorem 4.

$$\left. \begin{array}{l} \lim_{x \to a} f(x) = L_1 \\[2mm] \lim_{x \to a} f(x) = L_2 \end{array} \right\} \Rightarrow L_1 = L_2 .$$

Proof. We show that $L_1 = L_2$ by the following device:

$$|L_1 - L_2| = |L_1 - f(x) + f(x) - L_2| \le |L_1 - f(x)| + |f(x) - L_2|,$$

where the x is now to be determined. Let $\varepsilon > 0$ be arbitrary; pick $N_1^*(a)$ such that $x \in N_1^*(a) \Rightarrow |L_1 - f(x)| < \dfrac{\varepsilon}{2}$, and pick $N_2^*(a)$ such that $x \in N_2^*(a) \Rightarrow |f(x) - L_2| < \dfrac{\varepsilon}{2}$. Now define $N^*(a) = N_1^*(a) \cap N_2^*(a)$; then $x \in N^*(a) \Rightarrow$ both of the preceding inequalities hold, so $x \in N^*(a) \Rightarrow$

$$|L_1 - L_2| < \frac{\varepsilon}{2} + \frac{\varepsilon}{2} = \varepsilon.$$

As L_1 and L_2 are fixed numbers, and as ε can be made arbitrarily small, it must follow that $L_1 = L_2$. ∎

Our next theorem, which we will need later, says that if a function has a *finite* limit at a, then the functional values are bounded in some nbd. of a.

Theorem 5. *If* $\lim_{x \to a} f(x) = L$ *then there exist a number* $M > 0$ *and an* $N_\delta^*(a)$ *such that* $x \in N_\delta^*(a) \Rightarrow |f(x)| < M.$

Proof. We must produce both a deleted nbd. of a and a positive M such that $x \in N_\delta^*(a) \Rightarrow$

$$-M < f(x) < M.$$

Since our hypothesis includes the statement that $\lim_{x \to a} f(x) = L$, we begin by picking a convenient ε ($\varepsilon = 1$ will do) and applying Definition 6. We know then that there exists $N_\delta^*(a)$ such that $x \in N_\delta^*(a) \Rightarrow f(x) \in N_1(L)$, i.e.,

$$x \in N_\delta^*(a) \Rightarrow L - 1 < f(x) < L + 1.$$

Now all we need do is exercise a little care in the choice of M (the fact that either $L - 1$ or $L + 1$ might be negative is what demands caution here). It turns out that a suitable M is $M = |L| + 1$, as we now show. It will be recalled that $-|L| \leq L \leq |L|$. Then, we can say for $x \in N_\delta^*(a)$

$$f(x) < L + 1 \leq |L| + 1 = M,$$

and

$$f(x) > L - 1 \geq -|L| - 1 = -M.$$

Thus $x \in N_\delta^*(a) \Rightarrow -M < f(x) < M$, or $|f(x)| < M$. ∎

One way of describing the assertion of Theorem 5 is to say that if a function has a limit at a, it cannot "immediately" go out of bounds. In the same vein, the next theorem says that if a function has a nonzero limit at a it cannot go immediately to zero, or it is "bounded away from zero." We now give the precise statement.

Theorem 6. *If* $\lim_{x \to a} f(x) = L$, *where* $L \neq 0$, *then there exist* $\varepsilon > 0$ *and* $N_\delta^*(a)$ *such that* $x \in N_\delta^*(a) \Rightarrow |f(x)| > \varepsilon$.

Proof. We choose $\varepsilon = \frac{1}{2}|L|$ and apply the hypothesis that $\lim_{x \to a} f(x) = L$. Then by Definition 6 we know there exists an $N_\delta^*(a)$ such that $x \in N_\delta^*(a) \Rightarrow f(x) \in N_\varepsilon(L)$, i.e.,

$$L - \varepsilon < f(x) < L + \varepsilon.$$

(i) Now, if $L > 0$, then $\varepsilon = \frac{1}{2}L$ and $L - \varepsilon = \frac{1}{2}L = \varepsilon$, so the left inequality says that $x \in N_\delta^*(a) \Rightarrow f(x) > \varepsilon$; since in this case $f(x) = |f(x)|$, we have that $x \in N_\delta^*(a) \Rightarrow |f(x)| > \varepsilon$.

(ii) If $L < 0$, then $\varepsilon = -\frac{1}{2}L$ and $L + \varepsilon = \frac{1}{2}L = -\varepsilon$, so the right inequality says that $x \in N_\delta^*(a) \Rightarrow f(x) < -\varepsilon$, or $-f(x) > \varepsilon$. Since in this case we are dealing with negative functional values, $-f(x) = |f(x)|$; thus our last inequality says that $x \in N_\delta^*(a) \Rightarrow |f(x)| > \varepsilon$. ∎

The fact is that this proof gives us a little more than we asserted. In case (i), $L > 0$, we found that $x \in N_\delta^*(a) \Rightarrow f(x) > \frac{1}{2}L > 0$, and in case (ii), $L < 0$, we found that $x \in N_\delta{}^*(a) \Rightarrow f(x) < \frac{1}{2}L < 0$ (see Figure 18). Another way of describing this is as follows:

Corollary 1. *If* $\lim\limits_{x \to a} f(x) = L \neq 0$, *then there exists a deleted nbd. of a within which the functional values have the same sign as L.*

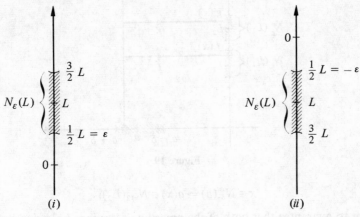

Figure 18

The next few theorems can be loosely verbalized as "the limit of a sum is the sum of the limits," "the limit of the difference is the difference of the limits," etc. It will be convenient for us to treat the sum and difference together and the product and quotient together.

Theorem 7.

$$\left.\begin{array}{l} \lim\limits_{x \to a} f(x) = L_1 \\[2mm] \lim\limits_{x \to a} g(x) = L_2 \end{array}\right\} \Rightarrow \left\{\begin{array}{l} \lim\limits_{x \to a} (f + g)(x) = \lim\limits_{x \to a} [f(x) + g(x)] = L_1 + L_2 \\[2mm] \lim\limits_{x \to a} (f - g)(x) = \lim\limits_{x \to a} [f(x) - g(x)] = L_1 - L_2. \end{array}\right.$$

Proof. One reason why the word "loose" was used in describing the verbalization of this and the next theorem is that the verbalization ignores the hypotheses: it is implicit that a is a cluster point of the domain of f and g, and it is explicit that both $\lim\limits_{x \to a} f(x)$ and $\lim\limits_{x \to a} g(x)$ exist as finite numbers.

To prove the assertion about $f + g$, we must (using Definition 6) for every possible choice of ε, produce an $N_\delta{}^*(a)$ such that $x \in N_\delta{}^*(a) \Rightarrow (f + g)(x) \in N_\varepsilon(L_1 + L_2)$. To this end, we consider an arbitrary $\varepsilon > 0$, and apply Definition 6 to both parts of the hypothesis; however, in applying Definition 6 to these limits, we use $\dfrac{\varepsilon}{2}$ rather than ε (see Figure 19). Then we know that there exist δ_1 and δ_2 such that

$$x \in N_{\delta_1}^*(a) \Rightarrow f(x) \in N_{\varepsilon/2}(L_1)$$

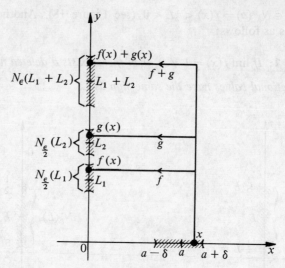

Figure 19

and

$$x \in N^*_{\delta_2}(a) \Rightarrow g(x) \in N_{\varepsilon/2}(L_2).$$

In order to guarantee that both of the preceding assertions hold simultaneously we choose $\delta =$ smaller (δ_1, δ_2) (this means that $N_\delta^*(a) = N^*_{\delta_1}(a) \cap N^*_{\delta_2}(a)$); then we can say that $x \in N_\delta^*(a) \Rightarrow$

$$L_1 - \frac{\varepsilon}{2} < f(x) < L_1 + \frac{\varepsilon}{2}$$

and

$$L_2 - \frac{\varepsilon}{2} < g(x) < L_2 + \frac{\varepsilon}{2}.$$

Adding these inequalities gives the statement that $x \in N_\delta^*(a) \Rightarrow$

$$L_1 + L_2 - \varepsilon < f(x) + g(x) < L_1 + L_2 + \varepsilon,$$

i.e., $(f + g)(x) \in N_\varepsilon(L_1 + L_2)$. Thus $\lim_{x \to a} (f + g)(x) = L_1 + L_2$, by Definition 6.

To prove the limit for $f - g$, we return to the inequalities displayed after the choice of δ, only we multiply by -1 the inequalities involving $g(x)$; then we can say $x \in N_\delta^*(a) \Rightarrow$

$$L_1 - \frac{\varepsilon}{2} < f(x) < L_1 + \frac{\varepsilon}{2}$$

and

$$-L_2 - \frac{\varepsilon}{2} < -g(x) < -L_2 + \frac{\varepsilon}{2}.$$

Adding, we have that $x \in N_\delta^*(a) \Rightarrow$

$$(L_1 - L_2) - \varepsilon < f(x) - g(x) < (L_1 - L_2) + \varepsilon;$$

i.e., $x \in N_\delta^*(a) \Rightarrow (f - g)(x) \in N_\varepsilon(L_1 - L_2)$. Thus, by Definition 6,

$$\lim_{x \to a} (f - g)(x) = L_1 - L_2. \quad \blacksquare$$

Theorem 8.

$$\left.\begin{array}{l} \lim_{x \to a} f(x) = L_1 \\ \\ \lim_{x \to a} g(x) = L_2 \end{array}\right\} \Rightarrow \left\{\begin{array}{l} \lim_{x \to a} (fg)(x) = \lim_{x \to a} [f(x)g(x)] = L_1 L_2 \\ \\ \lim_{x \to a} \left(\dfrac{f}{g}\right)(x) = \lim_{x \to a} \dfrac{f(x)}{g(x)} = \dfrac{L_1}{L_2}; \quad \text{here we also assume} \quad L_2 \neq 0. \end{array}\right.$$

Proof. For the proof of this theorem we shall work with Definition 6a rather than Definition 6.

We first formulate in a usable fashion the information which the hypotheses give us to work with:

(i)   for every $\varepsilon_1 > 0$ there exists $\delta_1 > 0$ such that

$$0 < |x - a| < \delta_1 \Rightarrow |f(x) - L_1| < \varepsilon_1$$

(ii)   for every $\varepsilon_2 > 0$ there exists $\delta_2 > 0$ such that

$$0 < |x - a| < \delta_2 \Rightarrow |g(x) - L_2| < \varepsilon_2.$$

In order to prove the assertion about the product we must, for every possible $\varepsilon > 0$, produce $\delta > 0$ such that $0 < |x - a| < \delta \Rightarrow |f(x)g(x) - L_1 L_2| < \varepsilon$. To this end, let $\varepsilon > 0$ be arbitrary; we want $|f(x)g(x) - L_1 L_2| < \varepsilon$. So that we can effectively use our hypotheses on this inequality, we write the left-hand side as

$$\begin{aligned} |f(x)g(x) - L_1 L_2| &= |(f(x)g(x) - f(x)L_2) + (f(x)L_2 - L_1 L_2)| \\ &\leq |f(x)g(x) - f(x)L_2| + |f(x)L_2 - L_1 L_2| \\ &= |f(x)| \cdot |g(x) - L_2| + |L_2| \cdot |f(x) - L_1|. \end{aligned}$$

We have achieved the following: the expression we want to "make small" is now dominated by the sum of two terms, each of which involves a factor we know we can control (by statements (i) and (ii)). The only possible source of trouble in this last expression is $|f(x)|$. But this in fact presents no difficulty because of Theorem 5; we know, slightly rephrasing Theorem 5, that

(iii)   there exist $\left.\begin{array}{l} \delta_3 > 0 \\ M > 0 \end{array}\right\}$ such that $0 < |x - a| < \delta_3 \Rightarrow |f(x)| < M.$

We now restrict x to satisfy $0 < |x - a| < \delta_3$; then we know

$$|f(x)g(x) - L_1 L_2| < M|g(x) - L_2| + |L_2| \cdot |f(x) - L_1|.$$

It is time to bring statements (i) and (ii) to the front: assuming $L_2 \neq 0$, we choose $\varepsilon_1 = \dfrac{\varepsilon}{2|L_2|}$ and we choose $\varepsilon_2 = \dfrac{\varepsilon}{2M}$; moreover, since the final inequalities of (i) and (ii) apply only when x is suitably restricted, we now define

$\delta = $ minimum $(\delta_1, \delta_2, \delta_3)$ (in the nbd. language, this means $N_\delta{}^*(a) = N_{\delta_1}{}^*(a) \cap$ $N_{\delta_2}{}^*(a) \cap N_{\delta_3}{}^*(a))$. Then, if $0 < |x - a| < \delta$, all the necessary restrictions on x apply and $|f(x) - L_1| < \varepsilon_1$, $|g(x) - L_2| < \varepsilon_2$, and $|f(x)| < M$. Thus, when $0 < |x - a| < \delta$, we know

$$|f(x)g(x) - L_1 L_2| < M \cdot \varepsilon_2 + |L_2|\varepsilon_1 = M\frac{\varepsilon}{2M} + |L_2|\frac{\varepsilon}{2L_2} = \varepsilon,$$

so Definition 6a is satisfied and $\lim_{x \to a} f(x)g(x) = L_1 L_2$.

The case $L_2 = 0$ can be quickly dispensed with. For, if $L_2 = 0$, the inequality given just after statement (iii) becomes

$$0 < |x - a| < \delta_3 \Rightarrow |f(x)g(x)| < M|g(x) - L_2| = M|g(x)|.$$

Now we choose $\varepsilon_2 = \dfrac{\varepsilon}{M}$ and define $\delta = $ minimum (δ_2, δ_3). Then, if $0 < |x - a| < \delta$ we know that $|f(x)| < M$ and $|g(x) - L_2| = |g(x)| < \varepsilon_2$, and

$$|f(x)g(x)| < M\varepsilon_2 = M\frac{\varepsilon}{M} = \varepsilon.$$

Thus, by Definition 6a, $\lim_{x \to a} [f(x)g(x)] = 0 = L_1 L_2$.

Before proceeding to the quotient part, we comment on the trick of adding and subtracting the term $f(x)L_2$. The purpose, of course, was to convert $f(x)g(x) - L_1 L_2$ into an expression which would enable us to use the hypotheses. This sort of device is frequently effective and should be kept in mind.

The proof for the limit of the quotient is very similar, in its general nature, to the proof just given. We have, in addition to the hypotheses already used, the essential one for this part that $L_2 \neq 0$. We want to produce, for any possible choice of $\varepsilon > 0$, a $\delta > 0$ such that $0 < |x - a| < \delta \Rightarrow$

$$\left|\frac{f(x)}{g(x)} - \frac{L_1}{L_2}\right| < \varepsilon.$$

As before, we transform the left-hand side of this inequality:

$$\left|\frac{f(x)}{g(x)} - \frac{L_1}{L_2}\right| = \left|\frac{f(x)L_2 - g(x)L_1}{g(x)L_2}\right|$$

$$= \frac{1}{|g(x)| \cdot |L_2|}|f(x)L_2 - f(x)g(x) + f(x)g(x) - g(x)L_1|$$

$$\leq \frac{1}{|g(x)| \cdot |L_2|}[|f(x)| \cdot |g(x) - L_2| + |g(x)| \cdot |f(x) - L_1|]$$

(recall that $|L_2 - g(x)| = |g(x) - L_2|$)

$$= \frac{|f(x)|}{|g(x)| \cdot |L_2|}|g(x) - L_2| + \frac{1}{|L_2|}|f(x) - L_1|.$$

Again we have the expression we want to "make small" dominated by a sum of two terms, each of which involves either $|g(x) - L_2|$ or $|f(x) - L_1|$, which we know we can control. But again there is a possible source of trouble (not the $|f(x)|$ in the first term—we know we have that under control): the factor $\dfrac{1}{|g(x)|}$ which appears in the first term. If $g(x)$ could get arbitrarily close to 0, $\dfrac{1}{|g(x)|}$ could get arbitrarily big. However, in this case it is Theorem 6 which comes to our rescue: since $L_2 \neq 0$, $g(x)$ must be "bounded away" from 0. More exactly, rephrasing Theorem 6,

(iv)   there exist $\begin{Bmatrix} \delta_4 > 0 \\ K > 0 \end{Bmatrix}$ such that

$$0 < |x - a| < \delta_4 \Rightarrow |g(x)| > \frac{1}{K} \text{ or } \frac{1}{|g(x)|} < K.$$

Since we would like to use the final inequalities of all four assertions, (i), (ii), (iii), and (iv), and since each of these involves a restriction on x, we define

$$\delta = \text{minimum} \quad (\delta_1, \delta_2, \delta_3, \delta_4),$$

which is to say (in nbd. language) that $N_\delta^*(a) = N_{\delta_1}^*(a) \cap N_{\delta_2}^*(a) \cap N_{\delta_3}^*(a) \cap N_{\delta_4}^*(a)$.

Then, if $0 < |x - a| < \delta$, we know that

$$|f(x) - L_1| < \varepsilon_1, |g(x) - L_2| < \varepsilon_2, |f(x)| < M, \quad \text{and} \quad \frac{1}{|g(x)|} < K;$$

i.e.,

$$\left| \frac{f(x)}{g(x)} - \frac{L_1}{L_2} \right| < \frac{MK}{|L_2|} \varepsilon_2 + \frac{1}{|L_2|} \varepsilon_1.$$

We choose $\varepsilon_1 = \dfrac{|L_2|\varepsilon}{2}$ and $\varepsilon_2 = \dfrac{|L_2|\varepsilon}{2MK}$; then if $0 < |x - a| < \delta$, we know that

$$\left| \frac{f(x)}{g(x)} - \frac{L_1}{L_2} \right| < \frac{MK}{|L_2|} \frac{\varepsilon|L_2|}{2MK} + \frac{1}{|L_2|} \frac{\varepsilon|L_2|}{2} = \varepsilon.$$

By Definition 6a, then, $\displaystyle\lim_{x \to a} \frac{f(x)}{g(x)} = \frac{L_1}{L_2}$. ∎

We remark that things got just a bit out of order in the final stages of this proof: strictly speaking, we should have chosen ε_1 and ε_2 and *then* defined $\delta = \min(\delta_1, \delta_2, \delta_3, \delta_4)$, since the size of δ_1 and δ_2 will depend upon the choice of ε_1 and ε_2, respectively. However, we know, by hypothesis, that suitable δ_1 and δ_2 exist for any choice of ε_1 and ε_2, so our procedure can be defended.

There is a useful corollary which follows from the product part of Theorem 8. Suppose, in fact, that g is a constant function, i.e., $g(x) = c$ for all x in the domain of g. Then, as is easily shown, $\displaystyle\lim_{x \to a} g(x) = c$. Thus we can state the following corollary.

Corollary 2.

$$\lim_{x \to a} f(x) = L \Rightarrow \lim_{x \to a} [cf(x)] = cL = c \lim_{x \to a} f(x).$$

This symbolic statement has the following verbalization: the limit of a constant times a function equals the constant times the limit of the function.

We next mention a few theorems which follow very easily from the preceding results. We give no proofs here but give hints or outlines of proofs in the exercises which follow.

Theorem 9. *Let p be a polynomial function. Then p is continuous at every point of its domain* **R**.

Theorem 10. *Let f and g be continuous at a point x_0 common to their domains. Then*

$$f + g, f - g, fg, \quad and \quad \frac{f}{g}$$

are also continuous at x_0, provided, in the case of f/g, that $g(x_0) \neq 0$.

The next result is a direct consequence of the two preceding theorems.

Theorem 11. *Let r be a rational function, i.e., $r = \dfrac{p_1}{p_2}$, where p_1 and p_2 are polynomials. Then r is continuous at every point of its domain, i.e., for all $a \in$ **R** such that $p_2(a) \neq 0$.*

The essence of Theorem 10 is that continuity is preserved under the usual arithmetic operations; the next propositions assure that continuity is also preserved by composition.

Theorem 12. *Let f and g be functions such that the composite function $h = f \circ g$ is defined. Suppose $\lim_{x \to a} g(x) = b$, f is continuous at b. Then $\lim_{x \to a} h(x) = f(b)$.*

An immediate consequence of Theorem 12 is the result that continuity is preserved by the operation of composition:

Corollary 3. *Let f and g be functions such that the composite function $h = f \circ g$ exists. Let $g(a) = b$ and suppose that g is continuous at a and f is continuous at b. Then h is continuous at a.*

We now state and briefly discuss four theorems which are of a deeper nature than the preceding ones. We shall need to use these theorems from time to time in what follows, so an understanding of their meanings is important. Fortunately, this understanding is easily gained. The proofs will be outlined in the exercises.

As a preliminary to the first theorem, we point out that a function might be continuous at every point of some set $X \subset \mathbf{R}$ (see Theorem 9). If we apply Definition 17(b) to such a function we would find that, for a *given fixed* ε, the choice of δ would depend upon the point $x_0 \in X$. For example, if

$$f(x) = \frac{1}{x}, \qquad x \in (0, 1] = X,$$

it can be shown that for a given ε the largest possible δ is described by

$$\delta_{\varepsilon, x_0} = \frac{x_0{}^2}{1 + \varepsilon x_0}\, \varepsilon. \tag{6}$$

Thus,

$$\delta_{\varepsilon, 1} = \frac{1}{1 + \varepsilon}\, \varepsilon \approx \varepsilon, \qquad \text{if } \varepsilon \text{ is small;}$$

but as x_0 is taken close to 0 the multiplier of ε in (6) approaches 0 so $\lim_{x_0 \to 0} \delta_{\varepsilon, x_0} = 0$. For every $x_0 \in (0, 1]$ $\delta_{\varepsilon, x_0}$ exists, but these δ's become arbitrarily small for x_0 close to 0. In particular, it would be impossible to find, for a given ε, a single δ which would be applicable to *every* $x_0 \in (0, 1]$.

The situation changes, however, if we consider the same function over the interval $X_1 = [1, 2]$. The expression, given in (6), for the maximum δ still applies, and it is possible to prove (although we shall not take time to do so) that

$$x_1 < x_2 \Rightarrow \delta_{\varepsilon, x_1} < \delta_{\varepsilon, x_2}$$

(note, by the way, that $\delta_{\varepsilon, 2} = \dfrac{4}{1 + 2\varepsilon}\, \varepsilon \approx 4\varepsilon$, if ε is small). Thus, since for every $x_0 \in [1, 2]$ it is true that

$$\delta_{\varepsilon, 1} \leq \delta_{\varepsilon, x_0},$$

it would be possible to use $\delta_{\varepsilon, 1} = \dfrac{1}{1 + \varepsilon}\, \varepsilon$ for every $x_0 \in [1, 2]$. This says that this function is *uniformly continuous* on $[1, 2]$.

Definition 18. *Let f have a domain which includes $X \subset \mathbf{R}$. Then*

$$\left.\begin{array}{l} f \text{ is } \textbf{\textit{uniformly}} \\ \textbf{\textit{continuous on }} X \end{array}\right\} \Leftrightarrow \left\{\begin{array}{l} \forall \varepsilon > 0 \Rightarrow \exists \delta_\varepsilon > 0 \text{ such that for all } x_1, x_2 \in X \\ \text{satisfying } |x_1 - x_2| < \delta_\varepsilon \Rightarrow |f(x_1) - f(x_2)| < \varepsilon. \end{array}\right.$$

The essential point about uniform continuity is that the choice of δ depends only upon the ε and not upon the $x \in X$. Clearly if f is uniformly continuous on X, then f is continuous on X. The remarkable fact is that by taking X to be a closed interval, one can obtain a converse of this result.

Theorem 13. *f continuous on $[a, b] \Rightarrow f$ uniformly continuous on $[a, b]$.*

Another property possessed by a function continuous on a closed interval is boundedness:

Theorem 14. f *continuous on* $[a, b] \Rightarrow \begin{cases} \exists K > 0 \text{ such that for all } x \in [a, b] \\ \text{it is true that } |f(x)| < K. \end{cases}$

Notice that the example $f(x) = \dfrac{1}{x}$ on $(0, 1]$ shows that it is necessary that the interval be closed. Continuity of f is also necessary, as the following example shows:

$$\begin{cases} f(x) = x, & x \in [0, 1], \quad x \text{ rational} \\ f(x) = \dfrac{1}{x}, & x \in [0, 1], \quad x \text{ irrational} \end{cases}.$$

By Theorem 14 the set of functional values of a function continuous on a closed interval $[a, b]$ is bounded both above and below; consequently, both

$$m = \text{glb}\{f(x) \mid x \in [a, b]\}$$

and   (7)

$$M = \text{lub}\{f(x) \mid x \in [a, b]\}$$

exist. But we can say more than this.

Theorem 15. *Let f be continuous on $[a, b]$ and let m and M be as defined in Equation* (7). *Then* $\exists x_1, x_2 \in [a, b]$ *such that* $f(x_1) = m, f(x_2) = M$.

(Is the conclusion of Theorem 15 true for $f(x) = x$ on $(0, 1)$?)

A popular way of verbalizing Theorem 15 is that a function continuous on a closed interval takes on its minimum and its maximum there. As a matter of fact, we can say more than that: it takes on every value in between.

Theorem 16. *Let f be continuous on $[a, b]$, let m and M be as defined in Equation* (7), *and let $y_0 \in [m, M]$. Then* $\exists x_0 \in [a, b]$ *such that* $f(x_0) = y_0$.

Observe that Theorem 16 says that if f is continuous on $[a, b]$ then it maps $[a, b]$ onto the closed interval $[m, M]$. However, this need not be a 1–1 mapping. For example, let $f(x) = 2x - x^2$, $x \in [0, 2]$. It is not hard to see that $m = 0$ and $M = 1$, so that $f : [0, 2] \longrightarrow [0, 1]$. But, with the exception of 1, $f(x)$ assumes twice every value in $[0, 1]$ (see Figure 20).

We finally mention what might be called a "squeezing theorem."

Theorem 17. *Suppose f, g, and h are such that* $\lim\limits_{x \to a} f(x) = \lim\limits_{x \to a} h(x) = L$, *and such that, for all x in some $N^*(a)$, $f(x) \le g(x) \le h(x)$. Then* $\lim\limits_{x \to a} g(x) = L$.

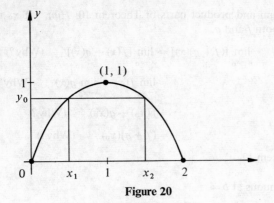

Figure 20

EXERCISES

Use any or all of Theorems 7–11, Corollaries 2–4, and Definition 17(a) to find the following limits. You should be able to justify each step.

1. $\lim\limits_{x\to 3} (4x^2 - 7x + 11) = \lim\limits_{x\to 3} 4x^2 - \lim\limits_{x\to 3} 7x + \lim\limits_{x\to 3} 11 = 4 \lim\limits_{x\to 3} x^2 - 7 \lim\limits_{x\to 3} x + 11 = \cdots$

2. $\lim\limits_{x\to 2} (x^3 - 2x^2 + 4x + 7).$

3. $\lim\limits_{x\to 3} \dfrac{x^2 + 13}{x^3 - 2}.$

4. $\lim\limits_{x\to 10} \dfrac{x - 11}{x^2 + 6}.$

5. $\lim\limits_{x\to a} (2x^2 - x + 13).$

6. $\lim\limits_{x\to 1} \sqrt{x^2 + 8}.$ Assume $f : x \to \sqrt{x}$ is continuous for $x \geq 0$.

7. $\lim\limits_{x\to 0} \dfrac{x^2 - 25}{x^2 - 2x - 15}.$

8. $\lim\limits_{x\to 5} \dfrac{x^2 - 25}{x^2 - 2x - 15}.$

9. $\lim\limits_{x\to 3} \sin\left(\dfrac{x^2 - 1}{x^2 + 1}\right).$ Assume $f : x \to \sin x$ is continuous for all $x \in \mathbf{R}$.

10. Prove Theorem 9. [*Hint.* Let $p(x) = c_0 x^n + c_1 x^{n-1} + \cdots + c_{n-1} x + c_n$. Then for every $a \in \mathbf{R}$,

$$\lim\limits_{x\to a} p(x) = \lim\limits_{x\to a} (c_0 x^n + c_1 x^{n-1} + \cdots + c_{n-1}x + c_n)$$

$$= \lim\limits_{x\to a} (c_0 x^n) + \lim\limits_{x\to a} (c_1 x^{n-1}) + \cdots + \lim\limits_{x\to a} c_n, \text{ etc.}]$$

11. Prove the sum and product parts of Theorem 10. *Hint.* If x_0 is a point in the domain of both f and g,

$$\lim_{x \to x_0} [(f+g)(x)] = \lim_{x \to x_0} [f(x) + g(x)] \qquad \text{(Why?)}$$

$$= \lim_{x \to x_0} f(x) + \lim_{x \to x_0} g(x) \qquad \text{(Why?)}$$

$$= f(x_0) + g(x_0) \qquad \text{(Why?)}$$

$$= (f+g)(x_0). \qquad \text{(Why?)}$$

12. Prove Theorem 12.
    Hints:
    1. f continuous at $b \Rightarrow$

    $$\forall N_\varepsilon(f(b)) \Rightarrow \exists N_\eta(b) \text{ such that } z \in N_\eta(b) \Rightarrow f(z) \in N_\varepsilon(f(b)).$$

    2. $\lim_{x \to a} g(x) = b \Rightarrow$

    $$\forall N_\eta(b) \Rightarrow \exists N_\delta^*(a) \text{ such that } x \in N_\delta^*(a) \Rightarrow g(x) = z \in N_\eta(b).$$

    3. Combine Hints 1 and 2 to get the desired result.

13. Prove Corollary 3. [*Hint.* Use Theorem 12.]

14. Prove Theorem 13: f continuous on $[a, b] \Rightarrow f$ uniformly continuous on $[a, b]$.
    Hints:
    1. Use a contrapositive approach: assume f not uniformly continuous on $[a, b]$. A negation of Definition 18 is:

    $\exists \varepsilon > 0$ such that for all $\delta > 0$ it is true that

    $$\exists x_1, x_2 \in [a, b], |x_1 - x_2| < \delta, \qquad \text{and} \quad |f(x_1) - f(x)| \ge \varepsilon.$$

    Convince yourself that this *is* a correct negation of Definition 18.
    2. Rewrite the statement of *Hint* 1 as:

    $\exists \varepsilon > 0$ such that for all $n = 1, 2, \ldots$, it is true that

    $$\exists x_n', x_n'' \in [a, b], |x_n' - x_n''| < \frac{1}{n}, \qquad \text{and} \quad |f(x_n') - f(x_n'')| \ge \varepsilon.$$

    3. Apply the Bolzano–Weierstrass Theorem (Exercise 6 in Section 3.8) to the set $\{x_n'\}$ to get a cluster point x_0 for $\{x_n'\}$. Note that $x_0 \in [a, b]$. Why?
    4. Show that x_0 is also a cluster point for the set $\{x_n''\}$.
    5. Now $x_0 \in [a, b] \Rightarrow$ (why?) f is continuous at x_0.
    Thus, using the ε of *Hint* 1, $\exists \delta > 0$ such that $x \in N_\delta(x_0) \Rightarrow$

    $$|f(x) - f(x_0)| < \frac{\varepsilon}{2}.$$

    6. Pick $n_1 \in \mathbf{N}$ large enough so that $x_{n_1}', x_{n_1}'', \in N_\delta(x_0)$. (Why can this be done?)
    7. Now we obtain a contradiction. For, on the one hand, by *Hint* 2,

    $$|f(x_{n_1}') - f(x_{n_1}'')| \ge \varepsilon.$$

Whereas, on the other hand, by Hints 6 and 5,

$$|f(x'_{n_1}) - f(x''_{n_1})| = |f(x'_{n_1}) - f(x_0) + f(x_0) - f(x''_{n_1})|$$

$$\leq |f(x'_{n_1}) - f(x_0)| + |f(x_0) - f(x''_{n_1})|$$

$$< \frac{\varepsilon}{2} + \frac{\varepsilon}{2} = \varepsilon.$$

15. Prove Theorem 14: f continuous on $[a, b] \Rightarrow \exists K > 0$ such that $|f(x)| < K$, for all $x \in [a, b]$.

Hints:

1. Use Theorem 13. Take $\varepsilon = 1$; then there exists δ_1 such that $|x_1 - x_2| < \delta_1 \Rightarrow |f(x_1) - f(x_2)| < 1$.

2. Pick $n_1 \in \mathbf{N}$ large enough so that $\dfrac{b - a}{n_1} < \delta_1$.

3. Form a regular partition π of $[a, b]$ with n_1 subintervals.

4. Then on each subinterval of π, f changes by less than 1. Since there are n_1 subintervals, the following holds for all $x \in [a, b]$:

$$f(a) - n_1 < f(x) < f(a) + n_1.$$

5. Define $K = |f(a)| + n_1$.

16. Prove Theorem 15:

$$\left.\begin{array}{l} f \text{ continuous on } [a, b] \\ m = \text{glb } f(x), \, x \in [a, b] \\ M = \text{lub } f(x), \, x \in [a, b] \end{array}\right\} \Rightarrow \begin{cases} \exists x_1, x_2 \in [a, b] \text{ such} \\ \text{that } f(x_1) = m, f(x_2) = M. \end{cases}$$

Hints for existence of x_2:

1. Suppose no such x_2 exists on $[a, b]$. Then $f(x) < M$ for all $x \in [a, b]$. Define a function g on $[a, b]$ by

$$g(x) = \frac{1}{M - f(x)}.$$

2. Show g is continuous on $[a, b]$. Hence g is bounded on $[a, b]$. (Why?)

3. *But,* $M = \text{lub } f(x) \Rightarrow \forall n \in \mathbf{N} \Rightarrow \exists x_n \in [a, b]$ such that

$$f(x_n) > M - \frac{1}{n},$$

i.e., $M - f(x_n) < \dfrac{1}{n}$, or $g(x_n) = \dfrac{1}{M - f(x_n)} > n$. And this says that g is unbounded

above, a contradiction. (Why?)

17. Prove the following lemma.

$$\left.\begin{array}{l} g \text{ continuous on } [a, b] \\ g(a)g(b) < 0 \end{array}\right\} \Rightarrow \begin{cases} \exists x_0 \in (a, b) \text{ such} \\ \text{that } g(x_0) = 0. \end{cases}$$

Hints:

1. Suppose, to be explicit, $g(a) < 0, g(b) > 0$.

Let

$$Q = \{x \in [a, b] \,|\, g(x) < 0\}, \, P = \{x \in [a, b] \,|\, g(x) > 0\}.$$

Then $a \in Q$, $b \in P$, and Q is bounded above by b.

2. Let $x_0 = \text{lub } Q$. Then $x_0 \in (a, b)$.

3. Show that the assumption that $g(x_0) < 0$ contradicts the choice of x_0 as *an* upper bound of Q. The Corollary to Theorem 6 will help.

4. Show that the assumption that $g(x_0) > 0$ contradicts the choice of x_0 as the *least* upper bound of Q.

5. Conclude that $g(x_0) = 0$.

18. Prove Theorem 16:

$$\left.\begin{array}{l} f \text{ continuous on } [a, b] \\ m = \text{glb } f(x), \, x \in [a, b] \\ M = \text{lub } f(x), \, x \in [a, b] \\ m \leq y_0 \leq M. \end{array}\right\} \Rightarrow \left\{\begin{array}{l} \exists x_0 \in [a, b] \text{ such} \\ \text{that } f(x_0) = y_0. \end{array}\right.$$

Hints:

1. Dispense quickly with the cases $m = M$, $y_0 = m$, or $y_0 = M$.

2. If $m < y_0 < M$, define g by $g(x) = f(x) - y_0$ and use the lemma of the preceding exercise.

19. Prove Theorem 17.

Chapter **4** Basic Theory of Differential Calculus

In this chapter we make use of our knowledge of limits and continuity to tie up some of the loose ends left hanging in Chapter 2 and also to develop further some of the theoretical ideas introduced there. Our interest here is in the part of calculus related to the derivative; we postpone until later a more searching look at the integral.

4.1 Differentiability and Continuity

The definition of a function with domain $X \subset \mathbf{R}$ is sufficiently broad to allow some very strange and pathological members to be included in the family of functions. However, in elementary work and in many of the applications, the functions encountered are usually "well behaved." What is meant by this last term is simply this: we have already introduced the properties of differentiability, integrability, and continuity, applicable to functions. Most of the functions we have met with thus far, with only isolated exceptions, have all of these properties. This is, roughly, what we mean by "well behaved."

Now the preceding three properties are by no means equivalent; nevertheless, we might expect that there are relations among them, and it becomes legitimate to inquire into the nature of these interrelationships. In particular, we shall find that differentiability implies continuity.

We first state a simple consequence of the limit definition which will be useful to us.

Lemma 1. *Let φ be a function. Then*

$$\lim_{t \to a} \varphi(t) = L \Rightarrow \varphi(t) = L + \eta(t), \qquad where \lim_{t \to a} \eta(t) = 0.$$

Proof. Exercise for student. ∎

It is now a triviality to prove the assertion about differentiability.

Theorem 1. *If f is differentiable at x_0, then f is continuous there. In symbols,*

$$f'(x_0) \text{ exists} \Rightarrow f \text{ continuous at } x_0.$$

Proof. By hypothesis

$$\lim_{h \to 0} \frac{f(x_0 + h) - f(x_0)}{h} = f'(x_0)$$

exists. Lemma 1, applied to $\dfrac{f(x_0 + h) - f(x_0)}{h} = \varphi(h)$, gives

$$\frac{f(x_0 + h) - f(x_0)}{h} = f'(x_0) + \eta(h), \qquad \text{where } \lim_{h \to 0} \eta(h) = 0;$$

thus

$$f(x_0 + h) = f(x_0) + f'(x_0)h + h\eta(h),$$

or

$$\lim_{h \to 0} f(x_0 + h) = f(x_0),$$

which is to say that f is continuous at x_0. ∎

It is important to realize that the converse of Theorem 1 is far from true. The absolute value function, $f: x \to |x|$, at $x_0 = 0$ gives a simple example of a function which is continuous, but nondifferentiable at a point. Even so, since being differentiable at a point implies, geometrically, having a unique tangent, or having a unique direction at that point, one would expect that continuous functions would *usually* be differentiable. If this deliberately vague statement is acceptable to the reader, he should have some understanding of the near-consternation created when K. Weierstrass (1815–1897) concocted a function continuous everywhere on **R** and differentiable nowhere. As such functions—other examples than Weierstrass's have since been found—fail to have a unique direction at every point, the natural request for "a picture of one" cannot be easily granted.

Note also, that the relation described between differentiability and continuity is quite different from that between continuity and integrability. For Theorem 2.9 (still unproven) tells us that continuity (on an interval) is a sufficient (but not necessary) condition for integrability over the interval.

To summarize this discussion, suppose $[a, b]$ is some fixed interval; let $\mathscr{D}$, $\mathscr{C}$, and $\mathscr{I}$ be the sets of functions which are, respectively, differentiable, continuous, and integrable on $[a, b]$. Then

$$\mathscr{D} \subset \mathscr{C} \subset \mathscr{I};$$

in each case the relation is a proper one.

EXERCISES

1. Prove Lemma 1. [*Hint.* Define $\eta(t) = \varphi(t) - L$.]

2. Find two examples of functions, other than the absolute value function, which are continuous at $x_0 = 0$, but which are nondifferentiable there.

3. Prove that every polynomial function and every rational function are continuous at every point of their domains. [*Hint.* Use Theorem 1.]

4.2 Differentials

We consider now another consequence of applying Lemma 1 to the defining expression for the derivative.

Let f be a function which is differentiable at x_0. Then, as in the proof of Theorem 1, we can write

$$f(x_0 + h) - f(x_0) = f'(x_0)h + \eta h, \tag{1}$$

where

$$\lim_{h \to 0} \eta = 0. \tag{2}$$

The left-hand side of Eq. (1) represents the change in f when the argument changes from x_0 to $x_0 + h$. The right-hand side expresses this change (or increment) in f as the sum of two terms, the second of which, by virtue of (2), will be quite small, compared to the first, when h is small. Figure 1 gives a geometric interpretation of Eq. (1). We leave it as an exercise to show that the length of the segment $\overline{P_1 T}$ is indeed $f'(x_0)h$.

(With regard to Figure 1, we remark that choices have been made so that the different quantities involved are all positive: $h > 0$, $f'(x_0) > 0$, $\eta > 0$. In general, some or all of these numbers might be negative. For example, if $h > 0$ and $f'(x_0) > 0$, but if the tangent at P_0 lies *above* the curve, then the segment $\overline{P_1 T}$ of length $f'(x_0)h$ will be longer than the segment $\overline{P_1 Q_0}$ of length $f(x_0 + h) - f(x_0)$; in other words, η and hence ηh will be negative. The reader should sketch this and several other variations of Figure 1.)

To return to Eq. (1), we can rephrase the preceding remark about the relative sizes (for small h) of the two terms on the right by saying that the *principal part* of the increment $f(x_0 + h) - f(x_0)$ is the term $f'(x_0)h$. This, as we shall see, is an important concept—important enough to warrant a special symbol and a special name.

Definition 1. *Let f be a function which is differentiable at a point x in its domain. The **differential** df of f is the function of two variables with value at (x, h) defined by*

$$df(x, h) = f'(x)h. \tag{3}$$

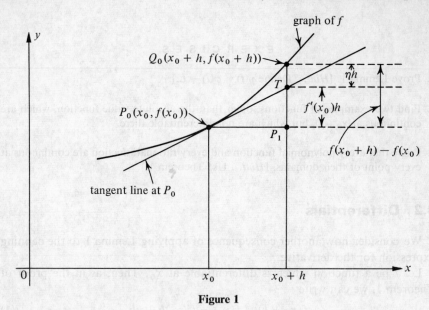

Figure 1

More exactly, if f' has domain $X' \subset \mathbf{R}$, then $df: X' \times \mathbf{R} \to \mathbf{R}$, the value of df at a point (x, h) of its domain being given by (3).

Notice that, although frequently in the use of the differential h will be small, nothing in Definition 1 requires that this be the case. (One way of suggesting that h is "small" would be to describe the domain of df as $X' \times N(0)$, where $N(0)$ is a nbd. of 0.)

If, following the notation of Leibniz, we let

$$\Delta f = \Delta f(x_0, h) = f(x_0 + h) - f(x_0),$$

then we can write equation (1) as

$$\Delta f(x_0, h) = df(x_0, h) + \eta h, \tag{4}$$

where, as usual, $\lim\limits_{h \to 0} \eta = 0$. As a matter of fact, Leibniz used Δx where we have used h. The idea is that Δx represents the increment or change in x, just as Δf represents the change in the functional values. With this modification (4) becomes

$$\Delta f = \Delta f(x_0, \Delta x) = df(x_0, \Delta x) + \eta \, \Delta x, \tag{5}$$

where

$$df(x_0, \Delta x) = f'(x_0) \, \Delta x.$$

Suppose we consider a simple example. Let f be the function defined by $f(x) = x^2$. Then $f'(x) = 2x$ and (5) becomes

$$\Delta f = 2x \, \Delta x + \eta \, \Delta x. \tag{6}$$

But in this case it is a simple matter to calculate Δf directly:

$$\Delta f = \Delta f(x, \Delta x) = f(x + \Delta x) - f(x) = (x + \Delta x)^2 - x^2$$
$$= x^2 + 2x\,\Delta x + \overline{\Delta x}^2 - x^2$$
$$= 2x\,\Delta x + \overline{\Delta x}^2$$
$$\Delta f = 2x\,\Delta x + (\Delta x)\,\Delta x. \tag{7}$$

A comparison of (6) and (7) shows that in this case $\eta = \Delta x$.

Moreover, this example has a simple geometric interpretation in terms of the area of a square (see Figure 2), and the change in this area produced by a change Δx in the side of the square.

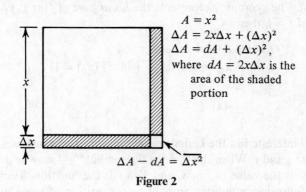

$$A = x^2$$
$$\Delta A = 2x\Delta x + (\Delta x)^2$$
$$\Delta A = dA + (\Delta x)^2,$$
where $dA = 2x\Delta x$ is the area of the shaded portion

$$\Delta A - dA = \overline{\Delta x}^2$$

Figure 2

As another example, but also as a means of obtaining a useful relation, suppose $f = j$, i.e., $f(x) = j(x) = x$. Then $j'(x) = 1$, all $x \in \mathbf{R}$, so

$$dj = dj(x, \Delta x) = 1 \cdot \Delta x = \Delta x. \tag{8}$$

Now the use of j for this function is not very widespread; in fact, the symbol x is used far more frequently than is j. This would suggest then that the corresponding differential function would be denoted by dx, i.e., $dj = dx$. When this is done (8) becomes

$$dx = dx(x, \Delta x) = \Delta x. \tag{9}$$

It is important that (9) be understood correctly. Conceptually dx and Δx are different objects. Since $dx = dj$ is a differential, it is a *function*, in fact a function of the two variables x and Δx. However, since $j' = 1$, the values of $dj = dx$ depend only on Δx:

$$dj(x, \Delta x) = dx(x, \Delta x) = \Delta x.$$

Thus the *number* Δx is the value of the *function* dx at the point $(x, \Delta x)$.

The following may help to indicate the nature of the differential and its role in approximation problems. We consider x_0 fixed and let $x_0 + h = x$, so that $h = x - x_0$. Then Eq. (1) can be written as

$$f(x) = f(x_0) + f'(x_0)(x - x_0) + \eta(x - x_0), \quad \lim_{x \to x_0} \eta = 0.$$

Dropping the "small" term $\eta(x - x_0)$, we have

$$f(x) \approx f(x_0) + f'(x_0)(x - x_0),$$

where $\approx$ means "is approximately equal to."

If we write

$$f_L(x) = f(x_0) + f'(x_0)(x - x_0) = f(x_0) + df(x_0, x - x_0),$$

then the graph of $y = f_L(x)$ is simply the tangent line to the curve at $(x_0, f(x_0))$ (see Figure 3). The symbol f_L represents the *linear part* of f (at x_0).

Note that if $f = j$, then

$$
\begin{aligned}
j_L(x) &= j(x_0) + j'(x_0)(x - x_0) \\
&= x_0 + x - x_0 \quad \text{(since } j'(x_0) = 1) \\
&= x \\
&= j(x)
\end{aligned}
$$

(see Figure 4).

We are still interested in the Leibniz notation. Sometimes one uses two names for a function: y and f. When this is done the symbol "y" may be doing double duty: $y = f(x)$ is the value of f at x, and also y is the function. Thus, when this is done, the following equations amount to a rewriting of some we have just introduced:

$$y = f(x)$$

$$\Delta y = f(x + \Delta x) - f(x)$$

$$dy = df(x, \Delta x) = f'(x)\,\Delta x.$$

$$dx = dj(x, \Delta x) = \Delta x.$$

Now, if we divide the penultimate of these equations by the last, we have

$$\frac{dy}{dx} = f'(x), \tag{10}$$

where $\dfrac{dy}{dx}$ is the symbol introduced originally by Leibniz for "the derivative, with respect to x, of the function $y = f(x)$."

The symbol $\dfrac{d}{dx}$ is completely equivalent to the symbol D introduced in Chapter 2: it stands for the operation of taking the derivative of the function which stands to the right of it. Thus

$$Dx^2 = \frac{d}{dx} x^2 = 2x = f'(x),$$

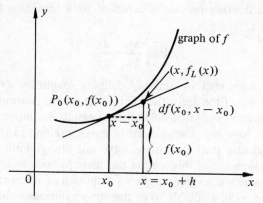

Figure 3

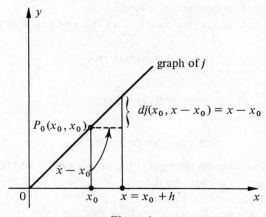

Figure 4

where $f: x \to x^2$. However, the form of the symbol, chosen deliberately by Leibniz, suggests that the derivative can be treated as a quotient (it is, to be sure, the *limit* of a quotient). For this reason we have thus far avoided using the symbol. But with the introduction of the differential function df (and its special case $dj = dx$), we see from the discussion leading up to Eq. (10) that it *is* possible to consider the value of the derivative $f'(x)$ as the quotient of the differentials dy and dx—or, to be exact, as the quotient of the values of these *differential functions*:

$$dy = df(x, h) = f'(x)h$$

$$dx = dx(x, h) = h.$$

We call attention to the cleverness of the Leibniz notation. By definition the derivative involves the limit of a quotient, which Leibniz wrote as $\dfrac{\Delta y}{\Delta x}$. Then, symbolically the limiting process is achieved by a transition from the Greek to the Latin letter:

$$\lim_{\Delta x \to 0} \frac{\Delta y}{\Delta x} = \frac{dy}{dx}.$$

The process is completed by suitably defining quantities dy and dx whose quotient is the value of the derivative. This notation has enormous manipulative advantages; in fact, it would be difficult to overstate its importance. Nevertheless, differentials have not always been in good standing in the mathematical world, partly because their definitions have not always been given with precision. The development of this section has perhaps been lengthier than necessary, but its purpose was to give a rigorous definition of differential which would at the same time make available to us the almost immeasurable advantages of the Leibniz notation—to have, in other words, the best of both worlds.

We conclude this section with a few illustrations of the use of the differential in approximating the increment of a function.

Consider first the change in the area of a circle due to a change in the radius: we have

$$A = A(r) = \pi r^2,$$

so

$$A'(r) = 2\pi r,$$

and

$$\Delta A \approx dA(r, \Delta r) = 2\pi r \, \Delta r.$$

Note that the expression on the right is the product of Δr and the circumference of the original circle: it could be thought of as the area of the "rectangle" of width Δr and length $2\pi r$ (see Figure 5).

In this case it is a simple matter to check that the error in using the value of dA in place of ΔA is

$$\Delta A - dA = \pi(\Delta r)^2.$$

Frequently, the use of df as an approximation to Δf occurs with functions which are more easily evaluated at some points than at others. We illustrate this, and another point, with the square root function. If

$$f(x) = \sqrt{x} = x^{1/2},$$

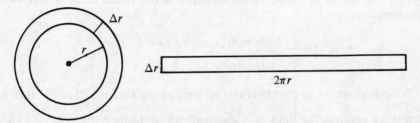

Figure 5

then

$$df(x, \Delta x) = \frac{1}{2} x^{-1/2} \Delta x = \frac{1}{2\sqrt{x}} \Delta x.$$

We might inquire how much the square root of a number changes when the number is changed by 1; using df as an approximation to Δf, we have

$$df(x, 1) = \frac{1}{2\sqrt{x}}.$$

Thus, if $x = 4$, $df(4, 1) = \frac{1}{4} = 0.25$. From this we can estimate $\sqrt{5}$ as $2 + 0.25 = 2.25$ (to the nearest thousandth, $\sqrt{5} = 2.236$). Or, if $x = 100$,

$$df(100, 1) = \tfrac{1}{20} = 0.05,$$

enabling us to estimate $\sqrt{101}$ as $10 + 0.05 = 10.05$ (to a few more places the correct value is 10.04988). We see from this that the quality of the approximation of df to Δf may vary with x (see Exercise 9).

Finally, we illustrate an application of the differential to errors. If we make an error of Δr in measuring the radius r of a circle, there will be induced an error ΔA in calculating the area A of the circle. As an approximation to ΔA we can use $dA = dA(r, \Delta r)$. Since

$$A = A(r) = \pi r^2,$$

$$dA = dA(r, \Delta r) = 2\pi r \, \Delta r.$$

In practice one does not usually know Δr, but can put an upper bound on the size of Δr—i.e., one might know that $|\Delta r| < 0.01$, say.

Frequently, the size of an error is less important than its size relative to the quantity measured. In general, if q is a function of x we define the relative error in x to be $\dfrac{\Delta x}{x}$, and, using the approximation dq,

$$\text{relative error in } q = \frac{dq}{q}.$$

In the case of this example, using the value obtained above, $\dfrac{dA}{A} = 2\dfrac{\Delta r}{r}$, i.e., the relative error in the area is twice the relative error in measuring the radius.

EXERCISES

1. Let $f(x) = x^3$.

   (a) Find $df(x, h)$.

   (b) Find $\Delta f(x, h)$. Can you interpret geometrically the terms in Δf?

   (c) Find $\Delta f - df$ and thus identify, for this case, $\eta(h)$ [see Eq. (1)].

2. For each of the following functions find $df(x, h)$:

(a) $f(x) = 2x - x^2$.

(b) $f(x) = \dfrac{1}{x}$.

(c) $f(x) = \sin x$.

(d) $f(x) = \dfrac{x}{1 + x^2}$.

(e) $f(x) = |x|$.

(f) $f(x) = x^3 - 2x^2 + 4x + 5$.

(g) $f(x) = \displaystyle\int_0^x \dfrac{2t}{t^2 + 4}\, dt$.

(h) $f(x) = [x]$. Give the domain of df.

(i) $f(x) = x^{1/3}$. What is the domain of df?

3. Show that the length of the segment $\overline{P_1 T}$ in Figure 1 is $|f'(x_0)h|$.

4. Draw figures analogous to Figure 1 for the following cases. In each case show Δf, df, and ηh.

(a) Curve similar to that in Figure 1, but $h < 0$.

(b) Curve for which $f'(x) > 0$, but for which the tangent lies above the curve; $h > 0$.

(c) Curve for which $f'(x) < 0$, tangent lies below the curve; take $h < 0$.

5. (a) Approximate the change in $\sin x$ when x changes $1°$. $\left[Hint: \ 1° = \dfrac{\pi}{180}. \right]$

(b) Find an approximate value for $\sin 31°$.

6. (a) Find an approximation to the change in $\sqrt[3]{x}$ when x changes by 1.

(b) Find, approximately, $\sqrt[3]{9}$, $\sqrt[3]{65}$, and $\sqrt[3]{1001}$.

(c) Use tables to compare the quality of each of these approximations.

7. Let $f(x) = mx + b$.

(a) Find $\Delta f(x, h)$.   (b) Find $df(x, h)$.

8. See Exercise 7. Consider a function f, a number $h \neq 0$.

(a) Is it possible that $\exists x_0$ such that $\Delta f(x_0, h) = df(x_0 h)$? If so, can you make a sketch?

(b) Suppose that for some x_0 and for every h in some deleted nbd. of 0

$$\Delta f(x_0, h) = df(x_0, h).$$

What can be said about f in a nbd. of x_0?

9. Let $f(x) = \dfrac{x}{1 - x}$, $0 \leq x < 1$.

(a) Find $df(x, h)$.   (b) Find $df(0.1, 0.1)$ and $df(0.8, 0.1)$.   (c) Find $\Delta f(x, h)$.

(d) Show that $\Delta f - df = \dfrac{h}{1 - x - h}\, df$. Thus show that at $(0.1, 0.1)$, $\Delta f - df = \tfrac{1}{8} df$; whereas at $(0.8, 0.1)$, $\Delta f - df = df$.

10. Show that the relative error in calculating the volume of a sphere by measuring the radius and then using the usual formula is three times the relative error in the radius.

11. In the course of an experiment it is necessary to find the square root of a number x_0 which is read from a meter. Show that the relative error in the square root is one-half the relative error in x_0.

12. Let $f(x) = x^m$. Show that the relative error in f is m times the relative error in x.

13. A definition. Let f and g be defined in a deleted nbd. of x_0 and let $g(x) \neq 0$ in this nbd. Then f is of lower order than g at x_0, or, in symbols

$$f = o(g) \Leftrightarrow \lim_{x \to x_0} \frac{f(x)}{g(x)} = 0.$$

The notation "$f = o(g)$" is usually read "f is little o of g."

For example, if $f(x) = x^3$, $g(x) = x^2$, $x_0 = 0$, then $f = o(g)$ at 0, since

$$\lim_{x \to 0} \frac{f(x)}{g(x)} = \lim_{x \to 0} x = 0.$$

Now let x_0 be fixed and consider $\Delta f(x_0, h)$ and $df(x_0, h)$ as functions of h. Show that

$$\Delta f - df = o(h), \qquad \text{as } h \to 0;$$

or, more exactly,

$$\Delta f - df = o(j), \qquad \text{as } h \to 0.$$

4.3 The Chain Rule and Implicit Differentiation

In Section 2.4 we introduced the important theorem, known as the chain rule, for the differentiation of composite functions. However, the proof given there, although reasonably natural, has a flaw, as we pointed out at the time. We now give a less natural but correct proof. The assertion is as follows.

Theorem 2.7. (*The Chain Rule*). *Suppose f and g are functions such that $F = f \circ g$ is defined at x_0: $F(x_0) = f(g(x_0))$. Suppose also that $f'(g(x_0))$ and $g'(x_0)$ exist. Then $F'(x_0)$ exists and*

$$F'(x_0) = (f \circ g)'(x_0) = f'(g(x_0))g'(x_0).$$

Proof. We begin (as we did in Chapter 2) with the definition:

$$F'(x_0) = \lim_{h \to 0} \frac{F(x_0 + h) - F(x_0)}{h}$$

$$= \lim_{h \to 0} \frac{f(g(x_0 + h)) - f(g(x_0))}{h}.$$

Now we let
$$u_0 = g(x_0)$$
$$u_0 + k = g(x_0 + h).$$
It follows that $k = g(x_0 + h) - g(x_0)$. Then
$$F'(x_0) = \lim_{h \to 0} \frac{f(u_0 + k) - f(u_0)}{h}. \tag{11}$$

At this point in the previous proof we multiplied by $\dfrac{k}{k}$ ——, and this is precisely where there could be an error, for it might happen that $k = 0$. To get around this difficulty we use a sneaky trick: we define a function φ as follows

$$\varphi(k) = \begin{cases} \dfrac{f(u_0 + k) - f(u_0)}{k}, & \text{if } k \neq 0 \\ f'(u_0), & \text{if } k = 0. \end{cases}$$

Then we note two things:

(i) $\lim\limits_{k \to 0} \varphi(k) = f'(u_0)$,

and

(ii) $f(u_0 + k) - f(u_0) = k\varphi(k)$,

whether or not $k = 0$.

Now we return to Eq. (11), and use φ and observation (ii):

$$F'(x_0) = \lim_{h \to 0} \frac{k\varphi(k)}{h}$$

$$= \lim_{h \to 0} \varphi(k) \lim_{h \to 0} \frac{k}{h}$$

$$= \lim_{h \to 0} \varphi(k) \lim_{h \to 0} \frac{g(x_0 + h) - g(x_0)}{h} \quad \text{(by definition of } k\text{)}$$

$$= \lim_{k \to 0} \varphi(k) \lim_{h \to 0} \frac{g(x_0 + h) - g(x_0)}{h} \quad \text{(since } \lim_{h \to 0} k = 0\text{—see below)}$$

$$= f'(u_0)g'(x_0) \quad [\text{by (i)}]$$

$$= f'(g(x_0))g'(x_0), \quad [\text{since } u_0 = g(x_0)].$$

It remains to show that $\lim\limits_{h \to 0} k = 0$ and that this result justifies writing
$$\lim_{h \to 0} \varphi(k) = \lim_{k \to 0} \varphi(k).$$

For the first of these we recall that $k = g(x_0 + h) - g(x_0)$ and that g is continuous at x_0, since, by hypothesis, $g'(x_0)$ exists. Thus
$$\lim_{h \to 0} k = \lim_{h \to 0} [g(x_0 + h) - g(x_0)] = 0.$$

The second assertion follows from Theorem 3.12. For, by its definition φ is continuous at $k = 0$: $\lim\limits_{k \to 0} \varphi(k) = \varphi(0)$. Also, by the preceding remark, $\lim\limits_{h \to 0} k = \lim\limits_{h \to 0} k(h) = 0$. Thus, using Theorem 3.12, we have

$$\lim_{h \to 0} \varphi(k) = \lim_{h \to 0} \varphi(k(h)) = \varphi(0) = \lim_{k \to 0} \varphi(k). \quad \blacksquare$$

It is worth pointing out that this theorem about *derivatives* of composite functions rests upon a theorem (Theorem 3.12) about *limits* of composite functions.

The chain rule enables us to extend many of the differentiation theorems. Consider, for example, the assertion on page 90 giving some (as yet unproven) differentiation results:

$$D_x \sin x = \cos x,$$
$$D_x \cos x = -\sin x,$$
$$D_x \log x = \frac{1}{x}, x > 0,$$
$$D_x e^x = e^x.$$

If, now, we let u represent a differentiable function then the above statement can be generalized (for the log function we require that $u(x) > 0$):

$$D_x \sin u = \cos u D_x u$$
$$D_x \cos u = -\sin u D_x u,$$
$$D_x \log u = \frac{1}{u} D_x u,$$
$$D_x e^u = e^u D_x u.$$

Thus, if $f(x) = \sin\left(2x - \dfrac{\pi}{3}\right)$, then $u(x) = 2x - \dfrac{\pi}{3}$, $u'(x) = 2$ and

$$f'(x) = \cos\left(2x - \frac{\pi}{3}\right) \cdot 2 = 2\cos\left(2x - \frac{\pi}{3}\right).$$

Or, if $g(x) = e^{-x^2}$, then $u(x) = -x^2$, $u'(x) = -2x$, so

$$g'(x) = e^{-x^2}(-2x) = -2x\, e^{-x^2}.$$

The Leibniz notation for the derivative makes the chain rule especially transparent. We have

$$F = f \circ g,$$

i.e.,

$$F(x) = f(g(x)) = f(z), \qquad \text{where } z = g(x).$$

By the chain rule,

$$\frac{dF}{dx} = F'(x) = f'(z)g'(x) = \frac{df}{dz} \cdot \frac{dz}{dx}.$$

In the last expression we are letting z do double duty in a way mentioned before. In fact, if we push this sort of thing one step further, we get the following very suggestive formulation: let

$$\left. \begin{array}{l} y = f(z) \\ z = g(x) \end{array} \right\} \text{ so that } y = f(g(x));$$

then

$$\frac{dy}{dx} = \frac{dy}{dz} \cdot \frac{dz}{dx}. \tag{12}$$

As we say, (12) is very suggestive, but it is also inaccurate; if we identify y and f, then y should not be used for the composite function F, for, in general, f and F are quite different functions. The statement of the chain rule in Theorem 2.7 is certainly more cumbersome than that of Eq. (12), but the earlier one is more explicit, as well as being completely accurate.

By means of the chain rule, and an assumption, we can obtain derivatives of functions defined implicitly by a relation of some sort.

Example 1. Consider the equation of a circle of radius a, center at the origin:

$$x^2 + y^2 - a^2 = 0. \tag{13}$$

If we *assume* there exists a differentiable function f, defined on some domain X, such that the functional values, when substituted for y in (13), make the left side of (13) equal 0; i.e., if we assume there exists a differentiable f such that

$$x^2 + (f(x))^2 - a^2 = 0, \tag{14}$$

then we can use the chain rule to find f'. For, differentiating (14), we obtain

$$2x + 2f(x)f'(x) = 0,$$

and, excluding any x for which $f(x) = 0$, we find

$$f'(x) = \frac{-x}{f(x)}.$$

Now it happens that in the present case it is an easy matter to express the upper half, say, of the circle as the graph of the function f, where

$$f(x) = \sqrt{a^2 - x^2} = (a^2 - x^2)^{1/2}, \qquad x \in [-a, a].$$

From this expression, and by means of the chain rule we can find an explicit formula for $f'(x)$:

$$f'(x) = \frac{1}{2}(a^2 - x^2)^{-1/2}(-2x) = \frac{-x}{\sqrt{a^2 - x^2}} \left(= \frac{-x}{f(x)} \right), \qquad x \in (-a, a).$$

(A similar result can easily be obtained for the function g, the graph of which is the lower half of the circle, $g(x) = -\sqrt{a^2 - x^2}$.)

However, frequently the relation which may define a function (or functions) implicitly is too complicated to permit the easy explicit solution obtainable in the preceding illustration. But, by assuming that the relation defines a differentiable function f and by using Theorem 2.7, we can find an expression for f'.

Example 2. Consider the relation

$$x^3 + y^3 - 3xy = 0$$

We assume there does exist a differentiable function f, defined on some domain, such that

$$x^3 + (f(x))^3 - 3xf(x) = 0.$$

We now differentiate this expression, using the chain rule and the product theorem:

$$3x^2 + 3(f(x))^2 f'(x) - 3[xf'(x) + f(x)] = 0.$$

The rest is elementary algebra:

$$[(f(x))^2 - x]f'(x) = f(x) - x^2,$$

or, for those x such that $(f(x))^2 \neq x$,

$$f'(x) = \frac{f(x) - x^2}{(f(x))^2 - x}.$$

It *is* possible to solve the original relation to find an explicit formula for f, but the task is a tedious one.

The assumption about the existence of a differentiable function f is an essential one. If we consider the relation

$$x^2 + y^2 + 4 = 0, \tag{15}$$

similar to the one used in (13), we can find, as before, that

$$f'(x) = \frac{-x}{f(x)}.$$

However, it is easy to see that in this case no function f with values which satisfy (15) can exist.

The study of conditions which assure the existence of a differentiable f with values which satisfy a relation such as (13) is usually made in works on advanced calculus.

EXERCISES

1. Find derivatives of each of the following functions by two methods and check that the results agree.

   (a) $f(x) = (1 - 3x^2)^2$.   (b) $f(x) = \dfrac{1}{(4x^3 + 1)^2}$.   (c) $f(x) = (3x^2 + 2x - 7)^3$.

2. Find derivatives of the following functions:

   (a) $f(x) = \sqrt{2x - 1}$

   (b) $f(x) = (x^2 + 1)^{3/2}$

   (c) $f(x) = \sin x^2$

   (d) $f(x) = \sin^2 x$

   (e) $f(x) = \sqrt{\dfrac{1 + x}{1 - x}}$

   (f) $f(x) = \dfrac{\sqrt{x^2 - 1}}{x + 3}$

   (g) $f(x) = \sqrt{1 - x^2}(4 + x^2)^{1/3}$

   (h) $f(x) = \dfrac{e^{ax} + e^{-ax}}{2}$

   (i) $f(x) = \dfrac{x}{\sqrt{x - 4}}$

   (j) $f(x) = 5\sqrt{(1 - x^2)^7} - 7\sqrt{(1 - x^2)^5}$

   (k) $f(x) = \frac{1}{3}\sqrt{(a^2 - x^2)^3} - a^2\sqrt{a^2 - x^2}$.

3. Note that the formula for the following function f can be written in several equivalent forms. Use each form to find f':

$$f(x) = \sqrt{\frac{1 - x^2}{1 + x^2}} = \frac{\sqrt{1 - x^2}}{\sqrt{1 + x^2}} = (1 - x^2)^{1/2}(1 + x^2)^{-1/2}.$$

4. Find f' for each of the following functions f.

   (a) $f(x) = (x^2 - x - 12)^4$
   (b) $f(x) = (x - 4)^4(x + 3)^4$

   (c) $f(x) = \dfrac{x}{\sqrt{x^2 + 4}} + \dfrac{\sqrt{x^2 + 4}}{x}$

   (d) $f(x) = \frac{1}{3}\sqrt{x^2 - 9} + 9\sqrt{x^2 - 9}$
   (e) $f(x) = (\frac{1}{5}x^2 - \frac{2}{15}a^2)\sqrt{(a^2 + x^2)^3}$

   (f) $f(x) = \dfrac{1}{b^2}\left[\dfrac{a}{2(a + bx)^2} - \dfrac{1}{a + bx}\right]$

   (g) $f(x) = \dfrac{\sin x}{x}$

   (i) $f(x) = \dfrac{\sin(x^2 + 1)}{x^2 + 1}$.

5. Assume that each of the following equations $F(x, y) = 0$ defines at least one differentiable function y such that in some domain $F(x, y(x)) = 0$. In each case find y'.

   (a) $x^2 - y^2 - 1 = 0$.   (b) $2x^2 - 3xy + y^2 - 4 = 0$.
   (c) $x^2y + 3xy - 4y^2 + 1 = 0$.   (d) $3x^2 - 4xy + y^3 = 0$.

6. With the chain rule we are in a position to prove that $Dx^n = nx^{n-1}$ is valid for rational n (recall that the proof in Chapter 2 applied only to integral n). Let

$f(x) = x^n$, $n = \dfrac{p}{q}$, where p and q are integers and $q > 0$. Then

$$f(x) = x^{p/q}$$

or

$$(f(x))^q = x^p.$$

Now differentiate both sides, using Theorem 3 on the left side, and then solve for $f'(x)$. You should obtain

$$f'(x) = \frac{p}{q} x^{\frac{p}{q}-1} = nx^{n-1}.$$

4.4 The Mean Value Theorem and Related Topics

We turn now to a few theoretical results of far-reaching consequences. In fact, we already found it necessary to introduce some of these propositions in Chapter 2.

We begin by proving Theorem 2.8 which was stated without proof on page 106.

Theorem 2.8. *Let f be a function whose domain includes the interval (a, b). Then*

$$\left.\begin{array}{l} f' \text{ exists on } (a, b) \\ x_0 \in (a, b) \\ f \text{ has relative maximum} \\ \text{ or minimum at } x_0 \end{array}\right\} \Rightarrow f'(x_0) = 0.$$

Proof. We prove the assertion involving a relative maximum—that for relative minimum is similar and will be left as an exercise. To say f has a relative maximum at x_0 means there exists $N(x_0)$ such that

$$x \in N(x_0) \Rightarrow f(x) \le f(x_0).$$

We choose h small enough so that $x_0 + h \in N(x_0)$. However, h may be either positive or negative; we consider both cases.

(i) $h > 0 \Rightarrow \dfrac{f(x_0 + h) - f(x_0)}{h} \le 0 \Rightarrow \lim\limits_{h \to 0^+} \dfrac{f(x_0 + h) - f(x_0)}{h} \le 0.$

(ii) $h < 0 \Rightarrow \dfrac{f(x_0 + h) - f(x_0)}{h} \ge 0 \Rightarrow \lim\limits_{h \to 0^-} \dfrac{f(x_0 + h) - f(x_0)}{h} \ge 0.$

But $f'(x_0)$ exists, by hypothesis. Thus the one-sided limits must not only exist but be equal, their common value being $f'(x_0)$. We conclude that $f'(x_0) = 0$. ∎

A review of the proof of Theorem 2.8 shows that we have used the existence of f' only at x_0. Taking this into account, we can state the following slightly stronger variation.

Theorem 2. *Let f be defined on (a, b). Then*

$$\left.\begin{array}{l} x_0 \in (a, b) \\ f \text{ has relative maximum} \\ \text{or minimum at } x_0 \end{array}\right\} \Rightarrow \left\{\begin{array}{l} \text{either } f'(x_0) = 0 \\ \text{or } f'(x_0) \text{ does not exist.} \end{array}\right.$$

Figure 6 illustrates several possibilities.

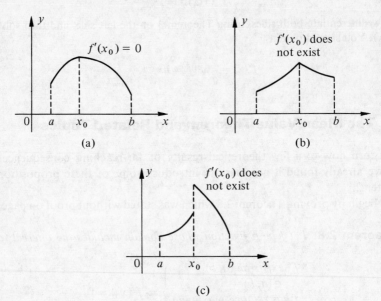

(a)

(b)

(c)

Figure 6

Our next theorem, geometrically obvious, is a consequence of Theorem 2.8.

Theorem 3. (*Rolle's Theorem*)

$$\left.\begin{array}{l} f \text{ continuous on } [a, b] \\ f' \text{ exists on } (a, b) \\ f(a) = f(b) \end{array}\right\} \Rightarrow \exists x_0 \in (a, b) \text{ such that } f'(x_0) = 0.$$

In Figure 7 we illustrate several of the possibilities. In Figure 7b the common value of $f(a)$ and $f(b)$ is shown as 0; frequently, this is included as part of the hypothesis of Rolle's Theorem, but this is not necessary.

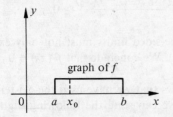

Figure 7

Proof of Theorem 3. Suppose we let $f(a) = f(b) = y_0$. The following three cases then exhaust all possibilities.

(i) $\forall x \in (a, b) \Rightarrow f(x) = y_0$ (Figure 7a). This simply says that f is constant on $[a, b]$; in this case f' is zero on (a, b) and x_0 can be taken as *any* point of (a, b).

(ii) $f(x) > y_0$ for some x on (a, b). In this case, the maximum value of f on $[a, b]$—recall that f continuous on $[a, b] \Rightarrow f$ *has* a maximum on $[a, b]$—must be greater than y_0 and so must be assumed at an *interior* point $x_0 \in (a, b)$. This absolute maximum will be, of course, a relative maximum, so Theorem 2.8 can be applied: $f'(x_0) = 0$.

(iii) $f(x) < y_0$ for some x on (a, b). This case is similar to that in (ii), except that it assures that f takes on its minimum value at an interior point $x_0 \in (a, b)$. Again, by Theorem 2.8, we have $f'(x_0) = 0$.

Note, by the way, that (ii) and (iii) are not mutually exclusive; should both cases occur it simply means there are several possible choices for x_0 (see Figure 8). ∎

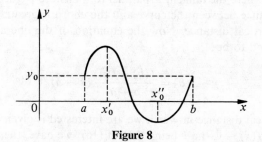

Figure 8

The next theorem, the main result of this section, is a fairly simple extension of Rolle's Theorem. It also has an obvious geometric interpretation. Roughly stated it is this: if a curve is continuous on an interval, and has a tangent at every interior point of the interval, then the tangent line at at least one interior point must be parallel to the chord joining the endpoints of the curve (see Figure 9).

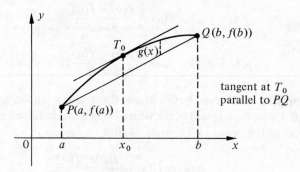

Figure 9

From another point of view, the Mean (or average) Value Theorem says that under suitable conditions the average rate of change of the function over an interval must be equal to the instantaneous rate at some point within the interval (if an automobile has an average speed of 70 mph on a 3-hr trip, then at at least one instant during the trip the speedometer had to read 70 mph).

A correct analytic statement is as follows.

Theorem 4. (*The Mean Value Theorem*)

$$\left.\begin{array}{r} f \text{ continuous on } [a, b] \\ f' \text{ exists on } (a, b) \end{array}\right\} \Rightarrow \left\{\begin{array}{l} \exists x_0 \in (a, b) \text{ such that} \\ f'(x_0) = \dfrac{f(b) - f(a)}{b - a}. \end{array}\right.$$

Proof. This theorem is one in which a careful study of the geometric interpretation rather quickly suggests a correct method for a rigorous proof. Note that, in Figure 9, as one considers the tangent line at different points on the curve, the place where the tangent is parallel to the chord PQ seems to be where the vertical distance between the curve and the chord is greatest. This suggests studying this vertical distance. Now the equation of the line along which PQ lies is easily found to be

$$y - f(a) = \frac{f(b) - f(a)}{b - a}(x - a). \tag{16}$$

Thus the vertical distance in which we are interested is given by the function g, where $g(x) = f(x) - y$, the y being that of (16); we have, then,

$$g(x) = f(x) - f(a) - \frac{f(b) - f(a)}{b - a}(x - a).$$

It is a simple matter to check that g satisfies all the hypotheses of Rolle's Theorem: as a sum of a continuous function and a linear function, g is continuous on $[a, b]$; and, as the sum of a differentiable function and a linear function, g is differentiable on (a, b). Also

$$g(a) = f(a) - f(a) - \frac{f(b) - f(a)}{b - a}(a - a) = 0$$

$$g(b) = f(b) - f(a) - \frac{f(b) - f(a)}{b - a}(b - a) = 0.$$

Thus, applying Theorem 3, we know there exists an $x_0 \in (a, b)$ such that $g'(x_0) = 0$. (Note that x_0 will occur where g has a maximum or minimum value—see the end of the proof of Theorem 3). But

$$g'(x) = f'(x) - \frac{f(b) - f(a)}{b - a};$$

consequently $g'(x_0) = 0$ gives

$$f'(x_0) = \frac{f(b) - f(a)}{b - a}. \quad \blacksquare$$

We remark that for a configuration such as in Figure 9 $g(x) \geq 0$ for $x \in [a, b]$. This, of course, need not be the case; in fact, g may be both positive and negative on $[a, b]$. This would simply mean that several possibilities exist for the choice of x_0 (see Figure 10 and the last sentence in the proof of Theorem 3).

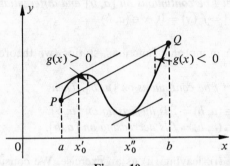

Figure 10

In some of the applications of Theorem 4 it turns out to be convenient to have the conclusion in a slightly different form from that given in the preceding statement. We list a few of these variations with a suggestion of how to obtain the variation:

$$f(b) = f(a) + f'(x_0)(b - a), \qquad x_0 \in (a, b): \tag{17}$$

$$f(x) = f(a) + f'(x_0)(x - a), \qquad x_0 \in (a, x) \quad \text{(replace } b \text{ by } x\text{)}; \tag{18}$$

$$f(a + h) = f(a) + f'(a + \theta h)h, \qquad 0 < \theta < 1 \tag{19}$$

(write $b = a + h$; then $a < x_0 < b$ can be written as $x_0 = a + \theta h$ with $0 < \theta < 1$).

Each of these forms expresses the value of f at the *right* end point of the interval in terms of its value at the *left* end, the length of the interval, and the value of the derivative at an interior point of the interval. We shall find later that by strengthening the hypotheses we can improve upon this sort of statement.

As applications of the Mean Value Theorem we turn now to consideration of Propositions 1 and 2 of Section 2.6; these were statements about the relation between derivatives and constant and monotonic functions.

Theorem 5. *Let f be defined on $[a, b]$. Then*

$$\left. \begin{array}{l} f \text{ continuous on } [a, b] \\ f'(x) = 0, \; x \in (a, b) \end{array} \right\} \Rightarrow f \text{ is constant on } [a, b].$$

Proof. Let $x \in (a, b]$. We apply the Mean Value Theorem to the interval $[a, x]$:

$$f(x) = f(a) + (x - a)f'(x_0), \qquad x_0 \in (a, x)$$
$$= f(a), \text{ since } f'(x_0) = 0.$$

Thus for every $x \in (a, b]$, $f(x) = f(a)$. ∎

Since the converse of Theorem 5 has already been proven (Theorem 2.1), we can assert the following.

Theorem 6. *Let f be continuous on* $[a, b]$ *and differentiable on* (a, b). *Then f is constant on* $[a, b] \Leftrightarrow f'(x) = 0$, $x \in (a, b)$.

We now consider monotonic functions, stating two theorems in one.

Theorem 7. *Let f be continuous on* $[a, b]$. *Then*

(i) $f'(x) > 0$, $x \in (a, b) \Rightarrow f$ *is increasing on* $[a, b]$.
(ii) $f'(x) < 0$, $x \in (a, b) \Rightarrow f$ *is decreasing on* $[a, b]$.

Proof. We prove (i), leaving (ii) as an exercise. We consider $x_1, x_2 \in [a, b]$, where $x_1 < x_2$, and apply the Mean Value Theorem to $[x_1, x_2]$:

$$f(x_2) = f(x_1) + f'(x_0)(x_2 - x_1), \qquad x_0 \in (x_1, x_2).$$

Now $f'(x_0) > 0$ and $x_2 - x_1 > 0$, so $f(x_2) > f(x_1)$. Since x_1 and x_2 were arbitrary points of $[a, b]$, subject to the condition that $x_1 < x_2$, we conclude that f is increasing. ∎

As a partial converse to Theorem 7 we have the following.

Theorem 8. *Let f be defined on* $[a, b]$ *and let f' exist on* (a, b). *Then*

(i) f *increasing on* $[a, b] \Rightarrow f'(x) \geq 0$, $x \in (a, b)$.
(ii) f *decreasing on* $[a, b] \Rightarrow f'(x) \leq 0$, $x \in (a, b)$.

Proof. Again we prove only (i), leaving the proof of (ii) as an exercise. We consider an arbitrary $x_0 \in (a, b)$.

(a) Suppose $h > 0$; then $x_0 < x_0 + h$ and $f(x_0) < f(x_0 + h)$. Thus

$$\frac{f(x_0 + h) - f(x_0)}{h} > 0,$$

so

$$\lim_{h \to 0^+} \frac{f(x_0 + h) - f(x_0)}{h} \geq 0.$$

(b) If $h < 0$, then $x_0 + h < x_0$ and $f(x_0 + h) < f(x_0)$. Thus

$$\frac{f(x_0 + h) - f(x_0)}{h} > 0,$$

and

$$\lim_{h \to 0^-} \frac{f(x_0 + h) - f(x_0)}{h} \geq 0.$$

Since $f'(x_0)$ exists, the one-sided limits in (a) and (b) must both exist and be equal to $f'(x_0)$. Thus $f'(x_0) \geq 0$. ∎

The function $f(x) = x^3$ on $[-1, 1]$ shows that we must retain the equal sign in Theorem 8, for f is increasing on this interval and $f'(0) = 0$.

E X E R C I S E S

1. Find the x_0 guaranteed by the Mean Value Theorem for each of the following functions and intervals.

   (a) $f(x) = \sqrt{x}$, $[0, 1]$.   (b) $f(x) = \sqrt{x}$, $[1, 4]$.   (c) $f(x) = x^3 - x$, $[-2, 2]$.
   (d) $f(x) = x^2 - 4x$, $[0, 2]$.   (e) $f(x) = x^2 - 4x$, $[0, 5]$.

2. Does the Mean Value Theorem hold for $f : x \to x^{2/3}$ on $[-1, 1]$? Explain.

3. Is the continuity of f essential as a hypothesis in Theorem 6?

4. Is the following assertion true?

   $$f \text{ increasing on } [a, b] \Rightarrow f'(x) \geq 0, \qquad x \in (a, b).$$

   If so, prove it; if not, find a counterexample.

5. Prove the assertion about the relative minimum of x_0 in Theorem 2.8.

6. Prove part (ii) of Theorem 7.

7. Prove part (ii) of Theorem 8.

4.5 The Extended Mean Value Theorem

The Mean Value Theorem (Theorem 4), which is itself an extension of Rolle's Theorem has a further extension, frequently called Cauchy's Theorem, involving two functions.

Theorem 9. *(Cauchy's Theorem)*

$$\left.\begin{array}{l} f \text{ continuous on } [a, b] \\ g \text{ continuous on } [a, b] \\ f' \text{ exists on } (a, b) \\ g' \text{ exists on } (a, b) \\ g'(t) \neq 0, \, t \in (a, b) \end{array}\right\} \Rightarrow \left\{\begin{array}{l} \exists t_0 \in (a, b) \text{ such that} \\ \dfrac{f'(t_0)}{g'(t_0)} = \dfrac{f(b) - f(a)}{g(b) - g(a)}. \end{array}\right.$$

Note that a separate application of Theorem 4 to both f and g would enable us to obtain t_1 and $t_2 \in (a, b)$ such that

$$\frac{f'(t_1)}{g'(t_2)} = \frac{f(b) - f(a)}{g(b) - g(a)};$$

however, in general, the t_1 and t_2 obtained in this way would be different. The present theorem guarantees the existence of a single number t_0 at which we evaluate both f' and g'.

The proof of Cauchy's Theorem can be given very quickly by producing a function φ which satisfies the hypotheses of Rolle's Theorem—by using, in other words, the same technique used in proving Theorem 4. We digress briefly, before turning to the proof, to show the source of the crucial function φ. The fact is that Cauchy's Theorem has a geometric interpretation similar to that of the Mean Value Theorem. Suppose the functions g and f represent, respectively, the abscissa and ordinate of a point in the plane:

$$\left.\begin{array}{l} x = g(t) \\ y = f(t) \end{array}\right\}, \qquad t \in [a, b].$$

One *could* think of t as time. In any case, the effect is that the functions g and f map the linear interval $a \leq t \leq b$ into the curve $\mathscr{C}$, a subset of the xy-plane (see Figure 11). Notice that this scheme enables one to assign a *direction* to a curve in a natural way: the positive direction along the curve is the direction determined by increasing t.

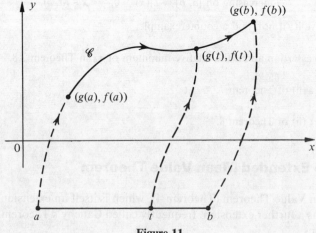

Figure 11

The geometric interpretation of the Cauchy Theorem says that at some *interior* point T of the curve $\mathscr{C}$ the tangent line is parallel to the chord determined by the endpoints of $\mathscr{C}$ (see Figure 12). For the slope m of the chord is

$$m = \frac{f(b) - f(a)}{g(b) - g(a)},\tag{20}$$

and if the portion of $\mathscr{C}$ between $t = a$ and $t = b$ is thought of as the graph of a function F, then the slope of the tangent at $(x_0, F(x_0))$, $x_0 = g(t_0)$, is

$$F'(x_0) = \frac{dy}{dx} = \frac{df(t_0, \Delta t)}{dg(t_0, \Delta t)} = \frac{f'(t_0)\,\Delta t}{g'(t_0)\,\Delta t} = \frac{f'(t_0)}{g'(t_0)}$$

(a rigorous proof appears in Chapter 11).

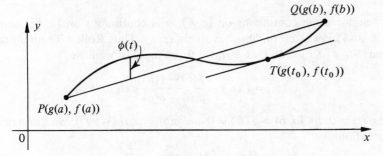

Figure 12

Now the chord PQ joining the endpoints of $\mathscr{C}$ has equation

$$y = f(a) + m(x - g(a)),\tag{21}$$

where m is given by (20). If we replace x in (21) by $g(t)$, then we have a representation in terms of t of the ordinate of that point on PQ which lies on the same vertical line as $(g(t), f(t))$ (see Figure 13). Thus

$$y(t) = f(a) + m(g(t) - g(a)).\tag{22}$$

The vertical distance φ between the curve and the chord is easily seen to be given by

$$\varphi(t) = f(t) - y(t)$$

or

$$\varphi(t) = f(t) - f(a) - \frac{f(b) - f(a)}{g(b) - g(a)}(g(t) - g(a)).\tag{23}$$

Proof of Theorem 9. We consider the function φ defined in (23). Note that

$$\varphi(a) = \varphi(b) = 0;$$

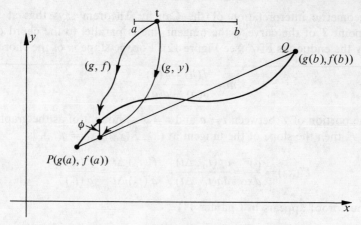

Figure 13

that, f and g being continuous on $[a, b]$, φ is continuous on $[a, b]$; and that since f' and g' exist on (a, b), φ' exists on (a, b). Thus Rolle's Theorem can be applied: $\exists t_0 \in (a, b)$ such that $\varphi'(t_0) = 0$. Using (23), we have

$$\varphi'(t_0) = f'(t_0) - \frac{f(b) - f(a)}{g(b) - g(a)} g'(t_0) = 0.$$

Since $g'(t) \neq 0$, $t \in (a, b) \Rightarrow g'(t_0) \neq 0$ *and* $g(b) \neq g(a)$ (Why?), we can write this last equation as

$$\frac{f(b) - f(a)}{g(b) - g(a)} = \frac{f'(t_0)}{g'(t_0)}, \qquad t_0 \in (a, b). \quad \blacksquare$$

Note that Theorem 9 reduces to Theorem 4 if $g(x) = x$, i.e., if $g = j$ on $[a, b]$.

Example 3. Let

$$\left.\begin{array}{l} f(t) = t^3 \\ g(t) = t^2 \end{array}\right\} \qquad t \in [0, 1].$$

Then $f(0) = g(0) = 0$, $f(1) = g(1) = 1$, so $m = 1$; also $f'(t) = 3t^2$, $g'(t) = 2t$. Thus

$$\frac{f'(t)}{g'(t)} = \frac{3t^2}{2t} = \frac{3}{2} t, \qquad t \neq 0,$$

and the value of t_0 guaranteed by Theorem 9 is $t_0 = \frac{2}{3}$.

Suppose, though, we use the interval $[-\frac{1}{2}, 1]$. We have $f(-\frac{1}{2}) = -\frac{1}{8}$, $g(-\frac{1}{2}) = \frac{1}{4}$, so

$$m = \frac{1 - (-\frac{1}{8})}{1 - \frac{1}{4}} = \frac{3}{2}.$$

As we still have $\dfrac{f'(t)}{g'(t)} = \dfrac{3}{2} t$, the value of t_0 would be in this case $t_0 = 1$, an *endpoint* of $[-\frac{1}{2}, 1]$. Why is this?

The geometrical ideas (representation of a curve by means of the *parameter t*) briefly introduced in this section are of considerable importance, and we shall give them further detailed study later.

EXERCISES

1. (a) Sketch the curve

$$\left. \begin{array}{l} y = f(t) = t^3 \\ x = g(t) = t^2 \end{array} \right\}$$

for $-\frac{1}{2} \le t \le 1$. This is the curve of the example at the end of the section.

(b) For the functions in (a) calculate the function $\varphi(t)$ and its derivative. Is there a value $t_0 \in (-\frac{1}{2}, 1)$ such that $\varphi'(t_0) = 0$? Why do things go wrong for the interval $[-\frac{1}{2}, 1]$?

2. In the proof of Theorem 9, the assertion is made that if $g'(t) \ne 0$ for $t \in (a, b)$ then $g(b) \ne g(a)$. Prove this.

3. Let $f(t) = \sin t$, $g(t) = \cos t$.

(a) If $x = g(t)$, $y = f(t)$, sketch the curve $\mathscr{C}$ for $0 \le t \le 2\pi$.

(b) Apply Theorem 9 for the interval $[0, \pi]$. Find the value of t_0 guaranteed by the theorem.

(c) Apply Theorem 9 for the interval $\left[-\frac{\pi}{2}, \frac{\pi}{6} \right]$. Find the value of t_0. Note that the conclusion of Theorem 9 holds even though $g'(0) = -\sin 0 = 0$, where $0 \in \left(-\frac{\pi}{2}, \frac{\pi}{6} \right)$.

(d) Apply Theorem 9 for the interval $\left[-\frac{\pi}{2}, \frac{\pi}{2} \right]$. Does anything go wrong? What and why?

4. Let

$$\left. \begin{array}{l} x = g(t) = \dfrac{1 - t^2}{1 + t^2} \\[2mm] y = f(t) = \dfrac{2t}{1 + t^2} \end{array} \right\} \qquad -\infty < t < \infty.$$

(a) Sketch the curve $\mathscr{C}$ determined by g and f. [*Hint.* One can always plot points.]

(b) Find the value of t_0 guaranteed by Theorem 9 for the interval $0 \le t \le 1$.

(c) Same as part (b) for the interval $[0, 2]$.

(d) Is there a value of t, say t_1, such that $g(t_1) = -1$, $f(t_1) = 0$? In other words, is $(-1, 0)$ on $\mathscr{C}$?

4.6 l'Hospital's Rule

Cauchy's Theorem enables us to prove several results which are extremely useful in evaluating limits. In order to cover all the different possibilities which arise we shall need several different theorems. Collectively these are, as the section heading implies, usually referred to as l'Hospital's Rule.

In truth, the full power and great utility of l'Hospital's Rule cannot be adequately appreciated until we have encountered the trigonometric, exponential, and logarithmic functions. We shall, however, gain some familiarity with it at this point, and return to the techniques at various times in subsequent chapters.

We now give the first of the assertions.

Theorem 10. $\left(l'Hospital's\ Rule,\ \dfrac{0}{0},\ Case\ 1\right)$. *Suppose f and g are functions such that $\lim\limits_{x \to a} f(x) = \lim\limits_{x \to a} g(x) = 0$, f' and g' exist in some $N^*(a)$, $g'(x) \neq 0$ for $x \in N^*(a)$. Then*

$$\lim_{x \to a} \frac{f(x)}{g(x)} = \lim_{x \to a} \frac{f'(x)}{g'(x)},$$

provided the limit on the right exists.

Proof.

(i) We begin by defining (or redefining, if necessary) $f(a) = g(a) = 0$. Then f and g will be continuous at a. If we take $x \in N^*(a)$, $x > a$, then we can apply the Cauchy Theorem (Theorem 9) to f and g on $[a, x]$. This guarantees $x_0 \in (a, x)$ such that

$$\frac{f(x) - f(a)}{g(x) - g(a)} = \frac{f'(x_0)}{g'(x_0)},$$

or, since $f(a) = g(a) = 0$,

$$\frac{f(x)}{g(x)} = \frac{f'(x_0)}{g'(x_0)}.$$

It follows, since $a < x_0 < x$, that if $\lim\limits_{x \to a} \dfrac{f'(x)}{g'(x)}$ exists,

$$\lim_{x \to a^+} \frac{f(x)}{g(x)} = \lim_{x \to a^+} \frac{f'(x)}{g'(x)}.$$

(ii) In a similar way, by taking $x < a$, $x \in N^*(a)$, we can show that

$$\lim_{x \to a^-} \frac{f(x)}{g(x)} = \lim_{x \to a^-} \frac{f'(x)}{g'(x)},$$

assuming $\lim\limits_{x \to a} \dfrac{f'(x)}{g'(x)}$ exists.

(iii) Combining (i) and (ii) gives the desired result, by means of Theorem 3.1. ∎

We consider a simple illustration.

Example 4. We find

$$\lim_{x \to 1} \frac{x^2 - 3x + 2}{x^2 - 1}.$$

It is easy to check that this is a $\frac{\text{``}0\text{''}}{0}$ type limit and that the hypotheses of Theorem 10 are all satisfied. Thus

$$\lim_{x \to 1} \frac{x^2 - 3x + 2}{x^2 - 1} = \lim_{x \to 1} \frac{2x - 3}{2x} = \frac{-1}{2}.$$

A warning! The use of Theorem 10 involves differentiating *separately* the numerator and denominator of the fraction. *Do not* differentiate as a quotient.

Sometimes the theorem must be applied more than once.

Example 5. Evaluate

$$\lim_{x \to 2} \frac{x^3 - 7x^2 + 16x - 12}{x^3 + x^2 - 16x + 20}.$$

Letting f and g be the polynomials in numerator and denominator, respectively, we verify that $f(2) = g(2) = 0$. Since f and g are polynomials, the conditions of Theorem 10 are clearly satisfied; we apply the rule:

$$\lim_{x \to 2} \frac{x^3 - 7x^2 + 16x - 12}{x^3 + x^2 - 16x + 20} = \lim_{x \to 2} \frac{3x^2 - 14x + 16}{3x^2 + 2x - 16} = \lim_{x \to 2} \frac{f'(x)}{g'(x)}.$$

But now we find that $f'(2) = g'(2) = 0$: the limit on the right does not exist. Rather than cause defeat, however, this observation simply allows us to apply the theorem to $\lim\limits_{x \to 2} \frac{f'(x)}{g'(x)}$, which we now do.

$$\lim_{x \to 2} \frac{f'(x)}{g'(x)} = \lim_{x \to 2} \frac{6x - 14}{6x + 2} = \frac{-2}{14} = \frac{-1}{7}.$$

If the last limit had again been a $\frac{0}{0}$ type we could, providing the other hypotheses were satisfied, again use Theorem 10.

The first extension of the basic rule asserts that it applies not only for finite a, but also as x gets big beyond all bounds.

Theorem 11. $\left(l'Hospital's\ Rule, \dfrac{0}{0}, Case\ 2\right)$. *Suppose* $\lim\limits_{x\to\infty} f(x) = \lim\limits_{x\to\infty} g(x) = 0$, f' *and* g' *exist in some* $N(\infty)$, *and* $g'(x) \neq 0$ *for* $x \in N(\infty)$. *Then*

$$\lim_{x\to\infty} \frac{f(x)}{g(x)} = \lim_{x\to\infty} \frac{f'(x)}{g'(x)},$$

provided the limit on the right exists. The conclusion also holds if ∞ *is replaced throughout with* $-\infty$.

Proof. Let $x = \dfrac{1}{t}$, so that $t = \dfrac{1}{x}$. Then $x \to \infty$ is equivalent to $t \to 0^+$, and

$$\lim_{x\to\infty} \frac{f(x)}{g(x)} = \lim_{t\to 0^+} \frac{f\left(\dfrac{1}{t}\right)}{g\left(\dfrac{1}{t}\right)} = \lim_{t\to 0^+} \frac{-\dfrac{1}{t^2}\, f'\left(\dfrac{1}{t}\right)}{-\dfrac{1}{t^2}\, g'\left(\dfrac{1}{t}\right)}$$

$$= \lim_{t\to 0^+} \frac{f'\left(\dfrac{1}{t}\right)}{g'\left(\dfrac{1}{t}\right)}$$

$$= \lim_{x\to\infty} \frac{f'(x)}{g'(x)}.$$

In this chain of equalities the transition from the second to the third expression is made by means of the chain rule and Theorem 10. ∎

Nontrivial illustrations of this theorem must wait until we have available the trigonometric, logarithmic, and exponential functions.

The final portion of l'Hospital's Rule which we take up is analogous to Theorem 10, except that it involves $\dfrac{``\infty"}{\infty}$. The proof of the following assertion is considerably more difficult than the demonstrations of the preceding theorems. We shall omit it here.

Theorem 12. $\left(l'Hospital's\ Rule, \dfrac{\infty}{\infty}\right)$. *Suppose* $\lim\limits_{x\to a} f(x) = \infty$, $\lim\limits_{x\to a} g(x) = \infty$, f' *and* g' *exist in some* $N^*(a)$, $g'(x) \neq 0$ *for* $x \in N^*(a)$, *and* $\lim\limits_{x\to a}\dfrac{f'(x)}{g'(x)} = L$. *Then*

$$\lim_{x\to a} \frac{f(x)}{g(x)} = L.$$

Theorem 12 remains valid, incidentally, if either—or both—of the ∞'s is replaced by $-\infty$. This follows from the fact that $\lim\limits_{x\to a} cF(x) = c \lim\limits_{x\to a} F(x)$. The result is also correct if a is replaced by ∞.

Example 6. Evaluate

$$\lim_{x \to \infty} \frac{x^2 - 3x + 2}{x^2 - 1}.$$

It is routine to check that the hypotheses of Theorem 12 are all satisfied. Thus

$$\lim_{x \to \infty} \frac{x^2 - 3x + 2}{x^2 - 1} = \lim_{x \to \infty} \frac{2x - 3}{2x} = \lim_{x \to \infty} \frac{2}{2} = 1.$$

As in Example 5 it was necessary to apply the rule twice, the second time to $\dfrac{f'(x)}{g'(x)}$, before arriving at a value for the limit.

Example 7. Evaluate

$$\lim_{x \to 0} \frac{\dfrac{1}{\sqrt{x}}}{\dfrac{1}{x^2}}.$$

Now it happens that this fits the pattern for application of Theorem 12. However, it would be both pointless and fruitless (try for yourself!) to use l'Hospital's Rule in the form of Theorem 12. Common sense suggests an algebraic simplification:

$$\lim_{x \to 0} \frac{\dfrac{1}{\sqrt{x}}}{\dfrac{1}{x^2}} = \lim_{x \to 0} \frac{x^2}{\sqrt{x}} = \lim_{x \to 0} x^{3/2} = 0.$$

If one encounters a limit of the type

$$\lim_{x \to a} [f(x)g(x)],$$

where $\lim_{x \to a} f(x) = 0$, $\lim_{x \to a} g(x) = \infty$ (a "$0 \cdot \infty$" type limit), use can be made of Theorems 10 or 12 by writing

$$\lim_{x \to a} [f(x)g(x)] = \lim_{x \to a} \frac{f(x)}{\dfrac{1}{g(x)}},$$

or

$$\lim_{x \to a} [f(x)g(x)] = \lim_{x \to a} \frac{g(x)}{\dfrac{1}{f(x)}}.$$

Whether the first or second of these is preferable depends upon the functions f and g.

Occasionally, too, a limit such as $\lim_{x \to a} [f(x) - g(x)]$, where $\lim_{x \to a} f(x) = \infty$, $\lim_{x \to a} g(x) = \infty$ occurs (this is referred to as an "$\infty - \infty$" type). It is generally possible to change the *form* of $f(x) - g(x)$ so that either Theorem 10 or Theorem 12 can be used. Meaningful examples will occur in Chapters 6 and 7.

EXERCISES

Evaluate the limits in numbers 1–20.

1. $\lim_{x \to -1} \dfrac{x^2 + 5x + 4}{x^2 - 4x - 5}$.

2. $\lim_{x \to 0} \dfrac{x^3 + 4x^2 - 5x}{x^3 - 2x}$.

3. $\lim_{x \to 1} \dfrac{4x^3 + 3x^2 - 8x + 1}{x^3 + 2x^2 + 3x - 6}$.

4. $\lim_{x \to \infty} \dfrac{4x^3 + 3x^2 - 8x + 1}{x^3 + 2x^2 + 3x - 6}$.

5. $\lim_{x \to -2} \dfrac{2x^2 + 3x - 2}{x^2 + 3x + 2}$.

6. $\lim_{x \to 2} \dfrac{x^2 + 3x - 10}{2x^2 - x - 6}$.

7. $\lim_{x \to 1} \dfrac{x^3 - 4x^2 - 2x + 5}{2x^3 + 3x^2 - 5}$.

8. $\lim_{x \to 1} \dfrac{x^3 - 6x^2 + 9x - 4}{3x^3 - 4x^2 - x + 2}$.

9. $\lim_{x \to 2} \dfrac{x^2 + 2x - 8}{x^2 - 9x + 14}$.

10. $\lim_{x \to -3} \dfrac{x^3 + 5x^2 + 3x - 9}{x^3 + 8x^2 + 21x + 18}$.

11. $\lim_{x \to \infty} \dfrac{x^3 - 4x^2 + 7x - 1}{2x^3 + 5x^2 - 8}$.

12. $\lim_{x \to \infty} \dfrac{x^3 - 7x^2 + 1}{x^4 + 3x^2 + 5}$.

13. $\lim_{x \to 0} \dfrac{\sqrt{x + 9} - 3}{x}$.

14. $\lim_{x \to 0} \dfrac{2 - \sqrt{x + 4}}{x}$.

15. $\lim_{x \to 1} \dfrac{x^3 - 7x + 6}{2x^3 - 3x^2 + 1}$.

16. $\lim_{x \to 1} \dfrac{x^3 - 5x + 4}{3x^3 + 2x^2 - x - 4}$.

17. $\lim_{x \to \infty} \dfrac{x^3 - 5x + 4}{3x^3 + 2x^2 - x - 4}$.

18. $\lim_{x \to 1} \dfrac{x^2 - 7x + 6}{x^2 - 4x - 3}$.

19. $\lim_{x \to 2} \dfrac{x^3 - 4x + 1}{x^2 - 4}$.

20. $\lim_{x \to 1} \dfrac{x^4 - 5x^3 + 9x^2 - 7x + 2}{x^4 - 6x^2 + 8x - 3}$.

Chapter 5 Applications of the Derivative

In Chapter 2 we showed how the derivative, as an abstract mathematical concept, arises as a result of careful consideration of various physical and geometrical problems. In this chapter we turn to a closer and more detailed look at some of these problems.

With regard to the balance between geometrical and physical problems, we remark that students frequently bring to the study of calculus a broader understanding of the background material essential to geometrical problems than that for physical problems. Consequently, it is easier to discuss the former type than the latter; however, we shall include as many physical problems as possible without going too far afield.

5.1 The Derivative as a Rate of Change

We begin by recalling that, whatever interpretation we give to the quantities involved, the derivative of a function, by its definition, provides a measure of the rate of change of the function with respect to the independent variable. There is a class of problems, mostly involving time, which can be solved very easily by techniques now available to us. We illustrate with a few examples.

Example 1. A spherical balloon is being inflated by pumping 20 cu ft of gas into it every second. How fast is the radius changing when it is 4 ft?

Solution. If we let r and V be, respectively, the radius and volume of the balloon, then we observe that both r and V are changing with time. In fact, we are given that

$$\frac{dV}{dt} = 20 \text{ cu ft/sec,}$$

and we are asked to find the value of $\dfrac{dr}{dt}$ when $r = 4$ ft (a convenient notation for this latter is $\dfrac{dr}{dt}\Big|_{r=4}$). Now, the fact that the balloon is spherical gives us a relation between V and r, valid for all meaningful t:

$$V = V(r) = \frac{4\pi}{3}\,r^3; \tag{1}$$

we also have that r is changing with t:

$$r = r(t). \tag{2}$$

As both the given and the required information involve rate of change with respect to time, it is natural to take derivatives in (1) with respect to time. By virtue of (2) this can be done using the chain rule:

$$\frac{dV}{dt} = \frac{dV}{dr} \cdot \frac{dr}{dt},$$

or

$$\frac{dV}{dt} = 4\pi r^2 \frac{dr}{dt}. \tag{3}$$

We can substitute the value of $\dfrac{dV}{dt}\,(=20)$ in (3) and obtain

$$\frac{dr}{dt} = \frac{20}{4\pi r^2},$$

which gives the rate of change of the radius r with respect to time for any meaningful value of r. In particular, we have

$$\frac{dr}{dt}\Big|_{r=4} = \frac{10}{2\pi(4)^2} = \frac{10}{32\pi} \approx 0.099 \text{ ft/sec.}$$

This solution tacitly assumes that the pressure remains constant within the balloon. A more realistic assumption might be that the pressure increases as the balloon becomes inflated. The effect of this will be that the 20 cu ft of gas pumped into the balloon every second, being under greater pressure once it is within the balloon, will in fact increase the volume of the sphere by less than 20 cu/ft. A simple model which takes this into account would be to let

$$\frac{dV}{dt} = 20 - cr, c > 0 \tag{4}$$

(recall that, by (2), r is a function of t). Then, using (4) in (3) enables us to write

$$\frac{dr}{dt} = \frac{20 - cr}{4\pi r^2}.$$

In practice one might have to estimate c experimentally.

Example 2. A ladder 25 ft long has one end against a vertical wall, the other end on the ground. The lower end is being moved away from the wall at the constant rate of 4 ft/sec.

(a) How fast is the top descending when the bottom is 7 ft from the wall?
(b) How far above the ground is the top of the ladder when it is descending at the rate of 8 ft/sec?

Solution. If we let x and y represent, respectively, the distances (in feet) from the bottom and top of the ladder to the foot of the wall, then the basic relation between x and y, *valid for any meaningful time t*, is

$$x^2 + y^2 = 25^2 \qquad (5)$$

(see Figure 1).

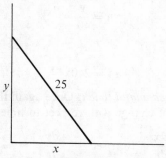

Figure 1

We observe that x and y are changing with time, and in fact we note that we are given $\dfrac{dx}{dt} = 4$ ft/sec and are asked to find in (a) the value of $\dfrac{dy}{dt}\bigg|_{x=7}$

As in Example 1, the obvious next step is to take derivatives in (5) with respect to t, this being possible because of the chain rule:

$$2x\frac{dx}{dt} + 2y\frac{dy}{dt} = 0. \qquad (6)$$

Since we are given $\dfrac{dx}{dt} = 4$ ft/sec, we can write (6) as

$$4x + y\frac{dy}{dt} = 0. \qquad (7)$$

To answer (a) we observe that when $x = 7$, $y = 24$ (from 5); thus

$$\frac{dy}{dt}\bigg|_{x=7} = \frac{-4x}{y} = \frac{-28}{24} \approx -1.17 \text{ ft/sec.}$$

To answer (b) we use in (7) the information that $\dfrac{dy}{dt} = -8$ ft/sec (why the minus sign?). Thus

$$4x - 8y = 0,$$

or $x = 2y$. Using this relation in (5) gives $y \approx 11.18$ ft.

Example 3. A spotlight is on the ground, 40 ft from a building and directed toward the building. A man 6 ft tall walks from the light toward the building at a speed of 10 ft/sec. How fast is the length of his shadow on the wall changing when the man is 20 ft from the building?

Solution. We let x be the distance the man is from the light and let y be the height of his shadow on the wall (see Figure 2). We can calculate in two ways the slope of the line from the light to the top of the man's head:

$$m = \frac{y}{40} = \frac{6}{x};$$

thus

$$y = 240x^{-1}, \tag{8}$$

a relation valid for any meaningful time t. Once again the information given and required involves rates of change with respect to time:

$$\frac{dx}{dt} = 10 \text{ ft/sec} \qquad \frac{dy}{dt}\bigg|_{x=20} = ?$$

Thus, using the chain rule we take the derivative of (8) with respect to t:

$$\frac{dy}{dt} = \frac{dy}{dx} \cdot \frac{dx}{dt},$$

or

$$\frac{dy}{dt} = 240(-1)x^{-2}\frac{dx}{dt}$$

$$= \frac{-2400}{x^2}, \qquad \text{since } \frac{dx}{dt} = 10 \text{ ft/sec.}$$

It is a simple matter now to find that

$$\frac{dy}{dt}\bigg|_{x=20} = \frac{-2400}{20^2} = -6 \text{ ft/sec;}$$

the negative answer indicates, of course, that the shadow is shortening.

At the risk of belaboring a fairly obvious point, we remark that the technique for handling the problems of the type illustrated is to obtain a relation between

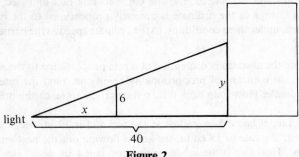

Figure 2

the changing quantities, a relation valid for all meaningful values of time, then differentiate this relation with respect to time, and finally substitute into the resulting expression particular numerical values so as to obtain the required information. In general, substitution of numerical values should be delayed to the final step: a common error is to substitute—too soon—an instantaneous value for a changing quantity.

E X E R C I S E S

1. The radius of a circular plate is increasing at the rate of 2 cm/sec. How fast is the area of the plate changing when the radius is 10 cm?

2. Suppose the radius of a circular plate is decreasing at a rate inversely proportional to the size of the radius, the units being chosen so that the constant of proportionality is one.

   (a) What can you say about the rate of change of the area of the plate?

   (b) If the radius was four units at the beginning of the process ($t = 0$), what is the meaningful time interval?

3. A ship, steaming at 13 knots (13 nautical mph, you landlubbers) leaves its anchorage A, travels east for three miles to a buoy B and then, at noon, heads north.

   (a) How fast is it steaming away from its anchorage at 1 pm?

   (b) How far is the ship from buoy B when the rate at which the ship is moving away from A exceeds 12 knots?

   (c) How far is the ship from B when the rate at which the ship is moving away from A exceeds $13 - \varepsilon$ knots?

   (d) Answer part (c) if $\varepsilon = \dfrac{1}{17}$ knots.

4. A particle is traveling along the curve $y = \sqrt{x}$. Its starting point (at time $t = 0$) is (64, 8).

(a) If the abscissa is decreasing at the constant rate of 2 units/sec, show that the rate of change of the ordinate is inversely proportional to the ordinate. What happens, under these conditions, to the ordinate speed as the particle approaches (0, 0)?

(b) Suppose the abscissa is decreasing at a rate proportional to the abscissa at any time t, the constant of proportionality being one. Find the rate of change of the ordinate. How long does it take the particle to reach the origin?

5. A conical funnel has a 5-in. radius at the top and is 12 in. deep. Water is being poured in at the rate of 18 cu in./sec and is flowing out the bottom at the rate of 8 cu in./sec. How fast is the liquid rising when it is 6 in. deep? (see Figure 3).

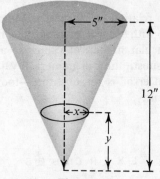

Figure 3

6. Little Benjamin is flying a kite. An accommodating wind keeps the kite at a constant height of 100 ft but moves it along horizontally at the rate of 20 ft/sec. How rapidly must Benjamin pay out the string when the kite is 400 ft away from him?

7. A man on a dock is pulling in a boat by the bow line. The man is pulling in the line, 12 ft above the water, at the rate of 3 ft/sec. How fast is the boat moving toward the dock when there are 20 ft of rope out?

8. A ship traveling north at 15 knots passes a whale which is heading east. By radar and some elementary calculations the whale's speed is determined to be 10 knots. Assuming that both whale and ship maintain the course and speed at the time of passing, find how fast they will be separating one hour later.

9. The equation describing the adiabatic expansion of air is $pv^{1.4} = c$, where p is pressure, v is volume, and c is a constant. At a certain instant the pressure is 50 lb/sq in. (psi) and the volume is 70 cu in., and is decreasing at the rate of 10 cu in./sec. Find the rate of change of the pressure at this instant.

10. When a certain type of sand is poured from a height, it forms a pile which is not only conical-shaped, but which is proportioned so that the radius of the base always equals one-half the height.

(a) If the sand is being poured at the rate of 9 cu ft/min, how fast is the height of the pile changing when the pile is 6 ft high?

(b) How fast is the base radius changing when the pile is 6 ft high?

11. A rod 15 in. long moves so that one end A stays on the x-axis and the other end B stays on the y-axis. Suppose A is moving away from the origin at the rate of 4 in./sec. Find, when A is 12 in. from the origin:

   (a) the rate at which B is moving toward the origin.

   (b) the rate of change of the area of the triangle OAB.

   (c) the rate of change of OM, where M is the midpoint of the rod.

5.2 Asymptotes

In this and the next few sections we turn our attention to geometric problems; in particular, we make use of the derivative to obtain information about the graph of a function. Recall that in Chapter 2 we began this discussion; we are now in a stronger position to develop useful techniques of curve sketching.

As it turns out, our major tool in this section will be the theory of limits rather than of derivatives. We will be concerned with detecting and locating—when they exist—asymptotes to a curve; such knowledge can be quite helpful in sketching the curve, as we shall see.

Roughly speaking, an asymptote is a line which gets arbitrarily close to the curve at points arbitrarily far from the origin (it follows, then, that curves like the circle and ellipse, which lie within bounded regions of the plane, cannot have asymptotes).

Suppose we look at a simple example before we consider the precise definition and some theorems. The function $f: x \to \dfrac{1}{x}$, $x \neq 0$, serves very well. It is fairly easy to see that arbitrarily large values of $|x|$ make $f(x) = \dfrac{1}{x}$ arbitrarily close to 0. Thus, the graph of f gets arbitrarily close to the x-axis at points with large abscissas. But we also notice that values of x close to 0 map into large values. Put geometrically, this says that close to the y-axis the graph is arbitrarily far from the x-axis. Thus both coordinate axes are asymptotes of the curve (see Figure 4). Note that $f'(x) = \dfrac{-1}{x^2} < 0$, $\forall x \neq 0$, and $\lim\limits_{x \to \pm\infty} f'(x) = 0$, $\lim\limits_{x \to 0} f'(x) = -\infty$: the tangent lines all have negative slopes, become nearly horizontal at points with large abscissas, and become nearly vertical at points with abscissas near zero. All this conforms with the sketch in Figure 4.

The graph of $y = \dfrac{1}{x}$ is a special case of a *hyperbola*; all hyperbolas have a pair of asymptotes, which, however, need not be perpendicular.

The general definition can be given as follows:

Definition 1.

(a) *The line $x = a$ is a **vertical asymptote** of the graph of $f \Leftrightarrow$ either* (i) $\lim\limits_{x \to a^-} f(x) = \pm\infty$ *or* (ii) $\lim\limits_{x \to a^+} f(x) = \pm\infty$. *(The " or " is used in the inclusive sense: $x = a$ is an asymptote of the graph if both* (i) *and* (ii) *hold.)*

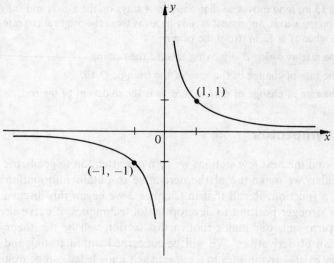

Figure 4

(b) *The line* $y = mx + b$ *is an **asymptote** of the graph of* $f \Leftrightarrow$ *either* (i) $\lim_{x \to -\infty} [f(x) - (mx + b)] = 0$ *or* (*inclusive*) (ii) $\lim_{x \to \infty} [f(x) - (mx + b)] = 0$.

Example 4. We find the asymptotes of the graph of $f : x \to x + \dfrac{1}{x}$. Since $\dfrac{1}{x}$ is small when x is large the essential part of the formula for f when x is large is the first term, suggesting that $y = x$ is an asymptote. Since $f(x) - x = \dfrac{1}{x}$, it is easily seen that part (b) of Definition 1 is satisfied. We can also see that $x > 0 \Rightarrow$ $f(x) > x$, whereas $x < 0 \Rightarrow f(x) < x$: in quadrant I the curve is above the asymptote; in quadrant III, below the asymptote,

By writing the formula for f as

$$f(x) = \frac{x^2 + 1}{x} \tag{9}$$

we can see that

$$\lim_{x \to 0^-} f(x) = -\infty, \quad \lim_{x \to 0^+} f(x) = \infty; \tag{10}$$

thus, by (a) of Definition 1, $x = 0$ is a vertical asymptote. The graph of f, a hyperbola, is shown in Figure 5.

Example 5. Consider $f(x) = \dfrac{x^2}{x^2 - 4} = \dfrac{x^2}{(x + 2)(x - 2)}$. From the second expression for f we see that when x is near ± 2 the numerator is near 4, whereas the denominator is near 0: put loosely

$$\lim_{x \to \pm 2} \frac{x^2}{(x + 2)(x - 2)} = \pm \infty.$$

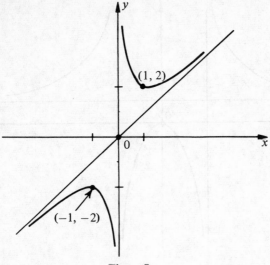

Figure 5

In other words, $x = -2$ and $x = 2$ are vertical asymptotes. Moreover, by writing, for $x \neq 0$,

$$f(x) = \frac{x^2}{x^2 - 4} = \frac{1}{1 - \dfrac{4}{x^2}}$$

we see that $\lim\limits_{x \to \pm\infty} f(x) = 1$; i.e., $y = 1$ is an asymptote. We can also obtain this fact by using Theorem 4.12, l'Hospital's Rule

$$\lim_{x \to \pm\infty} \frac{x^2}{x^2 - 4} = \lim_{x \to \pm\infty} \frac{2x}{2x} ;$$

clearly, $\lim\limits_{x \to \pm\infty} f(x) = 1$.) Since $f(0) = 0$, and since the graph is symmetric with respect to the y-axis, it is easy now to obtain a sketch as in Figure 6.

If we calculate f' for this example (as the student should do), we will find that $f'(0) = 0$, $x < 0$, $x \neq -2 \Rightarrow f'(x) > 0$, $x > 0$, $x \neq 2 \Rightarrow f'(x) < 0$. Interpret these statements geometrically.

It should be fairly apparent that $x = \pm 2$ are vertical asymptotes to the curve in Example 5 as a result of the form of the formula for f: a fraction whose denominator has zeros at $x = -2$ and $x = 2$. The following theorem, although not as sharp as it could be made, covers the cases usually encountered.

Theorem 1. *Let f be a function which is the ratio of two functions g_1 and g_2, both continuous at $a : f = \dfrac{g_1}{g_2}$. Suppose $g_1(a) \neq 0$, $g_2(a) = 0$, and the domain of f includes a deleted nbd. of a. Then $x = a$ is a vertical asymptote of the graph of f.*

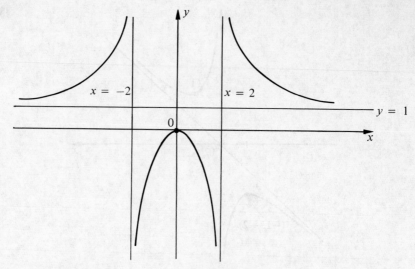

Figure 6

Proof. We give the essentials of the proof.

(1) $\left.\begin{array}{l} g_1 \text{ continuous at } a \\ g_1(a) \neq 0 \end{array}\right\} \Rightarrow \exists \left\{\begin{array}{l} \varepsilon > 0 \\ N_1(a) \end{array}\right\}$ such that $x \in N_1(a) \Rightarrow |g_1(x)| > \varepsilon.$ (Why?)

(2) $\left.\begin{array}{l} g_2 \text{ continuous at } a \\ g_2(a) = 0 \end{array}\right\} \Rightarrow$ $\forall n = 1, 2, 3, \ldots \Rightarrow \exists$ nbd. $Q_n{}^*(a)$ such that

$$x \in Q_n{}^*(a) \Rightarrow |g_2(x)| < \frac{\varepsilon}{n}. \quad \text{(Why?)}$$

(3) If, now we use (1) and (2) and define $N_n{}^*(a) = N_1(a) \cap Q_n{}^*(a)$, we can say

$$\forall n = 1, 2, \ldots, \Rightarrow \exists N_n{}^*(a) \text{ such that } x \in N_n{}^*(a) \Rightarrow |f(x)| = \left|\frac{g_1(x)}{g_2(x)}\right| > \frac{\varepsilon}{\dfrac{\varepsilon}{n}} = n; \text{ thus}$$

$$\lim_{x \to a} |f(x)| = \infty. \quad \blacksquare$$

This proof applies in case the domain of f includes only one-sided nbds. of a for g_1 and g_2.

Note also that the proof would be valid if we assumed about g_2 only that $\lim_{x \to a} g_2(x) = 0$.

It follows from Theorem 1 that if the numerator and denominator of a rational function have no common linear factors then the graph of the function has vertical asymptotes at every zero of the denominator polynomial. For example, the graph of

$$f(x) = \frac{(x + 2)(x - 1)(x - 6)}{x^2(x - 3)(x - 5)} \tag{11}$$

has vertical asymptotes at $x = 0$, $x = 3$, and $x = 5$.

For rational functions it is possible to give a simple criterion for the existence of horizontal asymptotes.

Theorem 2. *Let f be a rational function:*

$$f(x) = \frac{a_0 x^m + a_1 x^{m-1} + \cdots + a_m}{b_0 x^n + b_1 x^{n-1} + \cdots + b_n}, \qquad a_0 b_0 \neq 0.$$

Then

(i) $m < n \Rightarrow y = 0$ *is a horizontal asymptote;*

(ii) $m = n \Rightarrow y = \dfrac{a_0}{b_0}$ *is a horizontal asymptote;*

(iii) $m > n \Rightarrow$ *there is no horizontal asymptote.*

Proof. Exercise for student. ∎

By Theorem 2, then, the graph of the function in Example 4 (Eq. 9) has no horizontal asymptote, the graph of the function in Example 5 has $y = 1$ as horizontal asymptote. Note that Theorem 2 is concerned only with horizontal asymptotes; the curve in Example 4 has no horizontal asymptote, but it does have $y = x$ and $x = 0$ as asymptotes.

Example 6. We consider the graph of $y = \dfrac{b}{a}\sqrt{x^2 - a^2}$, $x \geq a$, where $a > 0$, $b > 0$. Since $-a^2$ is constant, x can be taken large enough so as to make the value of y approximately $y = \dfrac{b}{a}\sqrt{x^2} = \dfrac{b}{a}x$. This suggests that $y = \dfrac{b}{a}x$ is an asymptote, a fact which, using Definition 1, we now prove. For

$$\lim_{x \to \infty}\left[\frac{b}{a}\sqrt{x^2 - a^2} - \frac{b}{a}x\right] = \frac{b}{a}\lim_{x \to \infty}\left[\sqrt{x^2 - a^2} - x\right]$$

$$= \frac{b}{a}\lim_{x \to \infty}\left[\frac{x^2 - a^2 - x^2}{\sqrt{x^2 - a^2} + x}\right]$$

$$= \frac{b}{a}\lim_{x \to \infty}\left[\frac{-a^2}{\sqrt{x^2 - a^2} + x}\right]$$

$$= 0.$$

Thus $y = \dfrac{b}{a}x$ is an asymptote of the curve.

We also have that

$$\frac{dy}{dx} = \frac{b}{a}\cdot\frac{1}{2}(x^2 - a^2)^{-1/2}(2x) = \frac{b}{a}\frac{x}{\sqrt{x^2 - a^2}}, \qquad x > a.$$

Thus $\dfrac{dy}{dx}$ (and the slope of the tangent to the curve) is positive for $x > a$; more-over, we can easily see that

$$\lim_{x \to \infty} \frac{dy}{dx} = \frac{b}{a} \quad \text{and} \quad \lim_{x \to a^+} \frac{dy}{dx} = \infty.$$

The graph, now easily obtained, is shown in Figure 7. The curve is part (one fourth to be exact) of a hyperbola.

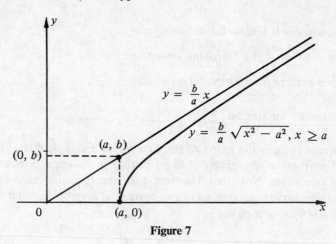

Figure 7

EXERCISES

In Exercises 1 through 17 find all asymptotes and sketch the graph.

1. $y = \dfrac{x_2 - 4}{x^2}$.   (see Example 5)   **2.** $y = \dfrac{x}{x^2 + 1}$.   (see Example 4)

3. $y = \dfrac{x}{x^2 - 4}$.   **4.** $y = \dfrac{x^2 - 4}{x}$.

5. $y = \dfrac{x}{x^2 - 3x + 2}$.   **6.** $y = \dfrac{x^2}{x^2 - 3x + 2}$.

7. $y = \dfrac{x^2 - 3x + 2}{x}$.   **8.** $y = \dfrac{x^2 - 3x + 2}{x^2}$.

9. $y = \dfrac{x^2 - 4}{x^2 + 4}$.   **10.** $y = \dfrac{x^2 + 4}{x^2 - 4}$.

11. $y = \dfrac{x^2 - 2x - 8}{x^2 + 2x - 8}$.   **12.** $y = \dfrac{x^2 + 2x - 8}{x^2 - 2x - 8}$.

13. $y = \dfrac{x^3 - 2x^2 - 15x}{x^2 + x - 20}$ **14.** $y = \dfrac{x^2 + x - 20}{x^3 - 2x^2 - 15x}$

15. $y = \dfrac{x^2 - 3x + 2}{x^2 + x - 6}$ **16.** $y = \dfrac{x^2 + x - 6}{x^2 - 3x + 2}$

17. $y = \dfrac{x^2 - 1}{(x^2 + 3)(x - 1)}$

18. This refers to the curve in Exercise 17. Consider the function f, $f(x) = \dfrac{x^2 - 1}{(x^2 + 3)(x - 1)}$ on $[0, 2]$. Does f have a maximum there? Why or why not?

19. (Continuation). Consider the function g, $g(x) = \dfrac{x + 1}{x^2 + 3}$ on $[0, 2]$. Does g have a maximum there? Why or why not? Does $g = f$? If not, how do they differ?

20. Prove Theorem 2. [*Hint.* Divide numerator and denominator by x^n.]

21. Supply the reasons for steps (1) and (2) in the proof of Theorem 1.

5.3 The Second Derivative

The second derivative of a function was introduced in Chapter 2 as a means of measuring acceleration in linear motion. In this and the following section we exploit it further.

We begin by recalling that, by definition, the second derivative is the derivative of the first derivative. If, as sometimes done, we use either y or f as the symbol for a function, then some of the different symbols for the second derivative are:

$$f''(x) = D_x f'(x) = D_x^2 f(x) = \frac{d}{dx}\left(\frac{dy}{dx}\right) = \frac{d^2 y}{dx^2}.$$

For example, if $f(x) = ax^2 + bx + c$, then $f'(x) = 2ax + b$ and $f''(x) = 2a$. Or, if $g(x) = \dfrac{1}{x} = x^{-1}$, then $g'(x) = -x^{-2} = \dfrac{-1}{x^2}$ and $g''(x) = 2x^{-3} = \dfrac{2}{x^3}$. And if $h(x) = x^{3/2}$ (defined for $x \geq 0$), then $h'(x) = \tfrac{3}{2}x^{1/2}$ (defined for $x \geq 0$), and $h''(x) = \tfrac{3}{4}x^{-1/2} = \dfrac{3}{4\sqrt{x}}$ (defined for $x > 0$).

As a first application we obtain an upper bound on the error introduced when the differential $df(x_0, h)$ is used as an approximation to the increment $\Delta f(x_0, h)$. Recall that (see Section 4.2) if $f'(x_0)$ exists, then

$$\Delta f(x_0, h) = f(x_0 + h) - f(x_0) = f'(x_0)h + \varepsilon h, \qquad \text{where } \lim_{h \to 0} \varepsilon = 0;$$

or, since $df(x_0, h) = f'(x_0)h$,

$$\Delta f(x_0, h) - df(x_0, h) = \varepsilon h, \qquad \text{where } \lim_{h \to 0} \varepsilon = 0. \qquad (12)$$

Theorem 3. *Let $I[x_0, h]$ be the closed interval with endpoints x_0, $x_0 + h$ (if $h < 0$, then $I[x_0, h] = [x_0 + h, x_0]$). Let f and f' be continuous on $I[x_0, h]$ and let f'' exist on the interior of $I[x_0, h]$. Then $\exists x_2$ in the interior of $I[x_0, h]$ such that*

$$|\Delta f(x_0, h) - df(x_0, h| < |f''(x_2)| \cdot h^2.$$

In particular, if $M > 0$ is an upper bound for $|f''|$ on the interior of $I[x_0, h]$, then

$$|\Delta f(x_0, h) - df(x_0, h)| < M \cdot h^2.$$

Proof. The proof involves only a double application of the Mean Value Theorem. We have, assuming $h > 0$,

$$\begin{aligned} \Delta f(x_0, h) - df(x_0, h) &= f(x_0 + h) - f(x_0) - f'(x_0)h \\ &= f'(x_1)h - f'(x_0)h, \\ &= [f'(x_1) - f'(x_0)]h, \end{aligned}$$

where x_1 lies between x_0 and $x_0 + h$ (see Figure 8).

Now we apply the Mean Value Theorem to the function f' on the interval between x_0 and x_1:

$$\Delta f - df = [f''(x_2)(x_1 - x_0)]h \qquad \text{(where x_2 lies between x_0 and x_1).}$$

Since $|x_1 - x_0| < h$, we have

$$|\Delta f - df| < |f''(x_2)| h^2.$$

Finally, if, for all x between x_0 and $x_0 + h$, $|f''(x)| < M$, then

$$|\Delta f(x_0, h) - df(x_0, h)| < Mh^2.$$

If $h < 0$ the details are similar and will be left as an exercise. ∎

In Exercise 22 we outline a proof for the assertion which, under the same hypotheses, guarantees an x_1 between x_0 and $x_0 + h$ such that

$$|\Delta f(x_0, h) - df(x_0, h)| < \tfrac{1}{2}|f''(x_1)| h^2; \tag{13}$$

or, if $|f''(x)| < M$ for x between x_0 and $x_0 + h$,

$$|\Delta f(x_0, h) - df(x_0, h)| < \tfrac{1}{2}Mh^2. \tag{14}$$

As an illustration of (14), we return to the example in Section 4.2 in which we estimated $\sqrt{101}$ by means of the differential. We have

$$f(x) = \sqrt{x} = x^{1/2}, \ x_0 = 100, \ h = 1$$

$$f'(x) = \frac{1}{2}x^{-1/2} = \frac{1}{2\sqrt{x}}$$

$$f''(x) = -\frac{1}{4}x^{-3/2} = \frac{-1}{4(\sqrt{x})^3}.$$

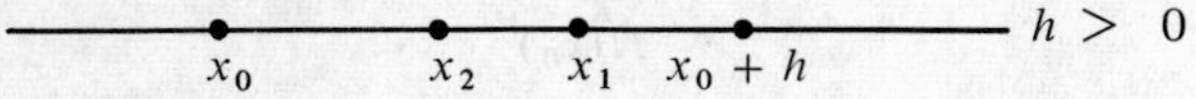

$$x_0 \qquad x_2 \qquad x_1 \quad x_0 + h \qquad\qquad h > 0$$

Figure 8

We have $df(x_0, h) = \dfrac{h}{2\sqrt{x_0}}$, so $df(100,1) = \dfrac{1}{20} = 0.05$. Thus $\sqrt{101} \approx 10.05$.

Now, for $h > 0$, $\sqrt{x_0 + h} > \sqrt{x_0}$, so

$$\frac{1}{\sqrt{x_0 + h}} < \frac{1}{\sqrt{x_0}}.$$

and

$$\frac{1}{4(\sqrt{x_0 + h})^3} < \frac{1}{4(\sqrt{x_0})^3}.$$

The implication of this last inequality is that $|f''(x)|$ is a decreasing function, so one can take its value at the left end of the interval $[x_0, x_0 + h]$ as an upper bound for its value on $(x_0, x_0 + h)$. Thus,

$$M = \frac{1}{4(\sqrt{x_0})^3} = \frac{1}{4 \cdot 10^3}, \qquad \text{if } x_0 = 100.$$

By (14) then, we have

$$|\Delta f(100, 1) - df(100, 1)| < \frac{1}{2} \cdot \frac{1}{4000} \cdot 1 = \frac{1}{8000} = 0.000125,$$

an upper bound for the error in using 10.05 as an approximation for $\sqrt{101}$.

We next plan to use f'' for the determination of relative maxima and minima. First, however, we must give criteria for such points in terms of the behavior of f'.

Theorem 4. *If $f'(x_0) = 0$ and if $f'(x)$ changes from negative to positive as x increases through x_0, then f has a relative minimum at x_0. In symbols,*

$$\left.\begin{array}{l} f'(x_0) = 0 \\[2mm] \exists N(x_0) \text{ such that } x \in N(x_0), \quad \begin{array}{l} x < x_0 \Rightarrow f'(x) < 0 \\ x > x_0 \Rightarrow f'(x) > 0 \end{array} \end{array}\right\} \Rightarrow \begin{array}{l} f \text{ has a relative} \\ \text{minimum at } x_0. \end{array}$$

Proof.

(1) Consider any $x_1 \in N(x_0)$, $x_1 < x_0$, and apply the Mean Value Theorem to $[x_1, x_0]$ (why can this be done?) This gives

$$f(x_0) - f(x_1) = (x_0 - x_1)f'(z_1) < 0, \qquad \text{since } z_1 \in (x_1, x_0) \text{ and } f'(z_1) < 0.$$

Thus, $f(x_0) < f(x_1)$ (see Figure 9).

(2) Pick any $x_2 \in N(x_0)$, $x_2 > x_0$. If we apply the Mean Value Theorem to $[x_0, x_2]$, then we know $\exists z_2 \in (x_0, x_2)$ such that

$$f(x_2) - f(x_0) = (x_2 - x_0)f'(z_2) > 0, \qquad \text{since } f'(z_2) > 0.$$

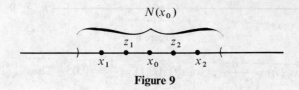

Figure 9

Thus $f(x_2) > f(x_0)$, and f has a relative minimum at x_0. ∎

We state, but do not prove, an analogous theorem for the existence of a relative maximum.

Theorem 5. *If $f'(x_0) = 0$ and if $f'(x)$ changes from positive to negative as x increases through x_0, then f has a relative maximum at x_0. In symbols,*

$$\left. \begin{array}{l} f'(x_0) = 0 \\[2mm] \exists N(x_0) \text{ such that } x \in N(x_0), \quad \begin{array}{l} x < x_0 \Rightarrow f'(x) > 0 \\ x > x_0 \Rightarrow f'(x) < 0 \end{array} \end{array} \right\} \Rightarrow \begin{array}{l} f \text{ has relative} \\ \text{maximum at } x_0. \end{array}$$

Proof. Exercise for student. ∎

We complete the picture with the following assertion.

Theorem 6. *If $f'(x_0) = 0$ but $f'(x)$ does not change sign as x increases through x_0, then f' has neither relative minimum nor relative maximum at x_0. In symbols,*

$$\left. \begin{array}{l} f'(x_0) = 0 \\[2mm] \exists N(x_0) \text{ such that } x \in N(x_0) \Rightarrow \begin{array}{c} f'(x) \geq 0 \\ or \\ f'(x) \leq 0 \end{array} \end{array} \right\} \Rightarrow \begin{array}{l} f \text{ has neither relative minimum} \\ \text{nor relative maximum at } x_0. \end{array}$$

Proof. We assume that $f'(x) \geq 0$ for $x \in N(x_0)$; the proof for $f'(x) \leq 0$ is similar and is left as an exercise.

(1) Suppose $x_1 < x_0$, $x_1 \in N(x_0)$, and apply the Mean Value Theorem to f on $[x_1, x_0]$. Then $\exists z_1 \in (x_1, x_0)$ such that

$$f(x_0) - f(x_1) = (x_0 - x_1)f'(z_1) \geq 0, \qquad \text{since} \quad f'(z_1) \geq 0.$$

Thus $f(x_1) \leq f(x_0)$.

(2) Suppose $x_2 > x_0$, $x_2 \in N(x_0)$, and apply the Mean Value Theorem to f on $[x_0, x_2]$. Then $\exists z_2 \in (x_0, x_2)$ such that

$$f(x_2) - f(x_0) = (x_2 - x_0)f'(z_2) \geq 0, \qquad \text{since} \quad f'(z_2) \geq 0.$$

Thus $f(x_2) \geq f(x_0)$, and f has neither relative maximum nor minimum at x_0. ∎

The advantage of the next theorem is that it enables us to determine the nature of a critical point by considering only the *sign* of $f''(x_0)$.

Theorem 7. *Suppose* $f'(x_0) = 0$. *Then*

(a) $f''(x_0) > 0 \Rightarrow f$ *has a relative minimum at* x_0.
(b) $f''(x_0) < 0 \Rightarrow f$ *has a relative maximum at* x_0.
(c) $f''(x_0) = 0 \Rightarrow f$ *may have relative minimum or relative maximum or neither at* x_0.

Proof.

(a) Since $f'(x_0) = 0$ and $f''(x_0) > 0$, we know $\exists N(x_0)$ such that

$$x_0 + h \in N(x_0) \Rightarrow \frac{f'(x_0 + h) - f'(x_0)}{h} = \frac{f'(x_0 + h)}{h} > 0. \qquad \text{(Why?)}$$

Thus, h and $f'(x_0 + h)$ must agree in sign: $h < 0 \Rightarrow f'(x_0 + h) < 0$, $h > 0 \Rightarrow f'(x_0 + h) > 0$. By Theorem 4, f has a relative minimum at x_0.

(b) Exercise for student.

(c) To demonstrate the assertion in (c) we simply list three functions. Table 5.1 tells all. ∎

TABLE 5.1

$f(x)$	$f'(x)$	$f''(x)$	$f'(0)$	$f''(0)$	Behavior of f at 0
x^4	$4x^3$	$12x^2$	0	0	minimum
$-x^4$	$-4x^3$	$-12x^2$	0	0	maximum
x^3	$3x^2$	$6x$	0	0	neither

The following result, which we shall need later, is an immediate consequence of Theorem 7.

Theorem 8. *Suppose f is such that $f'(x_0) = 0$ and $f''(x_0)$ exists. Then*

(i) f *has relative minimum at* $x_0 \Rightarrow f''(x_0) \geq 0$;
(ii) f *has relative maximum at* $x_0 \Rightarrow f''(x_0) \leq 0$.

Proof. Obvious. ∎

We now turn to some examples.

Example 7. Consider f with the formula

$$f(x) = 2x^3 - 3x^2 - 36x + 1.$$

We differentiate twice:

$$f'(x) = 6x^2 - 6x - 36 = 6(x^2 - x - 6) = 6(x + 2)(x - 3);$$

$$f''(x) = 6(2x - 1).$$

Clearly,

$$f'(-2) = 0, \qquad f''(-2) < 0,$$
$$f'(3) = 0, \qquad f''(3) > 0.$$

Thus, by Theorem 7, f has a relative maximum at $x = -2$, and a relative minimum at $x = 3$. We show the graph of f in Figure 10.

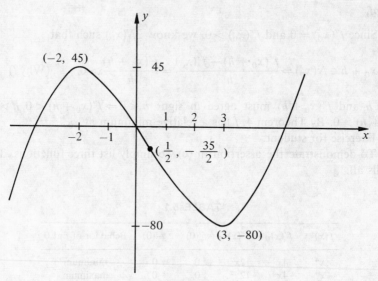

Figure 10

The student should verify the following assertions about f':

$$x < -2 \Rightarrow f'(x) > 0$$
$$-2 < x < 3 \Rightarrow f'(x) < 0$$
$$3 < x \Rightarrow f'(x) > 0.$$

Example 8. Consider $f(x) = x^5 - 5x^4 = x^4(x - 5)$. If we differentiate twice, we find

$$f'(x) = 5(x^4 - 4x^3) = 5x^3(x - 4)$$
$$f''(x) = 20(x^3 - 3x^2) = 20x^2(x - 3).$$

Thus,

$$f'(4) = 0, \qquad f''(4) > 0,$$
$$f'(0) = 0, \qquad f''(0) = 0.$$

Theorem 7 tells us f has a relative minimum at $(4, -256)$, but it does not describe the behavior of f at $(0, 0)$. For this we use Theorem 5; for

$$x < 0 \Rightarrow f'(x) > 0,$$
$$0 < x < 4 \Rightarrow f'(x) < 0.$$

Thus, by Theorem 5, f has a relative maximum at $(0, 0)$. The graph of f is shown in Figure 11.

Example 9. We consider now $f(x) = x^4 - 4x^3 = x^3(x - 4)$. Then

$$f'(x) = 4(x^3 - 3x^2) = 4x^2(x - 3),$$

$$f''(x) = 12(x^2 - 2x) = 12x(x - 2).$$

We see that

$$f'(3) = 0, \qquad f''(3) > 0,$$

$$f'(0) = 0, \qquad f''(0) = 0,$$

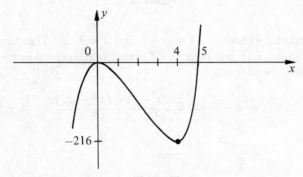

Figure 11

so Theorem 7 tells us f has a relative minimum at $x = 3$, but it does not give information about the behavior at $x = 0$. However, we notice that

$$x < 0 \Rightarrow f'(x) < 0$$

$$0 < x < 3 \Rightarrow f'(x) < 0;$$

thus f' does not change sign as x goes through 0, so the origin is neither a relative minimum nor a relative maximum. The graph of f is shown in Figure 12.

Of course, if f is not a polynomial, the computation of f'' may be tedious and recourse to Theorems 4 and 5 may be preferable to the use of Theorem 7.

Example 10. Consider the rational function f,

$$f(x) = \frac{x^2 - x}{x^2 - 2x - 3} = \frac{x(x - 1)}{(x + 1)(x - 3)} = \frac{x^2 - x}{x^2 - x - (x + 3)}$$

From the factored form we see that $f(0) = f(1) = 0$ and that the graph has as

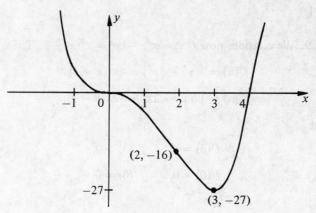

Figure 12

vertical asymptotes (Theorem 1) $x = -1$ and $x = 3$. By Theorem 2, $y = 1$ is also an asymptote. The last form for f shows that $f(x) = 1 \Leftrightarrow x + 3 = 0$, i.e., $\Leftrightarrow x = -3$. Now we compute f':

$$f'(x) = \frac{(x^2 - 2x - 3)(2x - 1) - (x^2 - x)(2x - 2)}{(x^2 - 2x - 3)^2}$$

$$= \frac{-(x^2 + 6x - 3)}{(x^2 - 2x - 3)^2}.$$

The equation $x^2 + 6x - 3 = 0$ has roots $r_1 = -3 - 2\sqrt{3} \approx -6.4$. $r_2 = -3 + 2\sqrt{3} \approx 0.4$. Thus we can write

$$f'(x) = \frac{-(x - r_1)(x - r_2)}{(x^2 - 2x - 3)^2}, \qquad \text{where} \quad r_1 < r_2.$$

It is now a simple matter to show that

$$x < r_1 \Rightarrow f'(x) < 0$$

$$\left.\begin{array}{c} r_1 < x < r_2 \\ x \neq -1 \end{array}\right\} \Rightarrow f'(x) > 0$$

$$\left.\begin{array}{c} r_2 < x \\ x \neq 3 \end{array}\right\} \Rightarrow f'(x) < 0.$$

From these statements and Theorems 4 and 5 we know that f has a relative minimum at $x = r_1 \approx -6.4$ and a relative maximum at $x = r_2 \approx 0.4$. It should be apparent that the calculation of f'' would be lengthy, if not difficult.

The information obtained above enables us to sketch the graph of f as shown in Figure 13.

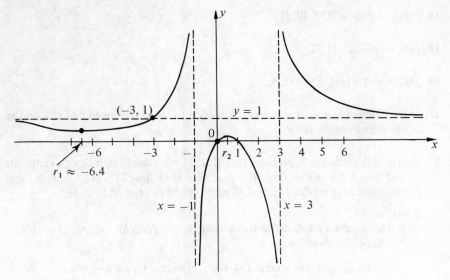

Figure 13

E X E R C I S E S

In Exercises 1–14 find all relative maxima and minima.

1. $f(x) = x^3 - 12x + 2$

2. $f(x) = x^2(x-4)^2$

3. $f(x) = x^2(x-4)^3$

4. $f(x) = x^3(x-4)^2$

5. $f(x) = x^3(x-4)^3$

6. $f(x) = \dfrac{x^2 - 4}{x^2 - 2x - 15}$

7. $f(x) = x - \dfrac{1}{x}$

8. $f(x) = x^{2/3}$

9. $f(x) = x(x-2)^2(x-4)^3$

10. $f(x) = x^2(x-2)^3(x-4)$

11. $f(x) = x^3(x-2)(x-4)^2$

12. $f(x) = \dfrac{x^2 - 3x}{x^2 - 6x + 8}$

13. $f(x) = \dfrac{4 - x^2}{x^2 - 9}$

14. $f(x) = \sin x.$

In Exercises 15–20 find the absolute maxima and minima on the intervals specified.

15. $f(x) = 4x - x^2$, $[0, 4]$

16. $f(x) = 4x - x^2$, $[0, 5]$

17. $f(x) = |x|$, $[-1, 1]$

18. $f(x) = 1 - (x - 1)^{2/3}$, $[0, 2]$

19. $f(x) = (x - 1)^3$, $[0, 2]$

20. $f(x) = x^n$, $[-1, 1]$, $n = 1, 2, 3, \ldots$

21. If the differential is used as an approximation to the increment to find $\sqrt{5}$, find an upper bound for the error.

22. Derive (13) under the hypotheses that $I[x_0, h]$ is a closed interval with endpoints x_0 and $x_0 + h$ (i.e., either $I[x_0, h] = [x_0, x_0 + h]$ or $I[x_0, h] = [x_0 + h, x_0]$), f and f' are continuous on $I[x_0, h]$, and f'' exists on the interior of $I[x_0, h]$.

Hints.

  1. For x_0 and h fixed, define the *constant* k by $\Delta f(x_0, h) - df(x_0, h) = \frac{1}{2}h^2 k$.
  2. Define the function φ by

$$\varphi(x) = f(x_0 + h) - f(x) - (x_0 + h - x)f'(x) - \frac{1}{2}(x_0 + h - x)^2 k.$$

  3. Verify that $\varphi(x_0) = \varphi(x_0 + h) = 0$ and that the other hypotheses of Rolle's Theorem (Theorem 4.3) are satisfied.
  4. Apply Rolle's Theorem to φ and obtain (13).

23. Prove Theorem 5.

24. Prove Theorem 6 for the case $f'(x) \leq 0$ for $x \in N(x_0)$.

25. Prove part (b) of Theorem 7.

26. This refers to Example 7 and Figure 10. Notice that $f''(\frac{1}{2}) = 0$, $x < \frac{1}{2} \Rightarrow f'' < (0.x)$ $x > \frac{1}{2} \Rightarrow f''(x) > 0$. Does this analytic behavior show up in any way in the graph of f?

27. Carry out the proof of Theorem 3 for the case $h < 0$.

28. Let $f(x) = x^n - nx^{n-1} = x^{n-1}(x - n)$.

  (a) Show that, for $k = 0, 1, 2, \ldots, n - 1$,

$$f^{(k)}(x) = n(n - 1) \cdots (n - k + 1)x^{n-k-1}(x - \overline{n - k}).$$

  (b) Show that $f^{(n)}(x) = n!$

  (c) Show that $f^{(k)}(n - k) = 0$, $k = 0, 1, \ldots, n - 1$.

  (d) Show that f has a relative minimum at $(n - 1, -(n - 1)^{n-1})$.

  (e) Show that n odd $\Rightarrow f$ has a relative maximum at $(0, 0)$.

  (f) Show that n even, $n > 2 \Rightarrow f$ has neither relative maximum nor relative minimum at $(0, 0)$.

5.4 Concavity

In this section we study the geometric property known as concavity. We shall see that the second derivative is useful in distinguishing the different kinds of concavity.

We illustrate the two kinds of concavity in Figure 14. At point A the tangent line lies *above* the curve, whereas at B the tangent line lies *below* the curve. More generally, at every point to the left of P the tangent will lie above the curve, and at every point to the right of P the tangent will lie below the curve. The following definition makes explicit these two kinds of points on a curve.

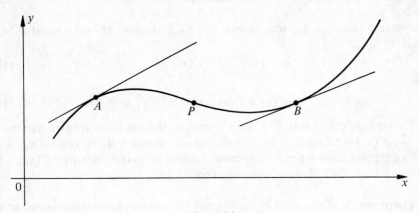

Figure 14

Definition 2. *A curve is **concave upward (downward)** at $(x_0, y_0) \Leftrightarrow \exists N(x_0)$ at every point of which the curve lies above (below) the tangent to the curve at (x_0, y_0).*

Note that concavity, as just defined, is fairly restrictive: the definition requires that there be a tangent line at the point.

We now search for an analytic description of the two types of concavity. To this end, we consider a curve, the graph of a function f, which is concave upward at x_0, and study the vertical distance φ between the tangent line at x_0 and the curve at points near $(x_0, f(x_0))$ (see Figure 15).

As the equation of the tangent line at x_0 is given by

$$y = f(x_0) + f'(x_0)(x - x_0),$$

the expression for the vertical distance φ is

$$\varphi(x) = f(x) - f(x_0) - f'(x_0)(x - x_0). \tag{15}$$

We note that $\varphi(x_0) = 0$, and, if the curve lies *above* the tangent line in a nbd. of x_0, then $x \in N^*(x_0) \Rightarrow \varphi(x) > 0$. Thus φ has a relative minimum at x_0. If

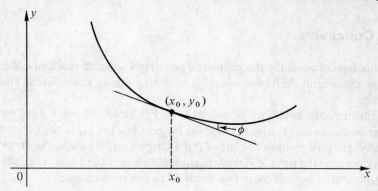

Figure 15

we assume that $f''(x_0)$ exists, as well as $f'(x_0)$, then so will $\varphi'(x_0)$ and $\varphi''(x_0)$ exist. In fact,

$$\varphi'(x) = f'(x) - f'(x_0), \tag{16}$$

and

$$\varphi''(x) = f''(x). \tag{17}$$

We see that $\varphi'(x_0) = 0$, and, by Theorem 8, since φ has a relative minimum at x_0, $\varphi''(x_0) = f''(x_0) \geq 0$. In case the curve is concave downward at x_0, and if $f''(x_0)$ exists, then a similar argument enables us to conclude that $f''(x_0) \leq 0$. Thus we have the following necessary conditions.

Theorem 9. *If the graph of the function f is concave upward (downward) at x_0 and if $f''(x_0)$ exists, then $f''(x_0) \geq 0$ ($f''(x_0) \leq 0$).*

As a near converse of Theorem 9, we can easily obtain the following sufficient conditions.

Theorem 10. *If $f''(x_0) > 0$ ($f''(x_0) < 0$) then the graph of f is concave upward (downward) at $(x_0, f(x_0))$.*

Proof. We first note that the existence of $f''(x_0) \Rightarrow$ the existence of $f'(x_0)$, so that one *can* discuss concavity of the graph of f at $(x_0, f(x_0))$. As in the preceding discussion, we consider the function φ of Eq. (15), the derivatives of which are given in (16) and (17). From (16) we see that $\varphi'(x_0) = 0$, and from (17) we have that $\varphi''(x_0) = f''(x_0)$. Thus, if $f''(x_0) > 0$, then $\varphi'(x_0) = 0$ and $\varphi''(x_0) > 0$, so φ has a relative minimum at x_0, by Theorem 7. But this means that, in a nbd. of x_0, $\varphi(x) \geq \varphi(x_0) = 0$; i.e., the curve lies above the tangent at $(x_0, f(x_0))$ in a nbd. of x_0. Similarly, if $f''(x_0) < 0$, φ has a relative maximum at x_0, so that the curve lies below the tangent at $(x_0, f(x_0))$. ∎

Example 11. Consider the graph of f where

$$f(x) = x^3 - x = x(x^2 - 1) = x(x + 1)(x - 1).$$

We calculate the first and second derivatives:

$$f'(x) = 3x^2 - 1,$$
$$f''(x) = 6x.$$

Clearly $x < 0 \Rightarrow f''(x) < 0$, $x > 0 \Rightarrow f''(x) > 0$; thus the curve is concave downward for all negative x, concave upward for all positive x. We note in passing that f has a relative minimum at $x_1 = \dfrac{1}{\sqrt{3}}$ and a relative maximum at $x_2 = \dfrac{-1}{\sqrt{3}}$.
The curve is shown in Figure 16.

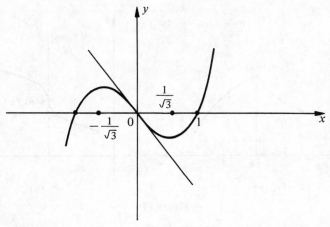

Figure 16

Note that at the point $(0, 0)$ where the concavity changes from downward to upward the tangent line *crosses* the curve. Such a point is called an *inflection point*.

Definition 3. *A point (x_0, y_0) on a curve is an **inflection point** of the curve $\Leftrightarrow$ the tangent to the curve at (x_0, y_0) lies above the curve on one side of (x_0, y_0) and below the curve on the other—we intend here that the points have abscissas which lie in some nbd. of x_0.*

The property possessed by an inflection point is, of course, a geometric property and we have borne this in mind in formulating Definition 3. There may, however, be some point in giving the analytic equivalent in terms of the function φ of Eq. (15).

Definition 3a. *A point $(x_0, y_0) = (x_0, f(x_0))$ on a curve is an **inflection point** of the curve $\Leftrightarrow \exists$ left and right nbds. of x_0, $N^-(x_0)$ and $N^+(x_0)$, such that either $\varphi(x) > 0$ in $N^-(x_0)$ and $\varphi(x) < 0$ in $N^+(x_0)$, or $\varphi(x) < 0$ in $N^-(x_0)$ and $\varphi(x) > 0$ in $N^+(x_0)$.*

Sometimes an inflection point is defined as a point where the concavity of a curve changes. The definition we have just given is more restrictive than this one. For example, each of the curves shown in Figure 17 has a change of concavity at x_0, but in neither case would (x_0, y_0) be an inflection point according to Definition 3 or 3a. The curve in Figure 17(a) has no tangent at (x_0, y_0) (a necessary condition, according to Definition 3, for (x_0, y_0) to be an inflection point); the curve in Figure 17(b) *has* a tangent at (x_0, y_0) but it is vertical, and the "above" and "below" conditions of Definition 3 are not meaningful (alternatively, the function φ of Eq. (15) is not defined when the tangent is vertical, so Definition 3a cannot be applied). Such points as these can be found by studying points where f'' fails to exist.

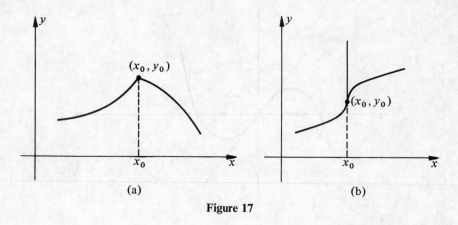

(a)   (b)

Figure 17

For the sake of emphasis we remark that at an inflection point a curve is neither concave upward nor concave downward.

The following analytical criterion for an inflection point follows almost immediately from Definition 3 and from Theorem 10.

Theorem 11. *If the point $(x_0, f(x_0))$ is an inflection point of the graph of f and if $f''(x_0)$ exists, then $f''(x_0) = 0$.*

Proof. Since $f''(x_0)$ exists, we must have exactly one of the following: (i) $f''(x_0) > 0$, (ii) $f''(x_0) < 0$, (iii) $f''(x_0) = 0$. If (i) holds, then, by Theorem 10, the curve is concave upward at $(x_0, f(x_0))$; if (ii) holds the curve is concave downward at $(x_0, f(x_0))$. Since these are incompatible with $(x_0, f(x_0))$ being an inflection point—see the preceding remark—it must be that $f''(x_0) = 0$. ∎

It is important to realize that the condition of Theorem 11, that $f''(x_0) = 0$, is neither necessary nor sufficient for $(x_0, f(x_0))$ to be an inflection point of the graph of f. For, on the one hand, if $f(x) = x^4$, then $f''(0) = 0$, but the point $(0, 0)$ is not an inflection point; in fact, the graph of this function is concave upward at all points, including $(0, 0)$. On the other hand, the graph of the function f with $f(x) = x^{5/3}$ has an inflection point at $(0, 0)$, although $f''(0) \neq 0$—for the very good reason that $f''(0)$ does not exist. The procedure in looking for inflection points and points where the concavity changes would be to consider as candidates all points x_0 where $f''(x_0) = 0$ or where $f''(x_0)$ fails to exist.

Example 12. We consider the graph of f, where

$$f(x) = x^{5/3}(x-1)(x-4) = x^{11/3} - 5x^{8/3} + 4x^{5/3}.$$

From the factored form for f we see that $f(0) = f(1) = f(4) = 0$, and

$$x < 0 \Rightarrow f(x) < 0,$$
$$0 < x < 1 \Rightarrow f(x) > 0,$$
$$1 < x < 4 \Rightarrow f(x) < 0$$
$$4 < x \Rightarrow f(x) > 0.$$

Computing f' and f'', we find

$$f'(x) = \tfrac{1}{3}(11x^{8/3} - 40x^{5/3} + 20x^{2/3}) = \tfrac{1}{3}x^{2/3}(11x^2 - 40x + 20),$$

and

$$f''(x) = \tfrac{1}{9}(88x^{5/3} - 200x^{2/3} + 40x^{-1/3}) = \tfrac{8}{9}x^{-1/3}(11x^2 - 25x + 5).$$

By solving the two quadratic equations

$$11x^2 - 40x + 20 = 0$$

and

$$11x^2 - 25x + 5 = 0,$$

we find that $f'(x) = 0$ when $x = 0$, $r_1 \approx 0.6$, $r_2 \approx 3.0$ and that $f''(x) = 0$ when $x = r_3 \approx 0.23$, $r_4 \approx 2.1$. Thus

$$f'(x) = \tfrac{1}{3}x^{2/3}(x - r_1)(x - r_2). \tag{18}$$
$$f''(x) = \tfrac{8}{9}x^{-1/3}(x - r_3)(x - r_4). \tag{19}$$

The relative locations of r_1, r_2, r_3, and r_4 are shown in Figure 18.

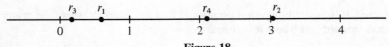

Figure 18

We assert that $f''(r_1) < 0$ and $f''(r_2) > 0$. Thus f has a relative maximum at $(0.6, 1.2)$ and a relative minimum at $(3.0, -12.5)$. At $(0, 0)$, where the tangent line is horizontal but where f'' does not exist, one can determine from Eq. (18) that f' does not change sign, so that $(0, 0)$ is neither a relative maximum nor a relative minimum.

The inflection points occur at r_3 and r_4, where f'' is zero, and also at 0, where f'' does not exist. The fact that $x = 0$ is an inflection point is easily seen by noting that, since $f(0) = f'(0) = 0$, the function φ of Eq. (15) is identical with f, which does change sign at $x = 0$. The graph of f is shown in Figure 19.

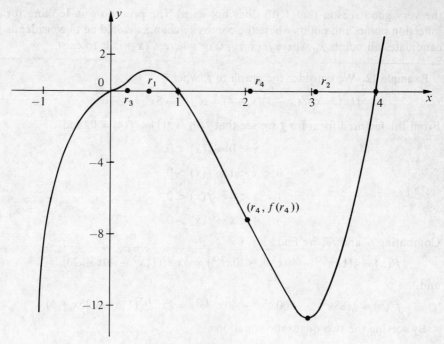

Figure 19

EXERCISES

1. Show that the graph of a quadratic function is either concave upward at every point or concave downward at every point.

2. Show that the graph of a cubic function (a polynomial of degree three) has exactly one inflection point.

In Exercises 3–16 find all inflection points and find the intervals where the graph of f is concave upward and where it is concave downward.

3. $f(x) = \dfrac{1}{1 + x^2}$ 4. $f(x) = x + \dfrac{1}{x}$

5. $f(x) = x^2(x - 4)^2$ 6. $f(x) = x^2(x - 4)^3$

7. $f(x) = x^3(x - 4)^2$ 8. $f(x) = x^3(x - 4)^3$

9. $f(x) = x^{1/3}$ 10. $f(x) = x^{2/3}$

11. $f(x) = \dfrac{x^2}{1 + x^2}$ 12. $f(x) = \begin{cases} 4x - x^2, & x < 0 \\ x^2 - 8x, & x \geq 0 \end{cases}$

13. $f(x) = \sin x$ 14. $f(x) = x^{1/3}(x - 4)$

15. $f(x) = x^{2/3}(x - 5)$ 16. $f(x) = x^4 - 4x^3 - 48x^2$

17. What do you think should be said about the concavity of a straight line?

18. Let f be the absolute value function. Is the graph of f concave upward or concave downward at $(0, 0)$?

19. Consider a function f with the following properties:

$$f(a) = b, \qquad a > 0, b > 0$$
$$x \geq a \Rightarrow f'(x) < 0$$
$$x \geq a \Rightarrow f''(x) < 0.$$

Prove that $\exists x_0 > a$ such that $f(x_0) = 0$.

20. See Exercise 19. Suppose a function f is such that

$$f(a) = b, a > 0, b > 0$$
$$x \geq a \Rightarrow f'(x) < 0$$
$$f''(a) < 0, x > a \Rightarrow f''(x) \quad \text{exists and is continuous.}$$

What must be true of f'' if the graph of f is to be asymptotic to the positive x-axis?

5.5 Maximum and Minimum Problems

We conclude this chapter with a few applications of maxima and minima. In most of the problems we will be interested in *absolute* maxima and minima; thus it becomes important to consider the endpoints of the domain of the function. A few examples may help.

Example 13. Find two positive numbers whose sum is a, and such that the product of the cube of one number and the square of the other is a maximum.

Solution. We let the two numbers be x and $a - x$; the problem is to maximize

$$f(x) = x^3(a - x)^2.$$

The admissible values of x are $0 < x < a$; we note, however, that

$$f(0) = f(a) = 0,$$

and

$$0 < x < a \Rightarrow f(x) > 0.$$

Thus f must have at least one maximum for $0 < x < a$. Differentiating, we find

$$f'(x) = x^3 \cdot 2(a - x)(-1) + 3x^2(a - x)^2$$
$$= x^2(a - x)[-2x + 3a - 3x]$$
$$= x^2(a - x)(3a - 5x).$$

Thus,

$$f'(0) = f'(a) = f'\left(\frac{3a}{5}\right) = 0;$$

the only value of interest to us is $x_0 = \dfrac{3a}{5}$, this clearly being between 0 and a.
The desired maximum is

$$f\left(\frac{3a}{5}\right) = \left(\frac{3a}{5}\right)^3 \left(\frac{2a}{5}\right)^2 = \frac{3^3 \cdot 2^2}{5^5}\, a^5 = 3^3 \cdot 2^2 \left(\frac{a}{5}\right)^5.$$

Notice that if a is divisible by 5, then $\dfrac{3a}{5}$ and $\dfrac{2a}{5}$ will be integers, but if a is not
a multiple of 5 then $\dfrac{3a}{5}$ and $\dfrac{2a}{5}$ will not be integral. In some cases it may be essential that the answers be integers. If, e.g., $a = 12$, and it is a condition that the
two summands be integral, one would take them as the integers nearest $\dfrac{3a}{5}$ and
$\dfrac{2a}{5}$; viz. 7 and 5.

Example 14. We consider a sphere of fixed radius a; the problem is to maximize the volume of a right circular cylinder contained within the sphere.

Solution. If we let the radius and height of the cylinder be x and y, respectively,
then the problem is to maximize

$$V = \pi x^2 y \tag{20}$$

subject to the condition (see Figure 20) that

$$x^2 + \frac{y^2}{4} = a^2. \tag{21}$$

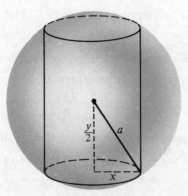

Figure 20

Now the admissible values of y are $0 < y < 2a$. From (21) we find

$$x^2 = \tfrac{1}{4}(4a^2 - y^2),\qquad (22)$$

which shows that $y = 2a \Rightarrow x = 0 \Rightarrow V = 0$; clearly, $y = 0 \Rightarrow V = 0$. Thus V has a maximum for y between 0 and $2a$.

From this point on there are two alternative methods:

(1) We substitute, from (22), for x^2 in (20), expressing V in terms of y,

$$V = V(y) = \frac{\pi}{4}(4a^2 - y^2)y = \frac{\pi}{4}(4a^2y - y^3).$$

Then

$$V'(y) = \frac{\pi}{4}(4a^2 - 3y^2),$$

so $V'(y) = 0$ leads to $y_0 = \dfrac{2a}{\sqrt{3}}$ (the negative value being meaningless here).

From this value we find, using (22), that $x_0 = \dfrac{\sqrt{2}a}{\sqrt{3}}$ (note that $y_0 = \sqrt{2}x_0$). Also

$$V_{\max} = \pi \left(\frac{2a^2}{3}\right)\left(\frac{2a}{\sqrt{3}}\right) = \frac{4\pi a^3}{3\sqrt{3}}$$

$$= \frac{1}{\sqrt{3}}\ \text{(volume of sphere).}$$

(2) The second method, less natural, proceeds as follows. We use (21) to define y as a function of x, but we do *not* actually solve for y in terms of x. We take derivatives, with respect to x, in both (20) and (21), using the chain rule when necessary:

$$\frac{dV}{dx} = \pi\left(x^2 \frac{dy}{dx} + 2xy\right),\qquad (23)$$

$$2x + \frac{1}{2}y\frac{dy}{dx} = 0.\qquad (24)$$

Setting $\dfrac{dV}{dx} = 0$ and dividing by x gives

$$x\frac{dy}{dx} + 2y = 0,\qquad (25)$$

a relation between x, y, and $\dfrac{dy}{dx}$ which should hold for maximum V. We can eliminate $\dfrac{dy}{dx}$ from this equation by using (24):

$$\frac{dy}{dx} = -\frac{4x}{y}.$$

Substituting this value in (25) gives

$$-\frac{4x^2}{y} + 2y = 0,$$

or

$$y^2 = 2x^2,$$

whence $y_0 = \sqrt{2}x_0$.

Note that, at this point, we have a relation between the height and radius of the cylinder of maximum volume, but not explicit formulas for the height and radius in terms of the radius of the sphere. These latter can be obtained, of course, by using (21). The distinction between the two methods lies mainly in the nature of the desired answer: if explicit formulas for x_0 and y_0 are sought, the first method is more direct; if only a relation between x_0 and y_0 is desired, then the second method is more direct. Of course, either method *can* be used in either case.

Example 15. We now give only a partial solution to a problem which at first glance seems quite simple.

A boat is at a point B, a miles from the nearest point M on a straight shore. A man in the boat wants to get to a point A which is b miles up the shore from M. If the speed of the boat is r_1 mph, and his speed on land is r_2 mph, how should he travel so as to get from B to A most quickly? See Figure 21.

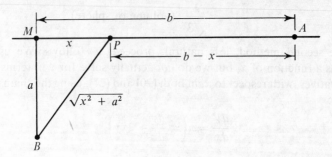

Figure 21

Solution. It is truly obvious that, for minimum time, the man should head for a point P on shore between M and A. If we let $\overline{MP} = x$ miles, then we can easily obtain an expression for the time T in hours to go from B to P to A:

$$T = T(x) = \frac{\sqrt{x^2 + a^2}}{r_1} + \frac{b - x}{r_2}, \qquad 0 \le x \le b.$$

We note in passing that

$$T(0) = \frac{a}{r_1} + \frac{b}{r_2}$$

$$T(b) = \frac{\sqrt{a^2 + b^2}}{r_1}.$$

In order to find the minimum value of T we differentiate:

$$T'(x) = \frac{1}{r_1} \cdot \frac{1}{2}(x^2 + a^2)^{-1/2}(2x) - \frac{1}{r_2}$$

$$= \frac{1}{r_1 r_2 \sqrt{x^2 + a^2}} (r_2 x - r_1 \sqrt{x^2 + a^2}).$$

Clearly $T'(x) = 0 \Rightarrow$

$$r_2 x - r_1 \sqrt{x^2 + a^2} = 0,$$

or

$$r_2^2 x^2 = r_1^2 x^2 + r_1^2 a^2,$$

or

$$(r_2^2 - r_1^2) x^2 = r_1^2 a^2, \tag{26}$$

If $r_1 \geq r_2$ this equation has no solution. Now common sense tells us that if the man can travel faster over water than on land then he should head directly for A (i.e., $x = b$). We can also obtain this analytically. If $r_1 \geq r_2$, $T'(x) = 0$ has no solutions, so the minimum must be an endpoint minimum. But $r_1 \geq r_2 \Rightarrow$

$$T(0) = \frac{a}{r_1} + \frac{b}{r_2} \geq \frac{a}{r_1} + \frac{b}{r_1} = \frac{a+b}{r_1} > \frac{\sqrt{a^2 + b^2}}{r_1} = T(b);$$

thus $T(b)$ is the minimum time if $r_1 \geq r_2$.

If $r_2 > r_1$ we can solve (26) for x_0:

$$x_0 = \frac{r_1 a}{\sqrt{r_2^2 - r_1^2}}. \tag{27}$$

We leave it as an exercise to show that $0 \leq x \leq b \Rightarrow T''(x) > 0$, so that the value of x_0 given in (27) *should* give a minimum value of T when $r_2 > r_1$. But the story is not yet ended, as you will see in the exercises.

We conclude with a summary of the procedure to be used in finding maxima and minima. Usually the meaningful domain of the function f to be maximized or minimized will be an interval (possible infinite).

(1) Determine this meaningful domain of f.
(2) Be sure to compute the value(s) of f at the endpoint(s) of the interval;
(3) Find the zeros of f' and test for maxima and minima; and
(4) If f' fails to exist at any points of the domain of f, study the behavior of f near these points.

EXERCISES

1. Find two positive numbers whose sum is 10, if the product of one by the square of the other is to be a maximum. What is the answer if the two numbers must be integers?

2. A rectangular area of fixed amount is to be enclosed, and divided into four equal lots by parallels to one of the sides. What should be the shape of the field to make the amount of fencing a minimum?

3. For a right triangle with given (fixed) hypotenuse, show that the area is a maximum when the triangle is isosceles.

4. A box is to be made of a piece of cardboard 8-in. square by cutting equal squares out of the corners and turning up the sides. Find the volume of the largest box that can be made in this way.

5. The perimeter of an isosceles triangle is 12 in. Find the maximum area.

6. Find the most economical proportions for a can which will contain a fixed volume.

7. A cylinder, without top, is to contain a fixed volume. Find the proportions which will minimize the material needed.

8. Find the most economical proportions for a box with an open top and a square base.

9. Find the most economical proportions for a box (with top) whose base is a rectangle with one side four times the other.

10. Find the proportions of the circular cylinder with given volume so the volume of the circumscribed sphere will be a minimum.

11. The strength of a rectangular beam is proportional to the breadth and the square of the depth. Find the shape of the strongest beam that can be cut from a log of a given size. Assume the log has circular cross section.

12. A Norman window consists of a rectangle surmounted by a semicircle. What shape gives the most light for a given perimeter?

13. Find the proportions of the circular cone of maximum volume which can be inscribed in a sphere of radius a.

14. Find the point on the curve $y = x^3$ that is nearest the point $(4, 0)$.

15. A ship lies 6 miles from shore, and opposite a point 12 miles farther along the shore another ship lies 18 miles offshore. A boat from the first ship is to land a passenger and then proceed to the other ship. What is the length of the shortest route that the boat can take?

16. A silo consists of a cylinder surmounted by a hemisphere. Find the proportion which will enclose a given volume with least surface area, including floor.

17. This refers to Example 15.

   (a) Suppose $r_2 = 2r_1$ and $a = 2b$. Compare the value of x_0 given in (27) with b.

   (b) Show that in this case the minimum value of T is $T(b)$.

18. This refers to both Example 15 and Exercise 17.

(a) Suppose $r_2 > r_1$. Show that

$$x < \frac{r_1 a}{\sqrt{r_2^2 - r_1^2}} = x_0 \Rightarrow T'(x) < 0.$$

(b) Thus show that if $x_0 = \dfrac{r_1 a}{\sqrt{r_2^2 - r_1^2}} > b$, then the minimum value of T is $T(b)$.

(c) Find conditions on a, b, r_1, r_2 for $x_0 > b$.

19. A wall b ft high is a horizontal distance of a ft from a building. Show that the shortest ladder which will reach from the ground to the building, touching the top of the wall, is $(a^{2/3} + b^{2/3})^{3/2}$ ft in length.

Chapter **6** Trigonometric Functions

This chapter is concerned with the calculus of the trigonometric functions. We begin with a brief review of the definitions and fundamental properties of the functions and then obtain their derivatives and antiderivatives. In order to define the inverse trigonometric functions, we give in Section 6.5, a discussion of inverse functions in general.

6.1 The Trigonometric Functions: Definition and Properties

The most elementary treatment of the trigonometric functions involves associating them with an angle in a right triangle and defining them as ratios of lengths of sides of the triangle (opposite divided by hypotenuse, etc.). In this context angle is defined in terms of amount of rotation of a half line about its fixed endpoint (see Figure 1); it is customary to measure angles in degrees (one complete rotation equals 360°), and, because of the application of these elementary trigonometric ideas to triangles and triangle solving, much of the work can be done with the angle θ limited to the interval $0° \leq \theta \leq 180°$.

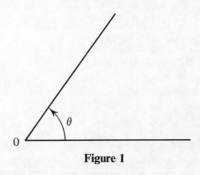

Figure 1

For our purposes, however, this approach is too narrow and restricted. It is necessary that we define the functions in a more general way so that, as functions, they have domains which are either all of **R**, or all of **R** except where division by zero would be involved. Moreover, it is inconvenient to have numbers in the domain tied to a rotation of a half line and thought of in terms of degrees. On the other hand, the more general definition should be devised so that the great utility of the angle concept is not lost: we want, in other words, the best of both worlds.

Fortunately, this is not only possible but possible by either of several methods, usually based on the geometry of the circle. We shall work with arc lengths of a circle. The dependence of our discussion upon geometry is indicated by our making explicit what we need to assume.

Assumption 1

(a) The circumference of a circle of radius r is $2\pi r$. Thus the circumference of a circle of radius 1 is 2π.

(b) If $\mathscr{C}_1$ and $\mathscr{C}_r$ are concentric circles of radius 1 and r, respectively, and if two half lines from the common center cut off arcs of length s_1 and s_r, respectively, then $s_r = rs_1$ (see Figure 2).

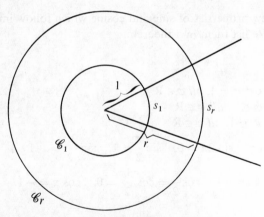

Figure 2

We shall initially focus attention on the sine and cosine. Once the definitions and basic properties of these functions have been given and developed it will be routine to obtain the corresponding properties of the other four trigonometric functions.

Definition 1. *Let $\mathscr{C}$ be the unit circle, i.e., the set of points in the plane determined by the equation $x^2 + y^2 = 1$. Let φ be any real number, and let P_φ be the point on $\mathscr{C}$ determined by the property that the length of arc on $\mathscr{C}$ from $(1, 0)$ to P_φ is φ; if $\varphi > 0$ the direction from $(1, 0)$ to P_φ is counterclockwise; if $\varphi < 0$, the* *direction is clockwise. If P_φ has coordinates (x, y), then by definition*

$$\cos \varphi = x$$
$$\sin \varphi = y.$$

(see Figure 3).

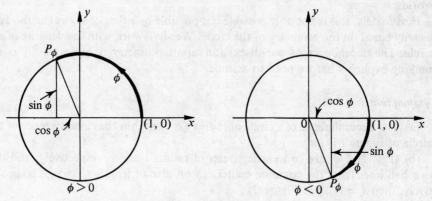

Figure 3

There are a few properties of sine and cosine which follow immediately from the definition. We list them in a theorem.

Theorem 1.

(1) $\sin^2 \varphi + \cos^2 \varphi = 1$, *all* $\varphi \in \mathbf{R}$
(2) $-1 \leq \sin \varphi \leq 1$, *all* $\varphi \in \mathbf{R}$
(3) $-1 \leq \cos \varphi \leq 1$, *all* $\varphi \in \mathbf{R}$
(4) $\sin 0 = \sin \pi = \sin 2\pi = 0$, $\quad \sin \dfrac{\pi}{2} = 1$, $\quad \sin \dfrac{3\pi}{2} = -1$
(5) $\cos 0 = \cos 2\pi = 1$, $\quad \cos \dfrac{\pi}{2} = \cos \dfrac{3\pi}{2} = 0$, $\quad \cos \pi = -1$.

Proof. Obvious (especially if you stop and think about it). ∎

It is frequently convenient to be able to work with a circle with a radius $r \neq 1$. This can easily be done in the following way.

Theorem 2. *Let $\mathscr{C}$ and $\mathscr{C}_r$ be circles of radii 1 and $r \neq 1$, respectively, and let φ be any number. Let the radial line through $P_\varphi(u, v)$ on $\mathscr{C}$ (determined as in Definition 1), extended if necessary, intersect $\mathscr{C}_r$ at $Q(x, y)$. Then*

$$\cos \varphi = \frac{x}{r}, \qquad \sin \varphi = \frac{y}{r}.$$

Proof. (See Figure 4.) Using the similar triangles OMP and ONQ, we have

$$\frac{\overline{ON}}{\overline{OM}} = \frac{\overline{OQ}}{\overline{OP}} \quad \text{or} \quad \frac{x}{u} = \frac{r}{1} \quad \text{or} \quad \frac{x}{r} = u = \cos \varphi.$$

Also

$$\frac{\overline{NQ}}{\overline{MP}} = \frac{\overline{OQ}}{\overline{OP}} \quad \text{or} \quad \frac{y}{v} = \frac{r}{1} \quad \text{or} \quad \frac{y}{r} = v = \sin \varphi. \quad \blacksquare$$

It follows from this result that if one wishes to identify φ with the central angle between the positive x-axis and the radius OQ and if it should happen that $0 < \varphi < \dfrac{\pi}{2}$, then the familiar designations of $\sin \varphi$ as "opposite over hypotenuse" and of $\cos \varphi$ as "adjacent over hypotenuse" are applicable.

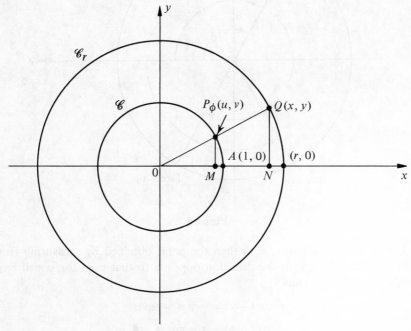

Figure 4

We now list a few additional properties of the sine and cosine.

Theorem 3

(1) $\sin (\varphi + 2n\pi) = \sin \varphi, \quad \cos (\varphi + 2n\pi) = \cos \varphi, \quad n = 0, \pm 1, \pm 2, \dots$
(2) $\sin (\varphi + \pi) = -\sin \varphi, \quad \cos (\varphi + \pi) = -\cos \varphi$
(3) $\sin (-\varphi) = -\sin \varphi, \quad \cos (-\varphi) = \cos \varphi.$

Proof. We refer to Figure 5.

(1) The assertion of (1) is equivalent to the geometric assertion that if, starting from any point P on $\mathscr{C}$, one describes an integral number of revolutions, in either direction, one ends at the same point P.

(2) If P has coordinates (x, y), then the diametrically opposite point, obtained by increasing the arc length by π units, has coordinates $(-x, -y)$. Thus

$$\sin(\varphi + \pi) = -y = -\sin\varphi,$$

$$\cos(\varphi + \pi) = -x = -\cos\varphi.$$

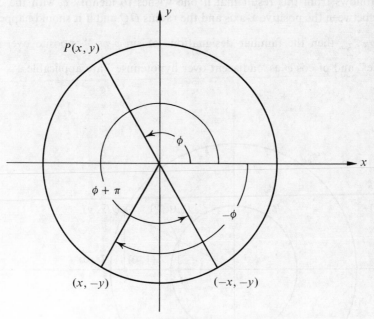

Figure 5

(3) If P has coordinates (x, y) then the point obtained by measuring from $(1, 0)$ $|\varphi|$ units along $\mathscr{C}$ in the direction opposite to that used for φ will have coordinates $(x, -y)$. Thus

$$\sin(-\varphi) = -y = -\sin\varphi$$

$$\cos(-\varphi) = x = \cos\varphi. \quad \blacksquare$$

Two remarks about Theorem 3 are in order. Statement 1 says that the sine and cosine functions are *periodic with period* 2π. A function f is *periodic* if and only if there exists a number $p > 0$ such that

$$f(x + p) = f(x)$$

for all x such that x and $x + p$ are in the domain of f. The minimum p for which this equation holds is *the period* of f. The fact that many physical phenomena are periodic suggests (and correctly so) that the trigonometric functions would be important in the application of mathematics to physical problems.

Statement (3) of Theorem 3 says that the sine is an *odd function* and the cosine is an *even function*. Recall that such functions have been discussed in Section 1.8.

For our next result we need the familiar law of cosines from the triangle-solving part of trigonometry. We now derive it.

Lemma 1 (*Law of Cosines*). *If a triangle has sides of lengths a, b, c, and if the angle between sides a and b is θ (angle opposite side c), then*

$$c^2 = a^2 + b^2 - 2ab \cos \theta.$$

Proof. We introduce a coordinate system such that side *a* lies along the positive *x*-axis and the angle θ is at the origin, and we consider a circle $\mathscr{C}$ of radius *b* (see Figure 6).

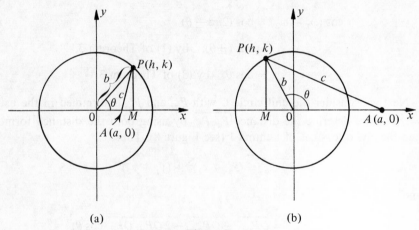

(a)   (b)

Figure 6

Using the distance formula, we have

$$c^2 = \overline{AP}^2 = (a - h)^2 + k^2$$
$$= a^2 - 2ah + h^2 + k^2$$
$$= a^2 + b^2 - 2ah,$$

since $P(h, k)$ lies on $\mathscr{C}_b$. But, by Theorem 2, $\cos \theta = \dfrac{h}{b}$, so $h = b \cos \theta$; thus

$$c^2 = a^2 + b^2 - 2ab \cos \theta. \quad \blacksquare$$

Note that, although it would usually be the case that the θ in Lemma 1 would satisfy $0 < \theta < \pi$, the result of the lemma still applies if $\theta = 0$ or if $\theta = \pi$ (see Figure 7).

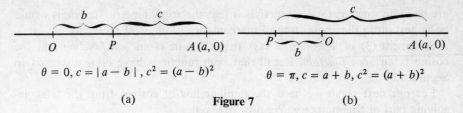

$\theta = 0, c = |a - b|, c^2 = (a - b)^2$ $\theta = \pi, c = a + b, c^2 = (a + b)^2$

(a)   **Figure 7**   (b)

We now derive an identity which will open a veritable treasure chest of other wonderful relationships.

Theorem 4. *For every* $\varphi_1, \varphi_2 \in \mathbf{R}$ *it is true that*

$$\cos(\varphi_1 - \varphi_2) = \cos \varphi_1 \cos \varphi_2 + \sin \varphi_1 \sin \varphi_2 .$$

Proof. We first remark that it is always possible to find an integer n and a number θ, $0 \le \theta \le \pi$, such that $\varphi_1 - \varphi_2 = 2n\pi \pm \theta$. Then

$$\cos(\varphi_1 - \varphi_2) = \cos(2n\pi \pm \theta)$$

$$= \cos(\pm\theta), \quad \text{by (1) of Theorem 3,}$$

$$= \cos \theta, \quad \text{by (3) of Theorem 3.}$$

Next we consider the unit circle C with P_{φ_1} and P_{φ_2} determined in the usual way and we describe the distance $\overline{P_{\varphi_1} P_{\varphi_2}}$ by using both the distance formula and the law of cosines of Lemma 1 (see Figure 8). Thus,

$$\overline{P_{\varphi_1} P_{\varphi_2}}^2 = (x_1 - x_2)^2 + (y_1 - y_2)^2$$

and

$$\overline{P_{\varphi_1} P_{\varphi_2}}^2 = \overline{OP_{\varphi_1}}^2 + \overline{OP_{\varphi_2}}^2 - 2\overline{OP_{\varphi_1}} \, \overline{OP_{\varphi_2}} \cos \theta.$$

Equating the right sides of the preceding two equations, and using the fact that C has radius one, we find

$$x_1^2 - 2x_1 x_2 + x_2^2 + y_1^2 - 2y_1 y_2 + y_2^2 = 2 - 2 \cos \theta,$$

or, since $x_1^2 + y_1^2 = x_2^2 + y_2^2 = 1$,

$$-2x_1 x_2 - 2y_1 y_2 = -2 \cos \theta.$$

Thus

$$\cos \theta = \cos \varphi_1 \cos \varphi_2 + \sin \varphi_1 \sin \varphi_2 ,$$

But $\cos \theta = \cos(\varphi_1 - \varphi_2)$, as previously noted, so

$$\cos(\varphi_1 - \varphi_2) = \cos \varphi_1 \cos \varphi_2 + \sin \varphi_1 \sin \varphi_2 . \quad \blacksquare$$

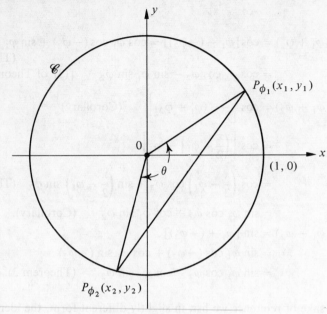

Figure 8

Corollary. *For all* $\varphi \in \mathbf{R}$ *it is true that*

(a) $\cos\left(\dfrac{\pi}{2} - \varphi\right) = \sin \varphi$

(b) $\sin\left(\dfrac{\pi}{2} - \varphi\right) = \cos \varphi.$

Proof. For (a) we use Theorem 4 with $\varphi_1 = \dfrac{\pi}{2}$, $\varphi_2 = \varphi$:

$$\cos\left(\frac{\pi}{2} - \varphi\right) = \cos\frac{\pi}{2}\cos\varphi + \sin\frac{\pi}{2}\sin\varphi$$

$$= \sin\varphi, \quad \text{by Theorem 1.}$$

For (b) we use the result of (a) with φ replaced by $\dfrac{\pi}{2} - \varphi$; thus

$$\sin\left(\frac{\pi}{2} - \varphi\right) = \cos\left[\frac{\pi}{2} - \left(\frac{\pi}{2} - \varphi\right)\right] = \cos\varphi. \quad\blacksquare$$

We are now able to obtain, very quickly, three more identities of the same type as that of Theorem 4.

Theorem 5. *For all* φ_1, $\varphi_2 \in \mathbf{R}$ *it is true that*

(a) $\cos(\varphi_1 + \varphi_2) = \cos\varphi_1 \cos\varphi_2 - \sin\varphi_1 \sin\varphi_2$

(b) $\sin(\varphi_1 + \varphi_2) = \sin\varphi_1 \cos\varphi_2 + \cos\varphi_1 \sin\varphi_2$

(c) $\sin(\varphi_1 - \varphi_2) = \sin\varphi_1 \cos\varphi_2 - \cos\varphi_1 \sin\varphi_2.$

Proof

(a) $\cos(\varphi_1 + \varphi_2) = \cos[\varphi_1 - (-\varphi_2)] = \cos\varphi_1\cos(-\varphi_2) + \sin\varphi_1\sin(-\varphi_2)$

(Theorem 4)

$\qquad\qquad\qquad = \cos\varphi_1\cos\varphi_2 - \sin\varphi_1\sin\varphi_2 \qquad$ [(3) of Theorem 3].

(b) $\sin(\varphi_1 + \varphi_2) = \cos\left[\dfrac{\pi}{2} - (\varphi_1 + \varphi_2)\right] \qquad$ (Corollary)

$\qquad\qquad\qquad = \cos\left[\left(\dfrac{\pi}{2} - \varphi_1\right) - \varphi_2\right]$

$\qquad\qquad\qquad = \cos\left(\dfrac{\pi}{2} - \varphi_1\right)\cos\varphi_2 + \sin\left(\dfrac{\pi}{2} - \varphi_1\right)\sin\varphi_2 \quad$ (Theorem 4)

$\qquad\qquad\qquad = \sin\varphi_1\cos\varphi_2 + \cos\varphi_1\sin\varphi_2 \qquad$ (Corollary).

(c) $\sin(\varphi_1 - \varphi_2) = \sin[\varphi_1 + (-\varphi_2)]$

$\qquad\qquad\qquad = \sin\varphi_1\cos(-\varphi_2) + \cos\varphi_1\sin(-\varphi_2)$

$\qquad\qquad\qquad = \sin\varphi_1\cos\varphi_2 - \cos\varphi_1\sin\varphi_2 \qquad$ (Theorem 3). ∎

For the sake of reference we list, in slightly different form, the identities just derived:

(1) $\sin(\varphi + \theta) = \sin\varphi\cos\theta + \cos\varphi\sin\theta$

(2) $\sin(\varphi - \theta) = \sin\varphi\cos\theta - \cos\varphi\sin\theta$

(3) $\cos(\varphi + \theta) = \cos\varphi\cos\theta - \sin\varphi\sin\theta$

(4) $\cos(\varphi - \theta) = \cos\varphi\cos\theta + \sin\varphi\sin\theta.$

We now give some of the immediate consequences of the preceding formulas:

(5) $\sin 2\varphi = 2\sin\varphi\cos\varphi \qquad$ [Set $\theta = \varphi$ in (1)]

(6) $\cos 2\varphi = \cos^2\varphi - \sin^2\varphi \qquad$ [Set $\theta = \varphi$ in (3)]

$\qquad\quad = 2\cos^2\varphi - 1 \qquad$ [Use Theorem 1]

$\qquad\quad = 1 - 2\sin^2\varphi \qquad$ [Use Theorem 1]

(7) $\sin\varphi\cos\theta = \dfrac{1}{2}[\sin(\varphi + \theta) + \sin(\varphi - \theta)] \qquad$ [Add (1) and (2)]

(8) $\cos\varphi\cos\theta = \dfrac{1}{2}[\cos(\varphi + \theta) + \cos(\varphi - \theta)] \qquad$ [Add (3) and (4)]

(9) $\sin\varphi\sin\theta = \dfrac{1}{2}[-\cos(\varphi + \theta) + \cos(\varphi - \theta)] \qquad$ [Subtract (3) from (4)]

(10) $\sin^2\varphi = \dfrac{1}{2}(1 - \cos 2\varphi)$

(11) $\cos^2\varphi = \dfrac{1}{2}(1 + \cos 2\varphi)$

[Use (6) in this list]

$$(12) \quad \sin^2 \frac{\theta}{2} = \frac{1}{2}(1 - \cos \theta)$$

$$(13) \quad \cos^2 \frac{\theta}{2} = \frac{1}{2}(1 + \cos \theta)$$

[Set $\theta = 2\varphi$ in (10) and (11)].

It is now a straightforward process to define the remaining four functions and determine their properties. Some of the proofs will be left as exercises.

The names of the functions we are about to define are *tangent*, *cotangent*, *secant*, and *cosecant*. These are usually abbreviated tan, cot, sec, and csc, respectively.

Definition 2

$$\tan \varphi = \frac{\sin \varphi}{\cos \varphi}, \qquad \varphi \neq \frac{\pi}{2} + n\pi, \qquad n = 0, \pm 1, \pm 2, \ldots$$

$$\cot \varphi = \frac{\cos \varphi}{\sin \varphi}, \qquad \varphi \neq n\pi, \qquad n = 0, \pm 1, \pm 2, \ldots$$

$$\sec \varphi = \frac{1}{\cos \varphi}, \qquad \varphi \neq \frac{\pi}{2} + n\pi, \qquad n = 0, \pm 1, \pm 2, \ldots$$

$$\csc \varphi = \frac{1}{\sin \varphi}, \qquad \varphi \neq n\pi, \qquad n = 0, \pm 1, \pm 2, \ldots.$$

We remark that the restrictions on the domains of these functions are, of course, because of the zeros of the sine and cosine. Also, it is evident that the tangent and cotangent are reciprocal functions.

A further observation is that the newly defined functions are all periodic as a consequence of their definitions and the periodicity of the sine and cosine. What is not immediately obvious is the fact that tangent and cotangent have period π. For, in the case of tangent,

$$\tan(\varphi + \pi) = \frac{\sin(\varphi + \pi)}{\cos(\varphi + \pi)} = \frac{-\sin \varphi}{-\cos \varphi}$$

$$= \tan \varphi.$$

A similar proof holds for cotangent. The period of secant and cosecant is 2π.

We should point out that, in terms of the coordinates of a point $P(x, y)$ on a circle of radius r (see Figure 4) the values of the tangent, etc., can be obtained from

$$\tan \varphi = \frac{y}{x}$$

$$\cot \varphi = \frac{x}{y}$$

$$\sec \varphi = \frac{r}{x}$$

$$\csc \varphi = \frac{r}{y}.$$

These expressions follow immediately from Definition 2, and the fact that $\sin \varphi = \dfrac{y}{r}$, $\cos \varphi = \dfrac{x}{r}$ (Theorem 2).

A few other properties of these functions are also immediate consequences of their definitions and corresponding properties of sine and cosine. For example, secant is an even function (since $\sec(-\varphi) = \dfrac{1}{\cos(-\varphi)} = \dfrac{1}{\cos \varphi} = \sec \varphi$), whereas tangent, cotangent, and cosecant are odd functions. And, since $|\sin \varphi| \leq 1$, $|\cos \varphi| \leq 1$, all $\varphi \in \mathbf{R}$, it follows that $|\csc \varphi| \geq 1$ and $|\sec \varphi| \geq 1$, all φ in the domains of these functions.

With regard to identities involving the functions of Definition 2, we can list the most important ones and give a proof of one or two, but leave for the reader the proofs of the rest. These equations hold for all φ and θ for which the functions involved are defined.

(14) $\tan^2 \varphi + 1 = \sec^2 \varphi$

(15) $1 + \cot^2 \varphi = \csc^2 \varphi$

(16) $\tan(\varphi + \theta) = \dfrac{\tan \varphi + \tan \theta}{1 - \tan \varphi \tan \theta}$

(17) $\tan(\varphi - \theta) = \dfrac{\tan \varphi - \tan \theta}{1 + \tan \varphi \tan \theta}$

(18) $\tan 2\varphi = \dfrac{2 \tan \varphi}{1 - \tan^2 \varphi}$

(19) $\tan \dfrac{1}{2}\varphi = \pm \sqrt{\dfrac{1 - \cos \varphi}{1 + \cos \varphi}} = \dfrac{\sin \varphi}{1 + \cos \varphi} = \dfrac{1 - \cos \varphi}{\sin \varphi}$.

Proofs. (14) Since $\sin^2 \varphi + \cos^2 \varphi = 1$ (Theorem 1), we obtain identity (14) by dividing both sides by $\cos^2 \varphi$:

$$\tan^2 \varphi + 1 = \sec^2 \varphi.$$

(16) $\tan(\varphi + \theta) = \dfrac{\sin(\varphi + \theta)}{\cos(\varphi + \theta)} = \dfrac{\sin \varphi \cos \theta + \cos \varphi \sin \theta}{\cos \varphi \cos \theta - \sin \varphi \sin \theta}$.

If, now, numerator and denominator of this last fraction are divided by $\cos \theta \cos \varphi$, we find

$$\tan(\varphi + \theta) = \dfrac{\dfrac{\sin \varphi}{\cos \varphi} + \dfrac{\sin \theta}{\cos \theta}}{1 - \dfrac{\sin \theta}{\cos \varphi} \dfrac{\sin \theta}{\cos \theta}}$$

or

$$\tan(\varphi + \theta) = \dfrac{\tan \varphi + \tan \theta}{1 - \tan \varphi \tan \theta}.$$

EXERCISES

1. If $\varphi = \dfrac{\pi}{4}$, and $P_\varphi(x, y)$, then $y = x$ (why)? Use this fact and the fact that P_φ lies on the unit circle to obtain:

(a) $\cos \dfrac{\pi}{4}$ (d) $\sin \dfrac{3\pi}{4}$ (g) $\cos \dfrac{7\pi}{4}$

(b) $\sin \dfrac{\pi}{4}$ (e) $\cos \dfrac{5\pi}{4}$ (h) $\sin \dfrac{7\pi}{4}$.

(c) $\cos \dfrac{3\pi}{4}$ (f) $\sin \dfrac{5\pi}{4}$

2. If $\varphi = \dfrac{\pi}{6}$, then $\dfrac{\pi}{2} - \varphi = \dfrac{\pi}{3}$ and the points P_φ and $P_{(\pi/2)-\varphi}$ are related by the fact that if (x, y) are the coordinates of P_φ, then (y, x) are the coordinates of $P_{(\pi/2)-\varphi}$ (see Figure 9). We can use both the distance formula and the law of cosines (Lemma 1) to obtain expressions for $\overline{P_\varphi P_{(\pi/2)-\varphi}}^2$.

(a) Do this, and obtain the result $\sin \dfrac{\pi}{6} = \dfrac{1}{2}$.

(b) From the result in (a) and an appropriate identity find $\cos \dfrac{\pi}{6}$.

(c) Find $\sin \dfrac{\pi}{3}$ and $\cos \dfrac{\pi}{3}$.

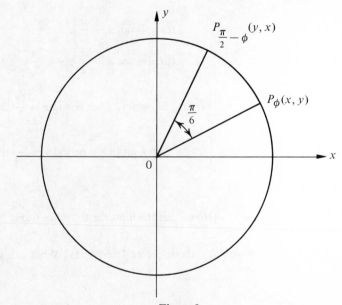

Figure 9

3. Use the results of Exercise 1 and 2 to find the values of

(a) $\sin \dfrac{2\pi}{3}$.

(h) $\tan \dfrac{\pi}{4}$.

(b) $\sin \dfrac{4\pi}{3}$.

(i) $\tan \dfrac{\pi}{6}$.

(c) $\cos \dfrac{5\pi}{6}$.

(j) $\tan \dfrac{\pi}{3}$.

(d) $\cos \dfrac{4\pi}{3}$.

(k) $\tan \dfrac{5\pi}{4}$.

(e) $\sin \dfrac{7\pi}{6}$.

(l) $\tan \dfrac{7\pi}{4}$.

(f) $\cos \dfrac{5\pi}{3}$.

(m) $\tan \dfrac{4\pi}{3}$.

(g) $\tan 0$.

(n) $\sec \dfrac{4\pi}{3}$.

4. Use identities and results of the preceding exercises to find the values of

(a) $\sin \dfrac{\pi}{12}$.

(d) $\cos \dfrac{13\pi}{12}$.

(b) $\cos \dfrac{5\pi}{12}$.

(e) $\tan \dfrac{\pi}{12}$.

(c) $\sin \dfrac{9\pi}{8}$.

(f) $\sec \dfrac{9\pi}{8}$.

5. Draw the graph of

(a) $y = \sin x,\ 0 \le x \le 2\pi$.

(c) $y = \tan x,\ -\dfrac{\pi}{2} < x < \dfrac{\pi}{2}$.

(b) $y = \cos x,\ -\dfrac{\pi}{2} \le x \le \dfrac{3\pi}{2}$.

(d) $y = \sec x,\ -\dfrac{\pi}{2} < x < \dfrac{3\pi}{2}$.

6. Draw the graph of $y = \sin 2x$. $\left[\textit{Hint.}\quad \text{Show } \sin 2x \text{ has period } \pi = \dfrac{2\pi}{2}\right].$

7. Draw the graph of $y = \sin \tfrac{1}{2}x$. $\left[\textit{Hint.}\quad \text{Show } \sin \tfrac{1}{2}x \text{ has period } 4\pi = \dfrac{2\pi}{\frac{1}{2}}\right].$

8. Draw the graph of $y = \sin 3x$.

9. What is the period of $\sin kx$? [*Hint.* See the hints for Exercises 6 and 7.]

10. If $\sin \varphi = \dfrac{1}{\sqrt{2}}$, what can you say about φ (see Exercise 1)? What can you say about $\cos \varphi$?

11. If $\cos \varphi = -\dfrac{\sqrt{3}}{2}$, what can be said about φ and $\sin \varphi$?

12. What can be said about φ if $\sin \varphi = \sqrt{2}$?

13. Find a description for all φ such that $2 \cos^2 \varphi - 1 = 0$.

14. Find a description for all φ such that $\sin 3\varphi = 1$.

15. Prove: $\tan\left(\alpha \pm \dfrac{\pi}{2}\right) = -\cot \alpha$. [*Hint.* Identities (16) and (17) are *not* applicable. Why? But Definition 2 and Identities (1)–(4) are.

16. Assign a positive direction to a line as the upward direction. The *angle of inclination* of a line is the angle α between the positive directions of the x-axis and the line; if the line is horizontal, $\alpha = 0$. Prove that the slope of a nonvertical line is described by $m = \tan \alpha$.

17. Prove the identities (15), (17), (18), and (19).

18. Prove:

$$\sec^2 x + \csc^2 x = \sec^2 x \csc^2 x.$$

For what values of x does this hold?

19. Graph:

(a) $y = \cot x, \ -\pi < x < 3\pi$
(b) $y = \csc x, \ -\pi < x < 3\pi.$

6.2 Derivatives and Graphs of Sine and Cosine

We found it convenient, in defining the trigonometric functions, to make an assumption about arcs of circles. As we shall see shortly, it will be convenient for finding the derivatives of these functions to make an additional assumption about the lengths of certain lines and arcs related to a circle. First, however, we see how far we can go with our present knowledge.

By definition,

$$D_x \sin x = \lim_{h \to 0} \frac{\sin (x + h) - \sin x}{h}.$$

Since we have available an identity (Theorem 5) for $\sin (x + h)$ we may as well use it:

$$D_x \sin x = \lim_{h \to 0} \frac{\sin x \cos h + \cos x \sin h - \sin x}{h}$$

$$= \lim_{h \to 0} \left[\cos x \, \frac{\sin h}{h} - \sin x \, \frac{1 - \cos h}{h} \right]$$

$$= \cos x \lim_{h \to 0} \frac{\sin h}{h} - \sin x \lim_{h \to 0} \frac{1 - \cos h}{h}.$$

Now we see that we need to know the values of the two limits in the preceding expression. In order not to leave this discussion in midair, we remark (and we shall very shortly prove) that the values of these limits are 1 and 0, respectively. It then follows that $D_x \sin x = \cos x$.

The proof of the limit assertion just made will be facilitated by the geometric assumption referred to before. We consider the portion of the unit circle C close to the point $(1, 0)$ (see Figure 10).

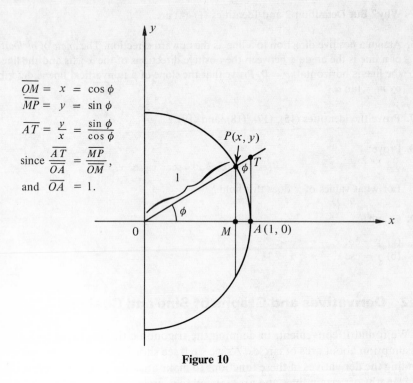

$$\overline{OM} = x = \cos \phi$$
$$\overline{MP} = y = \sin \phi$$
$$\overline{AT} = \frac{y}{x} = \frac{\sin \phi}{\cos \phi}$$
since $\dfrac{\overline{AT}}{\overline{OA}} = \dfrac{\overline{MP}}{\overline{OM}},$
and $\overline{OA} = 1.$

Figure 10

Assumption 2. The line segments MP and AT and the arc $\overset{\frown}{AP}$ satisfy

$$\overline{MP} < \overset{\frown}{AP} < \overline{AT}. \tag{1}$$

The crucial part of this assumption is that involving the *arc length* $\overset{\frown}{AP}$. As arc length of a curve is still to be defined (in Section 11.6), we make explicit that we are using a fact not yet developed (see the remark after Assumption 1).

In terms of φ and its sine and cosine this assumption becomes (for $\varphi > 0$)

$$\sin \varphi < \varphi < \frac{\sin \varphi}{\cos \varphi}. \tag{2}$$

Note that if $\varphi < 0$ the lengths of the corresponding line segment and arc in the first inequality of (2) would still be in the same relationship to each other. In other words, we can conclude from (1) that

$$\left.\begin{array}{c} |\sin \varphi| < |\varphi| \\[2mm] \text{or} \\[2mm] \sin^2 \varphi < \varphi^2 \end{array}\right\}. \tag{3}$$

Now we are in a position to evaluate the limits encountered before.

Lemma 2.

(i) $\displaystyle \lim_{\varphi \to 0} \frac{1 - \cos \varphi}{\varphi} = 0.$

(ii) $\displaystyle \lim_{\varphi \to 0} \frac{\sin \varphi}{\varphi} = 1.$

Proof. We consider (i) first. Regardless of the sign of $\varphi \neq 0$, identity (12) from Section 6.1 gives

$$0 < 1 - \cos \varphi = 2 \sin^2 \frac{\varphi}{2}.$$

By (3) this can be written

$$0 < 1 - \cos \varphi < 2\left(\frac{\varphi}{2}\right)^2 = \frac{\varphi^2}{2}.$$

We want to divide by φ but this requires paying attention to sign:

(a) $\displaystyle \varphi > 0 \Rightarrow 0 < \frac{1 - \cos \varphi}{\varphi} < \frac{\varphi}{2}.$

(b) $\displaystyle \varphi < 0 \Rightarrow 0 > \frac{1 - \cos \varphi}{\varphi} > \frac{\varphi}{2}.$

Since $\displaystyle \lim_{\phi \to 0} \frac{\varphi}{2} = 0$, we have, by Theorem 3.17, the "squeezing" theorem for limits,

$$\lim_{\varphi \to 0} \frac{1 - \cos \varphi}{\varphi} = 0.$$

Before proceding to the proof of (ii) we pause to collect a bonus from (i). The fact is that we have shown that the derivative of the cosine exists at zero and is equal to zero. To see this let $g(x) = \cos x$; then, by definition,

$$g'(0) = \lim_{\varphi \to 0} \frac{g(0 + \varphi) - g(0)}{\varphi}$$

$$= \lim_{\varphi \to 0} \frac{\cos \varphi - 1}{\varphi}, \qquad \text{since } \cos 0 = 1.$$

As the expression involved here is the negative of that in (i), we can conclude that $g'(0) = 0$. But this is not all: for if a function has a derivative at a point it is continuous at that point; thus the cosine function is continuous at 0, which is to say that $\lim_{\phi \to 0} \cos \varphi = \cos 0 = 1$.

Now we can dispense quickly with (ii). If $\varphi > 0$, we have, by (2),

$$\sin \varphi < \varphi < \frac{\sin \varphi}{\cos \varphi}.$$

Dividing by $\sin \varphi$ gives

$$1 < \frac{\varphi}{\sin \varphi} < \frac{1}{\cos \varphi}$$

or, inverting,

$$\cos \varphi < \frac{\sin \varphi}{\varphi} < 1.$$

But the same inequalities hold if $\varphi < 0$, as we now show. For, $\varphi < 0 \Rightarrow (-\varphi) > 0$, so

$$\sin (-\varphi) < (-\varphi) < \frac{\sin (-\varphi)}{\cos (-\varphi)}$$

or

$$-\sin \varphi < -\varphi < \frac{-\sin \varphi}{\cos \varphi}.$$

Dividing by $(-\sin \varphi)$ gives

$$1 < \frac{-\varphi}{-\sin \varphi} < \frac{1}{\cos \varphi},$$

or, inverting,

$$\cos \varphi < \frac{\sin \varphi}{\varphi} < 1.$$

Now if we use the "squeezing" theorem (Theorem 3.17) and the fact proven earlier, that $\lim_{\varphi \to 0} \cos \varphi = 1$, we have

$$\lim_{\varphi \to 0} \frac{\sin \varphi}{\varphi} = 1. \quad \blacksquare$$

Theorem 6 *For all $x \in \mathbf{R}$ the derivative of the sine function exists and*

$$D_x \sin x = \cos x.$$

Moreover, if u is a differentiable function of x, then

$$D_x \sin u = \cos u \, D_x u.$$

Proof. The first assertion follows from Lemma 2 and the discussion preceding it. The second assertion follows from the chain rule. $\blacksquare$

Theorem 7. *For all $x \in R$ the derivative of the cosine function exists and*

$$D_x \cos x = -\sin x.$$

Moreover, if u is a differentiable function of x, then

$$D_x \cos u = -\sin u \, D_x u.$$

Proof. Since $\cos x = \sin \left(\dfrac{\pi}{2} - x \right)$ (Corollary to Theorem 4).

$$D_x \cos x = D_x \sin \left(\frac{\pi}{2} - x \right)$$

$$= \cos \left(\frac{\pi}{2} - x \right)(-1) \quad \text{(by Theorem 6)}$$

$$= -\sin x \quad \text{(Corollary to Theorem 4)}.$$

The second assertion follows from the chain rule. ∎

We are now in a strong position to determine the nature of the graph of the sine and cosine functions. We begin with $\sin x$ and observe first of all that, because of the periodicity, knowledge of its geometric behavior in *any* interval of length 2π will suffice to obtain a description for *all* x. For reasons which will shortly be apparent we use the interval from $-\pi$ to π. Secondly, we can use the fact that $\sin x$ is an odd function to cut this interval in half, and study $\sin x$ for $0 \le x \le \pi$. To this end Table 6.1 will be useful:

TABLE 6.1

x	$\sin x$	$\dfrac{d}{dx} \sin x = \cos x$
$0 \to \dfrac{\pi}{2}$	$0 \to 1$	$1 \to 0$
$\dfrac{\pi}{2} \to \pi$	$1 \to 0$	$0 \to (-1)$

The various entries show that for $0 \le x \le \pi$, $\sin x \ge 0$ and, since $\dfrac{d}{dx} \sin x = \cos x > 0$ for $0 \le x \le \dfrac{\pi}{2}$, $\sin x$ is increasing in that interval. Similarly, since $\cos x < 0$ for $\dfrac{\pi}{2} < x \le \pi$, $\sin x$ is decreasing in that interval. Clearly $\sin x$ has a relative maximum of 1 at $x = \dfrac{\pi}{2}$ $\left(\text{note that } \cos \dfrac{\pi}{2} = 0 \right)$.

Thus, for $0 \leq x \leq \pi$, the graph of $y = \sin x$ appears as in Figure 11.

Now, drawing on the above-mentioned properties (odd, periodic), we can extend the graph to an interval of any length, as in Figure 12.

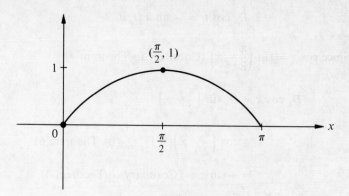

Figure 11

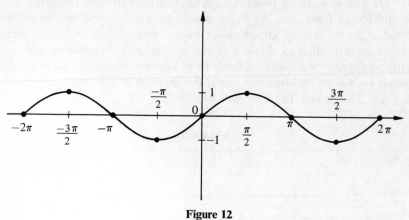

Figure 12

The graph of $y = \cos x$ can be studied in a similar fashion, but there is an even easier way: since

$$\sin\left(x + \frac{\pi}{2}\right) = \sin x \cos \frac{\pi}{2} + \cos x \sin \frac{\pi}{2},$$

or

$$\sin\left(x + \frac{\pi}{2}\right) = \cos x,$$

we can write

$$\cos x = \sin\left[x - \left(-\frac{\pi}{2}\right)\right].$$

The significance of this statement is simply that the graph of $y = \cos x$ is the same as the graph of $y = \sin x$ translated $\dfrac{\pi}{2}$ units to the left. This is shown in Figure 13.

Figure 13 also illustrates the relationships between these functions and their derivatives, as given by Theorems 6 and 7. Thus, wherever the one graph crosses the x-axis the other has either a maximum or a minimum. And $\sin x$ is increasing wherever $\cos x > 0$, $\cos x$ is increasing wherever $\sin x < 0$. And so on.

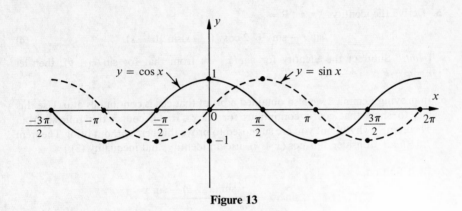

Figure 13

EXERCISES

1. Near the end of Section 6.2 reference was made to a "translation" property of curves. We illustrate this property.

   (a) Sketch all of the following curves on the same set of axes:
      (i) $y = x$.
      (ii) $y = x - 1$.
      (iii) $y = x + 2 = x - (-2)$.
      (iv) $y = x - a$.

   (b) Same as (a), only for
      (i) $y = x^2$.
      (ii) $y = (x - 2)^2$.
      (iii) $y = (x + 3)^2 = (x - (-3))^2$.
      (iv) $y = (x - a)^2$.

2. Find $\dfrac{dy}{dx}$:

   (a) $y = \sin x \cos x$.
   (b) $y = \sin^2 x$.
   (c) $y = \sin x^2$.
   (d) $y = 2 \sin^3 x + 3 \cos^2 x$.
   (e) $y = 4 \sin (x^2 + 1)$.
   (f) $y = 2 \sin^2 (x^3 - 1)$.

   (g) $y = \sqrt{\dfrac{1 - \sin^2 x}{1 + \sin^2 x}}$.

   (h) $y = \sqrt{\dfrac{1 - \cos x}{1 + \cos x}}$.

3. Let $f(x) = \sin x$.

(a) Find $f'(x), f''(x), f'''(x), f^{(\mathrm{iv})}(x), f^{(\mathrm{v})}(x)$.

(b) Find $f^{(143)}(x), f^{(258)}(x), f^{(600)}(x)$.

4. As Figure 13 shows, the graphs of sine and cosine are essentially the same. Show that these two functions satisfy the same differential equation:

$$\frac{d^2 y}{dx^2} + y = 0.$$

5. Derive the identity: $\forall r, s \in \mathbf{R} \Rightarrow$

$$\sin r - \sin s = 2 \cos \tfrac{1}{2}(r+s) \sin \tfrac{1}{2}(r-s). \tag{4}$$

[*Hint.* Subtract the identity for $\sin(\varphi - \theta)$ from that for $\sin(\varphi + \theta)$; then let $r = \varphi + \theta, s = \varphi - \theta$.]

6. In proving Lemma 2 we also obtained a proof that cos is continuous at 0. Use this fact to show that cos is continuous for all $x \in \mathbf{R}$. Of course this follows from Theorem 7 (why?), but you are supposed to prove this here without using Theorem 7. [*Hint.* Consider $\lim_{h \to 0} \cos(x + h)$, use an identity, and inequality (3).]

7. By definition

$$D_x \sin x = \lim_{h \to 0} \frac{\sin(x+h) - \sin x}{h}.$$

Evaluate this limit by using (4) in Exercise 5. Do you need the result of Exercise 6?

8. Use l'Hospital's Rule (see Section 4.6) to evaluate each of the following limits:

(a) $\lim_{x \to 0} \dfrac{x - \sin x}{x^2}$.

(b) $\lim_{x \to \pi} \dfrac{1 + \cos x}{\sin 2x}$.

(c) $\lim_{x \to 0} \dfrac{\cos x - 1}{\cos 2x - 1}$.

(d) $\lim_{x \to 0} \dfrac{\sin^2 x}{x}$.

(e) $\lim_{x \to 0} \dfrac{x - \sin^2 x}{1 - \cos 2x}$.

(f) $\lim_{x \to 0} \dfrac{x \cos x - \sin x}{x}$.

(g) $\lim_{x \to \infty} \dfrac{\dfrac{1}{x^2}}{\sin^2 \left(\dfrac{2}{x}\right)}$.

9. Find $\dfrac{dy}{dx}$:

(a) $y = \dfrac{\sin x}{\cos x}$.

(b) $y = \cos(2x + 1)$.

(c) $y = \dfrac{\sin x}{x}$.

(d) $y = \sin 3x \cos 4x$.

(e) $y = x^2 \sin x$.

(f) $y = \sin^4 x$.

(g) $y = \dfrac{x^2}{\sin^2 x}$.

(h) $y = \sin \sqrt{x}$.

(i) $y = \sqrt{\sin x}$.

(j) $y = \dfrac{1}{\cos x}$.

10. Use implicit differentiation to find $y' = \dfrac{dy}{dx}$:

   (a) $x + \sin xy = 1$

   (b) $\cos(x + y) + 2x - 3y = 0$.

6.3 Derivatives and Graphs of the Other Trigonometric Functions

We now investigate the derivatives of the remaining trigonometric functions. The results are obtained from the theorems already available about derivatives —there is no need to make use of the limit process. We illustrate the technique for tangent:

$$D_x \tan x = D_x \frac{\sin x}{\cos x} = \frac{\cos x \, D_x \sin x - \sin x \, D_x \cos x}{\cos^2 x}$$

$$= \frac{\cos^2 x + \sin^2 x}{\cos^2 x}$$

$$= \frac{1}{\cos^2 x}$$

$$= \sec^2 x.$$

We can summarize the complete results as follows:

Theorem 8. *Let u be a differentiable function (of x). Then the following derivative formulas hold*:

   (a) $D_x \tan u = \sec^2 u \, D_x u$.

   (b) $D_x \cot u = -\csc^2 u \, D_x u$.

   (c) $D_x \sec u = \sec u \tan u \, D_x u$.

   (d) $D_x \csc u = -\csc u \cot u \, D_x u$.

The proof of (a) follows from the preceding discussion and the chain rule. The proofs of (b), (c), and (d) are left as exercises. ∎

It should be noted that the derivatives of tan, cot, sec, and csc exist for all points in their respective domains; i.e., if f represents any one of these four functions, then f and f' have the same domain. It follows from this that these— and therefore *all*—trigonometric functions are continuous at all points of their domains.

It is now an easy matter to discuss the graphs of these functions. We shall investigate the graphs of $y = \tan x$ and $y = \sec x$, leaving the graphs of $y = \cot x$ and $y = \csc x$ as exercises.

In the study of the graph of $y = \tan x$ we first note that $\dfrac{dy}{dx} = \sec^2 x > 0$, so the graph is everywhere monotonic increasing. Next, since the period of tan is π, we can restrict ourselves to the interval $-\pi/2 < x < \pi/2$. But, taking advantage of the fact that tan is an odd function, we can further restrict the interval to $0 \le x < \dfrac{\pi}{2}$. Now $\tan 0 = 0$ and $\tan \dfrac{\pi}{4} = 1$, and the major remaining question concerns the behavior of $\tan x$ as $x \to \dfrac{\pi}{2}$ from the left. This is easily settled:

$$\lim_{x \to (\pi/2)^-} \tan x = \lim_{x \to (\pi/2)^-} \frac{\sin x}{\cos x} = \infty,$$

i.e., $\tan x$ gets big beyond all bounds as $x \to \dfrac{\pi^-}{2}$, since $\sin x \to 1$ and $\cos x \to 0$ through positive values. We can also compute the second derivative: $D_x{}^2 \tan x = 2\sec^2 x \tan x > 0$ for $0 < x < \dfrac{\pi}{2}$; thus the graph is concave upward in this interval.

Putting together this information we obtain the sketch in Figure 14.

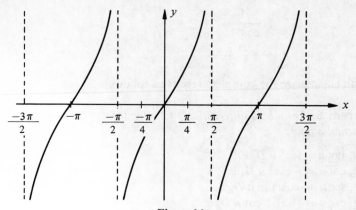

Figure 14

To obtain the graph of $y = \sec x$ we use periodicity and the even property to restrict our study to the set $\left\{x \mid 0 \le x < \dfrac{\pi}{2}\right\} \cup \left\{x \mid \dfrac{\pi}{2} < x \le \pi\right\}$. Since $D_x \sec x = \sec x \tan x = \dfrac{\sin x}{\cos^2 x}$, we observe that the sec is increasing for x in this set. However, $\sec x \ge 1$ for $x \in \left[0, \dfrac{\pi}{2}\right)$ and $\sec x \le -1$ for $x \in \left(\dfrac{\pi}{2}, \pi\right]$. Also,

$$\lim_{x \to (\pi/2)^-} \sec x = \lim_{x \to (\pi/2)^-} \frac{1}{\cos x} = \infty,$$

$$\lim_{x \to (\pi/2)^+} \sec x = \lim_{x \to (\pi/2)^+} \frac{1}{\cos x} = -\infty.$$

Collecting this information we obtain the sketch as shown in Figure 15. This figure also shows the graph of $y = \cos x$. Recalling that cos and sec are, by definition, reciprocal functions would make it easy to obtain the graph of one of these from the graph of the other.

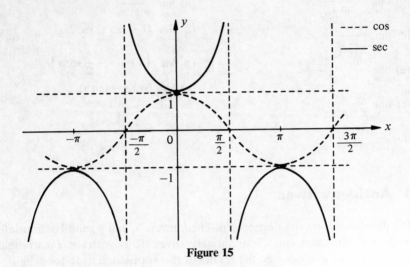

Figure 15

EXERCISES

1. Find $\dfrac{dy}{dx}$:

(a) $y = \sec x \tan x.$

(b) $y = \tan^2 x.$

(c) $y = \cot^3 x.$

(d) $y = -\cot^2 x \csc^2 x.$

(e) $y = \dfrac{1 + \tan^2 x}{1 - \tan^2 x}.$

(f) $y = \sqrt{1 + \tan^2 x}.$

(g) $y = -\sqrt{\csc^2 x - 1}.$

(h) $y = -\cot x - x.$

(i) $y = \tan x - x.$

(j) $y = x \sec^2 x.$

2. Let $f(x) = \tan x.$ Find the first five derivatives of f. Does there seem to be a pattern or a periodicity such as exists for the derivatives of sin?

3. Prove parts (b), (c), and (d) of Theorem 8.

4. Graph $y = \cot x$ for x between $-\pi$ and 3π.

5. Graph $y = \sin x$ for $-\dfrac{\pi}{2} \le x \le 2\pi$. Use this graph and the fact that csc x and sin x are reciprocals to draw, on the same axes, the graph of $y = \csc x$.

6. Use l'Hospital's Rule (see Section 4.6) to evaluate the following limits.

(a) $\lim\limits_{x\to\pi/4} \dfrac{1+\cos 4x}{\sec^2 x - 2\tan x}$.

(b) $\lim\limits_{x\to 0} \dfrac{x-\tan x}{\sin x}$.

(c) $\lim\limits_{x\to\pi/4} \dfrac{\cos^2 2x}{1-\tan x}$.

(d) $\lim\limits_{x\to 0} \dfrac{\sin x - \tan x}{x^3}$.

(e) $\lim\limits_{x\to 0} \dfrac{\tan 3x}{x\cos x}$.

(f) $\lim\limits_{x\to\pi/2} \dfrac{\tan 3x}{\tan 5x}$.

(g) $\lim\limits_{x\to\pi/2} \dfrac{\sec x + 1}{\tan x}$.

(h) $\lim\limits_{x\to 0} \dfrac{\csc x}{\cot^2 x}$.

(i) $\lim\limits_{x\to\pi/4} (1-\tan x)\sec 2x$.

(j) $\lim\limits_{x\to\pi/2} \left(x\tan x - \dfrac{\pi}{2}\sec x\right)$.

(k) $\lim\limits_{x\to\pi/2} (\sec x - \tan x)$.

6.4 Antiderivatives

The derivative formulas described in Theorems 6, 7, and 8 can all be translated immediately into statements about antiderivatives. Thus, with some rearranging and rewriting, we can describe the results of this translation as follows:

Theorem 9

$$\int \sin u\, du = -\cos u + c$$

$$\int \cos u\, du = \sin u + c$$

$$\int \sec^2 u\, du = \tan u + c$$

$$\int \csc^2 u\, du = -\cot u + c$$

$$\int \sec u \tan u = \sec u + c$$

$$\int \csc u \cot u\, du = -\csc u + c.$$

However, it is readily seen that these formulas give us the antiderivatives of only *two* of the six trigonometric functions: we still need to find primitives for the last four functions defined. As it turns out, the easiest of the four is cot: by its definition

$$\cot u = \frac{\cos u}{\sin u} = \frac{D(\sin u)}{\sin u}.$$

Thus

$$\int \cos u\, du = \log|\sin u| + c.$$

In a similar manner we can obtain

$$\int \tan u \, du = -\log |\cos u| + c$$

$$= \log |\sec u| + c.$$

The antiderivatives of the remaining two functions also involve logarithms, but the fact is that their exact form can most easily be obtained by use of a far from transparent trick. Thus

$$\sec u = \sec u \left(\frac{\sec u + \tan u}{\sec u + \tan u} \right)$$

$$= \frac{(\sec u \tan u + \sec^2 u)}{\sec u + \tan u}$$

$$= \frac{D(\sec u + \tan u)}{\sec u + \tan u}.$$

This near skulduggery enables us to write

$$\int \sec u \, du = \log |\sec u + \tan u| + c.$$

We collect the preceding results and the corresponding one for csc in the following theorem.

Theorem 10

$$\int \tan u \, du = -\log |\cos u| + c = \log |\sec u| + c$$

$$\int \cot u \, du = \log |\sin u| + c$$

$$\int \sec u \, du = \log |\sec u + \tan u| + c$$

$$\int \csc u \, du = -\log |\csc u + \cot u| + c.$$

EXERCISES

1. Find:

   (a) $\int (\cos x - x) \, dx.$
   (b) $\int (\tan x + \sin x) \, dx.$
   (c) $\int (\sec x + \tan x) \, dx.$
   (d) $\int (\sec^2 x + \tan^2 x) \, dx.$

   (e) $\int (\sec^2 x - \tan^2 x) \, dx.$
   (f) $\int (\csc x + \cot x) \, dx.$
   (g) $\int (\tan x + \csc x) \, dx.$

2. Find the area bounded by $y = \sin x$ and the x-axis between 0 and π.

3. Find the area bounded by $y = \tan x$ and the x-axis between $x = 0$ and $x = \dfrac{\pi}{4}$.

4. Can you find the number x_0, $0 < x_0 < \frac{\pi}{2}$, such that the area bounded by $y = \tan x$ and $y = 0$ between $x = 0$ and $x = x_0$ is 1 square unit?

5. (a) Sketch $y = \cos x$ and $y = \sec x$ on the same axes for $0 \le x \le \frac{\pi}{3}$.

   (b) Find the area bounded by $y = \cos x$ and the x-axis between $x = 0$ and $x = \frac{\pi}{3}$.

   (c) Find the area bounded by $y = \sec x$ and the x-axis between $x = 0$ and $x = \frac{\pi}{3}$.

   (d) Find the area between the curves $y = \sec x$ and $y = \cos x$, $0 \le x \le \frac{\pi}{3}$.

6. Prove
$$\int \csc x \, dx = -\log |\csc x + \cot x| + c.$$

7. Prove
$$-\log |\csc x + \cot x| = \log |\csc x - \cot x|.$$

8. Prove
$$\int \csc x \, dx = \log |\csc x - \cot x| + c.$$

9. Resolve the following "dilemma":

   Since $\frac{d}{dx} (\sin^2 x) = 2 \sin x \cos x$,

$$\int 2 \sin x \cos x \, dx = \sin^2 x,$$

   but $\frac{d}{dx} (-\cos^2 x) = 2 \sin x \cos x$; thus

$$\int 2 \sin x \cos x \, dx = -\cos^2 x.$$

   Yet

$$\sin^2 x \ne -\cos^2 x.$$

10. Sketch $y = \sin x$ and $y = \cos x$ for $0 \le x \le \frac{\pi}{4}$. Which area is larger: the area between the two curves or the area between the sine curve and the x-axis?

6.5   Inverse Functions: A Brief Sketch

In this section, as a preliminary to the discussion of the inverse trigonometric functions, we give a short exposition of the basic theory of inverse functions in general.

We consider a function f with domain $X \subset \mathbf{R}$, and we let $Y = f[X]$; thus $f: X \longrightarrow Y$ (recall that the double arrowhead means f maps X *onto* Y).

In Chapter 1, in our discussion of the operation of composition of functions, we pointed out that the function j serves as the identity for this operation;

$$j \circ f = f \circ j = f,$$

For, let $x \in X$; then

$$(j \circ f)(x) = j(f(x)) = f(x),$$

and

$$(f \circ j)(x) = f(j(x)) = f(x).$$

We are now interested in the possibility of an inverse with respect to the operation of composition.

Definition 3. *Let $f: X \longrightarrow Y$; then f has an inverse $f^{-1} \Leftrightarrow \exists$ a function f^{-1} such that $f^{-1} \circ f = j_X$, i.e., $\forall x \in X \Rightarrow f^{-1}(f(x)) = x$.*

It is fairly apparent from the definition of f^{-1} that its domain is Y and that it maps Y onto X. We state this formally.

Theorem 11

$$\left.\begin{array}{c} f: X \longrightarrow Y \\ f^{-1} \text{ exists} \end{array}\right\} \Rightarrow f^{-1}: Y \longrightarrow X.$$

Proof. Let $y \in Y$ be arbitrary; then $\exists x \in X$ such that $f(x) = y$ (since f maps X onto Y). By Definition 3, $f^{-1}(f(x)) = x$; but this says that $f^{-1}(y) = x \in X$. Thus $f^{-1}: Y \to X$. Also the mapping is onto; for $x \in X \Rightarrow f(x) = y \in Y$, and

$$f^{-1}(y) = f^{-1}(f(x)) = x,$$

which says that every $x \in X$ is an image under f^{-1}. ∎

We mention next an occasionally useful property of f^{-1}.

Theorem 12.

$$\left.\begin{array}{c} f: X \longrightarrow Y \\ f^{-1} \text{ exists} \end{array}\right\} \Rightarrow f \circ f^{-1} = j_Y.$$

Proof. Let $y \in Y$; then $\exists x \in X$ such that $f(x) = y$ and, by Definition 3,

$$f^{-1}(y) = f^{-1}(f(x)) = x.$$

Thus,

$$(f \circ f^{-1})(y) = f(f^{-1}(y)) = f(x) = y. ∎$$

We remark that it would generally be in error to say that $f^{-1} \circ f = f \circ f^{-1}$. For Definition 3 requires that $f^{-1} \circ f = j_X$ and Theorem 12 says that $f \circ f^{-1} = j_Y$.

Thus $f^{-1} \circ f = f \circ f^{-1} \Leftrightarrow X = Y$. We give several examples now which illustrate this and other points about f^{-1}.

Example 1. Let $f : x \to \frac{1}{2}x + 3$. Clearly $X = Y = \mathbf{R}$. In seeking f^{-1} we look for a function such that for $x \in \mathbf{R}$

$$f^{-1}(f(x)) = x,$$

i.e.,

$$f^{-1}(\tfrac{1}{2}x + 3) = x.$$

If we let $y = \frac{1}{2}x + 3$, then we can easily determine that $x = 2(y - 3)$, so $f^{-1} : y \to 2(y - 3)$. Or, if we write x instead of y (the symbol used for an element of the domain has no relation to the nature of the function), we see that

$$f^{-1}(x) = 2(x - 3).$$

Note that (cf. Definition 3 and Theorem 12)

$$(f^{-1} \circ f)(x) = f^{-1}(f(x)) = 2[f(x) - 3] = 2[\tfrac{1}{2}x + 3 - 3] = x,$$

and

$$(f \circ f^{-1})(x) = f(f^{-1}(x)) = \tfrac{1}{2}f^{-1}(x) + 3 = \tfrac{1}{2}[2(x - 3)] + 3 = x - 3 + 3 = x.$$

Figure 16 shows the graphs of f and f^{-1}. These graphs appear to be (and, in fact, *are*) symmetric with respect to the line $y = x$ (the graph of j).

Example 2. As a slightly more complicated example, consider the function defined by

$$f(x) = \sqrt{x^2 - 1}.$$

A little reflection shows that

$$X = \{x \mid x^2 \geq 1\} = \{x \mid x \leq -1\} \cup \{x \geq 1\},$$

$$Y = \{y \mid y \geq 0\}.$$

Proceeding as in Example 1, we look for f^{-1} such that $f^{-1}(f(x)) = x$, i.e., such that

$$f^{-1}(\sqrt{x^2 - 1}) = x.$$

If we set $y = \sqrt{x^2 - 1}$, we find $y^2 = x^2 - 1$ or $x^2 = y^2 + 1$. But now we are faced with a dilemma in solving for x: should we take $x = \sqrt{y^2 + 1}$ or $x = -\sqrt{y^2 + 1}$? As Figure 17 shows, each $y \geq 0$ is the image of two different x's under f, so it is not possible to define an inverse to f in the sense of Definition 3.

We can, however, salvage something from this. Suppose we restrict the domain of f to eliminate the difficulty encountered before. Thus we let

$$f_+(x) = \sqrt{x^2 - 1}, \qquad x \geq 1 > 0.$$

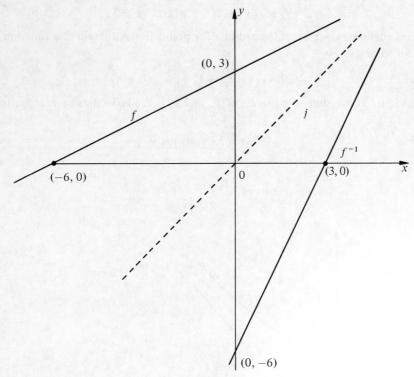

Figure 16

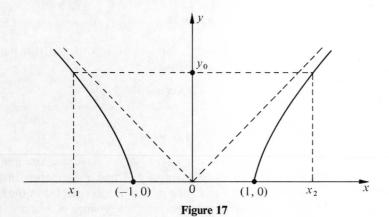

Figure 17

Then the dilemma encountered before in solving for x disappears, for $x > 0$ indicates that we *must* take the positive square root: $x = \sqrt{y^2 + 1}$. This means

$$f_+^{-1}(y) = \sqrt{y^2 + 1}, \qquad \text{where} \quad y \geq 0.$$

If, as is customary, we use x instead of y for points in the domain of a function, we can write

$$f_+^{-1}(x) = \sqrt{x^2 + 1}, \qquad x \geq 0.$$

In Figure 18 we show the graphs of f_+ and f_+^{-1}. We leave it as an exercise to verify that

(i) $$x \geq 1 \Rightarrow (f_+^{-1} \circ f_+)(x) = x,$$

and

(ii) $$x \geq 0 \Rightarrow (f_+ \circ f_+^{-1})(x) = x.$$

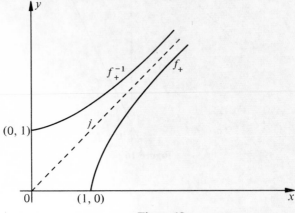

Figure 18

A remark about the graphs of f and f^{-1} might be in order at this point. Suppose $f \colon X \twoheadrightarrow Y$ and f^{-1} exists. Then the two sets

$$\{(x, y) \mid y = f(x), \, x \in X\}$$

and

$$\{(x, y) \mid x = f^{-1}(y), \, y \in Y\}$$

are equal; this means that, described in this way, f and f^{-1} have the same graph. However, writing x for points in the domain of f^{-1} and y for points in the range of f^{-1} causes the graph of f^{-1} to be the mirror image, reflected in the line $y = x$, of the graph of f—in other words, upon this interchange of x and y, the graphs of f and f^{-1} are symmetric with respect to the graph of j.

We now give two theorems which guarantee the existence of f^{-1}.

Theorem 13. *Let* $f: X \rightarrow Y$. *Then* f^{-1} *exists* $\Leftrightarrow f$ *is* 1–1.

Proof. We first prove the implication $\Rightarrow$. The hypothesis that f^{-1} exists means that $f^{-1}(f(x)) = x$ for every $x \in X$. To show that f is 1–1, let $x_1, x_2 \in X, x_1 \neq x_2$; we must show $f(x_1) \neq f(x_2)$. Now,

$$f^{-1}(f(x_1)) = x_1 \quad \text{and} \quad f^{-1}(f(x_2)) = x_2.$$

Suppose $f(x_1) = f(x_2) = y_0$, say. The two preceding equations would then say that $f^{-1}(y_0) = x_1, f^{-1}(y_0) = x_2$, where $x_1 \neq x_2$. This is contrary to the definition of a function, so we must reject the supposition that $f(x_1) = f(x_2)$. Thus f is 1–1.

For the implication $\Leftarrow$ we have as hypothesis that f is 1–1, i.e., that $x_1, x_2 \in X$, $x_1 \neq x_2, \Rightarrow f(x_1) \neq f(x_2)$. We show that f^{-1} exists, $f^{-1}: Y \rightarrow X$, by defining this function as follows: If $y \in Y$, then there exists $x \in X$, which is, by our hypothesis, unique, such that $y = f(x)$. We define $f^{-1}(y) = x$, where x is determined as indicated, i.e., $f(x) = y$. In this way f^{-1} is defined on Y and for every $x \in X$ we have

$$f^{-1}(f(x)) = f^{-1}(y) = x,$$

which is to say $f^{-1} \circ f = j_X$. ∎

Theorem 14. *Let* $f: X \rightarrow Y$ *and let* f *be monotonic increasing or monotonic decreasing on* X. *Then* f^{-1} *exists.*

Proof. If f is either monotonic increasing or monotonic decreasing, f is surely 1–1. By Theorem 13, f^{-1} exists. ∎

Before stating the next theorem it will be convenient to give a definition.

Definition 4. *Let* x_0 *be an element of the set* X. *Then* x_0 *is an* **interior point** *of* $X \Leftrightarrow \exists N(x_0) \subset X$. *The set of interior points of a set* X *is called the* **interior** *of* $X, \mathscr{I}(X)$.

For example, every point of an open interval is an interior point; the endpoints of a closed interval are not interior points and are, in fact, the only points which are not interior points.

Theorem 15. *Let* $f: X \rightarrow Y$, X *an interval, let* f *be continuous on* X *and let* f' *exist on the interior of* X. *If either* $f'(x) > 0$ *for all* $x \in \mathscr{I}(X)$ *or* $f'(x) < 0$ *for all* $x \in \mathscr{I}(X)$, *then* f^{-1} *exists.*

Proof. The hypotheses guarantee that f is either monotonic increasing or monotonic decreasing on X. Hence, by Theorem 14, f^{-1} exists. ∎

There is a minor point in this proof which will be discussed in Exercise 16 at the end of the section.

Our next theorem shows how certain properties of f carry over to f^{-1}.

Theorem 16

$$\left.\begin{array}{l} f : X \twoheadrightarrow Y \\ X \text{ an interval} \\ f \text{ monotonic increasing} \\ \quad\text{(decreasing) on } X \\ f \text{ continuous on } X \end{array}\right\} \Rightarrow \left\{\begin{array}{l} f^{-1} \text{ exists } (f^{-1} : Y \twoheadrightarrow X) \\ f^{-1} \text{ monotonic increasing} \\ \quad\text{(decreasing) on } Y \\ f^{-1} \text{ continuous on } Y \end{array}\right.$$

Proof.

(i) Since f is monotonic on X, by Theorem 14, f^{-1} exists.

(ii) Suppose f is monotonic increasing on X. We show f^{-1} is monotonic increasing on Y. Let $y_1, y_2 \in Y$, $y_1 < y_2$. Then $\exists x_1, x_2 \in X$ such that $f(x_1) = y_1$, $f(x_2) = y_2$, and $f^{-1}(y_1) = x_1$, $f^{-1}(y_2) = x_2$. Suppose $x_1 \geq x_2$; then, since f is monotonic increasing,

$$y_1 = f(x_1) \geq f(x_2) = y_2,$$

contrary to the choice of y_1 and y_2. Thus we must have $x_1 < x_2$. Similarly, if f is monotonic decreasing on X, we can show f^{-1} is monotonic decreasing on Y.

(iii) Finally we show that f^{-1} is continuous. We assume that f is monotonic increasing on X. The proof for decreasing f is similar.

Let $y_0 \in Y$; then $\exists x_0 \in X$ such that $f(x_0) = y_0$ and $f^{-1}(y_0) = f^{-1}(f(x_0)) = x_0$. We consider $N_\varepsilon(f^{-1}(y_0)) = N_\varepsilon(x_0)$ and show $\exists N_\delta(y_0)$ which is mapped by f^{-1} into $N_\varepsilon(f^{-1}(y_0))$. Assume $\varepsilon > 0$ is small enough so that $x_0 - \varepsilon$ and $x_0 + \varepsilon$ are both in X; let $f(x_0 - \varepsilon) = c$, $f(x_0 + \varepsilon) = d$, where $c < d$, since f is increasing (see Figure 19).

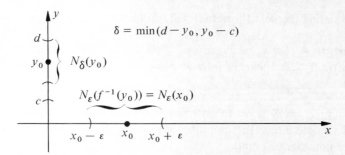

$$\delta = \min(d - y_0, y_0 - c)$$

Figure 19

Now if we take stock we have the following facts:

(a) $f^{-1}(c) = f^{-1}(f(x_0 - \varepsilon)) = x_0 - \varepsilon$,

(b) $f^{-1}(d) = f^{-1}(f(x_0 + \varepsilon)) = x_0 + \varepsilon$,

(c) f monotonic increasing $\Rightarrow f^{-1}$ monotonic increasing

(d) f continuous $\Rightarrow f$ maps $N_\varepsilon(x_0)$ onto (c, d) (why?).

Thus, $y \in (c, d) \Rightarrow f^{-1}(y)$ exists (by (d)) and satisfies

$$f^{-1}(c) < f^{-1}(y) < f^{-1}(d) \qquad \text{(by (c))},$$

which, by (a) and (b), means that

$$x_0 - \varepsilon < f^{-1}(y) < x_0 + \varepsilon.$$

This tells us that f^{-1} maps (c, d) into (onto, in fact) $N_\varepsilon(f^{-1}(y_0))$. All that remains to be done is to define $\delta = \min (d - y_0, y_0 - c)$. Then $N_\delta(y_0) \subset (c, d)$ and

$$f^{-1} : N_\delta(y_0) \to (x_0 - \varepsilon, x_0 + \varepsilon) = N_\varepsilon(f^{-1}(y_0));$$

thus f^{-1} is continuous at y_0.

If X is a closed or half-open interval, and if y_0 is such that $f^{-1}(y_0) = x_0$ is an endpoint of X, then one simply uses right or left neighborhoods in the proof. Thus, if $X = [a, b)$ and if $x_0 = a$, then right nbds. of x_0 and of $f(x_0) = y_0$ should be used. ∎

Our final theorem of this section also concerns the carryover of a property of f to f^{-1}, in this case the existence of the derivative.

Theorem 17. *Let $f : X \to Y$, X an interval, and suppose f' exists and does not change sign on the interior of X, i.e., either $f'(x) > 0$ for all $x \in \mathscr{I}(X)$ or $f'(x) < 0$ for all $x \in \mathscr{I}(X)$. Then f^{-1} exists and if $x_0 \in \mathscr{I}(X)$, $f(x_0) = y_0$, $(f^{-1})'(y_0)$ exists; in fact,*

$$(f^{-1})'(y_0) = \frac{1}{f'(f^{-1}(y_0))}$$

$$= \frac{1}{f'(x_0)}. \tag{5}$$

Proof. By definition,

$$(f^{-1})'(y_0) = \lim_{k \to 0} \frac{f^{-1}(y_0 + k) - f^{-1}(y_0)}{k} \tag{6}$$

It is clear from (6) that we must take k small enough so that $y_0 + k \in Y$. This means that $\exists x_1 \in X$ such that $f(x_1) = y_0 + k$. It will be convenient, however, to let $x_1 = x_0 + h$. Then we have the following useful relations:

$$f(x_0 + h) = y_0 + k = f(x_0) + k,$$

or

$$k = f(x_0 + h) - f(x_0); \tag{7}$$

and

$$f^{-1}(y_0 + k) = f^{-1}(f(x_0 + h)) = x_0 + h = f^{-1}(y_0) + h,$$

or

$$f^{-1}(y_0 + k) - f^{-1}(y_0) = h. \tag{8}$$

For the remainder of the proof we assume that $f'(x) < 0$ for all $x \in \mathscr{I}(X)$; the proof for the case $f'(x) > 0$ is similar.

If, now, we substitute (7) and (8) into (6) we have

$$(f^{-1})'(y_0) = \lim_{k \to 0} \frac{h}{f(x_0 + h) - f(x_0)}$$

$$= \lim_{k \to 0} \frac{1}{\dfrac{f(x_0 + h) - f(x_0)}{h}}.$$

This last step is possible because $f'(x) < 0 \Rightarrow f$ decreasing $\Rightarrow f^{-1}$ decreasing. Thus $k \neq 0 \Rightarrow h \neq 0$. As a matter of fact, one can say more about the relation between h and k: $\lim_{k \to 0} h = 0$ and $\lim_{h \to 0} k = 0$. For, f^{-1} is continuous (why), and, by (8)

$$\lim_{k \to 0} h = \lim_{k \to 0} [f^{-1}(y_0 + k) - f^{-1}(y_0)] = 0.$$

In a similar way, using (7) and the continuity of f, one shows $\lim_{h \to 0} k = 0$. Thus the preceding equation for $(f^{-1})'(y_0)$ can be written

$$(f^{-1})'(y_0) = \lim_{h \to 0} \frac{1}{\dfrac{f(x_0 + h) - f(x_0)}{h}}$$

$$= \lim_{h \to 0} \frac{1}{\dfrac{f(x_0 + h) - f(x_0)}{h}}$$

$$= \frac{1}{f'(x_0)} = \frac{1}{f'(f^{-1}(y_0))}. \quad\blacksquare$$

The relation between f' and $(f^{-1})'$, as stated in Theorem 17, seems rather monstrous. In the Leibniz notation this relation takes a much simpler and more suggestive form. If we denote the function f (of x) by y, then f' is denoted by $\dfrac{dy}{dx}$. On the other hand, if we can solve for x the functional relation between x and y to obtain $x = f^{-1}(y)$, then $(f^{-1})'$ is denoted by $\dfrac{dx}{dy}$. In this notation the relation between the derivatives is

$$\frac{dx}{dy} = \frac{1}{\dfrac{dy}{dx}}.$$

For,

$$\frac{dx}{dy} = (f^{-1})'(y_0) = \frac{1}{f'(x_0)} = \frac{1}{\dfrac{dy}{dx}}.$$

The Leibniz formulation *is* simple, but it is not very explicit and it is somewhat ambiguous, for it does not indicate at what points the functions are being evaluated. There is, however, no harm in using it as long as it is understood.

Example 3. We return to the function f_+ of Example 2:

$$f_+(x) = \sqrt{x^2 - 1}, \qquad X = \{x \mid x \geq 1\}.$$

Recall that we found f_+^{-1} was described by

$$f_+^{-1}(x) = \sqrt{x^2 + 1}, \qquad x \geq 0. \tag{9}$$

We calculate f_+' :

$$f_+'(x) = \frac{1}{2}(x^2 - 1)^{-1/2}(2x) = \frac{x}{\sqrt{x^2 - 1}};$$

clearly $x \in \mathscr{I}(X) = \{x \mid x > 1\} \Rightarrow f_+'(x) > 0$. Thus $(f_+^{-1})'$ exists, and, using (5),

$$(f_+^{-1})'(x) = \frac{1}{f_+'(f_+^{-1}(x))}$$

$$= \frac{1}{\dfrac{f_+^{-1}(x)}{\sqrt{[(f_+^{-1})(x)]^2 - 1}}} = \frac{\sqrt{[f_+^{-1}(x)]^2 - 1}}{f_+^{-1}(x)}$$

$$= \frac{\sqrt{x^2 + 1 - 1}}{\sqrt{x^2 + 1}} \qquad \text{[from (9)]}$$

$$= \frac{x}{\sqrt{x^2 + 1}} \qquad (\text{since } x > 0 \Rightarrow \sqrt{x^2} = x).$$

Obviously, this result could be obtained directly and more easily from Eq. (9), but the technique just illustrated will be useful in the next section when the direct method is not available.

EXERCISES

In Exercises 1–11 find the domain and range of each function f and find, if it exists, the inverse. If the inverse fails to exist, restrict the domain of f so that the cutdown f will have an inverse, and find it. Also, find the derivatives of f and f^{-1} when they exist. In each case sketch the graph of f and f^{-1} on the same figure.

1. $f(x) = 2x - 3$.

2. $f(x) = -\frac{1}{3}x + 4$.

3. $f(x) = mx + b, m \neq 0$.

4. $f(x) = \sqrt{x}$.

5. $f(x) = x^3$.

6. $f(x) = \sqrt[5]{x}$.

7. $f(x) = x^4$.

8. $f(x) = \dfrac{x^2}{x^2+1}$.

9. $f(x) = \dfrac{1}{x}$.

10. $f(x) = 1 - x$.

11. $f(x) = \sqrt{1 - x^2}, \quad 0 \le x \le 1$.

12. Let f, g, and h be functions with domains and ranges such that $f \circ g$, $g \circ h$, $(f \circ g) \circ h$, $f \circ (g \circ h)$ are all meaningful. Show that
$$(f \circ g) \circ h = f \circ (g \circ h).$$

13. Let $g(x) = \sqrt{x^2 - 1}$, $x \le -1$. Find g^{-1}.

14. This refers to the f_+ and f_+^{-1} of Example 2. Verify that
$$f_+^{-1} \circ f_+ = j_X,$$
$$f_+ \circ f_+^{-1} = j_Y.$$

15. Let $f: X \longrightarrow Y$; assume f^{-1} exists. Let
$$G_1 = \{(x, y) \mid y = f(x), \quad x \in X\},$$
$$G_2 = \{(x, y) \mid x = f^{-1}(y), \quad y \in Y\}.$$
Show that $G_1 = G_2$.

16. Let $f: X \longrightarrow Y$, where X is an interval. Suppose f is continuous on X and f' exists on $\mathscr{I}(X)$ and is either positive on all of $\mathscr{I}(X)$ or negative on all of $\mathscr{I}(X)$. Show that f is monotonic on X. [*Hint.* Use the Mean Value Theorem.]

17. Show that Theorem 16 remains valid if the hypothesis that f is continuous on X is dropped. [*Hint.* The essential fact is that without continuity of f, not every point of (c, d) need be in Y. Thus, in the final steps of the proof, one must consider $(c, d) \cap Y$.]

18. In the proof of Theorem 17, why can it be asserted that f^{-1} is continuous?

19. Is anything wrong with the following proof of Theorem 17? If so, what?
(1) $f^{-1} \circ f = j_X$ (Definition 3)
(2) $(f^{-1} \circ f)(x) = j(x)$ (evaluating at $x \in X$)
(3) $(f^{-1})'(f(x)) \cdot f'(x) = 1$ (chain rule and $j'(x) = 1$)
(4) $(f^{-1})'(f(x)) = \dfrac{1}{f'(x)}$, $(f'(x) \ne 0)$.

20. In Exercises 9, 10, and 11, it happened that $f^{-1} = f$. If $f: X \longrightarrow Y$, give necessary conditions for $f^{-1} = f$.

21. Let $f: X \longrightarrow Y$. Prove that if f^{-1} exists it is unique. [*Hint.* We know (why?) that $f^{-1} \circ f = j_X$, $f \circ f^{-1} = j_Y$. Suppose there exists $g: Y \longrightarrow X$ such that $g \circ f = j_X$ and $f \circ g = j_Y$. Consider $g \circ f \circ f^{-1}$ and show $g = f^{-1}$.]

6.6   The Inverse Trigonometric Functions

We now apply the results of the preceding section to the trigonometric functions, our purpose being to obtain, if possible, functions inverse to the six
trigonometric functions.

It will be convenient to consider the sine and cosine together. Portions of the
graphs of these functions are shown in Figure 20.

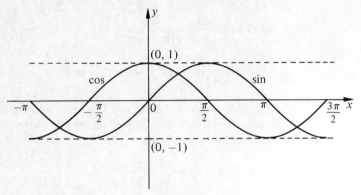

Figure 20

From Theorem 13 we know that we can find an inverse if and only if the function is 1–1. A glance at the graph of the sine function shows that it will be essential to restrict that function to an interval of length at most π units. However,
since the range of the sine is the interval $[-1, 1]$, we see that if we choose properly an interval π units long we will be able to encompass the entire range. Even
so there are many possible choices of such intervals: $\left[-\dfrac{\pi}{2}, \dfrac{\pi}{2}\right]$, $\left[\dfrac{\pi}{2}, \dfrac{3\pi}{2}\right]$, $\left[\dfrac{7\pi}{2}, \dfrac{9\pi}{2}\right]$
are some in which the restricted domain is *connected* (i.e., roughly, all in one
piece); but even this is not essential—we *could* take $\left[-\dfrac{\pi}{2}, 0\right] \cup \left[2\pi, \dfrac{5\pi}{2}\right]$, or
many others.

It seems sensible to choose the restricted domain to be connected, and, if asked
to make a single choice satisfying this requirement, it further would seem natural
to choose a domain "close to" 0. For the sine function the interval $\left[-\dfrac{\pi}{2}, \dfrac{\pi}{2}\right]$
becomes the "natural" one. Suppose we denote by f the sine function restricted
to $\left[-\dfrac{\pi}{2}, \dfrac{\pi}{2}\right]$. Then

$$f: x \to \sin x, \quad X_f = \left[-\frac{\pi}{2}, \frac{\pi}{2}\right], \quad Y_f = Y_{\sin} = [-1, 1].$$

Also,

$$f'' : x \to \cos x,$$

and $x \in X_f \Rightarrow f'(x) \geq 0$, with equality holding only at the endpoints $-\dfrac{\pi}{2}$ and $\dfrac{\pi}{2}$.

Thus Theorems 15, 16 and 17 assure us that f^{-1} exists on $[-1, 1]$, $f^{-1} : [-1, 1] \to \left[-\dfrac{\pi}{2}, \dfrac{\pi}{2}\right]$, f^{-1} is increasing and continuous there, and that $(f^{-1})'$ exists on $(-1, 1)$ and is positive there. Moreover, we can use Theorem 17 to obtain an explicit formula for $(f^{-1})'$. For we know

$$(f^{-1})'(y) = \frac{1}{f'(f^{-1}(y))}$$

$$= \frac{1}{\cos f^{-1}(y)}, \qquad \text{since } f' = \cos.$$

Now if we draw on the identity $\sin^2 x + \cos^2 x = 1$, we can quickly obtain a more satisfactory form for this derivative. For this identity leads to $\cos^2 x = 1 - \sin^2 x$, or, in this case, because

$$f^{-1} : Y_f \to X_f = \left[-\frac{\pi}{2}, \frac{\pi}{2}\right],$$

and because the cosine is non-negative on X_f (see Figure 20), $\cos x = \sqrt{1 - \sin^2 x}$ —in other words, there is no ambiguity about the sign in taking the square root. Thus,

$$(f^{-1})'(y) = \frac{1}{\sqrt{1 - \sin^2 f^{-1}(y)}}.$$

But here $f = \sin$, so $\sin^2 f^{-1}(y) = [f(f^{-1}(y))]^2 = y^2$, by Theorem 12, so

$$(f^{-1})'(y) = \frac{1}{\sqrt{1 - y^2}}.$$

Notice that Theorem 17 does not guarantee the existence of $(f^{-1})'$ at $y = \pm 1$, and, in fact, the derivative does not exist at either of these points.

In summary, using the standard notation $\sin^{-1}$ for f^{-1} (arc sin is also used), we have

$$f : x \to \sin x, \qquad X_f = \left[-\frac{\pi}{2}, \frac{\pi}{2}\right], \qquad Y_f = Y_{\sin} = [-1, 1],$$

$$f^{-1} : x \to \sin^{-1} x, \qquad x \in Y_f, \qquad \sin^{-1} x \in X_f,$$

and

$$(f^{-1})'(x) = \frac{1}{\sqrt{1 - x^2}}, \qquad -1 < x < 1.$$

The functional identities of Definition 3 and Theorem 12

$$f^{-1} \circ f = j_{X_f}, \quad \text{and} \quad f \circ f^{-1} = j_{Y_f},$$

become

$$\sin^{-1}(\sin x) = x, \quad -\frac{\pi}{2} \leq x \leq \frac{\pi}{2} \quad \text{and} \quad \sin(\sin^{-1} x) = x, \quad -1 \leq x \leq 1,$$

respectively.

In Figure 21 we show the graphs of f and f^{-1}.

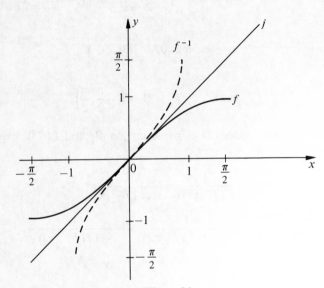

Figure 21

We now assert the following about the cosine function. We shall not prove any part of this assertion, but leave the proofs as an exercise for the reader; the proofs, in fact, are quite analogous to those just given for the sine function.

It is natural to use as restricted domain for the cosine function the interval $[0, \pi]$ (why are we unable to use $\left[-\frac{\pi}{2}, \frac{\pi}{2}\right]$ as we did for the sine?). Thus, we let f be the cosine function with domain cut down to $[0, \pi]$.

$$f : x \to \cos x, \qquad X_f = [0, \pi], \qquad Y_f = [-1, 1].$$
$$f' : x \to -\sin x, \quad -\sin x < 0 \text{ for } x \in (0, \pi).$$
$$f^{-1} \text{ exists on } [-1, 1], \quad f^{-1} : [-1, 1] \to [0, \pi].$$

f^{-1} is continuous and monotonic decreasing on $[-1, 1]$.

$(f^{-1})'$ exists on $(-1, 1)$, and if $x \in (-1, 1)$ then

$$(f^{-1})'(x) = \frac{-1}{\sqrt{1 - x^2}}.$$

The graphs of f and f^{-1} are as shown in Figure 22.

The tangent function presents no problem at all. We insist that it is very natural to take as restricted domain for the tangent function the open interval $\left(-\frac{\pi}{2}, \frac{\pi}{2}\right)$. Thus we can list in the usual way the properties of this restricted function and its inverse. We ask the reader to supply the reasons for the steps leading to the expression for $(f^{-1})'(x)$.

We let

$$f: x \to \tan x, \quad X_f = \left(-\frac{\pi}{2}, \frac{\pi}{2}\right), \qquad Y_f = \mathbf{R};$$

then

$$f': x \to \sec^2 x > 0, \qquad \text{all } x \in X_f.$$

Therefore

$$f^{-1} \text{ exists}, \qquad f^{-1}: \mathbf{R} \to \left(-\frac{\pi}{2}, \frac{\pi}{2}\right),$$

f^{-1} is continuous and monotonic increasing on $\mathbf{R}$, and $(f^{-1})'$ exists on $\mathbf{R}$. Moreover, for all $x \in \mathbf{R}$,

$$(f^{-1})'(x) = \frac{1}{f'(f^{-1}(x))} = \frac{1}{\sec^2 (f^{-1}(x))}$$

$$= \frac{1}{1 + \tan^2 (f^{-1}(x))} = \frac{1}{1 + [f(f^{-1}(x))]^2}$$

$$= \frac{1}{1 + x^2}.$$

The graphs of f and f^{-1} are shown in Figure 23.

The case of the secant function is a little more interesting and requires more careful study. Now the secant is, after all, the reciprocal of the cosine, and for this reason it would seem natural to try to use the same restricted domain for the secant as for the cosine. It turns out that, provided we exclude the point $x = \frac{\pi}{2}$ where the secant is not defined $\left(\cos \frac{\pi}{2} = 0\right)$, this set $[0, \pi]$ satisfies all the desired conditions. However, for reasons which will become clear later, we are going to use a slightly different—and, to be sure, somewhat less natural—choice of restricted domain.

Suppose we denote by f the secant function with domain restricted to $\left[0, \frac{\pi}{2}\right) \cup \left[\pi, \frac{3\pi}{2}\right)$:

$$f: x \to \sec x, \qquad X_f = \left[0, \frac{\pi}{2}\right) \cup \left[\pi, \frac{3\pi}{2}\right), \qquad Y_f = (-\infty, -1] \cup [1, \infty).$$

Note that $Y_f = Y_{\sec}$. Then

$$f' : x \to \sec x \tan x.$$

Now it is true that $x \in \left(0, \dfrac{\pi}{2}\right) \Rightarrow f'(x) > 0$, whereas $x \in \left(\pi, \dfrac{3\pi}{2}\right) \Rightarrow f'(x) < 0$;

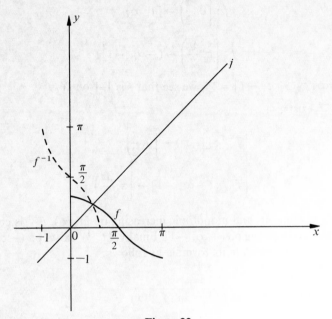

Figure 22

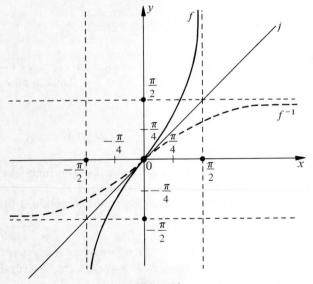

Figure 23

thus f' does change sign on this restricted domain, but a glance at the graph of the secant (see Figure 24) shows that f is 1–1 on X_f. In fact, since f is clearly 1–1 when f is restricted to $\left[0, \dfrac{\pi}{2}\right)$ and also when f is restricted to $\left[\pi, \dfrac{3\pi}{2}\right)$, and since

$$f: \left[0, \frac{\pi}{2}\right) \to [1, \infty)$$

$$f: \left[\pi, \frac{3\pi}{2}\right) \to (-\infty, -1],$$

where $[1, \infty) \cap (-\infty, -1] = \varnothing$, we see that f is 1–1 on X_f.

Thus, f^{-1} exists,

$$\left.\begin{cases} f^{-1}: [1, \infty) \to \left[0, \frac{\pi}{2}\right) \\[2mm] f^{-1}: (-\infty, -1] \to \left[\pi, \frac{3\pi}{2}\right) \end{cases}\right\}. \tag{10}$$

Also, f^{-1} is continuous and monotonic increasing on $[1, \infty)$, f^{-1} is continuous and monotonic decreasing on $(-\infty, -1]$. Finally, $(f^{-1})'$ exists on $(-\infty, -1) \cup (1, \infty)$, and we can calculate its formula as follows:

$$(f^{-1})'(x) = \frac{1}{f'(f^{-1}(x))} = \frac{1}{\sec f^{-1}(x) \tan f^{-1}(x)}$$

$$= \frac{1}{x \tan f^{-1}(x)} = \frac{1}{x[\pm\sqrt{\sec^2 f^{-1}(x) - 1}]}, \quad \text{since } \tan^2 x = \sec^2 x - 1$$

$$= \frac{1}{x[\pm\sqrt{x^2 - 1}]}, \quad \text{since } \sec^2 f^{-1}(x) = x^2.$$

The case of the ambiguous sign is settled easily: for every $x \in (-\infty, -1) \cup (1, \infty)$ we see, by consulting (10) that $\tan f^{-1}(x) > 0$. Thus in all cases we use the $+$ sign and we can write

$$(f^{-1})'(x) = \frac{1}{x\sqrt{x^2 - 1}}, \quad |x| > 1.$$

The graphs of f and f^{-1} are shown in Figure 24. The functions $\cot^{-1}$ and $\csc^{-1}$ will be discussed in the exercises which follow.

By way of summary, we state the following theorem, obtained from the preceding results and the chain rule.

Theorem 18. *The following differentiation formulas hold; in every case u is assumed to be a differentiable function of x. In parts* (a), (b), *and* (d) *the values of $u(x)$ are assumed to be restricted as indicated.*

(a) $\dfrac{d}{dx} \sin^{-1} u = \dfrac{\dfrac{du}{dx}}{\sqrt{1 - u^2}}$, $-1 < u(x) < 1$.

(b) $\dfrac{d}{dx} \cos^{-1} u = \dfrac{-\dfrac{du}{dx}}{\sqrt{1 - u^2}}$, $-1 < u(x) < 1$.

(c) $\dfrac{d}{dx} \tan^{-1} u = \dfrac{\dfrac{du}{dx}}{1 + u^2}$.

(d) $\dfrac{d}{dx} \sec^{-1} u = \dfrac{\dfrac{du}{dx}}{u\sqrt{u^2 - 1}}$, $|u(x)| > 1$.

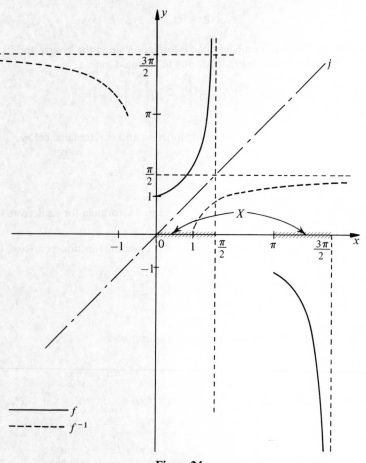

Figure 24

Example 4. Thus, if $f(x) = \sin^{-1} 3x$, then

$$f'(x) = \frac{3}{\sqrt{1 - 9x^2}}, \qquad -\tfrac{1}{3} < x < \tfrac{1}{3}.$$

Or, if $g(x) = \tan^{-1}(4x + 1)$, then

$$g'(x) = \frac{4}{1 + (4x + 1)^2}.$$

And

$$h(x) = \sec^{-1}(2x - 1) \Rightarrow h'(x) = \frac{2}{(2x - 1)\sqrt{(2x - 1)^2 - 1}},$$

where either $x < 0$ or $x > 1$ (why?).

EXERCISES

1. Use the theorems of Section 6.5 to find information about the inverse and its derivative for the sine function restricted to the following domains:

   (a) $\left[\dfrac{\pi}{2}, \dfrac{3\pi}{2}\right]$ (b) $\left[\dfrac{3\pi}{2}, \dfrac{5\pi}{2}\right]$ (c) $\left[-\dfrac{\pi}{2}, 0\right] \cup \left[\dfrac{\pi}{2}, \pi\right)$

2. Same as Exercise 1, only for the cosine function and the domains below:

   (a) $[-\pi, 0]$ (b) $\left[0, \dfrac{\pi}{2}\right] \cup \left[\pi, \dfrac{3\pi}{2}\right]$ (c) $[\pi, 2\pi]$

3. Let $f : x \to \cot x$, $0 < x < \pi$. Discuss f^{-1} and find a formula for its derivative.

4. Discuss the inverse and its derivative for the cosecant function restricted to each of the following domains:

   (a) $\left[-\dfrac{\pi}{2}, 0\right) \cup \left(0, \dfrac{\pi}{2}\right]$ (b) $\left(0, \dfrac{\pi}{2}\right] \cup \left(\pi, \dfrac{3\pi}{2}\right]$

5. Find the derivatives of each of the functions described.

   (a) $f(x) = \sin^{-1}(2x - 1)$.
   (b) $f(x) = \tan^{-1} x^2$.
   (c) $g(x) = x^2 \cos^{-1}(1 - x)$.
   (d) $h(x) = \dfrac{1}{x} \tan^{-1} 2x \cdot$
   (e) $g(x) = \sec^{-1} \dfrac{1}{x}$.

   (f) $f(x) = \sin^{-1} \dfrac{x + 1}{\sqrt{2}}.$
   (g) $g(x) = x \sin^{-1} x + \sqrt{1 - x^2}.$
   (h) $f(x) = \dfrac{x}{\sqrt{4 - x^2}} - \sin^{-1} \dfrac{x}{2} \cdot$
   (i) $g(x) = (x^2 + 1) \tan^{-1} x - x.$
   (j) $f(x) = \sec^{-1}(4 - 3x).$

6. Evaluate the following limits:

(a) $\lim\limits_{x\to 0} \dfrac{\tan^{-1} x}{x}$. 　　(b) $\lim\limits_{x\to 0} \dfrac{2x - \sin^{-1} x}{2\tan^{-1} x - x}$. 　　(c) $\lim\limits_{x\to 0} \dfrac{\sin^{-1} x}{\tan^{-1} x}$.

6.7 A Few Applications

Example 5. Late one afternoon Mr. Sean Dinge is watching a flying saucer hovering overhead at an altitude which he estimates to be 1000 ft. When the saucer begins to move—horizontally—Mr. Dinge uses an instrument he has invented to measure the angle of elevation and its rate of change. One set of readings showed that the angle of elevation was decreasing at the rate of 20 rad/min when the angle was $\dfrac{\pi}{6}$ rad. How fast was the saucer traveling at that instant?

We refer to Figure 25. Letting θ denote the angle of elevation and x the *horizontal* distance between the flying saucer and Mr. Dinge, we have

$$x = 1000 \cot \theta \tag{11}$$

and

$$\left.\frac{d\theta}{dt}\right|_{\theta=\pi/6} = -20 \text{ rad/min.}$$

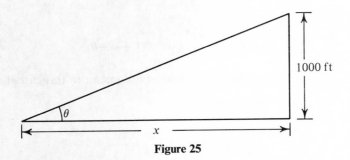

Figure 25

As we are asked to find the rate of change of x with respect to time, we differentiate (11) with respect to t:

$$\frac{dx}{dt} = -1000 \csc^2 \theta \, \frac{d\theta}{dt}.$$

Substituting in the given value for $\dfrac{d\theta}{dt}$, we have

$$\left.\frac{dx}{dt}\right|_{\theta=\pi/6} = (-1000)(4)(-20) = 80{,}000 \text{ ft/min}$$

$$\approx 909 \text{ mph.}$$

Example 6. Find the volume of the right circular cone of maximum volume which can be inscribed in a sphere of radius a (see Figure 26).

In terms of the distances x and y shown in the figure, the expression to be maximized is

$$V = \frac{\pi}{3} x^2 (a + y).$$

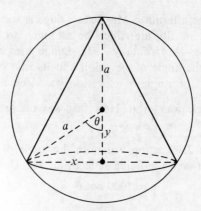

Figure 26

We can, however, express x and y as functions of θ:

$$x = a \sin \theta, \; y = a \cos \theta.$$

Then we can write

$$V = V(\theta) = \frac{\pi a^3}{3} [\sin^2 \theta (1 + \cos \theta)].$$

As usual, we should determine the meaningful domain; in this case it is easily seen to be $0 < \theta \leq \frac{\pi}{2}$. Note that

$$V(0) = 0, \qquad V\left(\frac{\pi}{2}\right) = \frac{\pi a^3}{3}.$$

Looking for a maximum on $\left(0, \frac{\pi}{2}\right]$, we find $\frac{dV}{d\theta}$:

$$\frac{dV}{d\theta} = \frac{\pi a^3}{3} [\sin^2 \theta (-\sin \theta) + (1 + \cos \theta)(2 \sin \theta \cos \theta)]$$

$$= \frac{\pi a^3}{3} \sin \theta [-\sin^2 \theta + 2 \cos \theta + 2 \cos^2 \theta]$$

$$= \frac{\pi a^3}{3} \sin \theta [3 \cos^2 \theta + 2 \cos \theta - 1].$$

It is routine to discern that the only value of $\theta \in \left(0, \dfrac{\pi}{2}\right]$ for which $\dfrac{dV}{d\theta} = 0$ is

$\theta_0 = \cos^{-1} \frac{1}{3}$. For this θ_0, $\sin^2 \theta_0 = \frac{8}{9}$ and

$$V\left(\cos^{-1}\frac{1}{3}\right) = \frac{\pi a^3}{3} \cdot \frac{8}{9} \cdot \frac{4}{3} = \frac{32\pi a^3}{81} = \frac{8}{27}\left(\frac{4\pi a^3}{3}\right).$$

Since $V\left(\cos^{-1}\dfrac{1}{3}\right) > V\left(\dfrac{\pi}{2}\right)$, we know (why?) that $V\left(\cos^{-1}\dfrac{1}{3}\right)$ gives the desired maximum.

Example 7. If we assume that the best position in which to stand to look at a painting is the position which maximizes the angle subtended by the painting, how far should one stand from a painting for which the bottom and top are a and b feet, respectively, above eye level? (see Figure 27).

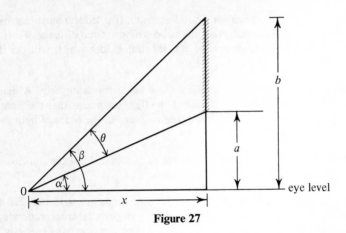

Figure 27

We let x equal the distance in feet from the painting. Then the angle to be maximized is

$$\theta = \beta - \alpha = \tan^{-1}\frac{b}{x} - \tan^{-1}\frac{a}{x}.$$

Clearly the domain of this function is $0 < x < \infty$. Also, $\lim\limits_{x \to 0^+} \theta = \lim\limits_{x \to \infty} \theta = 0$, so there must be at least one maximum for $x \in (0, \infty)$ (why?). Using Theorem 18, we have

$$\frac{d\theta}{dx} = \frac{\dfrac{-b}{x^2}}{1 + \dfrac{b^2}{x^2}} + \frac{\dfrac{a}{x^2}}{1 + \dfrac{a^2}{x^2}} = \frac{-b}{x^2 + b^2} + \frac{a}{x^2 + a^2},$$

or

$$\frac{d\theta}{dx} = \frac{(b-a)(ab-x^2)}{(x^2+a^2)(x^2+b^2)}.$$

Obviously (why?), θ has a maximum for $x = \sqrt{ab}$.

E X E R C I S E S

1. Find the volume of the right circular cylinder of maximum volume which can be inscribed in a sphere of radius a. Compare this volume with the volume of the sphere.

2. A kite is flying 100 ft above the level at which the string is being held. An obliging wind moves it along at the same height, causing the boy to pay out 50 ft of string a minute. How fast is the angle which the string makes with the horizontal changing when 500 ft of string are out?

3. A ladder is to be put up against a building, but it (the ladder) must pass over a wall near the building. If the wall is b ft high and is a horizontal distance of a ft from the building, show that the length of the shortest ladder which will do the job is $(a^{2/3} + b^{2/3})^{3/2}$ ft.

4. A lighthouse two miles off a straight shore has a revolving light. A man 4 miles down the shore from the point nearest the light ascertains that the light revolves once every two minutes. What is the (linear) speed of the beam of light as it passes the man?

5. A cylinder is to be inscribed in a sphere of radius a. Find the dimensions of the cylinder if its lateral surface is a maximum.

6. A long strip of sheet metal 24 in. wide is to be made into a trapezoidal gutter by bending up the edges. If the base is 8 in. and the trapezoidal cross section is isosceles, what should be the width across the top for maximum carrying capacity?

7. A ladder 20 ft long has been placed against a wall. The ladder begins to slide, its top moving at the rate of 3 ft/sec. How fast is the angle of elevation of the ladder changing when the lower end is 16 ft from the wall?

8. A searchlight is located 15 ft from the nearest point 0 of a straight walk. A man is walking along the walk at the rate of 6 ft/sec. If the searchlight is trained on the man, how fast is it revolving when the man is 20 ft from 0?

9. Let θ be a function of x, $\theta = \theta(x)$, for x in some interval. Then tan θ is also a function of x. Show that θ has a maximum or minimum exactly when tan θ has a maximum or minimum. [Chain rule, anyone?]

10. From a point on the positive x-axis lines are drawn to the points $(1, 1)$ and $(4, 2)$ on the parabola $y = \sqrt{x}$. Find the point on the positive x-axis at which the angle between the lines is a maximum. [*Hint*. Identity (17) in Section 6.1 and Exercise 9 may be of use.]

Chapter 7 The Logarithm and Exponential Functions

In this chapter we define the logarithm function (log) by means of an integral. The exponential function $f(x) = e^x$ is then introduced as the inverse of the log function; in discussing the properties of the exponential function we make considerable use of the theory of inverse functions from Chapter 6. The logarithm and exponential functions to bases other than e are subsequently studied, as are, briefly, the hyperbolic functions.

7.1 The Logarithm Function

It may be recalled that in the antidifferentiation formula

$$\int x^n \, dx = \frac{x^{n+1}}{n+1}$$

there is an obvious, necessary exception: $n = -1$. Thus this formula does not provide an antiderivative for

$$\int \frac{dx}{x}.$$

But for $x > 0$ we know by the Fundamental Theorem of Calculus (Theorem 2.13) that the function $F(x) = \int_a^x \frac{1}{t} \, dt$ has all sorts of nice properties. To be explicit, we shall consider $x > 0$, take $a = 1$ and call the function so defined by the name log (short for "logarithm"—in fact, short for "logarithm to the base e," where e is to be introduced later).

311

Definition 1. *For $x > 0$ the **log function** is defined by*

$$\log x = \int_1^x \frac{dt}{t}. \tag{1}$$

The geometric significance of Definition 1 is illustrated in Figure 1.

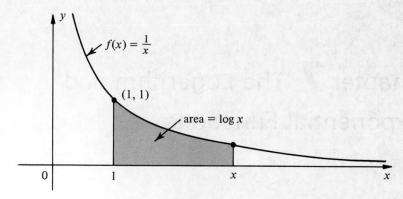

Figure 1

We can immediately obtain some properties of log. First of all we note that, by Theorem 2.13,

$$D \log x = \log' x = \frac{1}{x} > 0. \tag{2}$$

Thus log is continuous for all $x > 0$ and is an increasing function. Second, it follows from (1) that

$$\log 1 = 0. \tag{3}$$

Combining (3) with the fact that log is increasing we have

$$0 < x < 1 \Rightarrow \log x < 0, \tag{4}$$

$$1 < x \Rightarrow \log x > 0. \tag{5}$$

We next describe the distinguishing property of the log function.

Theorem 1. *For all $a > 0$, $b > 0$,*

$$\log ab = \log a + \log b. \tag{6}$$

Proof. By definition,

$$\log ab = \int_1^{ab} \frac{dt}{t}$$

$$= \int_1^a \frac{dt}{t} + \int_a^{ab} \frac{dt}{t}$$

$$= \log a + \int_a^{ab} \frac{dt}{t}.$$

In the remaining integral we let $t = au$, so that $dt = a\,du$, and the upper and lower limits become b and 1, respectively (full justification for this step will appear in Chapter 8). We then have

$$\log ab = \log a + \int_1^b \frac{a\,du}{au} = \log a + \int_1^b \frac{du}{u},$$

or

$$\log ab = \log a + \log b. \quad \blacksquare$$

From Theorem 1 we can obtain the following important consequences.

Theorem 2. *If $a > 0$, then $\log \dfrac{1}{a} = -\log a$.*

Proof. Since $a \cdot \dfrac{1}{a} = 1$, we have

$$0 = \log 1 = \log \left(a \cdot \frac{1}{a} \right) = \log a + \log \frac{1}{a}. \qquad \text{(Theorem 1)}$$

Thus

$$\log \frac{1}{a} = -\log a. \quad \blacksquare$$

Theorem 3. *For $a > 0$ and for all integers $n \in \mathbf{Z}$,*

$$\log a^n = n \log a. \tag{7}$$

Proof.

(a) $n > 0$. If we set $b = a$ in Theorem 1, we have $\log a^2 = 2 \log a$. The extension to all positive integers n can now be done by mathematical induction.

(b) $n = 0$. This is equivalent to $\log 1 = 0$.

(c) $n < 0$. Let $n = -m$, where $m > 0$; then $\log a^n = \log a^{-m} = \log \dfrac{1}{a^m} = -\log a^m = -m \log a = n \log a$. $\quad \blacksquare$

We can, in fact, make a further extension of the identity in (7).

Theorem 4. *For $a > 0$ and for all rational numbers $r \in \mathbf{Q}$,*

$$\log a^r = r \log a. \tag{8}$$

Proof. Let $r = \dfrac{m}{n}$, where m and n are integers and $n \geq 1$. Let $b = a^r = a^{m/n}$. Then $b^n = a^m$ and $\log b^n = \log a^m$. By Theorem 3, $n \log b = m \log a$. Thus

$$\log a^r = \log b = \frac{m}{n} \log a = \ \log a. \quad \blacksquare$$

This is, however, as far as we can go in this direction, for the simple reason that a^x, where x is an arbitrary real number, has not yet been defined.

Our next aim is to show that the range of log is $\mathbf{R}$, i.e., for every $y_0 \in \mathbf{R}$ there exists $x_0 > 0$ such that $\log x_0 = y_0$. To this end we prove the following result.

Lemma 1.

$$\tfrac{1}{2} < \log 2 < 1 < \log 4.$$

Proof. Since $\log' x$ exists for all $x > 0$ we can apply the Mean Value Theorem to the interval $[1, 2]$:

$$\frac{\log 2 - \log 1}{2 - 1} = \log' x_0, \quad \text{where} \quad 1 < x_0 < 2.$$

As $\log' x_0 = \dfrac{1}{x_0}$, and as $\log 1 = 0$, we find

$$\log 2 = \frac{1}{x_0} \quad \text{for} \quad 1 < x_0 < 2.$$

Inverting the inequalities for x_0 gives

$$1 > \frac{1}{x_0} = \log 2 > \frac{1}{2}, \quad \text{our first result.}$$

Next we have

$$\log 4 = \log 2^2 = 2 \log 2 > 2(\tfrac{1}{2}) = 1. \quad \blacksquare$$

Lemma 2. *For every $n \in \mathbf{N}$ there exists $x_n > 0$ such that $\log x_n > n$ and* $\log \dfrac{1}{x_n} < -n.$

Proof. Given any $n \in \mathbf{N}$, we take $x_n = 4^n$. Then

$$\log x_n = \log 4^n = n \log 4 > n, \quad \text{by Lemma 1.}$$

For the same x_n we also have $\log \dfrac{1}{x^n} = -\log x_n < -n.$ $\blacksquare$

We can now prove the previously announced result about the range of log.

Theorem 5. *The range of the log function is $\mathbf{R}$.*

Proof. Let $y_0 \in \mathbf{R}$ be arbitrary.

(i) If $y_0 > 0$, choose $n_1 \in \mathbf{N}$ such that $n_1 > y_0$. Then, by Lemma 2, $\log 4^{n_1} > n_1 > y_0$. Since log is continuous for all $x > 0$, if we apply the intermediate value theorem (Theorem 3.16) to log on the closed interval $[1, 4^{n_1}]$, we obtain $x_0 \in (1, 4^{n_1})$ such that $\log x_0 = y_0$.

(ii) If $y_0 < 0$, let $-y_0 = u_0$. Then $u_0 > 0$ and, by (i), $\exists x_0$ such that $\log x_0 = u_0$.

By Theorem 2, $\log \dfrac{1}{x_0} = -\log x_0 = -u_0 = y_0$.

(iii) Of course, if $y_0 = 0$ we take $x_0 = 1$. ∎

We have seen that domain $\log = \{x \mid x > 0\}$, range $\log = \mathbf{R}$, i.e., $\log$: $(0, \infty) \to \mathbf{R}$. Also, $D \log \dfrac{1}{x} = x > 0$, all $x \in (0, \infty)$, so $\log$ is continuous and monotonic increasing. Similarly, $D^2 \log x = -x^{-2} < 0$, for $x > 0$, so the graph of $\log$ is everywhere concave downward. The graph crosses the x-axis at $(1, 0)$ where its tangent line has slope one. Note that for large x the slope of the tangent $\left(\dfrac{1}{x}\right)$ approaches zero, so the tangent line becomes nearly horizontal when x is large. But remember! The range of $\log$ is $\mathbf{R}$, so the graph does not have a horizontal asymptote, but will go above *every* line $y = c$, no matter how large c is taken. However, the rate of increase of $\log$ is very slow for x large.

It is thus reasonable to draw the graph of $y = \log x$ as in Figure 2.

We conclude this section with a theorem on derivatives, easily obtainable from Eq. (2).

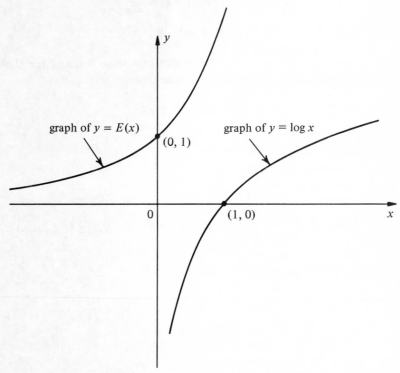

graph of $y = E(x)$

graph of $y = \log x$

$(0, 1)$

0

$(1, 0)$

x

y

Figure 2

Theorem 6

(a) *For all* $x > 0$, $\dfrac{d}{dx} \log x = \dfrac{1}{x}$.

(b) *If u is a differentiable function and if* $u(x) > 0$, *then*

$$\frac{d}{dx} \log u(x) = \frac{1}{u(x)} \frac{du}{dx} = \frac{u'(x)}{u(x)}.$$

(c) *For all* $x \neq 0$,

$$\frac{d}{dx} \log |x| = \frac{1}{x}. \tag{9}$$

(d) *If u is differentiable and* $u(x) \neq 0$, *then*

$$\frac{d}{dx} \log |u(x)| = \frac{1}{u(x)} \frac{du}{dx} = \frac{u'(x)}{u(x)}. \tag{10}$$

Proof. Part (a) is simply Eq. (2). Part (b) follows from (a) and the chain rule. Part (c) follows from (a) if $x > 0$. If $x < 0$, then $|x| = -x > 0$, and by (b) (with $u(x) = -x$),

$$\frac{d}{dx} \log |x| = \frac{d}{dx} \log (-x) = \frac{-1}{-x} = \frac{1}{x}.$$

Part (d) follows from (c) and the chain rule. ∎

From Theorem 6 we can write an antidifferentiation formula for the case $n = -1$ referred to at the beginning of this section:

$$\int \frac{du}{u} = \log |u| + c. \tag{11}$$

Example 1

(a) $\dfrac{d}{dx} \log (x^2 + 1) = \dfrac{2x}{x^2 + 1}$.

(b) $\dfrac{d}{dx} \log |\sin x| = \dfrac{\cos x}{\sin x} = \cot x$, $\quad (x \neq n\pi, \quad n = 0, \ \pm 1, \pm 2, \ldots)$.

(c) $\displaystyle\int \frac{3x^2}{x^3 + 4} \, dx = \int \frac{D(x^3 + 4)}{x^3 + 4} \, dx = \log |x^3 + 4| + c$.

EXERCISES

1. Let $a > 0$, $b > 0$. Prove that

$$\log \frac{a}{b} = \log a - \log b.$$

2. Use mathematical induction to prove that

$$\forall\, n \in \mathbf{N} \Rightarrow \log x^n = n \log x, \quad \text{where} \quad x > 0.$$

Find derivatives of the following functions.

3. $f(x) = \log (1 - x)$.   **4.** $f(x) = \log (x^2 + 1)$.

5. $f(x) = \log \dfrac{x^2 - 1}{x^2 + 1}$.   **6.** $f(x) = x \log \sqrt{x - 1}$.

7. $f(x) = \log \sin x$.   **8.** $f(x) = \sin \log x$.

9. $f(x) = \log \dfrac{2x + 3}{3x - 4}$.   **10.** $f(x) = \log \sqrt{\dfrac{x^2 - 1}{x^2 + 1}}$.

11. $f(x) = \frac{1}{2}[x \sqrt{x^2 + a^2} + a^2 \log (x + \sqrt{x^2 + a^2})]$.

12. $f(x) = \sqrt{x^2 + a^2} - a \log \left(\dfrac{a + \sqrt{x^2 + a^2}}{x} \right)$.

13. $f(x) = \log |x + \sqrt{x^2 - a^2}|$.

14. $f(x) = \dfrac{1}{4} \left[x \sqrt{(x^2 - a^2)^3} - \dfrac{3a^2 x}{2} \sqrt{x^2 - a^2} + \dfrac{3a^4}{2} \log |x + \sqrt{x^2 - a^2}| \right]$.

15. $f(x) = x \log x - x$.   **16.** $f(x) = x(\log x)^2 - 2x \log x + 2x$.

17. $f(x) = \log (\log x)$.   **18.** $f(x) = x^4 \left[\dfrac{\log x}{4} - \dfrac{1}{16} \right]$.

19. $f(x) = \frac{1}{2}x \sin \log x - \frac{1}{2}x \cos \log x$.   **20.** $f(x) = \dfrac{x^2}{2} \log x - \dfrac{x^4}{4}$.

21–30. Write the results of 11–20 in the form of antidifferentiation formulas.

31. Let $f(x) = \log x^2$, $g(x) = 2 \log x$.

    (a) What are the domains of f and g?

    (b) True or false: $f = g$? Explain.

32. Estimate log 3 by considering the area under $f(x) = \dfrac{1}{x}$ for $1 \le x \le 3$.

    (a) Divide the area between $x = 1$ and $x = 3$ into two parts by constructing the ordinate at $x = 2$. Now approximate the area under the curve by the sum of the areas of the two trapezoids (see Figure 3a).

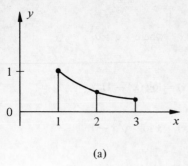

(a)   (b)

Figure 3

(b) Same as in (a), only use four trapezoids, as in Figure 3b. The tables give
   log 3 = 1.0986.

33. Using log 2 ≈ 0.7 and log 3 ≈ 1.1 (actually, to five places, log 2 ≈ 0.69315,
   log 3 ≈ 1.09861), find

   (a) log 1.5   (f) log 12
   (b) log 4   (g) log 24
   (c) log 6   (h) log $\sqrt[3]{2}$
   (d) log 8   (i) log 3^{100}.
   (e) log 9

34. Prove Lemma 1 by approximating the areas (see Figure 1) by rectangles.

35. Evaluate the following limits (l'Hospital's Rule, Section 4.6).

   (a) $\lim_{x \to 1} \dfrac{\log x}{x^2 - 1}$

   (f) $\lim_{x \to 0+} (x \log \sin x)$

   (b) $\lim_{x \to 0} \dfrac{\log \sec 2x}{\log \sec x}$

   (g) $\lim_{x \to 1} \left[\dfrac{1}{\log x} - \dfrac{1}{x - 1} \right]$

   (c) $\lim_{x \to \infty} \dfrac{\log x}{x}$

   (h) $\lim_{x \to 0+} x^n \log x \ (n > 0)$.

   (d) $\lim_{x \to 0+} \dfrac{\log \sin x}{\log \tan x}$

   (i) $\lim_{x \to 0+} [\sin x \log \sin x]$

   (e) $\lim_{x \to \infty} \dfrac{\log (\log x)}{\log x}$

   (j) $\lim_{x \to \frac{1}{2}+} \dfrac{\log (2x - 1)}{\tan \pi x}$.

7.2 The Function *E*

We have already pointed out in Section 7.1 that the log function defined there,
having a positive derivative on its domain $(0, \infty)$, is increasing; hence log has
an inverse.

Definition 2. *Let* log *be the function with domain* $(0, \infty)$,

$$\log x = \int_1^x \frac{dt}{t}.$$

Then E is the function inverse to log.

We note immediately that, since log: $(0, \infty) \twoheadrightarrow \mathbf{R}$, $E : \mathbf{R} \twoheadrightarrow (0, \infty)$; in particular, since log $1 = 0$, $E(0) = 1$. Moreover, drawing on our knowledge of inverse functions (Theorem 6.16), we can say that E is continuous and monotonic increasing on $\mathbf{R}$. In addition, since $E \circ \log = j_{\mathbf{R}+}$ and $\log \circ E = j$, we have

$$\begin{cases} \text{(a) } \forall x > 0, & E(\log x) = x \\ \text{(b) } \forall x \in \mathbf{R}, & \log E(x) = x \end{cases}. \tag{12}$$

Finally, Theorem 6.17 assures us that E' exists for all $x \in \mathbf{R}$. We describe the complete assertion formally.

Theorem 7. *The function E is differentiable for all $x \in \mathbf{R}$, Moreover, $E' = E$;* i.e., *for all $x \in \mathbf{R}$ it is true that*

$$E'(x) = E(x). \tag{13}$$

Proof. By Theorem 6.17 we know that

$$E'(x) = \frac{1}{\log' E(x)}$$

$$= \frac{1}{\dfrac{1}{E(x)}}, \qquad \left(\text{since } \log' u = \frac{1}{u}\right)$$

$$= E(x). \quad \blacksquare$$

Geometrically, Theorem 7 says that at every point of the graph of E the *slope* of the tangent line to the curve is equal to the *ordinate*. The curve is shown in Figure 2.

As we noted in Chapter 6, it is generally true that when a function has an inverse some of the properties of the original function carry over to the inverse. The characteristic property of log was described in Theorem 1: $\log ab = \log a + \log b$. We now show that the inverse function E has an analogous identity.

Theorem 8. *For all $a, b \in \mathbf{R}$ we have*

$$E(a + b) = E(a) \, E(b). \tag{14}$$

Proof. We have for $a, b \in \mathbf{R}$,

$$E(a + b) = E[\log E(a) + \log E(b)] \qquad \text{(by 12b)}$$

$$= E[\log E(a) \, E(b)] \qquad \text{(by Theorem 1)}$$

$$= E(a) \, (Eb). \qquad \text{(by 12a).} \quad \blacksquare$$

In the preceding section we were able to extend, in a series of steps, the result of Theorem 1 to the more general assertion of Theorem 4: $\log a^r = r \log a$, r rational. This statement also has an analog for the function E, but we can obtain it directly.

Theorem 9. *For all $a \in \mathbf{R}$ and for all rational r,*

$$E(ra) = [E(a)]^r \tag{15}$$

Proof. The scheme is similar to that used in the proof of Theorem 8. We start with the right side of (15):

$$
\begin{aligned}
[E(a)]^r &= E(\log [E(a)]^r) && \text{by (12a)} \\
&= E(r \log E(a)) && \text{(by Theorem 4)} \\
&= E(ra) && \text{(by 12b).} \quad \blacksquare
\end{aligned}
$$

As we pointed out after Theorem 4, we cannot improve upon the preceding result quite yet, because the concept of exponent is meaningful to us only when the exponent is rational. We are, however, now in a position to extend this concept so that it applies to all numbers in **R**. This next step is the "crucial" one of the entire present logical development.

First of all, we use the E function to define one of the most important numbers in all of mathematics.

Definition 3. *The number e is defined by*

$$e = E(1).$$

The symbol for this number was provided by Euler (1707–1783), one of the most prolific mathematicians of all time, who apparently named the number after himself. The number lies between 2 and 3 (a more exact description will be given shortly), and is not only irrational but *transcendental*, by which we mean that it does not appear as the root of a polynomial equation with integral coefficients. It is true that π is also transcendental, whereas $\sqrt{2}$ is irrational but not transcendental (not transcendental = algebraic), since $\sqrt{2}$ is a root of $x^2 - 2 = 0$.

We could also have defined e in terms of log, for, by (12b),

$$1 = \log E(1) = \log e; \tag{16}$$

i.e., e is the number which log maps into 1.

For a preliminary estimate of the size of e we use Lemma 1, which says

$$\log 2 < 1 < \log 4.$$

Now we operate on all members with $E : E(\log 2) < E(1) < E(\log 4)$. (Why is the order relation preserved?) But this says, using (12a),

$$2 < e < 4.$$

Returning to our major task of extending the meaning of exponents, we call on Eq. (15) (Theorem 9), and set $a = 1$:

$$E(r) = [E(1)]^r = e^r. \tag{17}$$

Now, summarizing briefly our knowledge about E, we have that E is defined, continuous, and differentiable for all $x \in \mathbf{R}$. Moreover, by (17), for every rational number r, $E(r) = e^r$. The temptation to define e^x for *all* $x \in \mathbf{R}$ in terms of $E(x)$ is too strong to resist.

Definition 4. *For all* $x \in \mathbf{R}$, $e^x = E(x)$.

Sometimes, especially if the exponent is more complicated than simply x, this function is referred to as exp. Thus

$$\exp x = E(x) = e^x.$$

From now on we shall favor the last form.

In terms of the e-notation the identities given in (12) become

$$\begin{cases} \text{(a)} \;\; e^{\log x} = x, & \text{all } x > 0, \\ \text{(b)} \;\; \log e^x = x, & \text{all } x \in \mathbf{R} \end{cases} \tag{18}$$

Other properties of the exponential function e^x can be summarized as follows.

Theorem 10. *For all* $x, y \in \mathbf{R}$ *the function* e^x *of Definition 4 has the following properties:*

(a) $e^x e^y = e^{x+y}$

(b) $e^{-x} = \dfrac{1}{e^x}$

(c) $\dfrac{e^x}{e^y} = e^{x-y}$

(d) $(e^x)^y = e^{xy}$.

Proof. Part (a) is a restatement of Theorem 8. Part (b) follows from Theorem 9 with $r = -1$. Part (c) follows from (a) and (b). Finally, we note that part (d), for either x or y rational, is simply Theorem 9; the proof of part (d) for arbitrary x and y will be given shortly. ∎

Theorem 11. *Let* u *be a differentiable function (of* x*). Then*

$$\frac{d}{dx} e^u = D_x e^u = e^u D_x u = e^u \frac{du}{dx}. \tag{19}$$

Proof. This assertion follows directly from Theorem 7 and the chain rule. ∎

Note that, from either Theorem 7 or Theorem 11, we obtain the following antidifferentiation result:

$$\int e^u \, du = e^u + c. \tag{20}$$

Example 2.

(a) $\dfrac{d}{dx} e^{x^2} = e^{x^2}(2x) = 2x \, e^{x^2}$.

(b) $D_x \, e^{\sin x} = e^{\sin x} \cos x = \cos x \, e^{\sin x}$.

(c) $\dfrac{d}{dx} \left[\dfrac{1}{2}(e^x + e^{-x}) \right] = \dfrac{1}{2}(e^x - e^{-x})$.

(d) Let $f(x) = \exp \left[-\dfrac{1}{2} \left(\dfrac{x - \mu}{\sigma} \right)^2 \right]$,

where μ and σ are constants. Then

$$f'(x) = \exp \left[-\frac{1}{2} \left(\frac{x - \mu}{\sigma} \right)^2 \right] \left(-\left(\frac{x - \mu}{\sigma} \right) \frac{1}{\sigma} \right)$$

$$= -\left(\frac{x - \mu}{\sigma^2} \right) \exp \left[-\frac{1}{2} \left(\frac{x - \mu}{\sigma} \right)^2 \right].$$

The function in (d) illustrates the remark about occasionally needing the exp notation. This function, by the way, is, apart from a multiplicative constant, the normal frequency function from probability. The constants μ and σ^2 are, respectively, the *mean* and the *variance*.

We conclude this section by developing a polynomial approximation for e^x. Suppose, to begin, we assume $x > 0$. As e^x is differentiable and continuous for all x, we can apply the Mean Value Theorem on the interval $[0, x]$:

$$\frac{e^x - e^0}{x - 0} = e^{x_0}, \qquad \text{where} \quad 0 < x_0 < x,$$

(recall that $\dfrac{d}{dx} e^x = e^x$). Since $e^0 = 1$, we have

$$e^x = 1 + e^{x_0} x.$$

We now integrate both sides over the interval $[0, x]$, using (20):

$$\int_0^x e^t \, dt = \int_0^x (1 + e^{x_0}t) \, dt,$$

or

$$e^x - 1 = x + \tfrac{1}{2} e^{x_0} x^2.$$

Thus

$$e^x = 1 + x + \tfrac{1}{2} e^{x_0} x^2, \qquad \text{where} \quad 0 < x_0 < x.$$

We can repeat the last step, integrating again:

$$\int_0^x e^t \, dt = \int_0^x \left(1 + t + \frac{1}{2} e^{x_0} t^2 \right) dt,$$

or

$$e^x - 1 = x + \frac{1}{2} x^2 + \frac{1}{2 \cdot 3} e^{x_0} x^3;$$

this gives

$$e^x = 1 + x + \frac{x^2}{2} + \frac{x^3}{3!} e^{x_0}, \qquad 0 < x_0 < x.$$

Performing the same step once more, we have

$$e^x = 1 + x + \frac{x^2}{2!} + \frac{x^3}{3!} + \frac{x^4}{4!} e^{x_0}.$$

By mathematical induction now, it is easy to show that for every positive integer n,

$$e^x = 1 + x + \frac{x^2}{2!} + \frac{x^3}{3!} + \cdots + \frac{x^n}{n!} + \frac{x^{n+1}}{(n+1)!} e^{x_0}, \qquad (21)$$

where $0 < x_0 < x$.

Although we specified earlier that $x > 0$, the fact is that Eq. (21) is valid for all $x \in \mathbf{R}$; however, if $x < 0$, then x_0 satisfies $x < x_0 < 0$.

In particular, if we take $x = 1$, then we have

$$e = 1 + 1 + \frac{1}{2!} + \frac{1}{3!} + \cdots + \frac{1}{n!} + \frac{e^{x_0}}{(n+1)!},$$

where, since $0 < x_0 < 1$, $1 < e^{x_0} < e < 4$. Thus, using the last inequalities for e^{x_0}, we can obtain the following inequalities for e, valid for every $n \in \mathbf{N}$:

$$1 + 1 + \frac{1}{2!} + \frac{1}{3!} + \cdots + \frac{1}{n!} + \frac{1}{(n+1)!} < e < 1 + 1 + \frac{1}{2!} + \cdots + \frac{1}{n!} + \frac{4}{(n+1)!}. \qquad (22)$$

By taking n suitably large one can obtain an estimate of e to any desired accuracy. We can find, for example, $e = 2.718281828459045 \ldots$.

EXERCISES

1. Draw graphs of the following functions:

   (a) $f(x) = e^{-x}$.

   (b) $f(x) = e^{2x}$.

   (c) $f(x) = e^{-x^2}$.

   (d) $f(x) = \dfrac{e^x + e^{-x}}{2}$.

   (e) $f(x) = \dfrac{e^x - e^{-x}}{2}$.

2. Find f'. Give the domain of both f and f'.

   (a) $f(x) = e^{x^2}$.

   (b) $f(x) = e^{\sin x}$.

   (c) $f(x) = \log e^x$.

   (d) $f(x) = e^{\log x}$.

   (e) $f(x) = e^{x^2 - \sin x} = \exp[x^2 - \sin x]$.

   (f) $f(x) = \sin e^x$.

   (g) $f(x) = \dfrac{e^{ax}}{a^2}(ax - 1)$.

   (h) $f(x) = \tfrac{1}{2}e^x(\sin x - \cos x)$.

   (i) $f(x) = \log \dfrac{e^x}{1 + e^x}$.

   (j) $f(x) = \dfrac{x}{a} - \dfrac{1}{a}\log(a + be^x)$.

   (k) $f(x) = e^{1/x}$.

   (l) $f(x) = e^{\sqrt{x}}$.

3. Write the results of parts (g), (h), (i), and (j) of Exercise 2 as antidifferentiation formulas.

4. Show in detail how part (c) of Theorem 10 can be obtained from parts (a) and (b).

5. Use the inequalities (22) with $n = 5$ to get a squeeze on the value of e. Compare your result with the value given for e just after (22).

6. How large must n be taken in (22) in order that the estimate for e be in error by less than 10^{-10}?
   Hint. Let a_n and b_n be the left and right members, respectively, of (22); note that $b_n - a_n = \dfrac{3}{(n+1)!}$, do some calculating and consult a table of factorials or use the fact that $14! \approx 8.7178 \times 10^{10}$.

7. Use l'Hospital's Rule (see Section 4.6) to evaluate:

   (a) $\lim\limits_{x \to 0} \dfrac{e^x - e^{-x}}{\sin x}$.

   (b) $\lim\limits_{x \to \infty} \dfrac{x^3}{e^x}$.

   (c) $\lim\limits_{x \to 0} \dfrac{e^x - e^{-x} - 2\sin x}{x^3}$.

   (d) $\lim\limits_{x \to 0} \dfrac{e^x + e^{-x} - 2}{\sin^2 x}$.

   (e) $\lim\limits_{x \to \infty} \dfrac{x^n}{e^x}$, $\quad n \in \mathbf{N}$.

   (f) $\lim\limits_{x \to -\infty} x^2 e^x$.

   (g) $\lim\limits_{x \to 0} \left[\dfrac{1}{x} - \dfrac{1}{e^x - 1}\right]$.

   (h) $\lim\limits_{x \to \infty} \sin e^{-x} \cdot \csc \dfrac{1}{x}$.

   (i) $\lim\limits_{x \to 0} \dfrac{e^{\cos x} \sin^{-1} x}{\cos^2 x \tan^{-1} x}$.

7.3 Other Bases

It is now a straightforward matter to define and discuss the logarithm and exponential functions to bases other than e.

Definition 5. *Let $a > 0$, $a \neq 1$. For every $x \in \mathbf{R}$,*

$$a^x = e^{x \log a}. \tag{23}$$

With this definition we can complete the proof of Theorem 10, the assertion that $(e^x)^y = e^{xy}$ holds for all $x, y \in \mathbf{R}$. For, let $e^x = a$. Then

$$(e^x)^y = a^y = e^{y \log a} = e^{y \log e^x} = e^{xy \log e} = e^{xy}.$$

We can also complete Theorem 4, showing that $\log a^x = x \log a$ holds for all $x \in \mathbf{R}$. For,

$$\log a^x = \log e^{x \log a} = x \log a, \qquad \text{by (18b)}.$$

The algebraic properties of the function a^x parallel those of e^x.

Theorem 12. *Let $a, b > 0$, $a \neq 1$, $b \neq 1$. Let $x, y \in \mathbf{R}$. Then*

(a) $a^x \cdot a^y = a^{x+y}$.

(b) $a^{-x} = \dfrac{1}{a^x}$.

(c) $\dfrac{a^x}{a^y} = a^{x-y}$.

(d) $(a^x)^y = a^{xy}$.

(e) $a^x b^x = (ab)^x$.

Proof. Exercise for student. ∎

The calculus properties of a^x also parallel those of e^x.

Theorem 13

(a) *Let $a > 0$, $a \neq 1$; then*

$$\frac{d}{dx} a^x = (\log a) a^x. \tag{24}$$

(b) *Let $a > 0$, $a \neq 1$, let u be a differentiable function. Then*

$$\frac{d}{dx} a^{u(x)} = (\log a) a^{u(x)} u'(x). \tag{25}$$

Proof. For (a) we have

$$\frac{d}{dx} a^x = \frac{d}{dx} e^{x \log a} = e^{x \log a} \log a = (\log a) a^x.$$

The proof of (b) follows from the chain rule. ∎

Several remarks are in order about the assertion of Theorem 13. First of all, a comparison of Theorems 11 and 13 shows the advantage of working with the base e: differentiating the function a^x where $a \neq e$ involves the multiplicative constant $\log a$; if, however, $a = e$, then $\log a = \log e = 1$, and the differentiation result is simpler.

Secondly, since $a^x > 0$ for all $x \in \mathbf{R}$, we see from Eq. (24) that the sign of $\dfrac{da^x}{dx}$ depends upon a:

$$0 < a < 1 \Rightarrow \log a < 0 \Rightarrow \frac{d}{dx}\, a^x < 0 \Rightarrow a^x \text{ decreasing};$$

$$1 < a \Rightarrow \log a > 0 \Rightarrow \frac{d}{dx}\, a^x > 0 \Rightarrow a^x \text{ increasing}.$$

In other words, if $a > 1$, then $f(x) = a^x$ has *essentially* the same properties as $E(x) = e^x$; if, however, $0 < a < 1$, then $f(x) = a^x$ behaves like e^{-x}.

Finally, we note that Theorem 13 enables us to write the following anti-differentiation formula:

$$\int a^u \, du = \frac{1}{\log a}\, a^u + c. \tag{26}$$

This might be a good time to look at the graphs of several of these functions. Suppose we take $a = 2$. Then if $y = 2^x = e^{x \log 2}$, $D_x y = (\log 2)\, 2^x > 0$. The graph of $y = 2^x$ is shown in Figure 4.

If we take $a = \dfrac{1}{2}$, then $y = \left(\dfrac{1}{2}\right)^x = \dfrac{1}{2^x} = 2^{-x}$, and the graph of this function is simply the mirror image in the y-axis of the graph already discussed. This graph is also shown in Figure 4.

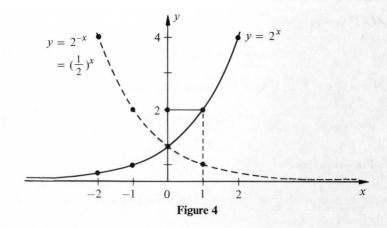

Figure 4

The logarithm function to base $a \neq e$ is the inverse of the exponential function a^x. We shall take $a > 1$; then $\log a > 0$, and

$$\frac{d}{dx} a^x = \log a \cdot a^x > 0,$$

so $g(x) = a^x$ is monotonic increasing and (Theorem 6.15) has an inverse.

Definition 6. *Let $g(x) = a^x$, where $a > 1$. Then the **logarithm to base a** is defined by*

$$\log_a x = g^{-1}(x).$$

Thus

$$y = \log_a x \Leftrightarrow x = a^y. \tag{27}$$

It may help to verbalize this last assertion: "y is the logarithm of x to base a" means that y is the *exponent* to which a must be raised to produce x.

The identities which correspond to (18) are

$$\begin{cases} \text{(a) } \log_a a^x = x, & \text{all } x > 0, \\ \text{(b) } \log_a a^x = x, & \text{all } x \in \mathbf{R} \end{cases} \tag{28}$$

These follow directly from Definition 6, Definition 6.3 and Theorem 6.12.

The following algebraic properties of logarithms are immediate consequences of the definition and of Theorem 12.

Theorem 14. *Let $a > 1$, $x, y > 0$, $q \in \mathbf{R}$. Then*

(a) $\log_a xy = \log_a x + \log_a y$.

(b) $\log_a \dfrac{x}{y} = \log_a x - \log_a y$.

(c) $\log_a x^q = q \log_a x$.

(d) $\log_a a = 1$.

Proof. Exercise for student. ∎

We next obtain a relation between logarithms to different bases.

Lemma 3. *Let $a > 0$, $b > 0$, $x > 0$. Then*

$$\log_b x = \log_a x \log_b a. \tag{29}$$

Proof. If we let $y = \log_a x$, then $x = a^y$. Taking logarithms to base b (a more exact way of describing this is "operating on both sides with the function $\log_b$") gives

$$\log_b x = \log_b a^y$$
$$= y \log_b a$$
$$= \log_a x \log_b a. \quad ∎$$

In particular, if we let $x = b$ in (29) and use the fact that $\log_b b = 1$, we find that

$$1 = (\log_a b)(\log_b a); \tag{30}$$

thus $\log_a b$ and $\log_b a$ are reciprocals. If we use this in (29) we obtain a result somewhat more useful than (29):

$$\log_b x = \left(\frac{1}{\log_a b}\right) \log_a x. \tag{31}$$

The advantage of (31) over (29) is that the right-hand side has only logarithms to the base a. This formula shows that shifting from one base to another involves only a multiplicative constant, dependent upon the two bases, but *not upon the number* x.

[We mention in passing the similarity between the *form* of the relation in (29) and that of the chain rule when it is written as

$$D_x y = D_u y \, D_x u.]$$

For $a = e$ and $b = 10$, we can find from tables that

$$\left.\begin{aligned} \log_{10} e &\approx 0.434294 \\ \log 10 &\approx 2.302585 \end{aligned}\right\} \tag{32}$$

Consequently,

$$\left.\begin{aligned} \log_{10} x &\approx 0.434294 \log x, \\ \log x &\approx 2.302585 \log_{10} x \end{aligned}\right\} \tag{33}$$

The numbers given in (32) are only rational approximations, both $\log_{10} e$ and $\log 10$ being irrational.

We can now find the derivative of $\log_a x$.

Theorem 15. *Let* $a > 1$.

(a) *For* $x > 0$,

$$\frac{d}{dx} \log_a x = \log_a e \cdot \frac{1}{x}. \tag{34}$$

(b) *More generally, if* u *is a differentiable function, then*

$$\frac{d}{dx} \log_a |u(x)| = \log_a e \, \frac{\dfrac{du}{dx}}{u(x)}, \qquad u(x) \neq 0. \tag{35}$$

Proof. From Lemma 3 we know that $\log_a x = \log_a e \log x$. Thus

$$\frac{d}{dx} \log_a x = \frac{d}{dx} \log_a e \log x = \log_a e \cdot \frac{1}{x}.$$

The proof of (35) follows in a similar way from Theorem 6. ∎

A comparison of Theorems 15 and 6 shows why e is the preferred base in calculus: When the base of logarithms is e the multiplicative constant $\log_a e$ appearing in the derivative is equal to one.

We next take another look at the number e. We consider the defining expression for the derivative of the log function at $x = 1$. Suppose we let $f = \log$; then we are looking for $f'(1)$. By definition

$$f'(1) = \lim_{h \to 0} \frac{f(1 + h) - f(1)}{h}$$

$$= \lim_{h \to 0} \frac{\log (1 + h) - \log 1}{h}$$

$$= \lim_{h \to 0} \frac{1}{h} \log (1 + h)$$

$$= \lim_{h \to 0} \log (1 + h)^{1/h}.$$

Now the function log is continuous, so we may interchange the operations "lim" and "log" (see Theorem 3.3). Thus

$$f'(1) = \log \lim_{h \to 0} (1 + h)^{1/h}.$$

But we already know that $f'(x) = \dfrac{1}{x}$, so $f'(1) = 1$. Since the number e is the (unique) number such that $\log e = 1$, the preceding results indicate that

$$e = \lim_{h \to 0} (1 + h)^{1/h}. \tag{36}$$

If we consider a special form for h in Equation (36), namely, $h = \dfrac{1}{n}$, where n is a positive integer, then we find that

$$e = \lim_{n \to \infty} \left(1 + \frac{1}{n}\right)^n. \tag{37}$$

Example 3. Find f' if $f(x) = x^a$, where $x > 0$. We have

$$\frac{d}{dx} x^a = \frac{d}{dx} e^{a \log x} = e^{a \log x} \cdot \frac{a}{x} = \frac{a}{x} x^a,$$

or

$$\frac{d}{dx} x^a = ax^{a-1}. \tag{38}$$

Thus $f'(x) = ax^{a-1}$, and we finally complete the story begun in Chapter 2 with $\dfrac{d}{dx} x^n = nx^{n-1}$, where n is a positive integer.

Example 4. Find f' if $f(x) = x^x$, $x > 0$.

Method 1. Since $f(x) = e^{x \log x}$,

$$f'(x) = e^{x \log x}\left(x \cdot \frac{1}{x} + \log x\right) = x^x(1 + \log x).$$

Method 2. We consider

$$\log f(x) = \log x^x = x \log x.$$

Then, taking derivatives,

$$\frac{f'(x)}{f(x)} = x \cdot \frac{1}{x} + \log x = 1 + \log x,$$

or

$$f'(x) = f(x)(1 + \log x) = x^x(1 + \log x).$$

Note that if we write the preceding derivative in the form

$$f'(x) = x \cdot x^{x-1} + (\log x)x^x,$$

it appears as the sum of the results of applying (38) and (25).

The second method used in the preceding example, taking logarithms before differentiating, can be useful in cases such as the following.

Example 5. Find f' if

$$f(x) = \frac{x^2 \sqrt[3]{x - 1}}{\sqrt{x^2 + 1}}.$$

Operating with log, we have

$$\log|f(x)| = 2 \log|x| + \tfrac{1}{3} \log|x - 1| - \tfrac{1}{2} \log(x^2 + 1).$$

Now taking derivatives,

$$\frac{f'(x)}{f(x)} = \frac{2}{x} + \frac{1}{3}\frac{1}{x - 1} - \frac{1}{2}\frac{2x}{x^2 + 1},$$

or

$$f'(x) = f(x)\left[\frac{2}{x} + \frac{1}{3(x - 1)} - \frac{x}{x^2 + 1}\right]$$

$$= \frac{x^2 \sqrt[3]{x - 1}}{\sqrt{x^2 + 1}}\left[\frac{2}{x} + \frac{1}{3(x - 1)} - \frac{x}{\sqrt{x^2 + 1}}\right].$$

The technique used in this example is known as "logarithmic differentiation."

EXERCISES

1. Find $\dfrac{dy}{dx}$:

(a) $y = \log_{10} \sqrt{x^2 + 1}$

(b) $y = \log_2 \sqrt{x^2 + 1}$

(c) $y = \log_a \dfrac{x^2 - 1}{x^2 + 1}$

(d) $y = x \log_a |x^2 - 4|$

(e) $y = (\log_a x)^2$

(f) $y = \dfrac{\log_a (x^2 + 1)}{2x}$.

2. Consider the two numbers e^π and π^e. Are they equal? If not, which is larger?

3. Use formula (32) to find:

(a) $\log 100$

(c) $\log 4$ $(\log_{10} 2 = 0.30103)$

(b) $\log 1000$

(d) $\log 6$ $(\log_{10} 3 = 0.47712)$.

4. Use the expression given in (37) to show that $e \leq 3$.

Hint. By (37), $e = \lim\limits_{n \to \infty} \left(1 + \dfrac{1}{n}\right)^n$. Using the binomial theorem,

$$\left(1 + \frac{1}{n}\right)^n = \sum_{k=0}^{n} \binom{n}{k} \frac{1}{n^k}$$

$$= \sum_{k=0}^{n} \frac{n(n-1)(n-2)\cdots(n-\overline{k-1})}{k!} \frac{1}{n^k}$$

$$= \sum_{k=0}^{n} \frac{n(n-1)(n-2)\cdots(n-\overline{k-1})}{n^k} \frac{1}{k!}$$

$$= \sum_{k=0}^{n} 1 \cdot \left(1 - \frac{1}{n}\right)\left(1 - \frac{2}{n}\right) \cdots \left(1 - \frac{k-1}{n}\right)\frac{1}{k!}$$

$$< \sum_{k=0}^{n} \frac{1}{k!} \qquad \text{(why?)}$$

$$= 1 + 1 + \frac{1}{2!} + \frac{1}{3!} + \cdots + \frac{1}{n!}$$

$$< 1 + \left(1 + \frac{1}{2} + \frac{1}{2^2} + \cdots + \frac{1}{2^{n-1}}\right) \qquad \text{(why?)}$$

$$= 1 + \frac{1 - \dfrac{1}{2^n}}{1 - \dfrac{1}{2}} = 1 + 2\left(1 - \frac{1}{2^n}\right)$$

$$= 3 - \frac{1}{2^{n-1}}$$

$$< 3, \qquad n = 1, 2, \ldots.$$

5. In this exercise we take a look at e from still another point of view. We are going to concern ourselves with a few prosaic facts related to compound interest. Now it turns out that the essential ideas are independent of the amount of money earning interest, so we shall keep matters simple by assuming the amount is one (dollar, say).

(a) If the interest is $i\%$ per year and is compounded annually, show that the amount A_n accumulated after n years is

$$A_n = (1+i)^n.$$

Hint. Clearly,

$$A_1 = 1+i,$$
$$A_2 = A_1 + A_1 i = A_1(1+i) = (1+i)(1+i) = (1+i)^2.$$

Now use mathematical induction.

(b) If the interest is $i\%$ per year but is compounded semi-annually, show that the amount $A_{2,n}$ accumulated after n years is

$$A_{2,n} = \left(1+\frac{i}{2}\right)^{2n}.$$

Hint. By the method used in (a),

$$A_{2,\frac{1}{2}} = 1 + i \cdot \frac{1}{2} = 1 + \frac{i}{2},$$

$$A_{2,1} = A_{2,\frac{1}{2}} + A_{2,\frac{1}{2}} i \cdot \frac{1}{2} = A_{2,\frac{1}{2}}\left(1+\frac{i}{2}\right) = \left(1+\frac{i}{2}\right)^2, \qquad \text{etc.}$$

(c) If the interest is $i\%$ per year but is compounded k times a year, show that the amount accumulated after n years is

$$A_{k,n} = \left(1+\frac{i}{k}\right)^{kn}.$$

(d) Suppose now that the annual interest rate remains $i\%$, but that the compounding is done continuously, which is to say that, for the result in (c), $k \to \infty$. Use (36) to show that the amount accumulated after n years is

$$A_{\infty,n} = e^{in}.$$

Hint. In the result of (c) let i be fixed, let $k = \dfrac{i}{h}$, so that

$$\left(1+\frac{i}{k}\right)^{kn} = (1+h)^{(i/h)n} = [1+h)^{1/h}]^{in}.$$

Now note that $h \to 0$ as $k \to \infty$ and use (36).

(e) Suppose \$100 is left at 6% interest for 5 years. What would be the final amounts if it were: (i) compounded annually, (ii) compounded continuously? [*Hint.* From tables, we can find $(1.06)^5 = 1.33822558$, $e^{0.3} = 1.3499$.]

6. Let $a > 0, b > 0$. Show that $b = a^{\log_a b}$. [*Hint.* $\log_a b = \log_a b \cdot \log_a a = \log_a a^{\log_a b}$.]

7. Let $a > 0, b > 0$. Show that

$$\frac{\log b}{\log a} = \log_a b.$$

8. Prove Theorem 12.

9. Prove Theorem 14.

10. Find f':

(a) $f(x) = 2^x$.
(b) $f(x) = 10^{x^2}$.
(c) $f(x) = (\sin x)^x$.

(d) $f(x) = x^{\sin x}$.
(e) $f(x) = x^a + a^x, \quad a > 1$.
(f) $f(x) = 3^{-x^2}$.

11. Use logarithmic differentiation (see Example 5) to find f':

(a) $f(x) = \dfrac{x^2\sqrt{x^2+1}}{(x+1)^3}$

(b) $f(x) = \dfrac{\sqrt{3x^2+4}\ \sqrt[3]{x^3-2}}{(x^2+4)^2}$

(c) $f(x) = \sqrt{x^2+1}\ \sqrt[3]{3x^2-4}\ \sqrt[5]{2x^4+3}$

(d) $f(x) = \dfrac{x^3(x-1)^{1/3}}{\sqrt[4]{x^2+2}}$.

12. Use l'Hospital's Rule to evaluate:

(a) $\lim\limits_{x\to 0+} x^x = \lim\limits_{x\to 0+} e^{x \log x}$ (Alternatively, let $y = x^x$, so $\log y = x \log x$)

(b) $\lim\limits_{x\to\infty} (1 + x^2)^{1/x}$.

(c) $\lim\limits_{x\to 0+} \left(\dfrac{\sin x}{x}\right)^{1/x}$.

(d) $\lim\limits_{x\to 0+} (1 + \sin x)^{\cot x}$.

(e) $\lim\limits_{x\to 0} (\cos x)^{1/x}$.

(f) $\lim\limits_{x\to(\pi/2)} (\tan x)^{\cos x}$.

7.4   A Few Applications

In this section we give, mainly by means of examples, a few applications of the exponential and logarithm functions.

Example 6. Find $\int_0^b e^{-x}\, dx$.

Letting $u = -x$, so $du = -dx$, we have

$$\int_0^b e^{-x}\, dx = -\int_0^b e^{-x}(-dx) = -e^{-x}\Big|_0^b = -(e^{-b} - 1) = 1 - \frac{1}{e^b}$$

(see Figure 5). Note that if we let A equal the area between the x-axis and the curve we have $0 < A < 1$. What can be said about A as $b \to \infty$?

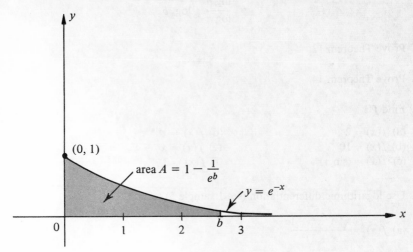

area $A = 1 - \dfrac{1}{e^b}$

$y = e^{-x}$

(0, 1)

Figure 5

Example 7. Sketch the curve $y = e^{-x^2}$.

We note that $y > 0$, all $x \in \mathbf{R}$, that the curve is symmetric with respect to the y-axis, that $(0, 1)$ is the only intercept, and, since $y = \dfrac{1}{e^{x^2}}$, that

$$\lim_{x \to \pm\infty} y = 0.$$

Also

$$\frac{dy}{dx} = -2xe^{-x^2},$$

so

$$x < 0 \Rightarrow \frac{dy}{dx} > 0, \qquad x > 0 \Rightarrow \frac{dy}{dx} < 0;$$

thus $(0, 1)$ is a maximum. The graph is shown in Figure 6.

A simple calculation of $\dfrac{d^2y}{dx^2}$ shows that there are inflection points at $x = \pm \dfrac{\sqrt{2}}{2}$.
This curve is closely related to the normal curve of probability theory.

Example 8. Sketch the curve $y = x \log x$.

The domain of the function $f(x) = x \log x$ is $\{x | x > 0\}$. Also we note that

(1, 0) is an intercept and that

$$0 < x < 1 \Rightarrow y < 0,$$

$$1 < x \Rightarrow y > 0,$$

$$\lim_{x \to \infty} y = \infty.$$

We leave it as an exercise to show by l'Hospital's Rule that $\lim_{x \to 0^+} y = 0$.

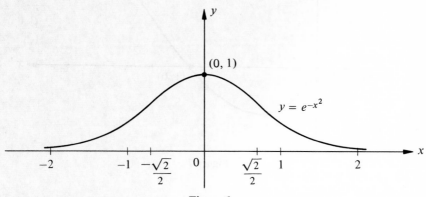

Figure 6

Calculating derivatives, we have

$$\frac{dy}{dx} = 1 + \log x,$$

$$\frac{d^2 y}{dx^2} = \frac{1}{x} > 0, \qquad \text{all} \quad x > 0.$$

It follows from the first of these equations that

$$x = e^{-1} \Rightarrow \frac{dy}{dx} = 0,$$

$$0 < x < e^{-1} \Rightarrow \frac{dy}{dx} < 0 \Rightarrow y \text{ decreasing}$$

$$e^{-1} < x \Rightarrow \frac{dy}{dx} > 0 \Rightarrow y \text{ increasing}.$$

As $\dfrac{d^2 y}{dx^2} > 0$ all $x > 0$, the curve is everywhere concave upward and the point $(e^{-1}, -e^{-1})$ is a minimum (see Figure 7).

Example 9. Sketch the curve $y = e^{-x} \sin x$, for $x \geq 0$.

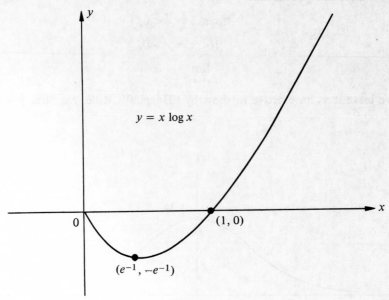

Figure 7

The function $f(x) = e^{-x} \sin x$ is of a rather special nature, and we modify our procedure to obtain geometric information. As $-1 \leq \sin x \leq 1$, we conclude that

$$-e^{-x} \leq e^{-x} \sin x \leq e^{-x}.$$

Thus the required curve will lie between $y = -e^{-x}$ and $y = e^{-x}$, touching these whenever $\sin x = -1$ or 1, respectively. Clearly, $y = e^{-x} \sin x$ will cross the x-axis when $x = n\pi$, $n = 0, 1, 2, \ldots$, and will touch one or the other of the curves $y = \pm e^{-x}$ when $x = (2n + 1)\left(\dfrac{\pi}{2}\right)$, $n = 1, 2, \ldots$.

Since the maximum and minimum values of $\sin x$ are 1 and -1, respectively, it might seem that the curve $y = e^{-x} \sin x$ would have relative maxima and minima at the points where it touches $y = e^{-x}$ and $y = -e^{-x}$, respectively. This, as it turns out, is not the case (these points are in fact, inflection points—exercise for student). For

$$\frac{dy}{dx} = e^{-x} \cos x - e^{-x} \sin x$$

$$= e^{-x}(\cos x - \sin x).$$

Thus

$$\frac{dy}{dx} = 0 \Rightarrow \cos x - \sin x = 0, \qquad \text{or} \quad \tan x = 1,$$

or

$$x = \frac{\pi}{4} + n\pi, \qquad n = 0, 1, 2, \ldots.$$

We show a portion of the curve in Figure 8, where we use different scales on the two axes.

The factor e^{-x} is called a *damping factor,* and the function $f(x) = e^{-x} \sin x$ can be used to describe the effect of friction or some other damping influence on oscillatory motion.

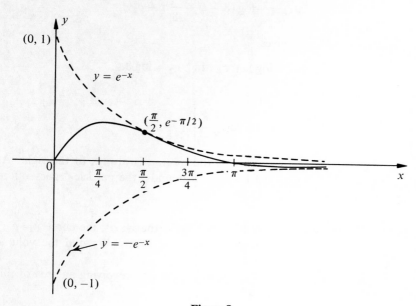

Figure 8

Example 10. During the time interval $0 \leq t \leq 8$ a particle moves along the x-axis according to the conditions

$$a(t) = \frac{1}{(8 - t)^2} \text{ ft/sec}^2,$$

$$v(0) = 4 \text{ ft/sec},$$

$$x(0) = 0.$$

We describe the motion.

To find the velocity we integrate the acceleration function:

$$v(t) = \int \frac{dt}{(8 - t)^2} = -\int (8 - t)^{-2}(-dt) = (- t)^{-1} + c_1.$$

Using the initial condition, $v(0) = 4$ ft/sec, we find c_1:

$$4 = \frac{1}{8} + c_1 \Rightarrow c_1 = \frac{31}{8},$$

so

$$v(t) = \frac{1}{8-t} + \frac{31}{8}.$$

To find the position function x we integrate again:

$$x(t) = -\log(8-t) + \frac{31}{8}t + c_2.$$

The initial condition on x gives

$$0 = -\log 8 + c_2 \quad \text{or} \quad c_2 = \log 8.$$

Thus

$$x(t) = \log\frac{8}{8-t} + \frac{31}{8}t.$$

For $0 \le t < 8$ we see that $v(t) > 0$; the motion is always to the right. As $t \to 8$ both $v(t)$ and $x(t)$ get big beyond all bounds: the particle "goes off to infinity" with a speed which is unbounded.

Example 11. The area bounded by the y-axis, the x-axis, the curve $y = e^{-x}$, and $x = b$ (see Figure 5) is revolved about the x-axis. We find the volume generated.

As we saw in Chapter 2 the volume V obtained by revolving an area of this sort about the x-axis is found by

$$V = \pi \int_0^b y^2 \, dx.$$

In the present case $y = e^{-x}$, $y^2 = e^{-2x}$, and we have

$$V = \pi \int_0^b e^{-2x} \, dx = -\frac{\pi}{2} \int_0^b e^{-2x}(-2 \, dx)$$

$$= -\frac{\pi}{2}\left[e^{-2x} \Big|_0^b \right] = -\frac{\pi}{2}(e^{-2b} - 1)$$

$$= \frac{\pi}{2}(1 - e^{-2b}) \text{ cubic units.}$$

Example 12. Suppose it has been found experimentally that the population of a colony of bacteria increases at a rate proportional to the population at time t.

We can describe this observation more precisely by resorting to symbols. Let $y = y(t)$ be the population at time t; then $\dfrac{dy}{dt} = y'(t)$ represents the rate of change of y with respect to time, and the condition just described says that

$$y'(t) = k^2 y(t), \tag{39}$$

where k^2 is the constant of proportionality, written as a square to guarantee that $y'(t) > 0$. We seek an explicit expression for the functional relation between y and t.

By writing (39) in either of the following forms

$$\frac{y'(t)}{y(t)} = k^2$$

or

$$\frac{y'(t)\,dt}{y(t)} = k^2\,dt \quad \text{or} \quad \frac{dy}{y} = k^2\,dt,$$

we see that we can perform an antidifferentiation of both sides. This enables us to write

$$\log y(t) = k^2 t + c \tag{40}$$

(in problems of this sort one must pay attention to the constant of integration). We can determine c by agreeing to choose a meaningful origin for the time scale t and letting $y(0) = y_0$, the population of the colony at the "beginning of time" (for this discussion, that is). Then substituting $t = 0$ in (40) gives

$$\log y_0 = 0 + c;$$

thus (40) can now be written as

$$\log \frac{y}{y_0} = k^2 t.$$

Finally, operating on both sides of this equation with the exponential function, we find

$$\frac{y}{y_0} = e^{k^2 t},$$

or

$$y = y(t) = y_0\, e^{k^2 t}, \tag{41}$$

the desired functional relation.

We conclude this section with the following remark. The student's original introduction to logarithms very likely emphasized the utility of logarithms in computational work; there is no denying the value of logarithms for certain types of computations.

However, with the invention of high-speed electronic computers it is clear that this aspect of logarithms will have diminished greatly in importance. It is natural, then, for the student to raise the questions "What good *are* they?," "Is there any real point in spending so much time studying these functions?" The complete answer cannot be given at this time, but rather more than a hint about one part of the answer is accessible. In the application of mathematics to various other fields many problems occur similar to that described in Example 12: some information is known about a rate of change of a function, and it is desired to find the form of the function. This leads to a differential equation problem; the solution of problems of this sort requires the availability of many different kinds of functions, and the logarithm and exponential functions carry their share of the burden in providing solutions. To put it differently, a great and serious gap would be created in trying to solve such problems if these functions were not part of the body of calculus.

EXERCISES

In Exercises 1–15 analyze (including finding maxima and minima and, where feasible, inflection points), and sketch.

1. $y = x^2 \log x$

2. $y = xe^{-x}$

3. $y = xe^{-x^2}$

4. $y = e^{-x} \log x$

5. $y = \log \cos x$

6. $y = \log \sec x$

7. $y = e^{-x} \cos x$

8. $y = e^{-1/x}$

9. $y = \begin{cases} e^{-1/x^2}, & x \neq 0 \\ 0, & x = 0 \end{cases}$

10. $y = 1 - e^{-x}$

11. $y = \dfrac{1}{1 - e^{-x}}$

12. $y = \dfrac{1}{1 + e^{-x}}$

13. $y = \dfrac{1}{1 - e^{-1/x}}$

14. $y = \dfrac{1}{1 - e^{-1/x^2}}$

15. $y = \dfrac{1}{1 + e^{-1/x^2}}$

16. Draw, with some care, the graphs of the following functions on the same set of axes

(a) $f(x) = \log_2 x$,   (b) $g(x) = \log x$,   (c) $h(x) = \log_{10} x$.

17. Find the area in the first quadrant bounded by the curve $y = xe^{-x^2}$, the x-axis, and the line $x = b$. What can be said about the area as $b \to \infty$?

18. A particle moves along the positive x-axis with velocity proportional to x. If $x = 1$ when $t = 0$ and $x = 4$ when $t = 1$, show that the motion can be described by

$$x(t) = 4^t, \qquad t \geq 0.$$

19. A particle moves along the x-axis with acceleration at time t described by $a(t) = e^{-t}$. If $v(0) = 2$ ft/sec and $x(0) = 1$ ft, find $x(t)$.

20. A particle starts at time $t = 0$ at the origin with an initial velocity of 0 and a velocity at time t given by

$$v(t) = \frac{1}{t^2 + 1}, \qquad t \geq 0.$$

(a) Find the position function x.

(b) Find the acceleration function a, discuss the sign of a and its relation to v.

21. The rate of disintegration (decay) of a radioactive substance is proportional to the amount y present at time t. If the amount at time $t = 0$ is $y = y_0$, find a formula for the amount present at time t.

22. See Exercise 21. Find the half life of the substance; i.e., find the value t_1 such that $y(t_1) = \frac{1}{2} y_0$.

7.5 The Hyperbolic Functions

In this section we discuss a class of functions which can be defined in terms of the exponential function. As we shall see, the six functions of this class have strong similarities to the trigonometric functions, and this fact is exploited in choosing names and symbols for these functions. There are, of course, points of distinction between the trigonometric functions and the hyperbolic functions, and we shall mention these differences at the appropriate times.

By way of introduction we remark that it is a not too difficult problem in mechanics to show that a cable, made of flexible but nonstretchable material, having its weight uniformly distributed, and hanging from two supports, will form a curve which, with suitable choice of coordinate system, is described by the equation

$$y = \frac{a}{2}(e^{x/a} + e^{-x/a}), \qquad a > 0.$$

The curve, called a *catenary*, is shown in Figure 9. Other problems, some of them also in mechanics, lead to a similar combination of exponential functions. Thus it is quite reasonable to give such a combination a special name and to devote a little attention to its properties.

For the sake of simplicity we take $a = 1$ in the preceding equation and call the resulting expression the *hyperbolic cosine of x*, abbreviated cosh x.

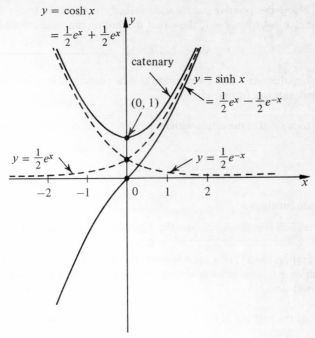

$y = \cosh x$

$= \frac{1}{2}e^x + \frac{1}{2}e^x$

catenary

$y = \sinh x$

$= \frac{1}{2}e^x - \frac{1}{2}e^{-x}$

$(0, 1)$

$y = \frac{1}{2}e^x$

$y = \frac{1}{2}e^{-x}$

Figure 9

Definition 7. *The* **hyperbolic cosine,** cosh, *is defined for all* $x \in \mathbf{R}$ *by*

$$\cosh x = \tfrac{1}{2}\,(e^x + e^{-x}). \tag{42}$$

Similarly, the **hyperbolic sine,** sinh, *is defined for all* $x \in \mathbf{R}$ *by*

$$\sinh x = \tfrac{1}{2}\,(e^x - e^{-x}). \tag{43}$$

It is customary to pronounce cosh about as it looks; sinh is pronounced "sinch." The reason for the name "hyperbolic" function will be disclosed later. It will sometimes be convenient to refer to the trigonometric functions as the circular functions in distinguishing them from the hyperbolic functions.

The following facts are immediately obtainable about cosh and sinh; they should be compared with corresponding statements about the circular cosine and sine. First of all, cosh is an *even* function (so the graph $y = \cosh x$ is symmetric with respect to the y-axis) and sinh is an *odd* function (its graph being, therefore, symmetric with respect to the origin. Next it is easy to compute from (42) and (43) that

$$D_x \cosh x = \sinh x, \tag{44}$$

and

$$D_x \sinh x = \cosh x. \tag{45}$$

As e^x and e^{-x} are positive for all x, it follows that $\cosh x > 0$, all $x \in \mathbf{R}$.

This observation, along with (45), then tells us that sinh is an increasing function; because $\sinh 0 = 0$, we also see that

$$x < 0 \Rightarrow \sinh x < 0,$$
$$x > 0 \Rightarrow \sinh x > 0.$$

But these statements, used with (44), imply that cosh is decreasing for $x < 0$, increasing for $x > 0$, and hence has a minimum (relative and absolute) at $x = 0$, $y = 1$. Further, as $D_x{}^2 \cosh x = \cosh x$ and $D_x{}^2 \sinh x = \sinh x$, we note that the graph of cosh is everywhere concave upward, whereas the graph of sinh is concave upward for $x > 0$, concave downward for $x < 0$.

This discussion enables us to draw the graphs of these functions, as shown in Figure 9. Note that in this figure we have also indicated how the graphs could be obtained from the graphs of $y = \frac{1}{2}e^x$ and $y = \frac{1}{2}e^{-x}$ and Definition 7.

We come now to some properties of the hyperbolic functions which are not immediately apparent from the definitions. We refer to the fact that cosh and sinh share a set of identities quite analogous to the identities which hold for the circular functions. To be explicit, we assert that the following are valid for all $x, y \in \mathbf{R}$.

$$\cosh^2 x - \sinh^2 x = 1 \tag{46}$$
$$\sinh(x + y) = \sinh x \cosh y + \cosh x \sinh y \tag{47}$$
$$\sinh(x - y) = \sinh x \cosh y - \cosh x \sinh y \tag{48}$$
$$\cosh(x + y) = \cosh x \cosh y + \sinh x \sinh y \tag{49}$$
$$\cosh(x - y) = \cosh x \cosh y - \sinh x \sinh y \tag{50}$$
$$\sinh 2x = 2 \sinh x \cosh x \tag{51}$$
$$\cosh 2x = \cosh^2 x + \sinh^2 x \tag{52}$$
$$= 1 + 2 \sinh^2 x \tag{53}$$
$$= 2 \cosh^2 x - 1 \tag{54}$$
$$\sinh^2 x = \tfrac{1}{2}(\cosh 2x - 1) \tag{55}$$
$$\cosh^2 x = \tfrac{1}{2}(\cosh 2x + 1). \tag{56}$$

The validity of these identities is established by using the definitions of cosh and sinh. We illustrate by proving the first two. For (46) we have

$$\cosh^2 x - \sinh^x x = \tfrac{1}{4}(e^x + e^{-x})^2 - \tfrac{1}{4}(e^x - e^{-x})^2$$
$$= \tfrac{1}{4}(e^{2x} + 2 + e^{-2x} - e^{2x} + 2 - e^{-2x})$$
$$= \tfrac{1}{4}(4) = 1.$$

The proof of (47) is more natural if we begin with the right-hand side:

$$\sinh x \cosh y + \cosh x \sinh y$$
$$= \tfrac{1}{2}(e^x - e^{-x}) \cdot \tfrac{1}{2}(e^y + e^{-y}) + \tfrac{1}{2}(e^x + e^{-x})\tfrac{1}{2}(e^y - e^{-y})$$
$$= \tfrac{1}{4}[e^{x+y} + e^{x-y} - e^{-x+y} - e^{-x-y} + e^{x+y} - e^{x-y} + e^{-x+y} - e^{-x-y}]$$
$$= \tfrac{1}{4}(2e^{x+y} - 2e^{-x-y}) = \tfrac{1}{2}(e^{x+y} - e^{-(x+y)})$$
$$= \sinh(x + y).$$

The proofs of (48), (49), and (50) are analogous to that of (47). Then (51) and (52) follow from (47) and (48) respectively, by replacing y by x. The details of these and the remaining proofs will be left as exercises.

Note that if we let

$$x = \cosh t,$$

$$y = \sinh t$$

and use the identity (46), $\cosh^2 t - \sinh^2 t = 1$, we have $x^2 - y^2 = 1$. This says that $(\cosh t, \sinh t)$ is a point on the equilateral hyperbola, just as $(\cos t, \sin t)$ is a point on the unit circle $x^2 + y^2 = 1$. This begins to suggest why the choice of names for these two sets of functions was made as it was (see Figure 10). The significance of t will be discussed shortly.

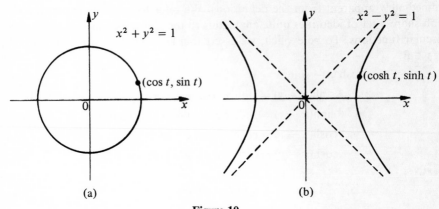

Figure 10

It is a simple matter now to define the remaining four hyperbolic functions, analogous to the way the last four circular functions were defined, and to obtain their essential properties.

Definition 8. *The **hyperbolic tangent, cotangent, secant** and **cosecant**, abbreviated* tanh, coth, sech, *and* csch, *respectively, are defined as follows:*

$$\tanh x = \frac{\sinh x}{\cosh x} = \frac{e^x - e^{-x}}{e^x + e^{-x}}, \qquad \text{all } x \in \mathbf{R}, \tag{57}$$

$$\coth x = \frac{\cosh x}{\sinh x} = \frac{e^x + e^{-x}}{e^x - e^{-x}}, \qquad x \neq 0, \tag{58}$$

$$\operatorname{sech} x = \frac{1}{\cosh x} = \frac{2}{e^x + e^{-x}}, \qquad \text{all } x \in \mathbf{R}, \tag{59}$$

$$\operatorname{csch} x = \frac{1}{\sinh x} = \frac{2}{e^x - e^{-x}}, \qquad x \neq 0. \tag{60}$$

The derivatives of these functions are similar to those of the circular functions. For the sake of completeness we describe the general form of the derivatives of all the hyperbolic functions as follows.

Theorem 16. *Let u be a differentiable function. Then*

$$D_x \sinh u = \cosh u \, D_x u$$

$$D_x \cosh u = \sinh u \, D_x u$$

$$D_x \tanh u = \operatorname{sech}^2 u \, D_x u$$

$$D_x \coth u = -\operatorname{csch}^2 u \, D_x u, \qquad u(x) \neq 0$$

$$D_x \operatorname{sech} u = -\operatorname{sech} u \tanh u \, D_x u$$

$$D_x \operatorname{csch} u = -\operatorname{csch} u \coth u \, D_x u, \qquad u(x) \neq 0.$$

Proof. The first two of these follow from (44) and (45) and the chain rule. For the tanh we proceed as follows:

$$D_x \tanh x = D_x\left(\frac{\sinh x}{\cosh x}\right) = \frac{\cosh x \cosh x - \sinh x \sinh x}{\cosh^2 x}$$

$$= \frac{\cosh^2 x - \sinh^2 x}{\cosh^2 x} = \frac{1}{\cosh^2 x} \qquad \text{[by (46)]}$$

$$= \operatorname{sech}^2 x.$$

An application of the chain rule then gives $D_x \tanh u$. The proofs of the remaining three are left as exercises. ∎

The functions of Definition 8 satisfy identities analogous to those which hold for the corresponding circular functions. We mention some of these.

$$1 - \tanh^2 x = \operatorname{sech}^2 x. \tag{61}$$

$$\coth^2 x - 1 = \operatorname{csch}^2 x. \tag{62}$$

$$\tanh(x + y) = \frac{\tanh x + \tanh y}{1 + \tanh x \tanh y}. \tag{63}$$

$$\tanh(x - y) = \frac{\tanh x - \tanh y}{1 - \tanh x \tanh y}. \tag{64}$$

$$\tanh 2x = \frac{2 \tanh x}{1 + \tanh^2 x}. \tag{65}$$

EXERCISES

1. Verify the identities (48), (49), (50), and (53).

2. Use the definition given in Eqs. (58), (59), and (60) to find $\dfrac{d}{dx} \coth x$, $\dfrac{d}{dx} \operatorname{sech} x$, and $\dfrac{d}{dx} \operatorname{csch} x$.

In numbers 3–10 find f'.

3. $f(x) = \tanh \sqrt[3]{x}$.

4. $f(x) = \sinh \log x$.

5. $f(x) = \operatorname{sech} \sqrt{x^2 - 1}$.

6. $f(x) = \cosh \sin x$.

7. $f(x) = \log \cosh x$.

8. $f(x) = e^{\coth x}$.

9. $f(x) = \tanh^2 x \operatorname{sech}^3 x$.

10. $f(x) = \cosh e^x$.

11. Using Definition 8, analyze the graph of each of the following, discussing such things as range (extent), maximum and minimum points, asymptotes, etc. Then sketch.

   (a) $y = \tanh x$.
   (b) $y = \coth x$.

   (c) $y = \operatorname{sech} x$.
   (d) $y = \operatorname{csch} x$.

12. Prove identities (62) and (64).

13. This exercise concerns $\int \operatorname{sech} x \, dx$.

   (a) Write
   $$\operatorname{sech} x = \frac{2}{e^x + e^{-x}} = \frac{2e^x}{e^{2x} + 1} = 2 \frac{e^x}{(e^x)^2 + 1}.$$

   Now recall, from Chapter 6, that $\dfrac{d}{dx} \tan^{-1} u = \dfrac{\dfrac{du}{dx}}{u^2 + 1}$ and find $\int \operatorname{sech} x \, dx$. Call your answer F_1.

   (b) Write
   $$\operatorname{sech} x = \frac{1}{\cosh x} = \frac{\cosh x}{\cosh^2 x} = \frac{\cosh x}{\sinh^2 x + 1},$$
   use the suggestion given in (a), and find $\int \operatorname{sech} x \, dx$. Call your answer F_2.

   (c) Prove that, for all $x \in \mathbf{R}$, $0 < F_1(x) < \pi$. [*Hint.* Remember that $e^x > 0$ and use the range of $\tan^{-1}$.]

(d) Prove that, for all $x \in \mathbf{R}$, $-\dfrac{\pi}{2} < F_2(x) < \dfrac{\pi}{2}$. [*Hint.* Use the range of sinh x and the range of $\tan^{-1}$.]

(e) Prove that $F_1(x) - F_2(x) = \dfrac{\pi}{2}$, all $x \in \mathbf{R}$.

14. This exercise concerns $\int \operatorname{csch} x \, dx$.

(a) Write

$$\operatorname{csch} x = \frac{2}{e^x - e^{-x}} = \frac{2e^x}{e^{2x} - 1} = 2 \frac{e^x}{(e^x)^2 - 1} = 2e^x \frac{1}{(e^x)^2 - 1}.$$

(b) Now verify that

$$\frac{1}{u^2 - 1} = \frac{1}{2}\left[\frac{1}{u - 1} - \frac{1}{u + 1}\right].$$

(c) Use the identity in (b) on the fraction in the last expression in (a). This will enable you to show

$$\int \operatorname{csch} x \, dx = \log\left|\frac{e^x - 1}{e^x + 1}\right|.$$

(d) Show that the result in (c) can also be written as

$$\int \operatorname{csch} x = \log\left|\tanh\frac{x}{2}\right|.$$

7.6   Inverse Hyperbolic Functions

In this section we give a brief discussion of the inverse hyperbolic functions. The fact is that four of the hyperbolic functions are monotonic throughout their domains and thus have unrestricted inverses. Only for the cosh and the sech must one restrict the domains in order to obtain an inverse. We shall focus our attention on the inverses of the sinh, cosh, and tanh.

Since the hyperbolic functions are defined in terms of the exponential function, the inverses, more or less predictably, can be expressed in terms of the logarithm function. Moreover, the form of the inverses can be found rather easily by elementary algebra.

Suppose we begin with the inverse of sinh. Temporarily, let

$$f(x) = \sinh x, \qquad \text{all } x \in \mathbf{R};$$

then

$$f'(x) = \cosh x > 0, \qquad \text{all } x \in \mathbf{R}.$$

Thus f has an inverse which we shall, for the present, call g; then

$$g(f(x)) = x, \qquad \text{all } x \in \mathbf{R},$$

i.e.,

$$g(\tfrac{1}{2}(e^x - e^{-x})) = x.$$

Suppose we let

$$\tfrac{1}{2}(e^x - e^{-x}) = y.$$

We multiply both sides of this equation by $2e^x$ and write the result as

$$e^{2x} - 2y\, e^x - 1 = 0.$$

This is a quadratic equation in e^x; applying the quadratic formula gives

$$e^x = y \pm \sqrt{y^2 + 1}.$$

As $e^x > 0$, all $x \in \mathbf{R}$, only the plus sign is applicable:

$$e^x = y + \sqrt{y^2 + 1},$$

or, taking logarithms,

$$x = \log(y + \sqrt{y^2 + 1}).$$

The form of the function g is, then,

$$g(y) = \log(y + \sqrt{y^2 + 1}).$$

Replacing y by x and using $\sinh^{-1}$ for g, we have

$$\sinh^{-1} x = \log(x + \sqrt{x^2 + 1}). \tag{66}$$

As $f = \sinh : \mathbf{R} \longrightarrow \mathbf{R}$, we know that

$$g = \sinh^{-1} : \mathbf{R} \longrightarrow \mathbf{R}.$$

From the formula in (66) for $\sinh^{-1}$ we can easily calculate the derivative:

$$\frac{d}{dx}\sinh^{-1} x = \frac{d}{dx}\log(x + \sqrt{x^2 + 1}) = \frac{1}{\sqrt{x^2 + 1}}. \tag{67}$$

(Compare this with the expression for $\dfrac{d}{dx}\sin^{-1} x$.)

For the inverse cosh it is necessary, as remarked above, to restrict the domain. Thus we consider

$$y = \cosh x = \tfrac{1}{2}(e^x + e^{-x}), \qquad x \ge 0, \quad y \ge 1.$$

By a technique such as used to find $\sinh^{-1}$ we can easily show that

$$\cosh^{-1} x = \log(x + \sqrt{x^2 - 1}), \qquad x \ge 1, \tag{68}$$

and

$$\frac{d}{dx}\cosh^{-1} x = \frac{1}{\sqrt{x^2 - 1}}, \qquad x > 1. \tag{69}$$

The tanh is monotonic, so the inverse can be found without restricting the domain. The results are

$$\tanh^{-1} x = \frac{1}{2} \log \frac{1+x}{1-x}, \qquad -1 < x < 1, \tag{70}$$

and

$$\frac{d}{dx} \tanh^{-1} x = \frac{1}{1-x^2}, \qquad -1 < x < 1. \tag{71}$$

Verification of the above assertions will be left as exercises.

The derivative formulas (67), (69), and (71) can be rewritten as antiderivatives. We give, however, a more general statement than that obtained from a simple translation:

$$\int \frac{du}{\sqrt{u^2 + a^2}} = \sinh^{-1} \frac{u}{a} = \log\left(\frac{u + \sqrt{u^2 + a^2}}{a}\right) + c, \tag{72}$$

$$\int \frac{du}{\sqrt{u^2 - a^2}} = \cosh^{-1} \frac{u}{a} = \log\left(\frac{u + \sqrt{u^2 - a^2}}{a}\right) + c, \tag{73}$$

$$\int \frac{du}{a^2 - u^2} = \frac{1}{a} \tanh^{-1} \frac{u}{a} = \frac{1}{2a} \log \frac{a + u}{a - u} + c, \qquad |u| < a. \tag{74}$$

We now return to the question of the relation between the circular and the hyperbolic functions. To make our point we resort to a parallel display of the solution of two analogous area problems (see Figure 11).

We consider the circle $x^2 + y^2 = 1$, the hyperbola $x^2 - y^2 = 1$, and a point

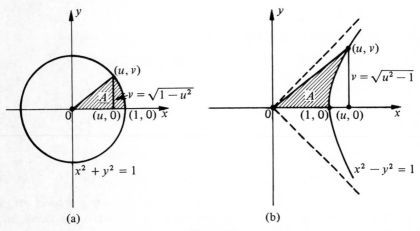

(a) (b)

Figure 11

(u, v) on each curve. In each case we seek the area A bounded by the x-axis, the curve, and the line from the origin to (u, v).

$x^2 + y^2 = 1$	$x^2 - y^2 = 1, \; x \geq 1$

$$A = \frac{1}{2} uv + \int_u^1 y \, dx$$

$$= \frac{1}{2} uv + \int_u^1 \sqrt{1 - x^2} \, dx.$$

$$A = \frac{1}{2} uv - \int_1^u y \, dx$$

$$= \frac{1}{2} uv - \int_1^u \sqrt{x^2 - 1} \, dx.$$

Let   Let

$$x = \cos t$$

$$dx = -\sin t \, dt$$

$$\sqrt{1 - x^2} = \sqrt{1 - \cos^2 t} = \sin t.$$

$$x = \cosh t$$

$$dx = \sinh t \, dt$$

$$\sqrt{x^2 - 1} = \sqrt{\cosh^2 t - 1} = \sinh t.$$

Then   Then

$$A = \frac{1}{2} uv - \int_{\cos^{-1} u}^0 \sin^2 t \, dt,$$

$$= \frac{1}{2} uv + \frac{1}{2} \int_0^{\cos^{-1} u} (1 - \cos 2t) \, dt,$$

$$A = \frac{1}{2} uv - \int_0^{\cosh^{-1} u} \sinh^2 t \, dt$$

$$= \frac{1}{2} uv - \frac{1}{2} \int_0^{\cosh^{-1} u} (\cosh 2t - 1) \, dt,$$

$(\sin^2 t = \frac{1}{2}(1 - \cos 2t))$

$$= \frac{1}{2}[uv + (t - \frac{1}{2}\sin 2t)|_0^{\cos^{-1} u}],$$

$$= \frac{1}{2}[uv + (t - \sin t \cos t)|_0^{\cos^{-1} u}],$$

$$= \frac{1}{2}[uv + (\cos^{-1} u - vu)],$$

$(\sinh^2 t = \frac{1}{2}(\cosh 2t - 1))$

$$= \frac{1}{2}[uv + (t - \frac{1}{2}\sinh 2t)|_0^{\cosh^{-1} u}],$$

$$= \frac{1}{2}[uv + (t - \sinh t \cosh t)|_0^{\cosh^{-1} u}],$$

$$= \frac{1}{2}[uv + (\cosh^{-1} u - vu)],$$

or   or

$$A = \frac{1}{2} \cos^{-1} u.$$

$$A = \frac{1}{2} \cosh^{-1} u.$$

In the steps leading to the penultimate line we used the facts that

$$\sin(\cos^{-1} u) = \sqrt{1 - u^2} = v$$

$$\sinh(\cosh^{-1} u) = \sqrt{u^2 - 1} = v.$$

Thus we see that

$$\cos^{-1} u = 2A$$

$$\cosh^{-1} u = 2A$$

or

$$u = \cos 2A$$

$$v = \sin 2A$$

$$u = \cosh 2A$$

$$v = \sinh 2A.$$

It follows, then, that the parameter t used in the preceding section before Figure 10 is in each case twice the area bounded by the x-axis, the curve, and the line from the origin to the point on the curve.

The substitution technique used in performing the two integrations will be discussed in detail in Chapter 8. Notice that to obtain all values of sin and cos we must use the entire circle $x^2 + y^2 = 1$, whereas to obtain all values of sinh and cosh we use only the branch of the hyperbola shown in Figure 11b). This dependence of these functions on their respective curves explains the basic difference between the circular and the hyperbolic functions: the former are periodic and the latter are not.

Example 13. We provide here the first half of another basis for comparing the hyperbolic and the circular functions. The second half will appear in Exercise 4.

We begin by taking $x > 0$ (this is a matter of convenience and is not essential) and applying the Mean Value Theorem to cosh on the interval $[0, x]$:

$$\frac{\cosh x - \cosh 0}{x - 0} = \sinh x_0,$$

since $\dfrac{d}{dx} \cosh x = \sinh x$. Here $0 < x_0 < x$; we let $q_0 = \sinh x_0$ and we recall that $\cosh 0 = 1$. Thus the above equation can be written

$$\cosh x = 1 + q_0 x.$$

Now we integrate this equation between 0 and x:

$$\int_0^x \cosh t \, dt = \int_0^x (1 + q_0 t) \, dt,$$

which gives

$$\sinh x = x + \tfrac{1}{2} q_0 x^2.$$

We continue, integrating *this* equation between 0 and x:

$$\int_0^x \sinh t \, dt = \int_0^x \left(t + \frac{1}{2} q_0 t^2 \right) dt,$$

or

$$\cosh x - 1 = \frac{1}{2} x^2 + \frac{1}{3!} q_0 x^2 ;$$

we write this as

$$\cosh x = 1 + \frac{x^2}{2!} + \frac{x^3}{3!} q_0 .$$

Again integrating between 0 and x,

$$\int_0^x \cosh t \, dt = \int_0^x \left(1 + \frac{t^2}{2!} + \frac{t^3}{3!} q_0 \right) dt,$$

or

$$\sinh x = x + \frac{x^3}{3!} + \frac{x^4}{4!} q_0 .$$

The next two steps would give

$$\cosh x = 1 + \frac{x^2}{2!} + \frac{x^4}{4!} + \frac{x^5}{5!} q_0$$

and

$$\sinh x = x + \frac{x^3}{3!} + \frac{x^5}{5!} + \frac{x^6}{6!} q_0.$$

It is now an easy matter, using mathematical induction, to show that for every $n \in \mathbf{N}$ we have

$$\cosh x = 1 + \frac{x^2}{2!} + \frac{x^4}{4!} + \cdots + \frac{x^{2n}}{(2n)!} + \frac{x^{2n+1}}{(2n+1)!} q_0, \tag{75}$$

$$\sinh x = x + \frac{x^3}{3!} + \frac{x^5}{5!} + \cdots + \frac{x^{2n+1}}{(2n+1)!} + \frac{x^{2n+2}}{(2n+2)!} q_0, \tag{76}$$

where $q_0 = \sinh x_0$, for $0 < x_0 < x$. If $x < 0$ the same results hold, only in this case $x < x_0 < 0$.

Clearly, a similar development is possible for cos and sin; we leave this for the exercises.

EXERCISES

1. Graph each of the following:

(a) $y = \sinh^{-1} x$.   (b) $y = \cosh^{-1} x$.   (c) $y = \tanh^{-1} x$.

2. Find the expression for $\cosh^{-1} x$ by the algebraic technique used in finding $\sinh^{-1} x$.

3. Find the expression for $\tanh^{-1} x$ by the technique used in the text for finding $\sinh^{-1} x$.

4. Use the method of Example 13 to show that, for all $n \in \mathbf{N}$, the following statements are valid:

$$\cos x = 1 - \frac{x^2}{2!} + \frac{x^4}{4!} - \cdots + (-1)^n \frac{x^{2n}}{(2n!)} + (-1)^{n+1} \frac{x^{2n+1}}{(2n+1)!} q_0 \tag{77}$$

$$\sin x = x - \frac{x^3}{3!} + \frac{x^5}{5!} - \cdots + (-1)^n \frac{x^{2n+1}}{(2n+1)!} + (-1)^{n+1} \frac{x^{2n+2}}{(2n+2)!} q_0 \tag{78}$$

Compare these with Eqs. (75) and (76). Note that in Eqs. (77) and (78) $q_0 = \sin x_0$, so $|q_0| \leq 1$. No such squeeze on q_0 is available for Eqs. (75) and (76).

The tanh is monotonic, so the inverse can be found without restricting the domain. The results are

$$\tanh^{-1} x = \frac{1}{2} \log \frac{1+x}{1-x}, \qquad -1 < x < 1, \tag{70}$$

and

$$\frac{d}{dx} \tanh^{-1} x = \frac{1}{1-x^2}, \qquad -1 < x < 1. \tag{71}$$

Verification of the above assertions will be left as exercises.

The derivative formulas (67), (69), and (71) can be rewritten as antiderivatives. We give, however, a more general statement than that obtained from a simple translation:

$$\int \frac{du}{\sqrt{u^2 + a^2}} = \sinh^{-1} \frac{u}{a} = \log\left(\frac{u + \sqrt{u^2 + a^2}}{a}\right) + c, \tag{72}$$

$$\int \frac{du}{\sqrt{u^2 - a^2}} = \cosh^{-1} \frac{u}{a} = \log\left(\frac{u + \sqrt{u^2 - a^2}}{a}\right) + c, \tag{73}$$

$$\int \frac{du}{a^2 - u^2} = \frac{1}{a} \tanh^{-1} \frac{u}{a} = \frac{1}{2a} \log \frac{a+u}{a-u} + c, \qquad |u| < a. \tag{74}$$

We now return to the question of the relation between the circular and the hyperbolic functions. To make our point we resort to a parallel display of the solution of two analogous area problems (see Figure 11).

We consider the circle $x^2 + y^2 = 1$, the hyperbola $x^2 - y^2 = 1$, and a point

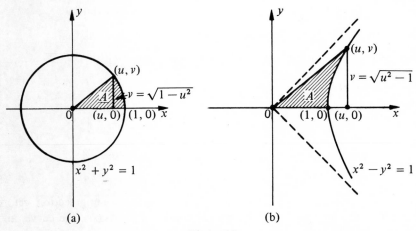

(a)   (b)

Figure 11

(u, v) on each curve. In each case we seek the area A bounded by the x-axis, the curve, and the line from the origin to (u, v).

$x^2 + y^2 = 1$	$x^2 - y^2 = 1, x \geq 1$

$$A = \frac{1}{2} uv + \int_u^1 y \, dx$$

$$= \frac{1}{2} uv + \int_u^1 \sqrt{1 - x^2} \, dx.$$

$$A = \frac{1}{2} uv - \int_1^u y \, dx$$

$$= \frac{1}{2} uv - \int_1^u \sqrt{x^2 - 1} \, dx.$$

Let

$$x = \cos t$$

$$dx = -\sin t \, dt$$

$$\sqrt{1 - x^2} = \sqrt{1 - \cos^2 t} = \sin t.$$

Then

$$A = \frac{1}{2} uv - \int_{\cos^{-1} u}^0 \sin^2 t \, dt,$$

$$= \frac{1}{2} uv + \frac{1}{2} \int_0^{\cos^{-1} u} (1 - \cos 2t) \, dt,$$

$(\sin^2 t = \frac{1}{2}(1 - \cos 2t))$

$$= \frac{1}{2}[uv + (t - \frac{1}{2} \sin 2t)|_0^{\cos^{-1} u}],$$

$$= \frac{1}{2}[uv + (t - \sin t \cos t)|_0^{\cos^{-1} u}],$$

$$= \frac{1}{2}[uv + (\cos^{-1} u - vu)],$$

or

$$A = \frac{1}{2} \cos^{-1} u.$$

Let

$$x = \cosh t$$

$$dx = \sinh t \, dt$$

$$\sqrt{x^2 - 1} = \sqrt{\cosh^2 t - 1} = \sinh t.$$

Then

$$A = \frac{1}{2} uv - \int_0^{\cosh^{-1} u} \sinh^2 t \, dt$$

$$= \frac{1}{2} uv - \frac{1}{2} \int_0^{\cosh^{-1} u} (\cosh 2t - 1) \, dt,$$

$(\sinh^2 t = \frac{1}{2}(\cosh 2t - 1))$

$$= \frac{1}{2}[uv + (t - \frac{1}{2} \sinh 2t)|_0^{\cosh^{-1} u}],$$

$$= \frac{1}{2}[uv + (t - \sinh t \cosh t)|_0^{\cosh^{-1} u}],$$

$$= \frac{1}{2}[uv + (\cosh^{-1} u - vu)],$$

or

$$A = \frac{1}{2} \cosh^{-1} u.$$

In the steps leading to the penultimate line we used the facts that

$$\sin(\cos^{-1} u) = \sqrt{1 - u^2} = v \qquad\qquad \sinh(\cosh^{-1} u) = \sqrt{u^2 - 1} = v.$$

Thus we see that

$$\cos^{-1} u = 2A \qquad\qquad\qquad \cosh^{-1} u = 2A$$

or

$$u = \cos 2A \qquad\qquad\qquad u = \cosh 2A$$

$$v = \sin 2A \qquad\qquad\qquad v = \sinh 2A.$$

It follows, then, that the parameter t used in the preceding section before Figure 10 is in each case twice the area bounded by the x-axis, the curve, and the line from the origin to the point on the curve.

Chapter **8** Techniques of Integration

8.1 Preliminary Remarks. More on Differentials

In this chapter we develop a few methods for finding antiderivatives. It is perhaps worth mentioning that, whereas a relatively few formulas (the number, if one is interested in counting, is between 20 and 30) will suffice for finding derivatives of the elementary functions, the inverse problem—that of finding antiderivatives—cannot be encompassed so neatly. One has only to consult a table of integrals (in, e.g., the *CRC Standard Mathematical Tables* or Peirce's *A Short Table of Integrals*) to be convinced of this.

The preceding sentence requires amplification on two points. One has to do with terminology. The process we have been referring to as "finding antiderivatives" has long been described as "integration." A minor disadvantage of the older name is that it suggests one is concerned with evaluating definite integrals (a related, but not identical, problem). The term "integration," meaning "antidifferentiation," is so well established, it would be folly to try to pretend it is not used in this way. Besides it is less cumbersome than its modern successor.

The other point which must be discussed involves tables of integrals. A good table of integrals is a necessary tool for anyone whose work requires frequent integration of functions, but it is by no means sufficient—it is not difficult to give easily integrable integrals which are not directly obtained from a good table. Moreover—and this is more serious—as a result of incorrect treatment of some of the inverse trigonometric functions, most of the current tables of integrals will give incorrect results for certain definite integrals; as an example we can mention

$$\int_{-2}^{\sqrt{2}} \frac{dx}{x^3\sqrt{x^2-1}}.$$

We shall return to this point later in the chapter.

Now from a manipulative point of view it turns out (this will be made quite clear in what follows) to be highly advantageous to approach the problem of integration in terms of differentials rather than derivatives. For this reason we conclude this section by reviewing the subject of differentials, introduced in Section 4.2.

Recall that, for a differentiable function f, the differential df is a function of two variables x and h, defined by

$$df(x, h) = f'(x)h. \tag{1}$$

Frequently, the symbol Δx is used in place of h, so that we can also write (1) as

$$df(x, \Delta x) = f'(x)\Delta x. \tag{2}$$

If the function f is the identity function j ($j(x) = x$, $j'(x) = 1$), then (2) becomes

$$dj(x, \Delta x) = 1 \cdot \Delta x = \Delta x,$$

or if, as is often done, we write dx for dj, we have

$$dx(x, \Delta x) = \Delta x. \tag{3}$$

Moreover, it is frequently the custom to omit the arguments of this differential and simply write

$$dx = \Delta x, \tag{4}$$

the point to remember being that dx is a *function* whose *value* at $(x, \Delta x)$ is Δx.

Now when y is used as a symbol for a function ($y = f(x)$), then the differential may be written

$$dy = f'(x)\Delta x, \tag{5}$$

and dividing (5) by (4) gives

$$\frac{dy}{dx} = f'(x). \tag{6}$$

The left-hand side of (6) is the symbol introduced by Leibniz for a derivative, the right-hand side is the symbol introduced by Lagrange.

But we can also use (6) (or (4) and (5) together) to write the differential of the function as

$$dy = f'(x)\, dx \tag{7}$$

a very useful notation.

One of the reasons for the utility of (7) is that it is invariant under a transformation. Suppose, for example, that, using the Leibniz notation, we have

$$y = \sin x, \qquad dy = \cos x\, dx \tag{8}$$

$$x = u^2 + 1, \qquad dx = 2u\, du. \tag{9}$$

If we substitute for x in the expression for y, we have

$$y = \sin (u^2 + 1),$$

so

$$\frac{dy}{du} = \cos (u^2 + 1)2u,$$

or

$$dy = \cos (u^2 + 1)2u \, du = \cos x \, dx,$$

by (9).

This result is generally true, as an application of the chain rule shows: let

$$y = f(x), \qquad dy = f'(x) \, dx$$
$$x = g(u), \qquad dx = g'(u) \, du.$$

Then

$$y = f(g(u)),$$

so, by the chain rule,

$$\frac{dy}{du} = f'(g(u))g'(u),$$

or

$$dy = f'(g(u)) \, g'(u) \, du = f'(x) \, dx.$$

EXERCISES

1. Use a table of integrals to find the value of each of the following integrals. Calculate the answer correct to two decimal places. Then draw a graph of the function involved for the interval $[-2, -\sqrt{2}]$ and use the graph to check the reasonableness of the answer.

(a) $\displaystyle\int_{-2}^{-\sqrt{2}} \frac{dx}{x^3\sqrt{x^2 - 1}}$ (b) $\displaystyle\int_{-2}^{-\sqrt{2}} \frac{\sqrt{x^2 - 1}}{x^3} \, dx$ (c) $\displaystyle\int_{-2}^{-\sqrt{2}} \frac{\sqrt{x^2 - 1}}{x} \, dx.$

2. Find $df(x, dx)$:

(a) $f(x) = \cos x, \, x = \dfrac{\pi}{3}, \, dx = 0.1$

(b) $f(x) = \cos x, \, x = \pi, \, dx = 0.1$

(c) $f(x) = e^x, \, x = 1, \, dx = 0.01$

(d) $f(x) = \log x, \, x = e, \, dx = 1$

(e) $f(x) = \sin^{-1} x, \, x = \frac{1}{2}, \, dx = \frac{1}{2}.$

3. Show that, if f is differentiable,

$$df(x, a_1 h_1 + a_2 h_2) = a_1 \, df(x, h_1) + a_2 \, df(x, h_2).$$

4. Let $r = f(\theta)$, $x = r \cos \theta$, $y = r \sin \theta$. Find:

(a) dx and dy.   (b) $\dfrac{dy}{dx}$ in terms of θ, r, and $r' = f'(\theta)$.

8.2 Basic Ideas

The basic technique in integration is simply a matching of the differential to be integrated with a differential whose integral is known. It is for this reason that it is essential to have available an extensive table of integrals. The preceding description may make the problem sound easy, but, as will be seen, the process of achieving an exact match (and it *must be exact*) may be a fairly difficult one requiring the use of various algebraic and trigonometric identities (to put it differently, this is where the fun lies).

We begin in a modest way by collecting the integration formulas we have developed thus far (plus a few more). Because the desired match is often achieved by a substitution we use the letter u in the formulas in Table 8.1, the idea being that u will represent a function of x (there will be numerous illustrations of this).

Formulas 17–19 are generalizations of formulas available from differentiation formulas obtained in Section 6.6. Their validity can be checked by differentiating the right-hand sides (also, see Exercise 37). Formula 20, the "integration by parts" formula will be derived and discussed in detail in a later section.

Of course, all of the formulas should include on the right side an arbitrary additive constant. Generally throughout this chapter we shall ignore this constant of integration. We now illustrate the use of these formulas with a few examples. The numbers in brackets refer to formulas in Table 8.1.

Example 1

$$\int \cos 2x \, dx = \frac{2}{2} \int \cos 2x \, dx = \frac{1}{2} \int \cos 2x2 \, dx \qquad [2]$$

$$= \frac{1}{2} \int \cos u \, du, \qquad \text{where} \quad u = 2x, \, du = 2dx,$$

$$= \frac{1}{2} \sin u \qquad [7]$$

$$= \frac{1}{2} \sin 2x, \qquad \text{since} \quad u = 2x.$$

The trick here is to note that [7] is the formula in Table 8.1 most nearly applicable; however, as originally given, the integral does not match that of [7]. Since all that is lacking is the multiplicative constant 2, an adjustment can be made by using [2].

TABLE 8.1

Very Brief Table of Integrals

1. $\int du = u$

2. $\int [af(u) + bg(u)]\, du = a \int f(u)\, du + b \int g(u)\, du$ (linearity property)

3. $\int u^n\, du = \dfrac{u^{n+1}}{n+1}, \qquad n \neq -1$

4. $\int \dfrac{1}{u}\, du = \log |u|$

5. $\int e^u\, du = e^u$

6. $\int a^u\, du = \dfrac{a^u}{\log a}$

7. $\int \sin u\, du = -\cos u$

8. $\int \cos u\, du = \sin u$

9. $\int \tan u\, du = -\log |\cos u| = \log |\sec u|$

10. $\int \cot u\, du = \log |\sin u|$

11. $\int \sec u\, du = \log |\sec u + \tan u|$

12. $\int \csc u\, du = -\log |\csc u + \cot u| = \log |\csc u - \cot u|$

13. $\int \sec^2 u\, du = \tan u$

14. $\int \csc^2 u\, du = -\cot u$

15. $\int \sec u \tan u\, du = \sec u$

16. $\int \csc u \cot u\, du = -\csc u$

17. $\int \dfrac{du}{\sqrt{a^2 - u^2}} = \sin^{-1}\dfrac{u}{a}, \qquad \sin^{-1}\dfrac{u}{a} \in \left[-\dfrac{\pi}{2}, \dfrac{\pi}{2} \right]$

18. $\int \dfrac{du}{a^2 + u^2} = \dfrac{1}{a}\tan^{-1}\dfrac{u}{a}, \qquad \tan^{-1}\dfrac{u}{a} \in \left(-\dfrac{\pi}{2}, \dfrac{\pi}{2} \right)$

19. $\int \dfrac{du}{u\sqrt{u^2 - a^2}} = \dfrac{1}{a}\sec^{-1}\dfrac{u}{a}, \qquad \sec^{-1}\dfrac{u}{a} \in \left[0, \dfrac{\pi}{2} \right) \cup \left[\pi, \dfrac{3\pi}{2} \right)$

20. $\int u\, dv = uv - \int v\, du$ (Integration by parts)

Example 2

$$\int x\sqrt{x^2+1}\,dx = \int x(x^2+1)^{1/2}\,dx = \frac{2}{2}\int (x^2+1)^{1/2}x\,dx$$

$$= \frac{1}{2}\int (x^2+1)^{1/2}2x\,dx \qquad [2]$$

$$= \frac{1}{2}\int u^{1/2}\,du, \qquad \text{where} \quad u = x^2+1, \, du = 2x\,dx$$

$$= \frac{1}{2}\frac{u^{3/2}}{3/2} \qquad [3]$$

$$= \frac{1}{3}(x^2+1)^{3/2}, \qquad \text{since} \quad u = x^2+1.$$

Once again, the trick is to identify the most likely candidate from Table 8.1. In this case it is [3], with $n = \frac{1}{2}$. But this requires that $u = x^2 + 1$, so we must have $du = 2x\,dx$. Since all that is lacking is the factor 2, we can achieve an exact match by using formula [2]. Note that this same technique would fail for either

$$\int x^2\sqrt{x^2+1}\,dx \quad \text{or} \quad \int \sqrt{x^2+1}\,dx.$$

Why?

Example 3

$$\int xe^{-x^2}\,dx = -\frac{1}{2}\int e^{-x^2}(-2x\,dx) \qquad [2]$$

$$= -\frac{1}{2}\int e^u\,du, \qquad \text{where} \quad u = -x^2, \, du = -2x\,dx$$

$$= -\frac{1}{2}e^u \qquad [5]$$

$$= -\frac{1}{2}e^{-x^2}.$$

The most likely candidate from Table 8.1 is [5]; if this is to be applicable, we must have $u = -x^2$, $du = -2x\,dx$. Since the required du is obtainable, the method is successful. Would the same method work for

$$\int e^{-x^2}\,dx?$$

Example 4

$$\int \frac{x\,dx}{x^2+1}.$$

The task of identifying in Table 8.1 the most likely candidate may not be so simple here as in the preceding examples. The essential clue is recognition that the numerator is "almost" the differential of the denominator, so one tries [4]. This means

$$u = x^2 + 1, \qquad du = 2x \, dx,$$

and we can write

$$\int \frac{x \, dx}{x^2 + 1} = \frac{1}{2} \int \frac{2x \, dx}{x^2 + 1} = \frac{1}{2} \log (x^2 + 1). \qquad [4]$$

Note that we have bypassed the writing of u; also, since $x^2 + 1 > 0$, we do not need absolute value signs.

Example 5

$$\int \sin^2 x \cos x \, dx.$$

One might be tempted to try some trigonometric identities on this, but the fact is that [3] is immediately applicable, with $u = \sin x, n = 2, du = \cos x \, dx$:

$$\int \sin^2 x \cos x \, dx = \int u^2 \, du = \frac{1}{3} u^3 = \frac{1}{3} \sin^3 x.$$

Example 6

$$\int \cos^3 x \, dx.$$

In this case [3] cannot be used (immediately) because if $n = 3, u = \cos x$, then $du = -\sin x \, dx$, and the factor $\sin x$ is neither present nor obtainable. The trick here is the *simultaneous* recognition that $\cos^3 x = \cos^2 x \cdot \cos x$, that $\cos x = D_x \sin x$, and that $\cos^2 x = 1 - \sin^2 x$. Thus

$$\int \cos^3 x \, dx = \int \cos^2 x \cos x \, dx = \int (1 - \sin^2 x) \cos x \, dx$$

$$= \int \cos x \, dx - \int \sin^2 x \cos x \, dx \qquad [2]$$

$$= \sin x - \frac{1}{3} \sin^3 x. \qquad [3] \text{ and } [8]$$

In all of the preceding examples the technique was essentially the same: the differential $f(x) \, dx$ to be integrated was put into the form

$$f(x) \, dx = h(g(x))g'(x) \, dx;$$

then we let $g(x) = u$, so $g'(x) \, dx = du$, and the problem of integrating $\int f(x) \, dx$

has been transformed to the problem of integrating $\int h(u)\,du$. In the examples this last integral was found from Table 8.1, say

$$\int h(u)\,du = H(u),$$

and we complete the story by writing

$$\int f(x)\,dx = H(g(x)).$$

Now, simply by differentiating the answers one can easily verify that the technique just described is valid in all of the preceding examples; but to ensure that this technique is always valid we state and prove the following assertion.

Theorem 1 (*First Substitution Theorem*). *Given a function f, suppose there exist a function h and a differentiable function g such that*

$$f = (h \circ g)g', \qquad i.e., \quad f(x) = h(g(x))g'(x);$$

suppose also that H is an antiderivative of h:

$$H' = h, \qquad i.e., \quad H(u) = \int h(u)\,du.$$

Then

$$\int f(x)\,dx = F(x),$$

where

$$F = H \circ g, \qquad i.e. \quad F(x) = H(g(x)).$$

Proof. The proof involves only an application of the chain rule: since

$$F'(x) = H'(g(x))g'(x) = h(g(x))g'(x) = f(x),$$

$$\int f(x)\,dx = F(x). \quad \blacksquare$$

Thus, in Example 2, after introducing the factor 2 into the integrand, we had

$$f(x) = (x^2 + 1)^{1/2}(2x) = (g(x))^{1/2}g'(x),$$

where $g(x) = x^2 + 1$, $g'(x) = 2x$, and $h(u) = u^{1/2}$.

In the next section we will introduce a somewhat different substitution technique which, properly used, has great power.

E X E R C I S E S

In Exercises 1–32 find antiderivatives. Check each problem by differentiating the result.

1. $\int (x+1)^3\,dx$.

2. $\int (x^2+1)^3\,dx$.

3. $\int x(x^2+1)^3\,dx$.

4. $\int (x+1)^{23}\,dx$.

5. $\int x^3 \sqrt{x^4 + 1}\, dx.$

6. $\int \dfrac{x^2\, dx}{x^3 - 1}.$

7. $\int \dfrac{x}{x+1}\, dx.$ $\quad \left[Hint. \quad \dfrac{x}{x+1} = \dfrac{x+1-1}{x+1} = 1 - \dfrac{1}{x+1} \right].$

8. $\int \dfrac{x^2 + 3x + 5}{x}\, dx.$

9. $\int \dfrac{5x^4 + 7x^3 - 3x^2 + 4x - 2}{x^2}\, dx.$

10. $\int \sqrt{x}\, dx.$

11. $\int x\sqrt{x}\, dx.$

12. $\int \dfrac{\cos x\, dx}{\sin^2 x}.$

13. $\int \tan^4 x \sec^2 x\, dx.$

14. $\int \dfrac{\sec^2 x}{\tan x}\, dx.$

15. $\int \sin^2 3x \cos 3x\, dx.$

16. $\int e^{3x}\, dx.$

17. $\int \dfrac{e^{\sqrt{x}}}{\sqrt{x}}\, dx.$

18. $\int \sec 2x \tan 2x\, dx.$

19. $\int \dfrac{x^2}{x^2 + 1}\, dx.$ $\quad \left[Hint. \quad \dfrac{x^2}{x^2 + 1} = \dfrac{x^2 + 1 - 1}{x^2 + 1} = 1 - \dfrac{1}{x^2 + 1} \right].$

20. $\int (x + 3)(x - 4)\, dx.$ $\qquad$ **21.** $\int \dfrac{(x+1)(x-2)(x+4)}{x}\, dx.$ $\qquad$ **22.** $\int \dfrac{e^x}{e^x + 1}\, dx.$

23. $\int \dfrac{1}{e^x + 1}\, dx$ $\quad$ [*Hint.* Multiply numerator and denominator by e^{-x}].

24. $\int e^{\log x}\, dx.$

25. $\int \log e^{x^2}\, dx.$

26. $\int \left(\sqrt{x} + \dfrac{1}{\sqrt{x}} \right)^2 dx.$

27. $\int \dfrac{2x + 4}{x^2 + 4x + 7}\, dx.$

28. $\int \dfrac{x}{\sqrt{1 - x^2}}\, dx.$

29. $\int \dfrac{1}{x} \log x\, dx.$

30. $\int \dfrac{dx}{x \log x}$

31. $\int \sin \tfrac{1}{2} x\, dx$

32. $\int \cot^4 2x \csc^2 2x\, dx$

33. By writing the function in the three ways indicated, find three antiderivatives for sin $2x$. Do the three answers agree?

$$
\begin{array}{ccc}
(1) & (2) & (3) \\
\end{array}
$$
$$
\sin 2x = \tfrac{1}{2}(\sin 2x)2 = 2 \sin x \cos x = -2 \cos x(-\sin x).
$$

34. Same as Exercise 33 for $\sec^2 x \tan x$:

$$
\begin{array}{ccc}
(1) & (2) & (3) \\
\end{array}
$$
$$
\sec^2 x \tan x = \tan x \sec^2 x = \sec x \sec x \tan x = (\cos x)^{-3} \sin x.
$$

35. Find $\displaystyle\int_{-e}^{-1} \frac{dx}{x}$. Suppose the absolute value signs were missing from formula [4]. Could you evaluate this integral?

36. Find

$$
\int_{2\pi/3}^{3\pi/4} \sec x \, dx.
$$

correct to two decimal places. Sketch the graph of $y = \sec x$ for $\dfrac{2\pi}{3} \le x \le \dfrac{3\pi}{4}$ and interpret geometrically the result of the integration.

37. In Section 6.6 we found the following differentiation formulas:

(i) $\dfrac{d}{dx} \sin^{-1} x = \dfrac{1}{\sqrt{1-x^2}}$, $x \in (-1, 1)$, $\sin^{-1} x \in \left(-\dfrac{\pi}{2}, \dfrac{\pi}{2}\right)$.

(ii) $\dfrac{d}{dx} \tan^{-1} x = \dfrac{1}{1+x^2}$, $x \in \mathbf{R}$, $\tan^{-1} x \in \left(-\dfrac{\pi}{2}, \dfrac{\pi}{2}\right)$.

(iii) $\dfrac{d}{dx} \sec^{-1} x = \dfrac{1}{x\sqrt{x^2-1}}$, $x \in (-\infty, -1) \cup (1, \infty)$,

$$
\sec^{-1} x \in \left(0, \dfrac{\pi}{2}\right) \cup \left(\pi, \dfrac{3\pi}{2}\right).
$$

These can immediately be written as integration formulas:

(iv) $\displaystyle\int \frac{dx}{\sqrt{1-x^2}} = \sin^{-1} x$.   (v) $\displaystyle\int \frac{dx}{1+x^2} = \tan^{-1} x$.

(vi) $\displaystyle\int \frac{dx}{x\sqrt{x^2-1}} = \sec^{-1} x$.

However, (iv), (v) and (vi) are not sufficiently general for most cases encountered. We can obtain [17] in Table 8.1 from (iv) as follows (we suppose $a > 0$):

$$
\int \frac{du}{\sqrt{a^2-u^2}} = \int \frac{\dfrac{1}{a}\,du}{\sqrt{1-\left(\dfrac{u}{a}\right)^2}}.
$$

Now let $\dfrac{u}{a} = x$ so that $\dfrac{1}{a}\,du = dx$; then the last integral becomes

$$\int \frac{dx}{\sqrt{1-x^2}} = \sin^{-1}x, \qquad \text{[by (iv)]};$$

thus

$$\int \frac{du}{\sqrt{a^2-u^2}} = \sin^{-1}\frac{u}{a}, \qquad \text{[by Theorem 1]}.$$

In a similar fashion derive [18] and [19] from (v) and (vi), respectively.

38. Use a table of integrals (such as that found in the *CRC Standard Mathematical Tables*) and attempt to find the integrals in Exercises 1–32. The major purpose of this exercise is to get you acquainted with the organization of a table of integrals and with the extent of its utility.

8.3   The Second Substitution Theorem

As we have already remarked, the substitution method discussed in the preceding section was simply one of expressing the integrand $f(x)\,dx$ in the form

$$f(x)\,dx = h(g(x))g'(x)\,dx;$$

then, if we set $g(x) = u$, so that $g'(x)\,dx = du$, the problem becomes that of finding

$$\int h(u)\,du = H(u).$$

If this latter integral can be found, then

$$\int f(x)\,dx = H(g(x)).$$

When this method is applicable the form of the function g used in the substitution is often evident by inspection (or simple manipulation) of the integral—in other words, the function g is usually almost explicitly present in f.

A second type of substitution, essentially different from that already discussed will now be considered. We begin with a particular illustration.

Example 7. Consider

$$\int \frac{x\,dx}{1+\sqrt{x}}.$$

A quick check through Table 8.1 shows there is no likely candidate, such as we were able to find in the examples in the preceding section. Now, a little reflection suggests that the source of the difficulty is the irrationality, $\sqrt{x}$. One way of eliminating this difficulty would be a change of variable: let

$$
\left.\begin{aligned}
\sqrt{x} = u, \qquad & x \geq 0,\, u \geq 0 \\
x = u^2, \qquad & dx = 2u\, du
\end{aligned}\right\}
\tag{10}
$$

or

Then

$$
\int \frac{x\, dx}{1 + \sqrt{x}} = \int \frac{u^2 (2u\, du)}{1 + u} = 2 \int \frac{u^3\, du}{1 + u},
$$

which involves only a rational function. This integral can be obtained by an elementary algebraic device: divide denominator into numerator. This gives

$$
\frac{u^3}{u + 1} = u^2 - u + 1 - \frac{1}{u + 1},
$$

so

$$
2 \int \frac{u^3\, du}{1 + u} = 2 \int \left(u^2 - u + 1 - \frac{1}{u + 1} \right) du
$$

$$
= \frac{2}{3} u^3 - u^2 + 2u - 2 \log (u + 1).
$$

Since $u = \sqrt{x}$, we should have

$$
\int \frac{x\, dx}{1 + \sqrt{x}} = \frac{2}{3} x^{3/2} - x + 2\sqrt{x} - 2 \log (\sqrt{x} + 1).
\tag{11}
$$

A routine differentiation shows that $\dfrac{x}{(1 + \sqrt{x})}$ is the derivative of the right-hand side. The technique was successful.

It may be of interest to point out that the substitution defined by (10) is not the only possible one. Thus we could use

$$
\left.\begin{aligned}
1 + \sqrt{x} = u \qquad & x \geq 0,\, u \geq 1 \\
x = (u - 1)^2 \qquad & dx = 2(u - 1)\, du
\end{aligned}\right\}.
\tag{12}
$$

Then

$$
\int \frac{x\, dx}{1 + \sqrt{x}} = \int \frac{(u - 1)^2 2(u - 1)\, du}{u} = 2 \int \frac{(u - 1)^3\, du}{u}
$$

$$
= 2 \int \left(u^2 - 3u + 3 - \frac{1}{u} \right) du
$$

$$
= \frac{2}{3} u^3 - 3u^2 + 6u - 2 \log u.
$$

Replacing u by $1 + \sqrt{x}$ gives

$$\int \frac{x \, dx}{1 + \sqrt{x}} = \frac{2}{3}(1 + \sqrt{x})^3 - 3(1 + \sqrt{x})^2 + 6(1 + \sqrt{x}) - 2 \log (1 + \sqrt{x}). \quad (13)$$

Once again it is routine to show that the derivative of the right-hand side is

$$\frac{x}{(1 + \sqrt{x})}.$$

Note that with this substitution method (unlike that of the preceding section) it is essential to be able to go from x to the function of u *and* from u back to x; in other words, *it is essential that the function involved in the substitution have an inverse.*

We next illustrate a technique which we plan to discuss in detail in Section 8.6.

Example 8. We consider

$$\int \sqrt{1 - x^2} \, dx.$$

Now the success of the scheme used in Example 7 might suggest letting $\sqrt{1 - x^2} = u$, etc. The reader is advised to try this substitution, convincing himself of its futility. In this case the irrationality involves the square root of a binomial. We point out that the trigonometric identity $1 - \sin^2 \theta = \cos^2 \theta$ expresses a binomial as a perfect square. This suggests letting

$$\left. \begin{aligned} x = \sin \theta, \qquad & x \in [-1, 1], \qquad \theta \in \left[-\frac{\pi}{2}, \frac{\pi}{2} \right] \\ dx = \cos \theta \, d\theta, & \\ \sqrt{1 - x^2} = \sqrt{1 - \sin^2 \theta} & = \sqrt{\cos^2 \theta} \\ = \cos \theta, \qquad & \text{since } \theta \in \left[-\frac{\pi}{2}, \frac{\pi}{2} \right] \Rightarrow \cos \theta \geq 0. \end{aligned} \right\} \quad (14)$$

Thus

$$\int \sqrt{1 - x^2} \, dx = \int \cos \theta \, (\cos \theta \, d\theta) = \int \cos^2 \theta \, d\theta. \quad (15)$$

But we are not out of the woods. However, in order not to lose sight of our major point, we remark that the trigonometric identity

$$\cos 2\theta = 2 \cos^2 \theta - 1$$

enables us to write

$$\cos^2 \theta = \tfrac{1}{2}(1 + \cos 2\theta).$$

Thus

$$\int \cos^2 \theta \, d\theta = \frac{1}{2} \int (1 + \cos 2\theta) \, d\theta = \frac{1}{2} \left[\int d\theta + \frac{1}{2} \int \cos 2\theta \, 2d\theta \right]$$

$$= \frac{1}{2} \left(\theta + \frac{1}{2} \sin 2\theta \right)$$

$$= \frac{1}{2} (\theta + \sin \theta \cos \theta).$$

We can use (14) to return to x:

$$\int \sqrt{1 - x^2} \, dx = \frac{1}{2} (\sin^{-1} x + x\sqrt{1 - x^2}).$$

Again, differentiating the right-hand side shows the result to be correct.

What was done here was to change the original integrand, by a substitution, from an algebraic function to a trigonometric function, the antiderivative of which could be found. As in Example 7 *it was essential that the function involved in the substitution have an inverse.*

If the integral in this example had been a definite integral—if, for instance, we wanted to find $\int_0^1 \sqrt{1 - x^2} \, dx$—the final step of translating back to x would have been unnecessary. Instead, we translate the x limits on the original integral to θ limits. Once more this shows the need to have the function involved in the transformation be invertible. In this case the transformation is given in (14); we have

$$x = 0 \Rightarrow \sin \theta = 0 \Rightarrow \theta = 0,$$

and

$$x = 1 \Rightarrow \sin \theta = 1 \Rightarrow \theta = \frac{\pi}{2}.$$

Thus

$$\int_0^1 \sqrt{1 - x^2} \, dx = \int_0^{\pi/2} \cos^2 \theta \, d\theta \qquad\qquad (16)$$

$$= \frac{1}{2} (\theta + \sin \theta \cos \theta) \Big|_0^{\pi/2}$$

$$= \frac{1}{2} \left(\frac{\pi}{2} + 0 \right) - \frac{1}{2} (0)$$

$$= \frac{\pi}{4}.$$

(We remark that the equality used in (16) is a valid one, whereas the first one which appears in (15) is meaningful only when it is used in conjunction with (14).)

The justification for the procedure of Examples 7 and 8 can now be given.

Theorem 2 (*Second Substitution Theorem*)

$$f \text{ has domain } X_f$$
$$x = \varphi(u), \qquad \varphi : X_\varphi \longrightarrow\!\!\!\!\!\rightarrow X_f$$
$$\varphi'(u) \neq 0, \qquad u \in \mathscr{I}(X_\varphi), \qquad dx = \varphi'(u)\, du$$
$$\varphi^{-1} \text{ exists}, \qquad \varphi^{-1}(x) = u, \qquad \varphi^{-1} : X_f \longrightarrow\!\!\!\!\!\rightarrow X_\varphi$$
$$k(u) = f(\varphi(u))\varphi'(u)$$
$$K' = k, \text{ i.e., } K(u) = \int k(u)\, du$$

$$\Rightarrow \begin{cases} \int f(x)\, dx = F(x) \\ \text{where } F = K \circ \varphi^{-1}, \\ \text{i.e., } F(x) = K(\varphi^{-1}(x)). \end{cases}$$

Proof. The proof depends (as did that of Theorem 1) on an application of the chain rule:

$$\begin{aligned}
F'(x) &= (K \circ \varphi^{-1})'(x) \\
&= K'(\varphi^{-1}(x))(\varphi^{-1})'(x) \qquad \text{(chain rule)} \\
&= k(\varphi^{-1}(x))(\varphi^{-1})'(x) \qquad (K' = k) \\
&= f(\varphi(\varphi^{-1}(x)))\varphi'(\varphi^{-1}(x))(\varphi^{-1})'(x) \qquad \text{(definition of } k) \\
&= f(x)\varphi'(\varphi^{-1}(x))(\varphi^{-1})'(x) \qquad \text{(Theorem 6.12)} \\
&= f(x)\varphi'(\varphi^{-1}(x))\frac{1}{\varphi'(\varphi^{-1}(x))} \qquad \text{(Theorem 6.17)} \\
&= f(x). \quad \blacksquare
\end{aligned}$$

The rather formidable appearance of the statement of Theorem 2 is simply a matter of assuring that the substitution function φ has all the required properties: its range equals the domain of f, φ is invertible and differentiable, and its derivative does not vanish on the interior of the domain of φ. Refer again to Example 8. The import of the theorem is that it justifies transferring the integration of $\int f(x)\, dx$ over to the integration of $\int k(u)\, du$.

As a corollary to Theorem 2 we obtain the justification for the substitution procedure used on the integral $\int_0^1 \sqrt{1 - x^2}\, dx$ in the discussion following Example 8.

Corollary. *Let* f, φ, k, *and* K *satisfy the hypotheses of Theorem 2; let* $a, b, \in X_f$, $\varphi^{-1}(a) = \alpha$, $\varphi^{-1}(b) = \beta$. *Then*

$$\int_a^b f(x)\, dx = \int_\alpha^\beta k(u)\, du.$$

Proof. We have

$$\begin{aligned}
\int_a^b f(x)\, dx &= F(b) - F(a) \\
&= K(\varphi^{-1}(b)) - K(\varphi^{-1}(a)) \qquad \text{(definition of } F \text{ in Theorem 2)} \\
&= K(\beta) - K(\alpha) \qquad \text{(definition of } \beta \text{ and } \alpha) \\
&= \int_\alpha^\beta k(u)\, du. \quad \blacksquare \qquad \text{(definition of } K \text{ in Theorem 2).}
\end{aligned}$$

As an illustration of this corollary, we return to the function of Example 7 and find

$$\int_0^4 \frac{x\,dx}{1+\sqrt{x}}.$$

The substitution used is given in (10); using the relations between x and u, we have

$$x = 0 \Rightarrow u = \sqrt{0} = 0,$$

$$x = 4 \Rightarrow u = \sqrt{4} = 2.$$

Thus

$$\int_0^4 \frac{x\,dx}{1+\sqrt{x}} = \int_0^2 \frac{2u^3\,du}{1+u} = \frac{2}{3}u^3 - u^2 + 2u - 2\log(u+1)\Big|_0^2$$

$$= \left(\frac{16}{3} - 4 + 4 - 2\log 3\right) - 0$$

$$= \frac{16}{3} - 2\log 3.$$

We conclude this section with another example.

Example 9. Find

$$\int \sin \sqrt{x}\,dx.$$

It would seem natural to try to eliminate the irrationality by the following substitution:

or

$$\left.\begin{array}{ll} \sqrt{x} = u, & x \geq 0, \qquad u \geq 0 \\[2mm] x = u^2, & dx = 2u\,du \end{array}\right\}. \qquad (17)$$

By Theorem 2, then, we have

$$\int \sin \sqrt{x}\,dx = \int \sin u \cdot 2u\,du = 2 \int u \sin u\,du,$$

and this, used with the relations in (17), is correct. However, we now run into trouble in trying to find $\int u \sin u\,du$. Table 8.1 does not help, and there seems to be no obvious trigonometric or algebraic trick which shows promise (see, however, Exercise 11). The essential difficulty of this last integral is due to its form as a product of two functions of different types (j and sin). This observation brings home the realization that we have not yet developed any means for integrating products. We turn to this in the next section.

EXERCISES

Find the integrals in Exercises 1–10. For each substitution used, indicate the domain and range.

1. $\int \dfrac{dx}{\sqrt{x+1}}.$

6. $\int \dfrac{\sin \sqrt{x}}{\sqrt{x}}\, dx.$

2. $\int x^3 \sqrt{x+2}\, dx.$

7. $\int \dfrac{x\, dx}{\sqrt{x-4}}.$

3. $\int \dfrac{x\, dx}{\sqrt{x-1}}.$

8. $\int \dfrac{\sin x + \cos x}{\sin x - \cos x}\, dx.$

4. $\int \dfrac{x\, dx}{\sqrt[3]{x+1}}.$

9. $\int \dfrac{\cos x\, dx}{\sqrt{\sin^5 x}}.$

5. $\int x\sqrt{2x-1}\, dx.$

10. $\int \dfrac{t+1}{\sqrt{t^2 + 2t + 5}}\, dt.$

11. Sometimes one can find an integral by intelligent guessing. Try this method on

$$\int x \sin x\, dx.$$

   [*Hints.* (1) We need a function whose derivative is $x \sin x$.

        (2) Recalling the rules for the derivative of cos and of a product, start with $x \cos x$.

        (3) This does not give the desired result, but you should be able to make the necessary adjustments to obtain a correct integral.]

12. Try the method of Exercise 11 on

$$\int \log x\, dx.$$

13. (a) Integrate

$$\int x^3 \sqrt{1 - x^2}\, dx$$

   by letting $x = \sin \theta.$ [*Hint.* $\sin^3 \theta = (1 - \cos^2 \theta) \sin \theta.$]

   (b) Now integrate

$$\int x^3 \sqrt{1 - x^2}\, dx$$

   by letting $u = \sqrt{1 - x^2}$ [*Hint.* $x^3\, dx = x^2(x\, dx).$]

14. Evaluate the following integrals:

(a) $\int_0^4 \dfrac{dx}{\sqrt{x+1}}.$

(d) $\int_{1/2}^5 x\sqrt{2x-1}\,dx.$

(b) $\int_{-1}^0 \sqrt{1-x^2}\,dx.$

(e) $\int_{-1}^6 \dfrac{x\,dx}{\sqrt[3]{x+2}}.$

(c) $\int_0^1 x^3\sqrt{1-x^2}\,dx.$

15. Turn to a table of integrals (such as in the *CRC Standard Mathematical Tables*) and try to find the integrals in Exercises 1–10.

8.4   Integration by Parts

An integral such as

$$\int x \sin x \, dx,$$

encountered at the end of the last section, does not fit any of the patterns described thus far. The essential feature of the integrand is that it is the *product* of two dissimilar functions:

$$f(x) = x \sin x = j(x)h(x), \qquad \text{where}$$

$$j(x) = x, \qquad h(x) = \sin x.$$

Up to this point we have said nothing about the integral of a product of two functions, except in the very special case where one of the functions is a constant. Because of the nature of the problem of antidifferentiation it would seem fitting to look to the formula for the derivative of a product for aid in finding the anti-derivative of a product.

Suppose u and v are differentiable functions (of x, say). Then

$$\frac{d}{dx}(uv) = u\frac{dv}{dx} + v\frac{du}{dx},$$

or, since we have agreed to work with differentials,

$$d(uv) = u\,dv + v\,du;$$

this can be rewritten as

$$u\,dv = d(uv) - v\,du.$$

If, now, we integrate both sides, remembering to use [2] and [1] from Table 8.1, we obtain

$$\int u\,dv = uv - \int v\,du,$$

which is [20] in Table 8.1.

Example 10. As a first application we consider the problem with which we introduced this section:

$$\int x \sin x \, dx.$$

The technique is to decompose $x \sin x \, dx$ into two parts, u and dv, apply [20], and hope that $\int v \, du$ can be obtained. *A necessary condition in choosing dv is that it be integrable.* In the present case this condition provides no help in making the choice, for one could take dv as either $x \, dx$ or $\sin x \, dx$. Drawing on the omniscience possessed by all authors, we choose

$$u = x,$$

$$dv = \sin x \, dx,$$

so that

$$du = dx$$

$$v = -\cos x.$$

Applying [20], then, we find

$$\int x \sin x \, dx = -x \cos x + \int \cos x \, dx$$

$$= -x \cos x + \sin x. \qquad \text{(by [8])}$$

A similar approach would work for integrals such as

$$\int x \cos x \, dx \quad \text{and} \quad \int x e^x \, dx.$$

Sometimes it is necessary to repeat the process.

Example 11. We consider

$$\int x^2 \sin x \, dx.$$

Let

$$u = x^2, \quad \text{so} \quad du = 2x \, dx,$$

$$dv = \sin x \, dx, \quad \text{so} \quad v = -\cos x.$$

Then, by [20],

$$\int x^2 \sin x \, dx = -x^2 \cos x + 2 \int x \cos x \, dx.$$

The integral on the right can be handled as in Example 10, and is left as an exercise.

Example 12. As a generalization of the preceding problem we consider

$$\int x^n \sin x \, dx, \qquad \text{where} \quad n \in \mathbf{N}.$$

Let

$$u = x^n, \qquad \text{so} \quad du = nx^{n-1} \, dx,$$

$$dv = \sin x \, dx, \qquad \text{so} \quad v = -\cos x.$$

Then

$$\int x^n \sin x \, dx = -x^n \cos x + n \int x^{n-1} \cos x \, dx. \tag{18}$$

We *could* leave it at that, but suppose we operate on the integral on the right of (18). Let, assuming, $n - 1 \geq 1$,

$$u = x^{n-1}, \qquad \text{so} \quad du = (n - 1)x^{n-2} \, dx$$

$$dv = \cos x \, dx, \qquad \text{so} \quad v = \sin x.$$

Then

$$\int x^{n-1} \cos x \, dx = x^{n-1} \sin x - (n - 1) \int x^{n-2} \sin x \, dx,$$

and the original integral can be written as

$$\int x^n \sin x \, dx = -x^n \cos x + nx^{n-1} \sin x - n(n - 1) \int x^{n-2} \sin x \, dx. \tag{19}$$

The advantage of (19) over (18) is that the integral remaining on the right side of (19) is the same type as that on the left-hand side, the troublesome exponent having been reduced by 2. Such an expression is known as a *reduction formula*. We shall encounter further examples of reduction formulas in the exercises below.

It may have been noticed that in all the preceding examples the choice made for dv was, to put it *very* roughly and imprecisely, the most complicated part of the integrand which could be integrated. This, in fact, can serve as a frequently (but not invariably) safe guiding principle. Occasionally, though, one has no choice in the decomposition.

Example 13. We consider $\int \log x \, dx$. Table 8.1 fails us, except for the possibility of integration by parts. And for this *we must* choose $u = \log x$. The usual display is:

$$u = \log x, \qquad \text{so} \quad du = \frac{1}{x} \, dx$$

$$dv = dx, \qquad \text{so} \quad v = x.$$

Thus

$$\int \log x \, dx = x \log x - \int dx = x \log x - x.$$

Sometimes, however, the crude principle just mentioned gives no help.

Example 14. We integrate

$$\int e^x \sin x \, dx.$$

The interesting point about this integrand is that its two factors behave in an essentially identical fashion under the operations of differentiation and integration (the function cos is essentially the same as the function sin). Thus it would seem to make little difference how we choose u and dv—we take them as they come:

$$u = e^x, \qquad du = e^x \, dx$$
$$dv = \sin x \, dx, \qquad v = -\cos x.$$

Then

$$\int e^x \sin x \, dx = -e^x \cos x + \int e^x \cos x \, dx.$$

The integral on the right is certainly no simpler than that on the left—is there any point in continuing? There is, and the outcome is mildly surprising. First, however, we note that we must resist the temptation to modify our choice of u and dv. We let

$$u = e^x, \qquad du = e^x \, dx$$
$$dv = \cos x \, dx, \qquad v = \sin x.$$

Then we have

$$\int e^x \sin x \, dx = -e^x \cos x + e^x \sin x - \int e^x \sin x \, dx; \tag{20}$$

we are back to our starting point! But if we add $\int e^x \sin x \, dx$ to both sides of (20) we get

$$2 \int e^x \sin x \, dx = e^x(\sin x - \cos x);$$

thus

$$\int e^x \sin x \, dx = \tfrac{1}{2} e^x(\sin x - \cos x).$$

We will see below how this same technique can be used on other integrals, not of this same type.

E X E R C I S E S

Find the integrals in Exercises 1–17. In each case check your result by differentiation.

1. $\int x^2 \cos x \, dx.$ 　　　　　　　　　　　　　　**2.** $\int x^2 e^{-x} \, dx.$

3. $\int x \log x \, dx.$ 　　　　　　　　　　　　　　**4.** $\int \sin^{-1} x \, dx.$

5. $\int \tan^{-1} x \, dx.$ 　　　　　　　　　　　　**6.** $\int e^x \cos x \, dx$

7. $\int e^{ax} \sin bx \, dx.$

8. $\int x^3 \sqrt{1 - x^2} \, dx = \dfrac{-1}{2} \int x^2 [(1 - x^2)^{1/2}(-2x \, dx)].$

9. $\int x \sqrt{1 - x^2} \, dx.$ 　　　　　　　　　　**10.** $\int x^3 e^x \, dx.$

11. $\int x \tan^{-1} x \, dx.$ 　　　　　　　　　　**12.** $\int \dfrac{x^3 \, dx}{\sqrt{1 - x^2}}$ [*Hint.* See Exercise 8.].

13. $\int \sec^3 x \, dx = \int \sec x \sec^2 x \, dx.$ 　　**14.** $\int x^2 (\log x)^2 \, dx.$

15. $\int x^2 \tan^{-1} x \, dx.$ 　　　　　　　　　　**16.** $\int \cos \sqrt{x} \, dx.$

17. $\int (x - 1)^2 (x - 4)^{12} \, dx.$

18. Evaluate the following integrals:

　　(a) $\displaystyle\int_0^3 x(x - 3)^5 \, dx.$ 　　　　　　　　(b) $\displaystyle\int_0^{\pi/2} x \cos x \, dx.$

19. Let

$$I_n = \int \sin^n x \, dx.$$

Write $\sin^n x = \sin^{n-1} x \sin x$ and show that

$$I_n = -\frac{1}{n} \sin^{n-1} x \cos x + \frac{n - 1}{n} I_{n-2}. \tag{21}$$

20. Use the result of Exercise 19 to show that

　　(a) n even $\Rightarrow \displaystyle\int_0^{\pi/2} \sin^n x \, dx = \dfrac{(n - 1)(n - 3) \cdots 3 \cdot 1}{n(n - 2) \cdots 4 \cdot 2} \dfrac{\pi}{2}.$

$$\tag{22}$$

　　(b) n odd $\Rightarrow \displaystyle\int_0^{\pi/2} \sin^n x \, dx = \dfrac{(n - 1(n - 3) \cdots 4 \cdot 2}{n(n - 2) \cdots 5 \cdot 3}.$

21. Use the methods of Exercise 19 and 20 to show that

$$\int_0^{\pi/2} \cos^n x \, dx = \int_0^{\pi/2} \sin^n x \, dx.$$

(The formulas obtained in Exercises 20 and 21, extremely useful, are called Wallis' formulas.)

22. In Example 10 (involving $\int x \sin x \, dx$) try letting $u = \sin x$, $dv = x \, dx$.

23. Try to find $\int e^{-x^2} \, dx$ by integration by parts.

24. This refers to Example 14. After the first integration by parts the integral

$$\int e^x \cos x \, dx$$

is found. Try to complete the original problem by letting $u = \cos x$, $dv = e^x \, dx$ in this integral.

25. Let

$$I_n = \int \sec^n x \, dx, \, n > 2.$$

Write $\sec^n x = \sec^{n-2} x \sec^2 x$, use integration by parts, and obtain the reduction formula

$$I_n = \frac{1}{n-1} \sec^{n-2} x \tan x + \frac{n-2}{n-1} I_{n-2} \qquad (23)$$

(see Exercise 13).

26. Use the result of Exercises 25 and 13 to find

$$\int \sec^5 x \, dx.$$

27. Explain the following: We use integration by parts on $\int x^{-1} \, dx$ by letting

$$u = x^{-1}, \quad \text{so} \quad du = -x^{-2} \, dx.$$

$$dv = dx, \quad \text{so} \quad v = x.$$

Then

$$\int x^{-1} \, dx = 1 + \int x^{-1} \, dx,$$

or, subtracting the common term from both sides,

$$0 = 1.$$

8.5   Trigonometric Integrands

In this section we consider the integration of certain combinations of trigo-nometric functions. To be specific, we shall be concerned with

(i) $\int \sin^m x \cos^n x \, dx$,

(ii) $\int \sec^m x \tan^n x \, dx$,

(iii) $\int \csc^m x \cot^n x \, dx$,

where, in every case, m and n represent nonnegative integers. Moreover, since the discussion of (ii) can be immediately applied to (iii), provided only that minus signs be inserted at suitable places, we shall restrict ourselves to (i) and (ii).

The guiding principle throughout is to make as much use as possible of [3],

$$\int u^n \, du = \frac{u^{n+1}}{n+1}.$$

Example 15. As a simple preliminary we look at $\int \sin^3 x \, dx$ (see Example 6). The successful scheme is to write $\sin^3 x$ as $\sin^2 x \sin x = (1 - \cos^2 x) \sin x$ and use $\sin x \, dx$ (with a minus inserted) as the differential of $\cos x$:

$$\int \sin^3 x \, dx = \int (1 - \cos^2 x) \sin x \, dx$$

$$= \int \sin x \, dx + \int \cos^2 x (-\sin x \, dx)$$

$$= -\cos x + \tfrac{1}{3} \cos^3 x. \qquad \text{[7] and [3]}$$

The presence of any power of $\cos x$ in the preceding integral would not have interfered with the success of the method used: thus

$$\int \sin^3 x \cos^n x \, dx = \int (1 - \cos^2 x) \sin x \cos^n x \, dx$$

$$= -\int \cos^n x (-\sin x \, dx) + \int \cos^{n+2} x (-\sin x \, dx)$$

$$= -\frac{1}{n+1} \cos^{n+1} x + \frac{1}{n+3} \cos^{n+3} x.$$

Moreover, a slight extension of this method would apply in the case of higher powers of $\sin x$, *provided only that the exponent is odd.*

Example 16. To be specific, consider

$$\int \sin^5 x \cos^7 x \, dx.$$

We exploit the identity $\sin^2 x + \cos^2 x = 1$, keeping one eye on [3]:

$$\int \sin^5 x \cos^7 x \, dx = \int \sin^4 x \cos^7 x \sin x \, dx$$

$$= \int (1 - \cos^2 x)^2 \cos^7 x (\sin x \, dx)$$

$$= \int (\cos^7 x - 2 \cos^9 x + \cos^{11} x)(\sin x \, dx)$$

$$= -\tfrac{1}{8} \cos^8 x + \tfrac{1}{5} \cos^{10} x - \tfrac{1}{12} \cos^{12} x.$$

Because the exponent on $\cos x$ is also odd, we have an alternative (but in this case longer) method.

$$\int \sin^5 x \cos^7 x \, dx = \int \sin^5 x (1 - \sin^2 x)^3 \cos x \, dx$$

$$= \int \sin^5 x (1 - 3 \sin^2 x + 3 \sin^4 x - \sin^6 x) \cos x \, dx$$

$$= \tfrac{1}{6} \sin^6 x - \tfrac{3}{8} \sin^8 x + \tfrac{3}{10} \sin^{10} x - \tfrac{1}{12} \sin^{12} x.$$

Thus we see that if at least one of the exponents on $\sin x$ and $\cos x$ is odd we can use [3], along with possibly [7] or [8]. This also points up when this approach will not be successful: when *both m and n are even*. In this case we turn to some trigonometric identities which have the effect of lowering exponents. We refer to the following:

$$\sin^2 \theta = \tfrac{1}{2}(1 - \cos 2\theta), \tag{24}$$

$$\cos^2 \theta = \tfrac{1}{2}(1 + \cos 2\theta), \tag{25}$$

$$\sin \theta \cos \theta = \tfrac{1}{2} \sin 2\theta; \tag{26}$$

These identities are simply revisions of the well-known identities for $\sin 2\theta$ and $\cos 2\theta$.

Example 17. Consider $\int \sin^4 x \, dx$. We begin with identity (24):

$$\sin^4 x = (\sin^2 x)^2 = \tfrac{1}{4}(1 - \cos 2x)^2$$
$$= \tfrac{1}{4}(1 - 2 \cos 2x + \cos^2 2x).$$

Now we use (25) on the last term, with $\theta = 2x$:

$$\cos^2 2x = \tfrac{1}{2}(1 + \cos 4x).$$

Thus,

$$\int \sin^4 x \, dx = \frac{1}{4} \int \left(1 - 2 \cos 2x + \frac{1}{2} + \frac{1}{2} \cos 4x\right) dx$$

$$= \frac{1}{4}\left[\frac{3}{2}x - \sin 2x + \frac{1}{8} \sin 4x\right]$$

$$= \frac{1}{8}[3x - 2 \sin 2x + \frac{1}{4} \sin 4x].$$

If both sin and cos appear, one should make as much use as possible of identity (26).

Example 18. Integrate $\int \sin^4 x \cos^2 x \, dx$. We write

$$\sin^4 x \cos^2 x = \sin^2 x (\sin x \cos x)^2$$

$$= \tfrac{1}{2}(1 - \cos 2x) \cdot \tfrac{1}{4} \sin^2 2x.$$

Thus

$$\int \sin^4 x \cos^2 x \, dx = \frac{1}{8} \int (\sin^2 2x - \sin^2 2x \cos 2x) \, dx$$

$$= \frac{1}{8} \left[\frac{1}{2} \int (1 - \cos 4x) \, dx - \frac{1}{2} \int \sin^2 2x \cos 2x (2 \, dx) \right]$$

$$= \frac{1}{16} \left[x - \frac{1}{4} \sin 4x - \frac{1}{3} \sin^3 2x \right].$$

We see, then, that products of integral powers of sin and cos can always be integrated, frequently by means of the power formula [3]. Consequently, we can turn our attention to the second of the three types mentioned at the beginning of the section.

We begin with the observation that any even power of the sec can be integrated. For example,

$$\sec^6 x = \sec^4 x \sec^2 x = (\sec^2 x)^2 \sec^2 x$$

$$= (1 + \tan^2 x)^2 \sec^2 x$$

$$= (1 + 2 \tan^2 x + \tan^4 x) \sec^2 x.$$

Thus,

$$\int \sec^6 x \, dx = \tan x + \tfrac{2}{3} \tan^3 x + \tfrac{1}{5} \tan^5 x.$$

Moreover, the presence in this integral of any power of tan would create no difficulty. The essential facts are that $\sec^2 x \, dx = d(\tan x)$ and $\sec^2 x = 1 + \tan^2 x$.

Example 19. We consider $\int \sec^6 x \tan^n x \, dx$. As above,

$$\int \sec^6 x \tan^n x \, dx = \int (1 + \tan^2 x)^2 \tan^n x \sec^2 x \, dx$$

$$= \int (1 + 2 \tan^2 x + \tan^4 x) \tan^n x \sec^2 x \, dx$$

$$= \frac{1}{n+1} \tan^{n+1} x + \frac{2}{n+3} \tan^{n+3} x + \frac{1}{n+5} \tan^{n+5} x.$$

The reasons for considering the particular combination $\sec^m x \tan^n x$ are simply that the derivatives of sec and tan involve the same pair of functions, and that, by means of the identity $1 + \tan^2 x = \sec^2 x$, it is possible to express *even* powers of the one function in terms of powers of the other. Suppose, now, that the method of Example 19 is not possible (this amounts to saying that the exponent of sec is odd); then it might be possible to set aside a $\sec x \tan x = D \sec x$ and express the remainer of the integrand in powers of the sec, again enabling us to use [3].

Example 20. We integrate $\int \sec^5 x \tan^5 x \, dx$, trying the method just mentioned.

$$\int \sec^5 x \tan^5 x \, dx = \int \sec^4 x \tan^4 x (\sec x \tan x \, dx)$$

$$= \int \sec^4 x (\sec^2 x - 1)^2 \sec x \tan x \, dx$$

$$= \int (\sec^8 x - 2 \sec^6 x + \sec^4 x) \sec x \tan x \, dx$$

$$= \tfrac{1}{9} \sec^9 x - \tfrac{2}{7} \sec^7 x + \tfrac{1}{5} \sec^5 x.$$

A little reflection shows that for this method to be successful the exponent on sec may be any number ≥ 1 and the exponent on tan must be an odd positive integer (odd, so that after a tan has been set aside as part of the differential the remaining exponent on tan is even).

Thus [3] can be employed successfully on integrals such as described in (ii) at the beginning of the section; in some cases $u = \tan x$ and in others $u = \sec x$. However, as was the case with the integrals $\int \sin^m x \cos^n x \, dx$, there are times when [3] is not applicable. We illustrate.

Example 21. Consider $\int \sec^3 x \tan^2 x \, dx$. First of all note that both exponents are wrong for using either $\sec x$ or $\tan x$ as u in [3]—convince yourself of this. However, the technique which can be used has already been described in Exercise 25 at the end of Section 8.4. We can write

$$\int \sec^3 x \tan^2 x \, dx = \int \sec^3 x (\sec^2 x - 1) \, dx$$

$$= \int \sec^5 x \, dx - \int \sec^3 x \, dx. \qquad (27)$$

Now using Eq. (23) in Exercise 25 of the preceding section, with $n = 5$, we find

$$\int \sec^5 x \, dx = \tfrac{1}{4} \sec^3 x \tan x + \tfrac{3}{4} \int \sec^3 x \, dx.$$

Substituting this in (27), we have

$$\int \sec^3 x \tan^2 x \, dx = \tfrac{1}{4} \sec^3 x \tan x - \tfrac{1}{4} \int \sec^3 x \, dx. \qquad (28)$$

Applying the reduction formula (23) again, this time with $n = 3$, we have

$$\int \sec^3 x \, dx = \tfrac{1}{2} \sec x \tan x + \tfrac{1}{2} \int \sec x \, dx$$

$$= \tfrac{1}{2} \left[\sec x \tan x + \log |\sec x + \tan x| \right].$$

Substituting this last in (28) gives

$$\int \sec^3 x \tan^2 x \, dx = \tfrac{1}{4}[\sec^3 x \tan x - \tfrac{1}{2} \sec x \tan x - \tfrac{1}{2} \log |\sec x + \tan x|]$$

$$= \tfrac{1}{8}[2 \sec^3 x \tan x - \sec x \tan x - \log |\sec x + \tan x|].$$

It is true that the three types of integrands mentioned at the beginning of this section by no means exhaust the possible combinations of trigonometric integrands. But it is also true that some other combinations can be reduced to one of those considered or perhaps can be integrated by methods already discussed. We give one illustration below; others appear in the exercises.

Example 22. We find $\int \sin^2 x \cot^3 x \, dx$. We have

$$\int \sin^2 x \cot^3 x \, dx = \int \sin^2 x \, \frac{\cos^3 x}{\sin^3 x} \, dx = \int \frac{\cos^3 x}{\sin x} \, dx$$

$$= \int \frac{\cos x(1 - \sin^2 x)}{\sin x} \, dx$$

$$= \int \cot x \, dx - \int \sin x \cos x \, dx$$

$$= \log |\sin x| - \tfrac{1}{2} \sin^2 x. \qquad [10] \text{ and } [3].$$

EXERCISES

In Exercises 1–20 find the integrals. Check each result by differentiating.

1. $\int \sin^3 x \cos^3 x \, dx.$

2. $\int \cos^4 2x \, dx.$

3. $\int \csc^3 x \cot^3 x \, dx.$

4. $\int \csc^6 x \, dx.$

5. $\int \sin 2x \cos^4 2x \, dx.$

6. $\int \sec^5 x \tan^3 x \, dx.$

7. $\int \sin^2 x \cos^4 x \, dx.$

8. $\int \sec^4 x \tan^3 x \, dx.$

9. $\int \sec^4 x \tan^2 x \, dx.$

10. $\int \sec^3 x \tan^3 x \, dx.$

11. $\int \sec x \tan^2 x \, dx.$

16. $\int \sin^4 x \cos^3 x \, dx.$

12. $\int \cos^3 x \tan^2 x \, dx.$

17. $\int \sin x \tan^2 x \csc^3 x \, dx.$

13. $\int \sin^2 x \sec^3 x \, dx.$

18. $\int \dfrac{\sin^2 x}{\sec^4 x} \, dx.$

14. $\int \sin^2 x \cos^3 x \, dx.$

19. $\int \cos^2 x \cot x \csc^3 x \, dx.$

15. $\int \sec^{10} x \tan^5 x \, dx.$

20. $\int \tan^2 x \csc^3 x \, dx.$

21. Do Example 18 by using only identities (24) and (25).

22. Let

$$I(m, n) = \int \sin^m x \cos^n x \, dx.$$

Show that

$$I(m, n) = -\frac{1}{m+n} \sin^{m-1} x \cos^{n+1} x + \frac{m-1}{m+n} I(m-2, n). \qquad (29)$$

[*Hint.* Use integration by parts, with $u = \sin^{m-1} x$, $dv = \cos^n x \sin x \, dx$.]

23. This refers to the $I(m, n)$ of Exercise 22. Show that

$$I(m, n) = \frac{1}{m+n} \sin^{m+1} x \cos^{n-1} x + \frac{n-1}{m+n} I(m, n-2). \qquad (30)$$

24. Use (29) and (30) in Exercises 22 and 23 to show that

(a) $\displaystyle\int_0^{\pi/2} \sin^7 x \cos^6 x \, dx = \frac{6 \cdot 4 \cdot 2 \cdot 5 \cdot 3 \cdot 1}{13 \cdot 11 \cdot 9 \cdot 7 \cdot 5 \cdot 3}.$

(b) $\displaystyle\int_0^{\pi/2} \sin^8 x \cos^6 x \, dx = \frac{7 \cdot 5 \cdot 3 \cdot 1 \cdot 5 \cdot 3 \cdot 1}{14 \cdot 12 \cdot 10 \cdot 8 \cdot 6 \cdot 4 \cdot 2} \cdot \frac{\pi}{2}.$

(c) $\displaystyle\int_0^{\pi/2} \sin^7 x \cos^7 x \, dx = \frac{6 \cdot 4 \cdot 2 \cdot 6 \cdot 4 \cdot 2}{14 \cdot 12 \cdot 10 \cdot 8 \cdot 6 \cdot 4 \cdot 2}.$

25. Can you generalize the results of Exercise 24 to find

$$\int_0^{\pi/2} \sin^m x \cos^n x \, dx?$$

26. Prove the following integration results. It is clearly necessary that $m \neq n$; frequently in applications m and n are integers, but this need not be the case.

(a) $\displaystyle\int \sin mx \sin nx \, dx = \frac{\sin (m-n)x}{2(m-n)} - \frac{\sin (m+n)x}{2(m+n)}.$

(b) $\int \cos mx \cos nx\, dx = \dfrac{\sin (m-n)x}{2(m-n)} + \dfrac{\sin (m+n)x}{2(m+n)}.$

(c) $\int \sin mx \cos nx\, dx = -\dfrac{\cos (m-n)x}{2(m-n)} - \dfrac{\cos (m+n)x}{2(m+n)}.$

[*Hint.* Use the identities (7), (8), (9) after Theorem 6.5.]

27. Find the integrals in the preceding problem if $m = n$.

28. Use the result of Exercise 26 to prove the following. Here $m \neq n$, and m and n are positive integers.

(a) $\displaystyle\int_{-\pi}^{\pi} \sin mx \sin nx\, dx = 0.$

(b) $\displaystyle\int_{-\pi}^{\pi} \cos mx \cos nx\, dx = 0.$

(c) $\displaystyle\int_{-\pi}^{\pi} \sin mx \cos nx\, dx = 0.$

8.6 Trigonometric Substitutions

In Example 8 of Section 8.3 we showed how the use of a trigonometric substitution enables one to find $\int \sqrt{1-x^2}\, dx$. As we explained there, the essential tool was the identity

$$1 - \sin^2 \theta = \cos^2 \theta$$

which converts a binomial into a perfect square. In this section we explore this technique in greater detail; in particular, we consider integrals of the following types:

(i) $\displaystyle\int f(x, \sqrt{a^2 - x^2})\, dx,$

(ii) $\displaystyle\int f(x, \sqrt{a^2 + x^2})\, dx,$

(iii) $\displaystyle\int f(x, \sqrt{x^2 - a^2})\, dx.$

We assume throughout that $a > 0$.

As we shall see, an appropriate trigonometric substitution will frequently convert such integrands into rational trigonometric integrands which can be treated by the methods of the preceding section.

As the basic principle is the same in all three of the above cases, we shall, rather than fragment the discussion, consider them simultaneously. The facts essential to the technique are contained in Table 8.2.

TABLE 8.2

If the radical is	use the identity	and let $x =$	where $\theta \in$	and the radical becomes
(i) $\sqrt{a^2 - x^2}$	$1 - \sin^2 \theta = \cos^2 \theta$	$a \sin \theta$	$\left[-\dfrac{\pi}{2}, \dfrac{\pi}{2} \right]$	$a \cos \theta$
(ii) $\sqrt{a^2 + x^2}$	$1 + \tan^2 \theta = \sec^2 \theta$	$a \tan \theta$	$\left(-\dfrac{\pi}{2}, \dfrac{\pi}{2} \right)$	$a \sec \theta$
(iii) $\sqrt{x^2 - a^2}$	$\sec^2 \theta - 1 = \tan^2 \theta$	$a \sec \theta$	$\left[0, \dfrac{\pi}{2} \right) \cup \left[\pi, \dfrac{3\pi}{2} \right)$	$a \tan \theta$

The domains for θ in the second column from the right assure the validity of the entries in the right-hand column. For example, in row (iii),

$$\sqrt{x^2 - a^2} = \sqrt{a^2 \sec^2 \theta - a^2} = a\sqrt{\sec^2 \theta - 1} = a\sqrt{\tan^2 \theta} = a \tan \theta,$$

since

$$\theta \in \left[0, \frac{\pi}{2} \right) \cup \left[\pi, \frac{3\pi}{2} \right) \Rightarrow \tan \theta \geq 0 \Rightarrow \sqrt{\tan^2 \theta} = \tan \theta.$$

It should be pointed out that for this case (integrals involving $\sqrt{x^2 - a^2}$) many integral tables use a different domain, and one must exercise caution when negative values of x are considered. In particular, some integral tables will give incorrect results for negative x.

The translation from θ back to x can be achieved by using the diagrams in Figure 1.

Thus, in (i) we can easily see that $\tan \theta = \dfrac{x}{\sqrt{a^2 - x^2}}$, in (ii) that $\sin \theta = \dfrac{x}{\sqrt{a^2 + x^2}}$, and so on, these equalities holding for both positive and negative x. The figure for (iii) in case $x \leq -a$ is not included because things do not work out so well for it as they do for negative x in (i) and (ii) and because one can always safely use the diagram given; for example, whether $x \geq a$ or $x \leq -a$, it is true that $\sin \theta = \dfrac{\sqrt{x^2 - a^2}}{x}$, and so on.

We illustrate now with a few examples.

Example 23. We find

$$I = \int x^2 \sqrt{4 - x^2} \, dx.$$

We let

$$x = 2 \sin \theta, \qquad \theta \in \left[-\frac{\pi}{2}, \frac{\pi}{2} \right]$$

$$dx = 2 \cos \theta \, d\theta, \quad \sqrt{4 - x^2} = 2 \cos \theta.$$

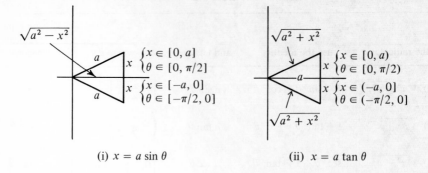

(i) $x = a \sin \theta$ (ii) $x = a \tan \theta$

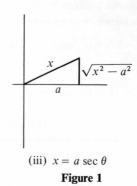

(iii) $x = a \sec \theta$

Figure 1

Then

$$I = \int 2^2 \sin^2 \theta \cdot 2 \cos \theta \cdot 2 \cos \theta \, d\theta = 2^4 \int \sin^2 \theta \cos^2 \theta \, d\theta$$

$$= 2^2 \int \sin^2 2\theta \, d\theta = 2 \int (1 - \cos 4\theta) \, d\theta$$

$$= 2\theta - \tfrac{1}{2}\sin 4\theta = 2\theta - \tfrac{1}{2}2 \sin 2\theta \cos 2\theta$$

$$= 2\theta - 2 \sin \theta \cos \theta (1 - 2 \sin^2 \theta).$$

The last few steps in this chain have been included so as to facilitate the translation from θ back to x; for it is now easy to write

$$I = 2 \sin^{-1} \frac{x}{2} - x \frac{\sqrt{4 - x^2}}{2} \left(1 - 2\frac{x^2}{4}\right)$$

$$= 2 \sin^{-1} \frac{x}{2} - \frac{1}{4} x\sqrt{4 - x^2}(2 - x^2).$$

It is routine to show that the derivative of this last function is $x^2\sqrt{4 - x^2}$.

Example 24. Consider

$$I = \int \frac{x^3 \, dx}{\sqrt{x^2 + 9}}.$$

The form of the radical suggests a tangent substitution. We let

$$x = 3 \tan \theta, \qquad \theta \in \left(-\frac{\pi}{2}, \frac{\pi}{2} \right),$$

$$dx = 3 \sec^2 \theta \, d\theta, \quad \sqrt{x^2 + 9} = 3 \sec \theta.$$

Then

$$I = \int \frac{3^3 \tan^3 \theta \cdot 3 \sec^2 \theta \, d\theta}{3 \sec \theta}$$

$$= 3^3 \int \tan^3 \theta \sec \theta \, d\theta = 3^3 \int \tan^2 \theta \cdot \sec \theta \tan \theta \, d\theta$$

$$= 3^3 \int (\sec^2 \theta - 1) \sec \theta \tan \theta \, d\theta$$

$$= 3^3 [\tfrac{1}{3} \sec^3 \theta - \sec \theta]$$

$$= 9(\sec^3 \theta - 3 \sec \theta).$$

Translating back to x, we have $\sec \theta = \dfrac{\sqrt{x^2 + 9}}{3}$, so

$$I = 9 \left[\left(\frac{\sqrt{x^2 + 9}}{3} \right)^3 - \sqrt{x^2 + 9} \right] = \frac{1}{3}(x^2 + 9)^{3/2} - 9\sqrt{x^2 + 9}$$

$$= \tfrac{1}{3}\sqrt{x^2 + 9}(x^2 - 18).$$

Example 25. We find

$$I = \int \frac{x^2 \, dx}{\sqrt{4x^2 - 5}}.$$

The form of the radical suggests a secant substitution; in this case, because the coefficient of x^2 is different from 1, we let

$$2x = \sqrt{5} \sec \theta, \qquad \theta \in \left[0, \frac{\pi}{2} \right) \cup \left[\pi, \frac{3\pi}{2} \right),$$

$$2 \, dx = \sqrt{5} \sec \theta \tan \theta \, d\theta; \qquad \sqrt{4x^2 - 5} = \sqrt{5} \tan \theta.$$

Then

$$I = \int \frac{\left(\frac{\sqrt{5}}{2} \right)^2 \sec^2 \theta \, \frac{\sqrt{5}}{2} \sec \theta \tan \theta \, d\theta}{\sqrt{5} \tan \theta}$$

$$= \frac{5}{2^3} \int \sec^3 \theta \, d\theta$$

$$= \frac{5}{2^4} [\sec \theta \tan \theta + \log |\sec \theta + \tan \theta|],$$

this integral having been found in a preceding section (see Example 21). Translating back to x gives

$$I = \frac{5}{2^4} \left[\frac{2x}{\sqrt{5}} \frac{\sqrt{4x^2 - 5}}{\sqrt{5}} + \log \left| \frac{2x}{\sqrt{5}} + \frac{\sqrt{4x^2 - 5}}{\sqrt{5}} \right| \right]$$

$$= \frac{1}{16} \left[2x\sqrt{4x^2 - 5} + 5 \log \left| \frac{2x + \sqrt{4x^2 - 5}}{\sqrt{5}} \right| \right].$$

In case the radicand is a quadratic function which is not of the form $cx^2 \pm a$ one can obtain this form by completing the square, as we illustrate in the next example.

There is a point, concerning notation, which we have touched on briefly before, which bears further comment. We refer to the use, in the preceding examples, of I to represent both the integral in terms of x and the (entirely different) integral in terms of θ. The justification for this loose use of equality lies in the fact that the functional relation between x and θ is—indeed, must be—invertible (see Theorem 2). At the risk of belaboring this point, we resort to a special form in writing the next example.

Example 26. Consider

$$I = \int \frac{x \, dx}{(\sqrt{4x - x^2})^3}.$$

By completing the square we can write $4x - x^2 = 4 - (x - 2)^2$. Then we let

$$\left. \begin{cases} x - 2 = 2 \sin \theta \quad \text{or} \quad x = 2 + 2 \sin \theta, \theta \in \left(-\frac{\pi}{2}, \frac{\pi}{2} \right), \\ dx = 2 \cos \theta \, d\theta, \sqrt{4x - x^2} = \sqrt{4 - (x - 2)^2} = 2 \cos \theta \end{cases} \right\} (*)$$

Thus

$$I = \int \frac{x \, dx}{(\sqrt{4x - x^2})^3}$$

$$= \int \frac{x \, dx}{[4 - (x - 2)^2]^{3/2}} \xrightarrow{\text{by } (*)} \int \frac{(2 + 2 \sin \theta)2 \cos \theta \, d\theta}{2^3 \cos^3 \theta}$$

$$= \frac{1}{2} \int \frac{1 + \sin \theta}{\cos^2 \theta} \, d\theta$$

$$= \frac{1}{2} \int (\sec^2 \theta + \sec \theta \tan \theta) \, d\theta =$$

$$= \frac{1}{2} \left[\frac{x - 2}{\sqrt{4x - x^2}} + \frac{2}{\sqrt{4x - x^2}} \right] \xleftarrow{\text{by } (*)} \frac{1}{2} [\tan \theta + \sec \theta]$$

$$= \frac{x}{2\sqrt{4x - x^2}}.$$

We conclude this section with an illustration of the use of the corollary to Theorem 2.

Example 27. We find $\int_{-2}^{-1} \dfrac{\sqrt{x^2-1}}{x^3}\,dx.$ Let

$$x = \sec\theta, \qquad \theta \in \left[\pi, \frac{4\pi}{3}\right], \qquad \text{since} \quad x \in [-2, -1],$$

$$dx = \sec\theta \tan\theta\, d\theta, \qquad \sqrt{x^2-1} = \tan\theta,$$

$$x = -2 \Rightarrow \sec\theta = -2 \Rightarrow \theta = \frac{4\pi}{3},$$

$$x = -1 \Rightarrow \sec\theta = -1 \Rightarrow \theta = \pi.$$

Then, by Corollary to Theorem 2,

$$\int_{-2}^{-1} \frac{\sqrt{x^2-1}}{x^3}\,dx = \int_{4\pi/3}^{\pi} \frac{\tan\theta \sec\theta \tan\theta\, d\theta}{\sec^3\theta}$$

$$= \int_{4\pi/3}^{\pi} \sin^2\theta\, d\theta = \int_{4\pi/3}^{\pi} \frac{1}{2}(1 - \cos 2\theta)\, d\theta$$

$$= \frac{\theta}{2} - \frac{1}{4}\sin 2\theta \Big|_{4\pi/3}^{\pi}$$

$$= \frac{\pi}{2} - \left(\frac{2\pi}{3} - \frac{\sqrt{3}}{8}\right)$$

$$= \frac{\sqrt{3}}{8} - \frac{\pi}{6}.$$

As the integrand is an odd function, one could also write

$$\int_{-2}^{-1} \frac{\sqrt{x^2-1}}{x^3}\,dx = -\int_{1}^{2} \frac{\sqrt{x^2-1}}{x^3}\,dx = -\int_{0}^{\pi/3} \sin^2\theta\, d\theta$$

$$= -\left(\frac{\pi}{6} - \frac{\sqrt{3}}{8}\right).$$

EXERCISES

In Exercises 1–18 find the antiderivatives.

1. $\displaystyle \int \frac{dx}{x^2\sqrt{x^2+9}}$

2. $\displaystyle \int \frac{dx}{x^2\sqrt{x^2-16}}$

3. $\displaystyle \int \frac{dx}{x^2\sqrt{(1-x^2)^3}}$

4. $\displaystyle\int \frac{x\,dx}{\sqrt{1-x^2}}$ **5.** $\displaystyle\int x^2\sqrt{3-2x^2}\,dx$ **6.** $\displaystyle\int \frac{\sqrt{6-x^2}}{x^2}\,dx$

7. $\displaystyle\int \frac{x\,dx}{\sqrt{2+x^2}}$ **8.** $\displaystyle\int \frac{\sqrt{x^2-4}\,dx}{x^3}$ **9.** $\displaystyle\int \frac{x\,dx}{\sqrt{x^2+2x-2}}$

10. $\displaystyle\int \frac{x\,dx}{x\sqrt{(3x^2+4)^3}}$ **11.** $\displaystyle\int \frac{dx}{x\sqrt{(x^2-a^2)^3}}$ **12.** $\displaystyle\int \frac{dx}{x^3\sqrt{x^2-8}}$

13. $\displaystyle\int \frac{dx}{x^3\sqrt{x^2+a^2}}$ **14.** $\displaystyle\int \frac{x\,dx}{\sqrt{6x-x^2-5}}$

15. $\displaystyle\int \frac{dx}{x\sqrt{x^2-2x}}=\int \frac{dx}{x^{3/2}\sqrt{x-2}}$. Find by at least two different methods.

16. $\displaystyle\int \frac{dx}{(x^2-8x+25)^{3/2}}$ **17.** $\displaystyle\int \frac{x\,dx}{\sqrt{4x-x^2}}$

18. $\displaystyle\int \frac{\sqrt{x^2+4x}}{x^2}\,dx=\int \frac{\sqrt{x+4}}{x^{3/2}}\,dx$. Find by at least two different methods.

Evaluate the integrals in Exercises 19–26.

19. $\displaystyle\int_0^a x^2\sqrt{a^2-x^2}\,dx$ **20.** $\displaystyle\int_1^2 \frac{\sqrt{4-x^2}}{x^2}\,dx$ **21.** $\displaystyle\int_{-1}^0 \frac{x^2\,dx}{\sqrt{4-x^2}}$

22. $\displaystyle\int_{-2}^{-\sqrt{2}} \frac{dx}{x^3\sqrt{x^2-1}}$ **23.** $\displaystyle\int_{-4}^{-2\sqrt{2}} \frac{dx}{x\sqrt{(x^2-4)^3}}$ **24.** $\displaystyle\int_{-6}^{-3\sqrt{2}} \frac{\sqrt{x^2-9}}{x^3}\,dx$

25. $\displaystyle\int_{-2}^{-\sqrt{2}} \frac{dx}{\sqrt{x^2-1}}$ **26.** $\displaystyle\int_0^2 \frac{x^3\,dx}{\sqrt{x^2+4}}$.

27. Find, by trigonometric substitution,

$$\int \frac{dx}{x^2-a^2}.$$

Keep in mind that one could have either $|x|<a$ or $|x|>a$. What does this have to do with anything?

28. (a) Sketch the graph of

$$y=\frac{x^2}{(\sqrt{x^2+1})^5},$$

for $x\geq0$.

(b) Find the area under the curve of part (a) between $x = 0$ and $x = 1$.

(c) Find the area under the curve of part (a) between $x = 0$ and $x = b$.

(d) What is the limit of the answer in part (c) as b gets big beyond all bounds? What is the geometric interpretation of this result?

8.7 The Method of Partial Fractions

In this section we show how to obtain integrals of rational functions (theoretically, at least—there are, it is true, serious practical difficulties which may arise; however, these are of an algebraic–arithmetic nature and we shall not pursue them here). The fact is that no new calculus techniques must be developed; our major interest will be the exposition of a few algebraic techniques which will enable us to transform a rational function into an identically equal but different-looking expression, called a *partial fraction decomposition*, which has the virtue of being integrable. Because, then, of the special nature of the problem, it may be helpful if we digress briefly to discuss some facts about polynomials and rational functions. The reader may wish to consult a book or two on algebra to fill in some of the details which we omit.

A rational function r is by definition a function which is the ratio of two polynomial functions p and q; thus the general form of r is given by

$$r(x) = \frac{p(x)}{q(x)} = \frac{a_0 x^m + a_1 x^{m-1} + \cdots + a_{m-1} x + a_m}{b_0 x^n + b_1 x^{n-1} + \cdots + b_{n-1} x + b_n}. \tag{31}$$

In discussing polynomial functions (such as q), one generally specifies the set of numbers from which the coefficients (the b_i, $i = 0, \ldots, n$) may be drawn. In our case this set is, of course, the field $\mathbf{R}$; then we say we are considering polynomials *over* $\mathbf{R}$. We might as well assume that $b_0 \neq 0$; then the nonnegative integer n is the *degree* of q. We shall write this as

$$dg(q) = n. \tag{32}$$

(If $n = 0$ and $b_0 \neq 0$, then q becomes a nonzero constant function, a polynomial of degree 0. The zero constant function is also considered to be a polynomial function, but problems arise in discussing its degree—we shall sidestep the issue by not attempting to assign a degree to this function.)

The Fundamental Theorem of Algebra guarantees that every polynomial q over the field $\mathbf{C}$ of complex numbers has a zero (a number a such that $q(a) = 0$) in $\mathbf{C}$. It is a fairly easy matter to show as a corollary of this theorem that every polynomial of degree n has exactly n zeros in the field of complex numbers. As $\mathbf{R}$ can be thought of as a subset of $\mathbf{C}$, it follows that every polynomial over $\mathbf{R}$ has n zeros (some of which may be equal) in $\mathbf{C}$. It can then be shown that

$$q(x) = b_0(x - c_1)(x - c_2) \cdots (x - c_n), \tag{33}$$

where $c_i \in \mathbf{C}$, and where the c_i need not all be distinct. Moreover, if, as we are assuming, the b_i are in $\mathbf{R}$, then any nonreal complex zeros must occur in conjugate pairs; i.e., if $c = a + bi$ is a zero, then so must $\bar{c} = a - bi$ be a zero. The corresponding factors in the representation (33) are

$$(x - a - bi) \quad \text{and} \quad (x - a + bi),$$

the product of which is $x^2 - 2ax + a^2 + b^2$, a *real quadratic factor* which is *irreducible* over $\mathbf{R}$ (i.e., the further decomposition into linear factors is possible only if one uses numbers in $\mathbf{C}$). Of course, a zero such as $a + bi$ may be repeated (occur more than once), in which case its conjugate $a - bi$ would also be repeated —the same number of times—and the quadratic factor $x^2 - 2ax + a^2 + b^2$ would occur with an exponent greater than 1 in the factored form of q. The result of this discussion is that every polynomial q of degree n over $\mathbf{R}$ can be written in the form

$$\left. \begin{aligned} q(x) = b_0(x - r_1)^{l_1} \cdots (x - r_h)^{l_h}(x^2 + a_1 x + c_1)^{m_1} \cdots (x^2 + a_k x + c_k)^{m_k}, \\[2mm] \text{where} \\[4mm] \sum_{i=1}^{h} l_i + 2 \sum_{j=1}^{k} m_j = n, \end{aligned} \right\} \quad \text{(34)}$$

and where $r_1, \ldots, r_h, a_1, \ldots, a_k, c_1, \ldots, c_k \in \mathbf{R}$. If this appears rather monstrous, consider it from a different point of view: it says that if a polynomial over $\mathbf{R}$ cannot be factored into products of powers of *linear* factors, the worst that can happen is that powers of quadratic factors must be included.

We need two further facts from algebra. For the first let q be a polynomial. Then

$$\left. \begin{aligned} x - a \text{ divides } q(x) \\ \text{or} \\ q(x) = (x - a)q_1(x) \end{aligned} \right\} \Leftrightarrow q(a) = 0.$$

This is the "factor theorem" and its converse. We shall refer to it as (∗).

The second fact (∗∗) asserts that if two polynomials, both of degree at most m, have equal values for k numbers in $\mathbf{R}$, where $k > m$, then the two polynomials are equal for all $x \in \mathbf{R}$, i.e., they are identically the same.

As motivation for the main problem of this section we carry out a simple routine from elementary algebra; we add two fractions, two rational functions:

$$\frac{2}{x - 3} + \frac{1}{x + 2} = \frac{2(x + 2) + (x - 3)}{(x - 3)(x + 2)},$$

or

$$\frac{2}{x - 3} + \frac{1}{x + 2} = \frac{3x + 1}{x^2 - x - 6} \qquad \text{(35)}$$

Now (35) is an identity: it is valid for all $x \in \mathbf{R}$, save -2 and 3. In algebra one usually proceeds in the direction we did: combine the two fractions into one.

But consider the problem of integrating the function displayed in two forms in (35). The two terms on the left-hand side can each be easily integrated $\left(\text{as } \int \frac{du}{u}\right)$, whereas the single term on the right presents a greater difficulty (by no means, in the case of this simple example, insurmountable). What we are getting at is that, given, for purposes of integration, a rational function such as illustrated in general in (31) or in particular in the right-hand side of (35), it would be useful to be able to transform this function into a sum of "simpler" rational functions such as those occurring in the left-hand side of (35). Note that the denominators on the left are factors of the denominator on the right. Note also the numerators on both sides: on the left they are constants, on the right the polynomial is of *lower* degree than that of the denominator.

We now begin our attack on the problem of integrating rational functions by observing that we can safely assume that the degree of the numerator is always less than the degree of the denominator; i.e., the rational function is *proper*. For if

$$r(x) = \frac{p(x)}{q(x)},$$

where $dg(p) \geq dg(q)$, we can divide q into p to obtain

$$r(x) = p_1(x) + \frac{p_2(x)}{q(x)},$$

where $dg(p_2) < dg(q)$. Since the integration of the polynomial p_1 presents no problem we can focus attention on the proper rational function p_2/q.

We consider the simplest case first.

Theorem 3

$$\left.\begin{array}{l} r(x) = \dfrac{p(x)}{q(x)} \\[2mm] q(x) = (x - c_1) \cdots (x - c_n) \\[2mm] c_i \in \mathbf{R} \\[2mm] i \neq j \Rightarrow c_i \neq c_j \text{ (the } c_i \text{ are distinct)} \\[2mm] dg(p) < n \end{array}\right\} \Rightarrow \begin{array}{l} \exists a_1, \ldots, a_n \in \mathbf{R} \\ \text{such that } \forall x \in \mathbf{R}, \\ x \neq c_1, \ldots, c_n, \Rightarrow \\ \dfrac{p(x)}{q(x)} = \dfrac{a_1}{x - c_1} + \cdots \dfrac{a_n}{x - c_n}. \end{array}$$

Proof. We assume that the set of a_i exist and find a necessary condition. We then show that if the a_i are chosen in accordance with this condition the desired result follows. Thus we assume that for all $x \in \mathbf{R}$, $x \neq c_1, \ldots, c_n$, it is true that

$$\frac{p(x)}{q(x)} = \frac{p(x)}{(x - c_1) \cdots (x - c_n)} = \frac{a_1}{x - c_1} + \cdots + \frac{a_n}{x - c_n}. \tag{36}$$

Now we define $q_i(x) = \dfrac{q(x)}{x - c_i}$; thus $q_1(x) = (x - c_2) \cdots (x - c_n)$, and $q_n(x) =$
$(x - c_1) \cdots (x - c_{n-1})$. Note the following about these n polynomials:

(i) $dg(q_i) = n - 1 < n$,
(ii) $q_i(c_i) \neq 0$,
(iii) $q_i(c_j) = 0$, $\quad j \neq i$.

We multiply the numerator and denominator of the ith fraction on the right-hand side of (36) by $q_i(x)$:

$$\frac{p(x)}{q(x)} = \frac{a_1 q_1(x)}{q(x)} + \cdots + \frac{a_n q_n(x)}{q(x)} = \frac{\sum_{i=1}^{n} a_i q_i(x)}{q(x)},$$

a relation which holds for all $x \in \mathbf{R}$, $x \neq c_1, \ldots, c_n$. It follows that for the same set of real numbers we must have

$$p(x) = \sum_{i=1}^{n} a_i q_i(x) \tag{37}$$

and since $dg(p) < n$, $dg(a_i q_i) \leq n - 1$, it further follows, from (**), that (37) holds for *all* $x \in \mathbf{R}$.

In (37) we set $x = c_j$; then, using (iii), we have

$$p(c_j) = a_j q_j(c_j),$$

or, since $q_j(c_j) \neq 0$,

$$a_j = \frac{p(c_j)}{q_j(c_j)}.$$

This is the desired necessary condition on the a_i.

We now show this condition is also sufficient. Consider

$$\sum_{i=1}^{n} \frac{a_i}{x - c_i} = \sum_{i=1}^{n} \frac{p(c_i)}{q_i(c_i)(x - c_i)} = \sum_{i=1}^{n} \frac{p(c_i) q_i(x)}{q_i(c_i)(x - c_i) q_i(x)}$$

$$= \frac{\sum_{i=1}^{n} \frac{p(c_i)}{q_i(c_i)} q_i(x)}{q(x)}$$

$$= \frac{P(x)}{q(x)},$$

where

$$P(x) = \sum_{i=1}^{n} \frac{p(c_i)}{q_i(c_i)} q_i(x).$$

We observe that P, a linear combination of the q_i is of degree at most $n - 1$. Next, for $j = 1, \ldots, n$,

$$P(c_j) = \sum_{i=1}^{n} \frac{p(c_i)}{q_i(c_i)} q_i(c_j)$$

$$= \frac{p(c_j)}{q_j(c_j)} q_j(c_j) \qquad \text{[because of (ii) and (iii)]}$$

$$= p(c_j).$$

As $dg(p) < n$, $dg(P) < n$, it follows from (**) that $P = p$. ∎

Example 28. We find

$$\int \frac{2x^3 + 5x^2 - 13x + 10}{x^3 - 7x + 6} \, dx.$$

Notice that the integrand $r(x)$ is not a *proper* rational function; thus we divide denominator into numerator:

$$\int \frac{2x^3 + 5x^2 - 13x + 10}{x^3 - 7x + 6} \, dx = \int \left(2 + \frac{5x^2 + x - 2}{x^3 - 7x + 6} \right) dx$$

$$= 2x + \int \frac{5x^2 + x - 2}{(x + 3)(x - 1)(x - 2)} \, dx.$$

The factoring of $q(x) = x^3 - 7x + 6$ into $(x + 3)(x - 1)(x - 2)$ can, in this case, be done by a combination of inspection and trial and error. This task *can* be the most difficult part of the whole problem with which we are involved.

Now we can use Theorem 3 on the remaining integral. We have

$$c_1 = -3, \ c_2 = 1, \ c_3 = 2,$$

$$q_1(x) = (x - 1)(x - 2), \qquad q_1(-3) = 20$$

$$q_2(x) = (x + 3)(x - 2), \qquad q_2(1) = -4$$

$$q_3(x) = (x + 3)(x - 1), \qquad q_3(2) = 5$$

$$p(x) = 5x^2 + x - 2, \qquad p(-3) = 40, \ p(1) = 4, \ p(2) = 20.$$

Consequently,

$$a_1 = \frac{p(-3)}{q_1(-3)} = 2, \qquad a_2 = \frac{p(1)}{q_2(1)} = -1, \qquad a_3 = \frac{p(2)}{q_3(3)} = 4,$$

and

$$\frac{p(x)}{q(x)} = \frac{2}{x + 3} - \frac{1}{x - 1} + \frac{4}{x - 2}.$$

We point out, however, that there is no need to memorize the formulas for the a_i as given in Theorem 3. We seek numbers A, B, C (which we *know* exist) such that

$$\frac{5x^2 + x - 2}{(x + 3)(x - 1)(x - 2)} = \frac{A}{x + 3} + \frac{B}{x - 1} + \frac{C}{x - 2}.$$

Multiplying both sides by $q(x)$ gives

$$5x^2 + x - 2 = A(x - 1)(x - 2) + B(x + 3)(x - 2) + C(x + 3)(x - 1),$$

an identity which holds for all $x \in \mathbf{R}$. Setting, in turn, $x = -3, 1, 2$, gives

$$x = -3 : 40 = A(20) \Rightarrow A = 2$$

$$x = 1 : 4 = B(-4) \Rightarrow B = -1$$

$$x = 2 : 20 = C(5) \Rightarrow C = 4.$$

Returning to the integral, we have

$$\int \frac{2x^3 + 5x^2 - 13x + 10}{x^3 - 7x + 6} = 2x + \int \left(\frac{2}{x + 3} - \frac{1}{x - 1} + \frac{4}{x - 2} \right) dx$$

$$= 2x + 2 \log |x + 3| - \log |x - 1| + 4 \log |x - 2|$$

$$= 2x + \log \frac{(x + 3)^2 (x - 2)^4}{|x - 1|}.$$

In case q has all real zeros, some of which are repeated, we need a more general result than that of Theorem 3. We omit the proof.

Theorem 4

$$\left.\begin{array}{l} r(x) = \dfrac{p(x)}{q(x)} \\[2mm] q(x) = (x - c)^m q_1(x), \; m \geq 1 \\[2mm] dg(q) = n \\[2mm] dg(p) = k < n \\[2mm] q_1(c) \neq 0 \end{array}\right\} \Rightarrow \left\{\begin{array}{l} \exists a \in \mathbf{R}, \; \exists \text{ polynomial } p_1, \\[2mm] \qquad dg(p_1) < dg(q) - 1 = n - 1 \\[2mm] \textit{such that} \\[2mm] \qquad \forall x \in \mathbf{R}, \qquad q(x) \neq 0, \qquad \Rightarrow \\[2mm] \dfrac{p(x)}{q(x)} = \dfrac{a}{(x - c)^m} + \dfrac{p_1(x)}{(x - c)^{m-1} q_1(x)}. \end{array}\right.$$

The (omitted) proof of Theorem 4 gives formulas for a and p_1, and hence it does give a sequential method of calculating all the desired numerical numerators. However, we now illustrate an alternative method.

Example 29. Consider

$$r(x) = \frac{p(x)}{q(x)} = \frac{-4x^3 + 16x^2 - 19x + 5}{x^4 - 5x^3 + 9x^2 - 7x + 2} = \frac{-4x^3 + 16x^2 - 19x + 5}{(x - 1)^3(x - 2)}.$$

(We leave it as an exercise for the student to obtain the factored form of q.) We use Theorem 4 three times to write

$$\frac{p(x)}{(x-1)^3(x-2)} = \frac{A}{(x-1)^3} + \frac{p_1(x)}{(x-1)^2(x-2)}$$

$$= \frac{A}{(x-1)^3} + \frac{B}{(x-1)^2} + \frac{p_2(x)}{(x-1)(x-2)}$$

$$= \frac{A}{(x-1)^3} + \frac{B}{(x-1)^2} + \frac{C}{x-1} + \frac{D}{x-2};$$

the fact that the last numerator is a constant follows from an argument involving the degrees of the successive numerators. This identity must hold for *all* $x \in \mathbf{R}$ except 1 and 2. Thus, multiplying by q, we get a polynomial identity which must hold for *all* $x \in \mathbf{R}$.

$$-4x^3 + 16x^2 - 19x + 5 = A(x-2) + B(x-1)(x-2)$$
$$+ C(x-1)^2(x-2) + D(x-1)^3.$$

We can then set $x = 1$ and $x = 2$ to obtain

$$x = 1: -2 = -A \Rightarrow A = 2$$
$$x = 2: -1 = D \Rightarrow D = -1.$$

To find the values of B and C we multiply out the right-hand side and use (**):

$$-4x^3 + 16x^2 - 19x + 5 = (C + D)x^3 + (B - 4C - 3D)x^2$$
$$+ (A - 3B + 5C + 3D)x + (-2A + 2B - 2C - D).$$

By (**), we must have $C + D = -4$ or $C = -D - 4 = -3$; also, equating coefficients of x^2,

$$B - 4C - 3D = 16,$$
$$B = 4C + 3D + 16 = -12 - 3 + 16 = 1.$$

The remaining two equations, using the coefficients of x and the constant terms, can be used to provide a check.

We have, then, for all $x \in \mathbf{R}$ except 1 and 2, that

$$r(x) = \frac{-4x^3 + 16x^2 - 19x + 5}{x^4 - 5x^3 + 9x^2 - 7x + 2} = \frac{2}{(x-1)^3} + \frac{1}{(x-1)^2} - \frac{3}{x-1} - \frac{1}{x-2}.$$

Consequently,

$$\int r(x)\,dx = 2\frac{(x-1)^{-2}}{-2} + \frac{(x-1)^{-1}}{-1} - 3\log|x-1| - \log|x-2|$$

$$= \frac{-1}{(x-1)^2} - \frac{1}{x-1} - \log|(x-1)^3(x-2)|$$

$$= \frac{-x}{(x-1)^2} - \log|(x-1)^3(x-2)|.$$

In the event that q has quadratic factors irreducible over **R** (which is to say that some of the zeros of q are complex numbers), the partial fraction decomposition of $r = p/q$ will involve terms with denominators such as $(ax^2 + bx + c)^m$ [see Eq. (34)]. In this case the numerator will usually be a first degree polynomial rather than a constant, but the resulting terms, of the type

$$\frac{Ax + B}{(ax^2 + bx + c)^m},$$

are still integrable. The necessary theoretical support for the decomposition is contained in Theorem 5 which is closely analogous to Theorem 4. We shall omit the proof.

Theorem 5

$$r(x) = \frac{p(x)}{q(x)}$$

$q(x) = (ax^2 + bx + c)^m q_1(x)$
$dg(q) = n,\ dg(q_1) = n - 2m$
$dg(p) = k < n$
$b^2 - 4ac < 0$

$ax^2 + bx + c$ does not divide
$q_1(x)$

$\Rightarrow$

$\exists A, B \in \mathbf{R}$ and
$\exists$ polynomial $p_1,\ dg(p_1) < n - 2$
such that for all $x \in \mathbf{R}$
for which $q_1(x) \neq 0$ it is true that

$$\frac{p(x)}{q(x)} = \frac{Ax + B}{(ax^2 + bx + c)^m}$$
$$+ \frac{p_1(x)}{(ax^2 + bx + c)^{m-1}q_1(x)}$$

We illustrate the use of this theorem with a few examples.

Example 30. We find

$$\int \frac{2x^2 - 2x - 3}{x^3 - 1}\, dx.$$

As $x^3 - 1 = (x^2 + x + 1)(x - 1)$, we can use Theorem 5 once to obtain the identity, valid for all $x \neq 1$,

$$\frac{2x^2 - 2x - 3}{(x^2 + x + 1)(x - 1)} = \frac{Ax + B}{x^2 + x + 1} + \frac{C}{x - 1}.$$

Multiplying both sides of this equation by $(x^2 + x + 1)(x - 1)$, we obtain the *polynomial* identity, valid for *all* $x \in \mathbf{R}$ (why?),

$$2x^2 - 2x - 3 = (Ax + B)(x - 1) + C(x^2 + x + 1).$$

If we set $x = 1$ we find C:

$$-3 = 3C \Rightarrow C = -1.$$

To find A and B use the method illustrated in Example 29, i.e., we multiply out the right-hand side, use (**), and equate coefficients of like powers of x:

$$2x^2 - 2x - 3 = (A + C)x^2 + (-A + B + C)x + (-B + C).$$

Thus $A + C = 2$, so $A = 2 - C = 2 - (-1) = 3$; and from $-B + C = -3$ we find $B = C + 3 = 2$. The remaining equation, $-A + B + C = -2$ serves as a check.

We have, then, that

$$\frac{2x^2 - 2x - 3}{x^3 - 1} = \frac{3x + 2}{x^2 + x + 1} - \frac{1}{x - 1}.$$

The integration of the second term on the right presents no problem, but we discuss the integration of the first term. A standard way is first to adjust, as we shall illustrate, the numerator so as to make it equal the derivative of the denominator. Thus

$$\int \frac{3x + 2}{x^2 + x + 1} \, dx = \frac{3}{2} \int \frac{2x + \frac{4}{3}}{x^2 + x + 1} \, dx$$

$$= \frac{3}{2} \int \frac{2x + 1 + \frac{1}{3}}{x^2 + x + 1} \, dx$$

$$= \frac{3}{2} \int \frac{(2x + 1) \, dx}{x^2 + x + 1} + \frac{1}{2} \int \frac{dx}{x^2 + x + 1}$$

$$= \frac{3}{2} \log (x^2 + x + 1) + \frac{1}{2} \int \frac{dx}{(x + \frac{1}{2})^2 + \frac{3}{4}}$$

$$= \frac{3}{2} \log (x^2 + x + 1) + \frac{1}{\sqrt{3}} \tan^{-1} \frac{2x + 1}{\sqrt{3}}.$$

The final result is then

$$\int \frac{2x^2 - 2x - 3}{x^3 - 1} \, dx = \frac{3}{2} \log (x^2 + x + 1) + \frac{1}{\sqrt{3}} \tan^{-1} \frac{2x + 1}{\sqrt{3}} - \log |x - 1|$$

$$= \log \frac{(x^2 + x + 1)^{3/2}}{|x - 1|} + \frac{1}{\sqrt{3}} \tan^{-1} \frac{2x + 1}{\sqrt{3}}.$$

Example 31. Consider

$$\int \frac{2x^4 + x^3 + x^2 + 3x - 2}{x^4 + 2x^2 + 1} \, dx.$$

As the degree of the numerator equals that of the denominator, we begin by dividing:

$$r(x) = \frac{2x^4 + x^3 + x^2 + 3x - 2}{x^4 + 2x^2 + 1} = 2 + \frac{x^3 - 3x^2 + 3x - 4}{x^4 + 2x^2 + 1}.$$

We now use Theorem 5 to change the form of the proper rational function on the right:

$$\frac{x^3 - 3x^2 + 3x - 4}{(x^2 + 1)^2} = \frac{Ax + B}{(x^2 + 1)^2} + \frac{Cx + D}{x^2 + 1},$$

an identity which, for suitable A, B, C, D, is to hold for all $x \in \mathbf{R}$. To find the constants we multiply both sides by $(x^2 + 1)^2$, obtaining a polynomial identity:

$$x^3 - 3x^2 + 3x - 4 = Ax + B + (Cx + D)(x^2 + 1)$$
$$= Cx^3 + Dx^2 + (A + C)x + B + D.$$

we now use (**):

$$C = 1, \ D = -3, \qquad A + C = 3, \qquad B + D = -4,$$

whence

$$A = 2, \qquad B = -1, \qquad C = 1, \qquad D = -3.$$

Thus

$$r(x) = 2 + \frac{2x - 1}{(x^2 + 1)^2} + \frac{x - 3}{x^2 + 1}. \tag{38}$$

To integrate the second term on the right of (38) we begin by pulling off the derivative of $x^2 + 1$:

$$\int \frac{2x - 1}{(x^2 + 1)^2} \, dx = \int (x^2 + 1)^{-2} 2x \, dx - \int \frac{dx}{(x^2 + 1)^2}$$

$$= \frac{(x^2 + 1)^{-1}}{-1} - \int \frac{dx}{(x^2 + 1)^2}.$$

For the remaining integral here we use a trigonometric substitution: $x = \tan \theta$, $dx = \sec^2 \theta \, d\theta$, $x^2 + 1 = \sec^2 \theta$. Thus

$$\int \frac{dx}{(x^2 + 1)^2} = \int \frac{\sec^2 \theta \, d\theta}{\sec^4 \theta} = \int \cos^2 \theta \, d\theta$$

$$= \frac{1}{2} \int (1 + \cos 2\theta) \, d\theta = \frac{\theta}{2} + \frac{1}{4} \sin 2\theta$$

$$= \frac{1}{2} \left(\tan^{-1} x + \frac{x}{x^2 + 1} \right).$$

To integrate the third term on the right of (38) we proceed as in Example 30:

$$\int \frac{x - 3}{x^2 + 1} \, dx = \frac{1}{2} \int \frac{2x - 6}{x^2 + 1} \, dx = \frac{1}{2} \int \frac{2x \, dx}{x^2 + 1} - 3 \int \frac{dx}{x^2 + 1}$$

$$= \frac{1}{2} \log (x^2 + 1) - 3 \tan^{-1} x.$$

Combining the above results, we have

$$\int r(x) \, dx = 2x - \frac{1}{x^2 + 1} - \frac{1}{2} \tan^{-1} x - \frac{1}{2} \frac{x}{x^2 + 1} + \frac{1}{2} \log (x^2 + 1) - 3 \tan^{-1} x$$

$$= 2x - \frac{1}{2} \left[\frac{x + 2}{x^2 + 1} + 7 \tan^{-1} x - \log (x^2 + 1) \right].$$

We conclude this section with two remarks.

The first is the observation (perhaps already noted by the student) that in a partial fraction decomposition of a rational function the number of constants to be determined is equal to the degree of the denominator polynomial.

The second concerns the difficulty referred to parenthetically in the opening sentence of this section. We had in mind there the problem of factoring the denominator polynomial $q(x)$ into the form represented by (34). This may be an extremely tough chore, but there are *some* helpful techniques available; we refer the reader to books on algebra.

EXERCISES

Find the integrals in Exercises 1–14.

1. $\int \dfrac{x-23}{x^2+3x-10}\,dx.$

2. $\int \dfrac{3x^3-6x^2-44x+59}{(x+3)(x-1)(x-4)}\,dx.$

3. $\int \dfrac{dx}{x^2-4}.$

4. $\int \dfrac{dx}{9-x^2}.$

5. $\int \dfrac{dx}{x^2-a^2}$ (see Exercise 27 in Section 8.6).

6. $\int \dfrac{x^2+2x+3}{(x-1)(x-2)(x-3)}\,dx.$

7. $\int \dfrac{x^3-2x+4}{x^5-4x^4+4x^3}\,dx.$

8. $\int \dfrac{3x^3+15x^2-50x-134}{(x+3)^2(x-2)(x-4)}\,dx.$

9. $\int \dfrac{7x^2-3x+2}{x^3+1}\,dx.$

10. $\int \dfrac{4x^3+8x-13}{(x^2+2x+5)(x^2+x+5)}\,dx.$

11. $\int \dfrac{x^4+7x^3+10x^2}{(x^2+x+1)(x^3-1)}\,dx.$

12. $\int \dfrac{x^5-x^4+x^3-x^2+x-1}{(x^2+1)^3}\,dx.$

13. $\int \dfrac{x^5+x^4+x^3+x^2+x+1}{(x^2+1)^3}\,dx.$

14. $\int \dfrac{-x^5+4x^4-3x^3+28x^2+4x+64}{(x-2)^2(x^2+4)^2}\,dx.$

15. There is a substitution, not at all transparent, which will convert a rational function of sines and cosines into a rational algebraic function. For example, if one must find

$$\int \frac{d\theta}{2\sin\theta - \cos\theta},$$

the substitution is to let

$$z = \tan \frac{\theta}{2} \quad \text{or} \quad \theta = 2\tan^{-1} z;$$

then

$$\sin \theta = 2 \sin \frac{\theta}{2} \cos \frac{\theta}{2} = \frac{2z}{1+z^2}$$

$$\cos \theta = \cos^2 \frac{\theta}{2} - \sin^2 \frac{\theta}{2} = \frac{1-z^2}{1+z^2} \tag{39}$$

$$d\theta = \frac{2\,dz}{1+z^2}$$

(a) Verify the equations given in (39) for $\sin \theta$, $\cos \theta$, $d\theta$ in terms of z.

(b) Use the substitution (39) to find

$$\int \frac{d\theta}{2\sin\theta - \cos\theta}.$$

(c) Use the substitution (39) to find

$$\int \frac{d\theta}{2\cos\theta + 3\sin\theta}.$$

(d) Same as (c) for

$$\int \frac{\cos\theta\,d\theta}{\sin\theta + 2\cos\theta}.$$

8.8 Elementary Differential Equations

In this section we consider briefly an aspect of the problem of integration which up to this point we have essentially been ignoring. We refer to the fact that every integration result obtained should have an arbitrary constant of integration tacked on the end. Or, from a more abstract point of view, the operation of integration maps a function into an equivalence class of functions (two functions being in the same class if and only if they differ by a constant); from this point of view we have been concerned in this chapter with the problem of finding *any* representative of the equivalence class. There are many problems, however, which include enough information to enable one to select a particular member of an equivalence class. We illustrate a few simple cases.

Example 32. Find the curve which goes through the point (2, 1) and which at the point with abscissa x has slope $m = e^x + 1$.

If we assume that such a curve exists and further assume that it is the graph of a function f, then the information about the slope can be expressed symbolically as

$$\frac{dy}{dx} = f'(x) = e^x + 1.$$

It follows that

$$y = \int f'(x)\,dx = \int (e^x + 1)\,dx = e^x + x + c,$$

for some value of c. But the condition that the curve go through $(2, 1)$ enables us to determine c:

$$1 = e^2 + 2 + c \Rightarrow c = -e^2 - 1.$$

Thus, the desired curve is the graph of f, where $f(x) = e^x - e^2 + x - 1$. (It is easy to check, and this is left as an exercise, that this curve does have the prescribed properties.)

This completes the solution of the problem as posed, but it is a simple matter to add further information. If we consider the equivalence class of functions f described by $f(x) = e^x + x + c$ we can easily show that exactly one curve from this family passes through each point of the plane. For, if (x_0, y_0) is an arbitrary point, we can find a *unique* value of c satisfying

$$y_0 = e^{x_0} + x_0 + c;$$

thus

$$c = y_0 - x_0 - e^{x_0}.$$

It follows that the graph of

$$y = f(x) = e^x - e^{x_0} + x - x_0 + y_0$$

goes through the point (x_0, y_0).

Example 33. The point $(-2, 1)$ lies on a curve; in addition, at every point (x, y) on the curve the slope of the tangent is $m = -\dfrac{y}{x}$. Find the equation of the curve.

Solution. The information about the slope of the tangent line enables us to write

$$\frac{dy}{dx} = -\frac{y}{x}. \tag{40}$$

This differential equation, however, is not quite so simple as the one occurring in the preceding example, because the right-hand side involves both x and y. It is in just such situations as these that the Leibniz notation for derivatives and differentials, and the agreement to work with differentials in problems of integration combine to facilitate finding the solution. We multiply both sides of (40) by $\dfrac{1}{y}\,dx$, giving

$$\frac{dy}{y} = -\frac{dx}{x}.$$

(a technique known as *separating the variables*). Now we can integrate:

$$\log |y| = -\log |x| + c,$$

or

$$\log |xy| = c,$$

or

$$|xy| = e^c,$$

or

$$xy = \pm e^c,$$

or

$$xy = c_1, \tag{41}$$

where $c_1 = \pm e^c$ (note that $c_1 \neq 0$). The particular curve from the family described by (41) which contains the point $(-2, 1)$ can now be found:

$$(-2)(1) = c_1,$$

so $c_1 = -2$, and the curve in question is $xy = -2$, or $y = \dfrac{-2}{x}$. (One, namely *you*, should check that this curve does have the prescribed properties.)

As long as $x_0 y_0 \neq 0$ (i.e., $P_0(x_0, y_0)$ lies on neither axis) there will be exactly one member of (41) which goes through (x_0, y_0).

Example 34. A particle is traveling on a straight line with acceleration

$$a(t) = -\omega^2 \cos \omega t \text{ ft/sec}^2, \tag{42}$$

where $t \geq 0$ and ω is a constant. Describe the motion.

Solution. By definition the acceleration in linear motion is the derivative of the velocity, so the velocity can be found by an antidifferentiation:

$$v(t) = -\omega \sin \omega t + c_1 \text{ ft/sec}. \tag{43}$$

Similarly, the position function s can be found by integrating the velocity function:

$$s(t) = \cos \omega t + c_1 t + c_2. \tag{44}$$

The fact that the position function s has two constants of integration is, of course, due to the fact that $a(t) = s''(t)$, so two integrations had to be performed. Put differently, (42), involving a second but no higher derivative, is a *second order* differential equation, the general solution of which, given in this case in (44), will involve two arbitrary constants.

We can obtain some information about the significance of c_1 and c_2 as follows.

If we let, as usual, $v(0) = v_0$, then, substituting $t = 0$ in (43) gives

$$v_0 = c_1.$$

Thus

$$v(t) = -\omega \sin \omega t + v_0. \tag{45}$$

Next, letting $s(0) = s_0$ and setting $t = 0$ in (44) gives

$$s_0 = 1 + c_2,$$

so $c_2 = s_0 - 1$, and

$$s(t) = \cos \omega t + v_0 t + s_0 - 1, \tag{46}$$

a more informative version of (44).

As a special case of the preceding motion, suppose $s_0 = 1$ ft, $v_0 = 0$ ft/sec. Then the equations of motion become

$$\left.\begin{array}{l} s(t) = \cos \omega t \\ v(t) = -\omega \sin \omega t \\ a(t) = -\omega^2 \cos \omega t \end{array}\right\} \tag{47}$$

Note, from the third of these, that the acceleration is always proportional to the distance s from the origin but bears the sign opposite to that of s: particle to right (left) of origin $\Rightarrow$ acceleration vector directed toward left (right).

The motion described by Eqs. (47) is clearly an oscillatory motion, taking place entirely between $s = -1$ and $s = 1$. In Table 8.3 we give a few values of s and v and a, which should suggest the nature of the motion.

TABLE 8.3

t	$s(t)$	$v(t)$	$a(t)$
0	1	0	$-\omega^2$
$\dfrac{\pi}{2\omega}$	0	$-\omega$	0
$\dfrac{\pi}{\omega}$	-1	0	ω^2
$\dfrac{3\pi}{2\omega}$	0	ω	0
$\dfrac{2\pi}{\omega}$	1	0	$-\omega^2$

This is an example of *simple harmonic motion*, which can also be described in the following way. Suppose an object is traveling counterclockwise round the unit circle at uniform angular speed of ω radians/sec. If one considers the motion of the projection onto the x-axis of this object it will be exactly that described by Eqs. (47) (see Figure 2).

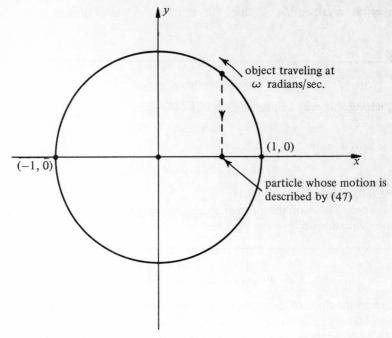

Figure 2

EXERCISES

In Exercises 1–8 find the equations of the curves satisfying the conditions given.

1. Slope at $(x, y) = m(x, y) = 3x^2 - 4x + 2$;   through $(4, -2)$.

2. Slope at $(x, y) = m(x, y) = \dfrac{x}{x+1}$; through $(0, 0)$. Sketch this curve; note that it is
concave upward (why?) for all $x \neq -1$.

3. Slope at $(x, y) = m(x, y) = \tan^{-1} x$;   through $(1, 3)$.

4. $m(x, y) = \dfrac{x^2}{\sqrt{1 - x^2}}$, $|x| < 1$;   through $(1, 0)$.

5. $m(x, y) = \log x$, $x > 0$;   through $(e, 1)$.

6. $m(x, y) = \dfrac{x^2 + 1}{x - 1}$, $x \neq 1$;   through $(-2, 8)$.

7. $m(x, y) = \dfrac{x^3}{\sqrt{x^2 - 1}}$, $x < -1$;   through $(-4, 4)$.

8. $m(x, y) = -\dfrac{2}{x^2};$ through $\left(-4, \dfrac{1}{2}\right).$

9. A family of curves has slope $m(x, y)$ at the point (x, y), where

$$x > 0 \Rightarrow m(x, y) = -2x$$
$$x < 0 \Rightarrow m(x, y) = 3x^2.$$

(a) Find the equation of the family of curves satisfying these conditions.

(b) What condition must hold for the curve to be defined and continuous at $x = 0$?

(c) Find the member of the family which contains $(-2, -9)$ and $(3, 10)$.

10. Find the member of each family of curves—as defined by the slope at (x, y)—which contains the point $(4, 5)$.

(a) $m(x, y) = \dfrac{x}{y}$　　　　(b) $m(x, y) = -\dfrac{x}{y}.$　　　　(c) $m(x, y) = \dfrac{y}{x}.$

11. This refers to Example 32. Find the condition that two points (x_1, y_1) and (x_2, y_2) determine the same value of c.

12. Find the velocity and position functions for the linear motions which satisfy:

(a) $a(t) = \dfrac{t^2 - 1}{t^2 + 1}, t \geq 0, v(0) = 0$ ft/sec,　　　$s(0) = 0$ ft.

(b) $a(t) = t \sin t, t \geq 0, v(0) = 1$ ft/sec,　　　$s(0) = 0$ ft.

13. Show that in evaluating the integral $\int_a^b f(x)\, dx$ by the Fundamental Theorem of Calculus it makes no difference which member of the equivalence class $\int f(x)\, dx$ one uses.

Chapter 9 The Integral, Theory and Developments

In Chapter 2 we gave an intuitive introduction to the integral, and we have subsequently made use of the concept whenever it suited our purposes. However, at the time the integral was introduced, our knowledge of the fundamentals of limits was inadequate for the task of giving a precise definition of the integral and for proving theorems about integrability and about the properties of integrals. Now that the necessary essentials have been developed, it is time that we attend to these matters.

In addition, we shall see in this chapter that the notion of integral can sometimes be extended in a natural and meaningful way in case the interval of integration is infinite or in case the function has infinite discontinuities within the interval of integration. These extensions are called *improper integrals.*

9.1 Two Definitions of the Integral

In Section 2.7 we gave a preliminary definition (Definition 2.10) of an integral as a limit of a sum. However, the nature of the limit was only suggested by examples and was not precisely described. Our first task in this section will be to say exactly what we mean by the limit and by the integral.

We consider a *bounded* function f on a finite interval $[a, b]$. Because f is assumed to be bounded, we can define the numbers m and M by

$$\begin{cases} m = \text{glb } f(x), & x \in [a, b] \\ M = \text{lub } f(x) & x \in a, b] \end{cases}. \tag{1}$$

We shall be working with partitions of $[a, b]$, a partition π being described by

$$\pi = \{a = x_0, x_1, x_2, \ldots x_{i-1}, x_i, \ldots, x_{n-1}, x_n = b\}$$

$$x_{i-1} < x_i, \qquad i = 1, \ldots, n. \tag{2}$$

We let, for each $i = 1, \ldots, n$,

$$\Delta x_i = x_i - x_{i-1} \tag{3}$$

and we define the *norm of the partition* $|\pi|$ by

$$|\pi| = \max_{i=1,\ldots,n} \Delta x_i. \tag{4}$$

If the Δx_i are all equal—the common value necessarily being $\dfrac{b-a}{n}$—we call the partition *regular*.

Finally, in order to define the integral we select, quite arbitrarily, a point z_i in each subinterval; i.e., for every $i = 1. \ldots, n$,

$$z_i \in [x_{i-1}, x_i]. \tag{5}$$

For a partition π and a choice of the n numbers z_i [Eq. (5)], we let

$$S(\pi) = \sum_{i=1}^{n} f(z_i)\, \Delta x_i. \tag{6}$$

The number $S(\pi)$ is called a *Riemann sum*.

The description $S(\pi)$ is slightly inadequate in that it does not show the dependence of S on the set $\{z_i\}$. However, the gain in precision by indicating this dependence is not worth the increased notational cumbersomeness.

Definition 1. *A function f, bounded on $[a, b]$, is **integrable (1) on** $[a, b] \Leftrightarrow$ there exists a number L such that for every $\varepsilon > 0$ there exists $\delta_\varepsilon > 0$ such that for all partitions π with $|\pi| < \delta_\varepsilon$ and for all possible choices of $\{z_i\}$ satisfying (5) the inequality*

$$|S(\pi) - L| < \varepsilon \tag{7}$$

*is satisfied. When f is integrable (1) on $[a, b]$ the number L is called the **integral** of f over $[a, b]$ and is denoted by*

$$L = \int_a^b f(x)\, dx = \int_a^b f. \tag{8}$$

For many applications the definition of the integral as a limit of a Riemann sum is a natural one, as we tried to suggest in Chapter 2. However, the arbitrariness in the choice of the set $\{z_i\}$ renders Definition 1 somewhat intractable as far as developing the theory is concerned. We shall, consequently, introduce a second definition, equivalent (this must be proven) to the first, which is more suitable for theoretical purposes.

For the second definition we use a partition π and let, for $i = 1, \ldots, n$,

$$\left. \begin{aligned} m_i &= \text{glb } f(x) \\ M_i &= \text{lub } f(x) \end{aligned} \right\}, \qquad x \in [x_{i-1}, x_i] \tag{9}$$

Definition 2. *For a function f, bounded on [a, b], and a partition π of [a, b] we define the **lower and upper sums** by, respectively,*

$$
\begin{aligned}
\underline{S}(\pi) &= \sum_{i=1}^{n} m_i \, \Delta x_i \\
\overline{S}(\pi) &= \sum_{i=1}^{n} M_i \, \Delta x_i
\end{aligned}
\left. \right\}.
\tag{10}
$$

From Definition 2 and Eq. (1) we have immediately that

$$
\underline{S}(\pi) = \sum_{i=1}^{n} m_i \, \Delta x_i \geq m \sum_{i=1}^{n} \Delta x_i = m(b - a);
$$

similarly

$$
\overline{S}(\pi) = \sum_{i=1}^{m} M_i \, \Delta x_i \leq M \sum_{i=1}^{n} \Delta x i = M(b - a).
$$

Thus, for every partition π, we have

$$
m(b - a) \leq \underline{S}(\pi) \leq \overline{S}(\pi) \leq M(b - a).
\tag{11}
$$

[It is obvious that the Riemann sums $S(\pi)$ must satisfy

$$
\underline{S}(\pi) \leq S(\pi) \leq \overline{S}(\pi).
$$

However, it should be pointed out that equality need not occur. As a simple example, let f be defined on $[0, 2]$ by

$$
f(x) = x, \ 0 \leq x < 1,
$$
$$
f(1) = \tfrac{1}{2},
$$
$$
f(x) = 2 - x, \ 1 < x \leq 2.
$$

Let $\pi = \{0, 1, 2\}$. Then $\underline{S}(\pi) = 0 \cdot 1 + 0 \cdot 1 = 0$, $\overline{S}(\pi) = 1 \cdot 1 + 1 \cdot 1 = 2$. However, the Riemann sums $S(\pi)$ must satisfy $0 \leq S(\pi) < 2$, so in this case

$$
\underline{S}(\pi) \leq S(\pi) < \overline{S}(\pi).
$$

In other words, the upper sum $\overline{S}(\pi)$ is not obtainable as a Riemann sum. Of course, if f is continuous on $[a, b]$ then both $\underline{S}(\pi)$ and $\overline{S}(\pi)$ will be Riemann sums (why?).]

It is clear from (11) that the lower and upper sums are bounded; before exploiting this observation, however, we want to indicate the way in which these sums change as one takes "smaller" partitions. For our purposes here, though, "smaller" is not interpreted in terms of the norm of the partition. Recall that a partition of $[a, b]$ is simply a set of points in $[a, b]$ which includes both a and b.

Definition 3. *Let π_1 and π_2 be partitions of $[a, b]$. Then π_2 is **finer than** π_1 or π_2 is a **refinement** of $\pi_1 \Leftrightarrow \pi_1 \subset \pi_2$.*

Lemma 1. *If f is bounded on $[a, b]$, if π_1 and π_2 are partitions of $[a, b]$, π_2 finer than π_1 ($\pi_1 \subset \pi_2$), then*

$$\underline{S}(\pi_1) \leq \underline{S}(\pi_2) \leq \bar{S}(\pi_2) \leq \bar{S}(\pi_1). \tag{12}$$

Proof. The middle inequality in (12) being obvious, we concentrate on showing the validity of the extreme inequalities. We let the points of π_1 be denoted by x_i, those of π_2 by x_k'. By hypothesis, every x_i is in π_2. Also, we let m_i and M_i be the lower and upper bounds of f on subintervals of π_1, m_k' and M_k' those on subintervals of π_2. Suppose we consider a subinterval $[x_{i-1}, x_i]$ of π_1. If no point of π_2 lies between x_{i-1} and x_i, then the corresponding terms in $\bar{S}(\pi_1)$ and in $\bar{S}(\pi_2)$ will be equal, and similarly for $\underline{S}(\pi_1)$ and $\underline{S}(\pi_2)$. Next, to be explicit, assume one point of π_2 lies in (x_{i-1}, x_i). The situation is illustrated in Figure 1.

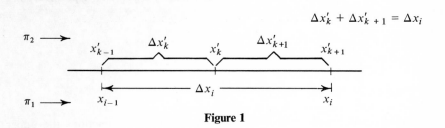

Figure 1

Now

$$\left. \begin{aligned} M_k' \leq M_i; \quad m_k' \geq m_i \\ M_{k+1}' \leq M_i; \quad m_{k+1}' \geq m_i \end{aligned} \right\} . \tag{13}$$

As a result of (13);

$$\left. \begin{aligned} M_k' \, \Delta x_k' + M_{k+1}' \, \Delta x_{k+1}' \leq M_i(\Delta x_k' + \Delta x_{k+1}') = M_i \, \Delta x_i, \\ m_k' \, \Delta x_k' + m_{k+1}' \, \Delta x_{k+1}' \geq m_i(\Delta x_k' + \Delta x_{k+1}') = m_i \, \Delta x_i \end{aligned} \right\} . \tag{14}$$

In case more than one point of π_2 lies in (x_{i-1}, x_i) the situation is similar to that just described, except that there will be more than two terms in the expressions for $\bar{S}(\pi_2)$ and $\underline{S}(\pi_2)$. It follows, then, that

$$\bar{S}(\pi_2) \leq \bar{S}(\pi_1)$$

and

$$\underline{S}(\pi_2) \geq \underline{S}(\pi_1);$$

these, along with the obvious inequality $\underline{S}(\pi_2) \leq \bar{S}(\pi_2)$, give (12). ∎

One of the consequences of this lemma is the assertion that every lower sum is less than or equal to every upper sum.

Lemma 2. *Let f be bounded on* $[a, b]$, *let* π_1 *and* π_2 *be any two partitions of* $[a, b]$. *Then*

$$\underline{S}(\pi_1) \leq \bar{S}(\pi_2).$$

Proof. Given the partitions π_1 and π_2, we form a new partition $\pi = \pi_1 \cup \pi_2$. Then π is a refinement of both π_1 and π_2. By Lemma 1,

$$\underline{S}(\pi_1) \leq \underline{S}(\pi) \leq \bar{S}(\pi) \leq \bar{S}(\pi_2). \quad \blacksquare$$

In summary, we see that as partitions are taken finer, the lower sums increase and the upper sums decrease; moreover, the lower sums are bounded above (by every upper sum), and the upper sums are bounded below (by every lower sum). The definition below follows naturally from these remarks.

Definition 4. *Let f be bounded on* $[a, b]$. *The **lower** and **upper** Darboux integrals of f on* $[a, b]$ *are, respectively,*

$$\int_{\underline{a}}^{b} f = \mathrm{lub}\; \underline{S}(\pi),$$

$$\int_{a}^{\bar{b}} f = \mathrm{glb}\; \bar{S}(\pi).$$

Intuitively, one would expect that for "well-behaved" functions the upper and lower Darboux integrals are equal. One would also expect that in general the value of the lower Darboux integral would not exceed that of the upper Darboux integral. These are correct assessments.

Theorem 1. *For every f bounded on* $[a, b]$ *the two Darboux integrals exist and*

$$\int_{\underline{a}}^{b} f \leq \int_{a}^{\bar{b}} f. \tag{15}$$

Proof. The existence of the Darboux integrals follows from Definition 4, and the remarks immediately preceding that definition. As for (15), let π_2 be any partition of $[a, b]$. Then, by Lemma 2,

$$\int_{\underline{a}}^{b} f = \mathrm{lub}\; \underline{S}(\pi) \leq \bar{S}(\pi_2).$$

This says that the lower integral is a lower bound for every upper sum (π_2 was arbitrary). Consequently,

$$\int_{\underline{a}}^{b} f \leq \mathrm{glb}\; \bar{S}(\pi) = \int_{a}^{\bar{b}} f. \quad \blacksquare$$

Finally, after all the foregoing preliminaries, we are ready for the second definition of integrability. In fact, the reader should have no trouble guessing correctly the form of the definition.

Definition 5. *A function f, bounded on* [a, b], *is* **integrable (2)** *on* **[a, b]** ⇔ $\underline{\int_a^b} f = \overline{\int_a^b} f$. *When f is integrable (2) on* [a, b] *the common value of the Darboux integrals is denoted by*

$$\int_a^b f = \int_a^b f(x)\,dx,$$

called the **integral** *of f over* [a, b].

As a reminder that not all functions are integrable and as an indication of the ease with which Definition 5 can sometimes be used, consider the function *f* defined on [0, 1] by

$$\left\{\begin{aligned} f(x) &= 0, \; x \text{ irrational} \\ f(x) &= 1, \; x \text{ rational} \end{aligned}\right\}.$$

Then clearly $\underline{S}(\pi) = 0$, $\bar{S}(\pi) = 1$, for all π, and

$$\underline{\int_0^1} f = 0, \qquad \overline{\int_0^1} f = 1.$$

This function is not integrable (2).

One of the advantages of the second definition of integrability is the fact that we can obtain a simple criterion for integrability.

Theorem 2 (*The Riemann Condition*). *Let f be a function bounded on* [a, b]. *Then*

$$f \text{ integrable (2) on } [a, b] \Leftrightarrow \left\{\begin{aligned} &\textit{for every } \varepsilon > 0 \Rightarrow \\ &\exists \textit{ partition } \pi \textit{ such} \\ &\textit{that } \bar{S}(\pi) - \underline{S}(\pi) < \varepsilon \end{aligned}\right\}.$$

Proof. We begin with the implication ⇒. Let $\varepsilon > 0$ be arbitrary. Since

$$\underline{\int_a^b} f = \operatorname*{lub}_\pi \underline{S}(\pi),$$

there exists a partition π_1 such that

$$\underline{\int_a^b} f - \frac{\varepsilon}{2} < \underline{S}(\pi_1) \le \underline{\int_a^b} f. \tag{16}$$

Similarly, the definition of the upper integral as

$$\overline{\int_a^b} f = \operatorname*{glb}_\pi \bar{S}(\pi)$$

implies that there exists a partition π_2 such that

$$\overline{\int_a^b} f \le \bar{S}(\pi_2) < \overline{\int_a^b} f + \frac{\varepsilon}{2}. \tag{17}$$

(see Figure 2).

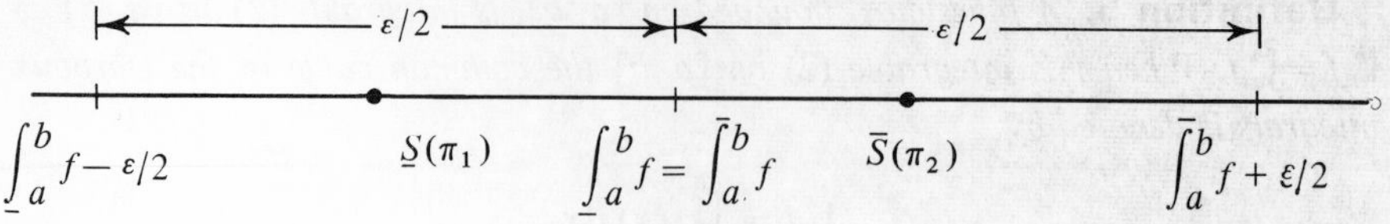

Figure 2

Now let $\pi = \pi_1 \cup \pi_2$. Then, as in the proof of Lemma 2,

$$\underline{S}(\pi_1) \le \underline{S}(\pi) \le \bar{S}(\pi) \le \bar{S}(\pi_2).$$

Using the right part of this chain with (17) gives

$$\bar{S}(\pi) \le \bar{S}(\pi_2) < \int_a^{\bar{b}} f + \frac{\varepsilon}{2}. \tag{18}$$

Using the left part of the preceding chain with (16) gives, after multiplication throughout by -1,

$$-\underline{S}(\pi) \le -\underline{S}(\pi_1) < -\int_{\underline{a}}^b f + \frac{\varepsilon}{2}. \tag{19}$$

Now adding the extreme members of (18) and (19) gives

$$\bar{S}(\pi) - \underline{S}(\pi) < \int_a^{\bar{b}} f - \int_{\underline{a}}^b f + \varepsilon = \varepsilon,$$

since f integrable (2) $\Rightarrow \int_a^{\bar{b}} f = \int_{\underline{a}}^b f$.

For the implication $\Leftarrow$ we begin with the hypothesis: this guarantees that for every $\varepsilon > 0$, there exists a partition π such that $\bar{S}(\pi) - \underline{S}(\pi) < \varepsilon$. But

$$\int_a^{\bar{b}} f \le \bar{S}(\pi)$$

and

$$\int_{\underline{a}}^b f \ge \underline{S}(\pi),$$

or, multiplying by -1,

$$-\int_{\underline{a}}^b f \le -\underline{S}(\pi).$$

Adding the first and third of these inequalities and using the hypothesis, we find

$$\int_a^{\bar{b}} f - \int_{\underline{a}}^b f \le \bar{S}(\pi) - \underline{S}(\pi) < \varepsilon.$$

As the upper and lower Darboux integrals are fixed numbers and as $\varepsilon > 0$ is arbitrary, it follows that

$$\int_a^{\bar{b}} f = \int_{\underline{a}}^b f,$$

which is to say that f is integrable (2) on $[a, b]$. ∎

We come now to the most important result of this section.

Theorem 3. *Let f be a function bounded on* $[a, b]$. *Then*

$$f \text{ is integrable (1) on } [a, b] \Leftrightarrow f \text{ is integrable (2) on } [a, b].$$

If f is integrable in either sense, the integrals determined by both senses are equal.

The proof of this assertion is, unfortunately, somewhat involved. We are going to omit it here. Those who are interested in seeing it will find a fairly complete outline in Exercises 8–10.

The effect of Theorem 3, as was suggested at the beginning of this section, is this: We can use the form of the integral as described in Definition 1 for applications to physical problems (see Section 9.5) and to mathematical problems, whereas the theoretical matters, such as sufficient conditions for a function to be integrable and the properties of the integral, can be discussed in terms of Definition 5 and the Riemann condition (Theorem 2). In the next section we shall give ample illustration of the utility of Theorem 2.

EXERCISES

1. Let $f(x) = [x]$, $0 \leq x \leq 4$.

    (a) Sketch the graph of f.

    (b) If $\pi = \{0, 1, 2, 3, 4\}$, find $\underline{S}(\pi)$ and $\bar{S}(\pi)$.

    (c) If $\pi = \{0, \frac{1}{2}, 1, \frac{3}{2}, 2, \frac{5}{2}, 3, \frac{7}{2}, 4\}$, find $\underline{S}(\pi)$ and $\bar{S}(\pi)$.

    (d) Let π be a regular partition with $n = 2^{k+2} = 4 \cdot 2^k$. Show that

    (i) $\underline{S}(\pi) = 6$.

    (ii) $\bar{S}(\pi) - \underline{S}(\pi) = \dfrac{1}{2^{k-2}}$. One way is to consider for how many i $M_i \neq m_i$.

    (iii) Prove that $\int_0^4 f = 6$.

2. Let f be defined on $[0, 2]$ by

$$\begin{aligned}
f(0) &= \tfrac{1}{2} \\
f(x) &= x, 0 < x < 1, \\
f(1) &= \tfrac{1}{2}, \\
f(x) &= 2 - x, 1 < x < 2 \\
f(2) &= \tfrac{1}{2}.
\end{aligned}$$

    (a) Sketch the graph of f.

    (b) If $\pi = \{0, 1, 2\}$ find $\underline{S}(\pi)$ and $\bar{S}(\pi)$. Show that every Riemann sum $S(\pi)$ for this partition must satisfy $\underline{S}(\pi) < S(\pi) < \bar{S}(\pi)$.

3. Let f be defined on $[0, 2]$ as in Exercise 2, except that $f(0) = f(1) = f(2) = 0$. Let $\pi = \{0, 1, 2\}$. Show that any Riemann sum $S(\pi)$ must satisfy

$$\underline{S}(\pi) \leq S(\pi) < \bar{S}(\pi).$$

What is the value of $\int_0^2 f$?

4. Find $\underline{S}(\pi)$ and $\bar{S}(\pi)$ for each of the following functions and the given partition.

(a) $f(x) = x$, $[0, 2]$, $\pi = \{0, \frac{1}{2}, 1, \frac{3}{2}, 2\}$.

(b) $f(x) = x$, $[0, 2]$, $\pi = \{0, \frac{1}{3}, \frac{4}{5}, \frac{7}{6}, \frac{4}{3}, \frac{3}{2}, \frac{15}{8}, 2\}$.

(c) $f(x) = x$, $[0, 2]$, π is the union of the partitions in (a) and (b).

(d) $f(x) = x^2$, $[0, 2]$, π is the regular partition with $n = 8$.

(e) $f(x) = 2x - x^2$, $[0, 2]$, π is the regular partition with $n = 8$.

(f) Same f, same interval as in (e). The partition is regular with $n = 16$.

5. Let f be defined by

$$f(x) = x - [x], \qquad 0 \leq x \leq 4.$$

(a) Sketch the graph of f.

(b) Find $\underline{S}(\pi)$ and $\bar{S}(\pi)$ for $\pi = \{0, 1, 2, 3, 4\}$.

(c) Same as (b), but for $\pi = \{0, \frac{1}{2}, 1, \frac{3}{2}, 2, \frac{5}{2}, 3, \frac{7}{2}, 4\}$.

(d) What is the value of $\int_0^4 f$?

6. Same as Exercise 5, only for

$$f(x) = x + [x], \qquad 0 \leq x \leq 4.$$

7. Prove that if f is continuous on $[a, b]$, then for every partition $\underline{S}(\pi)$ and $\bar{S}(\pi)$ are obtainable as Riemann sums.

8. In this exercise we begin outlining the proof of Theorem 3. The first step will be to prove a lemma.

Lemma 3. *Let f be bounded on $[a, b]$. Then*

$$\lim_{|\pi| \to 0} \bar{S}(\pi) = \int_a^b f \quad and \quad \lim_{|\pi| \to 0} \underline{S}(\pi) = \int_a^b f. \qquad (20)$$

The limits are taken in the same sense as that in Definition 1.

Hints.

(1) Assume $f(x) > 0$ for $x \in [a, b]$. If not, there is a k such that $f(x) + k > 0$ for $x \in [a, b]$, and one can take $g(x) = f(x) + k$.

(2) For arbitrary $\varepsilon > 0$ there exists (why?) a partition π_0 such that

$$\bar{S}(\pi_0) < \int_a^b f + \frac{\varepsilon}{2}.$$

(3) Let $n_0 =$ number of points in π_0, let

$$\delta = \frac{\varepsilon}{2 n_0 M},$$

where $M = \text{lub } f(x)$, $x \in [a, b]$. Why is $M > 0$?

(4) Let π be any partition with $|\pi| < \delta$. Divide the subintervals of π into two types.

Type 1: Subinterval of π contained within subinterval of π_0.

Type 2: Subinterval of π has one (or more) subdivision points of π_0 in the interior.

Let $\bar{S}_1$ and $\bar{S}_2$ be the sums from $\bar{S}(\pi)$ over the Type 1 and Type 2 subintervals, respectively. Then

$$\bar{S}(\pi) = \bar{S}_1 + \bar{S}_2.$$

(5) Now

$$\bar{S}_1 \le \bar{S}(\pi_0) < \int_a^{\bar{b}} f + \frac{\varepsilon}{2} \qquad \text{(why?)}$$

(6) Also

$$\bar{S}_2 \le Mn_0 \, \delta < \frac{\varepsilon}{2} \qquad \text{(why?)}.$$

(7) Thus, from 4, 5, and 6,

$$\bar{S}(\pi) = \bar{S}_1 + \bar{S}_2 < \int_a^{\bar{b}} f + \varepsilon.$$

Consequently,

$$\int_a^{\bar{b}} f \le \bar{S}(\pi) < \int_a^{\bar{b}} f + \varepsilon,$$

or

$$\lim_{|\pi| \to 0} \bar{S}(\pi) = \int_a^{\bar{b}} f.$$

In an exactly similar way prove

$$\lim_{|\pi| \to 0} \underline{S}(\pi) = \int_{\underline{a}}^b f.$$

9. Prove the implication $\Leftarrow$ of Theorem 3.

[*Hint.* For all partitions π, $\underline{S}(\pi) \le S(\pi) \le \bar{S}(\pi)$. Now use the hypothesis and Lemma 3 in Exercise 8.]

10. Prove the implication $\Rightarrow$ in Theorem 3.

[*Hints.* Show first that

$$\lim_{|\pi| \to 0} \bar{S}(\pi) = \lim_{|\pi| \to 0} \underline{S}(\pi)$$

by the following procedure.

(1) For arbitrary $\varepsilon > 0$ and a partition π choose $z_i \in [x_{i-1}, x_i]$ such that

$$M_i - \frac{\varepsilon}{b-a} < f(z_i) \le M_i, \qquad i = 1, \ldots, n.$$

Why can this be done?

(2) Multiply each member of the preceding inequality by Δx_i and sum over i to obtain

$$\bar{S}(\pi) - \varepsilon < S(\pi) \leq \bar{S}(\pi).$$

(3) Subtract $S(\pi)$ from each member:

$$[\bar{S}(\pi) - S(\pi)] - \varepsilon < 0 \leq [\bar{S}(\pi) - S(\pi)].$$

(4) Conclude from the statement in (3) that

$$0 \leq [\bar{S}(\pi) - S(\pi)] < \varepsilon.$$

(5) From Lemma 3, the hypothesis for this portion of the proof, and hint (4), conclude that

$$\int_a^{\bar{b}} f = \int_a^b f.$$

In a similar way show that

$$\int_{\underline{a}}^b f = \int_a^b f.$$

Thus f is integrable (2) and the values of the integrals are equal.]

9.2 Properties of the Integral

In this section we prove a few of the important results about the integral, including several theorems which were stated without proof in Chapter 2.

We begin with an obvious hereditary property.

Lemma 4. *Suppose that f is integrable on $[a, b]$ and that $[c, d] \subset [a, b]$. Then f is integrable on $[c, d]$.*

Proof. We use the Riemann condition (Theorem 2). Since f is integrable on $[a, b]$, there exists a partition π such that $\bar{S}(\pi) - \underline{S}(\pi) < \varepsilon$. Let $\pi_1 = \pi \cup \{c, d\}$. Then π_1 is a refinement of π, and

$$\underline{S}(\pi) \leq \underline{S}(\pi_1) \leq \bar{S}(\pi_1) \leq \bar{S}(\pi),$$

which implies that $\bar{S}(\pi_1) - \underline{S}(\pi_1) < \varepsilon$.

Now let

$$\bar{S}(\pi_1) = \bar{S}(\pi_1 \,|\, [c, d]) + \bar{S}(\pi_1 |\, [c, d]'), \tag{21}$$

where $\bar{S}(\pi_1 \,|\, [c, d])$ and $\bar{S}(\pi_1 |\, [c, d]')$ refer to, respectively, the portion of $\bar{S}(\pi_1)$ from the interval $[c, d]$ and the portion outside of $[c, d]$. Similarly, for the lower sum:

$$\underline{S}(\pi_1) = \underline{S}(\pi_1 \,|\, [c, d]) + \underline{S}(\pi_1 |\, [c, d]'). \tag{22}$$

From (21) and (22), we obtain

$$\bar{S}(\pi_1 \,|\, [c, d] - \underline{S}(\pi_1 |\, [c, d]) = [\bar{S}(\pi_1) - \underline{S}(\pi_1)] + [\underline{S}(\pi_1 \,|\, [c, d]' - \bar{S}(\pi_1 |\, [c, d]')]$$

$$\leq \bar{S}(\pi_1) - \underline{S}(\pi_1) \tag{23}$$

$$< \varepsilon,$$

since the term in the second brackets on the right of (23) is nonpositive. Thus, by Theorem 2, f is integrable on $[c, d]$. ∎

Our next result is equivalent to the linearity condition described in Theorem 2.10.

Theorem 4. *Let f and g be functions integrable on $[a, b]$, let $c \in \mathbf{R}$. Then*

(a) $f + g$ *is integrable on $[a, b]$ and*

$$\int_a^b (f + g) = \int_a^b f + \int_a^b g.$$

(b) *cf is integrable on $[a, b]$ and*

$$\int_a^b cf = c \int_a^b f.$$

Proof. For this proof we use the first definition of integrability.

(a) Let $\varepsilon > 0$ be arbitrary. Since, by hypothesis, f and g are integrable over $[a, b]$, we know there exist δ_1 and δ_2 such that

$$|\pi| < \delta_1 \Rightarrow \left| S_f(\pi) - \int_a^b f \right| < \frac{\varepsilon}{2}$$

$$|\pi| < \delta_2 \Rightarrow \left| S_g(\pi) - \int_a^b g \right| < \frac{\varepsilon}{2}.$$

We define $\delta = \min(\delta_1, \delta_2)$; since $S_{f+g}(\pi) = S_f(\pi) + S_g(\pi)$ (Exercise 1 below), we have, for $|\pi| < \delta$,

$$\left| S_{f+g}(\pi) - \left(\int_a^b f + \int_a^b g \right) \right| = \left| \left[S_f(\pi) - \int_a^b f \right] + \left[S_g(\pi) - \int_a^b g \right] \right|$$

$$\leq \left| S_f(\pi) - \int_a^b f \right| + \left| S_g(\pi) - \int_a^b g \right|$$

$$< \frac{\varepsilon}{2} + \frac{\varepsilon}{2} = \varepsilon.$$

By Definition 1, $f + g$ is integrable on $[a, b]$ and

$$\int_a^b (f + g) = \int_a^b f + \int_a^b g.$$

The proof of (b), similar to and a bit easier than that of (a), will be left as an exercise. ∎

We note that part (a) of Theorem 4 says that the integral is additive with respect to *functions*. We now prove the theorem which says that the integral is additive with respect to *intervals*.

Theorem 2.11. *Suppose that f is integrable on $[a, b]$; let $c \in [a, b]$. Then f is integrable on $[a, c]$ and on $[c, b]$, and*

$$\int_a^c f + \int_c^b f = \int_a^b f. \tag{24}$$

Proof. The integrability of f on $[a, c]$ and $[c, b]$ follows from Lemma 4; consequently, we need only prove (24). Let π be an arbitrary partition of $[a, b]$ and let $\pi_1 = \pi \cup \{c\}$. Then

$$\underline{S}(\pi) \leq \underline{S}(\pi_1) = \underline{S}(\pi_1|[a, c]) + \underline{S}(\pi_1|[c, b]) \leq \int_{\underline{a}}^c f + \int_{\underline{c}}^b f.$$

This says that the number $\int_{\underline{a}}^c f + \int_{\underline{c}}^b f$ is *an* upper bound of $\underline{S}(\pi)$. But, by definition, $\int_{\underline{a}}^b f$ is the *least* upper bound of the lower sums. Thus

$$\int_{\underline{a}}^b f \leq \int_{\underline{a}}^c f + \int_{\underline{c}}^b f = \int_a^c f + \int_c^b f \tag{25}$$

(the equality holds because of the integrability of f on $[a, c]$ and on $[c, b]$). Similarly,

$$\bar{S}(\pi) \geq \bar{S}(\pi_1) = \bar{S}(\pi_1|[a, c]) + \bar{S}(\pi_1|[c, b]) \geq \int_a^{\bar{c}} f + \int_c^{\bar{b}} f,$$

which says that the upper sums are bounded below by $\int_a^{\bar{c}} f + \int_c^{\bar{b}} f$. But, by definition, $\int_a^{\bar{b}} f$ is the *greatest* lower bound of the upper sums for the interval $[a, b]$; so

$$\int_a^{\bar{b}} f \geq \int_a^{\bar{c}} f + \int_c^{\bar{b}} f = \int_a^c f + \int_c^b f, \tag{26}$$

since f is integrable on $[a, c]$ and on $[c, b]$. By hypothesis, f is integrable on $[a, b]$; this means

$$\int_{\underline{a}}^b f = \int_a^{\bar{b}} f = \int_a^b f. \tag{27}$$

From (27), (26), and (25) we conclude that

$$\int_a^b f = \int_a^c f + \int_c^b f. \ \blacksquare$$

We remind the reader of Definition 2.11 and Theorem 2.12 which, together with the preceding theorem, guarantee the validity of Eq. (24) provided only that f is integrable on an interval which contains a, b, and c, *regardless of the relative positions of these points.*

We turn now to the proof of Theorem 2.9, which gives three sufficient conditions for a function to be integrable on $[a, b]$. We give a slightly different formulation of the assertion in Chapter 2.

Theorem 5. *Let f be bounded on* $[a, b]$. *Then*

(i) *f continuous on* $[a, b] \Rightarrow f$ *integrable on* $[a, b]$.
(ii) *f nondecreasing on* $[a, b] \Rightarrow f$ *integrable on* $[a, b]$.
(iii) *f nonincreasing on* $[a, b] \Rightarrow f$ *integrable on* $[a, b]$.

Proof. For (i) we draw on Theorem 3.13 which says that f continuous on $[a, b] \Rightarrow f$ uniformly continuous on $[a, b]$. This means that, for arbitrary $\varepsilon > 0$, there exists $\delta > 0$, such that if $x_1, x_2 \in [a, b]$, $|x_1 - x_2| < \delta$, then

$$|f(x_1) - f(x_2)| < \frac{\varepsilon}{b - a}. \tag{28}$$

If, now, we take any partition π of $[a, b]$ with $|\pi| < \delta$, then

$$\bar{S}(\pi) - \underline{S}(\pi) = \sum_{i=1}^{n} M_i \, \Delta x_i - \sum_{i=1}^{n} m_i \, \Delta x_i$$

$$= \sum_{i=1}^{n} (M_i - m_i) \, \Delta x_i.$$

Since f is continuous on $[a, b]$, f actually takes on its lub and glb on each sub-interval of π (Theorem 3.15); in other words, for each $i = 1, \ldots, n$, there exist x_i' and $x_i'' \in [x_{i-1}, x_i]$ such that

$$f(x_i') = M_i, \qquad f(x_i'') = m_i.$$

Because $|\pi| < \delta$, we have, by virtue of (28),

$$M_i - m_i < \frac{\varepsilon}{b - a}, \qquad i = 1, \ldots, n.$$

Thus,

$$\bar{S}(\pi) - \underline{S}(\pi) < \sum_{i=1}^{n} \frac{\varepsilon}{b - a} \, \Delta x_i = \frac{\varepsilon}{b - a} \sum_{i=1}^{n} \Delta x_i = \varepsilon.$$

By the Riemann condition (Theorem 2), f is integrable on $[a, b]$.

The proofs of (ii) and (iii) are similar to each other; we give here the proof of (iii) and leave (ii) for an exercise. Again we shall use the Riemann condition. We use a *regular* partition π with

$$|\pi| = \Delta x = \frac{b - a}{n}.$$

Since f is nonincreasing on $[a, b]$, for each $i = 1, \ldots, n$, the lub occurs at the left endpoint of the subinterval and the glb at the right:

$$M_i = f(x_{i-1}), \qquad m_i = f(x_i).$$

Thus

$$\bar{S}(\pi) - \underline{S}(\pi) = \sum_{i=1}^{n} f(x_{i-1}) \, \Delta x - \sum_{i=1}^{n} f(x_i) \, \Delta x$$

$$= \sum_{i=1}^{n} [f(x_{i-1}) - f(x_i)] \, \Delta x$$

$$= \frac{b-a}{n} \sum_{i=1}^{n} [f(x_{i-1}) - f(x_i)]$$

$$= \frac{b-a}{n} [f(a) - f(b)],$$

since the sum telescopes. Now if we choose n large enough so that

$$n > \frac{(b-a)[f(a) - f(b)]}{\varepsilon},$$

then

$$\bar{S}(\pi) - \underline{S}(\pi) < \varepsilon$$

and the Riemann condition guarantees integrability of f on $[a, b]$. ∎

As we indicated in Chapter 2, we can assure integrability of f under more generous conditions than those of the preceding theorem. We begin our discussion of this point with the following more or less obvious assertion.

Lemma 5. *Suppose f is integrable on $[a, b]$ and $c \in [a, b]$. Then the value of f can be altered at c without either affecting the integrability of f or altering the value of the integral.*

The proof of this lemma is slightly messy although not difficult. The essential idea is that c can be included in a subinterval so small that the effect of the new $f(c)$ on the lower or upper sum is arbitrarily small. We outline a proof in Exercise 6 below.

We next define a jump discontinuity for a function.

Definition 6. *Let x_0 be a point in the domain of a function f. Then f has a **jump discontinuity** at x_0 ⟺ the one-sided limits $\lim_{x \to x_0^-} f(x)$ and $\lim_{x \to x_0^+} f(x)$ exist but are not equal* (see Figure 3).

The value of $f(x_0)$ is irrelevant: it *could* be either of the one-sided limits, midway between them, or none of these.

Now, we introduce the concepts of piecewise continuity and piecewise monotonicity for functions.

Definition 7. *A function f whose domain includes the interval $[a, b]$ is **piecewise continuous** on $[a, b]$ ⟺ f is continuous on $[a, b]$ with the exception of a finite number of jump discontinuities.*

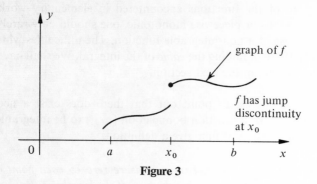

Figure 3

Definition 8. *A function f whose domain includes the interval* $[a, b]$ *is* **piecewise monotonic** *on* $[a, b]$ $\Leftrightarrow$ *there exists a partition* π *of* $[a, b]$ *such that f is monotonic on each of the open subintervals of* π.

The sketch in Figure 3 shows a simple example of a function which is piecewise continuous on $[a, b]$. In Figure 4 we illustrate a function which is piecewise monotonic on $[a, b]$.

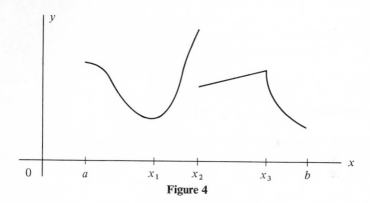

Figure 4

Now if a function f is either piecewise continuous or piecewise monotonic on an interval $[a, b]$ there will be determined a partition of $[a, b]$ on each sub-interval of which f is continuous or monotonic, hence integrable. Thus we can let

$$\int_a^b f = \sum_{i=1}^n \int_{x_{i-1}}^{x_i} f$$

the x_i being the points of the partition. To be sure, either the continuity or the monotonicity of f at the endpoints of the subintervals may present minor problems, but this is where Lemma 5 comes into the picture. As a consequence we can make the following assertion.

Theorem 6. *If a bounded function f is either piecewise continuous or piecewise monotonic on* $[a, b]$, *then f is integrable on* $[a, b]$.

As almost all of the functions encountered in elementary work are either piecewise continuous or piecewise monotonic, one should only rarely encounter difficulties because of a non-integrable function. The difficulties which *do* occur are likely to be those of finding the *value* of the integral. We shall have something to say on this subject in the next section.

[It may be of interest to point out that there does exist a necessary and sufficient condition for a function bounded on $[a, b]$ to be integrable on $[a, b]$. In order to state it we must first give a definition.

Definition. *A set S has* **Lebesgue measure zero** $\Leftrightarrow$ *each point of S can be enclosed in an open interval such that the sum of the lengths of the intervals is less than* ε, *no matter how small* $\varepsilon > 0$ *is chosen.*

As an illustration, the set of rational numbers in $[0, 1]$ has Lebesgue measure zero (no proof given here).

The promised condition is, then, as follows. We shall not prove this assertion which is due to Lebesgue (1875–1941).

Theorem. *Let f be bounded on* $[a, b]$. *Then*

$$f \text{ integrable on } [a, b] \Leftrightarrow \begin{cases} \text{the set of points} \\ \text{of discontinuity of } f \\ \text{on } [a, b] \text{ has Lebesgue} \\ \text{measure zero.} \end{cases}$$

As an example, let f be defined on $[0, 1]$ as follows:

$$f(0) = 0, \qquad f(1) = 1,$$

$$f(x) = 0, \qquad x \text{ irrational,}$$

$$f\left(\frac{p}{q}\right) = \frac{1}{q},$$

where p and q are positive integers with no common factors. Then (no proof) f is continuous at all irrational points, discontinuous at all rational points. Hence f is integrable on $[0, 1]$. What should be the value of the integral?]

The final piece of unfinished business left from Chapter 2 is the proof of the First Mean Value Theorem of the Integral Calculus. The statement is as follows.

Theorem 2.14. *Let f be continuous on* $[a, b]$. *There there exists* $x_0 \in [a, b]$ *such that*

$$\int_a^b f(x)\, dx = f(x_0)(b - a).$$

Proof. Let

$$m = \mathrm{glb}\, f(x), \qquad M = \mathrm{lub}\, f(x), \qquad x \in [a, b].$$

Then, clearly,

$$m(b - a) \le \int_a^b f(x)\, dx \le M(b - a).$$

It follows that there exists y_0, $m \le y_0 \le M$, such that

$$\int_a^b f(x)\, dx = y_0(b - a). \tag{29}$$

Since f is continuous on $[a, b]$, there exists (by Theorem 3.16) $x_0 \in [a, b]$ such that $f(x_0) = y_0$. This, combined with (29), gives the assertion of the theorem. ∎

We conclude this section by collecting an important bonus from several of the results already obtained.

Occasionally one encounters the following. The function F is the product of two functions, say $F = fg$. In attempting to set up a Riemann sum for the integral of F it is not possible to evaluate f and g at the same point in the subinterval. Instead we find ourselves considering, for a partition π of $[a, b]$,

$$S^*(\pi) = \sum_{i=1}^n f(z_i')g(z_i'')\, \Delta x_i, \qquad z_i', z_i'' \in [x_{i-1}, x_i]. \tag{30}$$

Is it still true that

$$\lim_{|\pi| \to 0} S^*(\pi) = \int_a^b F = \int_a^b fg\,?$$

The answer is in the affirmative, provided $F = fg$ is continuous.

Theorem 7. *Let $F = fg$ be continuous on $[a, b]$. If $S^*(\pi)$ is defined as in (30), then*

$$\lim_{|\pi| \to 0} S^*(\pi) = \int_a^b fg.$$

Proof. We need only assemble a few already established facts. We know

$$\underline{S}(\pi) \le S^*(\pi) \le \bar{S}(\pi).$$

Also, by Lemma 3,

$$\lim_{|\pi| \to 0} \bar{S}(\pi) = \int_a^{\bar b} F = \int_a^{\bar b} fg;$$

$$\lim_{|\pi| \to 0} \underline{S}(\pi) = \int_{\underline a}^b F = \int_{\underline a}^b fg.$$

But $F = fg$ continuous $\Rightarrow \int_{\underline a}^b fg = \int_a^{\bar b} fg = \int_a^b fg$. This statement, together with the preceding three gives us the desired result. ∎

Corollary. *Let* $F = \sqrt{f^2 + g^2}$, *where* f *and* g *are continuous on* $[a, b]$. *For a partition* π *of* $[a, b]$ *let*

$$S^*(\pi) = \sum_{i=1}^{n} \sqrt{(f(z_i'))^2 + (g(z_i''))^2}\,\Delta x_i, \quad z_i',\, z_i'' \in [x_{i-1}, x_i].$$

Then

$$\lim_{|\pi| \to 0} S^*(\pi) = \int_a^b F = \int_a^b \sqrt{f^2 + g^2}. \tag{31}$$

The proof is similar to that of the theorem, the essential point being that f, g continuous on $[a, b] \Rightarrow F$ continuous on $[a, b] \Rightarrow F$ integrable on $[a, b]$. Indeed, it is easy to see that a more general result could be formulated; the assertion analogous to that in (31) will remain valid so long as the hypotheses are sufficiently strong to assure the continuity of the function F, obtained by various operations from a finite number—not necessarily two—of other functions.

E X E R C I S E S

1. Let π be a partition of $[a, b]$, let f and g be functions whose domains include $[a, b]$. Prove:

   (a) $S_{f+g}(\pi) = S_f(\pi) + S_g(\pi)$.   (b) $S_{cf}(\pi) = cS_f(\pi)$, $c \in \mathbf{R}$.

2. Let f and g be functions defined $[a, b]$.

   (a) Prove that

   $$\underset{x \in [a, b]}{\text{lub}} [f(x) + g(x)] \le \underset{x \in [a, b]}{\text{lub}} f(x) + \underset{x \in [a, b]}{\text{lub}} g(x). \tag{32}$$

   (b) Give an example of functions f and g for which the strict inequality holds in (32).

   (c) What is the statement for glb corresponding to (32)?

   (d) If π is a partition of $[a, b]$, show that

   $$\bar{S}_{f+g}(\pi) \le \bar{S}_f(\pi) + \bar{S}_g(\pi),$$
   $$\underline{S}_{f+g}(\pi) \ge \underline{S}_f(\pi) + \underline{S}_g(\pi).$$

   [Compare with the result in Exercise 1(a).]

   (e) Show that

   $$\bar{S}_{f+g}(\pi) - \underline{S}_{f+g}(\pi) \le [\bar{S}_f(\pi) + \bar{S}_g(\pi)] - [\underline{S}_f(\pi) + \underline{S}_g(\pi)].$$

3. Prove (b) of Theorem 4, i.e., show that

$$\left.\begin{array}{l} f \text{ integrable on } [a, b] \\ c \in \mathbf{R} \end{array}\right\} \Rightarrow \left\{\begin{array}{l} cf \text{ integrable on } [a, b] \\ \text{and } \displaystyle\int_a^b cf = c \int_a^b f. \end{array}\right.$$

4. Prove (ii) of Theorem 5, i.e., prove that f nondecreasing on $[a, b] \Rightarrow f$ integrable on $[a, b]$.

5. (a) Is the function sketched in Figure 3 piecewise monotonic?

   (b) Is the function sketched in Figure 4 piecewise continuous?

   (c) Give an example of a function which is continuous on an interval but not piece-wise monotonic. [*Hint.* Let f be defined on $[0, 1]$ by
   $$\left[\begin{cases} f(x) = x \sin \dfrac{1}{x}, & x \in (0, 1] \\ f(0) = 0 \end{cases} \right].$$

   (d) Give an example of a function which is monotonic on an interval but not piece-wise continuous.

6. Prove Lemma 5.

   Hints.

   (1) Let π be any partition of $[a, b]$. Suppose that $c \in [x_{k-1}, x_k]$. If f is *increased* at c from $f(c)$ to $y_0 > f(c)$, if $S_0(\pi)$ is the Riemann sum for the altered f and $S(\pi)$ the Riemann sum for the original f, show that
   $$|S_0(\pi) - S(\pi)| \le |y_0 - f(z_k)| \, \Delta x_k$$
   $$\le (y_0 - m)|\pi|.$$

   (2) If f is *decreased* at c from $f(c)$ to $y_0 < f(c)$, show that
   $$|S_0(\pi) - S(\pi)| \le |f(z_k) - y_0| \, \Delta x_k$$
   $$\le (M - y_0)|\pi|.$$

   (3) Let $\varepsilon > 0$ be arbitrary. Choose δ such that
   $$\text{(i)} \quad |\pi| < \delta \Rightarrow \left| S(\pi) - \int_a^b f \right| < \frac{\varepsilon}{2},$$

   and

   $$\text{(ii)} \quad \delta < \frac{\varepsilon}{2(y_0 - m)} \quad \text{or} \quad \delta < \frac{\varepsilon}{2(M - y_0)},$$
   depending upon whether f is increased or decreased at c.

   (4) Then, if $|\pi| < \delta$,
   $$\left| S_0(\pi) - \int_a^b f \right| = \left| S_0(\pi) - S(\pi) + S(\pi) - \int_a^b f \right|$$
   $$\le \left| S_0(\pi) - S(\pi) \right| + \left| S(\pi) - \int_a^b f \right|$$
   $$< \frac{\varepsilon}{2} + \frac{\varepsilon}{2} = \varepsilon.$$

   Conclusion?

9.3   Approximate Integration

As is the case with many mathematical concepts (limits, in general; the derivative, in particular), the definition of the integral does not provide a convenient or
an efficient method for computation of the value of the integral. For most of the
elementary work, evaluation of definite integrals is achieved by means of the
Fundamental Theorem of Calculus which furnishes an extremely simple technique, provided one can find an antiderivative of the function to be integrated.
There are, however, elementary functions for which the antiderivatives are not
elementary functions. Examples of these are the functions f and g described by
the formulas

$$f(x) = e^{-x^2}, \qquad g(x) = \frac{\sin x}{x}.$$

[The proof of the assertion that the antiderivatives of these functions are not
elementary functions is not elementary. For proof of *this* assertion the reader is
referred to the little book by Ritt, J. F., *Integration in Finite Terms*, New York,
Columbia Univ. Press, 1948).] For such functions it becomes essential to develop
a procedure for computing, approximately, if necessary, the value of an integral,
and for this purpose modifications of the first definition of the integral prove to
be highly satisfactory. The fact is that there are numerous methods for approximating the value of an integral, varying in complexity and in the degree of accuracy. In this section we shall discuss only two of the simpler methods, each of
which has strong intuitive appeal.

Before getting down to cases, however, we mention a further reason for the
need to develop approximate methods of integration. In certain kinds of experi-
mental work the values of a function may be obtained empirically; if it is desired
to integrate the function over some interval, the formula for the function *could*
be found by means of one of several available curve-fitting methods, and the
integration could then be performed by the usual antidifferentiation process.
However, because the fundamental data are only approximate, it would seem
reasonable to use directly an approximation method for the integration, thus
bypassing the curve-fitting portion of the problem.

THE TRAPEZOIDAL RULE. The most obvious method of approximating the value
of an integral is to use a Riemann sum associated with a partition. Geometrically this amounts to approximating the area under a curve by a sum of areas of
rectangles. Clearly an improvement in the approximation would be obtained by
joining adjacent points on the curve (corresponding to partition points) by
straight-line segments, thus using trapezoids instead of rectangles. See Figure 5.
The area A_i of one of the approximating trapezoids is, then,

$$A_i = (x_i - x_{i-1})\tfrac{1}{2}[f(x_{i-1}) + f(x_i)]$$

$$= \tfrac{1}{2}(y_{i-1} + y_i)\Delta x_i.$$

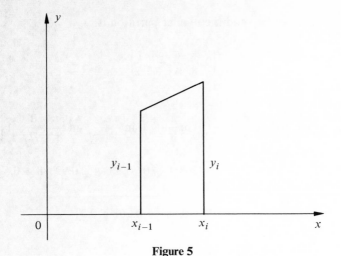

Figure 5

It is easy to see that the calculations will be simplified if we use a regular partition. Then

$$\Delta x = \frac{b - a}{n},$$

where n is the number of subintervals and the integration is over the interval $[a, b]$. It follows that

$$\sum_{i=1}^{n} A_i = \frac{1}{2} [(y_0 + y_1) + (y_1 + y_2) + \cdots + (y_{n-2} + y_{n-1}) + (y_{n-1} + y_n)] \Delta x,$$

or

$$\int_a^b f(x)\, dx \approx \frac{b - a}{n} \left[\frac{1}{2} y_0 + y_1 + y_2 + \cdots + y_{n-2} + y_{n-1} + \frac{1}{2} y_n \right], \qquad (33)$$

where $y_i = f(x_i)$, $i = 0, 1, \ldots, n$. The formula in (33) is known as the *trapezoidal rule*. It is fairly clear that the quality of the approximation will increase with n.

It can be shown that the maximum error E in using the trapezoidal rule is

$$E < \frac{(\Delta x)^2}{12} (b - a) K_2,$$

where $|f''(x)| < K_2$ for all $x \in [a, b]$. We omit the proof.

Example 1. As a simple illustration of the trapezoidal rule, we find

$$\int_0^{\pi/2} \sqrt{\sin x}\, dx,$$

using $n = 4$.

We have $\Delta x = \dfrac{\pi}{2 \cdot 4} = \dfrac{\pi}{8}$ and the regular partition is

$$\left\{ 0, \frac{\pi}{8}, \frac{\pi}{4}, \frac{3\pi}{8}, \frac{\pi}{2} \right\}.$$

By (33), then,

$$\int_0^{\pi/2} \sqrt{\sin x}\; dx \approx \frac{\pi}{8} \left[0 + \sqrt{\sin \frac{\pi}{8}} + \sqrt{\sin \frac{\pi}{4}} + \sqrt{\sin \frac{3\pi}{8}} + \frac{1}{2}\sqrt{1} \right]$$

$$= \frac{\pi}{8} \left[\sqrt{0.38268} + \sqrt{0.70711} + \sqrt{0.92388} + 0.5 \right]$$

$$= \frac{\pi}{8} \left[0.619 + 0.841 + 0.961 + 0.5 \right]$$

$$= \frac{\pi}{8} (2.921)$$

$$= 1.145.$$

As the graph of $y = \sqrt{\sin x}$ is concave downward everywhere, the approximation given by the trapezoidal rule will be an underestimate. Why?

SIMPSON'S RULE. The trapezoidal rule amounts to using a linear, or first degree approximation for the function to be integrated. A superior method is obtained by using a second degree polynomial to approximate f. To be explicit, we again use a regular partition of the interval $[a, b]$ and, taking the subintervals two at a time, approximate f between x_{i-1} and x_{i+1} by a quadratic function $q(x) = ax^2 + bx + c$ which passes through the points $P_{-1}(x_{i-1}, f(x_{i-1}))$, $P_0(x_i, f(x_i))$, and $P_1(x_{i+1}, f(x_{i+1}))$ (see Figure 6). Clearly, for this approach the number of subintervals in the partition should be even—hardly a severe restriction.

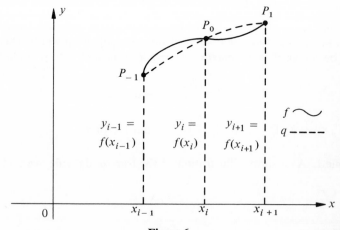

Figure 6

The preceding description may convey the impression that the labor involved in the use of the parabolic approximation is considerable. This is not so, mainly because of the following assertion.

Lemma 6. *Let* $q(x) = ax^2 + bx + c$; *let* $y_j = q(x_j)$ *for* $j = -1, 0, 1$, *where* $x_1 - x_0 = x_0 - x_{-1} = h$. *Then*

$$\int_{x_{-1}}^{x_1} q(x)\, dx = \frac{h}{3} [y_{-1} + 4y_0 + y_1].$$

The proof, which is rather easy, is outlined in Exercise 11.

If, now, we approximate f on each pair of subintervals of the partition by q—in general, a different q for each pair of subintervals—then repeated application of Lemma 6 will enable us to write

$$\int_a^b f(x)\, dx \approx \frac{h}{3} [(y_0 + 4y_1 + y_2) + (y_2 + 4y_3 + y_4)$$
$$+ (y_4 + 4y_5 + y_6) + \cdots + (y_{2n-2} + 4y_{2n-1} + y_{2n})].$$

For the preceding equation we assume the regular partition has $2n$ subintervals and

$$h = \Delta x = x_i - x_{i-1} = \frac{b-a}{2n}.$$

It follows, then, that

$$\int_a^b f(x)\, dx \approx \frac{b-a}{6n} [y_0 + 4y_1 + 2y_2 + 4y_3 + 2y_4 + \cdots$$
$$+ 2y_{2n-2} + 4y_{2n-1} + y_{2n}]. \quad (34)$$

The formula in (34) is known as *Simpson's Rule.*

Example 2. We use Simpson's Rule to approximate $\int_0^1 e^{-x^2}\, dx$.

For the sake of simplicity we take $2n = 4$ or $n = 2$. The regular partition of $[0, 1]$ is, then, $\pi = \{0, 0.25, 0.5, 0.75, 1\}$. From tables of the exponential function we obtain the following values.

x	0	0.25	0.50	0.75	1
y	1	0.939	0.779	0.570	0.368

Thus, using (34), we have

$$\int_0^1 e^{-x^2}\, dx \approx \frac{1}{12} [1 + 4(0.939) + 2(0.779) + 4(0.570) + 0.368]$$

$$= \frac{1}{12} [1 + 3.756 + 1.558 + 2.280 + 0.368]$$

$$= \frac{1}{12} [8.962]$$

$$= 0.747.$$

It can be shown—but we shall not do it here—that for a partition of $2n$ subintervals the maximum error E in using Simpson's Rule is

$$E = \frac{h^4(b-a)}{180} K_4 = \frac{nh^5}{90} K_4,$$

where $x \in [a, b] \Rightarrow |f^{iv}(x)| < K_4$.

EXERCISES

In Exercises 1–5 use the trapezoidal rule with the value of n given to find the approximate value of the integral.

1. $\int_0^1 \sqrt{1+x^3}\, dx$, $n = 4$.   **2.** $\int_0^1 \frac{dx}{\sqrt{1+x^4}}$, $n = 5$.

3. $\int_0^1 \frac{dx}{\sqrt{1+x^4}}$, $n = 8$.   **4.** $\int_0^1 \frac{dx}{1+x^3}$, $n = 4$.

5. $\int_0^1 e^{-x^2}\, dx$, $n = 4$ [Compare with the result in Example 2].

In Exercises 6–10, use Simpson's Rule with the value of $2n$ given to find, approximately, the value of the integral.

6. $\int_0^1 \frac{dx}{1+x^3}$, $2n = 4$ [Compare with Exercise 4].

7. $\int_0^1 \frac{dx}{\sqrt{1+x^4}}$, $2n = 4$.   **8.** $\int_0^{\pi/2} \sin x^2\, dx$, $2n = 4$.

9. $\int_0^{\pi/2} \frac{\sin x}{x}\, dx$, $2n = 4$ [Define $f(0) = 1$].   **10.** $\int_0^1 \sqrt{1-x^4}\, dx$, $2n = 4$.

11. Prove Lemma 6.

    Hints.

    1. Show that

$$\int_{-h}^{h} (ax^2 + bx + c)\, dx = \frac{h}{3}\, [2ah^2 + 6c].$$

    2. Let $q(-h) = y_{-1}$, $q(0) = y_0$, $q(h) = y_1$; show that $y_{-1} + 4y_0 + y_1 = 2ah^2 + 6c$.

    3. Explain why it is sufficient to work with the special interval $[-h, h]$ rather than the general interval $[x_0 - h, x_0 + h]$.

9.4 Improper Integrals

The definition and resulting theorems about the integral of a function over an interval are predicated on the assumptions that the interval is *finite* and that the function is *bounded* on the interval. There are times when it is desirable to remove one or the other—or both—of these restrictions; and frequently this can be done in a very natural way, as we shall see. We begin with a simple example.

Example 3. Consider $\int_0^b e^{-x} \, dx$. Clearly,

$$\int_0^b e^{-x} \, dx = -e^{-x} \Big|_0^b = -e^{-b} + 1 = 1 - \frac{1}{e^b}.$$

It is easy to see, then, that

$$\lim_{b \to \infty} \int_0^b e^{-x} \, dx = \lim_{b \to \infty} \left[1 - \frac{1}{e^b} \right] = 1,$$

and it is natural to express this result as

$$\int_0^\infty e^{-x} \, dx = 1.$$

Consider, on the other hand, the following.

Example 4. Since

$$\int_1^b \frac{1}{x} \, dx = \log x \Big|_1^b = \log b,$$

we see that

$$\lim_{b \to \infty} \int_1^b \frac{1}{x} \, dx = \lim_{b \to \infty} \log b = \infty.$$

Thus the limit fails to exist.

In any case, though, the following extension of the integral is a reasonable one.

Definition 9

(i) *Let f be defined and integrable on* [a, b] *for every b > a. Then*

$$\int_a^\infty f(x) \, dx = \lim_{b \to \infty} \int_a^b f(x) \, dx, \tag{35}$$

provided the limit on the right exists.

(ii) *Let f be defined and integrable on* [a, b] *for every a < b. Then*

$$\int_{-\infty}^b f(x) \, dx = \lim_{a \to -\infty} \int_a^b f(x) \, dx, \tag{36}$$

provided the limit on the right exists.

The integrals in Definition 9 are called *improper integrals*. When the limit exists the improper integral is said to *converge*, otherwise the improper integral *diverges*. Thus the improper integrals in the preceding two examples are, respectively, convergent and divergent.

Sometimes it is possible to extend an integral over all of **R** .

Definition 10. *Let f be defined and integrable over every finite interval* $[a, b] \subset \mathbf{R}$. *Then*

$$\int_{-\infty}^{\infty} f(x)\,dx = \int_{-\infty}^{a} f(x)\,dx + \int_{a}^{\infty} f(x)\,dx, \tag{37}$$

provided both integrals on the right converge. If at least one of the intervals on the right of (37) diverges, then the integral $\int_{-\infty}^{\infty} f$ *diverges. The "dividing point," a, can be any number in* **R**. *Frequently* $a = 0$ *is a convenient choice.*

The preceding definition may appear to be a little more cumbersome and less natural than the possible alternative

$$\int_{-\infty}^{\infty} f(x)\,dx = \lim_{b \to \infty} \int_{-b}^{b} f(x)\,dx. \tag{38}$$

However, the two definitions are not equivalent, as the following illustration shows.

Example 5. Consider $\int_{-\infty}^{\infty} \dfrac{x\,dx}{x^2 + 1}$. Since the function f defined by $f(x) = \dfrac{x}{x^2+1}$ is odd, we have

$$\int_{-b}^{b} \frac{x\,dx}{x^2 + 1} = 0,$$

for every b. Thus

$$\lim_{b \to \infty} \int_{-b}^{b} \frac{x\,dx}{x^2 + 1} = \lim_{b \to \infty} 0 = 0.$$

However,

$$\int_{0}^{\infty} \frac{x\,dx}{x^2+1} = \lim_{b \to \infty} \int_{0}^{b} \frac{x\,dx}{x^2+1} = \lim_{b \to \infty} \frac{1}{2}\log(x^2+1)\Big|_{0}^{b}$$

$$= \lim_{b \to \infty} \frac{1}{2}\log(b^2+1) = \infty.$$

Thus, by (38) the integral would converge (to the value 0), but by Definition 10 the integral diverges. We must hold to Definition 10 and accept the latter judgment: the integral $\int_{-\infty}^{\infty} \dfrac{x\,dx}{x^2+1}$ diverges.

Geometrically it is easy to see the reason for the different results (see Figure 7). The integral over any interval symmetric with respect to the origin is 0. But the area between the right half of the curve, the x-axis, and the ordinate at $x = b$ gets big beyond all bounds as $b \to \infty$.

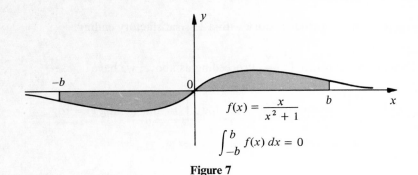

$$f(x) = \frac{x}{x^2 + 1}$$

$$\int_{-b}^{b} f(x)\, dx = 0$$

Figure 7

Example 6. Consider $\int_0^\infty x\, e^{-x^2}\, dx$. We have

$$\int_0^\infty x\, e^{-x^2}\, dx = \lim_{b \to \infty} -\frac{1}{2} \int_0^b e^{-x^2}(-2x\, dx) = \lim_{b \to \infty} \left[-\frac{1}{2} e^{-x^2} \Big|_0^b \right]$$

$$= \lim_{b \to \infty} \left[\frac{1}{2}(1 - e^{-b^2}) \right] = \frac{1}{2}.$$

Since the function f defined by $f(x) = x\, e^{-x^2}$ is odd, we know immediately that $\int_{-\infty}^0 x\, e^{-x^2}\, dx = -\frac{1}{2}$. Thus, by Definition 10, the original integral converges (to zero).

The second type of improper integral arises from lifting the restriction of *boundedness*. Again we begin with an example.

Example 7. Consider $\int_0^1 \frac{dx}{\sqrt{x}}$. We see immediately that, if f is defined by

$$f(x) = \frac{1}{\sqrt{x}},$$

$$\lim_{x \to 0^+} f(x) = \infty;$$

f is not bounded on $[0, 1]$. But f is bounded on every interval $[\varepsilon, 1]$, where $\varepsilon > 0$. Thus it is natural to investigate

$$\lim_{\varepsilon \to 0^+} \int_\varepsilon^1 \frac{dx}{\sqrt{x}} = \lim_{\varepsilon \to 0^+} 2\sqrt{x} \Big|_\varepsilon^1 = \lim_{\varepsilon \to 0^+} [2(1 - \sqrt{\varepsilon})] = 2.$$

From this result we would be led to write

$$\int_0^1 \frac{dx}{\sqrt{x}} = 2,$$

even though the integrand is not bounded on $[0, 1]$.

Again we must include a story with a less satisfactory ending.

Example 8. Consider $\int_0^1 \frac{dx}{x}$. Proceeding as above, we have

$$\int_0^1 \frac{dx}{x} = \lim_{\varepsilon \to 0^+} \int_\varepsilon^1 \frac{dx}{x} = \lim_{\varepsilon \to 0^+} \log x \Big|_\varepsilon^1 = \lim_{\varepsilon \to 0^+} (- \log \varepsilon) = \infty,$$

since $\lim_{\varepsilon \to 0^+} \log \varepsilon = -\infty$. The limit does not exist.

These examples, however, suggest a definition. See Figure 8.

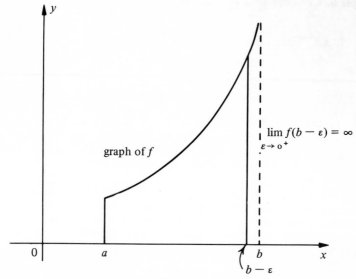

Figure 8

Definition 11

(i) *Suppose f is defined on $(a, b]$ and $\lim_{\varepsilon \to 0^+} f(a + \varepsilon) = \pm\infty$. If, for every $\varepsilon > 0$, f is integrable on $[a + \varepsilon, b]$, then*

$$\int_a^b f(x)\, dx = \lim_{\varepsilon \to 0^+} \int_{a+\varepsilon}^b f(x)\, dx, \tag{39}$$

provided the limit on the right exists.

(ii) *Suppose f is defined on* $[a, b)$ *and* $\lim\limits_{\varepsilon \to 0^+} f(b - \varepsilon) = \pm\infty$. *If, for every* $\varepsilon > 0$, *f is integrable on* $[a, b - \varepsilon]$, *then*

$$\int_a^b f(x)\, dx = \lim_{\varepsilon \to 0^+} \int_a^{b-\varepsilon} f(x)\, dx, \tag{40}$$

provided the limit on the right exists.

As with the first type of improper integral, we say the integral converges when the limit exists, diverges otherwise.

Example 9. Consider $\displaystyle\int_0^2 \frac{dx}{\sqrt[3]{2 - x}}$. Using Definition 11, we have

$$\int_0^2 \frac{dx}{\sqrt[3]{2 - x}} = \lim_{\varepsilon \to 0^+} \int_0^{2-\varepsilon} (2 - x)^{-1/3}\, dx = \lim_{\varepsilon \to 0^+} \left. -\frac{3}{2}(2 - x)^{2/3} \right|_0^{2-\varepsilon}$$

$$= \lim_{\varepsilon \to 0^+} \left[-\frac{3}{2}(\varepsilon^{2/3} - 2^{2/3}) \right] = \frac{3}{2} \cdot 2^{2/3}$$

$$= \frac{3}{\sqrt[3]{2}}.$$

The analog to Definition 10 is the following.

Definition 12. *Suppose f is defined for all* $x \in [a, b]$, *with the exception of* $c \in (a, b)$. *Suppose* $\lim\limits_{x \to c} f(x) = \pm\infty$. *Then*

$$\int_a^b f(x)\, dx = \int_a^c f(x)\, dx + \int_c^b f(x)\, dx, \tag{41}$$

provided both integrals on the right exist (in the sense of Definition 11).

Example 10. Consider $\displaystyle\int_{-1}^1 \frac{dx}{x^2}$. A careless, mechanical, handling of the problem leads to

$$\int_{-1}^1 \frac{dx}{x^2} = \left. -\frac{1}{x} \right|_{-1}^1 = -1 - 1 = -2,$$

an absurd answer, since $f(x) = \dfrac{1}{x^2} > 0$. The "dilemma" is caused by the fact that f is unbounded in every nbd of zero. Thus, we should consider

$$\int_0^1 \frac{dx}{x^2} = \lim_{\varepsilon \to 0^+} \int_\varepsilon^1 x^{-2}\, dx = \lim_{\varepsilon \to 0^+} \left. -\frac{1}{x} \right|_\varepsilon^1 = \lim_{\varepsilon \to 0^+} \left(-1 + \frac{1}{\varepsilon} \right) = \infty.$$

Clearly the original improper integral diverges, and the apparent answer of -2 is not meaningful.

It is possible that both types of impropriety might occur in the same integral. For example, in considering $\int_a^\infty f(x)\,dx$ it may happen that, for $c \in (a, \infty)$, $\lim_{x \to c} f(x) = \pm\infty$. Obviously one should then decompose the integral into several, isolating the improprieties:

$$\int_a^\infty f(x)\,dx = \int_a^c f(x)\,dx + \int_c^d f(x)\,dx + \int_d^\infty f(x)\,dx.$$

The integral on the left will converge if and only if all three integrals on the right converge.

EXERCISES

In numbers 1–20 determine whether or not the improper integral converges. If it does, find its value.

1. $\int_1^\infty \dfrac{dx}{x^2}.$

2. $\int_4^7 \dfrac{dx}{\sqrt{x-4}}.$

3. $\int_0^\infty \dfrac{x\,dx}{\sqrt{x+2}}.$

4. $\int_0^\infty \sin x\,dx.$

5. $\int_1^\infty \dfrac{dx}{x(1+x^2)}.$

6. $\int_{-\infty}^\infty \dfrac{dx}{x^2+1}.$

7. $\int_{-a}^a \dfrac{dx}{\sqrt{a^2-x^2}}.$

8. $\int_0^1 \dfrac{\log x\,dx}{x}.$

9. $\int_1^4 \dfrac{dx}{(x-1)^{2/3}}.$

10. $\int_{-\infty}^2 \dfrac{dx}{\sqrt{3-x}}.$

11. $\int_{-\infty}^\infty \dfrac{dx}{x^{3/4}}.$

12. $\int_{-1}^1 \dfrac{dx}{\sqrt[5]{x}}.$

13. $\int_{-1}^1 \dfrac{dx}{x^3}.$

14. $\int_1^3 \dfrac{dx}{\sqrt{x^2-1}}.$

15. $\int_0^2 \dfrac{dx}{4-x^2}.$

16. $\int_0^4 \dfrac{dx}{9-x^2}.$

17. $\int_1^\infty \dfrac{dx}{x^4+x^2}.$

18. $\int_{-\infty}^\infty \dfrac{dx}{(x-1)^2}.$

19. $\int_1^2 \dfrac{x\,dx}{\sqrt{x^2-1}}.$

20. $\int_{-\infty}^\infty \dfrac{dx}{e^x+e^{-x}}.$

21. Consider $\displaystyle\int_1^\infty \frac{dx}{x^n}$.

    (a) Show that the integral diverges for $0 \le n \le 1$ and converges for $n > 1$.

    (b) In the latter case for part (a), to what value does it converge?

22. (a) Show that $\displaystyle\int_0^1 \frac{dx}{\sqrt[n]{x}}$ converges for $n > 1$.

    (b) What happens to the integral in part (a) if $0 \le n < 1$?

23. Show that a trigonometric substitution converts the improper integral $\displaystyle\int_0^1 \frac{dx}{\sqrt{1-x^2}}$ to a proper integral.

24. Prove the following assertion.

    Theorem. *Suppose f is bounded and integrable on $[a, b-\varepsilon]$, for every $\varepsilon > 0$. Assume $\displaystyle\lim_{x \to b} f(x) = \pm \infty$. Let $F'(x) = f(x)$ and suppose F is continuous at b. Then*

$$\int_a^b f(x)\, dx = F(b) - F(a).$$

25. Apply the Theorem in Exercise 24 to show that $\displaystyle\int_0^1 \frac{dx}{(1-x)^{1/n}}$ converges if $n > 1$.

9.5 Further Applications of the Integral

    Now that the correct theoretical foundations of the integral have been established, it is appropriate that we consider briefly a few additional applications of the integral.

    WORK. We learn from elementary physics that if a force of magnitude F pounds, say, moves a particle a distance of x feet, then, by definition, the *work* done by the force is

$$W = Fx \text{ ft lbs.} \tag{42}$$

    Thus, a person lifting a twenty pound bucket of sand a vertical distance of four feet exerts a force which does work equal, by (42), to

$$W = (20)(4) = 80 \text{ ft lbs.}$$

    Of course, the implicit assumption of the preceding definition is that the magnitude of the force is constant. If the magnitude of the force is variable (if, e.g., the bucket had a hole in it), then one must proceed differently in defining work. It is here where the integral plays a role, just as it does in defining area under a curve.

    However, before addressing ourselves to this point, we must first attend to one other. We refer to the fact that force is a *vector* quantity, having both *magnitude* and *direction*. As we shall study vectors in Chapter 11, we sidestep the issue at this time by assuming that the force vector lies along the line of motion. In this way we need concern ourselves only with the magnitude of the force. (See Section 14.9 for a more general discussion.)

In order, then, to arrive at a satisfactory definition of the work done by a force of variable magnitude, we proceed as follows. We suppose the force directed along the x-axis, its magnitude at point x being given by the value $F(x)$ of a function F. We desire to measure the work done when the force moves a particle from $x = a$ to $x = b$ $(a < b)$. We first take a partition $\pi = \{a = x_0, x_1, \ldots, x_{i-1}, x_i, \ldots, x_{n-1}, x_n = b\}$ of $[a, b]$ and choose a point $z_i \in [x_{i-1}, x_i]$ for $i = 1, 2, \ldots, n$. If we evaluate F at z_i and assume that $F(x)$ does not differ much from $F(z_i)$ for $x \in [x_{i-1}, x_i]$, we can use (42) n times to obtain an approximation to the desired measure:

$$W \approx \sum_{i=1}^{n} F(z_i) \, \Delta x_i. \tag{43}$$

It is natural, then, to consider the limit of the right-hand side of (43), the limit being taken in the sense of Definition 1. Thus we are led to the following formulation.

Definition 13. *If a force directed along the x-axis has magnitude $F(x)$ at $x \in [a, b]$, then the **work** W done by the force in moving a particle from a to b is*

$$W = \int_a^b F(x) \, dx. \tag{44}$$

It is assumed here that F is integrable on $[a, b]$.

Example 11. If a force of magnitude $F(x) = x^2$ lbs moves an object from $x = 2$ to $x = 6$ (units in ft) along the x-axis, then, by (44), the work done is

$$W = \int_2^6 x^2 \, dx = \tfrac{1}{3}x^3 \Big|_2^6 = 69\tfrac{1}{3} \text{ ft lbs.}$$

Suppose, however, that the particle moves from $x = 2$ to $x = 6$ along the x-axis, but that F is a frictional force. In this case it would be directed opposite to the direction of motion, and we should write $F(x) = -x^2$. Thus, by (44), $W = -69\tfrac{1}{3}$ ft lbs, and we say, accounting for the minus sign, that the work is done *against* the force.

Example 12. A spring with natural length of 6 inches requires a force of 3 lbs to stretch it to 7 in. How much work is done in stretching the spring from its natural length to a length of 10 in.?

Solution. This problem requires knowledge of Hooke's law, which says that the force required to stretch a spring x in. is $F(x) = kx$, for $0 \leq x \leq L$, where

k and L depend upon the material of which the spring is made. In this case, we know that $F(1) = 3$, which implies $k = 3$, or $F(x) = 3x$. Assuming $L \geq 4$, we have, from (44), that

$$W = \int_0^4 3x \, dx = \tfrac{3}{2} x^2 \Big|_0^4 = 24 \text{ in. lbs.}$$

Example 13. A tank in the shape of a cone is placed with its vertex at the bottom. The radius at the top is 4 ft and the height is 12 ft. The tank contains liquid to a depth of 9 ft. If the liquid weighs w lb per cu ft, find the measure of work done in pumping the liquid out over the top. See Figure 9.

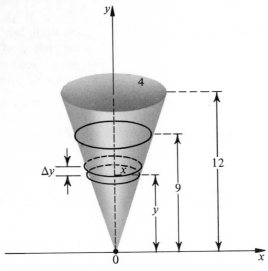

Figure 9

Solution. We begin by noting that the force involved here is the vertical force necessary to overcome the force of gravity. For the magnitude of this force on an object we use the weight of the object.

We choose a coordinate system with the y-axis along the axis of the cone, the origin being at the vertex (bottom of the tank). Now we think of the liquid in the tank as being made up of disk-like slabs of thickness Δy. Thus the work done in lifting the slab at height y to the top of the tank is, approximately,

$$(12 - y)\pi w x^2 \Delta y,$$

where x is the radius of the slab. It follows that the total work done will be given by

$$W = \int_0^9 \pi w x^2 (12 - y) \, dy. \tag{45}$$

We can use similar triangles to express x in terms of y; thus

$$\frac{x}{4} = \frac{y}{12} \text{ or } x = \frac{1}{3} y.$$

Using this value of x in (45) we have

$$W = \pi w \int_0^9 \frac{y^2}{9} (12 - y) \, dy = \frac{\pi w}{9} \left[4y^3 - \frac{1}{4} y^4 \Big|_0^9 \right]$$

$$= \pi w 9^2 \left(4 - \frac{9}{4} \right) = \frac{567 \pi w}{4} \text{ ft lbs.}$$

(If the liquid is water, $w \approx 62.5$ lbs, and $W \approx 27818.5$ ft lbs.)

Example 14. According to Newton's law of gravitation, two particles attract each other with a force which is proportional to the product of the masses and inversely proportional to the square of the distance between them. If we consider a particle of mass m fixed at the origin and a movable particle of mass one on the x-axis, then the force of attraction is $F(x) = \dfrac{km}{x^2}$. Thus the work done in moving the particle of unit mass from a to b on the x-axis is

$$W_a^b = \int_a^b \frac{km}{x^2} dx = \frac{km}{a} - \frac{km}{b}.$$

Notice that, because the improper integral converges, we have

$$W_a^\infty = \frac{km}{a},$$

the work done in moving the particle "to infinity." This quantity, km/a, is called the *potential* of the particles.

HYDROSTATIC PRESSURE. Our second application, like the first, involves a brief excursion into the realm of physics. We shall be concerned with forces due to the weight of fluids; for our purposes we muster the following facts.

1. Pressure is force per unit area.
2. If the liquid is at rest, the pressure is the same in all directions.
3. If $w = $ weight/cu unit, $d = $ depth and $p = $ pressure, then $p = wd$, i.e., the pressure is proportional to the depth.
4. As a result of 1 and 3, if a region of area A is such that all points of the region are at the same depth, then the hydrostatic force on the region is given by

$$F = pA. \tag{46}$$

Now we consider the following problem. We have a plane region R which is submerged vertically in a liquid. Our aim is to measure the force on one side of the region. We begin by introducing a coordinate system with the x-axis on the surface of the liquid and the y-axis directed positively *downward*. Now we consider the region R to be composed of strips of height Δy and width $f(y)$, say, so that the force on one strip is given by $wyf(y)\,\Delta y$. More exactly, if c and d are the minimum and maximum depths of points of R, we form a partition of $[c, d]$, choose a point $v_i \in [y_{i-1}, y_i]$, and evaluate the width function f at this point. If $y_i - y_{i-1} = \Delta y_i$ is small, all points of the ith strip will have approximately the same depth, and the force on the strip will be, approximately,

$$wv_i\,f(v_i)\Delta y_i.$$

Thus, the force on R will be given approximately by

$$\sum_{i=1}^{n} wv_i\,f(v_i)\,\Delta y_i, \quad v_i \in [y_{i-1}, y_i],$$

and it is reasonable to *define* F by

$$F = \int_c^d wyf(y)\,dy, \tag{47}$$

where f is the function which gives the width of R at depth y. See Figure 10.

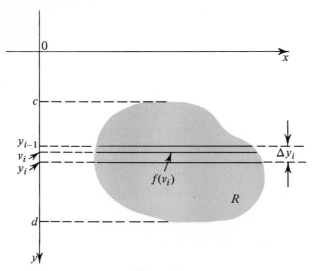

Figure 10

Example 15. The ends of a trough are equilateral triangles 4 ft on a side. If the trough is full of water, find the force on one end. See Figure 11.

Solution. In order to use (47) we must find the width function. If we take the y-axis as the vertical line of symmetry of the equilateral triangle, it is elementary

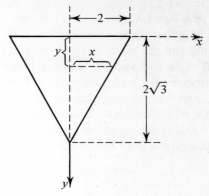

Figure 11

to show that the horizontal distance x from the y-axis to one edge of the triangle is, at depth y, $x = 2 - \dfrac{1}{\sqrt{3}} y$. This being half the desired width, we have $f(y) = 4 - \dfrac{2}{\sqrt{3}} y$. Thus, using (47), we have

$$F = w \int_0^{2\sqrt{3}} y\left(4 - \frac{2}{\sqrt{3}} y\right) dy$$

$$= w\left[2y^2 - \frac{2}{3\sqrt{3}} y^3 \Big|_0^{2\sqrt{3}}\right]$$

$$= 8w \text{ lbs.}$$

E X E R C I S E S

1. For a spring of natural length 20 in. a force of 10 lbs is required to stretch it to 22 in. How much work is done in stretching the spring from 22 to 25 in.?

2. A spring has natural length 8 in. If a force of 4 lbs is required to stretch it to 9 in., how much work is done by the force in stretching the spring from 9 to 13 in.?

3. If a spring has natural length L in., is the work done in stretching it from L to $L + 2$ in. the same as that done in stretching it from $L + 2$ to $L + 4$?

4. Show that the work done in stretching a spring from length $L + a$ to $L + b$, where L is the natural length, is

$$W_a^b = \frac{k}{2}(b^2 - a^2) \text{ in. lbs.}$$

5. The work done in stretching a spring from 10 in. to 12 in. is 30 in. lbs; to stretch the spring from 11 to 13 in. the force does work of 40 in. lbs. What is the natural length of the spring?

6. A tank in the shape of a right circular cylinder is 10 ft high and has a 3 ft radius. The tank is buried underground, its top being 5 ft below ground level. The tank is full of water, and it is planned to pump the water out of the tank up to the surface of the earth. Find the measure of the work done.

7. A cistern is in the shape of a rectangular parallelepiped with base dimensions 8 ft by 12 ft, and height 6 ft. The cistern is buried underground, its top being 5 ft below ground level. If the cistern is half full of water, find the work done in pumping its contents to the surface of the earth.

8. A conical tank (as in Example 13) is 20 ft high and has a radius at the top of 6 ft. It is filled to a depth of 12 ft with a liquid weighing 80 pounds per cu. ft. Find the work done in pumping the contents to a height 4 ft above the top of the tank.

9. A rectangular floodgate 6 ft wide and 4 ft deep has its top at the surface of the water. Find the force on the gate.

10. A rectangular floodgate is a ft wide and $3b$ ft deep. The top of the gate is at the surface of the water. Show that the forces on the middle and bottom thirds of the gate are, respectively, 3 and 5 times the force on the top third.

11. A trough full of water has ends which are parabolic segments. The end of the trough is 4 ft wide at the top, and 4 ft deep. Find the force on one end.

12. The ends of a water trough are in the shape of one arch of a sine curve; thus each end is π ft wide at the top and has a depth of 1 ft. If the trough is full of water, find the force on one end.

Chapter **10** Polar Coordinates and Conic Sections

10.1 Introduction

The use of coordinates enables us to associate points in the plane with ordered pairs of real numbers and thus use arithmetic, algebraic, or, more generally, analytic methods in the study of the geometric properties of curves and other sets of points in the plane. Thus far we have made the association between points and ordered pairs of numbers in just one way, leading to what is usually called a rectangular cartesian coordinate system. There are, however, other ways of establishing the correspondence between points and ordered pairs of numbers —other types of coordinate systems. For example, one could use a pair of axes which intersect at some angle other than $\frac{\pi}{2}$. The fact is, though, that only one system other than rectangular cartesian coordinates is widely used in plane geometry, the system of *polar coordinates* which we now describe and proceed to study.

The basic scheme is as follows: one chooses a point, O, called the *pole* and, using O as the initial point, draws a ray, or half line, called the *polar axis*. Customarily one draws the polar axis horizontally to the right from O. Finally, one must choose a unit of distance. Now let P be an arbitrary point in the plane and draw the line segment OP. The polar coordinates of P are the numbers (r, θ), where r is the length of OP and θ is the angle measured from the polar axis in a counterclockwise direction to OP (see Figure 1).

Conversely, given an ordered pair $\left(2, \frac{3\pi}{4}\right)$, say, one associates a point P with it by drawing the terminal side of the angle $\frac{3\pi}{4}$ (the initial side being the polar

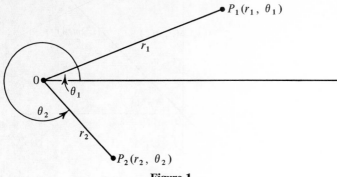

Figure 1

axis, the vertex being the pole O) and measuring 2 units from O along this terminal side. Figure 2 shows this point $\left(2, \dfrac{3\pi}{4}\right)$ and several others.

Although the polar axis is, by definition, a half line, it is customary to draw the entire line, indicating the position of the pole.

A little reflection shows that it is possible to "cover" the entire plane by using values of $r \geq 0$ and values of θ in the interval $0 \leq \theta < 2\pi$. In fact, these restrictions on r and θ *almost* give a 1–1 correspondence between the points in the plane and the set of ordered pairs $\{(r, \theta) \mid r \geq 0, 0 \leq \theta < 2\pi\}$. The exception, of course, is the pole, for which $r = 0$ but for which θ could have any value. As it turns out, however, such limitations on r and θ would be too restrictive for our purposes, and the usual convention is to allow both r and θ to have any value in **R**. However, we must now establish agreements for the use of negative values of r and θ. In the case of θ there is no problem: if $\theta < 0$ we simply measure the angle in the *clockwise* direction from the polar axis. To interpret negative values of r we take our cue from the treatment of numbers on the x-axis: a and $-a$ are equidistant from O, but in opposite directions. Thus if $r < 0$ we agree to

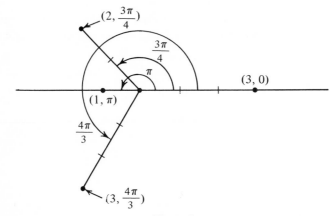

Figure 2

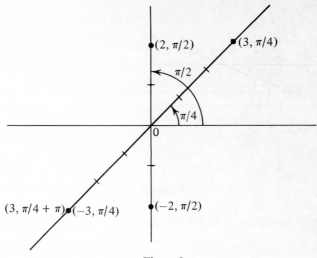

Figure 3

extend the terminal side of the angle θ "backwards" through the pole and locate P on this segment $|r|$ units from the pole. In this way (r, θ) and $(-r, \theta)$ are symmetric to each other with respect to the pole. (We illustrate in Figure 3.)

We can also describe the convention regarding negative values of r by saying that $(-r, \theta)$ and $(r, \theta + \pi)$ refer to the same point in the plane (see Figure 3).

With these conventions we lose all hope of a 1–1 correspondence between the points in the plane and the ordered pairs (r, θ). In fact, it is now the case that every point in the plane has infinitely many sets of coordinates. For, the two infinite sets

$$(r, \theta + 2n\pi), \qquad n = 0, \pm 1, \pm 2, \ldots$$

and

$$(-r, \theta + (2n + 1)\pi), \qquad n = 0, \pm 1, \pm 2, \ldots$$

all describe the same point. (We illustrate in Figure 4.)

When we consider any coordinate system it is informative to investigate the sets of points obtained by letting each coordinate equal a constant. These sets are called (in the plane) the *coordinate curves*. In this case the coordinate curves are

$$r = c$$

and

$$\theta = c.$$

$$\left(-2, \frac{7\pi}{6} + 2n\pi\right)$$

$$\left(2, \frac{\pi}{6} + 2n\pi\right)$$

$$n = 0, \pm 1, \pm 2, \ldots$$

Figure 4

For each c the equation $r = c$ is a circle with center at the pole and radius $|c|$; for each value of c the equation $\theta = c$ is a line through the pole. Thus, some of the coordinate curves are as shown in Figure 5.

Polar coordinate graph paper simply contains some of the coordinate curves, with the values of c equally spaced.

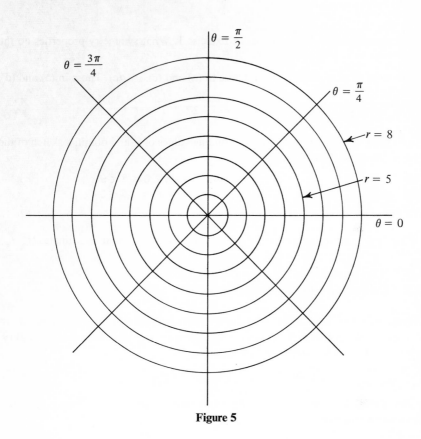

Figure 5

EXERCISES

1. Plot each of the following points—the context is polar coordinates.

(a) $\left(3, \dfrac{\pi}{6}\right)$.

(b) $\left(3, -\dfrac{\pi}{6}\right)$.

(c) $\left(3, \dfrac{5\pi}{6}\right)$.

(d) $\left(3, \dfrac{7\pi}{6}\right)$.

(e) $\left(-3, \dfrac{\pi}{6}\right)$.

(f) $(2, \pi)$.

(g) $(-2, 0)$.

(h) $(1, 1)$.

(i) $\left(1, \dfrac{\pi}{2}\right)$.

(j) $\left(1, -\dfrac{\pi}{2}\right)$.

(k) $\left(1, \dfrac{3\pi}{2}\right)$.

(l) $\left(3, \dfrac{13\pi}{6}\right)$.

2. This question refers to the points in Exercise 1. What symmetry properties do the following pairs of points have?

   (a) Those in (a) and (b).   (b) Those in (a) and (c).   (c) Those in (a) and (d).

3. What set of points is represented by $r = -2$?

4. Give values to θ, compute the corresponding values of r, and obtain a sketch of the set of points (r, θ) such that

   (a) $r = \theta$

   (b) $r = \theta + 1$

   (c) $r\theta = 1$

   (d) $r = \sin \theta, 0 \le \theta < \pi$

   (e) $r = \sin \theta, \pi \le \theta < 2\pi$.

5. What are the coordinate curves $x = c$ and $y = c$ in rectangular coordinates?

10.2   Curves in Polar Coordinates

An equation or inequality involving r and θ will determine a set of points in the plane: the points whose coordinates satisfy the equation or inequality. Frequently we will be interested in sets such as

$$\{(r, \theta) \mid r = f(\theta), \text{ where } f \text{ is a function}\}.$$

Our immediate concern will be to indicate and illustrate how geometric information can sometimes be extracted from the formula for f.

INTERCEPTS. The intersections (if any) of the curve with the polar axis can be found by setting $\theta = n\pi$, $n = 0, \pm 1, \pm 2, \ldots$. Also, intersections with the line through the pole perpendicular to the polar axis, the $\dfrac{\pi}{2}$-axis, can be obtained by setting $\theta = (2n + 1)\dfrac{\pi}{2}$, $n = 0, \pm 1, \pm 2, \ldots$. Intersections with the pole are found by solving the equation $f(\theta) = 0$.

SYMMETRY. As the points (r, θ) and $(r, -\theta)$ are symmetric to each other with respect to the polar axis, a curve will be symmetric with respect to the polar axis if $f(-\theta) = f(\theta)$. In particular, since $\cos(-\theta) = \cos \theta$, if θ appears in f only as $\cos \theta$ the curve will be symmetric with respect to the polar axis.

Symmetry with respect to the $\frac{\pi}{2}$-axis can be useful, also. The points (r, θ) and $(r, \pi - \theta)$ are symmetric with respect to this line, so a curve will have such symmetry if $f(\pi - \theta) = f(\theta)$. In particular, since $\sin (\pi - \theta) = \sin \theta$, if θ appears in the formula for f only as $\sin \theta$, the curve will be symmetric with respect to the $\frac{\pi}{2}$-axis.

Finally, we mention symmetry with respect to the pole. Two ways of describing the point symmetric to (r, θ) with respect to the pole are $(r, \theta + \pi)$ and $(-r, \theta)$. Thus if $f(\theta + \pi) = f(\theta)$—this would be the case if θ appeared in the formula for f only as $\tan \theta$ or $\cot \theta$—or if the relation between r and θ were not explicitly a functional one and r appeared as r^2 or as an even power only (Example: $r^2 = \cos 2\theta$), then the resulting curve would be symmetric with respect to the pole.

The various types of symmetry are illustrated in Figure 6.

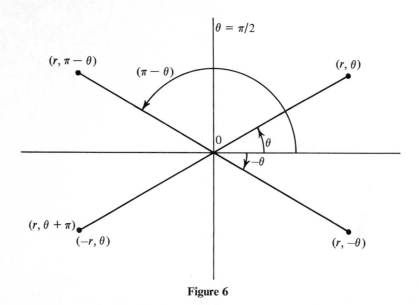

Figure 6

Because of the multiplicity of coordinates for a given point there are various tests for the different types of symmetry: the preceding ones are some of the more useful—but by no means the only—ones. Others will be introduced later.

Frequently, one can easily discern from the formula for f whether or not r is bounded for all values of θ, in which case the curve will lie entirely within a circle with center at the pole, or whether r—and hence the curve—will be unbounded. For example, the curve described by $r = \theta$ is clearly unbounded, whereas the curve described by $r = 1 + \cos \theta$ is readily seen to lie entirely within the circle $r = 2$.

We illustrate these points, as well as some others, in a few examples.

Example 1. We begin with $r = \theta$. In this example we consider $\theta \geq 0$ only. Clearly r is unbounded; there is, for $\theta \geq 0$, none of the symmetry previously discussed; and the curve intersects the polar axis infinitely many times ($\theta = n\pi$, $n = 0, 1, 2, \ldots$) and the $\frac{\pi}{2}$-axis infinitely many times $\left(\text{at all odd multiples of } \frac{\pi}{2}\right)$.
It is easy to see that the graph is a spiral (see Figure 7 and Exercise 16).

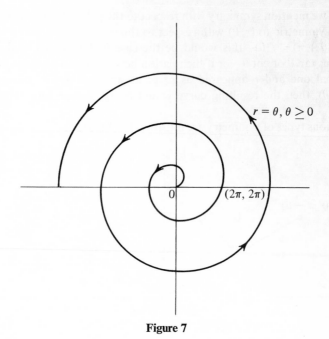

Figure 7

Example 2. We graph $r = 2 \cos \theta$.
The following facts are readily discernable:

1. Because of the periodicity of cos, we need consider only values of θ in $[0, 2\pi)$. In fact, as we shall see, the interval $0 \leq \theta < \pi$ will suffice.

2. Intersections with the pole and polar axis occur at $\left(0, \frac{\pi}{2}\right)$, $\left(0, \frac{3\pi}{2}\right)$, and $(2, 0)$, $(-2, \pi)$, respectively.

3. Clearly $|r| \leq 2$, for all θ, so the entire curve lies within the circle of radius 2, center at 0.

4. Since for all θ, $\cos \theta = - \cos (\theta - \pi)$, it follows that for $\pi < \theta < 2\pi$ the points obtained are identical with those already found for $0 < \theta < \pi$. Thus, the entire curve is described once for $0 \leq \theta < \pi$.

5. The curve is symmetric with respect to the polar axis.

We show a sketch in Figure 8. As *appears* to be the case (and, as we shall show in the next section, unquestionably *is* the case) the curve is a circle.

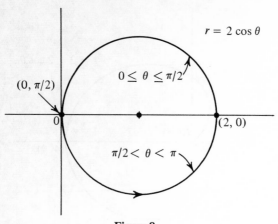

$r = 2 \cos \theta$

$(0, \pi/2)$

$0 \le \theta \le \pi/2$

$(2, 0)$

$\pi/2 < \theta < \pi$

Figure 8

Example 3. We modify very slightly the formula of the preceding example and graph

$$r = 2 + 2 \cos \theta = 2(1 + \cos \theta).$$

Discussion

1. There is symmetry with respect to the polar axis, so we need consider only values of θ in $[0, \pi]$.
2. Intercepts occur at $(4, 0)$, $\left(2, \dfrac{\pi}{2}\right)$, $(0, \pi)$.
3. The values of r are bounded: $|r| \le 4$.
4. Table 10.1 may be of help.

TABLE 10.1

θ	$2 \cos \theta$	$r = 2 + 2 \cos \theta$
increases from 0 to $\dfrac{\pi}{2}$	decreases from 2 to 0	decreases from 4 to 2
increases from $\dfrac{\pi}{2}$ to π	decreases from 0 to -2	decreases from 2 to 0

5. The curve, shown in Figure 9, is called a *cardioid*.

Example 4. We find the graph of $r = \sin 3\theta$. For this curve we use the following method. It is clear that r varies between -1 and 1, and we record, in Table 10.2, this variation.

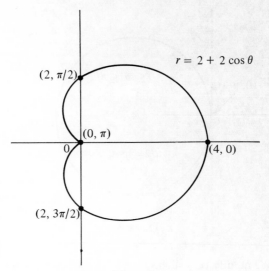

Figure 9

TABLE 10.2

3θ	$\sin 3\theta = r$	θ
0 to $\dfrac{\pi}{2}$	0 to 1	0 to $\dfrac{\pi}{6}$
$\dfrac{\pi}{2}$ to π	1 to 0	$\dfrac{\pi}{6}$ to $\dfrac{\pi}{3}$
π to $\dfrac{3\pi}{2}$	0 to -1	$\dfrac{\pi}{3}$ to $\dfrac{\pi}{2}$
$\dfrac{3\pi}{2}$ to 2π	-1 to 0	$\dfrac{\pi}{2}$ to $\dfrac{2\pi}{3}$
2π to $\dfrac{5\pi}{2}$	0 to 1	$\dfrac{2\pi}{3}$ to $\dfrac{5\pi}{6}$
$\dfrac{5\pi}{2}$ to 3π	1 to 0	$\dfrac{5\pi}{6}$ to π

Now, using the last two columns of Table 10.2, we obtain the sketch as shown in Figure 10.

Notice that Table 10.2 takes θ only between 0 and π; it is not hard to see that the interval $[\pi, 2\pi]$ will simply produce a retracing of the curve already obtained.

This curve is often called a *rose curve*. We give further examples in the following exercises.

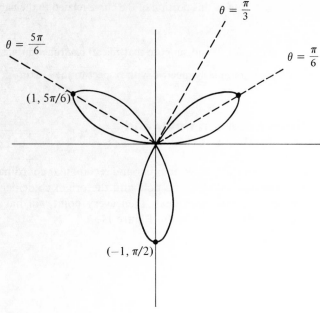

$\theta = \dfrac{\pi}{3}$

$\theta = \dfrac{5\pi}{6}$

$\theta = \dfrac{\pi}{6}$

$(1, 5\pi/6)$

$(-1, \pi/2)$

Figure 10

E X E R C I S E S

In Exercises 1–15 sketch the graphs of the functions given.

1. $r = 2 \sin \theta$.   **2.** $r = 1 - \cos \theta$.

3. $r = 1 - \sin \theta$.   **4.** $r = 1 + \sin \theta$.

5. $r = 1 - 2 \cos \theta$. [*Hint.* Be sure to find all θ such that $r = 0$.]

6. $r = e^\theta$.   **7.** $r = \cos 3\theta$.

8. $r = \sin 2\theta$ (four leaved rose).   **9.** $r = \sin 4\theta$ (eight leaved rose).

10. $r = \cos 2\theta$.   **11.** $r \cos \theta = 2$.

12. $r = 2 + \cos \theta$.

13. $r = \tan \theta$. [*Hints.* $\tan (\theta + \pi) = \tan \theta \Rightarrow$ sym. with respect to ?
                      $\tan (\pi - \theta) = -\tan \theta \Rightarrow$ sym. with respect to ?]

14. $r = \dfrac{2}{1 - \cos \theta}$.   **15.** $r = \cos \dfrac{\theta}{2}$.

16. Draw $r = \theta$ for $\theta \le 0$. How is this portion of the curve related to the part drawn in Example 1?

17. Suppose f is a function (of θ) and suppose that f is an *odd* function, i.e., $f(-\theta) = -f(\theta)$. Show that the graph is symmetric with respect to the $\dfrac{\pi}{2}$-axis.

10.3 Relations Between Polar and Rectangular Coordinates

We now consider the relation between polar and rectangular coordinates. If the two systems are superimposed with the pole and the origin coincident and the polar axis and positive x-axis coincident, then every point will have a set of co-ordinates in each system, as shown in Figure 11.

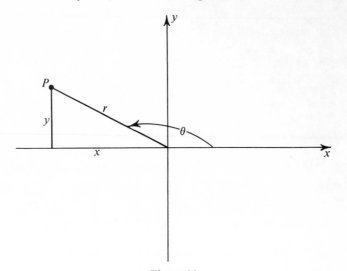

Figure 11

We note that

$$\left.\begin{aligned} x &= r \cos \theta \\ y &= r \sin \theta \end{aligned}\right\}. \tag{1}$$

Conversely, we can write

$$\left.\begin{aligned} r^2 &= x^2 + y^2 \\ \tan \theta &= \frac{y}{x} \end{aligned}\right\}. \tag{2}$$

The equations in (2) *can* be solved explicitly for r and θ:

$$\left.\begin{aligned} r &= \pm\sqrt{x^2 + y^2} \\ \theta &= \tan^{-1}\frac{y}{x} + n\pi, \qquad n = 0, \pm 1, \pm 2, \ldots \end{aligned}\right\}, \tag{3}$$

but in many cases it is preferable to work with the form in (2). With regard to the expression for θ in (3) recall that $\tan^{-1} \frac{y}{x} \in \left(-\frac{\pi}{2}, \frac{\pi}{2}\right)$, and θ in polar coordinates need not lie in this interval.

It is useful to have some facility in translating back and forth beween the two systems. For example, suppose we find the cartesian equivalent of $r = 2 \cos \theta$. If we multiply both sides by r (the geometric effect of this is to add the pole to the curve, but it was there already as $\left(0, \frac{\pi}{2}\right)$ so the locus is unchanged) we have

$$r^2 = 2r \cos \theta,$$

or, using one equation from each of (2) and (1),

$$x^2 + y^2 = 2x,$$

the equation of a circle with center $(1, 0)$, radius 1 (see Example 2).

Similarly, consider the cardioid of Example 3:

$$r = 2 + 2 \cos \theta. \tag{4}$$

Again we multiply through by r:

$$r^2 = 2r + 2r \cos \theta,$$

or, using (2) and (1),

$$x^2 + y^2 = 2r + 2x.$$

This can be written

$$x^2 + y^2 - 2x = 2r,$$

or

$$x^2 + y^2 - 2x = 2\sqrt{x^2 + y^2};$$

squaring both sides gives

$$(x^2 + y^2 - 2x)^2 = 4(x^2 + y^2). \tag{5}$$

The student should compare the graphing of $r = 2 + 2 \cos \theta$, as carried out in Example 3, with the prospect of graphing the curve defined by Eq. (5).

To emphasize the point of the preceding remark consider the function graphed in Example 1 (in Section 10.2): $r = \theta$. It takes only a little thought to discern the nature of the curve in polar coordinates, a spiral of infinite extent. Now an explicit use of Eqs. (3) would give, as a rectangular equivalent of $r = \theta$, the equation

$$\pm\sqrt{x^2 + y^2} = \tan^{-1} \frac{y}{x} + n\pi, \qquad n = 0, \pm 1, \pm 1, \ldots .$$

But the somewhat ambiguous nature of the right-hand side suggests a different approach: we take the tangent of both sides *before* translating. This gives

$$\tan r = \tan \theta,$$

or using (3) and (2),

$$\tan \left(\pm\sqrt{x^2 + y^2}\right) = \frac{y}{x},$$

which can also be written

$$\tan \sqrt{x^2 + y^2} = \pm \frac{y}{x}. \tag{6}$$

It is hardly an understatement to say that the geometric nature of the curve described by (6) is not immediately apparent.

The translation from rectangular to polar coordinates can usually be achieved by means of Eqs. (1) and (2). Consider, for example, the parabola $y^2 = 4x$; using (1) we have

$$r^2 \sin^2 \theta = 4r \cos \theta.$$

We can safely divide by r since the pole also appears as $\left(0, \dfrac{\pi}{2}\right)$; this gives

$$r \sin^2 \theta = 4 \cos \theta;$$

or, solving for r,

$$r = \frac{4 \cos \theta}{\sin^2 \theta} = 4 \csc \theta \cot \theta.$$

(Is it " obvious " what sort of curve this equation represents?)

Finally, we consider the straight line $y = mx + b$. A direct use of Eqs. (1) gives

$$r \sin \theta = mr \cos \theta + b,$$

or

$$r(\sin \theta - m \cos \theta) = b.$$

Solving for r we have

$$r = \frac{b}{\sin \theta - m \cos \theta}.$$

In summary, we remark that it is frequently essential to be able to translate back and forth between polar and rectangular coordinates. A byproduct of our illustrations is a demonstration of the fact that certain curves are much more easily sketched in polar coordinates whereas other curves are more readily analyzed for their geometrical features in rectangular coordinates. This provides one answer to the question, " Why bother with a second coordinate system when we already have a perfectly good one?"

EXERCISES

In Exercises 1–10 translate to rectangular coordinates and sketch each curve from one of the two forms.

1. $r = 4 \sin \theta$.

2. $r = 1 - 2 \sin \theta$.

3. $r \cos \theta = 2$.

4. $r = \tan \theta$.

5. $r = \cos 2\theta$.

6. $r = 3 - \cos \theta$.

7. $r = \dfrac{2}{\sin \theta - \cos \theta}$.

8. $r = 2 \cos \theta - 4 \sin \theta$.

9. $r = \dfrac{1}{1 - \cos \theta}$.

10. $r = 4 \csc \theta$.

In Exercises 11–19 translate to polar coordinates, then draw a sketch of the curve, using whichever coordinate system seems preferable.

11. $y = 3\sqrt{x}$.

12. $y = 4x^2 + 8x + 5$.

13. $x^2 + y^2 - 2y = 0$.

14. $(x^2 + y^2 + 2y)^2 = 4(x^2 + y^2)$.

15. $2x - 3y + 4 = 0$.

16. $x^2 - y^2 = 1$.

17. $(x^2 + y^2)^2 = x^2 - y^2$.

18. $y = \dfrac{1}{x^2 + 1}$.

19. $x + y = 0$.

20. Transform $r = \sin 3\theta$ to rectangular coordinates. [*Hint.*

$$\sin 3\theta = \sin (2\theta + \theta)$$
$$= 3 \sin \theta - 4 \sin^3 \theta.]$$

21. Consider the *normal form* of the equation of a straight line

$$(\cos \omega)x + (\sin \omega)y - p = 0;$$

(see Figure 12). Show that the polar coordinate equation is

$$r = \frac{p}{\cos (\theta - \omega)}.$$

22. Let $f : \theta \to f(\theta)$, where f involves θ only in the form of $\cos \theta$ (e.g., $r = 1 + \cos \theta$). Use Eqs. (1) to show that the geometric effect of replacing $\cos \theta$ everywhere by $\sin \theta$ is a reflection in the line $\theta = \dfrac{\pi}{4}$ (or $y = x$).

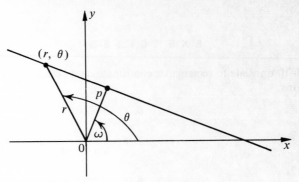

Figure 12

23. We turn our attention to a circle with center at $C(h, k) = C(c, \gamma)$ and radius a (see Figure 13). Use the law of cosines to show that in polar coordinates the equation is

$$r^2 - 2c \cos (\theta - \gamma)r = a^2 - c^2.$$

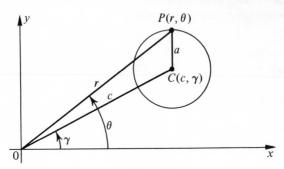

Figure 13

24. Sketch the *conchoid* $r = \sec \theta + 2$. [*Hints*. Consider

$$\lim_{\theta \to \pi/2} x = \lim_{\theta \to \pi/2} r \cos \theta.]$$

Also, find values of θ such that $r = 0$, $r > 0$, and $r < 0$.

25. Let $P_1(r_1, \theta_1)$ and $P_2(r_2, \theta_2)$ be two points. Show that the distance $\overline{P_1P_2}$ between them is given by

$$\overline{P_1P_2}^2 = r_1^2 + r_2^2 - 2r_1r_2 \cos (\theta_1 - \theta_2).$$

10.4 The Tangent Line to a Curve

As we might expect, the analytic description of the tangent line to a curve in polar coordinates is quite different from that in rectangular coordinates. In particular, if the curve is the graph of a function f, i.e., $f : \theta \to r = f(\theta)$, then $f'(\theta)$

measures the rate of change of $r = f(\theta)$ and need not be—and usually is not—the slope of the tangent to the curve at (r, θ). We shall find that the expression for the slope of the tangent is a bit more complicated than that.

There is however, a particular case which gives an immediate and very simple description of the tangent line: if $r = 0$ for $\theta = \theta_0$, i.e., if the curve comes in to the pole at an angle of θ_0, then the tangent to the curve at the pole is the line $\theta = \theta_0$. To see this, refer to Figure 14. We assume that θ_0 makes $r = 0$, and we describe the tangent line at $(0, \theta_0)$. If we pick a nearby point (r, θ) on the curve, then the slope of the tangent at the pole is

$$m_{\text{tan}} = \lim_{\theta \to \theta_0} \frac{y}{x} = \lim_{\theta \to \theta_0} \frac{r \sin \theta}{r \cos \theta} = \lim_{\theta \to \theta_0} \tan \theta = \tan \theta_0,$$

since the tangent is continuous at every point of its domain. Moreover, the assertion remains valid if θ_0 is an odd multiple of $\frac{\pi}{2}$.

Thus, in Example 2 (see Figure 8), where $r = 2 \cos \theta$, the curve comes into the pole for $\theta = \frac{\pi}{2}$. The line $\theta = \frac{\pi}{2}$ is, therefore, the tangent at $\left(0, \frac{\pi}{2}\right)$. Or, in Example 4, where the curve comes into the pole for $\theta = \frac{\pi}{3}$, $\theta = \frac{2\pi}{3}$, and $\theta = \pi$ (see Figure 10), we conclude that each of these lines is tangent to the curve at the pole.

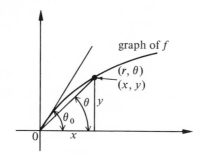

graph of f

(r, θ)

(x, y)

Figure 14

For the general case of the tangent to a curve we proceed as follows (see, however, Exercise 10). We assume the curve is the graph of a differentiable function f (of θ), and we exploit the relations (1) between polar and rectangular coordinates.

$$x = r \cos \theta = f(\theta) \cos \theta,$$
$$y = r \sin \theta = f(\theta) \sin \theta.$$

Then (see p. 219 in Section 4.5)

$$dx = dx(\theta, d\theta) = [-f(\theta) \sin \theta + f'(\theta) \cos \theta] \, d\theta,$$
$$dy = dy(\theta, d\theta) = [f(\theta) \cos \theta + f'(\theta) \sin \theta] \, d\theta.$$

Consequently the slope of the tangent to the curve is given by

$$\frac{dy}{dx} = \frac{[f(\theta)\cos\theta + f'(\theta)\sin\theta]\,d\theta}{[-f(\theta)\sin\theta + f'(\theta)\cos\theta]\,d\theta}$$

$$= \frac{f(\theta)\cos\theta + f'(\theta)\sin\theta}{-f(\theta)\sin\theta + f'(\theta)\cos\theta},$$

or

$$\frac{dy}{dx} = \frac{r\cos\theta + r'\sin\theta}{-r\sin\theta + r'\cos\theta}, \qquad \text{where} \quad r = f(\theta). \tag{7a}$$

If we assume $r'\cos\theta \neq 0$ we can change (7a) into a more revealing form by dividing numerator and denominator on the right by $r'\cos\theta$:

$$\frac{dy}{dx} = \frac{\dfrac{r}{r'} + \tan\theta}{-\dfrac{r}{r'}\tan\theta + 1}$$

or

$$\frac{dy}{dx} = \frac{\tan\psi + \tan\theta}{1 - \tan\psi\tan\theta}, \tag{7b}$$

where we let

$$\tan\psi = \frac{r}{r'}, \tag{8}$$

the nature of ψ to be explored shortly. Now, if we let α be the angle of inclination of the tangent line $(0 \leq \alpha < \pi)$ and if we recall that the right-hand side of (7b) is in the form of the tangent of the sum of ψ and θ, we can rewrite (7b) as

$$\tan\alpha = \tan(\psi + \theta). \tag{9}$$

From (9) we conclude that

$$\alpha = \psi + \theta \pm n\pi, \qquad n = 0, 1, 2, 3, \ldots. \tag{10}$$

Now we must investigate the angle ψ. Suppose we consider the sketch in Figure 15. From this drawing we observe that we can take ψ as the angle between the radial line OP and the "backward" side of the tangent. As we shall be able to prove later (see Section 11.9), this is typical: we can always take ψ, $0 \leq \psi \leq \pi$, between the radial line OP and the backward half of the tangent to the curve at P. Figure 16 shows another possible relation between α, ψ, and θ.

We give an illustration.

Example 5. Consider the curve defined by

$$r = 1 + 2\cos\theta.$$

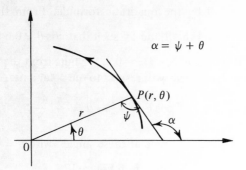

Figure 15

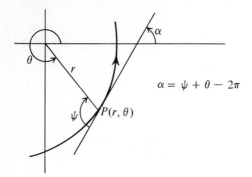

Figure 16

We calculate

$$r' = -2 \sin \theta,$$

and

$$\tan \psi = \frac{r}{r'} = \frac{1 + 2 \cos \theta}{-2 \sin \theta}.$$

By (7b) and the preceding equation we have

$$\frac{dy}{dx} = \frac{-\dfrac{1 + 2 \cos \theta}{2 \sin \theta} + \dfrac{\sin \theta}{\cos \theta}}{1 + \dfrac{1 + 2 \cos \theta}{2 \sin \theta} \dfrac{\sin \theta}{\cos \theta}} = \frac{-\cos \theta - 2 \cos^2 \theta + 2 \sin^2 \theta}{2 \sin \theta \cos \theta + \sin \theta + 2 \sin \theta \cos \theta},$$

or

$$\frac{dy}{dx} = -\frac{4 \cos^2 \theta + \cos \theta - 2}{\sin \theta (1 + 4 \cos \theta)}. \tag{11}$$

From (11) we see that $\dfrac{dy}{dx}$ does not exist for $\theta = 0$ and π and for the second and third quadrant angles for which $\cos \theta = -\frac{1}{4}$. Moreover, we can solve

$4 \cos^2 \theta + \cos \theta - 2 = 0$ by the quadratic formula. From this we learn that $\dfrac{dy}{dx} = 0$ for angles in quadrants I and IV such that $\cos \theta \approx 0.6$ and for angles in quadrants II and III such that $\cos \theta \approx -0.8$. We note from the original equation for r that the curve is symmetric with respect to the polar axis. Also,

$$r = 0 \Rightarrow \cos \theta = -\frac{1}{2} \Rightarrow \theta = \frac{2\pi}{3}, \frac{4\pi}{3}.$$

Thus the curve comes into the pole at these angles with $\theta = \dfrac{2\pi}{3}$ and $\theta = \dfrac{4\pi}{3}$ as tangent lines. The sketch of the curve is in Figure 17.

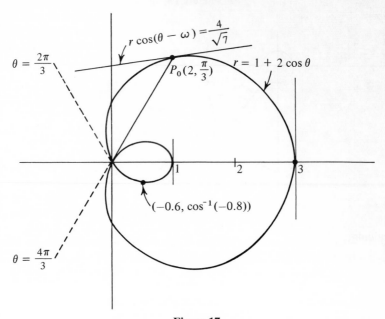

Figure 17

Example 6. This is a continuation of Example 5. We find the equation of the tangent line to the curve at the point $P_0\left(2, \dfrac{\pi}{3}\right)$. From (11) we compute

$$\left.\frac{dy}{dx}\right|_{\theta = \pi/3} = -\frac{1 + \frac{1}{2} - 2}{\dfrac{\sqrt{3}}{2}(1 + 2)} = \frac{\frac{1}{2}}{\dfrac{3\sqrt{3}}{2}} = \frac{\sqrt{3}}{9}.$$

In rectangular coordinates $P_0\left(2, \dfrac{\pi}{3}\right)$ is $P_0\left(2 \cos \dfrac{\pi}{3}, 2 \sin \dfrac{\pi}{3}\right)$ or $P_0(1, \sqrt{3})$. Thus the tangent line at P_0 is

$$y - \sqrt{3} = \frac{\sqrt{3}}{9}(x - 1),$$

or

$$x - 3\sqrt{3}\,y + 8 = 0,$$

which in polar coordinates becomes

$$r(\cos\theta - 3\sqrt{3}\sin\theta) + 8 = 0.$$

or $r\cos(\theta - \omega) = \dfrac{4}{\sqrt{7}}$, where $\cos\omega = \dfrac{-1}{2\sqrt{7}}$ (see Exercise 21 after Section 10.3).

EXERCISES

In Exercises 1–6 find the expression for the slope of the tangent line and for $\tan\psi$. Draw a sketch of the curve in each case. Also, find the (polar coordinate) equation of the tangent line to the curve at the given P_0.

1. $r = 2 + \cos\theta,\ P_0\left(\dfrac{5}{2}, \dfrac{\pi}{3}\right).$

4. $r = \cos\frac{1}{2}\theta,\ P_0\left(-\dfrac{1}{\sqrt{2}}, \dfrac{3\pi}{2}\right).$

2. $r = \dfrac{2}{1 + \sin\theta},\ P_0\left(\dfrac{4}{3}, \dfrac{5\pi}{6}\right).$

5. $r = \sec\theta,\ P_0\left(2, \dfrac{\pi}{3}\right).$

3. $r^2 = 4\cos 2\theta,\ P_0\left(\sqrt{2}, \dfrac{5\pi}{6}\right).$

6. $r = \tan\theta,\ P_0\left(1, \dfrac{\pi}{4}\right).$

7. In the text, in transforming Eq. (7a) to (7b) we assumed that $r'\cos\theta \neq 0$. Show that (10) remains valid even if $r'\cos\theta = 0$. [*Hints.* First of all, we assume $r \neq 0$ (if $r = 0$, the discussion at the beginning of the section applies). Secondly, consider the following cases

(i) $\cos\theta = 0,\ r' \neq 0$. Show $\theta = (2n+1)\dfrac{\pi}{2},\ |\alpha - \psi| = \dfrac{\pi}{2}$. Remember that

$\quad 0 \le \alpha < \pi,\ 0 \le \psi < \pi.$

(ii) $r' = 0,\ \cos\theta \neq 0$. Show $\psi = \dfrac{\pi}{2},\ \theta = \alpha + \dfrac{\pi}{2} + n\pi.$

(iii) $r' = 0,\ \cos\theta = 0$. Show $\alpha = 0,\ \psi = \dfrac{\pi}{2},\ \theta = (2n+1)\dfrac{\pi}{2}.\Big]$

8. Sketch each of the following curves with care.

(a) $r = 3 + 3\sin\theta.$ (c) $r = 3 + \sin\theta.$

(b) $r = 3 + 6\sin\theta.$ (d) $r = 4 + 3\sin\theta.$

[*Hints.*

1. Every curve is symmetric with respect to the $\dfrac{\pi}{2}$-axis.

1, Every curve is described completely for $0 \le \theta < 2\pi$.

3. Find values of θ such that $r = 0$.

4. Calculate the expression for $\dfrac{dy}{dx}$ and find θ such that $\dfrac{dy}{dx} = 0.$]

9. See Exercise 8. Consider $r = a + b \sin \theta$, where $a > 0$, $b > 0$. In particular, suppose $a > b$. Distinguish between the cases

   (i) $b < a < 2b$,   (ii) $a \geq 2b$.

   [*Hint.*   Consider the points where $\dfrac{dy}{dx} = 0$.]

10. Derive Eq. (7a) by considering the slope of the tangent at (r, θ) as $\lim\limits_{\Delta\theta \to 0} m_{\text{sec}}$, where m_{sec} is the slope of the line between (r, θ) and $(r + \Delta r, \theta + \Delta\theta)$. Here we let the values of r be determined by a differentiable function f. [*Hints.*   Use (1) in this chapter and Lemma 6.2.]

11. Use whatever techniques seem appropriate to sketch the following curves:

    (a) $r = a(\sec \theta - \cos \theta)$, the *cissoid of Diocles*.
        [*Hint.*   Consider $\lim\limits_{\theta \to \pi/2} x = \lim\limits_{\theta \to \pi/2} r \cos \theta$.]

    (b) $r = a \cos 2\theta$, the *strophoid*.

        [*Hint.*   See hint for part (a).]

    (c) $r = a \sin \theta \cos^2 \theta$, the *bifolium*.

    (d) $r = \csc \theta + 2$, the *conchoid of Nicomedes*.
        [*Hint.*   Consider $\lim\limits_{\theta \to 0} y = \lim\limits_{\theta \to 0} r \sin \theta$.]

    (e) $r = 2 \csc \theta + 1$.
        [*Hint.*   See hint for part (d).]

10.5   Area in Polar Coordinates

We saw in Section 10.4 that one of the fundamental geometric problems of calculus—finding slope of the tangent line to a curve—has quite a different solution in polar coordinates from the more familiar one in rectangular coordinates; in other words, if a curve is the graph of a function f (of θ), the slope of the tangent to the curve at (r, θ) is not given by $f'(\theta)$. This observation should prepare us for the fact that when we turn to another fundamental geometric problem of calculus—finding area bounded in part by a curve—the polar coordinate solution will be different from the rectangular coordinate solution; again, if the curve is the graph of a function f of (θ), the area will *not* be given by $\int_\alpha^\beta f(\theta)\, d\theta$.

In order to see how the nature of the coordinate system plays a role in the area problem we review briefly the approach to area in rectangular coordinates. Let the region involved have a boundary which includes the graph of a function f (of x), a segment $[a, b]$ of the x-axis, and vertical lines at $x = a$ and $x = b$ (see Figure 18).

The basic idea is to *approximate* the desired area by a sum of "elementary" areas, these being, in the case of rectangular coordinates, areas of rectangles.

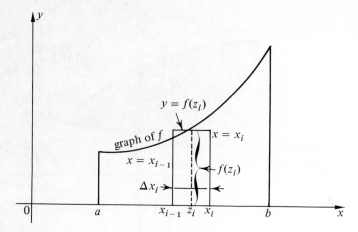

Figure 18

In particular, we form a partition of the interval $[a, b]$, the interval of the independent variable, use ordinates at the partition points to divide the region into subregions, and then use rectangular approximations for the areas of these subregions. Now, the ordinates which subdivide the region are in fact portions of one set of *coordinate curves*, the vertical lines $x = x_{i-1}$ and $x = x_i$; and the "tops" of the rectangles which we use for approximation purposes are in fact portions of the *other* set of coordinate curves, $y = f(z_i)$. By taking as known the usual formula for the area of a rectangle we complete our approximation as

$$A \approx \sum_{i=1}^{n} f(z_i) \, \Delta x_i,$$

and go on, by the usual limiting process, to the integral $\int_a^b f(x) \, dx$.

We propose now to try to follow the same procedure, making the modifications suggested by the use of polar coordinates. Suppose, then, we consider a curve which is the graph of a function f (of θ—to indicate the use of polar coordinates) and a region of the plane bounded by the lines $\theta = \alpha$ and $\theta = \beta$ ($\alpha < \beta$) and the portion of the curve for the θ interval $[\alpha, \beta]$ (see Figure 19). Our aim is to develop a measure of the area of the region (the shaded part in Figure 19).

We begin by forming a partition of the interval $[\alpha, \beta]$:

$$\{\alpha = \theta_0 < \theta_1 < \theta_2 < \cdots < \theta_{i-1} < \theta_i < \cdots < \theta_n = \beta\}.$$

The coordinate curves $\theta = \theta_i$, $i = 0, 1, \ldots, n$, provide us with a subdivision of the original area (just as do the vertical lines $y = x_i$ in the case of rectangular coordinates). We show a typical subdivision in Figure 20.

Still following the pattern of rectangular coordinates, we choose, quite arbitrarily, a number $\varphi_i \in [\theta_{i-1}, \theta_i]$ in each subinterval and, evaluating f at φ_i, use the coordinate curve—in this case an arc of a circle—$r = f(\varphi_i)$ as the outer boundary for the approximating part. In this way the approximating pieces become sectors of circles, each with central angle $\Delta\theta_i = \theta_i - \theta_{i-1}$ and radius $f(\varphi_i)$. Now, as we shall show below, the area of a sector of a circle with central

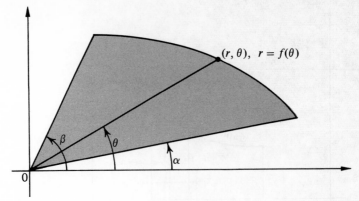

Figure 19

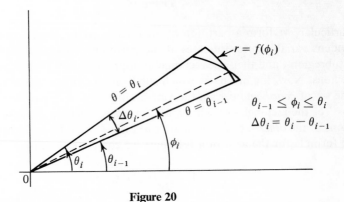

Figure 20

angle γ and radius a is $\frac{1}{2}a^2\gamma$. Thus the sum of the areas of the approximating pieces—and hence our approximation, corresponding to the partition of $[\alpha, \beta]$ and the choice of the φ_i—is

$$\sum_{i=1}^{n} \frac{1}{2} (f(\varphi_i))^2 \, \Delta\theta_i.$$

If f is continuous or monotonic or piecewise continuous or piecewise monotonic on $[\alpha, \beta]$, then $g = \frac{1}{2}f^2$ will have at least one of these properties and hence will be integrable.

With the preceding discussion as motivation, it is natural, then, to make the following definition.

Definition 1. *Let f be a function which is piecewise continuous or piecewise monotonic and let R be a region of the plane bounded by the lines $\theta = \alpha$ and $\theta = \beta$ ($\alpha < \beta$) and by the graph of f (in polar coordinates) for $\theta \in [\alpha, \beta]$. Then **the area of R** is*

$$A = \int_{\alpha}^{\beta} \frac{1}{2} (f(\theta))^2 \, d\theta = \int_{\alpha}^{\beta} \frac{1}{2} r^2 \, d\theta. \qquad (12)$$

Before looking at some examples we give the promised proof about the area of a sector of a circle.

Lemma 1. *The area of a sector of a circle of radius a, determined by a central angle γ, is $\frac{1}{2}a^2\gamma$.*

Proof. Consider Figure 21. We divide the desired area A into the two parts A_1 and A_2 ($A = A_1 + A_2$) and, noting that the region for A_1 is a triangle, so that $A_1 = \frac{1}{2}(a\cos\gamma)(a\sin\gamma) = \frac{1}{4}a^2\sin 2\gamma$, we concentrate on A_2. Now

$$A_2 = \int_{a\cos\gamma}^{a} \sqrt{a^2 - x^2}\, dx.$$

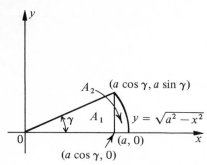

Figure 21

We integrate this by a trigonometric substitution, letting

$$x = a\cos\theta, \quad 0 \le \theta \le \frac{\pi}{2}$$

$$dx = -a\sin\theta\, d\theta$$

$$\sqrt{a^2 - x^2} = \sqrt{a^2\sin^2\theta} = a\sin\theta.$$

Then $x = a\cos\gamma \Rightarrow a\cos\theta = a\cos\gamma \Rightarrow \theta = \gamma$, and $x = a \Rightarrow a\cos\theta = a \Rightarrow \cos\theta = 1 \Rightarrow \theta = 0$. Thus,

$$A_2 = \int_{\gamma}^{0} a\sin\theta(-a\sin\theta)\, d\theta = a^2 \int_{0}^{\gamma} \sin^2\theta\, d\theta$$

$$= \frac{1}{2}a^2 \int_{0}^{\gamma}(1 - \cos 2\theta)\, d\theta = \frac{1}{2}a^2\left(\theta - \frac{1}{2}\sin 2\theta\right)\Big|_{0}^{\gamma}$$

$$= \frac{1}{2}a^2\gamma - \frac{1}{4}a^2\sin 2\gamma.$$

Combining this result with the preceding one for A_1, we have $A = A_1 + A_2 = \frac{1}{4}a^2\sin 2\gamma + \frac{1}{2}a^2\gamma - \frac{1}{4}a^2\sin 2\gamma = \frac{1}{2}a^2\gamma$. ∎

We now look at an extremely simple example.

Example 7. We show that by Definition 1 the area of a right triangle of base a and height b is $A = \frac{1}{2}ab$ (see Figure 22).

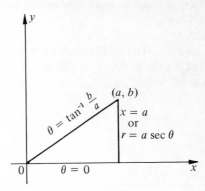

Figure 22

By Definition 1, the desired area is

$$A = \frac{1}{2} \int_0^{\tan^{-1} b/a} r^2 \, d\theta,$$

where $r = a \sec \theta$. Thus

$$A = \frac{1}{2} \int_0^{\tan^{-1} b/a} a^2 \sec^2 \theta \, d\theta = \frac{1}{2} a^2 \tan \theta \Big|_0^{\tan^{-1} b/a}$$

$$= \frac{1}{2} a^2 \left(\frac{b}{a}\right)$$

$$= \frac{1}{2} ab.$$

From this result it follows immediately that, by Definition 1, the area of a rectangle of sides a and b is $A = ab$.

Now, it may seem a bit foolish to take time to work out the details of a simple (and *known*) result such as that of Example 7. But the fact is that this result and that of Lemma 1 have a bearing on the following question. Suppose one uses rectangular coordinates and the usual technique to find the area of a plane region R; then one shifts to polar coordinates and finds the area of R by Definition 1. Will the two results agree? Without going into this in detail, we remark that Lemma 1 uses rectangular coordinates to find the area of an *elementary* region for polar coordinates, whereas Example 7 guarantees that the polar coordinate method gives the correct result for the area of an elementary region (a rectangle) for rectangular coordinates. These facts suggest that the two methods will produce the same answer to a given problem.

Example 8. We find the area enclosed by the cardioid $r = a(1 + \cos \theta)$ (Figure 23).

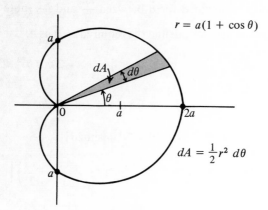

Figure 23

By (12), the area A is given by

$$A = \frac{1}{2} \int_0^{2\pi} a^2 (1 + \cos \theta)^2 \, d\theta$$

$$= \frac{1}{2} a^2 \int_0^{2\pi} (1 + 2 \cos \theta + \cos^2 \theta) \, d\theta$$

$$= \frac{1}{2} a^2 \int_0^{2\pi} \left[1 + 2 \cos \theta + \frac{1}{2} (1 + \cos 2\theta) \right] d\theta$$

$$= \frac{1}{2} a^2 \left(\frac{3}{2} \theta + 2 \sin \theta + \frac{1}{4} \sin 2\theta \right) \Big|_0^{2\pi}$$

$$= \frac{3\pi a^2}{2}.$$

Note that the symmetry of the curve with respect to the polar axis would enable us to find the area as

$$A = 2 \int_0^\pi \frac{1}{2} r^2 \, d\theta = \int_0^\pi a^2 (1 + \cos \theta)^2 \, d\theta.$$

In Figure 23 we show an "element of area," the shaded portion. Intuitively, it is often convenient to think of the integral as summing up all these elements of area to give the desired answer.

In rectangular coordinates one must be concerned about the sign of the functional values. Because of the nature of the integrand in Eq. (12) no such problem arises in polar coordinates.

Example 9. We find the area of the small inner loop in the limaçon $r = a(1 + 2\cos\theta)$, shown in Figure 24.

The inner loop is obtained for θ between $\dfrac{2\pi}{3}$ and $\dfrac{4\pi}{3}$ (note that $r \leq 0$ here), but, using the symmetry, we can find the required area as

$$A = 2\int_{2\pi/3}^{\pi} \frac{1}{2}r^2\,d\theta = a^2\int_{2\pi/3}^{\pi}(1 + 2\cos\theta)^2\,d\theta$$

$$= a^2\int_{2\pi/3}^{\pi}(1 + 4\cos\theta + 4\cos^2\theta)\,d\theta$$

$$= a^2[\theta + 4\sin\theta + 2\theta + \sin 2\theta]\,|_{2\pi/3}^{\pi}$$

$$= a^2\left[\pi + 2\pi - \left(\frac{2\pi}{3} + 2\sqrt{3} + \frac{4\pi}{3} - \frac{\sqrt{3}}{2}\right)\right]$$

$$= a^2\left(3\pi - 2\pi - \frac{3}{2}\sqrt{3}\right) = a^2\left(\pi - \frac{3\sqrt{3}}{2}\right)$$

$$\approx 0.54a^2.$$

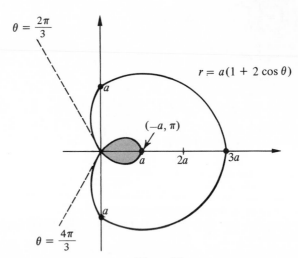

$\theta = \dfrac{2\pi}{3}$

$r = a(1 + 2\cos\theta)$

$(-a, \pi)$

a $2a$ $3a$

$\theta = \dfrac{4\pi}{3}$

Figure 24

Example 10. We find the area common to the circle $r = 2\sin\theta$ and the cardioid, $r = 1 + \cos\theta$ (see Figure 25).

To find the points of intersection we solve the two equations simultaneously, equating the expressions for r:

$$1 + \cos\theta = 2\sin\theta.$$

Squaring and converting $\sin^2\theta$ to $1 - \cos^2\theta$ gives

$$1 + 2\cos\theta + \cos^2\theta = 4 - 4\cos^2\theta,$$

or

$$5 \cos^2 \theta + 2 \cos \theta - 3 = 0,$$

or

$$(5 \cos \theta - 3)(\cos \theta + 1) = 0.$$

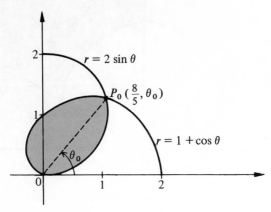

Figure 25

Thus the curves intersect at the pole ($\theta = \pi$) and at P_0 ($\frac{8}{5}$, θ_0), where $\cos \theta_0 = \frac{3}{5}$. The outer boundary of the area is the circle for $\theta \in [0, \theta_0]$ and is the cardioid for $\theta \in [\theta_0, \pi]$. Thus the desired area A is given by

$$A = \frac{1}{2} \int_0^{\theta_0} 4 \sin^2 \theta \, d\theta + \frac{1}{2} \int_{\theta_0}^{\pi} (1 + \cos \theta)^2 \, d\theta.$$

We leave it as an exercise for the student to show that

$$A = \tfrac{1}{4} (3\pi + \cos^{-1} \tfrac{3}{5}) - \tfrac{7}{5} \approx 1.19 \text{ square units.}$$

Example 11. We find the area inside the circle $r = 3 \sin \theta$ and outside the cardioid $r = 1 + \sin \theta$. The sketch is in Figure 26.

From the equations we note that both curves are symmetric with respect to the line $\theta = \frac{\pi}{2}$. To find the points of intersection we solve the equations simultaneously:

$$3 \sin \theta = 1 + \sin \theta,$$

whence $\sin \theta = \frac{1}{2}$, or $\theta = \frac{\pi}{6}, \frac{5\pi}{6}$, the value of r being $\frac{3}{2}$. (Notice, by the way, that the two curves also intersect at the pole, although the simultaneous solution did not disclose this fact. The reason for this is that the circle comes in to the pole at $\theta = 0$ and $\theta = \pi$, whereas the cardioid comes in to the pole at $\theta = \frac{3\pi}{2}$. This—the occurrence of points of intersection which do not show up when

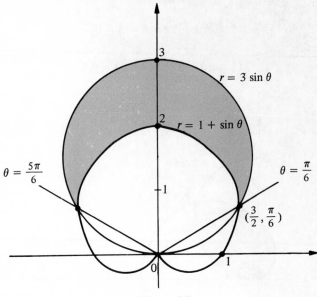

Figure 26

equations are solved simultaneously—is due to the fact that a point has many sets of coordinates. The student must be alert for this possibility.)

To return to the area problem, we make use of the symmetry and concentrate on the first quadrant; the desired area will be found by doubling the area in the first quadrant. Suppose we let r_1 be the r of the circle, r_2 that of the cardioid. Then

$$A = 2 \left[\int_{\pi/6}^{\pi/2} \frac{1}{2} r_1^2 \, d\theta - \int_{\pi/6}^{\pi/2} \frac{1}{2} r_2^2 \, d\theta \right]$$

$$= \int_{\pi/6}^{\pi/2} (r_1^2 - r_2^2) \, d\theta = \int_{\pi/6}^{\pi/2} (9 \sin^2 \theta - 1 - 2 \sin \theta - \sin^2 \theta) \, d\theta$$

$$= \int_{\pi/6}^{\pi/2} (8 \sin^2 \theta - 2 \sin \theta - 1) \, d\theta = \int_{\pi/6}^{\pi/2} (4 - 4 \cos 2\theta - 2 \sin \theta - 1) \, d\theta$$

$$= 3\theta - 2 \sin 2\theta + 2 \cos \theta \, |_{\pi/6}^{\pi/2}$$

$$= \frac{3\pi}{2} - \left(\frac{\pi}{2} - \sqrt{3} + \sqrt{3} \right)$$

$$= \pi \text{ square units.}$$

E X E R C I S E S

In Exercises 1–10 find the area of the region described.

1. Inside the limaçon $r = a(1 - 2 \cos \theta)$ but outside the small inner loop.

2. Inside one leaf of the rose $r = a \sin 3\theta$.

3. Within the lemniscate $r^2 = a^2 \cos 2\theta$.

4. Inside the limaçon $r = 4 + 3 \cos \theta$.

5. Outside the cardioid $r = 1 - \sin \theta$ and inside the circle $r = -3 \sin \theta$.

6. Inside the cardioid $r = 1 - \sin \theta$ and outside the circle $r = -3 \sin \theta$.

7. Inside the lemniscate $r^2 = 4 \cos 2\theta$ but outside the rose $r = 2 \cos 2\theta$.

8. Inside the lemniscate $r^2 = 2 \cos 2\theta$ but outside the rose $r = 2 \cos 2\theta$.

9. Common to the circle $r = -4 \cos \theta$ and the cardioid $r = 2 - 2 \sin \theta$.

10. Common to the circles $r = 2 \cos \theta$ and $r = -4 \sin \theta$.

11. Find the area bounded by the parabola $r = \dfrac{2}{1 + \cos \theta}$ and the line $\theta = \dfrac{\pi}{2}$.

$$\left[Hint. \quad \frac{1}{2}(1 + \cos \theta) = \cos^2 \frac{\theta}{2}. \right]$$

12. Find the area of Exercise 11 by translating to rectangular coordinates.

13. Find the area bounded by the loop of the strophoid,

$$r = a \cos 2\theta \sec \theta.$$

(See Exercise 11b after Section 10.4.)

14. Find the area enclosed by the bifolium,

$$r = a \sin \theta \cos^2 \theta.$$

(See Exercise 11c after Section 10.4.]

10.6   The Conic Sections (1)

In this section we introduce a family of curves which have been studied in various ways since the days of classical Greece. The reason for the name of the family, the conic sections, will be made clear a little later.

The definition of the conic section curves which is most convenient in terms of polar coordinates (alternate definitions will be introduced subsequently) involves a fixed point, the *focus*, a fixed line, the *directrix*, which does not go through the focus, and a positive number, the *eccentricity*. It is customary to denote the eccentricity by the letter e; this usage opens the possibility of confusion with the base e of natural logarithms, but in fact the context usually makes it clear which number is intended when e is used.

Definition 2. *Let l be a fixed line, F a fixed point not on l, and let e > 0 be a fixed number. The set of points*

$$\left\{ P \;\middle|\; \frac{\overline{PF}}{d(P,\,l)} = e \right\}$$

*is called a **conic section curve**. By d(P, l) we mean the perpendicular distance from P to the line l.*

To obtain the polar coordinate equation of a conic section curve we take the focus at the pole and the directrix perpendicular to the polar axis and $2p$ units to the left of the line $\theta = \dfrac{\pi}{2}$ (thus the directrix is the line $r \cos\theta + 2p = 0$, where $p > 0$) (see Figure 27).

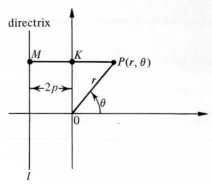

Figure 27

Let $P(r, \theta)$ be a point on the curve. Then, by Definition 2,

$$\frac{\overline{OP}}{\overline{PM}} = e,$$

i.e.,

$$r = e\,\overline{PM} = e(\overline{PK} + \overline{KM}),$$

or

$$r = e(r \cos\theta + 2p).$$

Solving for r, we have

$$r = \frac{2ep}{1 - e \cos\theta}. \tag{13}$$

We shall consistently work with the form given in (13). However, it is not hard to see that several variations are possible. For example, if we took the focus at the pole but took the directrix perpendicular to the polar axis and $2p$ units to the *right* of $\theta = \dfrac{\pi}{2}$ (i.e., l is $r \cos \theta - 2p = 0$), then the equation would be

$$r = \frac{2ep}{1 + e \cos \theta}. \tag{14}$$

Or, by taking the directrix parallel to and either $2p$ units below or $2p$ units above the polar axis, the focus still being at the pole, one would obtain

$$r = \frac{2ep}{1 - e \sin \theta} \tag{15}$$

or

$$r = \frac{2ep}{1 + e \sin \theta}, \tag{16}$$

respectively.

From Eq. (13) we see that the curves are symmetric with respect to the polar axis, that the complete curve is obtained for $0 \le \theta < 2\pi$, that $r \ne 0$ for all admissible θ, and that r remains bounded or gets arbitrarily large, depending upon whether $1 - e \cos \theta \ne 0$ for all admissible θ, or $1 - e \cos \theta = 0$ for some θ. But this last equation holds $\Leftrightarrow \cos \theta = \dfrac{1}{e}$. Thus this last characteristic (boundedness or unboundedness) depends upon e. We consider three cases: (1) $e = 1$, (2) $e < 1$, and (3) $e > 1$.

(1) If $e = 1$, Eq. (13) becomes

$$r = \frac{2p}{1 - \cos \theta}; \tag{17}$$

clearly we must have $\theta \ne 0$, i.e., we take $0 < \theta < 2\pi$. To obtain further information about the curve we use (8) to find $\tan \psi$. We first calculate $r' = \dfrac{dr}{d\theta}$:

$$r' = -2p(1 - \cos \theta)^{-2} \sin \theta = \frac{-2p \sin \theta}{(1 - \cos \theta)^2}.$$

Thus

$$\tan \psi = \frac{r}{r'} = \frac{1 - \cos \theta}{-\sin \theta}.$$

A few values of r and $\tan \psi$ will aid in obtaining a sketch:

θ	r	$\tan \psi$	ψ
$\dfrac{\pi}{2}$	$2p$	-1	$\dfrac{3\pi}{4}$
π	p	—	$\dfrac{\pi}{2}$

Using this table and the symmetry with respect to the polar axis, we obtain a partial sketch, as shown in Figure 28.

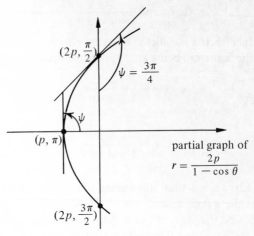

Figure 28

A question arises about the behavior of the curve as $\theta \to 0^+$. Clearly $r \to \infty$, but that does not settle the matter. What may help is information about the *ordinate* as $\theta \to 0^+$. Thus we consider $\lim\limits_{\theta \to 0^+} y$. Since

$$y = r \sin \theta = \frac{2p}{1 - \cos \theta} \sin \theta$$

$$= 2p \frac{\sin \theta}{1 - \cos \theta} \cdot \frac{1 + \cos \theta}{1 + \cos \theta}$$

$$= 2p \frac{\sin \theta (1 + \cos \theta)}{1 - \cos^2 \theta}$$

$$= 2p \frac{1 + \cos \theta}{\sin \theta},$$

we see that $\lim\limits_{\theta \to 0^+} y = \infty$. In fact, the last form for y shows that as θ decreases from π to 0, y increases from $2p$, getting big beyond all bounds (see Figure 29). The curve is a *parabola*.

Suppose we transform Eq. (17) to rectangular coordinates; we can write it as

$$r - r \cos \theta = 2p,$$

or

$$r = x + 2p;$$

squaring

$$r^2 = (x + 2p)^2,$$

or

$$x^2 + y^2 = x^2 + 4px + 4p^2.$$

Thus

$$y^2 = 4p(x + p). \tag{18}$$

From this we see that, since $y^2 \geq 0$, we must have $x \geq -p$. Also, differentiating Eq. (18) (implicitly), we have

$$2yy' = 4p,$$

so

$$y' = \frac{2p}{y}.$$

This shows that $y > 0 \Rightarrow y' > 0$, $y < 0 \Rightarrow y' < 0$; if $y = 0$, the tangent to the curve is vertical (see Figure 29). Some properties of the parabola will be brought out in the exercises which follow.

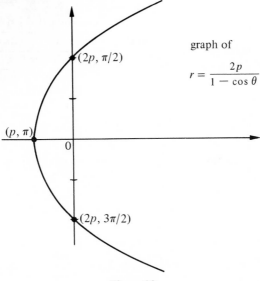

graph of

$$r = \frac{2p}{1 - \cos \theta}$$

Figure 29

The discussion of the cases $e \neq 1$ can be done more efficiently if we utilize the fact that some of the analysis of the curves does not depend upon distinguishing between $e < 1$ and $e > 1$. In particular, this applies to the calculation of r', $\tan \psi$, and $\dfrac{dy}{dx}$, which we now proceed to find.

From

$$r = \frac{2ep}{1 - e \cos \theta},$$

we find

$$r' = -2ep(1 - e \cos \theta)^{-2}(e \sin \theta)$$

$$= \frac{-2e^2 p \sin \theta}{(1 - e \cos \theta)^2}.$$

Thus

$$\tan \psi = \frac{r}{r'} = \frac{\dfrac{2ep}{1 - e \cos \theta}}{\dfrac{-2e^2 p \sin \theta}{(1 - e \cos \theta)^2}},$$

or

$$\tan \psi = \frac{1 - e \cos \theta}{-e \sin \theta} = \frac{\dfrac{1}{e} - \cos \theta}{-\sin \theta}. \tag{19}$$

Also,

$$\frac{dy}{dx} = \tan \alpha = \frac{\tan \psi + \tan \theta}{1 - \tan \psi \tan \theta} = \frac{\dfrac{1 - e \cos \theta}{-e \sin \theta} + \dfrac{\sin \theta}{\cos \theta}}{1 + \dfrac{1 - e \cos \theta}{e \sin \theta} \dfrac{\sin \theta}{\cos \theta}},$$

or

$$\frac{dy}{dx} = \frac{e - \cos \theta}{\sin \theta}. \tag{20}$$

Before obtaining sketches of the curves we transform the equation to the cartesian form. From

$$r = \frac{2ep}{1 - e \cos \theta}$$

we have $r - er \cos \theta = 2ep$, or

$$r = e(x + 2p).$$

Squaring this equation and then replacing r^2 by $x^2 + y^2$, we have

$$x^2 + y^2 = e^2(x^2 + 4px + 4p^2),$$

or

$$(1 - e^2)x^2 + y^2 - 4e^2px - 4e^2p^2 = 0. \tag{21}$$

This equation, like that in (18), is a second degree equation in x and y. Note that if $e < 1$ the coefficients of x^2 and y^2 will both be positive, whereas if $e > 1$ the second degree terms will be of opposite sign. We shall return to this remark and to Eq. (21) a little later.

(2) We now consider $0 < e < 1$. The basic equation (13) can be written

$$r = \frac{2p}{\dfrac{1}{e} - \cos \theta}. \tag{22}$$

It follows, since $\dfrac{1}{e} > 1$, that r remains bounded for all θ, $0 \le \theta < 2\pi$. In fact, the maximum value of r is easily seen to occur when $\cos \theta$ is a maximum, i.e., when $\theta = 0$; then $r_{max} = \dfrac{2ep}{1 - e}$.

From Eq. (20) we see that the tangent line to the curve is vertical when $\theta = 0$ and $\theta = \pi$; the tangent is horizontal when $\cos \theta = e$; and that, for $0 < \theta < \pi$, when $\sin \theta > 0$, the tangent has negative slope if $\cos \theta > e$, positive slope if $\cos \theta < e$. Using this information and the symmetry with respect to the polar axis, we can sketch the curve as in Figure 30.

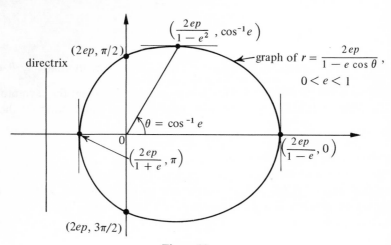

Figure 30

(3) If $e > 1$, then a glance at the equation in the form displayed in Eq. (22) shows that $|r|$ increases beyond bounds for θ in the vicinity of those values for which $\cos \theta = \dfrac{1}{e}$. From (20) we see that $\dfrac{dy}{dx}$ does not exist when $\theta = 0$ and $\theta = \pi$—the tangent line is vertical for these points. From the same equation we observe that the tangent line is never horizontal and that the slope of the tangent line is positive exactly when $\sin \theta$ is:

$$0 < \theta < \pi \Rightarrow \frac{dy}{dx} > 0,$$

$$\pi < \theta < 2\pi \Rightarrow \frac{dy}{dx} < 0.$$

For the remainder of this discussion suppose we let $p = 1$, $e = 2$, so that we are considering

$$r = \frac{4}{1 - 2 \cos \theta}.$$

We look at the way in which r varies with θ, as described in Table 10.3.

TABLE 10.3

θ	r
$0 \to \dfrac{\pi}{3}$	$-4 \to -\infty$
$\dfrac{\pi}{3} \to \dfrac{\pi}{2}$	$+\infty \to 4$
$\dfrac{\pi}{2} \to \pi$	$4 \to \dfrac{4}{3}$

Now it would seem that the lines $\theta = \dfrac{\pi}{3}$ and $\theta = \dfrac{5\pi}{3}$ $\left(\text{or, alternatively, } \theta = -\dfrac{\pi}{3}\right)$ are asymptotes for the curve. This, however, is not the case: the asymptotes are in fact lines parallel to the ones just mentioned but intersecting on the polar axis at the point $\left(\dfrac{8}{3}, \pi\right)$. The curve, a *hyperbola*, sketched by using the information detailed above, is shown in Figure 31.

Notice that both the hyperbola in Figure 31 and the ellipse in Figure 30 have a vertical axis of symmetry, as well as a horizontal one (the polar axis). This observation suggests that these curves would have *two* foci and *two* directrices, which is indeed so. Proof of this assertion will be made later in terms of cartesian coordinates.

E X E R C I S E S

In Exercises 1–12 sketch each of the curves. It may help to write the equation in one of the forms $r = \dfrac{2ep}{1 \pm e \cos \theta}$ or $r = \dfrac{2ep}{1 \pm e \sin \theta}$.

1. $r = \dfrac{1}{2 - \cos \theta}$.   **2.** $r + r \cos \theta = 2$.

3. $r - r \sin \theta = 4$.   **4.** $2r + r \sin \theta = 2$.

5. $r = \dfrac{6}{3 + 2 \sin \theta}$.   **6.** $10r + r \cos \theta = 1$.

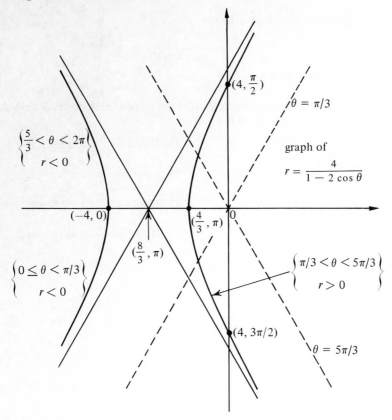

Figure 31

7. $r = \dfrac{9}{10 + 9 \cos \theta}$.

8. $r = 4 - 2r \sin \theta$.

9. $r = \dfrac{8}{1 + 2 \cos \theta}$.

10. $r = \dfrac{10}{1 - 5 \sin \theta}$.

11. $r + 3r \sin \theta = 12$.

12. $9r - 10r \cos \theta = 20$.

13. Sketch on the same axes the graph of

$$r = \frac{4}{1 - e \cos \theta}$$

for $e = \frac{5}{4}, \frac{3}{2}, 3$, and 5.

14. Sketch on the same axes the graph of

$$r = \frac{2p}{1 - \cos \theta}$$

for $p = \frac{1}{4}, \frac{1}{2}, 1$ and 4.

15. Sketch on the same axes the graph of

$$r = \frac{4}{1 - e \cos \theta}$$

for $e = \frac{1}{100}, \frac{1}{10}, \frac{1}{4}, \frac{3}{4}$, and $\frac{9}{10}$.

In Exercises 16–23 find the equation of each of the conic section curves described, and sketch. In each case the focus is at the pole.

16. Directrix: $r = 3 \csc \theta$, $e = 1$.   **17.** Directrix: $r = -2 \sec \theta$, $e = \frac{1}{2}$.

18. Directrix: $r = -4 \csc \theta$, $e = 0.01$.   **19.** Directrix: $r = \sec \theta$, $e = \frac{4}{5}$.

20. Directrix: $r = -2 \csc \theta$, $e = \frac{1}{3}$.   **21.** Directrix: $r = 2 \csc \theta$, $e = \frac{7}{4}$.

22. Directrix: $r = -4 \sec \theta$, $e = \frac{5}{3}$.   **23.** Directrix: $r = 2 \sec \theta$, $e = \frac{5}{2}$.

24. Consider a point $P(r, \theta)$ on the parabola

$$r = \frac{2p}{1 - \cos \theta},$$

where $0 < \theta < \pi$. Show that

$$\tan \alpha = \tan \frac{\theta}{2}$$

(identity 19 in Section 6.1 may help), and hence $\alpha = \frac{\theta}{2}$. From this, show that, using the notation indicated in Figure 32, $\beta = \alpha = \frac{\theta}{2}$. This says that the tangent to the curve makes equal angles with OP, the *focal radius*, and with the horizontal line through P. This is the reflector property of the parabola which is the basis for parabolic mirrors and reflectors—a source of light at the focus will be reflected horizontally by a parabolic reflector.

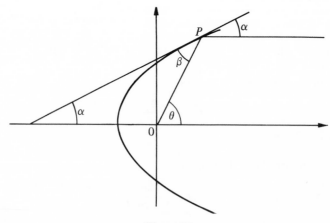

Figure 32

25. Consider the parabola

$$r = \frac{2p}{1 - \cos \theta};$$

let $\theta = \theta_0$, where $0 < \theta_0 < \pi$, be a line through the focus. The segment of this line cut off by the parabola is a *focal chord*. Show that the length of a focal chord is $4p \csc^2 \theta_0$. [*Hint.* The two points of intersection of $\theta = \theta_0$ with the parabola are found by using θ_0 and $\theta_0 + \pi$.]

26. This refers to Exercise 25. Show that the tangents to the parabola at the ends of a focal chord intersect *orthogonally*, i.e., at right angles. If you really want to show off, prove that this point of intersection lies on the directrix.

27. Let e satisfy $0 < e < 1$ so that the equation

$$r = \frac{2ep}{1 - e \cos \theta} \tag{23}$$

defines an ellipse. The points A and P, determined so that A is the point of the ellipse farthest from the focus (the pole) and P the point closest to the focus, are called, respectively, the *aphelion* and the *perihelion*. (These names are related to the fact that the orbit of a planet is an ellipse with the sun as focus.)

(a) Find A and P for the ellipse in (23).

(b) Show that

$$\frac{\overline{OA} - \overline{OP}}{\overline{OA} + \overline{OP}} = e.$$

10.7   The Conic Sections (2)

In this section we continue our discussion of the conic section curves. It turns out that there are certain things which need to be said about these curves which are most effectively said in terms of rectangular coordinates.

We begin with a brief look at the parabola ($e = 1$), our starting point being Eq. (18):

$$y^2 = 4p(x + p).$$

If we let

$$h = -p$$

$$k = 0$$

and

$$\begin{cases} x' = x - h \\ y' = y - k \end{cases}, \tag{24}$$

then Eq. (18) becomes

$$y'^2 = 4px'. \tag{25}$$

The geometric effect of the substitution (24) is to move the origin to the point (h, k), at the same time introducing new axes *parallel to the original axes* (in the present case, $k = 0$, the new x'-axis coincides with the original x-axis). Once this has been done each point in the plane will have two sets of coordinates, the relations between these sets being given by Eq. (24) and the companion equations

$$\begin{cases} x = x' + h \\ y = y' + k \end{cases}. \qquad (26)$$

For example, the focus—$(0, 0)$ in the original—becomes $(p, 0)$ in the new, and the directrix—$x + 2p = 0$ in the original—becomes $x' + p = 0$ in the new (see Figure 33).

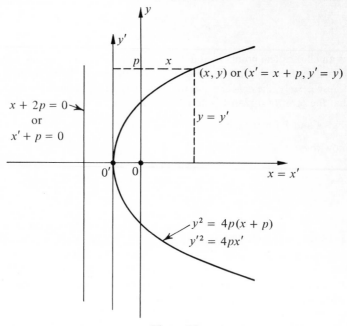

Figure 33

One of the chief purposes of such a change of coordinates—called a *translation of coordinates*—is to simplify the equation of the curve. To be sure, in the case just considered little simplification was achieved. Rather more is gained in the case of the ellipse and hyperbola, to which we turn shortly.

First, however, we summarize briefly some of the important facts about the parabola. Every parabola has one axis of symmetry, perpendicular to the directrix, and on which the focus lies. The point of intersection of the curve with its axis of symmetry is called the *vertex*.

If the vertex is at $V(h, k)$, and the axis of symmetry is $y = k$, the equation of the parabola is $(y - k)^2 = 4p(x - h)$; if the vertex is at $V(h, k)$, and the axis of symmetry is the vertical line $x = h$, the equation will be $(x - h)^2 = 4p(y - k)$.

These equations are of the forms

$$Cy^2 + Dx + Ey + F = 0$$

and

$$Ax^2 + Dx + Ey + F = 0,$$

respectively.

Given an equation of either of these types one can, by completing the square in the variable which has a second degree term, convert the equation to one of the standard forms just mentioned, from which it is easy to read the coordinates of the vertex and the equation of the axis of symmetry.

Example 12. Consider

$$y^2 - 3x + 2y - 8 = 0.$$

We complete the square in y:

$$y^2 + 2y + 1 = 3x + 8 + 1,$$

or

$$(y + 1)^2 = 3(x + 3).$$

Thus the vertex is $V(-3, -1)$; $4p = 3$, so $p = \frac{3}{4}$; the axis of symmetry is $y = -1$; and the focus is $F(-3 + \frac{3}{4}, -1) = F(-\frac{9}{4}, -1)$. Notice that setting $x = 0$ in the original equation gives $y^2 + 2y - 8 = 0$ or $(y + 4)(y - 2) = 0$; thus the y-intercepts are $(0, 2)$ and $(0, -4)$.

By setting $x + 3 = x'$ and $y + 1 = y'$, we could write the equation of the curve as

$$y'^2 = 3x'.$$

The graph is shown in Figure 34.

For the ellipse we take Eq. (21) in the preceding section as our starting point:

$$(1 - e^2)x^2 - 4e^2px + y^2 = 4e^2pe, \qquad 0 < e < 1.$$

If we complete the square, we obtain (the omitted algebra is not difficult)

$$\frac{\left(x - \dfrac{2e^2p}{1 - e^2}\right)^2}{\dfrac{4e^2p^2}{(1 - e^2)^2}} + \frac{y^2}{\dfrac{4e^2p^2}{1 - e^2}} = 1. \tag{27}$$

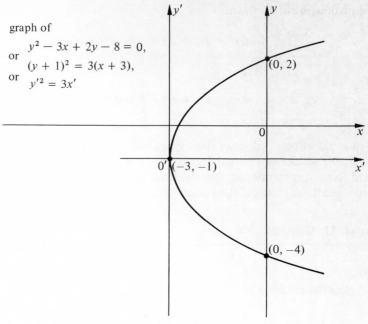

graph of

or

$y^2 - 3x + 2y - 8 = 0,$

$(y + 1)^2 = 3(x + 3),$

or

$y'^2 = 3x'$

Figure 34

The form can be greatly simplified by setting

$$x' = x - \frac{2e^2 p}{1 - e^2} = x - h, \qquad h = \frac{2e^2 p}{1 - e^2}$$

$$y' = y = y - k, \qquad k = 0$$

$$a^2 = \frac{4e^2 p^2}{(1 - e^2)^2}$$

$$b^2 = \frac{4e^2 p^2}{1 - e^2}$$

$$\left. \right\} . \tag{28}$$

Equation (27) then becomes

$$\frac{x'^2}{a^2} + \frac{y'^2}{b^2} = 1. \tag{29}$$

If we drop the primes on x and y we have the *standard* form of the equation of the ellipse in rectangular coordinates:

$$\frac{x^2}{a^2} + \frac{y^2}{b^2} = 1. \tag{30}$$

The analysis of the geometric nature of the graph is straightforward and is left as an exercise.

We note that $0 < e < 1 \Rightarrow 1 - e^2 < 1 \Rightarrow \dfrac{1}{1-e^2} > 1 \Rightarrow a^2 > b^2$. Thus we can define

$$c^2 = a^2 - b^2$$

and calculate

$$c^2 = \frac{4e^4p^2}{(1-e^2)^2}.$$

In general, then, taking positive square roots,

$$a = \frac{2ep}{1-e^2}, \qquad b = \frac{2ep}{\sqrt{1-e^2}}, \qquad c = \frac{2e^2p}{1-e^2} = ea;$$

thus $\dfrac{c}{a} = e$. The graph of a typical ellipse is shown in Figure 35.

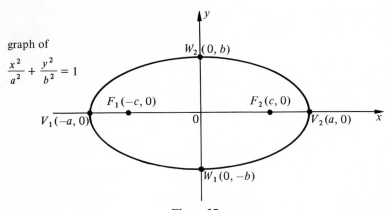

graph of
$$\frac{x^2}{a^2} + \frac{y^2}{b^2} = 1$$

Figure 35

Some of the terminology associated with the ellipse will now be given briefly: The origin is the *center*; the points $V_1(-a, 0)$ and $V_2(a, 0)$ are called the *vertices*; the segment $\overline{V_1 V_2}$ is the *major axis*, a being the length of the *semi-major axis*; the segment $\overline{W_1 W_2}$, where $W_1(0, -b)$, $W_2(0, b)$, is the *minor axis*, so b is the length of the *semi-minor axis*. The eccentricity e can be loosely thought of as the measure of how much the ellipse departs from a circle: for a fixed a, as $e \to 0$ the foci move toward the origin, $b \to a$, and the ellipse approaches a circle.

As will be developed in Exercise 25 the ellipse can also be defined as the locus of a point the sum of whose distances from two fixed points, the foci, remains constant ($2a$).

If $a > b$, the equation

$$\frac{y^2}{a^2} + \frac{x^2}{b^2} = 1$$

represents an ellipse with major axis on the y-axis. More generally, if h and k are any numbers, then

$$\frac{(x-h)^2}{a^2} + \frac{(y-k)^2}{b^2} = 1, \tag{31}$$

represents an ellipse with center at (h, k), major axis on $y = k$, and minor axis on $x = h$. Analogous remarks apply to

$$\frac{(y-k)^2}{a^2} + \frac{(x-h)^2}{b^2} = 1. \tag{32}$$

The general form of (31) and (32) is

$$Ax^2 + Cy^2 + Dx + Ey + F = 0, \qquad AC > 0. \tag{33}$$

Conversely, given an equation of type (33) one can, by completing the squares in x and y, reduce it to either (31) or (32).

Example 13. We analyze and sketch

$$4x^2 + 9y^2 - 16x + 18y - 11 = 0,$$

which is of the type in (33).

Completing the squares in x and y, we have

$$4(x^2 - 4x + 4) + 9(y^2 + 2y + 1) = 11 + 16 + 9,$$

or

$$4(x-2)^2 + 9(y+1)^2 = 36;$$

dividing by 36 gives

$$\frac{(x-2)^2}{9} + \frac{(y+1)^2}{4} = 1.$$

Thus we see that $h = 2$, $k = -1$, $a = 3$, $b = 2$. We can quickly sketch the graph as in Figure 36.

In order to discuss the hyperbola, we return to Eq. (21) of the preceding section, but rewrite it slightly, taking account of the fact that now $e > 1$:

$$(e^2 - 1)x^2 - y^2 + 4e^2px + 4e^2p^2 = 0.$$

Again we complete the square in x, obtaining (after the usual messy algebra)

$$\frac{\left(x + \dfrac{2e^2p}{e^2-1}\right)^2}{\dfrac{4e^2p^2}{(e^2-1)^2}} - \frac{y^2}{\dfrac{4e^2p^2}{e^2-1}} = 1.$$

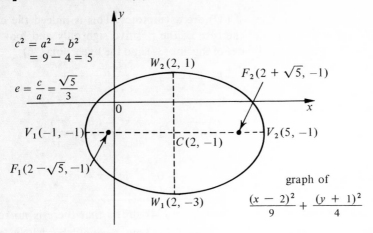

$$c^2 = a^2 - b^2$$
$$= 9 - 4 = 5$$

$$e = \frac{c}{a} = \frac{\sqrt{5}}{3}$$

$W_2(2, 1)$

$F_2(2 + \sqrt{5}, -1)$

$V_1(-1, -1)$

$C(2, -1)$

$V_2(5, -1)$

$F_1(2 - \sqrt{5}, -1)$

graph of

$W_1(2, -3)$

$$\frac{(x - 2)^2}{9} + \frac{(y + 1)^2}{4}$$

Figure 36

We set

$$\left.\begin{aligned}
x' &= x + \frac{2e^2 p}{e^2 - 1} = x - h, \qquad h = \frac{-2e^2 p}{e^2 - 1} \\[2mm]
y' &= y = y - k, \qquad k = 0 \\[2mm]
a^2 &= \frac{4e^2 p^2}{(e^2 - 1)^2} \\[2mm]
b^2 &= \frac{4e^2 p^2}{e^2 - 1}
\end{aligned}\right\}. \tag{34}$$

The preceding equation takes the form (we have dropped the short-lived primes on x and y):

$$\frac{x^2}{a^2} - \frac{y^2}{b^2} = 1. \tag{35}$$

For a geometric analysis of the graph of this equation we note that there is symmetry with respect to both axes, that $(\pm a, 0)$ are x-intercepts, and that there is no intersection with the y-axis. Solving for y gives

$$y = \pm \frac{b}{a}\sqrt{x^2 - a^2}, \tag{36}$$

from which we see that we must have $|x| \geq a$. If we modify (36) as

$$y = \pm \frac{b}{a} x\sqrt{1 - \frac{a^2}{x^2}},$$

we see that large values of x^2 will cause the ordinate to equal approximately

$$y = \pm \frac{b}{a} x; \tag{37}$$

this suggests that the lines of (37) are asymptotes. This is indeed the case, as we now show. We consider the case of the positive sign only and look at the difference between the ordinates of the line (37) and the hyperbola (36):

$$y_l - y_h = \frac{b}{a}x - \frac{b}{a}\sqrt{x^2 - a^2}$$

$$= \frac{b}{a}[x - \sqrt{x^2 - a^2}] = \frac{b}{a}\frac{x^2 - (x^2 - a^2)}{x + \sqrt{x^2 - a^2}}$$

$$= \frac{ab}{x + \sqrt{x^2 - a^2}} \to 0, \qquad \text{as} \quad x \to \infty.$$

A study of the values of a^2 and b^2 in (34) shows that there is no relation imposed upon them (e.g., $e = \sqrt{2} \Rightarrow a = b$). Thus c cannot be defined as it is with the ellipse. The definition is

$$c^2 = a^2 + b^2 = \left(\frac{2e^2 p}{e^2 - 1}\right)^2.$$

Notice again from (34) that $x' = x + c$; thus, since a focus is at the pole ($x = 0$), the number c gives the x' abscissa of a focus.

To complete our analysis, we seek information about the slope of the tangent. Differentiating Eq. (35) implicitly with respect to x, we have

$$\frac{2x}{a^2} - \frac{2yy'}{b^2} = 0,$$

from which we find $y' = \frac{b^2}{a^2}\frac{x}{y}$. This shows that y' is never 0 (since x cannot equal 0), that y' is not defined when $y = 0$, and that $y' > 0$ at points of the curve in quadrants I and III, $y' < 0$ in quadrants II and IV.

We can now easily sketch the graph as in Figure 37.

A brief survey of terminology relating to the hyperbola will now be given, The origin is the *center*; the x-axis, on which lie the *vertices* $V_1(-a, 0)$ and $V_2(a, 0)$ is the *transverse axis*; the y-axis, the other axis of symmetry, is the *conjugate* axis; the *foci* are at $F_1(-c, 0)$ and $F_2(c, 0)$; the *asymptotes* are the lines $y = \pm \frac{b}{a}x$ (through the center—cf. the discussion preceding Figure 31 in Section 10.6).

Notice that the rectangle with vertices (a, b), $(-a, b)$, $(-a, -b)$, $(a, -b)$ has its diagonals on the asymptotes. If $a = b$, the rectangle becomes a square, and the hyperbola is called *equilateral*. The two hyperbolas

$$\frac{x^2}{a^2} - \frac{y^2}{b^2} = 1 \quad \text{and} \quad \frac{y^2}{b^2} - \frac{x^2}{a^2} = 1$$

are called *conjugate hyperbolas*; they share the same asymptotes.

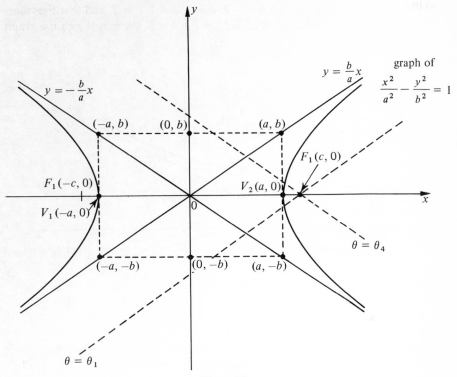

Figure 37

The equation

$$\frac{(x-h)^2}{a^2} - \frac{(y-k)^2}{b^2} = 1 \qquad (38)$$

is easily seen to represent a hyperbola with center at $C(h, k)$, transverse axis $y = k$, conjugate axis $x = h$, and vertices at $(h \pm a, k)$. The general form of (38) is

$$Ax^2 + Cy^2 + Dx + Ey + F = 0, \qquad AC < 0. \qquad (39)$$

Conversely, one can, by completing the squares in x and y, transform an equation of type (39) to that of (38) or the related equation representing a hyperbola with transverse axis parallel to the y-axis.

Example 14. We graph

$$x^2 - 4y^2 + 4x + 8y + 4 = 0,$$

which is the same type as (39).

Completing the squares, we have

$$(x^2 + 4x + 4) - 4(y^2 - 2y + 1) = -4 + 4 - 4.$$

Dividing by -4 gives

$$\frac{(y-1)^2}{1} - \frac{(x+2)^2}{4} = 1.$$

From this equation we see that $h = -2$, $k = 1$, $a = 1$, $b = 2$, and that the transverse axis is $x = -2$. Also, $c^2 = a^2 + b^2 = 1 + 4 = 5$. We can sketch the graph as in Figure 38.

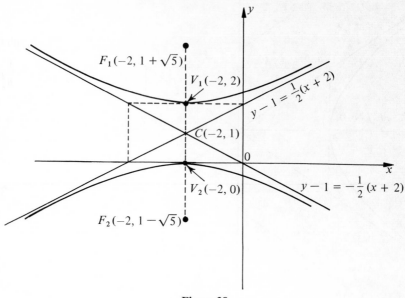

Figure 38

Analogous to the alternative definition of the ellipse is the following alternative definition of a hyperbola: given two fixed points F_1 and F_2, a positive constant $2a$, a hyperbola is the set of all points P satisfying $|\overline{PF_1} - \overline{PF_2}| = 2a$, where $\overline{PF_1}$ is the distance between P and F_1 (see Exercise 26 below).

We conclude this section with a brief remark about the name *conic section curves*. As the geometers of classical Greece well knew (Apollonius wrote an eight-volume treatise on the subject in the third century B.C.), the curves we have just been considering can all be obtained as intersections of planes with a circular cone, the particular curve depending upon the relation of the plane to the cone. In Figure 39 we show how different curves occur.

Exhaustive study of the properties of these curves had been made by synthetic (i.e., noncoordinate) methods. With the introduction of coordinates it was found that this same family of curves was described by the equations of second degree in x and y, i.e., by equations of the type

$$Ax^2 + Bxy + Cy^2 + Dx + Ey + F = 0, \qquad (40)$$

where at least one of A, B, C is not zero. The fact is that all of the equations of this type encountered in this section have had $B = 0$. We can assert on the basis of what has already been said, that if an axis of symmetry of a conic section curve is parallel to one of the coordinate axes, then $B = 0$. Conversely, if $B \neq 0$ in

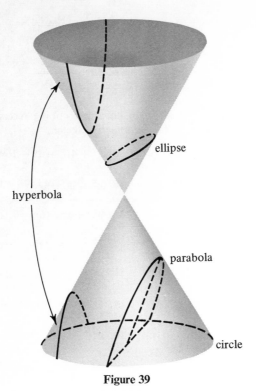

Figure 39

(40), then the curve (if it is not "degenerate"—see below) is a conic section with axis of symmetry not parallel to either coordinate axis (example: $xy = 1$).

Equation (40) includes all the conic section curves in the plane; it also includes degenerate cases thereof: (i) pairs of intersecting lines, (ii) pairs of coincident lines, (iii) pairs of parallel lines, (iv) points, and (v) the empty set. As examples of these respective cases, we cite

(i) $x^2 - y^2 = 0$ $(A = 1, C = -1, B = D = E = F = 0)$
(ii) $x^2 = 0$ $(A = 1, B = C = D = E = F = 0)$
(iii) $y^2 - 3y + 2 = 0$ $(A = B = D = 0, C = 1, E = -3, F = 2)$
(iv) $x^2 + y^2 = 0$ $(A = C = 1, B = D = E = F = 0)$
(v) $x^2 + y^2 + 1 = 0$ $(A = C = F = 1, B = D = E = 0)$.

EXERCISES

In numbers 1–6 transform to rectangular coordinates and then translate the axes so that the vertex or center is at the new origin. Sketch each curve.

1. $r = \dfrac{2}{1 + \sin \theta}$.

2. $r = \dfrac{12}{2 + 3 \cos \theta}$.

3. $r = \dfrac{8}{4 - \sin \theta}$.

5. $r = \dfrac{3}{1 - \sin \theta}$.

4. $r = \dfrac{4}{1 - \sqrt{2} \cos \theta}$.

6. $r = \dfrac{16}{4 + 3 \cos \theta}$.

In Exercises 7–24 complete the square(s), thus determining vertex (if the curve is a parabola) or center and axis or axes of symmetry. Sketch.

7. $x^2 - 4x - 4y - 8 = 0$.

8. $x^2 + 4y^2 + 6x - 16y + 21 = 0$.

9. $x^2 - y^2 - 10x - 6y + 15 = 0$.

10. $y^2 + 4x + 4y - 8 = 0$.

11. $x^2 - 8x + 2y + 16 = 0$.

12. $9x^2 + y^2 - 6y = 0$.

13. $x^2 - y^2 - 2x + 5 = 0$.

14. $x^2 - y^2 - 2x - 3 = 0$.

15. $4x^2 + 9y^2 - 24x + 18y + 45 = 0$.

16. $x^2 - 4y^2 - 2x - 16y - 15 = 0$.

17. $x^2 + y^2 + 6x = 0$.

18. $10x^2 - 80x - y + 162 = 0$.

19. $2x^2 + y^2 + 4x - 4y + 8 = 0$.

20. $x^2 - 100y^2 - 100 = 0$.

21. $x^2 + 100y^2 - 100 = 0$.

22. $x^2 + 100y^2 + 100 = 0$.

23. $-x^2 + 100y^2 - 100 = 0$.

24. $9x^2 - 24xy + 16y^2 = 0$.

25. Let $0 < c < a$, and let $F_1(-c, 0)$, $F_2(c, 0)$ be two fixed points. Consider the set of all points $P(x, y)$ such that

$$\overline{PF_1} + \overline{PF_2} = 2a.$$

Show that the coordinates of P must satisfy

$$\frac{x^2}{a^2} + \frac{y^2}{b^2} = 1,$$

where $b^2 = a^2 - c^2$. This gives an alternate definition of the ellipse.

26. Let $c > 0$, $a > 0$, and let $F_1(-c, 0)$, $F_2(c, 0)$ be two fixed points. Consider the set of all points $P(x, y)$ such that

$$|\overline{PF_1} - \overline{PF_2}| = 2a.$$

Show that the coordinates of P must satisfy

$$\frac{x^2}{a^2} - \frac{y^2}{b^2} = 1,$$

where $b^2 = c^2 - a^2$. This is another way of defining a hyperbola.

27. Show that the tangent to the ellipse

$$\frac{x^2}{a^2} + \frac{y^2}{b^2} = 1$$

at (x_1, y_1) has equation

$$\frac{x_1 x}{a^2} + \frac{y_1 y}{b^2} = 1.$$

28. Show that the equation of the tangent to the hyperbola

$$\frac{x^2}{a^2} - \frac{y^2}{b^2} = 1$$

at (x_1, y_1) can be written

$$\frac{x_1 x}{a^2} - \frac{y_1 y}{b^2} = 1.$$

29. Find the equation of the tangent to the parabola $y^2 = 4px$ at the point (x_1, y_1) on the parabola.

30. Show that the area of the ellipse

$$\frac{x^2}{a^2} + \frac{y^2}{b^2} = 1$$

is $A = \pi ab$.

31. Consider the parabola $y = cx^2$, where $c > 0$. Show that the area bounded by the parabola, the x-axis, and the ordinate at $x = a$ is equal to one-third the area of the rectangle determined by the axes and the lines $x = a$ and $y = ca^2$.

32. Let $P_0(x_0, y_0)$ be a point in the first quadrant on the hyperbola $\dfrac{x^2}{a^2} - \dfrac{y^2}{b^2} = 1$, so that $y_0 = \dfrac{b}{a}\sqrt{x_0^2 - a^2}$. Consider the region bounded by the line OP_0, the hyperbola from the vertex $A(a, 0)$ to P_0, and the x-axis from O to A. Show that the area A of this region is given by

$$A = \frac{1}{2} ab \log\left(\frac{x_0}{a} + \frac{y_0}{b}\right).$$

Chapter **11** Vectors and Parametric Equations

11.1   Introduction and Informal Discussion

In this chapter we begin the study of a subject—vectors—which will prove to be important for several reasons. Originally, vectors became a part of the body of useful mathematics as a result of the interplay between mathematics and physics. The utility of the concept from this point of view remains, as we shall see. However, a more recent development is the use of vectors, from the abstract algebraic point of view, to improve and simplify the discussion of calculus for functions of several variables.

Our discussion in this section will be an informal one describing the physical approach to vectors. With this description as motivation, but with an eye to the future, we can then, in subsequent sections, give the formal definitions which lay the foundations for our study of vectors.

We begin by pointing out that the physical concepts *force, velocity*, and *acceleration*, among others, although all different from one another, have a common property; they cannot usually be represented by a single number; instead they require, for a complete description, a specification of both *magnitude* and *direction*. (It is true that in our discussion of motion in Chapter 2, we represented velocity by a number, but that was because we limited ourselves there to motion along a line; there were consequently only two different directions available, and these could be distinguished by means of sign.) The mathematical approach to such a situation is to abstract the common features and to observe that such quantities as force and velocity can be described mathematically as *directed line segments*, the length of the segment indicating the magnitude, and the direction, of course, the direction. Thus we can think of a *vector* as a *directed line* segment (see Figure 1).

vector $\mathbf{PQ} = \mathbf{v}$
initial point P
terminal point Q
magnitude $|\mathbf{PQ}| = |\mathbf{v}|$

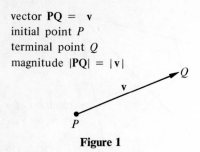

Figure 1

A problem arises in trying to arrive at a definition of equality for vectors. Since the characterizing features of a vector are its magnitude and direction, it would seem reasonable to call equal two vectors whose magnitudes and directions are the same. However, in some contexts it becomes important to take into account the position of the vector, its location in the plane (we will study vectors in space later). In this case two vectors would be equal if and only if they have the same magnitudes and directions *and* initial points. Under the first agreement vectors are referred to as *free*; under the second, as *fixed*. Either approach has strong arguments both for and against, but it suits our purposes to work with free vectors. Thus in Figure 2 the vectors $\mathbf{P_1Q_1} = \mathbf{v_1}$ and $\mathbf{P_2Q_2} = \mathbf{v_2}$ are equal.

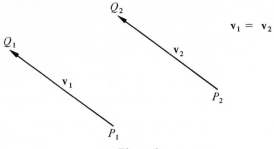

Figure 2

The vectors $\mathbf{PQ}$ and $\mathbf{QP}$ certainly have the same magnitudes $|\mathbf{PQ}| = |\mathbf{QP}|$ and, in a way, they have the same direction, since they lie on the same line; clearly, however, they should be distinguished. We shall say that $\mathbf{PQ}$ and $\mathbf{QP}$ have *opposite sense*, and we write

$$\mathbf{QP} = -\mathbf{PQ}.$$

A physical object may be subject to several forces acting on it, or a particle in motion may have a velocity which is the resultant of several component velocities (in the case of a boat, for example, the velocity may be due to the velocity imparted by the motor and the direction of the rudder and to that imparted by a current in the water). It has been found experimentally that forces and velocities and the other physical quantities conveniently described by vectors combine by the "parallelogram law," as illustrated in Figure 3.

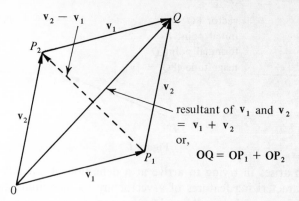

Figure 3

The scheme is to draw $\mathbf{v}_1$ and $\mathbf{v}_2$ with the same initial point, complete the parallelogram thus determined, and represent the resultant of $\mathbf{v}_1$ and $\mathbf{v}_2$ by the diagonal with initial point at O. Note, though, that since $\mathbf{P}_1\mathbf{Q} = \mathbf{v}_2$, we could also describe the process as follows: draw $\mathbf{v}_2$ with its initial point coincident with the terminal point of $\mathbf{v}_1$ and draw the resultant, which it is natural to call $\mathbf{v}_1 + \mathbf{v}_2$, with its initial point at that of $\mathbf{v}_1$, its terminal point at that of $\mathbf{v}_2$. (This second description shows that $\mathbf{v}_2 + \mathbf{v}_1 = \mathbf{v}_1 + \mathbf{v}_2$.)

As a simple example of the preceding description consider a man in a rowboat heading directly for the opposite shore of a river and rowing at a speed (magnitude of velocity) which would enable him to travel three miles in an hour *if* he were rowing in still water. However, the river has a swift current, its downstream speed being four miles per hour. The resultant velocity of the rowboat (and consequently of the man) is as shown in Figure 4.

As we have already indicated, the addition of vectors is commutative. One can

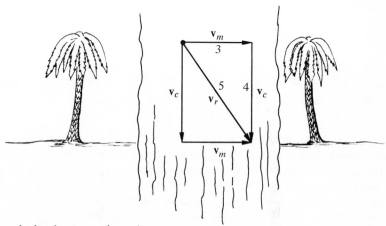

$\mathbf{v}_m$, velocity due to man's rowing
$\mathbf{v}_c$, velocity of current
$\mathbf{v}_r = \mathbf{v}_m + \mathbf{v}_c$, resultant velocity of boat

Figure 4

also show by a geometric argument (see Exercise 5) that this addition is associa-tive, but we shall prove both of these properties in a different manner in the next section.

A second way of getting new vectors from old is suggested by the following: if a boat, traveling through still water maintains its direction but suddenly doubles its speed, it would be natural to describe the new velocity vector as $2\mathbf{v}$, where $\mathbf{v}$ was the original velocity vector. More generally, if $\mathbf{v}$ is a vector and c a number, $c > 0$ (it is the custom, when discoursing about vectors, to refer to numbers as *scalars*), then $\mathbf{w} = c\mathbf{v}$ is a vector with the same direction—and sense —as that of $\mathbf{v}$, but the magnitude is $|\mathbf{w}| = c\,|\mathbf{v}|$. If c is a negative scalar, then $\mathbf{w} = c\mathbf{v}$ has the same direction as $\mathbf{v}$, but opposite sense, and $|\mathbf{w}| = |c|\,|\mathbf{v}|$. The operation just described is known as *multiplication by a scalar*.

By geometric arguments, which we shall ask you to carry out in the exercises, the following identities are easily shown—we shall indicate a different method of proof in the next section.

$$\begin{cases} (h + k)\mathbf{v} = h\mathbf{v} + k\mathbf{v}, & h, k \text{ scalars,} \\ c(\mathbf{v}_1 + \mathbf{v}_2) = c\mathbf{v}_1 + c\mathbf{v}_2, & c \text{ scalar,} \\ h(k\mathbf{v}) = (hk)\mathbf{v}, & h, k \text{ scalars.} \end{cases} \tag{1}$$

We next point out that subtraction of vectors is possible. We can think of $\mathbf{v}_2 - \mathbf{v}_1$ as $\mathbf{v}_2 + (-1)\mathbf{v}_1$. Note that in Figure 3 $\mathbf{v}_2 - \mathbf{v}_1 = \mathbf{P}_1\mathbf{P}_2$, the diagonal of the parallelogram other than $\mathbf{v}_1 + \mathbf{v}_2$. For

$$\mathbf{v}_2 - \mathbf{v}_1 = (-1)\mathbf{v}_1 + \mathbf{v}_2 = \mathbf{P}_1\mathbf{O} + \mathbf{OP}_2 = \mathbf{P}_1\mathbf{P}_2.$$

We conclude this section with an illustration of the use of vectors in geometry. We hasten to mention, though, that we do not plan to pursue this type of applica-tion of vector techniques.

Example 1. We show that the medians of a triangle are concurrent. Consider the triangle OAB as in Figure 5, M_1, M_2, M_3 being the midpoints of, respec-tively, OA, AB, OB. Let $\mathbf{OA} = \mathbf{a}$, $\mathbf{OB} = \mathbf{b}$; then $\mathbf{AB} = \mathbf{b} - \mathbf{a}$. Also, $\mathbf{OM}_1 = \frac{1}{2}\mathbf{a}$, $\mathbf{AM}_2 = \frac{1}{2}(\mathbf{b} - \mathbf{a})$, $\mathbf{OM}_3 = \frac{1}{2}\mathbf{b}$. Thus

$$\mathbf{OM}_2 = \mathbf{OA} + \mathbf{AM}_2 = \mathbf{a} + \tfrac{1}{2}(\mathbf{b} - \mathbf{a}) = \tfrac{1}{2}\mathbf{a} + \tfrac{1}{2}\mathbf{b},$$

$$\mathbf{AM}_3 = \mathbf{AO} + \mathbf{OM}_3 = -\mathbf{a} + \tfrac{1}{2}\mathbf{b},$$

$$\mathbf{BM}_1 = \mathbf{BO} + \mathbf{OM}_1 = -\mathbf{b} + \tfrac{1}{2}\mathbf{a} = \tfrac{1}{2}\mathbf{a} - \mathbf{b}.$$

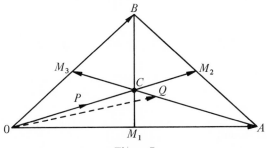

Figure 5

If P is a variable point on OM_2, then

$$\mathbf{OP} = p\mathbf{OM_2} = \tfrac{1}{2}p\mathbf{a} + \tfrac{1}{2}p\mathbf{b}, \qquad 0 \le p \le 1.$$

Similarly, if Q is a variable point on AM_3, then

$$\mathbf{OQ} = \mathbf{OA} + q\mathbf{AM_3} = \mathbf{a} + (-q)\mathbf{a} + \tfrac{1}{2}q\mathbf{b} = (1-q)\mathbf{a} + \tfrac{1}{2}q\mathbf{b}, \qquad 0 \le q \le 1.$$

The intersection of the two medians OM_2 and AM_3 is the point C determined by the equation $\mathbf{OP} = \mathbf{OQ}$; equating the expressions for $\mathbf{OP}$ and $\mathbf{OQ}$ gives

$$\tfrac{1}{2}p\mathbf{a} + \tfrac{1}{2}p\mathbf{b} = (1-q)\mathbf{a} + \tfrac{1}{2}q\mathbf{b}.$$

Equating the coefficients of $\mathbf{a}$ and $\mathbf{b}$, we find $p = q = \tfrac{2}{3}$. Thus $\mathbf{OC} = \tfrac{1}{3}\mathbf{a} + \tfrac{1}{3}\mathbf{b}$.

By an exactly similar technique we can show that the intersection of the medians OM_2 and BM_1 is also at C. (Alternatively, one can show that $\mathbf{OB} + \tfrac{2}{3}\mathbf{BM_1} = \mathbf{OC}$.)

EXERCISES

1. Given vectors $\mathbf{a}$ and $\mathbf{b}$ as in Figure 6, draw each of the following vectors, making a separate figure for each one.

   (a) $\mathbf{a} + \mathbf{b}$

   (b) $\mathbf{b} + \mathbf{a}$

   (c) $\mathbf{a} - \mathbf{b}$

   (d) $2\mathbf{a} + \mathbf{b}$

   (e) $3\mathbf{a} - 2\mathbf{b}$

   (f) $-\mathbf{a} + 4\mathbf{b}$

   (g) $\mathbf{a} - \mathbf{a}$

   (h) $-2\mathbf{a} - 3\mathbf{b}$.

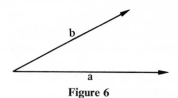

Figure 6

2. Let $\mathbf{a}$ and $\mathbf{b}$ be as in Figure 6, let $\mathbf{c}$ be any vector in the plane. Do there exist scalars h_c and k_c such that $\mathbf{c} = h_c\mathbf{a} + k_c\mathbf{b}$? Experiment with different vectors $\mathbf{c}$.

3. Suppose we desire that addition of vectors be closed, i.e., the sum of two vectors is a vector. What should be said about $\mathbf{PQ} + \mathbf{QP}$?

4. See Exercise 3. In the discussion of multiplication of a vector by a scalar c we omitted the case $c = 0$. What is a reasonable meaning to assign to $\mathbf{w} = c\mathbf{v}$ if $c = 0$?

5. Let $\mathbf{a}$, $\mathbf{b}$, $\mathbf{c}$ be three vectors. Show by means of a drawing that

$$(\mathbf{a} + \mathbf{b}) + \mathbf{c} = \mathbf{a} + (\mathbf{b} + \mathbf{c}).$$

[*Hint.* Draw the vectors in sequence, i.e., with the initial point of $\mathbf{b}$ at the terminal point of $\mathbf{a}$, and so on.]

6. See Exercises 3, 4, and 5. Consider a triangle ABC. What can be said about $\mathbf{AB} + \mathbf{BC} + \mathbf{CA}$?

7. (a) Define the zero vector (see Exercises 3, 4, and 6).

   (b) Is it true that $\mathbf{a} + \mathbf{0} = \mathbf{a}$, for every vector $\mathbf{a}$?

   (c) Is it true that, for every vector $\mathbf{a}$, $\mathbf{a} + (-\mathbf{a}) = \mathbf{0}$?

   (d) What direction should the zero vector have?

8. Use drawings to show that the identities in (1) are valid.

9. (a) Give a definition of: "vector $\mathbf{v}_1$ is parallel to vector $\mathbf{v}_2$."

   (b) In the triangle in Figure 5 show that $|\mathbf{M}_3 \mathbf{M}_2|$ is parallel to $\mathbf{a} = \mathbf{OA}$.

   (c) What can you show, by vector methods, about $|\mathbf{M}_3 \mathbf{M}_2|$?

10. A *unit vector* is a vector with magnitude one. Let $\mathbf{a}$ be any vector such that $|\mathbf{a}| \neq 0$. Show that there exists a unit vector $\mathbf{u_a}$ with the same direction (and sense) as $\mathbf{a}$. [*Hint.* $\mathbf{u_a} = c\mathbf{a}$ for suitable choice of the scalar c.]

11.2 Definitions and Examples

In this section we use the ideas suggested in the informal discussion of the previous section to give formal definitions of vectors in the plane and of some of the operations involving vectors.

Definition 1. *Let* $A(a_1, a_2)$ *and* $B(b_1, b_2)$ *be points in the plane. The **vector** $\mathbf{AB}$ is the ordered pair* $(b_1 - a_1, b_2 - a_2)$:

$$\mathbf{AB} = (b_1 - a_1, b_2 - a_2)$$

(see Figure 7). *The **length** or **magnitude** or **norm** of* $\mathbf{AB}$ *is*

$$|\mathbf{AB}| = \sqrt{(b_1 - a_1)^2 + (b_2 - a_2)^2}.$$

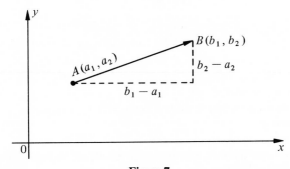

Figure 7

Definition 2. *Let $A(a_1, a_2)$, $B(b_1, b_2)$, $C(c_1, c_2)$, $D(d_1, d_2)$ be points in the plane. Then*

$$\mathbf{AB} = \mathbf{CD} \Leftrightarrow \begin{cases} b_1 - a_1 = d_1 - c_1 \\ \text{and} \\ b_2 - a_2 = d_2 - c_2 \end{cases}$$

(see Figure 8).

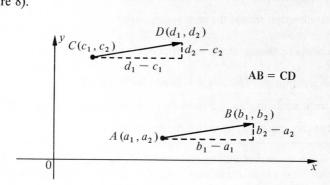

Figure 8

[A remark is in order at this point. Equality in mathematics is almost invariably defined to mean "is identically the same as." Definition 2, defining equal vectors, is a deliberate violation of this principle. A more correct way, consistent with the usual agreement about equality is the following. Let A, B, C, D be as in Definition 2. Then define the *arrow* $\mathbf{AB} = (b_1 - a_1, b_2 - a_2)$. If the arrows $\mathbf{AB}$ and $\mathbf{CD}$ satisfy the condition of Definition 2 we call them *equivalent* and write

$$\mathbf{AB} \sim \mathbf{CD}.$$

This relation is, in fact, easily proven to be an equivalence relation:

(i) $\mathbf{AB} \sim \mathbf{AB}$,

(ii) $\mathbf{AB} \sim \mathbf{CD} \Rightarrow \mathbf{CD} \sim \mathbf{AB}$,

(iii) $\left. \begin{array}{l} \mathbf{AB} \sim \mathbf{CD} \\ \mathbf{CD} \sim \mathbf{EF} \end{array} \right\} \Rightarrow \mathbf{AB} \sim \mathbf{EF}.$

Consequently, the equivalence relation $\sim$ divides the set of all arrows into equivalence classes. We define a *vector* to be an equivalence class of arrows and agree that we can use any arrow in a class as a *representative* of its vector. The length of a vector is $\sqrt{(b_1 - a_1)^2 + (b_2 - a_2)^2}$, where $(b_1 - a_1, b_2 - a_2)$ is any representative of the vector; etc.

This approach is, as we have said, correct, but it is occasionally cumbersome, and we eschew it.]

It is clear that our definition of vector is simply an ordered pair of numbers, two vectors being equal if the two ordered pairs are identical. As we also use an ordered pair of numbers to determine a point in the plane, the natural question arises about the distinction between vectors and points.

If we were working with fixed vectors, i.e., vectors with initial point at the origin, there would be a 1–1 correspondence between points and vectors: (i) every *point* $P_0(x_0, y_0)$ corresponds to the *vector* $\mathbf{OP_0} = (x_0, y_0)$ from the origin to P_0; (ii) every *vector* $\mathbf{a} = (a_1, a_2)$ corresponds to the *point* $A(a_1, a_2)$ such that $\mathbf{a} = \mathbf{OA}$. Moreover, different points correspond to different vectors, different vectors correspond to different points.

Working with free vectors, we still have available the correspondences just described, but we can also use an arbitrary point of the plane as the initial point of a vector. Thus, given a vector $\mathbf{a} = (a_1, a_2)$ and a *point* $P_0(x_0, y_0)$, we can define a point $P_1(x_1, y_1)$ by

$$x_1 = x_0 + a_1, \qquad y_1 = y_0 + a_2$$

so that $\mathbf{a} = \mathbf{P_0 P_1}$ (see Figure 9).

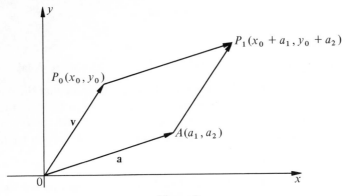

Figure 9

For the operations of addition of vectors and multiplication of a vector by a scalar we have the following definitions.

Definition 3. *Let* $\mathbf{a} = (a_1, a_2)$, $\mathbf{b} = (b_1, b_2)$ *be vectors,* $c \in \mathbf{R}$ *a scalar. Then*

$$\mathbf{a} + \mathbf{b} = (a_1 + b_1, a_2 + b_2)$$

$$c\mathbf{a} = (ca_1, ca_2).$$

We illustrate $\mathbf{a} + \mathbf{b}$, $\mathbf{b} - \mathbf{a}$, and $c\mathbf{a}$, for several values of c, in Figure 10. Note that the definition of addition is consistent with the parallelogram law mentioned in Section 10.1.

We let the zero vector $\mathbf{0} = (0, 0)$, and $\mathbf{b} - \mathbf{a} = \mathbf{b} + (-\mathbf{a})$, where $-\mathbf{a} = (-1)(\mathbf{a}) = (-a_1, -a_2)$. Thus

$$\mathbf{b} - \mathbf{a} = (b_1 - a_1, b_2 - a_2).$$

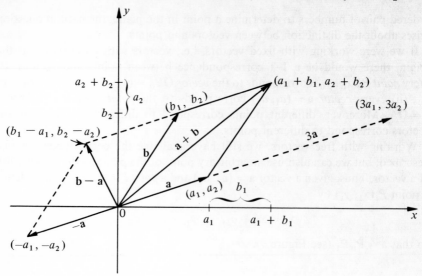

Figure 10

By Definitions 3 and 1,

$$|c\mathbf{a}| = |(ca_1, ca_2)| = \sqrt{c^2 a_1^2 + c^2 a_2^2} = |c|\sqrt{a_1^2 + a_2^2} = |c|\,|\mathbf{a}|.$$

With these agreements and Definition 3 it is easy to show that the operations on vectors thus far introduced have the properties listed in the next theorem.

Before stating the theorem we introduce the notation $\mathbf{R}^2$ for the set of all vectors in the plane, with equality and two operations as defined in Definitions 2 and 3.

Theorem 1. *Let* $\mathbf{a}, \mathbf{b}, \mathbf{c} \in \mathbf{R}^2$, *r and* $s \in \mathbf{R}$. *Then the following are true.*

1. $\mathbf{a} + \mathbf{b}$ *is a vector.*
2. $\mathbf{a} + \mathbf{b} = \mathbf{b} + \mathbf{a}$
3. $\mathbf{a} + (\mathbf{b} + \mathbf{c}) = (\mathbf{a} + \mathbf{b}) + \mathbf{c}$.
4. $\exists \mathbf{0}$ *such that* $\mathbf{a} + \mathbf{0} = \mathbf{a}$.
5. *For every* $\mathbf{a}$, $\exists(-\mathbf{a})$ *such that* $\mathbf{a} + (-\mathbf{a}) = \mathbf{0}$.
6. $r\mathbf{a}$ *is a vector.*
7. $r(\mathbf{a} + \mathbf{b}) = r\mathbf{a} + r\mathbf{b}$.
8. $(r + s)\mathbf{a} = r\mathbf{a} + s\mathbf{a}$.
9. $(rs)\mathbf{a} = r(s\mathbf{a})$.
10. $1\mathbf{a} = \mathbf{a}$.

Proof. Exercise for student. ∎

An abstract algebraic approach to the study of vectors would begin with the field $\mathbf{R}$ (or some other field) and a set of objects (the vectors) on which an addition and a multiplication by numbers in $\mathbf{R}$ are defined. Then the ten properties of the preceding theorem would be taken as *axioms* for the *vector space*.

We are at this time, however, interested in the geometric rather than the algebraic aspect of vectors. To this end we introduce the unit (length one) vectors in the directions of the positive side of the coordinate axes.

Definition 4. *The vectors* **i** *and* **j** *are defined as*

$$\mathbf{i} = (1, 0), \qquad \mathbf{j} = (0, 1).$$

Every vector in the plane can be written as a linear combination of **i** and **j**. For, if $\mathbf{v} = (x_0, y_0)$ is any vector, we have

$$\mathbf{v} = (x_0, y_0) = (x_0, 0) + (0, y_0) = x_0(1, 0) + y_0(0, 1) = x_0\mathbf{i} + y_0\mathbf{j}.$$

In this context x_0 and y_0 are called the *components* of **v**.

Note that if $\mathbf{a} = (a_1, a_2) = a_1\mathbf{i} + a_2\mathbf{j}$ and $\mathbf{b} = b_1\mathbf{i} + b_2\mathbf{j}$, then

$$\mathbf{a} + \mathbf{b} = (a_1 + b_1, a_2 + b_2) = (a_1 + b_1)\mathbf{i} + (a_2 + b_2)\mathbf{j},$$

$$c\mathbf{a} = (ca_1, ca_2) = (ca_1)\mathbf{i} + (ca_2)\mathbf{j}.$$

Thus addition of two vectors is achieved by adding the components, etc.

We next mention several facts about magnitude and direction of vectors, which, although more or less obvious, are worthy of comment.

First, let $\mathbf{a} = a_1\mathbf{i} + a_2\mathbf{j}$ be any nonzero vector: $|\mathbf{a}| = \sqrt{a_1^2 + a_2^2} \neq 0$. Then

$$\mathbf{u_a} = \frac{1}{|\mathbf{a}|}\,\mathbf{a} = \frac{a_1}{\sqrt{a_1^2 + a_2^2}}\,\mathbf{i} + \frac{a_2}{\sqrt{a_1^2 + a_2^2}}\,\mathbf{j} \qquad (2)$$

is a *unit* vector with the same direction—*and sense*—as **a**. Also, $-\mathbf{u_a}$ is a *unit* vector with the same direction as **a**, but with opposite sense.

It is natural to call *parallel* two vectors with the same direction. (Are two parallel vectors with the same length necessarily equal?) If we consider two vectors $\mathbf{a} = a_1\mathbf{i} + a_2\mathbf{j}$ and $\mathbf{b} = b_1\mathbf{i} + b_2\mathbf{j}$ (see Figure 11) then we can make the following observations—we exclude the zero vector from this discussion.

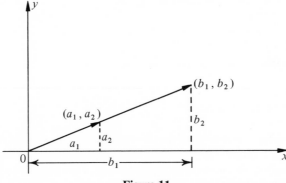

Figure 11

(i) The vectors **a** and **b** are horizontal $\Leftrightarrow a_2 = b_2 = 0$.

(ii) The vectors **a** and **b** are vertical $\Leftrightarrow a_1 = b_1 = 0$.

(iii) If **a** and **b** are neither horizontal nor vertical, so that $a_1 a_2 b_1 b_2 \neq 0$, then (using $\parallel$ to mean "is parallel to")

$$\mathbf{a} \parallel \mathbf{b} \Leftrightarrow \frac{b_2}{a_2} = \frac{b_1}{a_1}.$$

If in case (iii) we let the common value of the ratio be t, then we can, observing that the following assertion is also valid for cases (i) and (ii), summarize these remarks formally.

Theorem 2. *Two nonzero vectors* $\mathbf{a} = a_1\mathbf{i} + a_2\mathbf{j}$ *and* $\mathbf{b} = b_1\mathbf{i} + b_2\mathbf{j}$ *are parallel $\Leftrightarrow$ corresponding components and are proportional. In symbols,*

$$\mathbf{a} \parallel \mathbf{b} \Leftrightarrow \exists t \neq 0 \ \textit{such that} \begin{cases} b_1 = a_1 t \\ b_2 = a_2 t. \end{cases} \tag{3}$$

If (3) *holds, then* **a** *and* **b** *have the same sense if* $t > 0$, *opposite sense if* $t < 0$.

We now illustrate some of these ideas.

Example 2. Given two points $A(1, 2)$ and $B(4, 3)$ we find the point $P_0(x_0, y_0)$ which is one-third of the way from A to B on the line segment AB (see Figure 12).

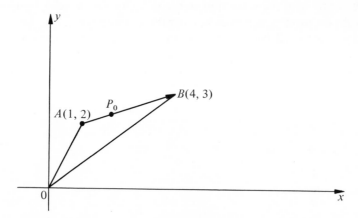

Figure 12

Let $\mathbf{v} = \mathbf{AB} = (4 - 1, 3 - 2) = 3\mathbf{i} + \mathbf{j}$. Then points P between A and B are described by the vector

$$\mathbf{OP} = \mathbf{OA} + t\mathbf{AB} = (\mathbf{i} + 2\mathbf{j}) + t(3\mathbf{i} + \mathbf{j}), \qquad 0 \leq t \leq 1.$$

In particular, the desired point P_0 is found by using $t = \frac{1}{3}$:

$$\mathbf{OP}_0 = (\mathbf{i} + 2\mathbf{j}) + \tfrac{1}{3}(3\mathbf{i} + \mathbf{j}),$$

or

$$\mathbf{OP}_0 = 2\mathbf{i} + \tfrac{7}{3}\mathbf{j};$$

from this we find P_0 as $P_0\,(2, \frac{7}{3})$.

In a similar way, one can, by suitable choice of t, find the point which divides any line segment into two parts with prescribed ratio.

Example 3. Let $\mathbf{v} = (2, 1) = 2\mathbf{i} + \mathbf{j}$ be a vector and let A be the point $A(3, 2)$. We find a point $P_0(x_0, y_0)$ such that $\mathbf{AP}_0 \parallel \mathbf{v}$ and $|\mathbf{AP}_0| = 5$.
  We have

$$\mathbf{AP}_0 = (x_0 - 3, y_0 - 2) = (x_0 - 3)\mathbf{i} + (y_0 - 2)\mathbf{j}.$$

By Theorem 2, $\mathbf{AP}_0 \parallel \mathbf{v} = 2\mathbf{i} + \mathbf{j} \Leftrightarrow$

$$x_0 - 3 = 2t, \qquad y_0 - 2 = t. \tag{4}$$

Using the condition about the length of $\mathbf{AP}_0$, we have

$$|\mathbf{AP}_0|^2 = (x_0 - 3)^2 + (y_0 - 2)^2 = 4t^2 + t^2 = 25;$$

thus $t^2 = 5$, or $t = \pm\sqrt{5}$. From (4) we find two candidates for P_0,

$$P_0(3 + 2\sqrt{5}, 2 + \sqrt{5}) \quad \text{and} \quad P_0'(3 - 2\sqrt{5}, 2 - \sqrt{5}).$$

Note that $\mathbf{AP}_0$ has the same sense as $\mathbf{v}$, $\mathbf{AP}_0'$ and $\mathbf{v}$ have opposite sense (see Figure 13).

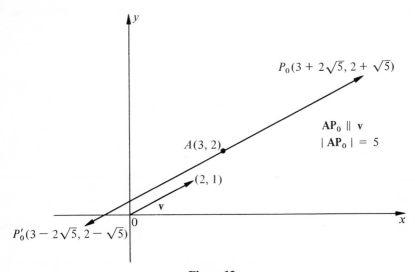

Figure 13

Example 4. We show that the figure obtained by joining the midpoints of adjacent sides of an arbitrary quadrilateral is a parallelogram.

First of all we choose the coordinate system so that one vertex of the quadrilateral $OABC$ is at the origin and one side lies along the positive x-axis (see Figure 14).

We use Theorem 1.19 to compute the coordinates of the midpoints M_1, M_2, M_3, M_4 as shown in Figure 14. It is now a simple matter to calculate the vectors $\mathbf{M_1M_2}$, $\mathbf{M_2\,M_3}$, $\mathbf{M_4\,M_3}$, and $\mathbf{M_1M_4}$:

$$\mathbf{M_1M_2} = \frac{b_1}{2}\mathbf{i} + \frac{b_2}{2}\mathbf{j} = \mathbf{M_4\,M_3},$$

$$\mathbf{M_2\,M_3} = \frac{c_1 - a_1}{2}\mathbf{i} + \frac{c_2}{2}\mathbf{j} = \mathbf{M_1M_4}.$$

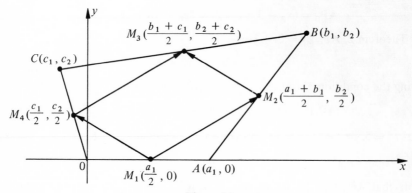

Figure 14

Since the opposite sides are equal vectors, hence parallel and of equal length, the figure $M_1M_2\,M_3\,M_4$ is a parallelogram. Notice that the use of vector methods enabled us to bypass the distance formula.

E X E R C I S E S

1. Let $\mathbf{a} = (-2, 3)$, $\mathbf{b} = (4, 2)$, $\mathbf{c} = (3, -5)$. Find:

   (a) $\mathbf{a} + \mathbf{b}$ and $\mathbf{b} + \mathbf{a}$.
   (b) $(\mathbf{a} + \mathbf{b}) + \mathbf{c}$ and $\mathbf{a} + (\mathbf{b} + \mathbf{c})$.
   (c) $(-1)\mathbf{a}$.
   (d) $\mathbf{a} - \mathbf{b}$ and $\mathbf{b} - \mathbf{a}$.
   (e) $2\mathbf{a} + 3\mathbf{b}$.
   (f) $3\mathbf{a} - 4\mathbf{b}$.

   (g) $\mathbf{a} + (-\mathbf{a})$.
   (h) $26\mathbf{a} + \mathbf{b} + 16\mathbf{c}$.
   (i) $2(\mathbf{a} + \mathbf{b})$ and $2\mathbf{a} + 2\mathbf{b}$.
   (j) $3\mathbf{a} + 4\mathbf{a}$ and $7\mathbf{a}$.
   (k) $-\dfrac{1}{26}\mathbf{b} - \dfrac{8}{13}\mathbf{c}$. Compare with $\mathbf{a}$.

2. Using the vectors $\mathbf{a}$, $\mathbf{b}$, and $\mathbf{c}$ of Exercise 1, draw $\mathbf{a} + \mathbf{b}$, $\mathbf{a} - \mathbf{b}$, $(\mathbf{a} + \mathbf{b}) + \mathbf{c}$, and $(-\mathbf{a})$.

3. Given the points $A(-2, -3)$, $B(4, 0)$, $C(6, 6)$, $D(-4, 1)$.

   (a) Find the vectors $\mathbf{AB}$, $\mathbf{BC}$, $\mathbf{CD}$, $\mathbf{DA}$.
   (b) What can be said about $\mathbf{AB}$ and $\mathbf{CD}$?
   (c) Find $|\mathbf{AD}|$.
   (d) Find a unit vector parallel to $\mathbf{BC}$.

4. Let $\mathbf{v} = (-4, 2) = -4\mathbf{i} + 2\mathbf{j}$.

   (a) Given the point $A(-5, -1)$, find B so that $\mathbf{AB} = \mathbf{v}$.
   (b) Given the point $D(-7, 2)$, find C so that $\mathbf{CD} = \mathbf{v}$.
   (c) Find $-\mathbf{u_v}$, a unit vector parallel to $\mathbf{v}$ but with opposite sense.

5. Let $\mathbf{v}_1 = (1, 1) = \mathbf{i} + \mathbf{j}$, $\mathbf{v}_2 = (-1, 2) = -\mathbf{i} + 2\mathbf{j}$. For each vector $\mathbf{a}$ given below find scalars c_1 and c_2 such that $\mathbf{a} = c_1\mathbf{v}_1 + c_2\mathbf{v}_2$.

   (a) $\mathbf{a} = (3, 0)$.   (d) $\mathbf{a} = (0, -4)$.
   (b) $\mathbf{a} = (-4, 3)$.   (e) $\mathbf{a} = (a_1, a_2)$.
   (c) $\mathbf{a} = (2, 5)$.

6. Given the points $A(-4, -3)$, $B(2, -2)$, $C(4, 5)$, $D(-1, 8)$, and $E(-7, 4)$, find:

   (a) $\mathbf{AB} + \mathbf{BC} + \mathbf{CD}$.   (b) $\mathbf{AE} + \mathbf{ED}$ (c) $\mathbf{AD}$.

7. Let $\mathbf{v}_1 = -3\mathbf{i} + 2\mathbf{j}$, $\mathbf{v}_2 = 6\mathbf{i} - 4\mathbf{j}$. Find scalars c_1 and c_2 such that $c_1\mathbf{v}_1 + c_2\mathbf{v}_2 = \mathbf{0}$.

8. Let $\mathbf{v}_1$ and $\mathbf{v}_2$ be vectors; suppose that there exist scalars c_1 and c_2, not both zero, such that $c_1\mathbf{v}_1 + c_2\mathbf{v}_2 = \mathbf{0}$. Prove that $\mathbf{v}_1$ and $\mathbf{v}_2$ are parallel.

9. Let $\mathbf{v}_1$ and $\mathbf{v}_2$ be two nonzero vectors. If $\mathbf{a} = a_1\mathbf{i} + a_2\mathbf{j}$ is any vector, is it possible to find scalars c_1 and c_2 such that $\mathbf{a} = c_1\mathbf{v}_1 + c_2\mathbf{v}_2$. [*Hints.* (i) See Exercise 5; and (ii) Suppose $\mathbf{v}_1$ and $\mathbf{v}_2$ are the two vectors of Exercise 7.]

10. Consider the point $P_0(-2, 3)$ and the line $y = x - 1$. Find the minimum (perpendicular) distance between P_0 and the line by the following method. Let $P(x, y)$ be any point on the line; find $\mathbf{P_0 P}$, and minimize $|\mathbf{P_0 P}|^2$.

11. Consider the point $A(-3, 2)$ and the vector $\mathbf{v} = (3, -4)$. Find the point $B(b_1, b_2)$ such that $\mathbf{AB}$ is parallel to $\mathbf{v}$ and $|\mathbf{AB}| = 10$. How many such points B are there?

12. If $\mathbf{a}$ and $\mathbf{b}$ are nonzero vectors, show that

$$\mathbf{v} = \frac{\mathbf{a}}{|\mathbf{a}|} + \frac{\mathbf{b}}{|\mathbf{b}|}$$

   bisects the angle between $\mathbf{a}$ and $\mathbf{b}$. Is this result still true if $\mathbf{a}$ and $\mathbf{b}$ are parallel but oppositely sensed?

13. Find the point P_0 described in each case below.

(a) P_0 is $\frac{1}{7}$ of the way from $A(-3, 2)$ to $B(4, -5)$.
(b) P_0 is $\frac{2}{5}$ of the way from $A(-2, -4)$ to $B(3, 1)$.
(c) P_0 is $\frac{2}{3}$ of the way from $A(-4, 2)$ to $B(8, 5)$.
(d) P_0 is on the line determined by $A(2, 1)$ and $B(6, 5)$, and A is the midpoint of $P_0 B$.

14. Prove Theorem 1.

11.3   The Inner Product

In this section we introduce a form of multiplication for vectors, the *inner product*. As we shall see, this product (also called the *dot product* or the *scalar product*) has many uses; in particular, it provides a convenient device for working with the angle between two vectors.

Definition 5. *Let* $\mathbf{a} = (a_1, a_2) = a_1\mathbf{i} + a_2\mathbf{j}$, $\mathbf{b} = (b_1, b_2) = b_1\mathbf{i} + b_2\mathbf{j}$. *Then the **inner product** of* $\mathbf{a}$ *and* $\mathbf{b}$ *is*

$$\mathbf{a} \cdot \mathbf{b} = a_1 b_1 + a_2 b_2. \tag{5}$$

The first point to remark about the inner product is that, by definition, the right-hand side of (5) is a scalar ($\in \mathbf{R}$). Thus the closure property does not hold; more exactly, the set of vectors in the plane is not closed with respect to this operation.

We next list a few properties of the inner product which follow easily from the definition.

Theorem 3. *Let* $\mathbf{a}$, $\mathbf{b}$, $\mathbf{c}$ *be arbitrary vectors, let* $h \in \mathbf{R}$. *Then*

1. $\mathbf{a} \cdot \mathbf{b} = \mathbf{b} \cdot \mathbf{a}$.
2. $h(\mathbf{a} \cdot \mathbf{b}) = (h\mathbf{a}) \cdot \mathbf{b} = \mathbf{a} \cdot (h\mathbf{b})$.
3. $\mathbf{a} \cdot (\mathbf{b} + \mathbf{c}) = \mathbf{a} \cdot \mathbf{b} + \mathbf{a} \cdot \mathbf{c}$.
4. $\mathbf{a} \cdot \mathbf{a} = |\mathbf{a}|^2$.

Proof. The commutativity is an immediate consequence of commutativity of multiplication in $\mathbf{R}$. For (2), let $\mathbf{a} = a_1\mathbf{i} + a_2\mathbf{j}$, $\mathbf{b} = b_1\mathbf{i} + b_2\mathbf{j}$. Then

$$h(\mathbf{a} \cdot \mathbf{b}) = h(a_1 b_1 + a_2 b_2) = ha_1 b_1 + ha_2 b_2,$$

$$(h\mathbf{a}) \cdot \mathbf{b} = (ha_1\mathbf{i} + ha_2\mathbf{j}) \cdot (b_1\mathbf{i} + b_2\mathbf{j}) = ha_1 b_1 + ha_2 b_2,$$

$$\mathbf{a} \cdot (h\mathbf{b}) = (a_1\mathbf{i} + a_2\mathbf{j}) \cdot (hb_1\mathbf{i} + hb_2\mathbf{j}) = ha_1 b_1 + ha_2 b_2.$$

The right-hand sides of these three equations being equal, the equality of the left-hand sides follows.

We leave the proof of (3), the distributivity, as an exercise. As for (4),

$$\mathbf{a} \cdot \mathbf{a} = a_1^2 + a_2^2 = |\mathbf{a}|^2,$$

by Definition 1. ∎

From (4) of Theorem 3, we see that

$$\left. \begin{array}{c} \mathbf{a} \cdot \mathbf{a} \geq 0, \\ \mathbf{a} \cdot \mathbf{a} = 0 \Leftrightarrow \mathbf{a} = \mathbf{0} \end{array} \right\}. \tag{6}$$

As a special case of the inner product we note the following results for the unit vectors $\mathbf{i}$ and $\mathbf{j}$:

$$\left\{ \begin{array}{c} \mathbf{i} \cdot \mathbf{i} = \mathbf{j} \cdot \mathbf{j} = 1 \\ \mathbf{i} \cdot \mathbf{j} = 0 \end{array} \right\}. \tag{7}$$

The following property is frequently used as the definition of the inner product. Notice that Eq. (8) is coordinate free.

Theorem 4. *Let* $\mathbf{a}$ *and* $\mathbf{b}$ *be arbitrary vectors. Then*

$$\mathbf{a} \cdot \mathbf{b} = |\mathbf{a}| \, |\mathbf{b}| \cos \theta, \tag{8}$$

where θ is the angle between the vectors when they are drawn with the same initial point, $0 \leq \theta \leq \pi$.

Proof. (See Figure 15.) We use the law of cosines on triangle OAB. As $\mathbf{AB} = \mathbf{b} - \mathbf{a}$, the equation given by the law of cosines, written in vector form, becomes

$$|\mathbf{b} - \mathbf{a}|^2 = |\mathbf{a}|^2 + |\mathbf{b}|^2 - 2|\mathbf{a}| \, |\mathbf{b}| \cos \theta.$$

If we use (4) of Theorem 3 the above equation becomes

$$(\mathbf{b} - \mathbf{a}) \cdot (\mathbf{b} - \mathbf{a}) = \mathbf{a} \cdot \mathbf{a} + \mathbf{b} \cdot \mathbf{b} - 2|\mathbf{a}| \, |\mathbf{b}| \cos \theta. \tag{9}$$

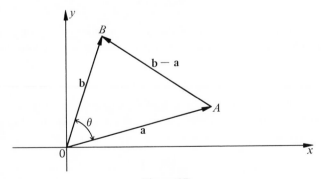

Figure 15

By (1), (2), and (3) of Theorem 3, we can transform the left side of (9) as follows:

$$(\mathbf{b} - \mathbf{a}) \cdot (\mathbf{b} - \mathbf{a}) = (\mathbf{b} - \mathbf{a}) \cdot \mathbf{b} - (\mathbf{b} - \mathbf{a}) \cdot \mathbf{a}$$
$$= \mathbf{b} \cdot (\mathbf{b} - \mathbf{a}) - \mathbf{a} \cdot (\mathbf{b} - \mathbf{a})$$
$$= \mathbf{b} \cdot \mathbf{b} - \mathbf{b} \cdot \mathbf{a} - \mathbf{a} \cdot \mathbf{b} + \mathbf{a} \cdot \mathbf{a}$$
$$= \mathbf{a} \cdot \mathbf{a} + \mathbf{b} \cdot \mathbf{b} - 2\mathbf{a} \cdot \mathbf{b}.$$

It follows from this equation and from (9) that

$$\mathbf{a} \cdot \mathbf{b} = |\mathbf{a}| \, |\mathbf{b}| \cos \theta. \quad \blacksquare$$

[This theorem provides us with a useful physical interpretation of the inner product, one which could serve as motivation for its definition in terms of $\mathbf{a} \cdot \mathbf{b} = |\mathbf{a}| \, |\mathbf{b}| \cos \theta$.

Recall that if a constant force of magnitude F moves a particle a distance r along a straight line, and if the force is also directed along this line, then the measure W of work done is, by definition, $W = Fr$. (see Section 9.5)

However, it may happen that the constant force vector $\mathbf{F}$ is not directed along the line of motion. In this case the work done is the product of the component of $\mathbf{F}$ along the line of motion and the distance. But if we introduce the displacement *vector* $\mathbf{r}$ (if the particle moves from A to B, then $\mathbf{r} = \mathbf{AB}$), it is easy to see (Figure 16) that the work done is precisely

$$W = |\mathbf{F}| \cos \theta \, |\mathbf{r}| = |\mathbf{F}| \, |\mathbf{r}| \cos \theta = \mathbf{F} \cdot \mathbf{r}. \tag{10}$$

In Section 14.9 we shall generalize this result.]

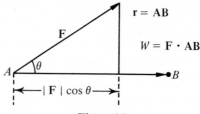

Figure 16

Further insight into the nature of the inner product is given by considering the result of Theorem 4 with $\mathbf{a}$ a unit vector, i.e., $|\mathbf{a}| = 1$. In this case Eq. (8) reduces to

$$\mathbf{a} \cdot \mathbf{b} = |\mathbf{b}| \cos \theta, \tag{11}$$

which is called the *scalar projection of* $\mathbf{b}$ *along* $\mathbf{a}$ (see Figure 17).

Related to this result is the following: if $\mathbf{a} = a_1 \mathbf{i} + a_2 \mathbf{j}$ is an arbitrary vector, then

$$\left. \begin{aligned} \mathbf{a} \cdot \mathbf{i} &= a_1 \\ \mathbf{a} \cdot \mathbf{j} &= a_2 \end{aligned} \right\}. \tag{12}$$

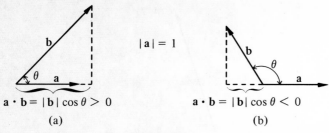

$$\mathbf{a} \cdot \mathbf{b} = |\mathbf{b}| \cos \theta > 0 \qquad\qquad \mathbf{a} \cdot \mathbf{b} = |\mathbf{b}| \cos \theta < 0$$

(a)   (b)

Figure 17

From Eq. (8) we obtain a convenient description for perpendicularity of vectors. First we make the agreement that the vector **0** is perpendicular to every vector.

Theorem 5. *The vectors* **a** *and* **b** *are perpendicular if and only if* $\mathbf{a} \cdot \mathbf{b} = 0$. *In symbols,*

$$\mathbf{a} \perp \mathbf{b} \Leftrightarrow \mathbf{a} \cdot \mathbf{b} = 0. \qquad\qquad (13)$$

Before giving the rather easy proof, we remark that the effect of this symbolic statement is to give an *arithmetic* description of the *geometric* property of perpendicularity.

Proof. Suppose first $\mathbf{a} \perp \mathbf{b}$. Then $\theta = \dfrac{\pi}{2}$, so $\cos \theta = 0$, and, by (8), $\mathbf{a} \cdot \mathbf{b} = 0$.
Next, if $\mathbf{a} \cdot \mathbf{b} = 0$, we have from (8) that

$$|\mathbf{a}|\,|\mathbf{b}| \cos \theta = 0.$$

Now, if either $\mathbf{a} = \mathbf{0}$ or $\mathbf{b} = \mathbf{0}$, then our result follows from the agreement made above about the zero vector. And if neither **a** nor **b** is the zero vector, then $|\mathbf{a}|\,|\mathbf{b}| \neq 0$, so we must have $\cos \theta = 0$, or $\theta = \dfrac{\pi}{2}$. Consequently, $\mathbf{a} \perp \mathbf{b}$. ∎

Example 5. We find the angle between the vectors **AB** and **AC**, where $A(2, 1)$, $B(5, 3)$, $C(4, 7)$ (see Figure 18).
    Let

$$\mathbf{b} = \mathbf{AB} = 3\mathbf{i} + 2\mathbf{j}$$

$$\mathbf{c} = \mathbf{AC} = 2\mathbf{i} + 6\mathbf{j}.$$

Then $\mathbf{b} \cdot \mathbf{c} = 3 \cdot 2 + 2 \cdot 6 = 18$; also,

$$|\mathbf{b}| = \sqrt{\mathbf{b} \cdot \mathbf{b}} = \sqrt{9 + 4} = \sqrt{13}$$

$$|\mathbf{c}| = \sqrt{\mathbf{c} \cdot \mathbf{c}} = \sqrt{4 + 36} = 2\sqrt{10}.$$

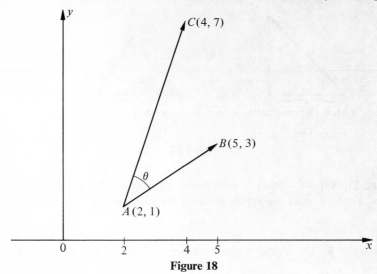

Figure 18

Since $\mathbf{b} \cdot \mathbf{c} = |\mathbf{b}|\,|\mathbf{c}| \cos \theta$, we have

$$\cos \theta = \frac{\mathbf{b} \cdot \mathbf{c}}{|\mathbf{b}|\,|\mathbf{c}|} = \frac{18}{\sqrt{13}(2\sqrt{10})} = \frac{9}{\sqrt{130}}$$

or

$$\theta = \cos^{-1} \frac{9}{\sqrt{130}} \approx \cos^{-1} 0.789 \approx 0.66 \approx 37° - 50'.$$

Example 6. We use the inner product to determine whether the angle between the vectors $\mathbf{a} = 3\mathbf{i} + 4\mathbf{j}$ and $\mathbf{b} = -7\mathbf{i} + 5\mathbf{j}$ is acute or obtuse (see Figure 19).

Since $\mathbf{a} \cdot \mathbf{b} = -21 + 20 = -1 < 0$, it follows that $\cos \theta < 0$; thus θ lies between $\dfrac{\pi}{2}$ and π.

Example 7. Let $\mathbf{a} = 3\mathbf{i} - 4\mathbf{j}$, $\mathbf{b} = 5\mathbf{i} + 12\mathbf{j}$. We find the scalar projection of $\mathbf{b}$ along $\mathbf{a}$. To this end we first find the unit vector $\mathbf{u_a}$ with the same direction (and sense) as $\mathbf{a}$:

$$\mathbf{u_a} = \tfrac{3}{5}\mathbf{i} - \tfrac{4}{5}\mathbf{j}, \qquad \text{since } |\mathbf{a}| = 5.$$

Then the scalar projection of $\mathbf{b}$ along $\mathbf{a}$ is given by

$$\mathbf{u_a} \cdot \mathbf{b} = \tfrac{3}{5} \cdot 5 + (-\tfrac{4}{5}) \cdot 12 = -6\tfrac{3}{5}.$$

Thus the length of this projection is $6\tfrac{3}{5}$ units, the minus sign indicates the projection lies on the negative extension of $\mathbf{a}$ (see Figure 20).

The inner product satisfies an important inequality, the Cauchy–Schwarz Inequality. For the simple case we are now considering the proof is an easy consequence of Theorem 4 (see Exercise 17); however we give a more general proof.

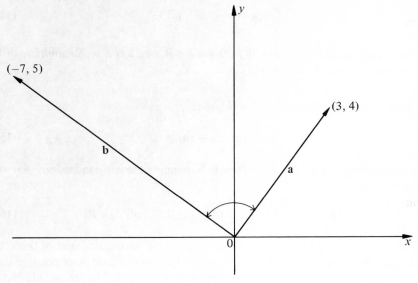

Figure 19

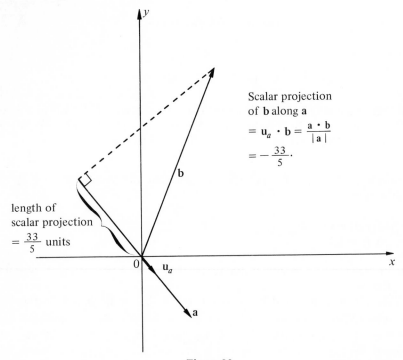

Scalar projection
of **b** along **a**

$= \mathbf{u}_a \cdot \mathbf{b} = \dfrac{\mathbf{a} \cdot \mathbf{b}}{|\mathbf{a}|}$

$= -\dfrac{33}{5}.$

length of
scalar projection
$= \dfrac{33}{5}$ units

Figure 20

Theorem 6. *(Cauchy–Schwarz Inequality). For any two vectors* **a** *and* **b**

$$(\mathbf{a} \cdot \mathbf{b})^2 \leq |\mathbf{a}|^2 \, |\mathbf{b}|^2. \tag{14}$$

Equality holds if and only if $\mathbf{a} = h\mathbf{b}$ *for some* $h \in \mathbf{R}$, i.e., **a** *is a scalar multiple of* **b** *(which means* **a** *and* **b** *are parallel).*

Proof. For all $t \in \mathbf{R}$ we have, by (6), that

$$(\mathbf{a} - t\mathbf{b}) \cdot (\mathbf{a} - t\mathbf{b}) \geq 0, \tag{15}$$

equality holding if and only if $\mathbf{a} - t\mathbf{b} = \mathbf{0}$. Expanding the left-hand side of (15) we have

$$(\mathbf{b} \cdot \mathbf{b})t^2 - 2(\mathbf{a} \cdot \mathbf{b})t + (\mathbf{a} \cdot \mathbf{a}) \geq 0, \qquad \text{all} \quad t \in \mathbf{R}. \tag{16}$$

Now the theory of quadratic equations tells us that the discriminant of the left-hand side of (16) must be nonpositive—for if the discriminant were positive the equation obtained by setting the left-hand side of (16) equal to zero would have two real and unequal roots; but this means that, for some values of t the expression would be negative, contradicting (15). This condition on the discriminant gives

$$4(\mathbf{a} \cdot \mathbf{b})^2 - 4(\mathbf{b} \cdot \mathbf{b})(\mathbf{a} \cdot \mathbf{a}) \leq 0,$$

or

$$(\mathbf{a} \cdot \mathbf{b})^2 \leq |\mathbf{a}|^2 \, |\mathbf{b}|^2.$$

Moreover, if equality holds in (14), then the left-hand side of (15) will equal zero for some value h of t. By (6), then, $\mathbf{a} - h\mathbf{b} = \mathbf{0}$, or $\mathbf{a} = h\mathbf{b}$. If, conversely, $\mathbf{a} = h\mathbf{b}$ for some $h \in \mathbf{R}$, it is easy to see that $(\mathbf{a} \cdot \mathbf{b})^2 = |\mathbf{a}|^2 \, |\mathbf{b}|^2$. ∎

Example 8. We find the value of c such that the vectors $\mathbf{a} = \mathbf{i} + 3\mathbf{j}$ and $\mathbf{b} = 2\mathbf{i} + c\mathbf{j}$ are

    (i) perpendicular,
    (ii) parallel.

(i) By Theorem 5, **a** and **b** are perpendicular $\Leftrightarrow \mathbf{a} \cdot \mathbf{b} = 0 \Leftrightarrow 2 + 3c = 0 \Leftrightarrow$
    $c = -\frac{2}{3}$.
(ii) By Theorem 6, **a** and **b** are parallel $\Leftrightarrow (\mathbf{a} \cdot \mathbf{b})^2 = |\mathbf{a}|^2 \, |\mathbf{b}|^2$; thus the condition is

$$(2 + 3c)^2 = 10(4 + c^2),$$

from which we find $c = 6$.

EXERCISES

In Exercises 1–10 find cos θ, where θ is the angle between the given vectors; also find the scalar projection of the second vector on the first.

1. $\mathbf{a} = 3\mathbf{i} - \mathbf{j}$, $\mathbf{b} = -2\mathbf{i} + 5\mathbf{j}$.   2. $\mathbf{a} = \mathbf{i} + 4\mathbf{j}$, $\mathbf{b} = -3\mathbf{i} + 2\mathbf{j}$.

3. $\mathbf{a} = 2\mathbf{i} - 7\mathbf{j}$, $\mathbf{b} = -4\mathbf{i} + 14\mathbf{j}$.   4. $\mathbf{a} = 4\mathbf{i} - 3\mathbf{j}$, $\mathbf{b} = 6\mathbf{i} + 8\mathbf{j}$.

5. **AB, CD**, where $A(3, -2)$, $B(3, 4)$, $C(-4, 1)$, $D(-1, -1)$.

6. **AB, CD**, where $A(0, 3)$, $B(3, 4)$, $C(-2, 0)$, $D(0, -4)$.

7. $\mathbf{a} = \mathbf{i} + \mathbf{j}$, $\mathbf{b} = \mathbf{i} - \mathbf{j}$.   8. $\mathbf{a} = 3\mathbf{i} + 4\mathbf{j}$, $\mathbf{b} = 5\mathbf{i} - 12\mathbf{j}$.

9. $\mathbf{a} = -4\mathbf{i} - 3\mathbf{j}$, $\mathbf{b} = 7\mathbf{i} + 24\mathbf{j}$.   10. $\mathbf{a} = -3\mathbf{i} + 5\mathbf{j}$, $\mathbf{b} = -3\mathbf{i} + 4\mathbf{j}$.

11. Find the cosines of the angles of the triangle with vertices $A(-3, -2)$, $B(5, 1)$, $C(2, 4)$.

12. Find c such that $\mathbf{a} = 3\mathbf{i} - 5\mathbf{j}$ and $\mathbf{b} = c\mathbf{i} + 6\mathbf{j}$ are perpendicular.

13. Find c such that the vectors of Exercise 12 intersect at an angle of $\dfrac{\pi}{3}$.

14. Find c such that the vectors $\mathbf{a} = -4\mathbf{i} + 3\mathbf{j}$ and $\mathbf{b} = \mathbf{i} + c\mathbf{j}$ intersect at an angle of $\dfrac{3\pi}{4}$.

15. Find b_1 and b_2 so that $\mathbf{b} = b_1\mathbf{i} + b_2\mathbf{j}$ is a unit vector perpendicular to $\mathbf{a} = 6\mathbf{i} - 8\mathbf{j}$.

16. Prove assertion (3) of Theorem 3.

17. Use Eq. (8) of Theorem 4 to prove Theorem 6.

18. Let
$$\mathbf{a} = 4\mathbf{i} + 3\mathbf{j},$$
$$\mathbf{b} = -\mathbf{i} + 2\mathbf{j},$$
$$\mathbf{v} = -13\mathbf{i} + 4\mathbf{j}.$$

Find scalars h and k such that $\mathbf{v} = h\mathbf{a} + k\mathbf{b}$. [*Hint.* Using both expressions for $\mathbf{v}$, calculate $\mathbf{v} \cdot \mathbf{a}$ and $\mathbf{v} \cdot \mathbf{b}$ and solve the resulting system of linear equations for h and k.]

19. See Exercise 18. Let $\mathbf{a}$ and $\mathbf{b}$ be fixed nonzero, nonparallel vectors. Let $\mathbf{v}$ be an arbitrary vector.

(a) Find scalars h and k such that $\mathbf{v} = h\mathbf{a} + k\mathbf{b}$. [*Hint.* Solve the system of equations obtained from $\mathbf{v} \cdot \mathbf{a}$ and $\mathbf{v} \cdot \mathbf{b}$.]

(b) Show that if **a** and **b** are perpendicular the h and k obtained in (a) reduce to

$$h = \frac{\mathbf{v} \cdot \mathbf{a}}{\mathbf{a} \cdot \mathbf{a}}, \qquad k = \frac{\mathbf{v} \cdot \mathbf{b}}{\mathbf{b} \cdot \mathbf{b}}.$$

(c) Find the h and k of part (a) on the assumption that **a** and **b** are unit vectors but not necessarily perpendicular.

(d) Show that, if **a** and **b** are unit vectors *and* perpendicular, then

$$h = \mathbf{v} \cdot \mathbf{a} \quad \text{and} \quad k = \mathbf{v} \cdot \mathbf{b}. \tag{17}$$

20. See Exercise 19. Let **a** be a unit vector which makes an angle α with the positive x-axis and let **b** be a unit vector which makes an angle of $+\dfrac{\pi}{2}$ with **a** (see Figure 21). The terminal points of **a** and **b** are, then, $(\cos \alpha, \sin \alpha)$ and $\left[\cos\left(\alpha + \dfrac{\pi}{2}\right), \sin\left(\alpha + \dfrac{\pi}{2}\right)\right] = (-\sin \alpha, \cos \alpha)$, respectively. Thus

$$\mathbf{a} = \cos \alpha \mathbf{i} + \sin \alpha \mathbf{j},$$
$$\mathbf{b} = -\sin \alpha \mathbf{i} + \cos \alpha \mathbf{j}.$$

Let $\mathbf{v} = x\mathbf{i} + y\mathbf{j}$ be an arbitrary vector. Use (17) to express **v** in terms of **a** and **b**.

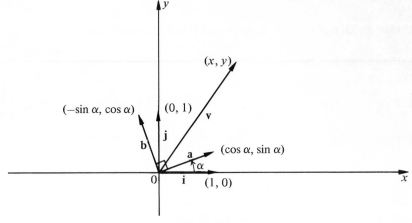

Figure 21

11.4   Vector Functions and Parametric Equations

In this section we introduce the concept of a vector function (more exactly, a vector-valued function—the precise definition will be given shortly) and exploit its geometric implications.

Recall that we introduced, just prior to Theorem 1, the symbol $\mathbf{R}^2$ for the set of all vectors in the plane (with the properties described by Definitions 1, 2, and 3). We shall also make use in what follows of a nonempty set $T \subset \mathbf{R}$; it will usually be satisfactory to think of T as an interval—finite, infinite, open, closed, possibly $T = \mathbf{R}$.

Definition 6. *By a vector function* **r**, *we mean a function which maps a non-empty set $T \subset \mathbf{R}$ into* $\mathbf{R}^2$. *In symbols,*

$$\mathbf{r} : T \to \mathbf{R}^2, \qquad T \subset \mathbf{R}, \qquad T \neq \emptyset.$$

As each $t_0 \in T$ determines a vector in $\mathbf{R}^2$, we can write

$$\mathbf{r}(t_0) = x_0 \mathbf{i} + y_0 \mathbf{j};$$

this statement holding true for every $t \in T$, we can write more generally that

$$\mathbf{r}(t) = x(t)\mathbf{i} + y(t)\mathbf{j},$$

where x and y are *scalar* functions (i.e., the functional values are in $\mathbf{R}$) determined by **r**. Conversely, given a pair of functions, f and g,

$$f : T \to \mathbf{R}$$

$$g : T \to \mathbf{R},$$

we can define a vector function **r** by

$$\mathbf{r}(t) = f(t)\mathbf{i} + g(t)\mathbf{j}, \qquad \forall t \in T.$$

Thus we see that, just as a vector is an ordered pair of scalars (numbers in $\mathbf{R}$), so is a vector function with domain T an ordered pair of scalar functions defined on T (with ranges in $\mathbf{R}$).

We now look at some examples.

Example 9. Suppose **r** is defined by the equation

$$\mathbf{r}(t) = (2t - 1)\mathbf{i} + (4 - t)\mathbf{j}.$$

In this case $T = \mathbf{R}$. We obtain a geometric interpretation of this function by considering, for every $t \in T$, $\mathbf{r}(t)$ as the vector from the origin to the point $(2t - 1, 4 - t)$. The set of these terminal points then describes a curve in the plane. As a crude method of determining the nature of this curve, it is possible to assign values to t and calculate corresponding values of x and y. Thus

$$\mathbf{r}(0) = -\mathbf{i} + 4\mathbf{j}$$

$$\mathbf{r}(1) = \mathbf{i} + 3\mathbf{j}$$

$$\mathbf{r}(2) = 3\mathbf{i} + 2\mathbf{j}, \text{ etc.}$$

(see Figure 22).

It would appear—and it is true—that the graph of **r** is in this case a straight line. In fact, if we consider the two scalar functions determined by **r**:

$$x = 2t - 1$$

$$y = 4 - t,$$

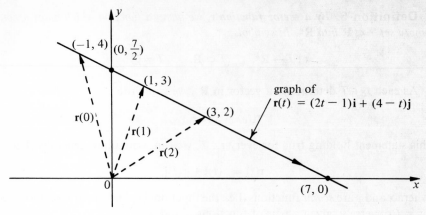

Figure 22

we see that we can solve the first of these for t and substitute into the second, thereby obtaining

$$y = 4 - \frac{x+1}{2} = -\frac{1}{2}x + \frac{7}{2},$$

the graph of which is clearly a line.

Example 10. Consider the function **r** defined by

$$\mathbf{r}(t) = \cos t\mathbf{i} + \sin t\mathbf{j}. \tag{18}$$

Clearly one can take $T = \mathbf{R}$. To discern the geometric description we note that for *every* t,

$$|\mathbf{r}(t)| = \sqrt{\cos^2 t + \sin^2 t} = 1.$$

Thus the vectors $\mathbf{r}(t)$ are all unit vectors and the curve described is the unit circle. Notice, however, that the circle is described completely for $0 \le t < 2\pi$, and we could take $T = [0, 2\pi)$. Choosing $T = [0, 4\pi)$ would give the circle described twice (see Figure 23).

Example 11. Let

$$\mathbf{r}(t) = \frac{1-t^2}{1+t^2}\mathbf{i} + \frac{2t}{1+t^2}\mathbf{j}. \tag{19}$$

Again we look at the magnitudes of the vectors $\mathbf{r}(t)$:

$$|\mathbf{r}(t)|^2 = \left(\frac{1-t^2}{1+t^2}\right)^2 + \left(\frac{2t}{1+t^2}\right)^2 = 1.$$

Thus it would appear that the set of points determined by (19) is the same as that determined by (18). A more complete description is this: every point determined by (19) is also determined by (18), but not conversely. In particular, the point $(-1, 0)$ cannot be obtained from (19); moreover, if t is not restricted, i.e., if t

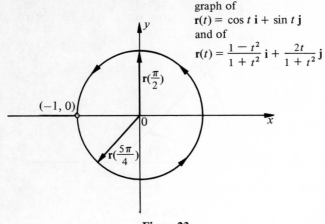

graph of
$$\mathbf{r}(t) = \cos t\,\mathbf{i} + \sin t\,\mathbf{j}$$
and of
$$\mathbf{r}(t) = \frac{1-t^2}{1+t^2}\,\mathbf{i} + \frac{2t}{1+t^2}\,\mathbf{j}$$

Figure 23

runs through all of **R**, Eq. (18) gives every point of the circle infinitely many times, whereas the points of (19) trace out the circle (minus $(-1, 0)$) exactly once for $-\infty < t < \infty$ (see Exercise 15).

Example 12. Consider the function **r** defined by

$$\mathbf{r}(t) = \cos^2\left(\frac{\pi}{2}t\right)\mathbf{i} + \sin^2\left(\frac{\pi}{2}t\right)\mathbf{j}.$$

Letting

$$x = \cos^2\frac{\pi}{2}t,$$

$$y = \sin^2\frac{\pi}{2}t,$$

we can see that for all $t \Rightarrow x + y = 1$, $x \geq 0$, $y \geq 0$. Thus the graph of this function is the line segment shown in Figure 24. Note, however, that the entire segment is obtained for $0 \leq t \leq 1$; the t interval, $1 \leq t \leq 2$, gives the same segment described in the opposite direction.

Several remarks are now in order. At first glance there may not seem to be any advantage in introducing vector functions; we have, geometrically, what was available all along; namely, curves in the plane defined either by functions or relations, and at the expense of having to work with an additional variable, t, which is usually called a *parameter*. However, there is considerably more to the story than that. First, when it comes to studying curves in three dimensions it becomes almost necessary to use vector functions (or their equivalent in three-space, triples of functions of a parameter). For, as we shall see, a single equation involving three variables (x, y, z, say) will usually determine a *two-dimensional* set of points, a *surface* (thus a sphere is determined by an equation such as $x^2 + y^2 + z^2 = 1$). Second, the use of vector equations and the parameter t

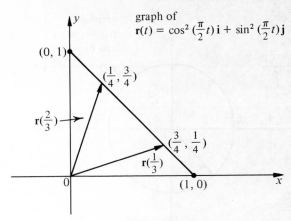

graph of
$$\mathbf{r}(t) = \cos^2\left(\frac{\pi}{2}t\right)\mathbf{i} + \sin^2\left(\frac{\pi}{2}t\right)\mathbf{j}$$

Figure 24

enables us to assign, in a natural way, a direction to a curve: the positive direction is that determined by increasing t. Moreover, vector functions provide a natural mechanism for dealing with problems of motion in the plane—we shall consider this topic in subsequent sections. Another advantage, which we will shortly investigate in detail, is the following: frequently a curve is defined by a geometric condition which is of such a nature that an analytic description of the curve is most easily and naturally obtained by introducing an auxiliary variable, in short, a *parameter*.

To be sure, as Examples 10 and 11 partially illustrated, a given curve may have several different (many different, in fact) representations in terms of a parameter, different *parametrizations*, as they are called (examples appear in the following exercises). Realization of this fact raises some questions. *Which* parametrization should one use? Do some parametrizations have advantages over others? These and other questions, which occur later, are legitimate, but the fact remains that the use of vector functions (or parametric equations) in the study of curves is a powerful tool which it is better not to be without.

E X E R C I S E S

In numbers 1–14 determine the nature of the curve described by the function $\mathbf{r}$. In each case indicate the positive direction along the curve.

1. $\mathbf{r}(t) = (t+1)\mathbf{i} + (t-1)\mathbf{j}$, $T = [0, 1]$.

2. $\mathbf{r}(t) = (t+1)\mathbf{i} + (t-1)\mathbf{j}$, $T = [1, \infty)$.

3. $\mathbf{r}(t) = (t+1)\mathbf{i} + (t-1)\mathbf{j}$, $T = (-\infty, \infty)$.

4. $\mathbf{r}(t) = t\mathbf{i} + \sqrt{4-t^2}\,\mathbf{j}$, $T = [-2, 2]$.

5. $\mathbf{r}(t) = t\mathbf{i} - \sqrt{4-t^2}\,\mathbf{j}$, $\qquad T = [-2, 2]$.

6. $\mathbf{r}(t) = (1-t^2)\mathbf{i} + t^2\mathbf{j}$, $\qquad T = [0, 1]$.

7. $\mathbf{r}(t) = (1-t)\mathbf{i} + t\mathbf{j}$, $\qquad T = [0, 1]$.

8. $\mathbf{r}(t) = t\mathbf{i} + t^2\mathbf{j}$, $\qquad T = \mathbf{R}$.

9. $\mathbf{r}(t) = t^2\mathbf{i} + t^3\mathbf{j}$, $\qquad T = \mathbf{R}$.

10. $\mathbf{r}(t) = t^3\mathbf{i} + t^2\mathbf{j}$, $\qquad T = \mathbf{R}$.

11. $\mathbf{r}(t) = \left(a\cos^4\dfrac{\pi}{2}t\right)\mathbf{i} + \left(a\sin^4\dfrac{\pi}{2}t\right)\mathbf{j}$, $\qquad a > 0, T = [0, 1]$.

12. $\mathbf{r}(t) = \left(a\cos^4\dfrac{\pi}{2}t\right)\mathbf{i} + \left(a\sin^4\dfrac{\pi}{2}t\right)\mathbf{j}$, $\qquad a > 0, T = [1, 2]$.

13. $\mathbf{r}(t) = \left(a\cos^3\dfrac{\pi}{2}t\right)\mathbf{i} + \left(a\sin^3\dfrac{\pi}{2}t\right)\mathbf{j}$, $\qquad a > 0, T = [0, 1]$.

14. $\mathbf{r}(t) = \left(a\cos^3\dfrac{\pi}{2}t\right)\mathbf{i} + \left(a\sin^3\dfrac{\pi}{2}t\right)\mathbf{j}$, $\qquad a > 0, T = [0, 4)$.

15. This refers to Example 11. Describe the portion of the circle determined by the following intervals.

(a) $T = (-\infty, -1]$.   (b) $T = [-1, 0]$.   (c) $T = [0, 1]$.   (d) $T = [1, \infty)$.

16. This refers to Example 11. Prove the assertion made in the text that $(-1, 0)$ does not lie on the curve determined by Eq. (19) (see Exercise 15).

17. Is there any relation between the curves described below? Explain.

(a) $\mathbf{r}(t) = t\mathbf{i} + t^2\mathbf{j}$, $\quad T = \mathbf{R}$.   (c) $\mathbf{r}(t) = t^5\mathbf{i} + t^{10}\mathbf{j}$, $\quad T = \mathbf{R}$.
(b) $\mathbf{r}(t) = t^3\mathbf{i} + t^6\mathbf{j}$, $\quad T = \mathbf{R}$.   (d) $\mathbf{r}(t) = (\cos t)\mathbf{i} + (1 - \sin^2 t)\mathbf{j}$, $\quad T = [0, \pi]$.

18. Compare the curves determined by the following functions.

(a) $\mathbf{r}(t) = t\mathbf{i} + t^3\mathbf{j}$, $\quad T = \mathbf{R}$.   (b) $\mathbf{r}(t) = t^3\mathbf{i} + t^9\mathbf{j}$, $\quad T = \mathbf{R}$.
(c) $\mathbf{r}(t) = (\cos t)\mathbf{i} + \tfrac{1}{4}(\cos 3t + 3\cos t)\mathbf{j}$, $\quad T = [0, \pi]$.

19. Let $A(1, 1)$ and $\mathbf{v} = \mathbf{i} + 2\mathbf{j}$. Find the vector function which describes the line through A in the direction of $\mathbf{v}$. [*Hint.* Let P be a point on the desired line. Then $\mathbf{OP} = \mathbf{OA} + \mathbf{AP} = (\mathbf{i} + \mathbf{j}) + t\mathbf{v}$. Let $\mathbf{r}(t) = \mathbf{OP}$.

20. Let $A(-3, 2)$ and $\mathbf{v} = 2\mathbf{i} - \mathbf{j}$. Find the vector function which describes the line through A in the direction of $\mathbf{v}$ (see Exercise 19).

21. Let $A(a, b)$ and $\mathbf{v} = h\mathbf{i} + k\mathbf{j}$. Find the vector function which describes the line through A in the direction of $\mathbf{v}$ (see Exercise 19).

22. Let $\mathbf{r}(t) = x(t)\mathbf{i} + y(t)\mathbf{j}$, where x and y are linear functions of t. Show that $\mathbf{r}$ determines a straight line. [*Hint.* Let

$$x(t) = a + ht$$
$$y(t) = b + kt$$

(see Exercise 21).]

23. Given a vector function $\mathbf{r}$ or, equivalently, a pair of scalar functions x and y, it is sometimes desirable to eliminate the parameter t from the scalar equations, obtaining therefrom a relation between x and y, possibly expressing y as a function of x. This latter can always be done, as was illustrated in Example 9, if one can find the function inverse to x, $t = x^{-1}$, and then substitute this result into the formula for y. In other cases, an identity, perhaps a trigonometric identity, can be used (see Example 12); e.g., in Example 10, where

$$x(t) = \cos t$$
$$y(t) = \sin t,$$

we find that $x^2 + y^2 = 1$. In still other cases, no obvious procedure presents itself, and one must conjure up whatever ingenuity one can. Eliminate the parameter from the following:

(a) $\begin{cases} x = t + 1 \\ y = t - 1 \end{cases}$ (See Exercise 1).

(b) $\begin{cases} x = t \\ y = \sqrt{4 - t^2} \end{cases}$ (See Exercise 4).

(c) $\begin{cases} x = t^2 \\ y = t^3 \end{cases}$ (See Exercise 9).

(d) $\mathbf{r}(t)$, as given in Exercise 14.

(e) $\mathbf{r}(t)$, as given in Exercise 17(a).

(f) $\mathbf{r}(t)$, as given in Exercise 17(d).

(g) $\begin{cases} x = 2a \cot \varphi \\ y = 2a \sin^2 \varphi \end{cases}$.

(h) $\begin{cases} x = a \cot \varphi \\ y = b \sin \varphi \cos \varphi \end{cases}$.

11.5   Use of a Parameter in Geometric Problems

In this section we devote a little attention to a problem mentioned in the discussion at the end of the preceding section: obtaining with the aid of a parameter an analytic representation of a curve which has been defined by some geometric condition. Our approach will be through a series of examples.

Example 13. We consider a curve which is defined in terms of two fixed auxiliary curves: a circle $\mathscr{C}$ of diameter a, center at $\left(\dfrac{a}{2}, 0\right)$; and the line l, $x = a$ (see Figure 25). The desired curve is the set of points P obtained as follows: a line is drawn through the origin making an angle θ, $-\dfrac{\pi}{2} < \theta < \dfrac{\pi}{2}$, with the positive x-axis, intersecting $\mathscr{C}$ at Q and l at M. The point P, on this variable line, is such that $\mathbf{OP} = \mathbf{QM}$.

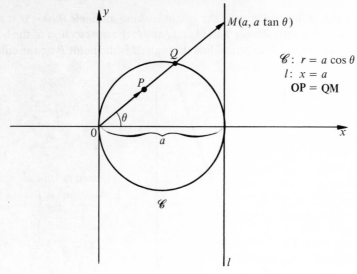

Figure 25

The polar coordinate equation of $\mathscr{C}$ is $r = a \cos \theta$. As $x = r \cos \theta$, $y = r \sin \theta$, the rectangular coordinates of Q are $Q(a \cos^2 \theta, a \sin \theta \cos \theta)$. Thus, taking the angle θ, $\theta \in \left(-\dfrac{\pi}{2}, \dfrac{\pi}{2}\right)$ as parameter, we have

$$\mathbf{OQ} = \mathbf{QM} = \mathbf{OM} - \mathbf{OQ}$$
$$= (a\mathbf{i} + a \tan \theta \mathbf{j}) - (a \cos^2 \theta \mathbf{i} + a \sin \theta \cos \theta \mathbf{j})$$
$$= a(1 - \cos^2 \theta)\mathbf{i} + a(\tan \theta - \sin \theta \cos \theta)\mathbf{j},$$
$$\mathbf{r}(\theta) = a \sin^2 \theta \mathbf{i} + a \frac{\sin^3 \theta}{\cos \theta} \mathbf{j},$$

where $\mathbf{r}(\theta) = \mathbf{OP}$.

The curve, called the Cissoid of Diocles, has parametric equations

$$\begin{cases} x = a \sin^2 \theta \\ y = a \dfrac{\sin^3 \theta}{\cos \theta} \end{cases}, \qquad -\frac{\pi}{2} < \theta < \frac{\pi}{2}. \tag{20}$$

We leave it as an exercise to show that if the parameter θ is eliminated one obtains

$$y^2 = \frac{x^3}{a - x}. \tag{21}$$

The curve, the nature of which is reasonably apparent from the original definition, is shown in Figure 26.

Example 14. Again we consider a curve defined in terms of a circle $\mathscr{C}$, $r = 2a \sin \theta$, and a straight line l, $y = 2a$. A point P on the curve is obtained as follows: a line is drawn through the origin making an angle θ ($0 < \theta < \pi$) with the positive x-axis, intersecting $\mathscr{C}$ at Q and l at M; the intersection of the horizontal line through Q and the vertical line through M is the point P on the curve (see Figure 27).

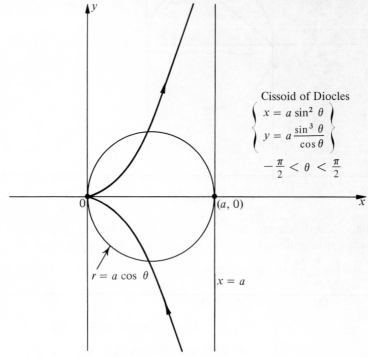

Cissoid of Diocles
$$\left\{ \begin{array}{l} x = a \sin^2 \theta \\ y = a \dfrac{\sin^3 \theta}{\cos \theta} \end{array} \right\}$$
$$-\frac{\pi}{2} < \theta < \frac{\pi}{2}$$

$r = a \cos \theta$

$x = a$

Figure 26

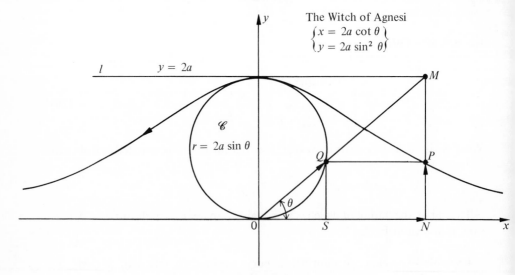

The Witch of Agnesi
$$\left\{ \begin{array}{l} x = 2a \cot \theta \\ y = 2a \sin^2 \theta \end{array} \right\}$$

$y = 2a$

$\mathscr{C}$

$r = 2a \sin \theta$

Figure 27

We take as parameter the angle θ. The polar equation of $\mathscr{C}$ being $r = 2a \sin \theta$, we have $\mathbf{OQ} = (2a \sin \theta \cos \theta)\mathbf{i} + (2a \sin^2 \theta)\mathbf{j}$. Also, since $|\mathbf{NM}| = 2a$, $\mathbf{ON} = 2a \cot \theta \mathbf{i}$. Thus

$$\mathbf{r}(\theta) = \mathbf{OP} = \mathbf{ON} + \mathbf{NP} = \mathbf{ON} + \mathbf{SQ},$$

$$\mathbf{r}(\theta) = (2a \cot \theta)\mathbf{i} + (2a \sin^2 \theta)\mathbf{j}. \tag{22}$$

This curve, shown in Figure 27, called the Witch of Agnesi, has parametric equations

$$\begin{cases} x = 2a \cot \theta \\ y = 2a \sin^2 \theta \end{cases}, \quad 0 < \theta < \pi. \tag{23}$$

Its nonparametric equation is

$$y = \frac{8a^3}{x^2 + 4a^2}$$

[see Exercise 23(g) after Section 11.4].

Example 15. For our next illustration we consider a curve defined by means of a circle of radius a and a straight line. In this case we fix a point on the circle and let the circle roll (without slipping) along the line. We are interested in the path of the specified point on the circle as the circle rolls along the line.

We choose the x-axis as the line along which the circle rolls and take as origin a point where the prescribed point on the circle touches the x-axis. We also assume the circle rolls to the right (see Figure 28).

Again we take as parameter an angle, this time the angle θ through which the circle has rolled from the "starting point" when P was at the origin. The essential fact in finding an analytic representation for the curve is the observation that

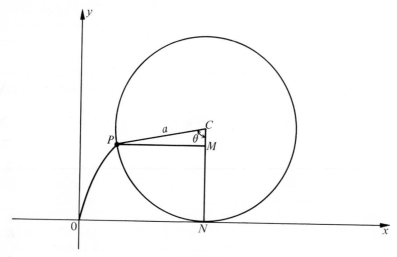

Figure 28

the length of the segment **ON** must equal the length of arc $\widehat{PN}$. Since $\widehat{PN} = a\theta$, we have $|\mathbf{ON}| = a\theta$. Thus

$$\mathbf{r}(\theta) = \mathbf{OP} = \mathbf{ON} + \mathbf{NM} + \mathbf{MP}$$

$$= a\theta\,\mathbf{i} + (a - a\cos\theta)\mathbf{j} + (-a\sin\theta)\mathbf{i},$$

so

$$\mathbf{r}(\theta) = a(\theta - \sin\theta)\mathbf{i} + a(1 - \cos\theta)\mathbf{j}. \tag{24}$$

This curve, a *cycloid*, has parametric equations

$$\begin{cases} x = a(\theta - \sin\theta) \\ y = a(1 - \cos\theta) \end{cases}. \tag{25}$$

A sketch of one period is given in Figure 29. This is the curve which, as John and James Bernoulli showed, provides a solution to the *brachistochrone problem* first discussed by Galileo: given two points in the same vertical plane, at different

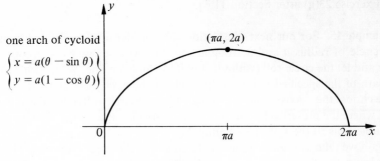

Figure 29

heights, although not on the same vertical line, to find a curve along which a bead would slide (without friction) from the upper point to the lower in minimum time. This is, of course, a minimization problem, but a deeper and more complicated one than those studied in elementary calculus, for it involves selecting from a suitably defined class of functions that one (if it exists) which minimizes an integral (the measure of time is expressed in terms of an integral). Euler also solved the brachistochrone problem and, in generalizing it, initiated the calculus of variations.

The problem associated with eliminating the parameter θ from Eq. (25) is discussed in Exercise 16.

So far nothing has been said about techniques of sketching a curve from a vector equation or a set of parametric equations. Intercepts can be found from the zeros of the parametric equations, the ranges of the functions for x and y may give useful information about extent of the curve, and in some cases suggestions about symmetry may be available. For example, in the case of the cissoid, it is clear from (20) that $0 \le x \le a$; moreover, the fact that the function for x is even whereas that for y is odd indicates symmetry with respect to the x-axis. Similarly, we see from Eqs. (23) that $0 \leq y \leq 2a$ and that the curve (the witch) is symmetric with respect to the y-axis. The Eqs. (25) for the cycloid indicate that $0 \leq y \leq 2a$ and that the curve is periodic.

Of course a more powerful tool for obtaining useful curve-sketching information is the derivative. We have already seen that we can, when y is a function of x, obtain the derivative $\dfrac{dy}{dx}$ as the ratio of the differentials dy and dx. It is a tribute to the power of the Leibniz notation that this result remains true under the current conditions when x and y are themselves functions of a parameter. The exact situation will now be described.

Theorem 7. *Let x and y be functions defined on a set $T \subset \mathbf{R}$. Suppose $\exists T_1 \subset T$ such that x' and y' exist on T_1 and also either $x'(t) > 0$, all $t \in T_1$, or $x'(t) < 0$, all $t \in T_1$. Then there is a function f defined on $x[T_1]$ and*

$$f'(x) = \frac{y'(t)}{x'(t)} = \frac{y'(t)\, dt}{x'(t)\, dt} = \frac{dy}{dx}. \tag{26}$$

Proof. The hypothesis about $x'(t)$ guarantees (see Theorem 6.15) that the function inverse to x exists on $x[T_1]$; we indicate this by saying that we can solve $x(t)$ for $t : t = t(x)$. If we define f by $f(x) = y(t(x))$, then, by the chain rule,

$$f'(x) = y'(t(x))t'(x).$$

But, by Theorem 6.17, $t'(x) = \dfrac{1}{x'(t)}$, so

$$f'(x) = \frac{y'(t)}{x'(t)}. \quad \blacksquare$$

To illustrate Theorem 7 we use the Eqs. (25) for the cycloid:

$$x = a(\theta - \sin \theta)$$

$$y = a(1 - \cos \theta).$$

Note that $x'(\theta) = a(1 - \cos \theta) \geq 0$, all θ. Thus x is an increasing function of θ and by (26), we have

$$\frac{dy}{dx} = \frac{y'(\theta)}{x'(\theta)} = \frac{a \sin \theta}{a(1 - \cos \theta)},$$

or

$$\frac{dy}{dx} = \frac{\sin \theta}{1 - \cos \theta}. \tag{27}$$

From this we see that $\dfrac{dy}{dx}$ fails to exist for $\theta = 2n\pi$, $n = 0, \pm 1, \pm 2, \ldots$. These values give the points on the cycloid where $y = 0$; it turns out (see Exercise 14) that the tangent line is vertical at these points. Equation (27) also shows that the tangent line to the curve is horizontal for $\theta = (2n + 1)\pi$; these give the maximum points where $y = 2a$.

We next find the second derivative $\dfrac{d^2y}{dx^2}$ for the cycloid. By definition

$$\frac{d^2y}{dx^2} = \frac{d}{dx}\left(\frac{dy}{dx}\right)$$

$$= \frac{d}{dx}\left(\frac{\sin\theta}{1-\cos\theta}\right) \qquad \text{(by (27))}$$

$$= \frac{d}{d\theta}\left(\frac{\sin\theta}{1-\cos\theta}\right)\frac{d\theta}{dx} \qquad \text{(the chain rule)}$$

$$= \frac{(1-\cos\theta)\cos\theta - \sin\theta(\sin\theta)}{(1-\cos\theta)^2}\frac{1}{\dfrac{dx}{d\theta}} \qquad \left(\frac{d\theta}{dx} = \frac{1}{\dfrac{dx}{d\theta}}\right)$$

$$= \frac{\cos\theta - 1}{(1-\cos\theta)^2}\frac{1}{x'(\theta)}$$

$$= \frac{-1}{1-\cos\theta}\cdot\frac{1}{a(1-\cos\theta)},$$

or

$$\frac{d^2y}{dx^2} = \frac{-1}{a(1-\cos\theta)^2}.$$

Thus $\dfrac{d^2y}{dx^2}$ fails to exist for $\theta = 2n\pi, n = 0, \pm1, \pm2, \ldots$, but for all other values of θ the second derivative is negative—the curve is everywhere concave downward.

We conclude this section with an example involving area.

Example 16. We find the area $A(0, b)$ bounded by the Witch of Agnesi, the x-axis, and the lines $x = 0$ and $x = b$ (see Figure 27).
The parametric equations for the Witch are

$$\begin{cases} x = 2a\cot\theta \\ y = 2a\sin^2\theta \end{cases}, \qquad 0 < \theta < \pi.$$

Thus

$$A(0, b) = \int_{x=0}^{x=b} y\,dx$$

$$= \int_{\theta=\pi/2}^{\theta=\tan^{-1}2a/b} (2a\sin^2\theta)(-2a\csc^2\theta)\,d\theta,$$

by Corollary 2, following Theorem 8.2. The upper limit in the θ integral is found by using $x = b$ in the preceding parametric equation. But this last integral reduces to

$$A(0, b) = 4a^2 \int_{\tan^{-1} 2a/b}^{\pi/2} d\theta$$

$$= 4a^2 \left[\frac{\pi}{2} - \tan^{-1} \frac{2a}{b} \right].$$

Suppose we consider letting b get big beyond all bounds. Then $\lim\limits_{b \to \infty} \dfrac{2a}{b} = 0$, and, since $\tan^{-1}$ is continuous everywhere, $\lim\limits_{b \to \infty} \tan^{-1} \dfrac{2a}{b} = 0$. Thus

$$A(0, \infty) = 2\pi a^2 = \int_0^\infty y\, dx.$$

As the curve is symmetric with respect to the y-axis, we conclude that the area A under the entire curve is $A = 4\pi a^2$—the same as the area of a circle with radius twice that of the circle used in defining this curve.

EXERCISES

In numbers 1–10 find $\dfrac{dy}{dx}$ and $\dfrac{d^2y}{dx^2}$.

1. $x = 2 + 3t,$ $y = 5 - t.$

2. $x = 3 - 2t,$ $y = 4 + 3t.$

3. $x = a + ht,$ $y = b + kt$ (see Exercise 22 after Section 11.4).

4. $x = t,$ $y = t^2.$

5. $x = t^2,$ $y = t^4.$ Compare with the result in Exercise 4; in particular, consider the situation for $t = 0.$

6. $x = a \cot t,$ $y = a \sin t.$

7. $x = \cos 2t,$ $y = \sin t.$

8. $x = a \cos t,$ $y = b \sin t.$

9. $x = 2a \cot \theta,$ $y = 2a \sin^2 \theta$ (see Example 14).

10. $x = a(t + \sin t),$ $y = a(1 - \cos t).$

11. This refers to Example 13. Eliminate θ from Eqs. (20) to obtain $y^2 = \dfrac{x^3}{a-x}$.

   [*Hint.* Show that $a - x = a \cos^2 \theta$; use this and the equation for x in the expression for y^2.]

12. By a variation of the definition of the Cissoid of Diocles (Example 13) we can obtain another curve, known as the *strophoid*. The same two auxiliary curves are used (see Figure 25); however, for the strophoid we define a point P on the curve by the condition that $\mathbf{PQ} = \mathbf{QM}$. Thus

$$\mathbf{OP} = \mathbf{OQ} + \mathbf{QP} = \mathbf{OQ} - \mathbf{QM}.$$

   (a) Use the preceding definition to show that parametric equations for the strophoid are

$$\begin{cases} x = a \cos 2\theta \\ y = a \cos 2\theta \tan \theta \end{cases}, \qquad -\frac{\pi}{2} < \theta < \frac{\pi}{2}.$$

   [*Hint.* Show that $\mathbf{OP} = 2\mathbf{OQ} - \mathbf{OM}$.]

   (b) Sketch the strophoid, indicating its *orientation*, i.e., the direction of the curve as determined by increasing θ.

   (c) Eliminate the parameter θ and show that

$$y^2 = x^2 \, \frac{a-x}{a+x}.$$

13. The curve called the *Serpentine* is defined as follows (see Figure 30). We use as auxiliary curves the line $y = a$ and the circle $r = b \cos \theta$. A line through the origin, making an angle θ with the positive x-axis, intersects $y = a$ at M and $r = b \cos \theta$

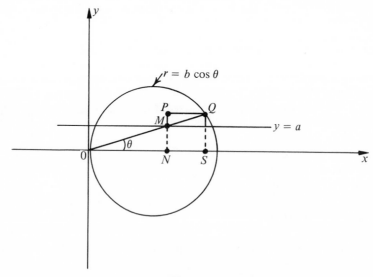

Figure 30

at Q. The point P on the Serpentine is the intersection of the vertical line through M and the horizontal line through Q.

(a) Let $\mathbf{r}(\theta) = \text{OP}$. Show that

$$\mathbf{r}(\theta) = a \cot \theta \mathbf{i} + b \sin \theta \cos \theta \mathbf{j}. \tag{28}$$

[*Hint.* Use $\text{OP} = \text{ON} + \text{NP} = \text{ON} + \text{SQ}$.]

(b) From (28) we obtain as parametric equations of the Serpentine

$$\begin{cases} x = a \cot \theta \\ y = b \sin \theta \cos \theta \end{cases}, \quad -\frac{\pi}{2} \le \theta \le \frac{\pi}{2}, \ \theta \ne 0. \tag{29}$$

Use these equations to sketch the curve. Note that when $-\dfrac{\pi}{2} \le \theta < 0$, the point P on the curve will lie in quadrant III.

(c) Show that

$$\frac{dy}{dx} = -\frac{b}{a} \sin^2 \theta \cos 2\theta.$$

From this it follows that the slope of the tangent at the origin is

$$\frac{dy}{dx}\bigg|_{\theta = \pi/2} = \frac{b}{a}.$$

Thus, the larger b is in comparison to a, the steeper the curve at the origin.

(d) Eliminate θ from (29), showing that

$$y = \frac{abx}{a^2 + x^2}.$$

14. This refers to the expression in (27) for the slope of the tangent to the cycloid.

(a) Show that $\displaystyle \lim_{\theta \to 2n\pi+} \frac{\sin \theta}{1 - \cos \theta} = \infty$.

(b) Show that $\displaystyle \lim_{\theta \to 2n\pi-} \frac{\sin \theta}{1 - \cos \theta} = -\infty$.

15. A *hypocycloid* is the curve traced out by a point P on a circle of radius b which is rolling (without slipping) on the *inside* of a fixed circle of radius a, $a > b$. We take the origin at the center of the fixed circle and assume that the specified point on the inner circle touches the fixed circle at a point on the x-axis (see Figure 31).

(a) If P has coordinates (x, y), show that

$$\begin{cases} x = (a - b) \cos \theta + b \cos \dfrac{a - b}{a} \theta \\ y = (a - b) \sin \theta - b \sin \dfrac{a - b}{b} \theta \end{cases} \tag{30}$$

[*Hint.*

$$x = \overline{ON} = \overline{OM} - \overline{NM},$$
$$y = \overline{NP} = \overline{NB} - \overline{PB} = \overline{MC} - \overline{PB}.]$$

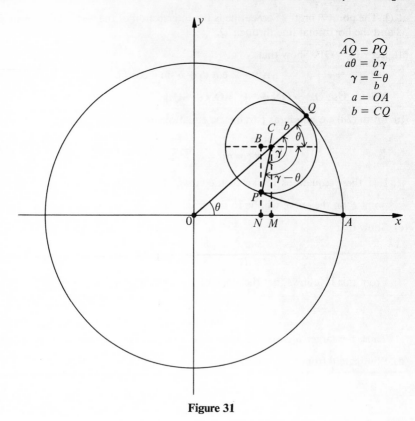

$$\widehat{AQ} = \widehat{PQ}$$
$$a\theta = b\gamma$$
$$\gamma = \frac{a}{b}\theta$$
$$a = OA$$
$$b = CQ$$

Figure 31

(b) If $\dfrac{b}{a}$ is irrational the curve will continue indefinitely, never repeating itself. How-

ever, if $\dfrac{b}{a}$ is rational the curve will ultimately return to A. Show, in particular,

that if $b = \frac{1}{4}a$, the equations in (30) reduce to

$$\begin{cases} x = a\cos^3\theta \\ y = a\sin^3\theta \end{cases}; \tag{31}$$

this curve, the hypocycloid of four cusps, is traced out completely for $0 \le \theta \le 2\pi$. [[*Hint.* Identities for $\sin 3\theta$ and $\cos 3\theta$ may be helpful.]

(c) Sketch the hypocycloid of four cusps.

(d) Eliminate θ from Eqs. (31), showing that the nonparametric equation is

$$x^{2/3} + y^{2/3} = a^{2/3}. \tag{32}$$

16. In attempting to eliminate the parameter θ from the equations for the cycloid, $x = a(\theta - \sin\theta)$, $y = a(1 - \cos\theta)$, one could solve the y-equation for $\cos\theta$:

$$\cos\theta = 1 - \frac{y}{a} = \frac{a-y}{a},$$

and then write

$$\theta = \cos^{-1} \frac{a - y}{a}$$

and substitute this in the x equation:

$$x = a \left[\cos^{-1} \frac{a - y}{a} - \sin \left(\cos^{-1} \frac{a - y}{a} \right) \right].$$

(a) Show that the second term in the brackets can be written as

$$\frac{\sqrt{2ay - y^2}}{a},$$

so the preceding equation becomes

$$x = a \cos^{-1} \frac{a - y}{a} - \sqrt{2ay - y^2}. \tag{33}$$

(b) How much of the cycloid curve does Eq. (33) represent? [*Hint.* Recall that $0 \le \cos^{-1} u \le \pi$.]

17. Find the area under one arch of the cycloid $x = a(\theta - \sin \theta)$, $y = a(1 - \cos \theta)$ (see Example 16).

11.6 Arc Length

In this section we continue our geometric digression (from vectors) in order to introduce a topic of obvious importance in its own right and also necessary to our purposes in the next section. We refer to the length of a curve.

To be specific, suppose we have a curve $\mathscr{C}$ defined by a pair of functions,

$$\mathscr{C} : \begin{cases} x = x(t) \\ y = y(t), \end{cases} \quad t \in [a, b], \tag{34}$$

where x and y are continuous on $[a, b]$. Our aim is to measure the length of $\mathscr{C}$.

We first describe briefly a method which has the virtue of leading us rather quickly to the desired result. However, the price we pay for this easy success is the need to draw on two assumptions which, in fact, are not only quite reasonable, but are valid for most of the curves one encounters in elementary calculus. We need the first of these to get going.

Assumption 1. Given a curve as in Eq. (34), we assume there exists a function s, defined on $[a, b]$, differentiable on (a, b), such that $s(a) = 0$, and $s(t)$ measures the length of arc from $A(x(a), y(a))$ to $P(x(t), y(t))$ (see Figure 32).

By assumption, s is differentiable on (a, b). We seek $s'(t)$, using the definition of a derivative:

$$s'(t) = \lim_{\Delta t \to 0} \frac{\Delta s}{\Delta t}.$$

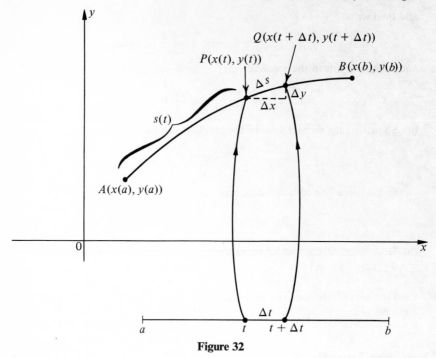

Figure 32

In order to make the expression on the right more tractable we introduce into it the length of the straight line segment $\overline{PQ}$, which is, intuitively, at least for small Δt, a good approximation for Δs. Since $\overline{PQ} = \sqrt{\overline{\Delta x}^2 + \overline{\Delta y}^2}$, we have

$$s'(t) = \lim_{\Delta t \to 0} \frac{\sqrt{\overline{\Delta x}^2 + \overline{\Delta y}^2}}{\Delta t} \cdot \frac{\Delta s}{\sqrt{\overline{\Delta x}^2 + \overline{\Delta y}^2}}$$

$$= \lim_{\Delta t \to 0} \sqrt{\left(\frac{\Delta x}{\Delta t}\right)^2 + \left(\frac{\Delta y}{\Delta t}\right)^2} \lim_{\Delta t \to 0} \frac{\Delta s}{|\mathbf{PQ}|}.$$

Now we add a hypothesis and the second assumption, both of which make good sense. The additional hypothesis is that the functions x and y have derivatives on (a, b). This, with the remark that the square root function is continuous, will enable us to take care of the first limit in the last equation. For the second we use the following.

Assumption 2. Given two "nearby" points P and Q on a curve the limit of the ratio of arc to chord length, as $Q \to P$, is one:

$$\lim_{Q \to P} \frac{\Delta s}{|\mathbf{PQ}|} = \lim_{Q \to P} \frac{\widehat{PQ}}{PQ} = 1. \tag{35}$$

It follows immediately that

$$s'(t) = \sqrt{\left(\frac{dx}{dt}\right)^2 + \left(\frac{dy}{dt}\right)^2}, \tag{36}$$

or

$$ds = \sqrt{\left(\frac{dx}{dt}\right)^2 + \left(\frac{dy}{dt}\right)^2} \; dt. \tag{37}$$

If we again strengthen our hypotheses to ensure that ds is integrable (e.g., require that x' and y' be continuous on $[a, b]$) we can conclude that

$$s = \int_a^b \sqrt{(x'(t))^2 + (y'(t))^2} \; dt, \tag{38}$$

since $s(a) = 0$.

In case $x = t$, $y = y(t) = f(x)$, the integral in (38) becomes

$$s = \int_a^b \sqrt{1 + (f'(x))^2} \; dx, \tag{39}$$

a frequently useful formula. Similarly, if $y = t$, $x = x(t) = g(y)$, we have

$$s = \int_a^b \sqrt{1 + \left(\frac{dx}{dt}\right)^2} \; dt = \int_a^b \sqrt{1 + (g'(y))^2} \; dy. \tag{40}$$

The preceding discussion not only produced, in (38), (39), and (40), correct results; the fact is that the hypotheses on x and y—that x' and y' be continuous on $[a, b]$—are sufficiently strong to guarantee that Assumptions 1 and 2 are valid. Of course, we have not proven this.

However, anyone having an understanding of the definition of the integral would no doubt anticipate that the approach to the measure of arc length would be via an approximation by sums of lengths of line segments and a limiting process. This conjecture is essentially correct; we proceed to a somewhat more rigorous discussion of arc length from this point of view.

We begin with a curve as defined in Eq. (34) and we take a partition π of $[a, b]$:

$$\pi = \{a = t_0, t_1, \ldots, t_{i-1}, t_i, \ldots, t_{n-1}, t_n = b\}.$$

Each point t_i of π determines a point P_i on the curve. We join successive points with straight line segments and consider the sum S_π of the lengths of these segments (see Figure 33).

Since

$$|\mathbf{P}_{i-1}\mathbf{P}_i| = \sqrt{(x(t_i) - x(t_{i-1}))^2 + (y(t_i) - y(t_{i-1}))^2},$$

we have

$$S_\pi = \sum_{i=1}^n |\mathbf{P}_{i-1}\mathbf{P}_i|$$

$$= \sum_{i=1}^n \sqrt{(x(t_i) - x(t_{i-1}))^2 + (y(t_i) - y(t_{i-1}))^2}. \tag{41}$$

Suppose, now, we consider all partitions of $[a, b]$. Then two possible cases may arise.

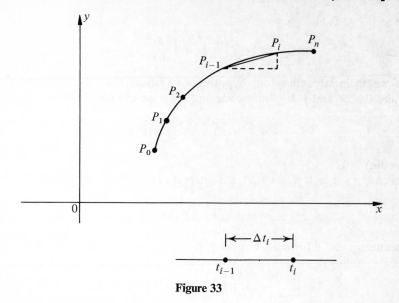

Figure 33

(1) The set of numbers $\{S_\pi\}$ is unbounded. In this case the curve has no length.

(2) The set of numbers $\{S_\pi\}$ is bounded above. As any value of S_π should, intuitively, be less than the length of arc, the following definition is reasonable.

Definition 7. *Let $\mathscr{C}$ be a curve as defined in* (34). *For a partition π of $[a, b]$, let S_π be defined as in* (41). *If the set $\{S_\pi\}$, for all π, is bounded above, then $\mathscr{C}$ is said to be **rectifiable** and its length s is defined to be*

$$s = \operatorname*{lub}_\pi S_\pi = \operatorname*{lub}_\pi \sum_{i=1}^{n} \sqrt{[x(t_i) - x(t_{i-1})]^2 + [y(t_i) - y(t_{i-1})]^2}.$$

It is worth remarking that there do exist curves which are not rectifiable. Without going into the proof, we mention that

$$\begin{cases} x = t, & 0 \le t \le 1 \\ y = t \sin\left(\dfrac{\pi}{2t}\right). & 0 < t \le 1 \\ y = 0, & t = 0 \end{cases}$$

is one such.

It consequently becomes highly desirable to have a criterion, a sufficient condition, for a curve to be rectifiable. The following theorem gives one in a constructive way.

Theorem 8. *Let $\mathscr{C}$ be a curve described by*

$$\begin{aligned} x &= x(t) \\ y &= y(t), \end{aligned} \quad t \in [a, b],$$

where x' and y' are continuous on [a, b]. Then $\mathscr{C}$ is rectifiable and the length s is given by

$$s = \int_a^b \sqrt{\left(\frac{dx}{dt}\right)^2 + \left(\frac{dy}{dt}\right)^2}\, dt = \int_a^b \sqrt{(x'(t))^2 + (y'(t))^2}\, dt. \tag{42}$$

Proof. For an arbitrary partition π of $[a, b]$ the length of the inscribed polygon is

$$S_\pi = \sum_{i=1}^n \sqrt{[x(t_i) - x(t_{i-1})]^2 + [y(t_i) - y(t_{i-1})]^2}.$$

We have, by hypothesis, that x' and y' exist (are, in fact, continuous) on $[a, b]$; thus we can use the Mean Value Theorem on both x and y on each subinterval to obtain $u_i, v_i \in (t_{i-1}, t_i)$ such that

$$x(t_i) - x(t_{i-1}) = x'(u_i)\Delta t_i,$$

$$y(t_i) - y(t_{i-1}) = y'(v_i)\Delta t_i,$$

where $\Delta t_i = t_i - t_{i-1}$. Consequently,

$$S_\pi = \sum_{i=1}^n \sqrt{(x'(u_i)\,\Delta t_i)^2 + (y'(v_i)\,\Delta t_i)^2},$$

or

$$S_\pi = \sum_{i=1}^n \sqrt{(x'(u_i))^2 + (y'(v_i))^2}\, \Delta t_i. \tag{43}$$

By the Corollary to Theorem 9.7, the limit of S_π, as $|\pi| \to 0$, is the integral in (42). ∎

Notice that the result of Theorem 8 is the same as that obtained by the more intuitive discussion leading to (38). It follows that the alternative formulas given in (39) and (40) are also consequences of Theorem 8. We shall illustrate the use of all of these shortly.

There is, however, one point we should clear up before we turn to examples. We refer to the fact that a given curve might be represented by different sets of parametric equations. Is the result of Theorem 8 independent of the parametrization? The affirmative answer is easily obtained by means of our ever useful friend, the chain rule.

Suppose, to be explicit, we have a curve $\mathscr{C}$ described by functions

$$\begin{cases} x = x(t) \\ y = y(t) \end{cases}, \qquad t \in [a, b] \tag{44}$$

and also by

$$\begin{cases} x = \xi(\tau) \\ y = \eta(\tau) \end{cases}, \qquad \tau \in [\alpha, \beta], \tag{45}$$

where τ and t are related by a function p:

$$\tau = p(t), \qquad \alpha = p(a), \qquad \beta = p(b), \qquad d\tau = p'(t)\,dt, \qquad p'(t) > 0$$

(see Figure 34).

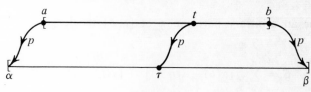

Figure 34

We have, then, substituting for τ in (45), $x(t) = \xi(p(t))$, $y(t) = \eta(p(t))$. Consequently, by the chain rule,

$$x'(t) = \xi'(p(t))p'(t) = \xi'(\tau)p'(t),$$
$$y'(t) = \eta'(p(t))p'(t) = \eta'(\tau)p'(t);$$

then

$$ds = \sqrt{(x'(t))^2 + (y'(t))^2}\, dt$$
$$= \sqrt{(\xi'(\tau))^2(p'(t))^2 + (\eta'(\tau))^2(p'(t))^2}\, dt$$
$$= \sqrt{(\xi'(\tau))^2 + (\eta'(\tau))^2}\, p'(t)\,dt, \qquad \text{since } p'(t) > 0,$$
$$= \sqrt{(\xi'(\tau))^2 + (\eta'(\tau))^2}\, d\tau, \qquad \text{since } d\tau = p'(t)\,dt.$$

It follows that

$$s = \int_a^b \sqrt{(x'(t))^2 + (y'(t))^2}\, dt = \int_\alpha^\beta \sqrt{(\xi'(\tau))^2 + (\eta'(\tau))^2}\, d\tau. \tag{46}$$

If one is working in polar coordinates and the curve is the graph of a function f (of θ), it is possible to use the relation between rectangular and polar coordinates,

$$x = r \cos \theta = f(\theta) \cos \theta$$
$$y = r \sin \theta = f(\theta) \sin \theta,$$

and, taking θ as parameter, show that the length of arc for $\alpha \le \theta \le \beta$ is given by

$$s = \int_\alpha^\beta \sqrt{(f(\theta))^2 + (f'(\theta))^2}\, d\theta = \int_\alpha^\beta \sqrt{r^2 + \left(\frac{dr}{d\theta}\right)^2}\, d\theta. \tag{47}$$

We leave as an exercise the verification of the formula in (47).

Example 17. We find the length of one arch of the cycloid (see Fig. 29):

$$\begin{cases} x = a(t - \sin t) \\ y = a(1 - \cos t) \end{cases}, \qquad 0 \le t \le 2\pi.$$

We calculate

$$\begin{cases} x'(t) = a(1 - \cos t) \\ y'(t) = a \sin t \end{cases},$$

$$\sqrt{(x'(t))^2 + (y'(t))^2} = \sqrt{a^2(1 - \cos t)^2 + a^2 \sin^2 t}$$

$$= a\sqrt{2(1 - \cos t)}$$

$$= 2a \sin \frac{t}{2}, \qquad 0 \le t \le 2\pi.$$

Thus, by Theorem 8,

$$s = \int_0^{2\pi} 2a \sin \frac{t}{2}\, dt$$

$$= 2^2 a \int_0^{2\pi} \sin \frac{t}{2} \frac{dt}{2} = 4a \left[-\cos \frac{t}{2} \right]\Big|_0^{2\pi}$$

$$= -4a(-1 - 1)$$

$$= 8a.$$

Example 18. We consider a portion of the parabola $y^2 = 4x$; to be explicit, the arc in the first quadrant between the origin and $P(1, 2)$ (see Figure 35).

If we consider the curve as the graph of f, where $f(x) = 2x^{1/2}$, we find $f'(x) = x^{-1/2}$, and (39) would lead to

$$s = \int_0^1 \sqrt{1 + \frac{1}{x}}\, dx.$$

This is, however, an improper integral, since the integrand $\to \infty$ as $x \to 0^+$. From Figure 35 it is intuitively clear that the curve should be rectifiable (after all, the

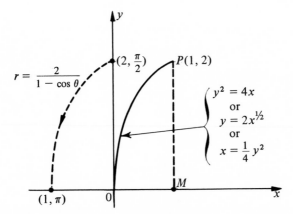

Figure 35

straight line path **OM + MP** from O to P has a length of 3 units), so we try a different approach.

The curve can also be considered as the graph of g, where $g(y) = \frac{1}{4}y^2$. Then $g'(y) = \frac{1}{2}y$ and (40) gives

$$s = \int_0^2 \sqrt{1 + \frac{1}{4}y^2}\, dy,$$

a perfectly well-behaved integral. This can be evaluated by the substitution

$$\frac{y}{2} = \tan\theta, \qquad 0 \le \theta \le \frac{\pi}{4},$$

$$dy = 2 \sec^2\theta\, d\theta,$$

which leads to

$$s = 2 \int_0^{\pi/4} \sec^3\theta\, d\theta = \sec\theta \tan\theta + \log(\sec\theta + \tan\theta)\Big|_0^{\pi/4},$$

or

$$s = \sqrt{2} + \log(\sqrt{2} + 1) \approx 2.295 \text{ units.}$$

(Note that $|\mathbf{OP}| = \sqrt{5} \approx 2.236$.)

Still another approach to the same problem is to observe that the polar coordinate equation

$$r = \frac{2}{1 - \cos\theta}, \qquad \frac{\pi}{2} \le \theta \le \pi,$$

describes the same arc in a slightly different position with respect to the coordinate system (see Figure 35). The calculations will be somewhat easier if we take advantage of the fact that

$$r = \frac{1}{\sin^2\dfrac{\theta}{2}} = \csc^2\frac{\theta}{2}.$$

Thus

$$\frac{dr}{d\theta} = -\csc^2\frac{\theta}{2}\cot\frac{\theta}{2},$$

and using (47), we find

$$s = \int_{\pi/2}^{\pi} \sqrt{\csc^4\frac{\theta}{2}\left(1 + \cot^2\frac{\theta}{2}\right)}\, d\theta$$

$$= \int_{\pi/2}^{\pi} \sqrt{\csc^6\frac{\theta}{2}}\, d\theta = \int_{\pi/2}^{\pi} \csc^3\frac{\theta}{2}\, d\theta.$$

It is a simple matter, by letting $\dfrac{\theta}{2} = \dfrac{\pi}{2} - \varphi$, to show that this last integral is equal to

$$2 \int_0^{\pi/4} \sec^3 \varphi \, d\varphi,$$

giving the same result as before.

We return to the improper integral encountered in our first attack on this problem:

$$s = \int_0^1 \sqrt{1 + \frac{1}{x}} \, dx$$

$$= \int_0^1 \frac{\sqrt{x+1}}{\sqrt{x}} \, dx.$$

This is not quite the standard integrand for a trigonometric substitution, but if we let

$$x = \tan^2 \theta, \qquad 0 \leq \theta \leq \frac{\pi}{4}$$

$$\sqrt{x} = \tan \theta, \qquad dx = 2 \tan \theta \sec^2 \theta \, d\theta$$

$$\sqrt{x+1} = \sec \theta,$$

an interesting result occurs: the equivalent θ-integral is

$$s = \int_0^{\pi/4} \frac{2 \tan \theta \sec^3 \theta \, d\theta}{\tan \theta} = 2 \int_0^{\pi/4} \sec^3 \theta \, d\theta,$$

familiar and no longer improper.

As we shall see in the exercises, even some of the simplest curves lead to arc-length integrals which cannot be evaluated by the usual elementary techniques: the supply of manageable, nontrivial curves is quite limited.

EXERCISES

In numbers 1–10 find the length of the arc described.

1. $\begin{cases} x = t^3 \\ y = t^2, \end{cases}$ $0 \leq t \leq 1.$

2. $\begin{cases} x = t^3 \\ y = t^2, \end{cases}$ $-2 \leq t \leq 0.$

3. $y = \log \cos x, \qquad 0 \leq x \leq \dfrac{\pi}{4}.$

4. $\begin{cases} x = a \cos^3 t \\ y = a \sin^3 t, \end{cases}$ $0 \leq t \leq 2\pi.$

5. $y = \cosh x, \qquad 0 \leq x \leq 2.$

6. $y = \dfrac{1}{3} x^3 + \dfrac{1}{4x}, \qquad 1 \leq x \leq 2.$

[*Hint.* $1 + \left(\dfrac{dy}{dx}\right)^2$ is a perfect square.]

7. $r = a(1 + \cos \theta),$ $0 \le \theta \le 2\pi.$ (Compare the result with that of Example 17.)

8. $y = e^x,$ $0 \le x \le 2.$ **9.** $y = \log x,$ $1 \le x \le e^2.$

10. $r = a\theta,$ $0 \le \theta \le \beta,$ where $0 < \beta < \dfrac{\pi}{2}.$

In numbers 11–15 *set up* the integrals for finding the length of arc described.

11. $y = \sin x,$ $0 \le x \le \dfrac{\pi}{2}.$ **12.** $y = \dfrac{1}{x},$ $1 \le x \le 3.$

13. $r^2 = a^2 \cos 2\theta,$ $0 \le \theta \le \dfrac{\pi}{4}.$ **14.** $y = \sqrt{x^2 - 1},$ $1 \le x \le 4.$

15. $y = x^3,$ $0 \le x \le 1.$ **16.** Derive the formula in (47).

17. Consider the curve defined by

$$\begin{cases} x = a \sin \theta \\ y = b \cos \theta \end{cases}, \quad a > b > 0, \quad 0 \le \theta < 2\pi.$$

(a) Show that the curve is an ellipse.

(b) Show that the integral for the length of arc of the ellipse lyiing in the first quadrant is

$$s = \int_0^{\pi/2} a\sqrt{1 - k^2 \sin^2 \theta}\, d\theta,$$

where $k^2 = 1 - \dfrac{b^2}{a^2} < 1.$ This is known as a *complete elliptic integral of the second kind*; tables are available giving its value for different values of k.

11.7 Derivatives of Vector Functions

In this section we return to the subject of vector functions introduced in Section 11.4. Our immediate aim is to obtain the derivative of a vector function, and for this purpose we need the idea of limit of such a function.

To be specific, suppose that $T \subset \mathbf{R}$ is an interval and that $\mathbf{r}$ is a function defined on T, the values of $\mathbf{r}$ being vectors in $\mathbf{R}^2$. As we saw in Section 11.4, we can represent such a function in terms of a pair of scalar functions x and y defined on T:

$$\mathbf{r}(t) = x(t)\mathbf{i} + y(t)\mathbf{j}.$$

Drawing on Definition 3.6, we can make a first attempt at a limit definition for $\mathbf{r}$ as follows:

Definition 8. $\lim_{t \to t_0} \mathbf{r}(t) = \mathbf{a} \Leftrightarrow$ *for every* $N_\varepsilon(\mathbf{a})$ *there exists* $N_\delta^*(t_0)$ *such that* $t \in N_\delta^*(t_0) \Rightarrow \mathbf{r}(t) \in N_\varepsilon(\mathbf{a}).$

The fact is that this definition will prove to be perfectly adequate as soon as we have defined $N_\varepsilon(\mathbf{a})$ for a vector $\mathbf{a}$. Moreover, although we do not have an order relation for vectors, we can use the absolute value form for a nbd, interpreting it in terms of magnitude of a vector:

Definition 9. *Let* $\mathbf{a} = (a_1, a_2) = a_1\mathbf{i} + a_2\mathbf{j}$; *a nbd.* $N_\varepsilon(\mathbf{a})$ *is defined as*

$$N_\varepsilon(\mathbf{a}) = \{\mathbf{v} = (x_1, x_2) \mid |\mathbf{v} - \mathbf{a}| < \varepsilon\}$$
$$= \{\mathbf{v} = (x_1, x_2) \mid (x_1 - a_1)^2 + (x_2 - a_2)^2 < \varepsilon^2\}.$$

In Figure 36 we show a vector $\mathbf{v} \in N_\varepsilon(\mathbf{a})$. Geometrically, $N_\varepsilon(\mathbf{a})$ consists of all those vectors with initial point at the origin, terminal point within the circle of radius ε and center at (a_1, a_2). (In Exercise 2 following we discuss an alternative form of $N(\mathbf{a})$.)

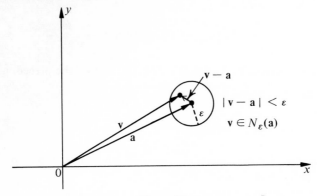

Figure 36

We can now assert that Definition 8, used along with Definition 9, gives the desired description of limit of a vector function. In addition, we can immediately define continuity for such a function.

Definition 10. *The function* $\mathbf{r}$ *is* ***continuous*** *at* $t_0 \in T \Leftrightarrow$

$$\lim_{t \to t_0} \mathbf{r}(t) = \mathbf{r}(t_0);$$

equivalently, for every $N_\varepsilon(\mathbf{r}(t_0))$ *there exists* $N_\delta(t_0)$ *such that*

$$t \in N_\delta(t_0) \Rightarrow \mathbf{r}(t) \in N_\varepsilon(\mathbf{r}(t_0)).$$

It is useful to know that continuity of a vector function $\mathbf{r}$ is equivalent to continuity of the associated scalar functions x and y.

Theorem 9. *Let* $\mathbf{r}(t) = x(t)\mathbf{i} + y(t)\mathbf{j}$. *Then* $\mathbf{r}$ *is continuous at* $t_0 \in T \Leftrightarrow x$ *and* y *are continuous at* t_0.

Proof. For the implication $\Rightarrow$ we know that, for arbitrary $\varepsilon > 0$, there exists $\delta > 0$ such that $t \in N_\delta(t_0) \Rightarrow \mathbf{r}(t) \in N_\varepsilon(\mathbf{r}(t_0))$. But

$$\mathbf{r}(t) \in N_\varepsilon(\mathbf{r}(t_0)) \Rightarrow |\mathbf{r}(t) - \mathbf{r}(t_0)| < \varepsilon;$$

this, in turn, means that

$$[x(t) - x(t_0)]^2 + [y(t) - y(t_0)]^2 < \varepsilon^2.$$

In order that the sum of the two terms on the left be less than ε^2, it must follow that each term be $< \varepsilon^2$; and this leads to

$$|x(t) - x(t_0)| < \varepsilon, \qquad |y(t) - y(t_0)| < \varepsilon.$$

As these inequalities hold for $t \in N_\delta(t_0)$, x and y are continuous at t_0.

For the implication $\Leftarrow$ we argue as follows. Let $\varepsilon > 0$ be given. The continuity of x and y at t_0 guarantees the existence of δ_1 and δ_2 such that

$$t \in N_{\delta_1}(t_0) \Rightarrow |x(t) - x(t_0)| < \frac{\varepsilon}{\sqrt{2}},$$

$$t \in N_{\delta_2}(t_0) \Rightarrow |y(t) - y(t_0)| < \frac{\varepsilon}{\sqrt{2}}.$$

If we define $\delta = \min(\delta_1, \delta_2)$ and take $t \in N_\delta(t_0)$, both of the preceding inequalities hold; thus

$$[x(t) - x(t_0)]^2 + [y(t) - y(t_0)]^2 < \varepsilon^2,$$

which is to say that $\mathbf{r}(t) \in N(\mathbf{r}(t_0))$. ∎

We now define the derivative of a vector function $\mathbf{r}$, following the same scheme as is used for a scalar function.

Definition 11. *Let $\mathbf{r}$ be a vector function with domain T, $t_0 \in T$. The **derivative** $\mathbf{r}'(t_0)$ of $\mathbf{r}$ at t_0 is*

$$\mathbf{r}'(t_0) = \lim_{h \to 0} \frac{1}{h} [\mathbf{r}(t_0 + h) - \mathbf{r}(t_0)],$$

*provided the limit exists. The **derived function** $\mathbf{r}'$ is the function whose value at t_0 is given by the preceding equation.*

By referring to Figure 37 we see that when $\mathbf{r}'(t_0)$ exists it represents a vector which, if drawn with its initial point at the point $P_0(x(t_0), y(t_0))$ on the graph of $\mathbf{r}$, lies along the tangent to the curve at P_0. For, by its very definition, $\mathbf{r}(t_0)$ is a limit of secant vectors.

Analogous to the result of Theorem 9, we note that existence of $\mathbf{r}'(t_0)$ is tied to that of $x'(t_0)$ and $y'(t_0)$.

Theorem 10. *Let $\mathbf{r}(t) = x(t)\mathbf{i} + y(t)\mathbf{j}$. Then*

$$\mathbf{r}'(t_0) \text{ exists} \Leftrightarrow x'(t_0) \text{ and } y'(t_0) \text{ exist.}$$

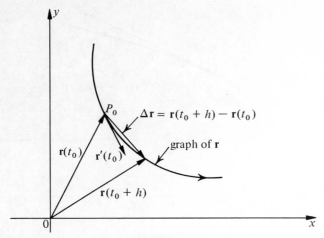

Figure 37

When either condition is satisfied

$$\mathbf{r}'(t_0) = x'(t_0)\mathbf{i} + y'(t_0)\mathbf{j}.$$

Proof.   We consider the implication ⇒. By definition

$$\mathbf{r}'(t_0) = \lim_{h \to 0} \frac{1}{h} [\mathbf{r}(t_0 + h) - \mathbf{r}(t_0)]$$

$$= \lim_{h \to 0} \frac{1}{h} [(x(t_0 + h) - x(t_0))\mathbf{i} + (y(t_0 + h) - y(t_0))\mathbf{j}]$$

$$= \left[\lim_{h \to 0} \frac{x(t_0 + h) - x(t_0)}{h}\right]\mathbf{i} + \left[\lim_{h \to 0} \frac{y(t_0 + h) - y(t_0)}{h}\right]\mathbf{j}$$

$$= x'(t_0)\mathbf{i} + y'(t_0)\mathbf{j},$$

since $\mathbf{r}'(t_0)$ is assumed to exist.

A reversal of these steps gives the implication ⇐. ∎

Example 19. As a simple illustration of the preceding ideas, suppose

$$\mathbf{r}(t) = t^2\mathbf{i} + t\mathbf{j}, \qquad t \in \mathbf{R}.$$

Then $\mathbf{r}'(t) = 2t\mathbf{i} + \mathbf{j}$. In particular,

$$\mathbf{r}(0) = \mathbf{0} \qquad \mathbf{r}(1) = \mathbf{i} + \mathbf{j}$$

$$\mathbf{r}'(0) = \mathbf{j}, \qquad \mathbf{r}'(1) = 2\mathbf{i} + \mathbf{j}$$

(see Figure 38).

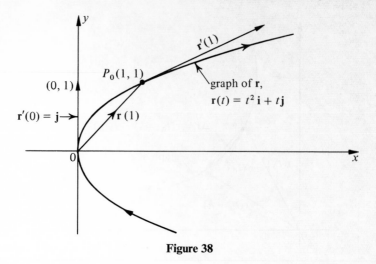

Figure 38

EXERCISES

1. Determine whether or not each of the following vectors is in $N_{1/2}(\mathbf{i}+\mathbf{j})$.

(a) $1.1\mathbf{i}+0.8\mathbf{j}$.   (c) $1.4\mathbf{i}+0.8\mathbf{j}$.   (e) $0.7\mathbf{i}+1.39\mathbf{j}$.

(b) $1.5\mathbf{i}+\mathbf{j}$.   (d) $0.7\mathbf{i}+1.4\mathbf{j}$.

2. An alternative definition for nbd. of a vector $\mathbf{a}$ is the following: Let $\mathbf{a}=a_1\mathbf{i}+a_2\mathbf{j}$, then

$$N_{\boxed{\varepsilon}}(\mathbf{a})=\{\mathbf{v}=x_1\mathbf{i}+x_2\mathbf{j}|\,|x_1-a_1|<\varepsilon,\,|x_2-a_2|<\varepsilon\}.$$

(a) Make a sketch which illustrates this definition.

(b) Which of the vectors in Exercise 1 are in $N_{\boxed{1/2}}(\mathbf{i}+\mathbf{j})$?

(c) Prove: For every $N_\varepsilon(\mathbf{a})$ there exists $N_{\boxed{\varepsilon_1}}(\mathbf{a})$ such that $N_{\boxed{\varepsilon_1}}(\mathbf{a})\subset N_\varepsilon(\mathbf{a})$.

(d) Prove: For every $N_{\boxed{\varepsilon}}(\mathbf{a})$ there exists $N_{\varepsilon_1}(\mathbf{a})$ such that $N_{\varepsilon_1}(\mathbf{a})\subset N_{\boxed{\varepsilon}}(\mathbf{a})$.

11.8 Tangent and Normal Vectors. Curvature

We next turn our attention to some geometrical applications which are of considerable interest and which are now accessible to us. Although our primary concern in this section is geometry, there is no harm in looking ahead to the topic of the next section and interpreting the vector function $\mathbf{r}$ as representing motion of a particle in the plane. In this light the parameter t can be thought of as time; moreover, we define the velocity vector $\mathbf{v}$ by

$$\mathbf{v}(t)=\mathbf{r}'(t). \tag{48}$$

Thus we are considering

$$\left.\begin{aligned}\mathbf{r}(t) &= x(t)\mathbf{i} + y(t)\mathbf{j}, \\ \mathbf{v}(t) &= \mathbf{r}'(t) = x'(t)\mathbf{i} + y'(t)\mathbf{j}\end{aligned}\right\}, \tag{49}$$

the first of these being the position vector from the origin to the point P and the second the velocity or tangent vector at P (i.e., with its initial point at P).

We now convert the tangent (velocity) vector $\mathbf{v}$ to a unit vector:

$$\mathbf{T} = \frac{\mathbf{v}}{|\mathbf{v}|} = \frac{\mathbf{r}'(t)}{|\mathbf{r}'(t)|}, \qquad |\mathbf{T}| = 1, \tag{50}$$

assuming $|\mathbf{r}'(t)| \neq 0$. There are two immediate consequences of Eq. (50) which we pursue. First of all we look at $|\mathbf{v}| = |\mathbf{r}'(t)|$. By the second equation in (49),

$$|\mathbf{v}(t)| = \sqrt{(x'(t))^2 + (y'(t))^2},$$

which we recognize as $\dfrac{ds}{dt}$ (this means we are taking $\dfrac{ds}{dt} \geq 0$, which implies that s increases with t). Thus

$$\mathbf{T} = \frac{\mathbf{r}'(t)}{|\mathbf{r}'(t)|} = \frac{\mathbf{r}'(t)}{\dfrac{ds}{dt}} = \mathbf{r}'(t)\frac{dt}{ds} = \frac{d\mathbf{r}}{ds}. \tag{51}$$

We can interpret (51) in the following way: If the arc length s is used as the parameter (as $\dfrac{ds}{dt} \geq 0$, it is legitimate to think of changing parameter from t to s), then $\dfrac{d\mathbf{r}}{ds}$ represents a unit tangent vector; its sense is that of the forward or positive direction along the curve.

The second point we wish to exploit is the fact that $\mathbf{T}$, being a unit vector, can be represented as

$$\mathbf{T} = \cos \alpha \mathbf{i} + \sin \alpha \mathbf{j}, \tag{52}$$

where α is the angle between the positive x-axis and the vector $\mathbf{T}$ (see Figure 39).

Clearly $\mathbf{T}$ will vary from point to point on the curve, but as its magnitude remains one, it is only the angle α which will change. To point this up we use one of the forms given for $\mathbf{T}$ in (51):

$$\begin{aligned}\mathbf{T} &= \mathbf{r}'(t)\frac{dt}{ds} = (x'(t)\mathbf{i} + y'(t)\mathbf{j})\frac{dt}{ds} \\ &= \left(x'(t)\frac{dt}{ds}\right)\mathbf{i} + \left(y'(t)\frac{dt}{ds}\right)\mathbf{j} \\ &= \frac{dx}{ds}\mathbf{i} + \frac{dy}{ds}\mathbf{j}.\end{aligned}$$

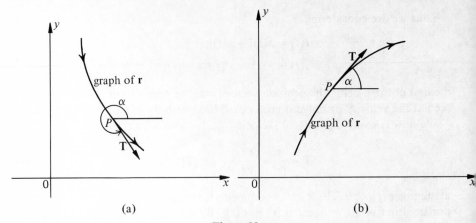

(a)   (b)

Figure 39

Comparing this result with (52), we have

$$
\left.
\begin{cases}
\cos \alpha = x'(t) \dfrac{dt}{ds} = \dfrac{dx}{ds} \\[2mm]
\sin \alpha = y'(t) \dfrac{dt}{ds} = \dfrac{dy}{ds}
\end{cases}
\right\},
\qquad (53)
$$

relations which can perhaps be kept in mind by the mnemonic and purely schematic device shown in Figure 40.

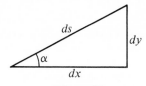

Figure 40

We now investigate the way in which **T** changes with s. Using the expression in (52) and the chain rule, we have

$$
\frac{d\mathbf{T}}{ds} = \frac{d\mathbf{T}}{d\alpha}\frac{d\alpha}{ds} = (-\sin \alpha \mathbf{i} + \cos \alpha \mathbf{j}) \frac{d\alpha}{ds}. \qquad (54)
$$

In order to obtain a geometric interpretation for this result we note first that $\dfrac{d\mathbf{T}}{d\alpha} = -\sin \alpha \mathbf{i} + \cos \alpha \mathbf{j}$ is clearly a unit vector. Second, since

$$
-\sin \alpha \mathbf{i} + \cos \alpha \mathbf{j} = \cos \left(\alpha + \frac{\pi}{2}\right)\mathbf{i} + \sin \left(\alpha + \frac{\pi}{2}\right)\mathbf{j},
$$

we see that $\dfrac{d\mathbf{T}}{d\alpha}$ is not only perpendicular to **T** (note that $\mathbf{T} \cdot \dfrac{d\mathbf{T}}{d\alpha} = 0$), but that

$\dfrac{d\mathbf{T}}{d\alpha}$ is obtained by rotating $\mathbf{T}$ through an angle of $\dfrac{\pi}{2}$ in the positive direction. In Figure 41 we illustrate some of the different cases.

As Figure 41 shows, differences occur both because of the concavity of the curve and because of the orientation (positive direction) of the curve. In each part of the figure we have indicated a unit vector $\mathbf{N}$, always directed toward the concave, or inner, side of the curve. In particular, we note that

$$\left.\begin{array}{l} \dfrac{d\alpha}{ds} > 0 \Rightarrow \mathbf{N} = \dfrac{d\mathbf{T}}{d\alpha} \\[4mm] \dfrac{d\alpha}{ds} < 0 \Rightarrow \mathbf{N} = -\dfrac{d\mathbf{T}}{d\alpha} \end{array}\right\} \tag{55}$$

In fact, we use Eqs. (55) as the definition of $\mathbf{N}$.

We now consider the magnitude of $\dfrac{d\mathbf{T}}{ds}$. As $\dfrac{d\mathbf{T}}{d\alpha}$ is a unit vector, it follows that

$$\left|\frac{d\mathbf{T}}{ds}\right| = \left|\frac{d\alpha}{ds}\right|.$$

Since $\dfrac{d\alpha}{ds}$ measures the rate of change of α with respect to length of arc, $\dfrac{d\alpha}{ds}$ can be interpreted as a measure of how rapidly the curve is turning away from the

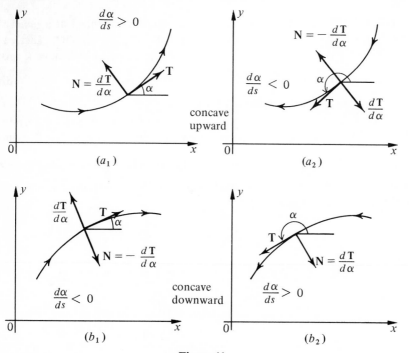

Figure 41

tangent line. From another—and perhaps cruder—point of view, we can describe $\frac{d\alpha}{ds}$ as follows: for a straight line α is constant, so $\frac{d\alpha}{ds} = 0$ at every point; thus one could think of the size of $\frac{d\alpha}{ds}$ as a measure of the degree that the curve departs from being a straight line. However, as Figure 41 shows, the sign of $\frac{d\alpha}{ds}$ depends upon both the concavity and the orientation of the curve, and the geometric property we have been discussing should be independent of such features. Thus the nature of the following definition.

Definition 12. *The **curvature** κ at a point P of a curve is defined as*

$$\kappa = \left| \frac{d\alpha}{ds} \right|,$$

where α is the inclination of the tangent line at P.

For future reference we point out that it is a consequence of (55) and Definition 12 that we always (i.e., whether $\frac{d\alpha}{ds} > 0$ or $\frac{d\alpha}{ds} < 0$) have

$$\kappa \mathbf{N} = \frac{d\alpha}{ds}\frac{d\mathbf{T}}{d\alpha} = \frac{d\mathbf{T}}{d\alpha}\frac{d\alpha}{ds} = \frac{d\mathbf{T}}{ds}. \tag{56}$$

It is worthwhile to emphasize that the curvature κ is defined at a *point* of a curve. In general, κ will vary from point to point. There are, in fact, exactly two classes of curves of constant curvature: the straight lines, which have $\kappa = 0$ at every point; and circles, for which at every point $\kappa = \frac{1}{a}$, where a is the radius. We leave the proof of this assertion for an exercise.

Before turning to examples we need to develop a few computational formulas. It is clear that knowledge of $\mathbf{r}(t) = x(t)\mathbf{i} + y(t)\mathbf{j}$ enables one to find $\mathbf{T}$ without difficulty. However, $\mathbf{N}$ and κ require an expression for $\frac{d\alpha}{ds}$, so we work toward that quantity. We can take as our starting point the equations in (53); division of the second by the first gives

$$\tan \alpha = \frac{y'(t)}{x'(t)}.$$

We now differentiate both sides of this equation with respect to s:

$$\sec^2 \alpha \, \frac{d\alpha}{ds} = \frac{d}{ds}\left(\frac{y'(t)}{x'(t)}\right)$$

$$= \frac{d}{dt}\left(\frac{y'(t)}{x'(t)}\right)\frac{dt}{ds}.$$

Thus, multiplying by $\cos^2 \alpha$ and performing the differentiation on the right, we have

$$\frac{d\alpha}{ds} = \frac{x'(t)y''(t) - y'(t)x''(t)}{(x'(t))^2} \frac{dt}{ds} \cos^2 \alpha.$$

If we make use of (53) again, replacing $\cos^2 \alpha$, we find

$$\frac{d\alpha}{ds} = \frac{x'(t)y''(t) - y'(t)x''(t)}{(x'(t))^2} \frac{dt}{ds} (x'(t))^2 \left(\frac{dt}{ds}\right)^2$$

$$= \frac{x'(t)y''(t) - y'(t)x''(t)}{\left(\dfrac{ds}{dt}\right)^3},$$

or

$$\frac{d\alpha}{ds} = \frac{x'(t)y''(t) - y'(t)x''(t)}{[(x'(t))^2 + (y'(t))^2]^{3/2}}, \tag{57}$$

since $\dfrac{ds}{dt} = |\mathbf{v}(t)| = [x'(t))^2 + (y'(t))^2]^{1/2}$.

It follows that

$$\kappa = \frac{|x'(t)y''(t) - y'(t)x''(t)|}{[(x'(t))^2 + (y'(t))^2]^{3/2}}. \tag{58}$$

In case $x = t$, $y = f(x)$, we find that $x'(t) = 1$, $y' = f'(x)$, $x''(t) = 0$, and $y'' = f''(x) = \dfrac{d^2y}{dx^2}$; then (58) becomes

$$\kappa = \frac{\left|\dfrac{d^2y}{dx^2}\right|}{\left[1 + \left(\dfrac{dy}{dx}\right)^2\right]^{3/2}}. \tag{59}$$

Similarly, one can show that

$$\kappa = \frac{\left|\dfrac{d^2x}{dy^2}\right|}{\left[1 + \left(\dfrac{dx}{dy}\right)^2\right]^{3/2}}, \tag{60}$$

occasionally useful in case $\dfrac{dy}{dx}$ is not defined.

It is clear from (59) that $\dfrac{d^2y}{dx^2} = 0 \Rightarrow \kappa = 0$. Consequently, at an inflection point where $\dfrac{d^2y}{dx^2}$ exists (where the tangent line crosses the curve) the curvature is zero—cf. the discussion preceding Definition 12.

Example 20. We continue with the function **r** introduced in Example 19 (Figure 38):

$$\mathbf{r}(t) = t^2\mathbf{i} + t\mathbf{j}.$$

For arbitrary t we find

$$\mathbf{r}'(t) = \mathbf{v}(t) = 2t\mathbf{i} + \mathbf{j}.$$

Thus $|\mathbf{v}(t)| = \dfrac{ds}{dt} = \sqrt{4t^2 + 1}$, and

$$\mathbf{T} = \frac{\mathbf{v}}{|\mathbf{v}|} = \frac{2t}{\sqrt{4t^2 + 1}}\mathbf{i} + \frac{1}{\sqrt{4t^2 + 1}}\mathbf{j} = \cos \alpha\mathbf{i} + \sin \alpha\mathbf{j}.$$

Since $x'(t) = 2t$, $y'(t) = 1$, $x''(t) = 2$, $y''(t) = 0$, we can calculate from (57) that

$$\frac{d\alpha}{ds} = \frac{-2}{(4t^2 + 1)^{3/2}} < 0, \qquad \text{for all } t.$$

Consequently

$$\kappa = \frac{2}{(4t^2 + 1)^{3/2}}$$

and

$$\mathbf{N} = -\frac{d\mathbf{T}}{d\alpha} = \sin \alpha\mathbf{i} - \cos \alpha\mathbf{j}$$

$$= \frac{1}{\sqrt{4t^2 + 1}}\mathbf{i} - \frac{2t}{\sqrt{4t^2 + 1}}\mathbf{j}.$$

It is easy to see that the maximum value of κ is 2, occurring when $t = 0$ at $(0, 0)$. For this curve κ is always different from zero, although $\lim_{t \to \pm\infty} \kappa = 0$.

Example 21. We consider one arch of the cycloid:

$$\mathbf{r}(t) = a(t - \sin t)\mathbf{i} + a(1 - \cos t)\mathbf{j}, \qquad 0 \le t \le 2\pi.$$

We calculate

$$\mathbf{v}(t) = \mathbf{r}'(t) = a(1 - \cos t)\mathbf{i} + a \sin t\mathbf{j},$$

$$|\mathbf{v}(t)| = a\sqrt{(1 - \cos t)^2 + \sin^2 t} = a\sqrt{2}\sqrt{1 - \cos t},$$

$$\mathbf{T} = \frac{\mathbf{v}(t)}{|\mathbf{v}(t)|} = \frac{\sqrt{1 - \cos t}}{\sqrt{2}}\mathbf{i} + \frac{\sin t}{\sqrt{2}\sqrt{1 - \cos t}}\mathbf{j}.$$

By means of some trigonometric identities we can write

$$\mathbf{T} = \sin \frac{t}{2}\mathbf{i} + \cos \frac{t}{2}\mathbf{j}, \qquad 0 \le t \le 2\pi.$$

From (52),

$$T = \cos \alpha \mathbf{i} + \sin \alpha \mathbf{j},$$

so

$$\frac{d\mathbf{T}}{d\alpha} = -\sin \alpha \mathbf{i} + \cos \alpha \mathbf{j}.$$

A comparison of the last two expressions for $\mathbf{T}$ indicates that $\cos \alpha = \sin \dfrac{t}{2}$, $\sin \alpha = \cos \dfrac{t}{2}$; consequently we can express $\dfrac{d\mathbf{T}}{d\alpha}$ as

$$\frac{d\mathbf{T}}{d\alpha} = -\cos \frac{t}{2}\mathbf{i} + \sin \frac{t}{2}\mathbf{j}.$$

To find $\dfrac{d\alpha}{ds}$ we note from $\mathbf{v}(t)$ that

$$x'(t) = a(1 - \cos t), \qquad y'(t) = a \sin t.$$

Hence

$$x''(t) = a \sin t, \qquad y''(t) = a \cos t.$$

Substituting in (57), we have

$$\frac{d\alpha}{ds} = \frac{a^2(1 - \cos t)\cos t - a^2 \sin^2 t}{(a\sqrt{2}\sqrt{1 - \cos t})^3}$$

$$= \frac{\cos t - 1}{a2^{3/2}(1 - \cos t)^{3/2}}$$

$$= \frac{-1}{4a \sin \dfrac{t}{2}}.$$

For $0 < t < 2\pi$, $\dfrac{d\alpha}{ds} < 0$. Thus

$$\mathbf{N} = -\frac{d\mathbf{T}}{d\alpha} = \cos \frac{t}{2}\mathbf{i} - \sin \frac{t}{2}\mathbf{j},$$

and

$$\kappa = \frac{1}{4a \sin \dfrac{t}{2}}.$$

In Table 11.1 we give the values of $\mathbf{r}$, $\mathbf{T}$, $\mathbf{N}$, κ, and α for a few values of t, and in Figure 42 we show the curve and these vectors.

TABLE 11.1

t	$\mathbf{r}$	$\mathbf{T}$	$\mathbf{N}$	κ	α
0	$\mathbf{0}$	$\mathbf{j}$	$\mathbf{i}$	—	$\dfrac{\pi}{2}$
$\dfrac{\pi}{2}$	$a\left(\dfrac{\pi}{2}-1\right)\mathbf{i}+a\mathbf{j}$	$\dfrac{1}{\sqrt{2}}(\mathbf{i}+\mathbf{j})$	$\dfrac{1}{\sqrt{2}}(\mathbf{i}-\mathbf{j})$	$\dfrac{\sqrt{2}}{4a}$	$\dfrac{\pi}{4}$
π	$a\pi\mathbf{i}+2a\mathbf{j}$	$\mathbf{i}$	$-\mathbf{j}$	$\dfrac{1}{4a}$	0
$\dfrac{3\pi}{2}$	$a\left(\dfrac{3\pi}{2}+1\right)\mathbf{i}+a\mathbf{j}$	$\dfrac{1}{\sqrt{2}}(\mathbf{i}-\mathbf{j})$	$-\dfrac{1}{\sqrt{2}}(\mathbf{i}+\mathbf{j})$	$\dfrac{\sqrt{2}}{4a}$	$-\dfrac{\pi}{4}$
2π	$2\pi a\mathbf{i}$	$-\mathbf{j}$	$-\mathbf{i}$	—	$-\dfrac{\pi}{2}$

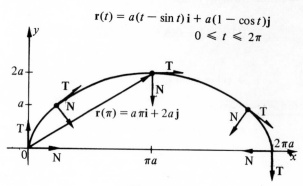

$$\mathbf{r}(t)=a(t-\sin t)\mathbf{i}+a(1-\cos t)\mathbf{j}$$
$$0\leqslant t\leqslant 2\pi$$

$$\mathbf{r}(\pi)=a\pi\mathbf{i}+2a\mathbf{j}$$

Figure 42

Notice that as t increases from 0 to 2π, α decreases from $\dfrac{\pi}{2}$ to $-\dfrac{\pi}{2}$. In particular, we do not restrict α to the interval $[0, 2\pi]$, for to do so would cause a discontinuity in α when $t=\pi$.

Example 22. Consider the graph of $y=\sin x$ for $0 \leq x \leq \pi$. We use (59) to calculate the curvature κ. Since

$$\frac{dy}{dx}=\cos x, \qquad \frac{d^2 y}{dx^2}=-\sin x,$$

we have

$$\kappa=\frac{\sin x}{(1+\cos^2 x)^{3/2}}$$

(see Figure 43).

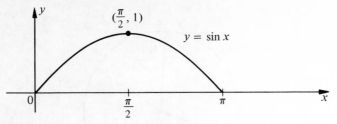

Figure 43

Note that $\kappa = 0$ for $x = 0$ and π, whereas $\kappa = 1$, a *maximum*, at the maximum point $\left(\dfrac{\pi}{2}, 1\right)$. In contrast, at the maximum point $(\pi a, 2a)$ of the cycloid the value of $\kappa = \dfrac{1}{4a}$ is a *minimum*; and $\kappa \to \infty$ as the cycloid approaches the x-axis.

We conclude this section with a little more geometry. We have already remarked that at every point of a circle of radius a the curvature $\kappa = \dfrac{1}{a}$, which is to say that the radius of the circle is the reciprocal of the curvature. Also, since at each point of a circle the radius is perpendicular to the tangent, the normal vector $\mathbf{N}$ will, at every point of a circle, be directed toward the center of the circle. A slight recasting of this enables us to say that if the graph of a vector function $\mathbf{r}$ is a circle, then for every t_0 in the domain of $\mathbf{r}$ the vector

$$\mathbf{r}(t_0) + a\mathbf{N} = \mathbf{OC}$$

will be the vector from the origin to the center C of the circle (see Figure 44).

We can generalize this discussion in the following way. We consider the graph of a vector function $\mathbf{r}$ and a point P_0 on the graph where the curvature κ is non-zero. We define the *radius of curvature* ρ to be the reciprocal of the curvature,

$$\rho = \frac{1}{\kappa};$$

we define the *center of curvature* to be the point C determined by

$$\mathbf{OC} = \mathbf{r}(t_0) + \rho\mathbf{N},$$

$\mathbf{N}$ being the unit normal at P_0; and, finally, we define the *circle of curvature*, or *osculating circle* to be the circle with center C and radius ρ. We emphasize that these definitions apply at each point of the curve where $\mathbf{T}$ and $\mathbf{N}$ exist and where $\kappa \neq 0$ exists. (The suggestive name "osculating circle" is the older of the two names given; the current trend seems to be toward superseding it with the name "circle of curvature.") Intuitively, the osculating circle is the circle which best fits the curve at P_0, the circle which "hugs the curve most closely."

These ideas have been formulated in terms of a curve which is the graph of a vector function. They clearly apply to a curve which may be represented by a set of points (x, y) where $y = f(x)$ for some function f, but the calculation for the center of curvature C is more straightforward in the context given.

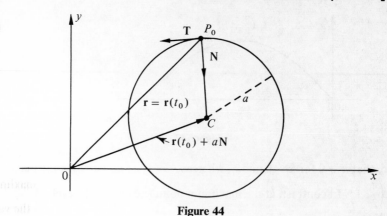

Figure 44

Example 23. We want to consider the graph of the exponential function $y = e^x$ at its y-intercept $(0, 1)$. However, we describe the curve in terms of the vector function **r** where

$$\mathbf{r}(t) = t\mathbf{i} + e^t\mathbf{j}, \qquad P_0(0, 1) \text{ corresponds to } t = 0.$$

We have

$$x(t) = t, \qquad y(t) = e^t,$$
$$x'(t) = 1, \qquad y'(t) = e^t,$$
$$x''(t) = 0, \qquad y''(t) = e^t.$$

Thus

$$\mathbf{v}(t) = \mathbf{r}'(t) = \mathbf{i} + e^t\mathbf{j}, \qquad |\mathbf{v}| = \sqrt{1 + e^{2t}},$$

$$\mathbf{T} = \frac{1}{\sqrt{1 + e^{2t}}}(\mathbf{i} + e^t\mathbf{j}) = \cos\alpha\mathbf{i} + \sin\alpha\mathbf{j},$$

$$\frac{d\alpha}{ds} = \frac{x'y'' - x''y'}{|\mathbf{v}|^3} = \frac{e^t}{(1 + e^{2t})^{3/2}} > 0, \quad \text{all } t.$$

Consequently,

$$\mathbf{N} = \frac{d\mathbf{T}}{d\alpha} = -\sin\alpha\mathbf{i} + \cos\alpha\mathbf{j} = \frac{1}{\sqrt{1 + e^{2t}}}(-e^t\mathbf{i} + \mathbf{j}),$$

and

$$\kappa = \frac{d\alpha}{ds} = \frac{e^t}{(1 + e^{2t})^{3/2}}, \qquad \rho = \frac{(1 + e^{2t})^{3/2}}{e^t},$$

In particular for the point $P_0(0, 1)$, where $t = 0$, we find

$$\mathbf{r} = \mathbf{j}, \qquad \mathbf{T} = \frac{1}{\sqrt{2}}(\mathbf{i} + \mathbf{j}), \qquad \mathbf{N} = \frac{1}{\sqrt{2}}(-\mathbf{i} + \mathbf{j}), \qquad \kappa = \frac{1}{2\sqrt{2}}, \qquad \rho = 2\sqrt{2}.$$

For P_0, then, the center of curvature C is defined by

$$OC = r + \rho N$$

$$= j + 2\sqrt{2} \cdot \frac{1}{\sqrt{2}}(-i + j)$$

$$= -2i + 3j,$$

which is to say C has coordinates $(-2, 3)$. Figure 45 shows the graph and the osculating circle at P_0. As Figure 45 shows, the circle of curvature at a point will usually cross the curve at that point.

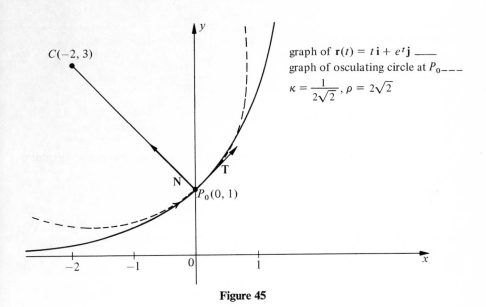

graph of $r(t) = ti + e^t j$ ———
graph of osculating circle at P_0 ‒‒‒
$\kappa = \dfrac{1}{2\sqrt{2}}, \rho = 2\sqrt{2}$

Figure 45

EXERCISES

1. Show by at least two methods that at every point of a circle of radius a, $\kappa = \dfrac{1}{a}$.

    [*Hints.* One method would be to use either $r(t) = a \cos ti + a \sin tj$ and (58) or $x^2 + y^2 = a^2$ and (59) or $y = \sqrt{a^2 - x^2}$ and (59). A second method is to use $\dfrac{d\alpha}{ds} = \lim\limits_{\Delta s \to 0} \dfrac{\Delta \alpha}{\Delta s}$ and the fact that, for a circle of radius a, $\Delta s = a\Delta\alpha$.

In numbers 2–11 find **T**, **N**, and κ at the point indicated. Make a sketch.

2. $r(t) = t^3 i + t^2 j,$ $t_0 = 1.$

3. $y = 4x - x^3,$ $P_0(1, 3)$. [*Hint.* $r(t) = ti + (4t - t^3)j, t_0 = 1.$]

4. $r(t) = a \cos^2 ti + a \sin^2 tj, \quad t_0 = \dfrac{\pi}{4}.$

5. $y = \cosh x, \ P_0(2, \cosh 2).$ (See hint for number 3.)

6. $r(t) = a \cos ti + b \sin tj, \quad t_0 = \dfrac{\pi}{6}.$

7. $xy = 1, \ P_0(-2, -\tfrac{1}{2}).$ (See hint for number 3.)

8. $y = \cos x, \ P_0\left(\dfrac{\pi}{4}, \dfrac{1}{\sqrt{2}}\right).$ (See hint for number 3.)

9. $r(t) = a \cos^3 ti + a \sin^3 tj, \quad t_0 = \dfrac{\pi}{4}.$

10. $y = \sqrt{x}, \ P_0(0, 0).$

11. $y = \log \cos x, \ P_0\left(\dfrac{\pi}{3}, -\log 2\right).$

12. Find the point(s) at which each of the following curves has maximum curvature.

(a) $y = ax^2$
(b) $y = \cos x.$

13. Consider the graph of $y = 4x - x^3$ for $x \geq 0$. Show that the point at which the curvature κ is a maximum is not the same point at which y has a maximum.

14. For each of the following curves find $\lim\limits_{x \to \infty} \kappa$.

(a) $y = \sqrt{x^2 - 1}.$ (b) $y = x^2.$ (c) $y = e^x.$

15. For each of the following curves find the circle of curvature at the point indicated. Make a sketch.

(a) $r(t) = ti + t^2j, \quad t_0 = 0.$
(b) $r(t) = \sin ti + \cos 2tj, \quad t_0 = \dfrac{\pi}{4}.$
(c) $r(t) = 3t^2i + (3t - t^3)j, \quad t_0 = 1.$

16. Find the value of a such that the curves

$$y = \cosh x \quad \text{and} \quad y = ax^2 + 1$$

have the same curvature at $(0, 1)$. Sketch (with some care) both curves.

17. Sketch with some care the graphs of

$$y = \sin x, \qquad 0 \leq x \leq \dfrac{\pi}{2}$$

and

$$y = \log x, \qquad 1 \leq x \leq e.$$

These curves have a number of similar features: the intervals are about the same length, each increases monotonically from 0 to 1, each is concave downward throughout the interval, for each the tangent line has slope of one at the leftend point, and the area under each is exactly one square unit.

There are also some dissimilarities: e.g., the slope of the tangent at the right end of the interval is zero for the sine, $\frac{1}{e}$ for the log curve.

Calculate the curvature κ for each curve and after a study of these functions decide whether this characteristic contributes to the similarities or dissimilarities of the curves. [*Hint.* Each κ is a monotonic function on its interval, but ....]

18. Given a curve $\mathbf{r}(t) = x(t)\mathbf{i} + y(t)\mathbf{j}$, we have defined the center of curvature C at a point by the vector $\mathbf{OC} = \mathbf{r}(t) + \rho\mathbf{N}$, where ρ is the radius of curvature and $\mathbf{N}$ is the unit normal vector. Show that

$$\mathbf{OC} = \left(x - y' \frac{x'^2 + y'^2}{x'y'' - x''y'}\right)\mathbf{i} + \left(y + x' \frac{x'^2 + y'^2}{x'y'' - x''y'}\right)\mathbf{j}. \qquad (61)$$

The set of such points C is a curve, the *evolute* of the curve $\mathbf{r}(t)$. [*Hints.*

$$\frac{ds}{dt} = \sqrt{x'^2 + y'^2},$$

$$\mathbf{T} = \cos\alpha\,\mathbf{i} + \sin\alpha\,\mathbf{j} = \left(x'\frac{dt}{ds}\right)\mathbf{i} + \left(y'\frac{dt}{ds}\right)\mathbf{j},$$

$$\frac{d\mathbf{T}}{d\alpha} = -\sin\alpha\,\mathbf{i} + \cos\alpha\,\mathbf{j} = -y'\frac{dt}{ds}\mathbf{i} + x'\frac{dt}{ds}\mathbf{j},$$

$$\rho\mathbf{N} = \frac{1}{\frac{d\alpha}{ds}}\frac{d\mathbf{T}}{d\alpha}, \quad \text{whether} \quad \frac{d\alpha}{ds} > 0 \quad \text{or} \quad \frac{d\alpha}{ds} < 0.]$$

19. See Exercise 20. Let

$$\mathbf{r}(t) = t\mathbf{i} + t^2\mathbf{i}.$$

Find the equation of the evolute. Sketch both curves on the same axes.

11.9 Motion in the Plane

In this section we consider motion of a particle in the plane. We will find that most of the necessary machinery has already been introduced.

To be specific, suppose that $\mathbf{r}$ is a vector function defined on some interval $T \subset \mathbf{R}$. We interpret t as time and $\mathbf{r}$ as the *position vector* for the moving particle, i.e., if $t_0 \in T$ then $\mathbf{r}(t_0)$ is the vector from the origin to the position of the object at time t_0. We define the *velocity vector* at time t_0 by

$$\mathbf{v}(t_0) = \mathbf{r}'(t_0), \qquad (61)$$

and the acceleration vector at t_0 by

$$\mathbf{a}(t_0) = \mathbf{v}'(t_0) = \mathbf{r}''(t_0). \tag{62}$$

In other words the velocity vector is the rate of change (with respect to time) of the position vector and the acceleration is the rate of change of the velocity vector.

When $\mathbf{r}$ is given by scalar functions x and y, the preceding relations become

$$\mathbf{r}(t) = x(t)\mathbf{i} + y(t)\mathbf{j} \tag{63}$$

$$\mathbf{v}(t) = x'(t)\mathbf{i} + y'(t)\mathbf{j} = \mathbf{r}'(t) \tag{64}$$

$$\mathbf{a}(t) = x''(t)\mathbf{i} + y''(t)\mathbf{j} = \mathbf{v}'(t) = \mathbf{r}''(t). \tag{65}$$

We have already seen in Section 11.8 that the magnitude of the velocity vector is

$$|\mathbf{v}(t)| = \sqrt{(x'(t))^2 + (y'(t))^2} = \frac{ds}{dt};$$

thus $|\mathbf{v}(t)|$ gives a measure of the rate of change of distance along the path of the motion. We call this the *speed* of the object and denote it by v:

$$\text{speed} = |\mathbf{v}(t)| = \frac{ds}{dt} = v. \tag{66}$$

Clearly, $v \geq 0$ for all $t \in T$.

Example 24. Let

$$\mathbf{r}(t) = \tfrac{1}{2}t^2\mathbf{i} + t\mathbf{j}, \qquad t \geq 0.$$

Then

$$\mathbf{v}(t) = t\mathbf{i} + \mathbf{j}, \qquad v = \sqrt{t^2 + 1},$$

$$\mathbf{a}(t) = \mathbf{i}.$$

For $t = 0$, $\mathbf{r} = 0$, $\mathbf{v} = \mathbf{j}$, $v = 1$, $\mathbf{a} = \mathbf{i}$; for $t = 2$ we find

$$\mathbf{r} = 2\mathbf{i} + 2\mathbf{j}, \qquad \mathbf{v} = 2\mathbf{i} + \mathbf{j}, \qquad v = \sqrt{5}, \qquad \mathbf{a} = \mathbf{i}.$$

These vectors and the path of motion are shown in Figure 46.

As the preceding example indicates, the acceleration vector does not usually lie along the tangent to the curve, as does the velocity vector $\mathbf{v}$. It is sometimes convenient to express the acceleration vector in terms of the unit tangent and normal vectors, $\mathbf{T}$ and $\mathbf{N}$, introduced in Section 11.8. This we now do. We need, however, the following fact about the derivative of a function which is the product of a scalar and a vector function.

Theorem 11. *Let the vector function* $\mathbf{F}$ *be the product of a scalar function* f *and a vector function* $\mathbf{g}$, *where* f *and* $\mathbf{g}$ *are differentiable on some common domain* T, $\mathbf{F} = f\mathbf{g}$. *Then* $\mathbf{F}$ *is differentiable, and for* $t \in T$,

$$\mathbf{F}'(t) = f'(t)\mathbf{g}(t) + f(t)\mathbf{g}'(t).$$

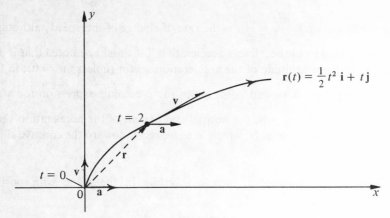

Figure 46

The proof is straightforward and is left as an exercise. Notice that the theorem simply says that the usual rule for the derivative of a product still holds if one of the factors is a vector function.

We next recall several facts from Section 11.8. By (51), which says that $\mathbf{T} = \dfrac{d\mathbf{r}}{ds}$, we have

$$\mathbf{v}(t) = \mathbf{r}'(t) = \frac{d\mathbf{r}}{ds}\frac{ds}{dt} = v\mathbf{T}. \tag{67}$$

Also, from Equation (56) we know that

$$\frac{d\mathbf{T}}{ds} = \kappa\mathbf{N}. \tag{68}$$

We can now quickly achieve our aim. We have

$$\mathbf{a}(t) = \mathbf{v}'(t) = \frac{d}{dt}(\mathbf{v}(t)) = \frac{d}{dt}(v\mathbf{T}) \qquad \text{[by Eq. (67)]}$$

$$= \frac{d}{dt}\left(\frac{ds}{dt}\mathbf{T}\right)$$

$$= \frac{d^2s}{dt^2}\mathbf{T} + \frac{ds}{dt}\left(\frac{d}{dt}\mathbf{T}\right) \qquad \text{(by Theorem 11)}$$

$$= \frac{d^2s}{dt^2}\mathbf{T} + \frac{ds}{dt}\left(\frac{d\mathbf{T}}{ds}\right)\frac{ds}{dt} \qquad \text{(by the chain rule)}$$

$$= \frac{d^2s}{dt^2}\mathbf{T} + \left(\frac{ds}{dt}\right)^2(\kappa\mathbf{N}). \qquad \text{(by 68)}$$

Thus we can write

$$\mathbf{a}(t) = \frac{d^2s}{dt^2}\mathbf{T} + \kappa v^2\mathbf{N}. \tag{69}$$

The coefficient of $\mathbf{T}$, $\dfrac{d^2s}{dt^2} = \dfrac{dv}{dt}$, is the rate of change of the speed; although it might be referred to as the "linear acceleration," it should be noted that it does not represent the magnitude of the acceleration vector (unless $\kappa v^2 = 0$); in fact, $\dfrac{d^2s}{dt^2}$ can be negative. A second point about the preceding expression for $\mathbf{a}(t)$ is that $\kappa v^2 \geq 0$; in other words, the normal component of the acceleration vector always has the same sense as $\mathbf{N}$, which is, as we recall, toward the concave side of the path of motion.

Example 25. We consider a particle traveling in the plane with position function $\mathbf{r}$ given by

$$\mathbf{r}(t) = 4\cos t\,\mathbf{i} + 3\sin t\,\mathbf{j}, \qquad 0 \leq t < 2\pi.$$

We calculate

$$\mathbf{v}(t) = -4\sin t\,\mathbf{i} + 3\cos t\,\mathbf{j}$$

$$\mathbf{a}(t) = -4\cos t\,\mathbf{i} - 3\sin t\,\mathbf{j} = -\mathbf{r}(t).$$

Also,

$$v = \frac{ds}{dt} = \sqrt{16\sin^2 t + 9\cos^2 t},$$

$$\frac{dv}{dt} = \frac{d^2s}{dt^2} = \frac{7\sin 2t}{2\sqrt{16\sin^2 t + 9\cos^2 t}}$$

$$\frac{d\alpha}{ds} = \frac{x'(t)y''(t) - x''(t)y'(t)}{v^3} = \frac{12\sin^2 t + 12\cos^2 t}{v^3} = \frac{12}{v^3}.$$

Since $\dfrac{d\alpha}{ds} > 0$, $\kappa = \dfrac{d\alpha}{ds} = \dfrac{12}{v^3}$, $\kappa v^2 = \dfrac{12}{v}$.

If we focus attention on the point where $t = \dfrac{\pi}{4}$ we find

$$\mathbf{r} = \frac{1}{\sqrt{2}}(4\mathbf{i} + 3\mathbf{j}),$$

$$\mathbf{v} = \frac{1}{\sqrt{2}}(-4\mathbf{i} + 3\mathbf{j}),$$

$$\mathbf{a} = \frac{1}{\sqrt{2}}(-4\mathbf{i} - 3\mathbf{j}),$$

$$v = \frac{5}{\sqrt{2}}, \qquad \frac{d^2s}{dt^2} = \frac{7\sqrt{2}}{10}, \qquad \kappa v^2 = \frac{12\sqrt{2}}{5} = \frac{24\sqrt{2}}{10},$$

$$\mathbf{T} = \frac{1}{5}(-4\mathbf{i} + 3\mathbf{j})$$

$$\mathbf{N} = \frac{1}{5}(-3\mathbf{i} - 4\mathbf{j}).$$

Substituting from this list into (69) we find

$$\mathbf{a} = \frac{7\sqrt{2}}{10}\mathbf{T} + \frac{24\sqrt{2}}{10}\mathbf{N} = \frac{\sqrt{2}}{10}(7\mathbf{T} + 24\mathbf{N}) \approx 0.99\mathbf{T} + 3.39\mathbf{N}$$

(see Figure 47).

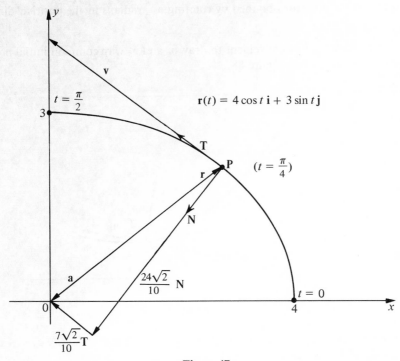

Figure 47

In the event that it is convenient to work in polar coordinates, one can use θ as parameter. As before, we can begin with $\mathbf{r} = x\mathbf{i} + y\mathbf{j}$. But if the path of motion is described by a function $r = f(\theta)$, we can use the relations between rectangular and polar coordinates to write

$$\mathbf{r} = \mathbf{r}(\theta) = r\cos\theta\mathbf{i} + r\sin\theta\mathbf{j}$$
$$= r(\cos\theta\mathbf{i} + \sin\theta\mathbf{j})$$
$$= r\,\mathbf{u}_\theta,$$

where $r = f(\theta)$ and $\mathbf{u}_\theta = \cos\theta\mathbf{i} + \sin\theta\mathbf{j}$. (There should be no confusion because of the two uses of the symbol "r": in general, $r = |\mathbf{r}|$.)

By Theorem 11, then,

$$\mathbf{v} = \mathbf{r}'(\theta) = f'(\theta)\mathbf{u}_\theta + f(\theta)\mathbf{u}_\theta',$$

or

$$\mathbf{v} = r'\mathbf{u}_\theta + r\mathbf{u}_\theta'. \tag{70}$$

The relation between $\mathbf{u}'_\theta$ and $\mathbf{u}_\theta$ is an especially simple one: since

$$\mathbf{u}_\theta = \cos\theta\,\mathbf{i} + \sin\theta\,\mathbf{j},$$

$$\mathbf{u}'_\theta = -\sin\theta\,\mathbf{i} + \cos\theta\,\mathbf{j} = \cos\left(\theta + \frac{\pi}{2}\right)\mathbf{i} + \sin\left(\theta + \frac{\pi}{2}\right)\mathbf{j}.$$

Thus $\mathbf{u}'_\theta$ is the unit vector obtained by rotating $\mathbf{u}_\theta \dfrac{\pi}{2}$ radians in the positive direction.

For our purposes it is convenient to draw $\mathbf{u}_\theta$ and $\mathbf{u}'_\theta$ with common initial point $P(r, \theta)$ on the curve (see Figure 48).

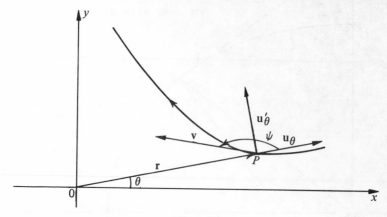

Figure 48

We leave it as an exercise for the student to show, using the identity $\mathbf{u}''_\theta = -\mathbf{u}_\theta$, that the acceleration vector is given by

$$\mathbf{a} = \mathbf{v}'(\theta) = (r'' - r)\mathbf{u}_\theta + 2r'\mathbf{u}'_\theta. \tag{71}$$

If we form the scalar product of $\mathbf{u}_\theta$ and $\mathbf{v}$ we obtain information about the angle ψ introduced in Section 10.4. From Eq. (70) we find

$$\mathbf{u}_\theta \cdot \mathbf{v} = \mathbf{u}_\theta \cdot (r'\mathbf{u}_\theta + r\mathbf{u}'_\theta) = r',$$

since $\mathbf{u}_\theta$ is perpendicular to $\mathbf{u}'_\theta$ and $|\mathbf{u}_\theta| = 1$. Also, by definition of the scalar product,

$$\mathbf{u}_\theta \cdot \mathbf{v} = |\mathbf{v}| \cos\psi, \qquad (\text{since } |\mathbf{u}_\theta| = 1)$$

where ψ is the angle between $\mathbf{u}_\theta$ and the tangent $\mathbf{v}$. From these equations we see

$$\cos\psi = \frac{r'}{|\mathbf{v}|}, \tag{72}$$

where, from (70), $|\mathbf{v}| = \sqrt{r'^2 + r^2}$.

Consideration of (72) discloses that

$$r' = \frac{dr}{d\theta} > 0 \Rightarrow \cos \psi > 0 \Rightarrow 0 < \psi < \frac{\pi}{2},$$

$$r' = \frac{dr}{d\theta} < 0 \Rightarrow \cos \psi < 0 \Rightarrow \frac{\pi}{2} < \psi < \pi,$$

as described in Chapter 10. Recall that in Section 10.4 we defined the angle ψ as the angle between the radial line and the "backward" portion of the tangent. It is easy to see that this is equal to the angle ψ described above (and shown in Figure 48). Finally, we remark that from (72) we can verify that $\tan \psi = \dfrac{r}{r'}$ (see Figure 49).

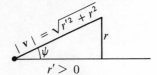
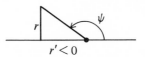

Figure 49

Example 26. Consider a particle traveling on the cardioid $r = 1 + \cos \theta$. We have

$$\mathbf{r}(\theta) = r\mathbf{u}_\theta = (1 + \cos \theta)\mathbf{u}_\theta$$

$$\mathbf{v} = \mathbf{r}'(\theta) = -\sin \theta \mathbf{u}_\theta + (1 + \cos \theta)\mathbf{u}_\theta'$$

$$\mathbf{a} = \mathbf{v}' = -\cos \theta \mathbf{u}_\theta - \sin \theta \mathbf{u}_\theta' - \sin \theta \mathbf{u}_\theta' + (1 + \cos \theta)\mathbf{u}_\theta''$$

$$= (-1 - 2 \cos \theta)\mathbf{u}_\theta - 2 \sin \theta \mathbf{u}_\theta'.$$

We calculate these vectors for several values of θ and show some of them in Figure 50:

$$\theta = \frac{\pi}{6}, \quad r = 1 + \frac{\sqrt{3}}{2}, \quad r' = -\frac{1}{2}, \quad \mathbf{v} = -\frac{1}{2}\mathbf{u}_\theta + \left(1 + \frac{\sqrt{3}}{2}\right)\mathbf{u}_\theta',$$

$$\mathbf{a} = (-1 - \sqrt{3})\mathbf{u}_\theta - \mathbf{u}_\theta', \quad \tan \psi = -2 - \sqrt{3};$$

$$\theta = \frac{7\pi}{4}, \quad r = 1 + \frac{1}{\sqrt{2}}, \quad r' = \frac{1}{\sqrt{2}}, \quad \mathbf{v} = \frac{1}{\sqrt{2}}\mathbf{u}_\theta + \left(1 + \frac{1}{\sqrt{2}}\right)\mathbf{u}_\theta',$$

$$\mathbf{a} = (-1 - \sqrt{2})\mathbf{u}_\theta + \sqrt{2}\mathbf{u}_\theta', \quad \tan \psi = 1 + \sqrt{2}.$$

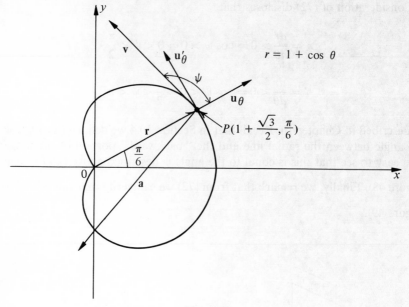

Figure 50

EXERCISES

In numbers 1–8 determine the path of motion and calculate $\mathbf{r}$, $\mathbf{v}$, v, $\mathbf{T}$, $\mathbf{N}$, and κ and express $\mathbf{a}$ in terms of $\mathbf{T}$ and $\mathbf{N}$ at the point indicated.

1. $\mathbf{r}(t) = 2t\mathbf{i} + \frac{1}{2}t^2\mathbf{j}$, $t_0 = 2$.

2. $\mathbf{r}(t) = (\cos t + \sin t)\mathbf{i} + (\cos t - \sin t)\mathbf{j}$, $t_0 = \dfrac{\pi}{2}$.

3. $\mathbf{r}(t) = (t + \sin t)\mathbf{i} + (1 - \cos t)\mathbf{j}$, $t \in [-\pi, \pi]$, $t_0 = \dfrac{\pi}{2}$.

4. $\mathbf{r}(t) = (t^2 + 1)\mathbf{i} + t^3\mathbf{j}$, $t_0 = -1$.

5. $\mathbf{r}(t) = a \cos^3 t\mathbf{i} + a \sin^3 t\mathbf{j}$, $t_0 = \dfrac{3\pi}{4}$.

6. $\mathbf{r}(t) = 2a \cot t\mathbf{i} + 2a \sin^2 t\mathbf{j}$, $t_0 = \dfrac{\pi}{4}$.

7. $\mathbf{r}(t) = \cos t\mathbf{i} + e^t\mathbf{j}$, $t \in [0, 2\pi]$, $t_0 = \dfrac{\pi}{2}$.

8. $\mathbf{r}(t) = \cos 2t\mathbf{i} + \sin t\mathbf{j}, \qquad t_0 = \dfrac{\pi}{4}.$

For numbers 9–12 find $\mathbf{v}$ and $\mathbf{a}$ at the point indicated. Sketch the path of motion.

9. $\mathbf{r}(\theta) = (1 + 2\cos\theta)\mathbf{u}_\theta, \qquad \theta = \dfrac{7\pi}{6}.$

10. $\mathbf{r}(\theta) = \dfrac{2}{1 - \cos\theta}\,\mathbf{u}_\theta, \qquad \theta = \dfrac{\pi}{2}.$

11. $\mathbf{r}(\theta) = \theta\mathbf{u}_\theta, \qquad \theta = \dfrac{\pi}{2} \quad \text{and} \quad \theta = \dfrac{5\pi}{2}.$

12. $\mathbf{r}(\theta) = \sin 3\theta, \qquad \theta = \dfrac{\pi}{4}.$

13. Does the acceleration vector ever lie along the tangent vector? If so, under what conditions?

14. Derive Eq. (71) for $\mathbf{a}$, using the expression given in (70) for $\mathbf{v}$.

15. Prove Theorem 11. [*Hint.* Let $\mathbf{g}(t) = x(t)\mathbf{i} + y(t)\mathbf{j}$. Then

$$\mathbf{F}(t) = (f(t)x(t))\mathbf{i} + (f(t)y(t))\mathbf{j}.]$$

16. A projectile is fired from the origin at time $t = 0$ with an initial velocity v_0 and an angle of elevation α.

(a) Show that, neglecting air resistance, its position vector $\mathbf{r}$ is given by

$$\mathbf{r}(t) = (v_0 \cos \alpha t)\mathbf{i} + (-\tfrac{1}{2}gt^2 + v_0 \sin \alpha t),\mathbf{j}$$

where g is the acceleration due to gravity.
[*Hints.*
(1) $\mathbf{a}(t) = 0 \cdot \mathbf{i} + (-g)\mathbf{j}.$
(2) $\mathbf{v}(0) = (v_0 \cos \alpha)\mathbf{i} + (v_0 \sin \alpha)\mathbf{j}.$
(3) $\mathbf{r}(0) = \mathbf{0}.]$

(b) Assuming level ground below the path of flight of the projectile, find the abscissa of the point at which it returns to earth.

(c) What value of α gives the greatest range?

(d) What curve describes the path of motion?

Chapter 12 Geometry and Vectors in Three Space

In this chapter we make a brief study of analytic geometry of three dimensions. Vectors, in the geometric sense, will provide us with a useful tool. Fortunately, the ideas developed in Chapter 11 carry over directly to three dimensions; we shall, however, introduce an operation on vectors not discussed in the earlier chapter. The enlarging of space by one dimension means that, in addition, to studying curves, as we did in plane geometry, we must also concern ourselves with surfaces, i.e., two-dimensional regions. The simplest of these are planes, but we shall also study more complicated—and more interesting—surfaces.

12.1 Rectangular Coordinates in Three Space

A rectangular cartesian coordinate system is established in three dimensions by the following procedure. One chooses a point O, the origin; three mutually perpendicular straight lines through O, the x-, y-, and z-axes; a positive direction for each axis; and a unit of length—we shall, unless specific mention is made to the contrary, always use the same unit of length on all three axes.

However, that is not the end of the story, for one more decision must be made. To show why this is so, suppose the origin O, the three mutually perpendicular lines through O, and the positive direction on each have all been chosen, but the labels x, y, z have not yet been assigned. There are, formally, six (3!) different ways in which these assignments can be made; actually, though, these six fall into two groups of three each, the three in each group being essentially the same —and basically different from the three in the other group. We show a representative of each group of three in Figure 1.

The system in Figure 1(a) is known as a *right-handed system* for the reason

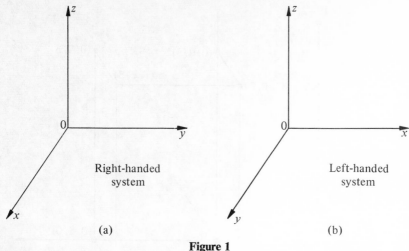

Right-handed
system

Left-handed
system

(a)   (b)

Figure 1

that a rotation in the direction from positive x- to positive y-axis is in the same direction that would cause an ordinary right-handed wood screw, positioned with its head at O, its pointed end in the direction of the positive z-axis, to advance into the wood. The system in Figure 1(b) is *left-handed*. We shall consistently use a right-handed system, although we may use one of the two other possible ways of labeling—e. g., letting x and y be the axes in the plane of the paper in their usual (i.e., two-dimensional) horizontal and vertical positions, and letting the positive z-axis be drawn to suggest coming out of the plane of the paper toward the reader.

We strongly recommend that the student draw all six possible ways of assigning labels to the positive axes and pick out the group of three which are right-handed.

The three coordinate axes taken two at a time determine three planes, called the *coordinate planes*. In Figure 1(a) the plane of the paper is the yz-plane, the horizontal plane perpendicular to the plane of the paper is the xy-plane, and the zx-plane is the vertical plane perpendicular to the plane of the paper. (For purposes of visualizing, it is often convenient to think of the origin as a corner of a room at the floor; the floor is the xy-plane, etc.) The coordinates of a point in space are then directed distances measured from the coordinate planes—and perpendicular to these planes. For example, the z-coordinate is the directed distance from the xy-plane, etc. See Figure 2, where several points are shown with their coordinates (x, y, z).

The three coordinate planes divide space into eight parts, called *octants*. In contrast to the practice of plane geometry, only one of the octants is assigned a number: the octant in which all three coordinates of a point are positive is called the *first octant*.

Each of the equations $x = c$, $y = c$, or $z = c$ determines a set of points known as a *coordinate surface*. In every case these coordinate surfaces are planes parallel to the coordinate planes. Thus $z = 1$ determines the plane parallel to the xy-

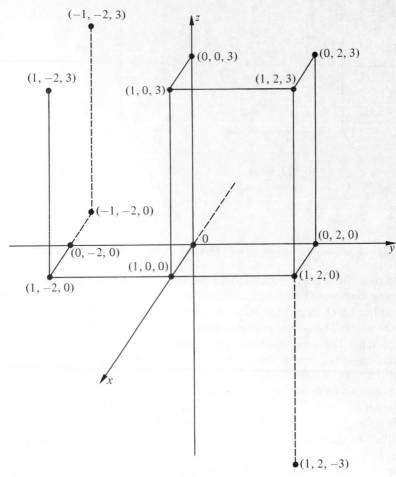

Figure 2

plane and one unit above it. The *xy*-plane is itself $z = 0$; similarly, the *yz*-plane and the *zx*-plane are, respectively, $x = 0$ and $y = 0$.

We shall use a natural extension of the Pythagorean theorem as a basis for defining distance in three dimensions.

Definition 1. *The **distance** between two points* $P_1(x_1, y_1, z_1)$ *and* $P_2(x_2, y_2, z_2)$ *is*

$$d(P_1, P_2) = \sqrt{(x_1 - x_2)^2 + (y_1 - y_2)^2 + (z_1 - z_2)^2}. \qquad (1)$$

It follows from this definition that the equation $x^2 + y^2 + z^2 = 1$ determines the set of points which are 1 unit from the origin: a sphere of radius one with center at the origin; we shall refer to this as the *unit sphere*.

The examples of the unit sphere and the coordinate surfaces serve to illustrate a fact that occasionally causes trouble for the three-space novitiate. We refer to the fact that, in general, a single equation in three-dimensional geometry determines a *surface*, a two-dimensional set of points. As we shall see, the analytic description of lines and curves in general is best achieved by means of parametric equations. However, the coordinate axes provide a mild exception to this statement. For example, the z-axis is represented by

$$\begin{Bmatrix} x = 0 \\ y = 0 \end{Bmatrix}.$$

The first of these equations is, of course, the yz-plane, the second the zx-plane; together they represent the intersection of these planes, i.e., the z-axis.

As an illustration of the important point of the preceding paragraph—and as a preview of a topic we look at later in more detail—consider the equation $x^2 + y^2 = 1$. In the xy-plane this equation determines the unit circle. To see that in three space it represents something more, recall that the equation imposes a *condition which must be satisfied* by the coordinates of the points on the graph. But the equation $x^2 + y^2 = 1$, with z absent, imposes no condition, i.e., no restriction, on z. Thus if x_0, y_0 are such that $x_0^2 + y_0^2 = 1$, then (x_0, y_0, z) is on the graph of $x^2 + y^2 = 1$ *for every value* of z. The resulting set of points is the right circular cylinder of radius one, symmetric with respect to the z-axis (see Figure 3).

In a similar way the equation $y + z = 1$, when restricted to the yz plane, describes a straight line. But when interpreted as defining a set of points in space it imposes no condition on x; thus, if y_0 and z_0 satisfy $y_0 + z_0 = 1$, the

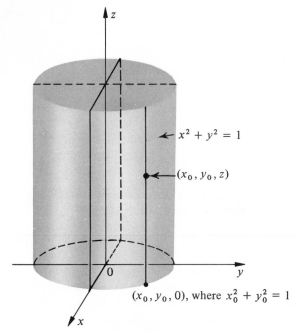

$$x^2 + y^2 = 1$$

(x_0, y_0, z)

$(x_0, y_0, 0)$, where $x_0^2 + y_0^2 = 1$

Figure 3

point (x, y_0, z_0) is on the surface for *every* x. As seems evident and as we shall verify later, this equation defines a plane, shown in part in Figure 4.

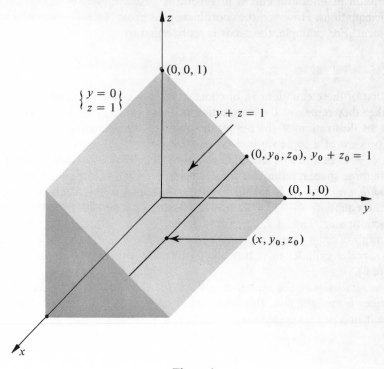

$\begin{Bmatrix} y = 0 \\ z = 1 \end{Bmatrix}$

$(0, 0, 1)$

$y + z = 1$

$(0, y_0, z_0), y_0 + z_0 = 1$

$(0, 1, 0)$

(x, y_0, z_0)

Figure 4

EXERCISES

1. Let $a > 0$, $b > 0$, $c > 0$. Sketch the point $P_0(a, b, c)$. Now give the coordinates of and sketch in on your figure the point which is symmetric to P_0 with respect to:

   (a) the xy-plane.
   (b) $x = 0$.
   (c) the x-axis.
   (d) the zx-plane.
   (e) the y-axis.
   (f) the origin.

2. Find the equation satisfied by the set of all points whose (perpendicular) distance from the y-axis is 2 units. Sketch.

3. Describe the set of points in space satisfying each of the following conditions.

   (a) $z > 0$.
   (b) $xy \geq 0$.
   (c) $\begin{Bmatrix} x > 0 \\ y = 0 \\ z = 0 \end{Bmatrix}$.
   (d) $x^2 + y^2 = 0$ (Careful!).
   (e) $\begin{Bmatrix} x^2 + y^2 = 1 \\ z = 1 \end{Bmatrix}$ (see Figure 3).
   (f) $\begin{Bmatrix} y + z = 1 \\ x = 2 \end{Bmatrix}$ (see Figure 4).
   (g) $\begin{Bmatrix} x = 2 \\ y = 1 \end{Bmatrix}$.

4. Describe each of the following sets of points in space.

(a) $x^2 + y^2 + z^2 \leq 1$.

(b) $z \geq 2$.

(c) $1 \leq x^2 + y^2 \leq 4$.

(d) $\begin{cases} x^2 + y^2 = 1 \\ y = 0 \end{cases}$.

(e) $\begin{cases} y = 1 \\ z = 0 \end{cases}$.

5. Let $A(0, 1, 2)$, $B(2, 1, 0)$. Find the equation satisfied by the coordinates of all points $P(x, y, z)$ which are equidistant from A and B. Sketch.

6. (a) Study the nature of the *curve* defined by $z = e^{-y}$ *when restricted to the yz-plane*.

(b) Now discuss the set of points in three space determined by $z = e^{-y}$.

7. (a) Reproduce Figure 1 and also draw the four figures obtainable by the other possible assignment of axes.

(b) Pick out the set of three right-handed systems and observe that any one can be transformed into any other of this set by a rigid motion.

(c) Now convince yourself that no such rigid motion will convert a right-handed system into a left-handed system.

8. Determine the geometric nature of the set of points determined by each of the following equations.

(a) $x^2 + y^2 + z^2 = 2x$. [*Hint.* Complete the square in x.]
(b) $x^2 + y^2 + z^2 = 2x + 2y$.
(c) $x^2 + y^2 + z^2 - 2x + 4y - 8z + 17 = 0$.
(d) $x^2 + y^2 = 2x$.
(e) $x = y$.

9. (a) Refer to Theorem 1.19. Develop a formula for the coordinates of the midpoint of the line segment between $P_1(x_1, y_1, z_1)$ and $P_2(x_2, y_2, z_2)$.

(b) Find the midpoint of the segment determined by $P_1(1, -1, 3)$ and $P_2(5, 3, -1)$.

10. Give an analytic description (equation, or equations, as necessary) of:

(a) The x-axis. (b) The y-axis.

12.2 Vectors in Three Space

The definitions and properties of geometric vectors in two dimensions, as formulated in Sections 11.2 and 11.3, all carry over in the obvious way, *mutatis mutandis*, to vectors in three dimensions.

In particular, a vector $\mathbf{a} \in \mathbf{R}^3$ will be interpreted geometrically as a directed line segment. Since we have agreed to work with *free* vectors, this means we can interpret $\mathbf{a} = (a_1, a_2, a_3)$ either as the line segment directed from the origin to the *point* (a_1, a_2, a_3); or, if $P_0(x_0, y_0, z_0)$ is any point, $\mathbf{a}$ can be interpreted as the line segment directed from P_0 to P_1, where P_1 has coordinates $P_1(x_0 + a_1, y_0 + a_2, z_0 + a_3)$ (see Figure 5).

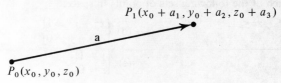

Figure 5

Conversely, if $P_0(x_0, y_0, z_0)$ and $P_1(x_1, y_1, z_1)$ are two points in three space, then the vector from P_0 to P_1 is

$$\mathbf{P_0\,P_1} = (x_1 - x_0, y_1 - y_0, z_1 - z_0).$$

The length $|\mathbf{a}|$ of the vector $\mathbf{a} = (a_1, a_2, a_3)$ is

$$|\mathbf{a}| = \sqrt{a_1^2 + a_2^2 + a_3^2}.$$

A vector of length one is called a *unit vector*.

We will make use of the unit vectors $\mathbf{i}$, $\mathbf{j}$, and $\mathbf{k}$, in the direction of the positive x-, y-, and z-axes, respectively. Thus, we can—and we often shall—write $\mathbf{a} = (a_1, a_2, a_3)$ as

$$\mathbf{a} = a_1\mathbf{i} + a_2\mathbf{j} + a_3\mathbf{k}.$$

Addition of vectors and multiplication of a vector by a scalar are carried out componentwise in terms of $\mathbf{i}$, $\mathbf{j}$, and $\mathbf{k}$: Thus

$$\left.\begin{array}{c}\mathbf{a} = a_1\mathbf{i} + a_2\mathbf{j} + a_3\mathbf{k} \\ \mathbf{b} = b_1\mathbf{i} + b_2\mathbf{j} + b_3\mathbf{k} \\ c \in \mathbf{R}\end{array}\right\} \Rightarrow \left\{\begin{array}{l}\mathbf{a} + \mathbf{b} = (a_1 + b_1)\mathbf{i} + (a_2 + b_2)\mathbf{j} + (a_3 + b_3)\mathbf{k}, \\ c\mathbf{a} = (ca_1)\mathbf{i} + (ca_2)\mathbf{j} + (ca_3)\mathbf{k}.\end{array}\right.$$

The inner product $\mathbf{a} \cdot \mathbf{b} = a_1 b_1 + a_2 b_2 + a_3 b_3$ has the same geometric interpretation as in Theorem 11.4:

$$\mathbf{a} \cdot \mathbf{b} = |\mathbf{a}|\,|\mathbf{b}|\cos\theta,$$

where θ is the angle $(0 \le \theta \le \pi)$ between $\mathbf{a}$ and $\mathbf{b}$. Consequently,

$$\mathbf{a} \perp \mathbf{b} \Leftrightarrow \mathbf{a} \cdot \mathbf{b} = 0,$$

and, if $\mathbf{a}$ and $\mathbf{b}$ are both nonzero, then θ can be found by

$$\cos\theta = \frac{\mathbf{a} \cdot \mathbf{b}}{|\mathbf{a}|\,|\mathbf{b}|} = \frac{a_1 b_1 + a_2 b_2 + a_3 b_3}{\sqrt{a_1^2 + a_2^2 + a_3^2}\sqrt{b_1^2 + b_2^2 + b_3^2}}.$$

We know that the *length* of a vector $\mathbf{v} = a\mathbf{i} + b\mathbf{j} + c\mathbf{k}$ is determined by the numbers a, b, c as $|\mathbf{v}| = \sqrt{a^2 + b^2 + c^2}$. But these numbers, or *components*, also determine the direction of $\mathbf{v}$. Suppose $\mathbf{v}$ has its initial point at the origin, as shown in Figure 6(a).

Definition 2. *The angles* α, β, γ *between the positive* x-, y-, *and* z-*axes, respectively, and the vector* $\mathbf{v} = a\mathbf{i} + b\mathbf{j} + c\mathbf{k} \ne \mathbf{0}$ *are the **direction angles** of* $\mathbf{v}$. *The direction angles lie in the interval* $[0, \pi]$.

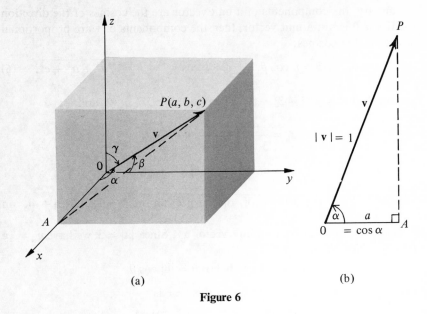

(a)   (b)

Figure 6

Now if the vector $\mathbf{v} = a\mathbf{i} + b\mathbf{j} + c\mathbf{k}$ is a unit vector, $|\mathbf{v}| = 1$, then, as indicated in Figure 6(b),

$$a = \cos \alpha, \; b = \cos \beta, \; c = \cos \gamma. \tag{2}$$

Because $\mathbf{v}$ is a unit vector we have

$$\cos^2 \alpha + \cos^2 \beta + \cos^2 \gamma = 1. \tag{3}$$

If $\mathbf{v} \neq \mathbf{0}$ is not a unit vector, then

$$\mathbf{u_v} = \frac{1}{|\mathbf{v}|}\mathbf{v} = \frac{a\mathbf{i} + b\mathbf{j} + c\mathbf{k}}{\sqrt{a^2 + b^2 + c^2}}$$

$$= \frac{a}{\sqrt{a^2 + b^2 + c^2}}\mathbf{i} + \frac{b}{\sqrt{a^2 + b^2 + c^2}}\mathbf{j} + \frac{c}{\sqrt{a^2 + b^2 + c^2}}\mathbf{k} \tag{4}$$

is a unit vector. Consequently,

$$\cos \alpha = \frac{a}{\sqrt{a^2 + b^2 + c^2}}, \quad \cos \beta = \frac{b}{\sqrt{a^2 + b^2 + c^2}}, \quad \cos \gamma = \frac{c}{\sqrt{a^2 + b^2 + c^2}}. \tag{5}$$

Again we notice that (3) holds. Thus we have the following assertion.

Theorem 1. *For every nonzero vector with direction angles* α, β, γ

$$\cos^2 \alpha + \cos^2 \beta + \cos^2 \gamma = 1.$$

In summary, the components of a unit vector are the cosines of the direction angles. If $v \neq 0$ is not a unit vector, then the components of v are proportional to these direction cosines:

$$a = k \cos \alpha, \qquad b = k \cos \beta, \qquad c = k \cos \gamma, \qquad k = \sqrt{a^2 + b^2 + c^2}. \quad \textbf{(6)}$$

Example 1. Let $a = 4i - 3j + 5k$. Then $|a| = \sqrt{50} = 5\sqrt{2}$, and

$$u_a = \frac{4}{5\sqrt{2}} i - \frac{3}{5\sqrt{2}} j + \frac{1}{\sqrt{2}} k$$

$$= \cos \alpha i + \cos \beta j + \cos \gamma k.$$

Example 2. Find the length of the projection of $b = -5i + 3j + 4k$ on $a = i - 2j + 2k$.

We begin by converting a to a unit vector u_a. Since $|a| = 3$, we have $u_a = \frac{1}{3}a = \frac{1}{3}(i - 2j + 2k)$. Now,

$$u_a \cdot b = |u_a| \cdot |b| \cos \theta = |b| \cos \theta,$$

the projection of b on a. The number in this case is

$$u_a \cdot b = \frac{1}{3}[(1)(-5) + (-2)(3) + (2)(4)] = -1.$$

The negative sign indicates $\frac{\pi}{2} < \theta < \pi$ (see Figure 7). The *length* of the projection of b on a is, therefore, 1.

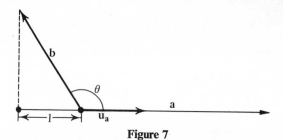

Figure 7

EXERCISES

In numbers 1–10 find the vector from P_1 to P_2 and in each case find the direction cosines of the vector.

1. $P_1(1, 2, -1), P_2(2, 0, 1)$.   2. $P_1(2, 0, 1), P_2(1, 2, -1)$.

3. $P_1(0, 0, 0), P_2(1, 1, 1)$.   4. $P_1(0, 0, 0), P_2(0, 1, 1)$.

5. $P_1(0, 0, 0), P_2(1, 0, 1)$.   6. $P_1(0, 0, 0), P_2(4, 0, 0)$.

7. $P_1(3, 4, 5)$, $P_2(0, 0, 0)$.   8. $P_1(1, 2, 1)$, $P_2(4, 6, 1)$.

9. $P_1(1, 1, 1)$, $P_2(1, -3, 4)$.   10. $P_1(1, 2, 3)$, $P_2(1, 2, 8)$.

11. Find $\cos \theta$, where θ is the angle between **a** and **b**, for each pair of vectors **a** and **b**.

     (a) $\mathbf{a} = 2\mathbf{i} + 2\mathbf{j} - \mathbf{k}$, $\mathbf{b} = 3\mathbf{i} - 4\mathbf{j} + 5\mathbf{k}$.
     (b) $\mathbf{a} = \mathbf{i} + \mathbf{j} - \mathbf{k}$, $\mathbf{b} = 3\mathbf{i} + 3\mathbf{k}$.
     (c) $\mathbf{a} = 4\mathbf{i} - \mathbf{j} + 2\mathbf{k}$, $\mathbf{b} = -\mathbf{i} + 2\mathbf{j} + 2\mathbf{k}$.

12. For each pair of vectors **a** and **b** of Exercise 11, find the length of the projection of **b** on **a**.

13. Show that the points $P_1(3, 4, -3)$, $P_2(7, 10, -11)$, $P_3(6, 1, 3)$, $P_4(10, 7, -5)$ are the vertices of a parallelogram. Is the parallelogram a rectangle?

14. Show, without using the length formula, that $P_1(4, 0, 7)$, $P_2(10, -4, 15)$, $P_3(12, 20, 11)$, and $P_4(18, 16, 19)$ are the vertices of a rectangle.

15. Given a vector $\mathbf{v} = a\mathbf{i} + b\mathbf{j} + c\mathbf{k}$. What is the geometric significance of each of the following?

     (a) $c = 0$ (d) $a = b = 0$
     (b) $b = c = 0$ (e) $a = b = c = 0$.
     (c) $a = 0$

16. The vector $\mathbf{v}_1 = \mathbf{j} - \mathbf{k}$ has its initial point at $P_0(0, 0, 1)$. The vector $\mathbf{v}_2$ also has its initial point at $P_0(0, 0, 1)$, is perpendicular to $\mathbf{v}_1$, lies in the zx-plane, and is $|a|$ units long. Find a such that the vector from the tip of $\mathbf{v}_1$ to the tip of $\mathbf{v}_2$ has a length of 10 units.

12.3 The Vector Product

In order to introduce the major topic of this section we need the idea of a *right-handed triple* of vectors.

Definition 3. *Given a set of three nonzero vectors,* **a**, **b**, **c**, *not coplanar, and with the same initial point, we say they form a* **right-handed triple**, *if the following is true. Establish a right-handed coordinate system with origin at the common initial point, with the xy-plane the plane of* **a** *and* **b**, *with the positive x-axis along* **a** *and with the positive y-axis on the same side of the x-axis as is* **b**. *Then* **c** *and the positive z-axis lie on the same side of the xy-plane.*

If the noncoplanar vectors **a**, **b**, **c** do not form a right-handed triple, they form a *left-handed triple* (see Figure 8).

Notice that if **a**, **b**, **c** form a right-handed triple, then so do **b**, **c**, **a** and **c**, **a**, **b**, whereas **a**, **c**, **b**; **b**, **a**, **c**; and **c**, **b**, **a** all are left-handed. For example (cf. Figure

8a), if the axes are moved so that the xy-plane is the **bc**-plane, the positive x-axis along **b**, the positive y-axis on the same side of **b** as is **c**, then **a** and the positive z-axis will lie on the same side of the xy-plane.

We now introduce a second type of multiplication for vectors. The definition is both involved and a little strange. However, rather than digress now to give motivational reasons (which lie in the realm of mechanics) for the form of the definition, we include a discussion in Exercise 13.

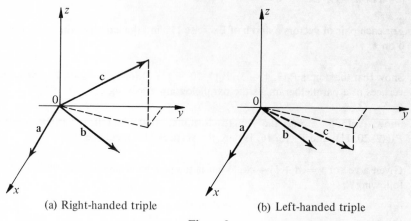

(a) Right-handed triple   (b) Left-handed triple

Figure 8

Definition 4. *Let* **a**, **b** *be vectors. The* **vector** *(or* **cross***)* **product** *of* **a** *and* **b** *is the vector*

$$\mathbf{a} \times \mathbf{b} = \mathbf{c},$$

where

   (i) $\mathbf{c} \perp \mathbf{a}, \mathbf{c} \perp \mathbf{b}$,
   (ii) **a**, **b**, **c** *form a right-handed triple,*
   (iii) $|\mathbf{c}| = |\mathbf{a}|\,|\mathbf{b}|\sin\theta$, θ *the angle between* **a** *and* **b**, $0 \le \theta \le \pi$.

In Figure 9 we show several examples of the vector product.

One of the peculiarities of the vector product is indicated in Figure 9: **b** × **a** and **a** × **b** are not equal. This follows from requirement (ii) of Definition 4; for if **a**, **b**, **a** × **b** form a right-handed triple, then **b**, **a**, **a** × **b** form a left-handed triple. The fact is that **b** × **a** = −**a** × **b**. We list this and other properties of the vector product formally.

Theorem 2. *The vector product has the following properties:*

   (i) $\mathbf{b} \times \mathbf{a} = -\mathbf{a} \times \mathbf{b}$.

   (ii) $\mathbf{a} \times \mathbf{b} = \mathbf{0} \Leftrightarrow \begin{cases} \mathbf{b} = k\mathbf{a}, \text{ some } k \\ \text{or } \mathbf{a} = k\mathbf{b} \end{cases}$

   (iii) $\mathbf{a} \times \mathbf{a} = \mathbf{0}$.

   (iv) $\mathbf{a} \parallel \mathbf{b} \Leftrightarrow \mathbf{a} \times \mathbf{b} = \mathbf{0}$.

(v) $(k\mathbf{a}) \times \mathbf{b} = \mathbf{a} \times (k\mathbf{b}) = k(\mathbf{a} \times \mathbf{b})$.

(vi) $\mathbf{i} \times \mathbf{i} = \mathbf{j} \times \mathbf{j} = \mathbf{k} \times \mathbf{k} = 0$,

   $\mathbf{i} \times \mathbf{j} = \mathbf{k}, \mathbf{j} \times \mathbf{k} = \mathbf{i}, \mathbf{k} \times \mathbf{i} = \mathbf{j}$,

   $\mathbf{j} \times \mathbf{i} = -\mathbf{k}, \mathbf{k} \times \mathbf{j} = -\mathbf{i}, \mathbf{i} \times \mathbf{k} = -\mathbf{j}$.

(vii) $|\mathbf{a} \times \mathbf{b}|$ = *area of parallelogram determined by* **a** *and* **b**.

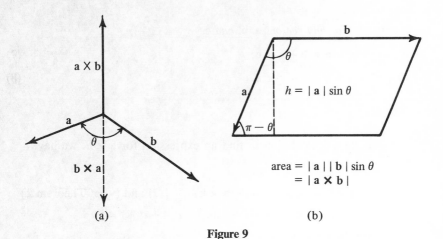

(a)   (b)

Figure 9

Proof. Concerning (i), we have already pointed out that reversing the order of **a** and **b** must change the sense of the vector product. But the other conditions (length and perpendicularity to the plane of **a** and **b**) will remain unchanged, so $\mathbf{b} \times \mathbf{a} = -\mathbf{a} \times \mathbf{b}$.

For (ii) we consider first the implication $\Rightarrow$. From (iii) of Definition 4, $\mathbf{a} \times \mathbf{b} = 0 \Rightarrow \mathbf{a} = 0$, or $\mathbf{b} = 0$, or $\sin \theta = 0$. If $\mathbf{a} = 0$, $\mathbf{a} = k\mathbf{b}$ for $k = 0$; if $\mathbf{b} = 0$, $\mathbf{b} = k\mathbf{a}$ for $k = 0$; finally, if $\sin \theta = 0$, then $\theta = 0$ or π and $\mathbf{b} = k\mathbf{a}$ for some k.

For the implication $\Leftarrow$, if $\mathbf{a} = k\mathbf{b}$ or $\mathbf{b} = k\mathbf{a}$, then $\theta = 0$ or π, $\sin \theta = 0$, and $\mathbf{a} \times \mathbf{b} = 0$.

Statement (iii) follows from (ii) with $k = 1$.

Statement (iv) is simply a rephrasing of (ii), for $\mathbf{a} \parallel \mathbf{b} \Leftrightarrow \{\mathbf{b} = k\mathbf{a} \text{ or } \mathbf{a} = k\mathbf{b}\}$ (with the agreement that the **0** vector is parallel to every vector).

We leave the proof of (v) as an exercise.

The first three equations of (vi) follow from (iii); the second three are direct consequences of the definitions of $\mathbf{a} \times \mathbf{b}$ and of **i**, **j**, and **k**. The last three equations follow from the second set of three and (i).

For (vii), we refer to Figure 9b. The altitude h of the parallelogram determined by **a** and **b** is $|a| \sin \theta$. Consequently, the area of the parallelogram is $|a|\,|b| \sin \theta = |\mathbf{a} \times \mathbf{b}|$. ∎

We would next like to find an expression for $\mathbf{a} \times \mathbf{b}$ in terms of the components of **a** and **b**. We shall need parts (v) and (vi) of Theorem 2, but these are not enough: we also need a distributive property. There are, in fact, two of these (because of lack of commutativity), one following from the other. It is possible to give a geometric argument for the distributivity, but it is also possible to give an analytic proof based on the distributivity of the inner product and on one other concept still to be introduced. Preferring this analytic proof, we shall state the distributive properties and use them, but defer the proof until a bit later.

Theorem 3. *For any vectors* **a**, **b**, *and* **c**,

(i) $\mathbf{a} \times (\mathbf{b} + \mathbf{c}) = \mathbf{a} \times \mathbf{b} + \mathbf{a} \times \mathbf{c}$;   (7)

(ii) $(\mathbf{b} + \mathbf{c}) \times \mathbf{a} = \mathbf{b} \times \mathbf{a} + \mathbf{c} \times \mathbf{a}$.   (8)

(Proof later.)

It is now a simple calculation to find an expression for $\mathbf{a} \times \mathbf{b}$; we have

$$\begin{aligned}
\mathbf{a} \times \mathbf{b} &= \mathbf{a} \times (b_1\mathbf{i} + b_2\mathbf{j} + b_3\mathbf{k}) \\
&= b_1(\mathbf{a} \times \mathbf{i}) + b_2(\mathbf{a} \times \mathbf{j}) + b_3(\mathbf{a} \times \mathbf{k}) \qquad [\text{(7) and (v) of Theorem 2}] \\
&= b_1(a_1\mathbf{i} + a_2\mathbf{j} + a_3\mathbf{k}) \times \mathbf{i} + b_2(a_1\mathbf{i} + a_2\mathbf{j} + a_3\mathbf{k}) \times \mathbf{j} \\
&\quad + b_3(a_1\mathbf{i} + a_2\mathbf{j} + a_3\mathbf{k}) \times \mathbf{k} \\
&= (a_1b_1)\mathbf{i} \times \mathbf{i} + (a_2b_1)\mathbf{j} \times \mathbf{i} + (a_3b_1)\mathbf{k} \times \mathbf{i} + (a_1b_2)\mathbf{i} \times \mathbf{j} \\
&\quad + (a_2b_2)\mathbf{j} \times \mathbf{j} + (a_3b_2)\mathbf{k} \times \mathbf{j} + (a_1b_3)\mathbf{i} \times \mathbf{k} + (a_2b_3)\mathbf{j} \times \mathbf{k} \\
&\quad + (a_3b_3)\mathbf{k} \times \mathbf{k};
\end{aligned}$$

using (vi) of Theorem 2, we can write

$$\mathbf{a} \times \mathbf{b} = (a_2 b_3 - a_3 b_2)\mathbf{i} + (a_3 b_1 - a_1 b_3)\mathbf{j} + (a_1 b_2 - a_2 b_1)\mathbf{k} \qquad (9)$$

There is a convenient mnemonic device for the equation in (9), making use of a pseudodeterminant:

$$\mathbf{a} \times \mathbf{b} = \begin{vmatrix} \mathbf{i} & \mathbf{j} & \mathbf{k} \\ a_1 & a_2 & a_3 \\ b_1 & b_2 & b_3 \end{vmatrix} \qquad (10)$$

If this is expanded by the cofactors of the first row, the result is exactly (9). The determinant is referred to as "pseudo" because its elements are in part vectors, in part numbers.

Example 3. Given $\mathbf{a} = 2\mathbf{i} + \mathbf{j} - 4\mathbf{k}$, $\mathbf{b} = -\mathbf{i} + 3\mathbf{j} - 2\mathbf{k}$, we find, using (10),

$$\mathbf{a} \times \mathbf{b} = \begin{vmatrix} \mathbf{i} & \mathbf{j} & \mathbf{k} \\ 2 & 1 & -4 \\ -1 & 3 & -2 \end{vmatrix}$$

$$= 10\mathbf{i} + 8\mathbf{j} + 7\mathbf{k}.$$

TRIPLE SCALAR PRODUCT. We consider three noncoplanar vectors **a**, **b**, **c** which form a right-handed triple. The product

$$\mathbf{a} \times \mathbf{b} \cdot \mathbf{c}$$

is known as the *triple scalar product*. The reason for the name is practically obvious: the vector product **a** × **b** must take precedence; then the inner product of **a** × **b** and **c** will result in a scalar.

We shall now show that the number **a** × **b** · **c** represents the volume of the parallelepiped with edges **a**, **b**, and **c** (see Figure 10).

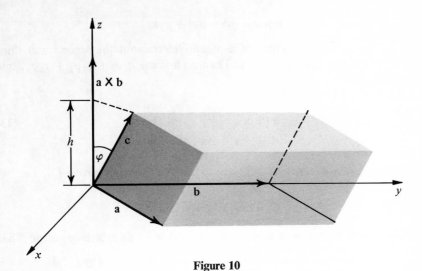

Figure 10

We know that

$$\mathbf{a} \times \mathbf{b} \cdot \mathbf{c} = |\mathbf{a} \times \mathbf{b}| \, |\mathbf{c}| \cos \varphi, \tag{11}$$

where φ is the angle between **a** × **b** and **c**. Now if, as is the case in Figure 10, the xy-plane is the plane of **a** and **b**, then **a** × **b** will lie along the positive z-axis. Since **a**, **b**, **c** form a right-handed triple, **c** lies on the positive (upper) side of the xy-plane, so $\varphi < \dfrac{\pi}{2}$, $\cos \varphi > 0$, and $|\mathbf{c}| \cos \varphi$ is the length of the projection of **c** on the z-axis. In other words, $|\mathbf{c}| \cos \varphi$ is the height h of the parallelpiped with edges **a**, **b**, **c**. We already know that $|\mathbf{a} \times \mathbf{b}|$ is the area of the base parallelogram; it follows, then, that the number in (11) is the volume of the parallelepiped.

[If **a**, **b**, **c** form a left-handed triple, a slight modification of the preceding argument will show that **a** × **b** · **c** < 0, but that $|\mathbf{a} \times \mathbf{b} \cdot \mathbf{c}|$ is the volume of the parallelepiped determined by the three vectors.]

Now notice that if we interchange the × and · in (11) the vectors will still form a right-handed triple, they will still determine the same parallelepiped, and an obvious modification of the argument following Eq. (11) will show that $\mathbf{a} \cdot \mathbf{b} \times \mathbf{c}$ represents the volume of this same parallelepiped. Thus

$$\mathbf{a} \cdot \mathbf{b} \times \mathbf{c} = \mathbf{a} \times \mathbf{b} \cdot \mathbf{c}; \tag{12}$$

or, in words, the $\cdot$ and $\times$ can be interchanged in a triple scalar product without changing the value. (As we will ask you to show in Exercise 8, if $\mathbf{a} \times \mathbf{b} \cdot \mathbf{c} = g$, then every possible arrangement of the vectors and of the operations must lead to either g or $-g$.)

It is occasionally useful to know that a triple scalar product can be expressed as a *real* (nonpseudo) determinant. Consider the left-hand side of (12), $\mathbf{a} \cdot \mathbf{b} \times \mathbf{c}$. We know that

$$\mathbf{b} \times \mathbf{c} = g_1 \mathbf{i} + g_2 \mathbf{j} + g_3 \mathbf{k},$$

where g_1, g_2, g_3 are cofactors of a pseudodeterminant the second and third rows of which are the b's and c's. Then $\mathbf{a} \cdot \mathbf{b} \times \mathbf{c} = a_1 g_1 + a_2 g_2 + a_3 g_3$, and this means

$$\mathbf{a} \cdot \mathbf{b} \times \mathbf{c} = \begin{vmatrix} a_1 & a_2 & a_3 \\ b_1 & b_2 & b_3 \\ c_1 & c_2 & c_3 \end{vmatrix}. \tag{13}$$

Proof of Theorem 3. Now we return to Theorem 3 and prove (7), i.e., we show

$$\mathbf{a} \times (\mathbf{b} + \mathbf{c}) = \mathbf{a} \times \mathbf{b} + \mathbf{a} \times \mathbf{c}.$$

Let $\mathbf{v}_1 = \mathbf{a} \times (\mathbf{b} + \mathbf{c})$, $\mathbf{v}_2 = \mathbf{a} \times \mathbf{b} + \mathbf{a} \times \mathbf{c}$ and let $\mathbf{w}$ be an arbitrary vector. Then

$$\mathbf{w} \cdot \mathbf{v}_1 = \mathbf{w} \cdot \mathbf{a} \times (\mathbf{b} + \mathbf{c}) = \mathbf{w} \times \mathbf{a} \cdot (\mathbf{b} + \mathbf{c}) \qquad \text{[by (12)]}$$

$$= \mathbf{w} \times \mathbf{a} \cdot \mathbf{b} + \mathbf{w} \times \mathbf{a} \cdot \mathbf{c}. \qquad \text{(since the inner product is distributive)}$$

Also,

$$\mathbf{w} \cdot \mathbf{v}_2 = \mathbf{w} \cdot (\mathbf{a} \times \mathbf{b} + \mathbf{a} \times \mathbf{c}) = \mathbf{w} \cdot \mathbf{a} \times \mathbf{b} + \mathbf{w} \cdot \mathbf{a} \times \mathbf{c} \qquad \text{(since the inner product is distributive)}$$

$$= \mathbf{w} \times \mathbf{a} \cdot \mathbf{b} + \mathbf{w} \times \mathbf{a} \cdot \mathbf{c}. \qquad \text{[by (12)]}$$

We see then that, for *arbitrary* $\mathbf{w}$,

$$\mathbf{w} \cdot \mathbf{v}_1 = \mathbf{w} \cdot \mathbf{v}_2,$$

and from this it follows (see Exercise 9, p. 587) that $\mathbf{v}_1 = \mathbf{v}_2$. The proof of the other part, Eq. (8), of Theorem 3 follows easily from (7) (see Exercise 10, p. 587.) ∎

Example 4. We find the area of the triangle with vertices $A(2, 1, 3)$, $B(-1, 2, 2)$, $C(3, 0, 2)$.

The sketch in Figure 11 is schematic and can be thought of as being in the plane determined by A, B, and C. The area of the triangle $\triangle ABC$ is half the area of the parallelogram determined by the vectors $\mathbf{AB} = \mathbf{b}$ and $\mathbf{AC} = \mathbf{c}$. In turn, this area is equal to $|\mathbf{b} \times \mathbf{c}|$. Thus our first step is to find $\mathbf{b}$, $\mathbf{c}$, and $\mathbf{b} \times \mathbf{c}$:

$$\mathbf{b} = \mathbf{AB} = -3\mathbf{i} + \mathbf{j} - \mathbf{k}$$

$$\mathbf{c} = \mathbf{AC} = \mathbf{i} - \mathbf{j} - \mathbf{k}.$$

Then

$$\mathbf{b} \times \mathbf{c} = -2\mathbf{i} - 4\mathbf{j} + 2\mathbf{k} = 2(-\mathbf{i} - 2\mathbf{j} + \mathbf{k}).$$

From this we find $|\mathbf{b} \times \mathbf{c}| = 2\sqrt{6}$, and the area of $\triangle ABC$ is $\sqrt{6}$ square units.

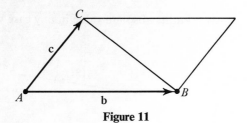

Figure 11

The next illustration shows how the vector product can be used to find a vector perpendicular to each of two given vectors.

Example 5. The points $A(1, 2, -1)$ and $B(3, -1, 2)$ determine a line in space; the points $C(1, 0, 2)$ and $D(2, 1, 3)$ determine another. We want to find the minimum distance between these two lines.

This seems at first glance like an ordinary minimum problem of calculus (and, indeed, it can be solved by methods discussed in Chapter 13) but we can give, by means of vectors, a fairly direct and short solution.

The fundamental idea is that the shortest distance will lie along a line which is *perpendicular to each of the given lines*—hence the use of the vector product. The direction of line AB is given by

$$\mathbf{v}_1 = \mathbf{AB} = 2\mathbf{i} - 3\mathbf{j} + 3\mathbf{k};$$

that of line CD by

$$\mathbf{v}_2 = \mathbf{CD} = \mathbf{i} + \mathbf{j} + \mathbf{k}.$$

Hence, the mutually perpendicular direction is that of

$$\mathbf{n} = \mathbf{v}_1 \times \mathbf{v}_2 = -6\mathbf{i} + \mathbf{j} + 5\mathbf{k}.$$

Because we are primarily interested in the information $\mathbf{n}$ has for us about *direction*, we convert it to a unit vector:

$$\mathbf{u_n} = \frac{1}{|\mathbf{n}|}\,\mathbf{n} = \frac{1}{\sqrt{62}}\,(-6\mathbf{i} + \mathbf{j} + 5\mathbf{k}).$$

In Figure 12 we show a schematic sketch which, necessarily inaccurate because it is drawn in a plane, suggests how to obtain the desired distance.

As $\mathbf{u_n}$ is perpendicular to both lines, if we take any vector from one line to the other, say $\mathbf{AD}$, and project it on $\mathbf{u_n}$ drawn with its initial point at A, the length of the projection obtained will be the desired minimum distance. Now $\mathbf{AD} = \mathbf{i} - \mathbf{j} + 4\mathbf{k}$; the projection is found from the inner product (remember: $\mathbf{u_n}$ is a unit vector):

$$\mathbf{AD} \cdot \mathbf{u_n} = \frac{1}{\sqrt{62}}(-6 - 1 + 20) = \frac{13}{\sqrt{62}} \approx 1.65 \text{ units.}$$

A different choice of vector between line AB and line CD, say $\mathbf{CB}$, may make the inner product negative; but its absolute value in any case would be $\dfrac{13}{\sqrt{62}}$.

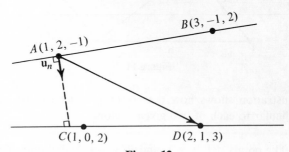

Figure 12

EXERCISES

1. Find a unit vector perpendicular to both of the vectors given in the following pairs:

   (a) $\mathbf{a} = \mathbf{i} + \mathbf{k}, \mathbf{b} = \mathbf{j} - \mathbf{k}$.
   (b) $\mathbf{a} = \mathbf{i} + 2\mathbf{j} - \mathbf{k}, \mathbf{b} = 2\mathbf{i} + \mathbf{j} + 4\mathbf{k}$.
   (c) $\mathbf{a} = \mathbf{i} - \mathbf{j} + 3\mathbf{k}, \mathbf{b} = -\mathbf{i} + \mathbf{j}$.

2. Find the area of the parallelogram determined by each of the pairs of vectors in Exercise 1.

3. Find the volume of the parallelepiped determined by each of the following triples of vectors.

   (a) $\mathbf{a} = \mathbf{i} + \mathbf{j}, \mathbf{b} = 3\mathbf{i} - 2\mathbf{j} + \mathbf{k}, \mathbf{c} = 2\mathbf{j} - \mathbf{k}$.
   (b) $\mathbf{a} = -\mathbf{i} + 2\mathbf{j} - 5\mathbf{k}, \mathbf{b} = 3\mathbf{i} + \mathbf{j}, \mathbf{c} = \mathbf{i} - \mathbf{k}$.
   (c) $\mathbf{a} = \mathbf{i} - \mathbf{j} + 2\mathbf{k}, \mathbf{b} = 2\mathbf{i} + \mathbf{j} - \mathbf{k}, \mathbf{c} = \mathbf{i} + 5\mathbf{j} - 8\mathbf{k}$.

4. (a) Use (9) or (10) to show that $\mathbf{b} \times \mathbf{a} = -\mathbf{a} \times \mathbf{b}$.

   (b) Is there circularity in the procedure of part (a)? If so, where?

5. Find the shortest distance between the lines determined by A, B and C, D, where

   (a) $A(1, 0, 0)$, $B(2, 1, 2)$; $C(3, -1, 4)$, $D(2, 0, 2)$.
   (b) $A(0, 1, 2)$, $B(1, 0, 3)$; $C(2, 1, 0)$, $D(-1, -1, 1)$.
   (c) $A(1, 2, 3)$, $B(-3, 0, -3)$; $C(-5, 4, 1)$, $D(7, 0, 5)$.

6. Consider the three points $A(1, 2, -1)$, $B(3, 0, 1)$, $C(2, -1, 0)$.

   (a) Find a unit vector perpendicular to the plane determined by A, B, and C.

   (b) Find the area of the triangle $\triangle ABC$.

   (c) Find, by vector methods, the distance between the origin and the plane of A, B, C.

7. Let

$$\mathbf{a} = 2\mathbf{i} + \mathbf{j} + \mathbf{k}$$
$$\mathbf{b} = \mathbf{i} - \mathbf{j} - 2\mathbf{k}$$
$$\mathbf{c} = \mathbf{i} + 3\mathbf{j} + \mathbf{k}.$$

   (a) Find $(\mathbf{a} \times \mathbf{b}) \times \mathbf{c}$.   (b) Find $\mathbf{a} \times (\mathbf{b} \times \mathbf{c})$.

   (c) Make an intelligent comment about the results of (a) and (b).

8. Given three vectors $\mathbf{a}$, $\mathbf{b}$, $\mathbf{c}$.

   (a) List all the formally possible triple scalar products, such as $\mathbf{a} \times \mathbf{b} \cdot \mathbf{c}$ and $\mathbf{b} \cdot \mathbf{a} \times \mathbf{c}$. There are twelve in all.

   (b) Suppose $\mathbf{a} \times \mathbf{b} \cdot \mathbf{c} = g$. Show that five of the others equal g and the remaining six have the value $(-g)$. Remember that the inner product is commutative.

9. Let $\mathbf{v}_1$ and $\mathbf{v}_2$ be vectors with the property that

$$\mathbf{w} \cdot \mathbf{v}_1 = \mathbf{w} \cdot \mathbf{v}_2$$

   for every possible choice of $\mathbf{w}$. Show that $\mathbf{v}_1 = \mathbf{v}_2$. [*Hint.* Suppose $\mathbf{v}_1 \neq \mathbf{v}_2$, i.e., $\mathbf{v}_1 - \mathbf{v}_2 \neq 0$; try $\mathbf{w} = \mathbf{v}_1 - \mathbf{v}_2$.]

10. Prove (ii) of Theorem 3; i.e., Eq. (8). [*Hint.* Use (i) of Theorem 2.]

11. Let $\mathbf{a}$, $\mathbf{b}$, $\mathbf{c}$ be vectors; let

$$\mathbf{a} \cdot \mathbf{b} \times \mathbf{c} = \begin{vmatrix} a_1 & a_2 & a_3 \\ b_1 & b_2 & b_3 \\ c_1 & c_2 & c_3 \end{vmatrix} = g.$$

   Show that

$$g > 0 \Rightarrow \mathbf{a}, \mathbf{b}, \mathbf{c} \text{ form a right-handed triple,}$$
$$g < 0 \Rightarrow \mathbf{a}, \mathbf{b}, \mathbf{c} \text{ form a left-handed triple,}$$
$$g = 0 \Rightarrow \mathbf{a}, \mathbf{b}, \mathbf{c}, \text{ are coplanar.}$$

12. Consider the triple vector product $(\mathbf{a} \times \mathbf{b}) \times \mathbf{c}$.

  (a) Show that this vector must lie in the plane of $\mathbf{a}$ and $\mathbf{b}$.

  (b) In a similar way, show that $\mathbf{a} \times (\mathbf{b} \times \mathbf{c})$ must lie in the plane of $\mathbf{b}$ and $\mathbf{c}$.

  (c) As (a) and (b) show, the triple vector product is not associative.

13. In this exercise we consider a motivating reason from mechanics for introducing the vector product.

    We shall be concerned with rotational motion (that of a wheel, for example) about an axis. Description of this motion is aided by introducing an *angular velocity* vector $\boldsymbol{\omega}$, which lies along the axis of rotation and which has a magnitude $|\boldsymbol{\omega}|$ = angular speed (in radians per second, say). The sense of $\boldsymbol{\omega}$ can be defined as follows: to an observer looking along the axis at the terminal end of $\boldsymbol{\omega}$ the motion is counterclockwise (see Figure 13).

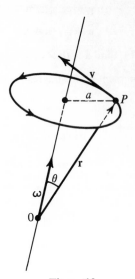

Figure 13

    We draw $\boldsymbol{\omega}$ with its initial point at an origin 0 on the axis, and we draw a position vector $\mathbf{r}$ from 0 to a point P on the rotating body. Also we introduce a linear velocity vector $\mathbf{v}$, with initial point at P; $\mathbf{v}$ will be tangent to the rotating body and its magnitude, the linear speed, is $|\mathbf{v}| = a|\boldsymbol{\omega}|$, where a is the radius of the rotating body. Show that

  (a) $|\mathbf{v}| = |\boldsymbol{\omega}| \, |\mathbf{r}| \sin \theta$, θ the angle between $\boldsymbol{\omega}$ and $\mathbf{r}$.

  (b) $\mathbf{v} \perp \boldsymbol{\omega}$, $\mathbf{v} \perp \mathbf{r}$.

  (c) $\mathbf{v} = \boldsymbol{\omega} \times \mathbf{r}$.

14. Show that for any three vectors $\mathbf{a}, \mathbf{b}, \mathbf{c}$, the following identity holds:

$$(\mathbf{a} \times \mathbf{b}) \times \mathbf{c} = (\mathbf{a} \cdot \mathbf{c})\mathbf{b} - (\mathbf{b} \cdot \mathbf{c})\mathbf{a}. \qquad (*)$$

[*Hints.*

(1) Set up a coordinate system as follows: The xy-plane is the plane determined by $\mathbf{a}$ and $\mathbf{b}$, with the positive x-axis along $\mathbf{a}$. When this is done we can write

$$\mathbf{a} = a_1\mathbf{i}$$
$$\mathbf{b} = b_1\mathbf{i} + b_2\mathbf{j}$$
$$\mathbf{c} = c_1\mathbf{i} + c_2\mathbf{j} + c_3\mathbf{k}.$$

(2) Show that $\mathbf{a} \times \mathbf{b} = a_1 b_2 \mathbf{k}$.

(3) Show that $(\mathbf{a} \times \mathbf{b}) \times \mathbf{c} = -a_1 b_2 c_2 \mathbf{i} + a_1 b_2 c_1 \mathbf{j}$.

(4) To the expression in (3) for $(\mathbf{a} \times \mathbf{b}) \times \mathbf{c}$ add and subtract $a_1 b_1 c_1 \mathbf{i}$.

(5) Calculate $\mathbf{a} \cdot \mathbf{c}$ and $\mathbf{b} \cdot \mathbf{c}$ and show that the expression in (4) is equal to the right-hand side of (*).]

15. Show that

$$\mathbf{a} \times (\mathbf{b} \times \mathbf{c}) = (\mathbf{a} \cdot \mathbf{c})\mathbf{b} - (\mathbf{a} \cdot \mathbf{b})\mathbf{c}. \qquad (**)$$

[*Hint.* Write $\mathbf{a} \times (\mathbf{b} \times \mathbf{c}) = -[(\mathbf{b} \times \mathbf{c}) \times \mathbf{a}]$ and use (*) in Exercise 14.]

16. Show that

$$|\mathbf{a} \times \mathbf{b}|^2 = |\mathbf{a}|^2|\mathbf{b}|^2 - (\mathbf{a} \cdot \mathbf{b})^2. \qquad (***)$$

[*Hints.*

(1) We know

$$|\mathbf{a} \times \mathbf{b}|^2 = (\mathbf{a} \times \mathbf{b}) \cdot (\mathbf{a} \times \mathbf{b})$$
$$= \mathbf{c} \cdot \mathbf{a} \times \mathbf{b} \quad \text{(temporarily letting } \mathbf{c} = \mathbf{a} \times \mathbf{b})$$
$$= \mathbf{c} \times \mathbf{a} \cdot \mathbf{b} \quad \text{[by (12)]}$$
$$= [(\mathbf{a} \times \mathbf{b}) \times \mathbf{a}] \cdot \mathbf{b} \quad \text{(since } \mathbf{c} = \mathbf{a} \times \mathbf{b}).$$

(2) Now use (*) from Exercise 14.]

17. Use Exercise 16 to prove the Cauchy–Schwarz inequality (Theorem 11.6).

12.4 Planes

In plane analytic geometry we know that the equations of first degree in x and y represent straight lines. In three-dimensional geometry the first degree equations represent planes (recall that a single equation in three-space geometry represents a surface).

The essential geometric property of lines is that they are curves of constant direction. Similarly, for our purposes, a plane is a surface of constant direction. One way of making this more explicit is as follows: a surface is a plane if and only if normal vectors (vectors perpendicular to the surface) drawn at any two points are parallel. With this as our working definition we can obtain an analytic description of a plane.

Suppose a plane has a normal vector $\mathbf{n} = a\mathbf{i} + b\mathbf{j} + c\mathbf{k}$. (It is the normal vector which describes the direction of a plane; of course, a plane, being a two-dimensional set of points, has many directions in it, but in order to distinguish one plane from another, both through the same point, we can call on the normal vector.) Suppose also the plane goes through the point $P_0(x_0, y_0, z_0)$. We seek conditions for $P(x, y, z)$ to be an arbitrary point on the plane (see Figure 14).

If $P \neq P_0$ is any point of the plane, then the vector $\mathbf{P_0 P}$ must be perpendicular to $\mathbf{n}$: $\mathbf{n} \cdot \mathbf{P_0 P} = 0$, or, since $\mathbf{P_0 P} = (x - x_0)\mathbf{i} + (y - y_0)\mathbf{j} + (z - z_0)\mathbf{k}$,

$$a(x - x_0) + b(y - y_0) + c(z - z_0) = 0, \tag{14}$$

the required equation of the plane.

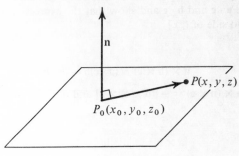

Figure 14

Equation (14) can be put in the form

$$ax + by + cz = ax_0 + by_0 + cz_0,$$

or

$$ax + by + cz = d. \tag{15}$$

Thus we see that a plane does have an equation of the first degree in x, y, and z. Notice that the coefficients of x, y, and z are precisely the components of the normal vector to the plane. Information about the *position* of the plane is contained in the constant d.

Example 6. One plane goes through the origin and has normal $\mathbf{n} = 2\mathbf{i} + \mathbf{j} + \mathbf{k}$. A second plane has the same normal and goes through $P_0(-3, 1, -7)$. Find their equations.

Using (14) and the given information, we have

first plane: $2x + y + z = 0$;

second plane: $2(x + 3) + (y - 1) + (z + 7) = 0$, or $2x + y + z = -12$.

The two planes are distinct but *parallel*.

If we agree that not all of a, b, c are zero, then the equation in (15) is one way of writing the most general linear (i.e., first degree) equation in x, y, and z. Will such an equation always represent a plane? The answer is easily seen to be in the affirmative. For, suppose $c \neq 0$; if we set $x = y = 0$, we can easily solve for z_0: $z_0 = \dfrac{d}{c}$, thereby obtaining a point $P_0\left(0, 0, \dfrac{d}{c}\right)$ on the surface determined by (15). But now we can write the equation in the form

$$a(x - 0) + b(y - 0) + c\left(z - \frac{d}{c}\right) = 0,$$

or

$$\mathbf{n} \cdot P_0 P = 0,$$

where $\mathbf{n} = a\mathbf{i} + b\mathbf{j} + c\mathbf{k}$ and $P(x, y, z)$ is an arbitrary point on the surface. This shows that $\mathbf{n}$ is perpendicular to the vector from P_0 to any other point on the surface, which is to say the surface is a plane.

The result of the preceding discussion can be summarized formally as follows (compare with Theorem 1.24).

Theorem 4. *A surface in three space is a plane $\Leftrightarrow$ it has an equation of the form*

$$ax + by + cz = d,$$

where a, b, c are not all zero. When this is so the vector $\mathbf{n} = a\mathbf{i} + b\mathbf{j} + c\mathbf{k}$ is normal to the plane.

Example 7. Consider the equation

$$4x + y + 2z = 8.$$

From Theorem 4 we know the equation represents (is) a plane, with normal vector $\mathbf{n} = 4\mathbf{i} + \mathbf{j} + 2\mathbf{k}$. We can easily find some points on the plane by looking for the intercepts with the axes. Thus, $y = z = 0 \Rightarrow x = 2$; $x = z = 0 \Rightarrow y = 8$; $x = y = 0 \Rightarrow z = 4$. We sketch in Figure 15 the portion of this plane which cuts across the first octant.

Example 8. In general, three points determine a plane. We find the plane determined by $A(1, 2, 1)$, $B(2, 0, 3)$, and $C(1, -2, 0)$.

Method 1. We can start with the equation $ax + by + cz = d$ and substitute in the coordinates of A, B, and C, obtaining a linear system for a, b, c, and d:

$$\left\{ \begin{array}{l} a + 2b + c = d \\ 2a \quad\;\; + 3c = d \\ a - 2b \quad\;\; = d \end{array} \right\}.$$

We can solve for a, b, and c in terms of d:

$$a = \frac{5d}{4}, \qquad b = \frac{d}{8}, \qquad c = -\frac{d}{2}.$$

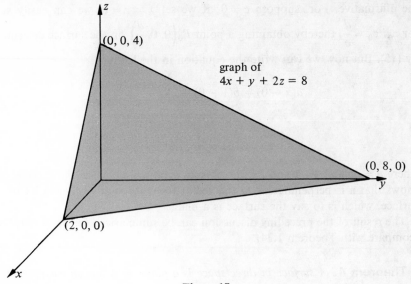

Figure 15

Taking $d = 8$ gives $a = 10$, $b = 1$, $c = -4$, and the desired equation is $10x + y - 4z = 8$. It is routine to check that coordinates of A, B, and C all satisfy this equation.

    Method 2. The vectors

$$\mathbf{b} = \mathbf{AB} = \mathbf{i} - 2\mathbf{j} + 2\mathbf{k}$$

and

$$\mathbf{c} = \mathbf{AC} = -4\mathbf{j} - \mathbf{k}$$

lie in the desired plane. Their vector product will be a normal to the plane (see Figure 16). Thus

$$\mathbf{n} = \mathbf{b} \times \mathbf{c} = 10\mathbf{i} + \mathbf{j} - 4\mathbf{k}.$$

Using the expression for $\mathbf{n}$ and the coordinates of A in (14) gives immediately

$$10x + y - 4z = 8,$$

as before.

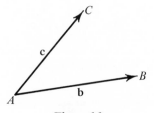

Figure 16

Example 9. Find the equation of a plane which is parallel to

$$3x - 5y + 2z = 7$$

and which contains the point $P_0(2, -1, -4)$.

If the two planes are parallel they share the same normal $\mathbf{n} = 3\mathbf{i} - 5\mathbf{j} + 2\mathbf{k}$, and the equation of the plane sought is

$$3x - 5y + 2z = d.$$

To find d we merely substitute in the coordinates of P_0:

$$3(2) + (-5)(-1) + 2(-4) = d,$$

or $d = 3$. Thus the required equation is

$$3x - 5y + 2z = 3.$$

EXERCISES

1. Find the equation of the plane through P_0 with normal vector $\mathbf{n}$.

(a) $P_0(0, 0, 0),\quad \mathbf{n} = a\mathbf{i} + b\mathbf{j} + c\mathbf{k}.$
(b) $P_0(-1, 3, 7),\quad \mathbf{n} = -2\mathbf{i} + 4\mathbf{j} - \mathbf{k}.$
(c) $P_0(1, 1, 0),\quad \mathbf{n} = \mathbf{i} + \mathbf{j}.$
(d) $P_0(1, 2, 3),\quad \mathbf{n} = \mathbf{k}.$
(e) $P_0(0, 1, 0),\quad \mathbf{n} = \mathbf{i}.$
(f) $P_0(1, 1, 1),\quad \mathbf{n} = \mathbf{j} - \mathbf{k}.$

2. Find the equation of the plane determined by the following points.

(a) $A(3, -4, 2),\ B(2, -1, 1),\ C(0, 1, 2).$
(b) $A(1, 0, 1),\ B(0, -1, 2),\ C(3, -4, 1).$
(c) $A(2, 3, 1),\ B(1, -1, 1),\ C(4, 0, 1).$

3. A plane through $(5, -1, 6)$ is parallel to $3x - 7y + z = 4$. Find its equation.

4. Find the equation of the plane which is parallel to $2x - 5y + 7z = 3$ and which contains the point $(3, -4, -6)$.

5. Find the equation satisfied by the set of points $P(x, y, z)$ which are equidistant from $(3, 0, 5)$ and $(1, -2, -1)$. Identify the set.

6. The vector normal to a plane is $\mathbf{n} = 4\mathbf{i} + 2\mathbf{j} + 7\mathbf{k}$. The point $(-1, 5, 8)$ lies in the plane. Find the equation of the plane.

7. A plane does not intersect the x-axis; it contains the points $(3, 8, 5)$ and $(2, 4, 6)$. Find its equation.

8. Give a necessary and sufficient condition for the plane $ax + by + cz = d$ to have no intersection with the y-axis.

9. Find the equation of the plane which does not intersect the y-axis and which contains the points $(1, 3, 2)$ and $(7, 1, -3)$.

10. Give a necessary and sufficient condition for the plane $ax + byc + z = d$ to intersect all three coordinate axes.

11. Find the equation of the plane through the points $(a, 0, 0)$, $(0, b, 0)$, $(0, 0, c)$, where $abc \neq 0$. Write the equation with the constant on the right-hand side equal to 1.

12. A plane through the origin has the z component of its normal vector equal to 0. If the point $(1, 1, 1)$ lies on the plane, find its equation.

13. Two planes are perpendicular if their normals are perpendicular. Find the equation of the plane which is perpendicular to $3x - 2y + z = 4$ and which contains $P_1(2, 0, 3)$ and $P_2(1, 4, -2)$.

14. Find the equation of the plane which is perpendicular to the xy-plane and which contains the points $P_1(2, 0, 0)$ and $P_2(0, 2, 0)$.

12.5 Lines

There are several ways to describe a line in space analytically. The most convenient and most tractable, however, is by means of a set of parametric equations.

Suppose the line (a curve of constant direction) has the same direction as the vector $\mathbf{v} = a\mathbf{i} + b\mathbf{j} + c\mathbf{k}$. We assume also that the line contains the point $P_0(x_0, y_0, z_0)$, Let $P(x, y, z)$ be any other point on the line. Then the vectors $\mathbf{v}$ and $\mathbf{P_0 P}$ are parallel. One analytic description of this is that

$$\mathbf{P_0 P} = t\mathbf{v},$$

or

$$(x - x_0)\mathbf{i} + (y - y_0)\mathbf{j} + (z - z_0)\mathbf{k} = t(a\mathbf{i} + b\mathbf{j} + c\mathbf{k}).$$

This single vector equation is equivalent to the following three scalar equations:

$$\begin{cases} x = x_0 + at \\ y = y_0 + bt \\ z = z_0 + ct \end{cases}. \tag{16}$$

These are the *parametric equations* of the line through $P_0(x_0, y_0, z_0)$ parallel to $a\mathbf{i} + b\mathbf{j} + c\mathbf{k}$.

Example 10. Find the equations of the line through $P_0(2, -1, 3)$ and $P_1(4, 2, 5)$.

We can find the direction as $P_0 P_1 = 2\mathbf{i} + 3\mathbf{j} + 2\mathbf{k}$. Then, using the coordinates of P_0, we have

$$\begin{cases} x = 2 + 2t \\ y = -1 + 3t \\ z = 3 + 2t \end{cases}.$$

In case $abc \neq 0$ we can solve each of the equations in (16) for t; equating these common values gives us the *symmetric form of the equations of a straight line*:

$$\frac{x - x_0}{a} = \frac{y - y_0}{b} = \frac{z - z_0}{c}. \tag{17}$$

It is even customary to use (17) if one or two of a, b, c equal zero; the understanding in this case is that the corresponding numerator(s) also be zero.

Example 11. Find the parametric and symmetric forms for the equations of the line through $P_0(4, 1, 2)$ and $P_1(5, 3, 2)$.

The vector $P_0 P_1 = \mathbf{i} + 2\mathbf{j}$. Thus the parametric form of the equation is

$$\begin{cases} x = 4 + t \\ y = 1 + 2t \\ z = 2 \end{cases}.$$

Clearly this line lies entirely in the plane $z = 2$. We can eliminate t from the first two equations and write

$$\begin{cases} \dfrac{x - 4}{1} = \dfrac{y - 1}{2} \\ z = 2 \end{cases}.$$

Of course, a line can be represented as the intersection of two planes, but only in especially simple cases (Example: $x = 0$, $z = 2$) is such an analytic description at all informative. We illustrate a technique for converting this type of representation to parametric form.

Example 12. Find parametric equations for the line of intersection of the planes

$$\begin{cases} x + 4y - z = 7 \\ 3x - y + 2z = 4 \end{cases}.$$

The normal $\mathbf{n}_1 = \mathbf{i} + 4\mathbf{j} - \mathbf{k}$ to the first plane is perpendicular to every line in that plane; similarly, the normal $\mathbf{n}_2 = 3\mathbf{i} - \mathbf{j} + 2\mathbf{k}$ is perpendicular to every line in the second plane. The line of intersection of the two planes will then be perpendicular to both normals; thus its direction will be given by the vector product

$$\mathbf{n}_1 \times \mathbf{n}_2 = 7\mathbf{i} - 5\mathbf{j} - 13\mathbf{k}.$$

All we need now is a point on the line, i.e., a point on both planes. There are many ways to extract one point from the above pair of equations. One such is to set one of the coordinates—we shall use y—equal to zero and solve for the other two:

$$\begin{cases} x - z = 7 \\ 3x + 2z = 4 \end{cases}.$$

The solution of this system is readily found to be $x_0 = \dfrac{18}{5}$, $z_0 = -\dfrac{17}{5}$—we already have $y_0 = 0$. Thus a parametric form for the equations is

$$\begin{cases} x = \dfrac{18}{5} + 7t \\ y = -5t \\ z = -\dfrac{17}{5} - 13t \end{cases}.$$

Example 13. Determine whether or not the two lines

$$\begin{cases} x = -2 + 4t \\ y = -2 + t \\ z = 5 - 2t \end{cases}, \qquad \begin{cases} x = -4 - 3s \\ y = 3 + 2s \\ z = 11 + 4s \end{cases}$$

intersect. If they do, find the point of intersection. [*Note.* These lines are not parallel. Even so, they might not intersect.]

For a point of intersection there would have to exist a value t_0 and a value s_0 which produce the same triple (x_0, y_0, z_0) in both sets of equations. Thus we equate the right sides of the respective equations and seek a common solution:

$$\begin{cases} -2 + 4t = -4 - 3s \\ -2 + t = 3 + 2s \\ 5 - 2t = 11 + 4s \end{cases}.$$

Rewritten, the system is

$$\begin{cases} 4t + 3s = -2 \\ t - 2s = 5 \\ -2t - 4s = 6 \end{cases}.$$

It is routine to find that the system is consistent, the unique solution being $t_0 = 1$, $s_0 = -2$. Using either of these values in its parametric system, we find the coordinates of the point of intersection to be $(2, -1, 3)$.

A line in space can also be represented analytically as a vector function of a special sort. To be explicit, suppose a line contains the point $P_0(x_0, y_0, z_0)$ and has a direction determined by the vector $\mathbf{v} = a\mathbf{i} + b\mathbf{j} + c\mathbf{k}$. Then the position vector $\mathbf{r} = \mathbf{OP}$ from the origin to a point on the line can be represented as (see Figure 17)

$$\mathbf{r} = \mathbf{OP} = \mathbf{OP_0} + \mathbf{P_0 P} = \mathbf{OP_0} + t\mathbf{v}$$

$$= x_0\mathbf{i} + y_0\mathbf{j} + z_0\mathbf{k} + t(a\mathbf{i} + b\mathbf{j} + c\mathbf{k}),$$

or

$$\mathbf{r} = \mathbf{r}(t) = (x_0 + at)\mathbf{i} + (y_0 + bt)\mathbf{j} + (z_0 + ct)\mathbf{k}, \qquad (18)$$

a *linear vector function* of t.

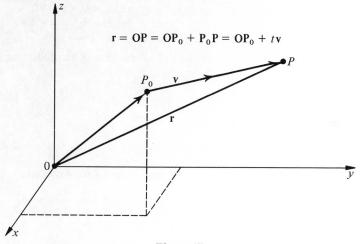

$$\mathbf{r} = \mathbf{OP} = \mathbf{OP_0} + \mathbf{P_0 P} = \mathbf{OP_0} + t\mathbf{v}$$

Figure 17

Conversely, if one begins with a *linear vector function* of t, one can assume it has the form of (18) and, by retracing the few preceding steps, show that it represents the position vector from the origin to a point on the line through P_0 in the direction of $\mathbf{v} = a\mathbf{i} + b\mathbf{j} + c\mathbf{k}$. We state this result formally.

Theorem 5. *A vector function $\mathbf{r}$ of the variable t represents a straight line $\Leftrightarrow$ $\mathbf{r}$ is linear, i.e., $\mathbf{r}$ has the form of Eq. (18).*

As an illustration, the line found in Example 10 (through $P_0(2, -1, 3)$ and $P_1(4, 2, 5)$) can be represented by the linear vector

$$\mathbf{r}(t) = (2 + 2t)\mathbf{i} + (-1 + 3t)\mathbf{j} + (3 + 2t)\mathbf{k}.$$

Since the domain of a linear vector function is all of $\mathbf{R}$, one can think of such a function as providing a map of the entire t-axis, possibly with stretching or shrinking, into a straight line in three space. In the next section we study other (than linear) vector functions.

EXERCISES

1. Find parametric, symmetric, and vector forms for the equations of the lines determined by the following pairs of points.

   (a) $P_0(4, -5, 2)$, $P_1(2, 7, -3)$.
   (b) $P_0(3, -3, 6)$, $P_1(5, -3, 2)$.
   (c) $P_0(-1, 0, 8)$, $P_1(2, 5, -4)$.

   (d) $P_0(3, 5, 2)$, $P_1(6, 5, 2)$.
   (e) $P_0(4, -1, 7)$, $P_1(4, 2, 5)$.

2. Write parametric equations for each of the following lines:

   (a) $x = 0$, $z = 2$.   (Answer. $x = 0, y = t, z = 2$)
   (b) $y = 3$, $z = 1$.
   (c) $x = 1$, $y = 2$.

   (d) $x = 0$, $y = 0$.
   (e) $x = 4$, $z = -1$.

3. Write parametric equations for the lines of intersection of the following pairs of planes.

   (a) $3x + y + z = 2$, $x + 3y + 4z = 7$.
   (b) $2x - y - 3z = 4$, $3x + y + 5z = 8$.
   (c) $x + y - 6z = 0$, $2x - 3y + 4z = 1$.
   (d) $x - 2y + 3z = 6$, $2x - 3y + 4z = 11$.

4. In this exercise we consider the geometric significance of the parameter t.

   (a) If a line is determined by the pair of points $P_0(x_0, y_0, z_0)$ and $P_1(x_1, y_1, z_1)$, show that a parametric representation is

   $$\begin{cases} x = x_0 + (x_1 - x_0)t \\ y = y_0 + (y_1 - y_0)t \\ z = z_0 + (z_1 - z_0)t \end{cases}. \tag{19}$$

   (b) Discuss the relation with P_0 and P_1 of points P on the line obtained by using values of t as follows:

   $$\text{(i) } t = 0$$
   $$\text{(ii) } t = 1$$
   $$\text{(iii) } 0 < t < 1$$
   $$\text{(iv) } t < 0$$
   $$\text{(v) } t > 0.$$

5. This is a continuation of the study, begun in Exercise 4, of the role of the parameter t.

   (a) Using the parametric representation of (19), show that the distance between P_0 and P on the line is

   $$d(P_0, P) = |t| \sqrt{(x_1 - x_0)^2 + (y_1 - y_0)^2 + (z_1 - z_0)^2}. \tag{20}$$

   (b) Show that if $d(P_0, P_1) = 1$, then the parameter t represents directed distance along the line.

6. Find the point of intersection of the line

$$\begin{cases} x = 2 + t \\ y = -1 + 2t \\ z = 3 - t \end{cases}$$

and the plane $x - 2y + 4z = 2$.

7. By definition, a line is *parallel* to a plane $\Leftrightarrow$ the line is perpendicular to the normal to the plane. Find the parametric equations for each of the following lines.

(a) Parallel to $2x - y + 3z = 6$ and to $x + 4y - 3z = 8$, and contains $P_0(5, -4, 2)$.

(b) Parallel to $x - 4y = 5$ and to $5y + z = 4$, and contains $P_0(1, 1, 1)$.

8. A line has the direction of $v = 2i - 7j + 4k$ and goes through the point of inter-section of the line $\dfrac{x}{1} = \dfrac{y - 2}{-3} = \dfrac{z - 1}{2}$ and the plane $3x + y + 6z + 4 = 0$. Express its equation in vector form.

9. Determine whether or not the following pairs of lines intersect. If they do find the point of intersection.

(a) $\begin{cases} x = 1 + 2t \\ y = 3 + t \\ z = -4 - 3t \end{cases}$, $\begin{cases} x = -3s \\ y = -1 + 2s \\ z = -2 + 4s \end{cases}$

(b) $\begin{cases} x = 1 - t \\ y = 2 + 4t \\ z = -3 + 2t \end{cases}$, $\begin{cases} x = 5 + 3s \\ y = -1 + s \\ z = 2 - 4s \end{cases}$.

12.6 Curves in Three Space

Just as a line in three dimensions *can* be thought of as the intersection of two planes, so can a curve be considered as the intersection of two surfaces. In neither case is the approach satisfactory from an analytic point of view. In fact, our study of curves in space will be undertaken in terms of vector functions— recall that we saw at the end of the preceding section that straight lines can be handled very satisfactorily by means of *linear* vector functions. In this section we shall be interested in somewhat more general vector functions and their geometric counterparts.

Let T be an interval, open, closed, half open, finite, infinite, possibly all of $\mathbf{R}$. Let $\mathbf{r}$ be a function, $\mathbf{r} : T \rightarrow \mathbf{R}^3$. Analogous to what we saw in Chapter 11 for vector functions with ranges in $\mathbf{R}^2$, $\mathbf{r}$ can be represented in terms of three scalar functions defined on T:

$$\mathbf{r}(t) = x(t)\mathbf{i} + y(t)\mathbf{j} + z(t)\mathbf{k}.$$

Rather than repeat the definitions of limit and continuity and derivative for vector functions, we call attention to the fact that these remain as given in

Section 11.7. It may be in order, however, to give the definition (an extension of Definition 11.9) of an ε-nbd of a vector in $\mathbf{R}^3$.

Definition 5. *Let* $\mathbf{a} = (a_1, a_2, a_3)$ *be a vector in* $\mathbf{R}^3$, $\varepsilon > 0$. *An* ε-**nbd.** *of* $\mathbf{a}$ *is*

$$N_\varepsilon(\mathbf{a}) = \{\mathbf{x} = (x_1, x_2, x_3) | (x_1 - a_1)^2 + (x_2 - a_2)^2 + (x_3 - a_3)^2 < \varepsilon^2\}.$$

The $\mathbf{R}^3$ analog of Theorems 11.9 and 11.10 remain valid (their proofs being essentially the same). Their import is that $\mathbf{r}$ is continuous if and only if x, y, and z are continuous, and that $\mathbf{r}'$ exists at $t_0 \in T$, if and only if x', y' and z' exist at t_0—and in this case

$$\mathbf{r}'(t_0) = x'(t_0)\mathbf{i} + y'(t_0)\mathbf{j} + z'(t_0)\mathbf{k}.$$

We shall, in fact, assume that $\mathbf{r}'$ exists and is continuous on T; in this case the geometric counterpart of $\mathbf{r}$ is called a *smooth curve* $\mathscr{C}$ in $\mathbf{R}^3$. Essentially, we can think of $\mathbf{r}$ as mapping the interval T on the t-axis into the smooth curve $\mathscr{C}$ in $\mathbf{R}^3$ (see Figure 18).

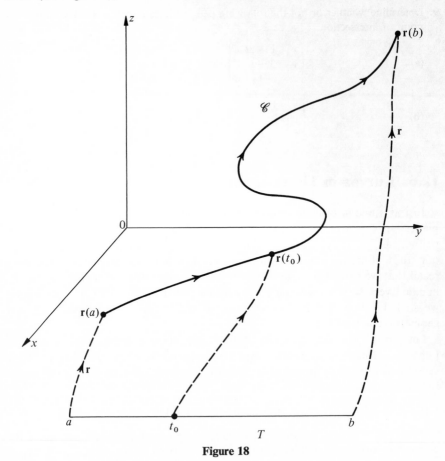

Figure 18

As we saw in Theorem 11.8, the assumption that $\mathbf{r}$ has continuous derivatives on $T = [a, b]$ is sufficient to guarantee that $\mathscr{C}$ is rectifiable on $[a, b]$, and the length of arc s is given by

$$s = \int_a^b \sqrt{(x'(t))^2 + (y'(t))^2 + (z'(t))^2} \, dt. \qquad (21)$$

From this equation and the Fundamental Theorem of Calculus we also know that for $t \in [a, b]$,

$$\frac{ds}{dt} = \sqrt{(x'(t))^2 + (y'(t))^2 + (z'(t))^2}. \qquad (22)$$

Because we shall at times wish to work with $\dfrac{dt}{ds}$ we make the further assumption that x', y', and z' are not simultaneously zero for $t \in T$. Then

$$\frac{dt}{ds} = \frac{1}{\sqrt{(x'(t))^2 + (y'(t))^2 + (z'(t))^2}}. \qquad (23)$$

It is easily seen (cf. Figure 19) that $\mathbf{r}'(t_0)$ is tangent to $\mathscr{C}$ at P_0, where $\mathbf{OP_0} = \mathbf{r}(t_0)$.

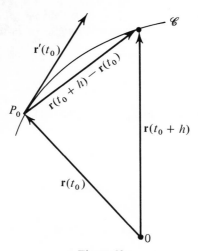

Figure 19

Since

$$\mathbf{r}'(t_0) = x'(t_0)\mathbf{i} + y'(t_0)\mathbf{j} + z'(t_0)\mathbf{k},$$

it follows that

$$|\mathbf{r}'(t_0)| = \left| \frac{d\mathbf{r}(t_0)}{dt} \right| = \sqrt{(x'(t_0))^2 + (y'(t_0))^2 + (z'(t_0))^2} = \frac{ds}{dt}.$$

As a result the vector $\mathbf{T} = \dfrac{d\mathbf{r}}{ds}$ is a unit vector tangent to $\mathscr{C}$; for

$$\mathbf{T} = \frac{d\mathbf{r}}{ds} = \frac{d\mathbf{r}}{dt}\frac{dt}{ds} = \frac{1}{\dfrac{ds}{dt}}\frac{d\mathbf{r}}{dt} \tag{24}$$

$$= \frac{1}{\left|\dfrac{d\mathbf{r}}{dt}\right|} \cdot \frac{d\mathbf{r}}{dt}.$$

We shall refer to $\mathbf{T}$ as *the tangent vector* at P_0.

From

$$\mathbf{T} \cdot \mathbf{T} = 1,$$

we obtain, using the result of Theorem 6 below,

$$\frac{d\mathbf{T}}{ds} \cdot \mathbf{T} + \mathbf{T} \cdot \frac{d\mathbf{T}}{ds} = 0$$

or

$$\frac{d\mathbf{T}}{ds} \cdot \mathbf{T} = 0.$$

This implies that $\dfrac{d\mathbf{T}}{ds} \perp \mathbf{T}$. In general, though, $\dfrac{d\mathbf{T}}{ds}$ is not a unit vector. We define

$$\kappa = \left|\frac{d\mathbf{T}}{ds}\right|, \tag{25}$$

and call κ the *curvature* of $\mathscr{C}$ at P_0. We further define the *unit* vector $\mathbf{N}$ by the equation

$$\frac{d\mathbf{T}}{ds} = \kappa\mathbf{N}. \tag{26}$$

The vector $\mathbf{N}$, then, is perpendicular to the tangent vector $\mathbf{T}$. We call $\mathbf{N}$ the *principal normal* to $\mathscr{C}$ at P_0.

As we saw in Chapter 11, κ, the magnitude of $\dfrac{d\mathbf{T}}{ds}$, serves as a measure of the rate of change of the tangent vector $\mathbf{T}$. Since $\mathbf{T}$ is a unit vector, only its direction can change. Thus we can interpret κ as a measure of how rapidly the curve $\mathscr{C}$ is turning away from its tangent at P_0.

The vectors $\mathbf{T}$ and $\mathbf{N}$, drawn with their initial points at P_0, determine a plane through P_0. This is called the *osculating plane* of $\mathscr{C}$ at P_0. If $\mathscr{C}$ were a plane curve, the osculating plane would be the plane of the curve. Roughly, the osculating plane of $\mathscr{C}$ at P_0 is the plane which best fits the curve at P_0, just as the tangent is the line which best fits the curve at P_0. All of these ideas are, of course, simply the three dimensional version of what was studied in Chapter 11.

However, because we *are* working in three dimensions, a further development is in order. We define

$$\mathbf{B} = \mathbf{T} \times \mathbf{N}, \tag{27}$$

and call $\mathbf{B}$ the *binormal* to $\mathscr{C}$ at P_0. The vectors $\mathbf{T}$, $\mathbf{N}$, $\mathbf{B}$ form an orthonormal (i.e., mutually perpendicular unit vectors) right-handed system at P_0. This triple is often called the *moving* trihedral, because there will be such a right-handed orthonormal system at each point P_0 of $\mathscr{C}$. The vectors $\mathbf{N}$ and $\mathbf{B}$ determine a plane through P_0, perpendicular to $\mathbf{T}$—and hence to $\mathscr{C}$. This plane is called the *rectifying plane*. Every vector through P_0 in the rectifying plane is a normal to $\mathscr{C}$. We have chosen, in $\mathbf{N}$ and $\mathbf{B}$, two of these normals.

It may be time to provide an illustration.

Example 14. Let $\mathbf{r}$ be defined by

$$\mathbf{r}(t) = (\cos t)\mathbf{i} + (\sin t))\mathbf{j} + t\mathbf{k}.$$

Note that, since $x(t) = \cos t$, $y(t) = \sin t$, $[x(t)]^2 + [y(t)]^2 = 1$ for all t; this implies that the entire curve lies on the right circular cylinder $x^2 + y^2 = 1$ (see Figure 20). The curve $\mathscr{C}$ is called a *circular helix*. We let $t_0 = \dfrac{\pi}{4}$, so P_0 is $P_0\left(\dfrac{1}{\sqrt{2}}, \dfrac{1}{\sqrt{2}}, \dfrac{\pi}{4}\right)$.

First we calculate $\mathbf{r}'(t)$:

$$\mathbf{r}'(t) = (-\sin t)\mathbf{i} + (\cos t)\mathbf{j} + \mathbf{k};$$

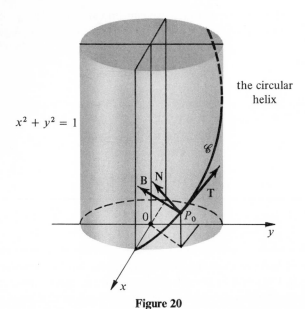

Figure 20

then

$$|\mathbf{r}'(t)| = \frac{ds}{dt} = \sqrt{\sin^2 t + \cos^2 t + 1} = \sqrt{2}, \quad \text{all } t.$$

Usually, $\frac{ds}{dt}$ is not a constant, but will vary with t.

We know then that $\frac{dt}{ds} = \frac{1}{\sqrt{2}}$ for all t and that

$$\mathbf{T} = \mathbf{r}'(t) \frac{dt}{ds} = \frac{1}{\sqrt{2}} (-\sin t\mathbf{i} + \cos t\mathbf{j} + \mathbf{k}).$$

Next we calculate

$$\frac{d\mathbf{T}}{ds} = \frac{d\mathbf{T}}{dt} \cdot \frac{dt}{ds} = \frac{d\mathbf{T}}{dt} \cdot \frac{1}{\sqrt{2}}$$

$$= \frac{1}{2} (-\cos t\mathbf{i} - \sin t\mathbf{j}).$$

Now $\frac{d\mathbf{T}}{ds} = \kappa\mathbf{N}$, where $\kappa \geq 0$ and $\mathbf{N}$ is a unit vector. From the preceding expression and these remarks it is clear that

$$\kappa = \tfrac{1}{2} \quad \text{and} \quad \mathbf{N} = -\cos t\mathbf{i} - \sin t\mathbf{j}.$$

(Once again we encounter in this example an especially simple situation; we refer in this case to the fact that here κ is constant, whereas in general κ is a function of t).

From the expressions for $\mathbf{T}$ and $\mathbf{N}$ we can find $\mathbf{B} = \mathbf{T} \times \mathbf{N}$:

$$\mathbf{B} = \frac{1}{\sqrt{2}} (\sin t\mathbf{i} - \cos t\mathbf{j} + \mathbf{k}).$$

Evaluating these vectors at $t_0 = \dfrac{\pi}{4}$, we find

$$\mathbf{T} = -\frac{1}{2}\mathbf{i} + \frac{1}{2}\mathbf{j} + \frac{1}{\sqrt{2}}\mathbf{k},$$

$$\mathbf{N} = -\frac{1}{\sqrt{2}}\mathbf{i} - \frac{1}{\sqrt{2}}\mathbf{j},$$

$$\mathbf{B} = \frac{1}{2}\mathbf{i} - \frac{1}{2}\mathbf{j} + \frac{1}{\sqrt{2}}\mathbf{k}.$$

There are some interesting further relationships among the vectors of the moving trihedral, but in order to develop them we need two differentiation results for vector functions—the ones we state are related to Theorem 11.11.

Theorem 6. *If* **f** *and* **g** *are vector functions whose derivatives exist, then both the inner and vector products are differentiable and*

$$\frac{d}{dt}[\mathbf{f}(t) \cdot \mathbf{g}(t)] = \mathbf{f}(t) \cdot \frac{d\mathbf{g}(t)}{dt} + \frac{d\mathbf{f}(t)}{dt} \cdot \mathbf{g}(t), \tag{28}$$

$$\frac{d}{dt}[\mathbf{f}(t) \times \mathbf{g}(t)] = \mathbf{f}(t) \times \frac{d\mathbf{g}(t)}{dt} + \frac{d\mathbf{f}(t)}{dt} \times \mathbf{g}(t). \tag{29}$$

Proof. Exercise for student. ∎

Note that these formulas have the same form as the product formula for scalar functions. However, because of the lack of commutativity of the vector product, the *order of the factors in* (29) *must be retained.*

Now recall that $\frac{d\mathbf{T}}{ds} = \kappa\mathbf{N}$. What of the derivatives (with respect to s) of the other vectors of the trihedral? We first investigate $\frac{d\mathbf{B}}{ds}$, beginning with the observation that **B** a unit vector implies

$$\mathbf{B} \cdot \mathbf{B} = 1.$$

We now use (28), differentiating with respect to s:

$$\mathbf{B} \cdot \frac{d\mathbf{B}}{ds} + \frac{d\mathbf{B}}{ds} \cdot \mathbf{B} = 0,$$

or

$$\mathbf{B} \cdot \frac{d\mathbf{B}}{ds} = 0.$$

This implies $\frac{d\mathbf{B}}{ds} \perp \mathbf{B}$.

Next we draw on the fact that $\mathbf{B} \perp \mathbf{T}$, or

$$\mathbf{B} \cdot \mathbf{T} = 0.$$

Differentiating by means of (28), we have

$$\mathbf{B} \cdot \frac{d\mathbf{T}}{ds} + \frac{d\mathbf{B}}{ds} \cdot \mathbf{T} = 0,$$

or, since $\frac{d\mathbf{T}}{ds} = \kappa\mathbf{N}$,

$$\kappa\mathbf{B} \cdot \mathbf{N} + \frac{d\mathbf{B}}{ds} \cdot \mathbf{T} = 0.$$

But $\mathbf{B} \perp \mathbf{N} \Rightarrow \mathbf{B} \cdot \mathbf{N} = 0$ and the above equation becomes

$$\frac{d\mathbf{B}}{ds} \cdot \mathbf{T} = 0;$$

this says that $\dfrac{d\mathbf{B}}{ds} \perp \mathbf{T}$.

We have shown that $\dfrac{d\mathbf{B}}{ds}$ is perpendicular to both $\mathbf{T}$ and $\mathbf{B}$. It must therefore have the same direction as $\mathbf{N}$. We can thus write

$$\frac{d\mathbf{B}}{ds} = \tau\mathbf{N}. \tag{30}$$

It is possible and perfectly correct to write this last expression as $\dfrac{d\mathbf{B}}{ds} = -\tau\mathbf{N}$, and this is often done, thereby assigning the opposite sign to τ. The number τ is, like κ, a measure of curvature, as we shall show shortly. Unlike κ, however, τ need not be nonnegative—it can be positive, negative, or zero. Like κ, τ is usually a function of t.

The number τ is called the *torsion* of $\mathscr{C}$ at P_0. From (30) we see that

$$|\tau| = \left| \frac{d\mathbf{B}}{ds} \right|,$$

since $\mathbf{N}$ is a unit vector. In other words, τ serves as a measure of the rate of change of the binormal vector $\mathbf{B}$. Since $\mathbf{B}$ is a unit vector, only its direction can change. Now if we recall that the binormal is perpendicular to the osculating plane, we see that we can interpret τ as a measure of the rate at which the curve is turning away from (or out of) the osculating plane. (The sign of τ indicates direction of turning.) This point is borne out by the assertion, which we shall not prove, that a curve $\mathscr{C}$ is a plane curve (i.e., lies in a plane) $\Leftrightarrow \tau = 0$ at every point. (Compare with the assertion, made in Chapter 11, that a curve is a straight line $\Leftrightarrow \kappa = 0$ at every point.)

Finally we look at $\dfrac{d\mathbf{N}}{ds}$. Since the vectors $\mathbf{T}$, $\mathbf{N}$, $\mathbf{B}$ form a right-handed ortho-normal set, we can write

$$\mathbf{N} = \mathbf{B} \times \mathbf{T}.$$

Differentiating with respect to s and using (29), we have

$$\frac{d\mathbf{N}}{ds} = \mathbf{B} \times \frac{d\mathbf{T}}{ds} + \frac{d\mathbf{B}}{ds} \times \mathbf{T}$$

$$= \mathbf{B} \times (\kappa\mathbf{N}) + (\tau\mathbf{N}) \times \mathbf{T} \qquad \text{[by (26) and (30)]}$$

$$= -\kappa\mathbf{T} - \tau\mathbf{B}.$$

The equations

$$\frac{d\mathbf{T}}{ds} = \kappa\mathbf{N}$$

$$\frac{d\mathbf{N}}{ds} = -\kappa\mathbf{T} - \tau\mathbf{B} \tag{31}$$

$$\frac{d\mathbf{B}}{ds} = \tau\mathbf{N}$$

are known as the Frenet–Serret formulas. They were discovered independently by Frenet (in 1847) and Serret (about 1850). They are fundamental for work in differential geometry.

Example 15. This is a continuation of the study, begun in Example 14, of the circular helix. Recall that we found $\dfrac{dt}{ds} = \dfrac{1}{\sqrt{2}}$ for all t; the binormal is

$$\mathbf{B} = \frac{1}{\sqrt{2}}(\sin t\mathbf{i} - \cos t\mathbf{j} + \mathbf{k}).$$

If we differentiate with respect to s, we find

$$\frac{d\mathbf{B}}{ds} = \frac{d\mathbf{B}}{dt}\frac{dt}{ds} = \frac{1}{\sqrt{2}}\frac{d\mathbf{B}}{dt},$$

or

$$\frac{d\mathbf{B}}{ds} = \frac{1}{2}(\cos t\mathbf{i} + \sin t\mathbf{j}) = -\frac{1}{2}(-\cos t\mathbf{i} - \sin t\mathbf{j})$$

$$= -\frac{1}{2}\mathbf{N}.$$

From this equation and from (30) we learn that the torsion τ for the helix has the value $\tau = -\frac{1}{2}$ at every point of the curve.

General formulas for computing κ and τ in terms of the original vector function $\mathbf{r}$ can be found by means of rather extensive calculations. The results are as follows:

$$\kappa = \frac{|\mathbf{r}'(t) \times \mathbf{r}''(t)|}{|\mathbf{r}'(t)|^3}, \tag{32}$$

$$\tau = -\frac{\mathbf{r}'(t) \times \mathbf{r}''(t) \cdot \mathbf{r}'''(t)}{|\mathbf{r}'(t) \times \mathbf{r}''(t)|^2}. \tag{33}$$

Example 16. Let $\mathbf{r}$ be defined by

$$\mathbf{r}(t) = t\mathbf{i} + \tfrac{1}{2}t^2\mathbf{j} + \tfrac{1}{3}t^3\mathbf{k}.$$

The curve $\mathscr{C}$ determined by $\mathbf{r}$ is called a *twisted cubic*.

We begin by calculating the first three derivatives of $\mathbf{r}$:

$$\mathbf{r}'(t) = \mathbf{i} + t\mathbf{j} + t^2\mathbf{k}$$

$$\mathbf{r}''(t) = \mathbf{j} + 2t\mathbf{k}$$

$$\mathbf{r}'''(t) = 2\mathbf{k}.$$

From the first of these we find

$$|\mathbf{r}'(t)| = \sqrt{1 + t^2 + t^4} = \frac{ds}{dt};$$

thus

$$\frac{dt}{ds} = \frac{1}{\sqrt{1 + t^2 + t^4}} = (1 + t^2 + t^4)^{-1/2}.$$

The tangent vector $\mathbf{T}$ is

$$\mathbf{T} = \frac{d\mathbf{r}}{ds} = \frac{d\mathbf{r}}{dt}\frac{dt}{ds} = \mathbf{r}'(t)\frac{dt}{ds} = \frac{\mathbf{i} + t\mathbf{j} + t^2\mathbf{k}}{\sqrt{1 + t^2 + t^4}}.$$

The calculation of

$$\frac{d\mathbf{T}}{ds} = \frac{d\mathbf{T}}{dt}\frac{dt}{ds} = \frac{d}{dt}\left(\frac{\mathbf{i} + t\mathbf{j} + t^2\mathbf{k}}{\sqrt{1 + t^2 + t^4}}\right)\frac{dt}{ds}$$

is straightforward but a little tedious. The result is

$$\frac{d\mathbf{T}}{ds} = -\frac{1}{(1 + t^2 + t^4)^2}[(t + 2t^3)\mathbf{i} + (t^4 - 1)\mathbf{j} - (2t + t^3)\mathbf{k}].$$

If we focus attention on the point P_0 on $\mathscr{C}$ determined by $t = 1$, we find

$$\frac{dt}{ds} = \frac{1}{\sqrt{3}}, \qquad \mathbf{r}(1) = \mathbf{i} + \frac{1}{2}\mathbf{j} + \frac{1}{3}\mathbf{k}, \qquad \text{or } P_0\left(1, \frac{1}{2}, \frac{1}{3}\right);$$

$$\mathbf{T} = \frac{1}{\sqrt{3}}(\mathbf{i} + \mathbf{j} + \mathbf{k}),$$

$$\frac{d\mathbf{T}}{ds} = -\frac{1}{9}(3\mathbf{i} - 3\mathbf{k}) = \frac{1}{3}(-\mathbf{i} + \mathbf{k}) = \frac{\sqrt{2}}{3}\left[-\frac{1}{\sqrt{2}}(\mathbf{i} - \mathbf{k})\right]$$

Thus $\kappa = \dfrac{\sqrt{2}}{3}$ and

$$\mathbf{N} = -\frac{1}{\sqrt{2}}(\mathbf{i} - \mathbf{k}).$$

From **T** and **N**, we can calculate **B** = **T** × **N**:

$$\mathbf{B} = -\frac{1}{\sqrt{6}}(-\mathbf{i} + 2\mathbf{j} - \mathbf{k}).$$

From the derivatives of **r** we have

$$\mathbf{r}'(1) = \mathbf{i} + \mathbf{j} + \mathbf{k}$$

$$\mathbf{r}''(1) = \mathbf{j} + 2\mathbf{k}$$

$$\mathbf{r}'''(1) = 2\mathbf{k}.$$

Then

$$\mathbf{r}'(1) \times \mathbf{r}''(1) = \mathbf{i} - 2\mathbf{j} + \mathbf{k}, \quad |\mathbf{r}'(1) \times \mathbf{r}''(1)| = \sqrt{6}.$$

Also,

$$|\mathbf{r}'(1)| = \sqrt{3}, \quad \mathbf{r}'(1) \times \mathbf{r}''(1) \cdot \mathbf{r}'''(1) = 2.$$

Substituting in (32) and (33), we find

$$\kappa = \frac{\sqrt{6}}{3\sqrt{3}} = \frac{\sqrt{2}}{3},$$

as before; and

$$\tau = -\tfrac{2}{6} = -\tfrac{1}{3}.$$

EXERCISES

In numbers 1–5 find **T**, **N**, **B**, κ and τ at the point indicated.

1. $\mathbf{r}(t) = \cos 2t\mathbf{i} + \sin 2t\mathbf{j} + t\mathbf{k}$; $t = \dfrac{\pi}{6}$.

2. $\mathbf{r}(t) = 2\mathbf{i} + t\mathbf{j} + \tfrac{1}{2}t^2\mathbf{k}$; $t = 2$.

3. $\mathbf{r}(t) = e^t\mathbf{i} + e^{-t}\mathbf{j} + \sqrt{2}t\mathbf{k}$; $t = 1$.

4. $\mathbf{r}(t) = (2at)\mathbf{i} + (a^2 \log t)\mathbf{j} + t^2\mathbf{k}$; $t = a$.

5. $\mathbf{r}(t) = \cosh t\mathbf{i} + \sinh t\mathbf{j} + t\mathbf{k}$; $t = 1$.

6. Find the length of arc of the curve $\mathscr{C}$ defined by

$$\mathbf{r}(t) = 2t\mathbf{i} + \sqrt{6}\,t^2\mathbf{j} + 2t^3\mathbf{k}$$

for $0 \le t \le 3$.

7. Find the length of the curve $\mathscr{C}$ defined by

$$\mathbf{r}(t) = (\cos at)\mathbf{i} + (\sin at)\mathbf{j} + bt\mathbf{k}$$

for $0 \leq t \leq 2\pi$.

8. Prove Theorem 6 [Eqs. (28) and (29).]
[*Hint for* (29).

$$\mathbf{f}(t_0 + h) \times \mathbf{g}(t_0 + h) - \mathbf{f}(t_0) \times \mathbf{g}(t_0) = \mathbf{f}(t_0 + h) \times \mathbf{g}(t_0 + h) - \mathbf{f}(t_0 + h) \times \mathbf{g}(t_0)$$

$$+ \mathbf{f}(t_0 + h) \times \mathbf{g}(t_0) - \mathbf{f}(t_0) \times \mathbf{g}(t_0).]$$

12.7 Surfaces

In this section we begin a brief study of the analytic geometry of surfaces. Specifically, we shall be interested in methods for extracting geometric information from equations such as $z = x^2 + y^2$, $z = x^2 - y^2$, $x^2 + y^2 - z^2 = 1$, $z = ye^x$, etc. In general, such equations will correspond to a two dimensional set of points, a surface. The types of information we look for are, for the most part, analogous to the sort of things we investigate in the study of curves in the plane: extent, intercepts, symmetry, and so on. There is, however, an additional and very considerable complication in the present problem. We refer to the difficulty of drawing in two dimensions (on paper or on a blackboard) a configuration which exists in three dimensions. At this point our only words of wisdom are that practice helps. We shall try to give some more explicit aid in what follows.

Intercepts with the coordinate axes can be found—if they exist—by setting two of the variables equal to zero. For example, with

$$x^2 + y^2 - z^2 = 1$$

we find $x = \pm 1$, $y = z = 0$; $x = 0$, $y = \pm 1$, $z = 0$; but putting $x = y = 0$ gives $-z^2 = 1$, which has no solution, indicating no intersection with the z-axis.

However, far more useful than the set of points obtained in this way is knowledge of the *traces* on the coordinate planes. These are the curves of intersection of the surface with the coordinate planes; they are found by setting one of the variables equal to zero. Using the above equation as an example, we have

$$z = 0 \ (xy\text{-plane}), \qquad x^2 + y^2 = 1 \ (\text{circle})$$

$$y = 0 \ (zx\text{-plane}), \qquad x^2 - z^2 = 1 \ (\text{hyperbola})$$

$$x = 0 \ (yz\text{-plane}), \qquad y^2 - z^2 = 1 \ (\text{hyperbola}).$$

Related to the traces on the coordinate planes are traces in planes parallel to the coordinate planes. For example, with the equation $z = x^2 + y^2$, we find from $z = 0$, $x^2 + y^2 = 0$, that the surface intersects the xy-plane only in a point, the origin. But if we consider planes parallel to and above the xy-plane, planes

$z = c$, $c > 0$, we find $z = c$, $x^2 + y^2 = c$, a circle with center on the z-axis, radius $= \sqrt{c}$. Clearly, the circles enlarge as c, the distance above the xy-plane, increases.

Similarly, with $z = x^2 - y^2$, the trace in the xy-plane, $z = 0$, $x^2 - y^2 = 0$, is simply a pair of straight lines; but in the plane $z = c$, $c \neq 0$, we find $z = c$, $x^2 - y^2 = c$, a hyperbola, the nature of the transverse axis depending upon whether c is positive or negative.

Symmetry with respect to the coordinate axes can be found, if it exists, by checking whether or not pairs of the variables can be replaced by their negatives without changing the nature of the relation (see Exercise 22). For example, $z = x^2 + y^2$ is unchanged if x and y are replaced by $-x$ and $-y$, respectively, indicating that the surface is symmetric with respect to the z-axis. But there is no symmetry with respect to the other axes. However, as with intercepts, symmetry with respect to the coordinate planes can be more helpful than with respect to axes. With this same example, $z = x^2 + y^2$, we see that replacing x by $-x$ leaves the equation unchanged, indicating symmetry with respect to the yz-plane (see Exercise 21). Similarly, there is symmetry with respect to the zx-plane (why?), but there is none with respect to the xy-plane (why?).

The equation $x^2 + y^2 - z^2 = 1$ immediately reveals symmetry with respect to all coordinate planes—and axes—whereas the equation $z = ye^x$ reveals no symmetry.

Obtaining information about *extent* of the surface depends very much, as regards ease or difficulty, upon the nature of the equation. With the equation $z = ye^x$, for example, we see that all pairs $(x, y) \in \mathbf{R}^2$ can be used on the right side, the sign of z depending upon the sign of y: the surface is above the xy-plane for $y > 0$, below for $y < 0$.

With the equation $z = x^2 + y^2$ it is easy to see that, all pairs $(x, y) \in \mathbf{R}^2$ can be used; in this case, clearly, $z \geq 0$: the entire surface lies above the xy-plane except for the origin, the vertex of this paraboloid.

If we write $x^2 + y^2 - z^2 = 1$ as $z^2 = x^2 + y^2 - 1$, we see that only (x, y) such that $x^2 + y^2 \geq 1$ (points on and outside the unit circle) can be used; also, *all* values of z can be obtained.

In contrast to the surfaces of these examples, the surface corresponding to

$$\frac{x^2}{a^2} + \frac{y^2}{b^2} + \frac{z^2}{c^2} = 1$$

lies entirely in a bounded region of space. For example, we can write the equation in the form

$$z^2 = c^2 \left[1 - \frac{x^2}{a^2} - \frac{y^2}{b^2} \right],$$

which shows at once that only pairs (x, y) such that $\dfrac{x^2}{a^2} + \dfrac{y^2}{b^2} \leq 1$ can be used and that, in any case, z must satisfy $-c \leq z \leq c$. In fact, this surface, having all kinds of symmetry, lies entirely within the box $\{(x, y, z) | \, |x| \leq a, |y| \leq b, |z| \leq c\}$. It is an ellipsoid.

Example 17. We illustrate some of the preceding ideas by obtaining a sketch of the surface represented analytically by $z = x^2 + y^2$.

We summarize the information already found, plus a little more, as follows.

TRACES.

xy plane	zx-plane	yz-plane	planes $z = c, c > 0$
$\begin{cases} z = 0 \\ x^2 + y^2 = 0 \end{cases}$	$\begin{cases} y = 0 \\ z = x^2 \end{cases}$	$\begin{cases} x = 0 \\ z = y^2 \end{cases}$	$\begin{cases} z = c \\ x^2 + y^2 = c \end{cases}$

SYMMETRY.

With respect to yz- and zx-planes.
With respect to z-axis.

EXTENT.

All $(x, y) \in \mathbf{R}^2$ admissible
$z \geq 0$ (surface lies on and above xy-plane).

As regards the sketching, the order in which the various traces are drawn may make a difference. A suggestion which may help is to draw first the trace, if any, in the plane of the paper (yz-plane); then draw in traces in the xy-plane and in planes parallel to the xy-plane. (With regard to the latter, if the surface is of infinite extent, chop it off somewhere with planes $z = c$.) Finally, draw in the trace in the zx-plane. We illustrate this suggestion (this *one* time) with a sequence of drawings for $z = x^2 + y^2$ (see Figure 21). This surface is a *circular paraboloid* or *paraboloid of revolution*, for it can be generated by revolving the parabola $z = y^2$ about the z-axis.

Example 18. For an illustration of an entirely different sort we sketch a portion of the graph of $z = e^{(-1/2)x} \cos^2 y$. In particular, we concern ourselves with that part which lies above the rectangle $S = \{(x, y) | 0 \leq x \leq 2, 0 \leq y \leq \pi\}$.

TRACES.

xy-plane	zx-plane	yz-plane
$\begin{cases} z = 0 \\ y = (2k + 1)\dfrac{\pi}{2}, k = 0, \pm 1, \pm 2, \ldots \end{cases}$	$\begin{cases} y = 0 \\ z = e^{(-1/2)x} \end{cases}$	$\begin{cases} x = 0 \\ z = \cos^2 y \end{cases}$

plane $y = \pi$	plane $x = 2$
$\begin{cases} y = \pi \\ z = e^{(-1/2)x} \end{cases}$	$\begin{cases} x = 2 \\ z = e^{-1} \cos^2 y \end{cases}$

SYMMETRY.

With respect to zx-plane.

EXTENT.

All $(x, y) \in \mathbf{R}^2$ admissible.

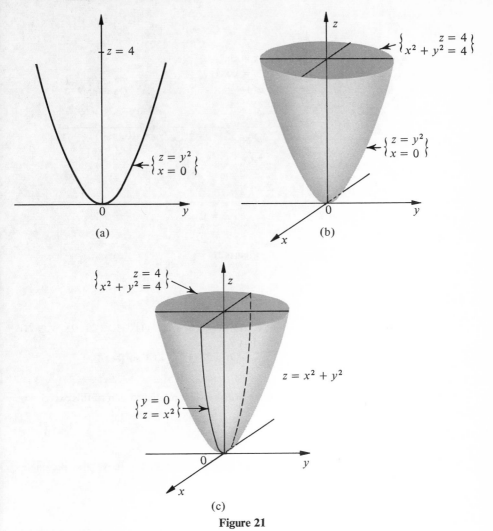

(a)

(b)

(c)

Figure 21

Also $x \geq 0 \Rightarrow 0 \leq z \leq 1$—on the positive side of the yz-plane the surface lies entirely on and between the planes $z = 0$ and $z = 1$. The sketch is shown in Figure 22.

EXERCISES

In numbers 1–20 perform a systematic analysis on the equation, extract as much geometric information as possible, and make a sketch.

1. $z = 4 - x^2 - y^2$ (Sketch the part for which $x^2 + y^2 \leq 4$).

2. $z = x^4 + y^4$.   **3.** $z = x + y$.

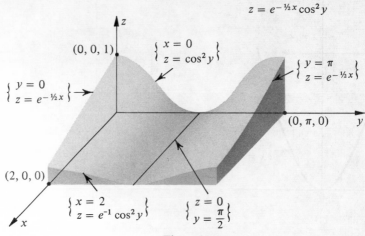

Figure 22

4. $z = y^2$ (This is a surface).

5. $z = e^{-x}$ (Sketch the portion above the rectangle $S = \{(x, y) \mid 0 \le x \le 1, 0 \le y \le 2\}$.

6. $z^2 = x^2 + y^2$.   **7.** $x^2 + y^2 = 4$ (A surface).

8. $z = \dfrac{1}{4 - x^2 - y^2}$. (How is the surface of Exercise 7 related to that of this exercise?)

9. $z = 1 + \sin y$.   **10.** $z = \log y$.

11. $z = \exp\left(-\tfrac{1}{2}x - \tfrac{1}{3}y\right) = e^{-\frac{1}{2}x}\, e^{-\frac{1}{3}y}$ (Sketch only the portion above the rectangle $S = \{(x, y) \mid 0 \le x \le 2, 0 \le y \le 3\}$).

12. $x^2 + y^2 + z^2 = 4$ (First octant only).

13. $x^2 + y^2 + 4z^2 = 4$ (First octant only).

14. $x^2 + 4y^2 + 9z^2 = 36$.

15. $x^2 + y^2 - z^2 = 1$.

16. $z = 4 - x^2 - 4y^2$.

17. $z = \dfrac{1}{x^2 + y^2}$.

18. $x = y^2 + z^2$. [*Hint. One* way would be to draw the axes so that the positive x-axis has the position usually occupied by the positive z-axis. Be sure the system is right handed.]

19. $y = 1 - z^2 - x^2$ (see hint for Exercise 18).

20. $z = xy$. [*Hint.* Consider traces in the planes $y = x$ and $y = -x$.]

21. (a) Define the following property. Points P_1 and P_2 are symmetric with respect to the xy-plane.

    (b) Given points $P_1(x_1, y_1, z_1)$ and $P_2(x_2, y_2, z_2)$. Find a necessary and sufficient condition on the coordinates for P_1 and P_2 to be symmetric with respect to the xy-plane.

    (c) Give a sufficient condition for a set $S \subset \mathbf{R}^3$ to be symmetric with respect to the xy-plane.

22. Same as Exercise 21 only replace "xy-plane" throughout with "z-axis."

12.8 Cylinders

A cylinder is an especially simple type of surface. However, the term connotes a broader class of surfaces than the reader may suspect. The familiar right circular cylinder encountered in Exercise 7 of the preceding section is only one type of many possible varieties of cylinder.

We can define a cylinder as follows. We consider a curve lying in a plane—this curve will be called the *base curve*. We let a straight line, perpendicular to the plane of the base curve, trace out the base curve. The set of points generated in this way constitutes the cylinder. If the base curve is a circle, then the cylinder is a right-circular cylinder. (The word "right" refers to the fact that the generating line is perpendicular to the plane of the base curve. We could consider cylinders other than right, but we shall not study these here.) We can, though, also have parabolic or elliptic or logarithmic cylinders.

If the base curve lies in a plane parallel to one of the coordinate planes, which implies that the generating line will be parallel to one of the coordinate axes, then the equation of the cylinder assumes a rather simple and easily recognizable form. Suppose, to be definite about it, we have a curve lying in the yz-plane; it could be represented analytically as

$$\left\{ \begin{aligned} f(y, z) &= 0 \\ x &= 0 \end{aligned} \right\},$$

where f is some function of two variables (e.g., $f(y, z) = y^2 + z^2 - 4$). If $(0, y_0, z_0)$ is a point on the base curve, i.e., y_0, z_0 satisfy the condition imposed by f, then (x, y_0, z_0) will be on the generating line—a fixed position of the generating line is called a *generator*—for *every* $x \in \mathbf{R}$ (see Figure 23). Thus (x, y_0, z_0) is on the cylinder for every $x \in \mathbf{R}$. Conversely, given any point (x_0, y_0, z_0) on the cylinder, $(0, y_0, z_0)$ must be on the base curve, which implies $f(y_0, z_0) = 0$ describes exactly the set of points on the cylinder with base curve $f(y, z) = 0$, $x = 0$, and with generators parallel to the x-axis. A similar argument applies to an equation with y or z missing.

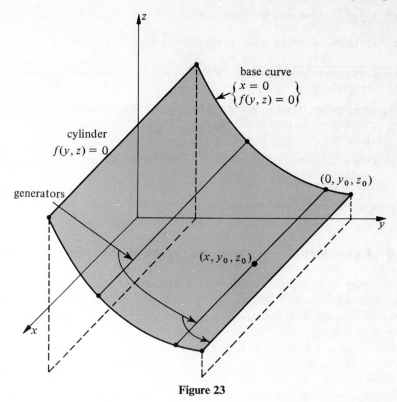

Figure 23

In summary, *if an equation in the geometry of three-space has a variable missing, it represents a cylinder with generators parallel to the axis of the missing variable.*

It follows that the surfaces in Exercises 4, 5, 9, and 10 just preceding are all cylinders.

Example 19. We consider the surface determined by

$$z = \sin^2 x.$$

It is clear from the preceding discussion that the surface is a cylinder with base curve in the zx-plane and with generators parallel to the y-axis. We show a portion of the cylinder in Figure 24.

SURFACES OF REVOLUTION. A right circular cylinder, in addition to being the most familiar example of a cylinder, is also an example of a *surface of revolution.* For example, the cylinder $x^2 + y^2 = 4$ can be thought of as generated by re- volving the straight line $x = 0$, $y = 2$ about the z-axis. The fact is that we encountered these surfaces, briefly, near the end of Chapter 2.

A special case of the most general situation will now be discussed. We consider a curve $\mathscr{C}$ in the yz-plane, the equation of which, in the yz-plane, is $z = f(y)$, where f is a function. We revolve $\mathscr{C}$ about the y-axis, thus generating a surface. We are interested in an analytic representation of the surface. Let

$P_0(0, y_0, z_0 = f(y_0))$ be a point on the curve, let $P_1(x_1, y_1, z_1)$ be an arbitrary point on the circle—hence on the surface—generated as P_0 is revolved about the y-axis (see Figure 25).

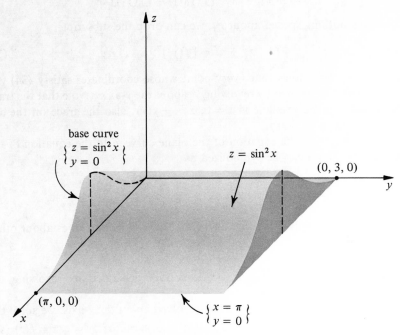

base curve
$\left\{ \begin{matrix} z = \sin^2 x \\ y = 0 \end{matrix} \right\}$

$z = \sin^2 x$

$(0, 3, 0)$

$(\pi, 0, 0)$

$\left\{ \begin{matrix} x = \pi \\ y = 0 \end{matrix} \right\}$

Figure 24

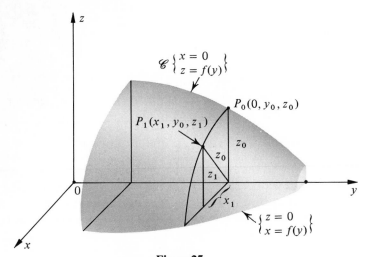

$\mathscr{C} \left\{ \begin{matrix} x = 0 \\ z = f(y) \end{matrix} \right\}$

$P_0(0, y_0, z_0)$

$P_1(x_1, y_0, z_1)$

z_0

z_0

z_1

x_1

$\left\{ \begin{matrix} z = 0 \\ x = f(y) \end{matrix} \right\}$

Figure 25

Referring to the figure, we can now obtain the following relations between the coordinates of P_0 and P_1:

$$y_1 = y_0,$$

$$x_1^2 + z_1^2 = z_0^2 = [f(y_0)]^2 = [f(y_1)]^2.$$

As there was nothing special about P_1, we can drop the subscript:

$$x^2 + z^2 = [f(y)]^2. \tag{34}$$

Reversing the steps shows that every point whose coordinates satisfy (34) will lie on the surface generated by revolving $\mathscr{C}$ about the y-axis. (Note that the trace of the surface on the yz-plane is $x = 0$, $z = \pm f(y)$; also the trace on the xy-plane is $z = 0$, $x = \pm f(y)$.)

The transition from the equation of the plane curve $\mathscr{C}$ to the equation of the surface of revolution can be symbolized as

$$z = f(y) \rightarrow z^2 = [f(y)]^2 \rightarrow x^2 + z^2 = [f(y)]^2.$$

Verbally this says: square both sides, then replace z^2 by $x^2 + z^2$.

Similar remarks apply to surfaces generated by revolving curves about other axes.

Example 20. Find the equation of the surface generated by revolving the parabola $z = y^2$ about the z-axis.

Because the curve in question is to be revolved about the z-axis, we solve the equation for y, limiting ourselves to half of the parabola: $y = \sqrt{z} = f(z)$ (see Figure 26).

As is clear from the figure, the equation of the surface is

$$x^2 + y^2 = [f(z)]^2 = (\sqrt{z})^2,$$

or

$$z = x^2 + y^2, \tag{35}$$

which was discussed in detail in Example 17.

The transition from the equation of the plane curve to the equation of the surface can be symbolized in this case as follows:

$$y = f(z) = \sqrt{z} \rightarrow y^2 = [f(z)]^2 = z \rightarrow x^2 + y^2 = z.$$

Similarly, returning to the right circular cylinder with which we began this discussion, if we start with the line $y = 2$ in the yz-plane and consider $y = 2$ as a constant function of z, then a transition identical in form with that just displayed, shows how to find the equation of the surface generated when this line is revolved about the z-axis:

$$y = f(z) = 2 \rightarrow y^2 = [f(z)]^2 = 4 \rightarrow x^2 + y^2 = 4.$$

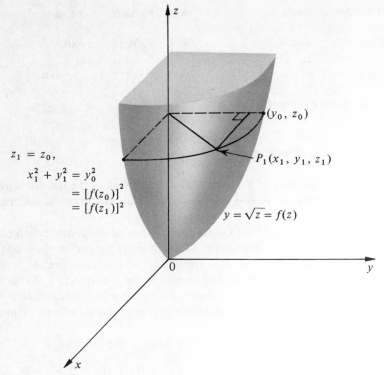

$$z_1 = z_0,$$
$$x_1^2 + y_1^2 = y_0^2$$
$$= [f(z_0)]^2$$
$$= [f(z_1)]^2$$

(y_0, z_0)

$P_1(x_1, y_1, z_1)$

$y = \sqrt{z} = f(z)$

Figure 26

E X E R C I S E S

In numbers 1–10 sketch the cylinder determined by the equation.

1. $\sqrt{z} = y$.   **2.** $x + y = 1$.

3. $z = e^{-y}$.   **4.** $z = \sin y + 1$.

5. $z = \log x$.   **6.** $x^2 + 4y^2 = 4$.

7. $xy = 1$.   **8.** $y = x$.

9. $x^2 y = 1$.   **10.** $z = 1 - y^2$.

In numbers 11–20 find the equation of the surface generated by revolving the plane curve $\mathscr{C}$ indicated about the prescribed axis. Sketch.

11. $\mathscr{C} : \sqrt{z} = y$; z-axis.   **12.** $\mathscr{C} : \sqrt{z} = y$; y-axis.

13. $\mathscr{C} : z = y$; z-axis.   **14.** $\mathscr{C} : yz = 1$; y-axis.

15. $\mathscr{C}: x = 2y;$ x-axis.   16. $\mathscr{C}: z = \sin y;$ y-axis.

17. $\mathscr{C}: z = e^{-x};$ x-axis.   18. $\mathscr{C}: z = e^{-x};$ z-axis.

19. $\mathscr{C}: z = 1 - y^2;$ z-axis.   20. $\mathscr{C}: y^2 - z^2 = 1;$ y-axis.

21. Is every plane a cylinder? Explain.

12.9 Quadric Surfaces

We conclude this study of surfaces with a description of the quadric surfaces —the three-dimensional analog of the conic section curves considered in Chapter 10.

From an analytic point of view the relation between the conic section curves and the quadric surfaces is very strong: The former are the curves obtained from the general equation of second degree in x and y; the latter are the surfaces represented by the general equation of second degree in x, y, and z. As we shall see, there are close geometric ties between the two families. In particular—and quite naturally—the traces of the quadric surfaces in the coordinate planes are conic section curves.

The equations we consider are all special cases of the following:

$$Ax^2 + By^2 + Cz^2 + Dyz + Ezx + Fxy + Gx + Hy + Iz + J = 0, \quad (36)$$

where not all of A, B, C, D, E, F are zero.

We shall look at several different classes of these surfaces. We begin with the only class, the *ellipsoids*, which lie in a bounded region of space. With a coordinate system suitably chosen, the equation takes the form

$$\frac{x^2}{a^2} + \frac{y^2}{b^2} + \frac{z^2}{c^2} = 1. \quad (37)$$

It is easy to see that the ellipsoid lies entirely within the box

$$S = \{(x, y, z) \mid x \leq |a|, \ y \leq |b|, \ z = |c|\}.$$

The analysis in terms of the procedures set forth in Section 7 is simple, straightforward, and fruitful. The traces in coordinate planes and in planes parallel to them are ellipses; and there is symmetry with respect to all coordinate planes and axes. A sketch is shown in Figure 27.

If two (but not three) of the numbers a, b, c are equal, the ellipsoid is called a *spheroid*; the spheroid is a surface of revolution. If all three of a, b, c are equal, the ellipsoid is, of course, a sphere.

If the center of the ellipsoid is not at the origin but the axes of symmetry are parallel to the coordinate axes, the equation of the ellipsoid will have terms of the first degree. The coordinates of the center and other essential information can easily be found by completing the squares in x, y, and z.

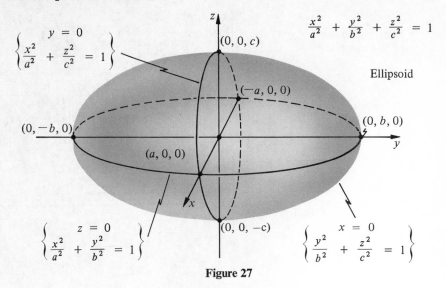

Figure 27

Another class of the family of quadric surfaces is called the *hyperboloids*. There are, as it turns out, two groups of these. The first ones we consider are called *hyperboloids of one sheet*, the simplest form of the equation being of the type

$$\frac{x^2}{a^2} + \frac{y^2}{b^2} - \frac{z^2}{c^2} = 1. \tag{38}$$

The systematic analysis is again routine. Traces in the xy- and parallel planes are ellipses; traces in the zx- and yz-planes are hyperbolas. There is symmetry to all coordinate planes and axes. By writing (38) in the form

$$z^2 = c^2 \left[\frac{x^2}{a^2} + \frac{y^2}{b^2} - 1 \right]$$

we see that (x, y) must satisfy $\dfrac{x^2}{a^2} + \dfrac{y^2}{b^2} \geq 1$. The hyperboloid of one sheet is unbounded. A sketch of one is shown in Figure 28.

The other group of hyperboloids are those of *two sheets*, the standard form of the equation having two minus signs on the left side—such as

$$-\frac{x^2}{a^2} + \frac{y^2}{b^2} - \frac{z^2}{c^2} = 1. \tag{39}$$

This surface has hyperbolas as traces in the xy- and yz-plane. There is no trace in the zx-plane ($y = 0$), but if $|k| > b$ the traces in the planes $y = k$ are ellipses. There is symmetry with respect to all coordinate planes and axes. If the equation in (39) is written as

$$y^2 = b^2 \left[1 + \frac{x^2}{a^2} + \frac{z^2}{c^2} \right],$$

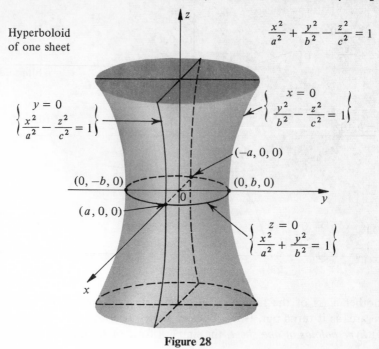

Hyperboloid
of one sheet

$$\frac{x^2}{a^2} + \frac{y^2}{b^2} - \frac{z^2}{c^2} = 1$$

$$\left\{ \begin{array}{l} y = 0 \\ \dfrac{x^2}{a^2} - \dfrac{z^2}{c^2} = 1 \end{array} \right\}$$

$$\left\{ \begin{array}{l} x = 0 \\ \dfrac{y^2}{b^2} - \dfrac{z^2}{c^2} = 1 \end{array} \right\}$$

$(-a, 0, 0)$

$(0, -b, 0)$ $(0, b, 0)$

$(a, 0, 0)$

$$\left\{ \begin{array}{l} z = 0 \\ \dfrac{x^2}{a^2} + \dfrac{y^2}{b^2} = 1 \end{array} \right\}$$

Figure 28

it becomes clear that we must have $|y| \geq b$. A sketch of a hyperboloid of two sheets is shown in Figure 29.

The preceding surfaces have all had centers; they are like the ellipses and hyperbolas in this respect. There are two types of *paraboloids*, neither of which is a central quadric surface.

The first of these is the *elliptic paraboloid*, the general form of the equation being

$$cz = \frac{x^2}{a^2} + \frac{y^2}{b^2}. \tag{40}$$

We have already, in Example 17 (Figure 21) in Section 7 given a complete analysis of this surface for $a = b = c = 1$, so no further discussion is necessary here. See also Example 20 in Section 8.

The *hyperbolic paraboloid* is in some ways the most interesting of the quadric surfaces. The form of the equation with which we shall work is

$$cz = -\frac{x^2}{a^2} + \frac{y^2}{b^2}. \tag{41}$$

The trace of this surface on the xy-plane is simply a pair of lines: $z = 0$, $b^2 x^2 = a^2 y^2$. However, traces in planes $z = k$ parallel to the xy-planes are hyperbolas, a shift in transverse axis occurring as k changes from positive to negative values. The trace in the yz-plane is the parabola $cz = \dfrac{y^2}{b^2}$, whereas that in the zx-plane is the parabola $cz = -\dfrac{x^2}{a^2}$.

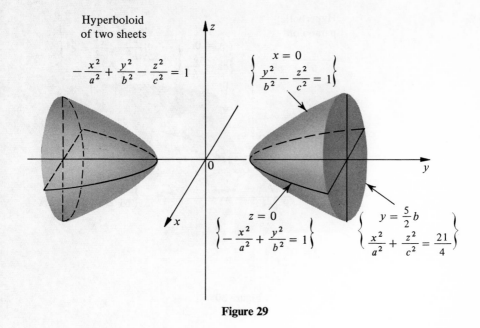

Hyperboloid
of two sheets

$$-\frac{x^2}{a^2} + \frac{y^2}{b^2} - \frac{z^2}{c^2} = 1$$

$$\left\{ \begin{array}{l} x = 0 \\ \dfrac{y^2}{b^2} - \dfrac{z^2}{c^2} = 1 \end{array} \right\}$$

$$\left\{ \begin{array}{l} z = 0 \\ -\dfrac{x^2}{a^2} + \dfrac{y^2}{b^2} = 1 \end{array} \right\}$$

$$\left\{ \begin{array}{l} y = \dfrac{5}{2}b \\ \dfrac{x^2}{a^2} + \dfrac{z^2}{c^2} = \dfrac{21}{4} \end{array} \right\}$$

Figure 29

There is symmetry with respect to the yz- and zx-planes, but not with respect to the xy-plane (see the preceding paragraph). There is also symmetry with respect to the z-axis.

The hyperbolic paraboloid is a saddle-shaped figure with a "minimax" point at the origin. Traveling in the yz-plane, one experiences a minimum at the origin, but one restricted to live in the zx-plane would look on the origin as a maximum point (see Figure 30 for a sketch).

The final class of quadric surfaces we take up should perhaps have been included earlier, among the other surfaces which have a center. We refer to the *cones*, which, with suitable choice of coordinate system, can be represented by equations such as

$$\frac{x^2}{a^2} + \frac{y^2}{b^2} - \frac{z^2}{c^2} = 0. \tag{42}$$

For this surface the traces are especially simple. In the xy-plane the trace is a point; in planes parallel to the xy-plane the traces are ellipses. In both the yz- and the zx-planes the traces are pairs of lines intersecting at the origin. (What are the traces in planes parallel to the yz- and zx-planes?)

It is easy to see that the surface in (42) has symmetry with respect to all coordinate planes and axes. A sketch appears in Figure 31.

Note that the equation of the cone is homogeneous in x, y, z: every term is of the same degree. This algebraic property is characteristic of cones in this position.

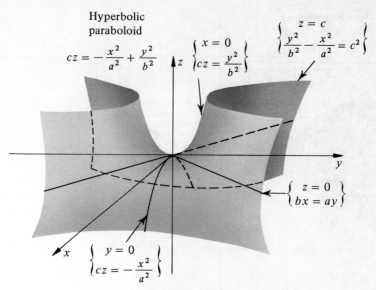

Hyperbolic
paraboloid

$$cz = -\frac{x^2}{a^2} + \frac{y^2}{b^2}$$

$$\left\{ \begin{array}{l} x = 0 \\ cz = \dfrac{y^2}{b^2} \end{array} \right\}$$

$$\left\{ \begin{array}{l} z = c \\ \dfrac{y^2}{b^2} - \dfrac{x^2}{a^2} = c^2 \end{array} \right\}$$

$$\left\{ \begin{array}{l} z = 0 \\ bx = ay \end{array} \right\}$$

$$\left\{ \begin{array}{l} y = 0 \\ cz = -\dfrac{x^2}{a^2} \end{array} \right\}$$

Figure 30

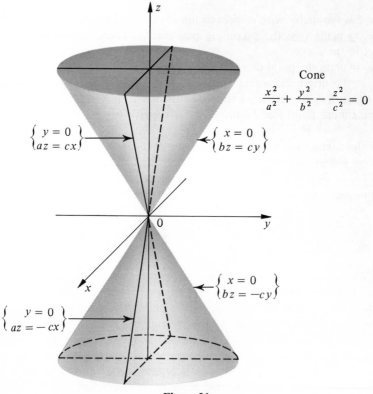

Cone

$$\frac{x^2}{a^2} + \frac{y^2}{b^2} - \frac{z^2}{c^2} = 0$$

$$\left\{ \begin{array}{l} y = 0 \\ az = cx \end{array} \right\}$$

$$\left\{ \begin{array}{l} x = 0 \\ bz = cy \end{array} \right\}$$

$$\left\{ \begin{array}{l} x = 0 \\ bz = -cy \end{array} \right\}$$

$$\left\{ \begin{array}{l} y = 0 \\ az = -cx \end{array} \right\}$$

Figure 31

It is easy to see that if $a = b$ in Eq. (42) the cone is then a surface of revolution: traces in planes parallel to the xy-plane will be circles rather than, as in the general case, ellipses.

We should point out that in discussing the different classes of quadric surfaces we have in each case used only one of several possible positions of the surface with respect to the coordinate system. Thus a paraboloid of revolution could have an equation such as $4x = y^2 + z^2$, its axis of symmetry being then the x-axis, or a hyperboloid of one sheet could have an equation such as $-x^2 + 4y^2 + 4z^2 = 4$. This surface would then surround the x-axis. As we remarked when discussing the ellipsoids, the presence of terms of first degree for the central quadric surfaces or of additional terms of first degree for the paraboloids would indicate a translation parallel to the axes. By completing the squares and, if desired, introducing new coordinates, as in Chapter 10, one can identify and describe the surface. Finally, if any of the cross-product terms, such as xy or zx, is present, the identification of the surface would be difficult in terms of the limited discussion we have had. A suitable rotation of axes will eliminate these cross-product terms. The theory which most efficiently describes this process lies in the part of linear algebra concerned with quadratic forms.

EXERCISES

In numbers 1–15 identify and sketch each of the surfaces.

1. $2x^2 + y^2 + z^2 = 2.$

2. $-2x^2 + y^2 + z^2 = 2.$

3. $2x^2 - y^2 - z^2 = 2.$

4. $x^2 + y^2 + z^2 = 2.$

5. $-2x + y^2 + z^2 = 2.$

6. $-2x + y^2 + z^2 = 0.$

7. $z = y^2 - x^2.$

8. $-2x^2 + y^2 + z^2 = 0.$

9. $-2x^2 + y^2 = 0.$

10. $-2x^2 + y = 0.$

11. $x^2 - y^2 - z^2 = 0.$

12. $3z = x^2 - 4y^2.$

13. $4y = x^2 + z^2.$

14. $x^2 - y^2 = 0.$

15. $z = xy.$

In numbers 16–26 find the equation of the surface generated when the *plane curve* given is revolved about the axis indicated. Name and sketch the surface.

16. $z = 2y$; z-axis.

17. $z = 2y$; y-axis.

18. $4y^2 - z^2 = 4$; y-axis.

19. $4y^2 - z^2 = 4$; z-axis.

20. $y^2 + 4z^2 = 4$; z-axis.   **21.** $y^2 + 4z^2 = 4$; y-axis.

22. $z = 3x$; x-axis.   **23.** $x^2 + y^2 = 1$; y-axis.

24. $x^2 + y^2 = 1$; x-axis.   **25.** $x^2 - 4y^2 = 4$; y-axis.

26. $x^2 - 4y^2 = 4$; x-axis.

27. The hyperboloid of one sheet contains two complete families of straight lines. Show that this is so for the particular hyperboloid $x^2 + y^2 - z^2 = 1$.
   [*Hints.*
   (1) Write the equation as $x^2 - z^2 = 1 - y^2$; now factor both sides.
   (2) Divide both sides by $(1 - y)(x + z)$.
   (3) Set each fraction equal to t; in each case multiply both sides of the equation by the denominator. This should give you

$$\begin{cases} x - z = t(1 - y) \\ 1 + y = t(x + z) \end{cases}.$$

   For each value of t this system is a straight line—every point of which lies on the hyperboloid.
   (4) Return to the factored equation found in Hint (1), and divide both sides by $(1 + y)(x + z)$. Set each fraction equal to s and follow through the procedure of Hint (3).]
      A surface of this sort is called a *ruled* surface.

28. See Exercise 27. Show that the hyperboloic paraboloid $z = y^2 - x^2$ is a ruled surface.

Chapter **13** Partial Derivatives

In this chapter we begin the study of the calculus of functions of several variables, i.e., functions $f: \mathbf{R}^n \to \mathbf{R}$, where $n \geq 2$. Much of our work will be with $n = 2$ or $n = 3$. In particular, if $n = 2$, the graph of f will be a surface in three space; this means we can, on the one hand, use geometric ideas to guide our thinking, and, on the other hand, apply the resulting theory to problems of a geometric nature. For $n = 3$, the domain of f will be a subset of three space, making geometry available to us, but the graph would require four space. And of course if $n > 3$ we are unable to draw on the geometry of our experience. Even so we can, and shall, use the language of geometry, where appropriate and useful.

Our primary concern in this chapter will be to extend the concepts of differential calculus. As much as possible, we try to follow the patterns established earlier for $n = 1$. As we shall see, many of the ideas generalize naturally, but others require modification or, at least, consideration from a somewhat different point of view.

13.1 Preliminary Definitions: Functions, Limits, Etc.

It is true that most of the basic ideas we need in this chapter have already been introduced. Nevertheless, we give a brief summary of definitions, along with a few examples, and establish agreement about notation.

The major point about the functions with which we shall be concerned is that they will have as domain a subset $X \subset \mathbf{R}^n$. As in the earlier chapters, the range of f is in $\mathbf{R}$. Frequently, the functions will be defined by a formula; in this case we will—unless otherwise specified—take the domain to be the largest admissible subset of $\mathbf{R}^n$. Thus, if $n = 2$, we might have

$$f(x, y) = x^2 + y^2, \tag{1}$$

or

$$g(x, y) = e^x \sin y, \tag{2}$$

or

$$h(x, y) = \log xy, \tag{3}$$

or

$$F(x, y) = \sqrt{1 - x^2 - y^2}. \tag{4}$$

It is easy to see that the domain for both f and g is $\mathbf{R}^2$; for h the domain is $\{(x, y) \,|\, xy > 0\}$, i.e., points in quadrants I and III, exclusive of the axes; and for F it is $\{(x, y) \,|\, x^2 + y^2 \leq 1\}$, or the points on and inside the unit circle. The ranges of these functions are as follows: for f, $\{z \,|\, z \geq 0\}$; for g and h, $\mathbf{R}$; and for F, $\{z \,|\, 0 \leq z \leq 1\}$.

When it is convenient, we may use vector notation for *points* in $\mathbf{R}^n$; thus, if $n = 3$,

$$f(\mathbf{x}) = \frac{x_1^2 - x_2^2}{x_3}$$

and

$$f(x, y, z) = \frac{x^2 - y^2}{z}$$

are simply different ways of describing the same function. (What is the domain— a subset of $\mathbf{R}^3$—for this f?)

For a discussion of limits of functions defined on $\mathbf{R}^n$, the essential need is a definition of neighborhood of a point. This definition has already been given (Definition 11.9) for $n = 2$. We now give a general formulation and specific examples.

Definition 1. *Let* $\mathbf{a} = (a_1 \ldots, a_n) \in \mathbf{R}^n$. *A* **$\delta$-neighborhood of** $\mathbf{a}$ *is the set of points in* $\mathbf{R}^n$ *described by*

$$N_\delta(\mathbf{a}) = \{\mathbf{x} \in \mathbf{R}^n | \, |\mathbf{x} - \mathbf{a}| < \delta\}, \tag{5}$$

or

$$N_\delta(\mathbf{a}) = \{(x_1, \ldots, x_n) \,|\, (x_1 - a_1)^2 + \cdots + (x_n - a_n)^2 < \delta^2\}. \tag{6}$$

This is a type of nbd. known as *spherical* (for a discussion of a *rectangular* ndb. in $\mathbf{R}^2$ see Exercise 2 after Section 11.7). We shall also refer to it as an *open ball* ("open," because the boundary points, $\{\mathbf{x} | \, |\mathbf{x} - \mathbf{a}| = \delta\}$, are not included).

For example, if $n = 2$, we have

$$N_\delta(2, 1) = \{(x, y) \,|\, (x - 2)^2 + (y - 1)^2 < \delta^2\},$$

the points interior to the circle with center at $(2, 1)$, radius δ (see Figure 1a). If $n = 3$, we have

$$N_\delta(2, 1, 3) = \{(x, y, z) \,|\, (x - 2)^2 + (y - 1)^2 + (z - 3) < \delta^2\},$$

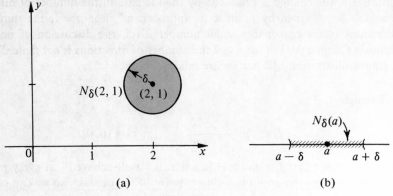

(a)   (b)

Figure 1

the points interior to the sphere with radius δ, center at $(2, 1, 3)$. Notice, finally, that if $n = 1$,

$$N_\delta(a) = \{x \mid (x - a)^2 < \delta^2\} = \{x \mid a - \delta < x < a + \delta\},$$

identical with our previous definition (see Figure 1b).

Of course, we define a deleted nbd. of a point as we did in Chapter 3.

Definition 2. *Let* $a \in \mathbf{R}^n$. *A **deleted δ-nbd. of** a is a δ-nbd. of a with the point a deleted.*

$$N_\delta^*(\mathbf{a}) = \{\mathbf{x} \in \mathbf{R}^n \mid 0 < |\mathbf{x} - \mathbf{a}| < \delta\}, \tag{7}$$

or

$$N_\delta^*(\mathbf{a}) = \{\mathbf{x} \in \mathbf{R}^n \mid 0 < (x_1 - a_1)^2 + \cdots + (x_n - a_n)^2 < \delta^2\}. \tag{8}$$

Next we review the definition of a *cluster point*.

Definition 3. *Let* $X \subset \mathbf{R}^n$, *let* $\mathbf{a} \in \mathbf{R}^n$. *Then* $\mathbf{a}$ *is a **cluster point** of* $X \Leftrightarrow$ *every* $N^*(\mathbf{a})$ *contains at least one point of* X. *In symbols,* $\mathbf{a}$ *is a c.p. of* $X \Leftrightarrow \forall N^*(\mathbf{a}) \Rightarrow N^*(\mathbf{a}) \cap X \neq \emptyset$. *The set of all cluster points of a set* X *will be denoted by* X'.

As we showed in Chapter 3, $\mathbf{a}$ is a cluster point of X if and only if every deleted nbd. of $\mathbf{a}$ contains, in fact, infinitely many points of X.

Now we can give the applicable version of the limit definition.

Definition 4. *If* $X \subset \mathbf{R}^n, f: X \to \mathbf{R}$, $\mathbf{a}$ *is a cluster point of* X, $b \in \mathbf{R}$, *then*

$$\lim_{\mathbf{x} \to \mathbf{a}} f(\mathbf{x}) = b \Leftrightarrow \begin{pmatrix} \textit{for every } N_\varepsilon(b) \Rightarrow \textit{there exists} \\ N_\delta^*(\mathbf{a}) \textit{ such that } \mathbf{x} \in N_\delta^*(\mathbf{a}) \\ \Rightarrow f(\mathbf{x}) \in N_\varepsilon(b) \end{pmatrix}.$$

The *form* is the same, but from one point of view the concept is enormously more complicated than that for a function of a single variable, even when $n = 2$.

Intuitively, the change is produced by the increase in the number of directions available for "a nearby point $\mathbf{x}$ to approach $\mathbf{a}$." For $n = 1$, the number of directions is the reasonably small number 2 (cf. the discussion of one-sided limits in Chapter 3), but for $n \geq 2$ the number of directions is *not finite*. We give a simple illustration of what we are talking about.

Example 1. Let

$$f(x, y) = \frac{xy}{x^2 + y^2}, \qquad (x, y) \neq (0, 0).$$

It is easy to see that f, a rational function is "well-behaved" at every point of its domain. Now the origin is a cluster point of the domain, so we can consider $\lim\limits_{(x, y) \to (0, 0)} f(x, y)$. Notice, by the way, that f has the value 0 at every point of both axes. But, in fact, $\lim\limits_{(x, y) \to (0, 0)} f(x, y)$ fails to exist. To see why this is so, and to point up the role of direction discussed above, suppose we consider points on the line $y = mx$. Then

$$f(x, mx) = \frac{mx^2}{x^2 + m^2 x^2} = \frac{m}{1 + m^2}.$$

Thus, at *every* point (excepting the origin) of the line $y = mx$ the value of f is the same, $\dfrac{m}{1 + m^2}$. Now, by varying m, one can cause $\dfrac{m}{1 + m^2}$ to take on every value between $-\frac{1}{2}$ and $\frac{1}{2}$. This means that *every* $N^*(0, 0)$ is mapped by f into the *entire* interval $[-\frac{1}{2}, \frac{1}{2}]$. Clearly, it is not possible for $\lim\limits_{(x,y) \to (0,0)} f$ to exist (see Figure 2).

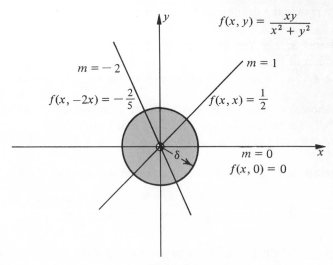

Figure 2

The definition of continuity of a function at a point parallels that for a function of a single variable.

Definition 5. *The function f is **continuous** at a point* **a** *of its domain* ⟺
$$\lim_{\mathbf{x} \to \mathbf{a}} f(\mathbf{x}) = f(\mathbf{a}).$$

Sometimes we shall want to consider functions continuous at every point of a set in its domain. Before stating this formally we describe several different kinds of subsets of $\mathbf{R}^n$.

Definition 6. *Let* $X \subset \mathbf{R}^n$, $\mathbf{a} \in X$. *Then* **a** *is an **interior point** of* $X \Leftrightarrow \exists N(\mathbf{a})$ *which lies entirely in* X. *The set of all interior points of* X *is called the **interior of** X,* $\mathscr{I}(X)$.

Notice that we always have $\mathscr{I}(X) \subset X$.

Definition 7. *Let* $X \subset \mathbf{R}^n$. *Then* X *is **open** ⟺ every point of* X *is an interior point. In symbols*
$$X \text{ open} \Leftrightarrow X = \mathscr{I}(X).$$

A neighborhood of a point in $\mathbf{R}^n$ is an open set. So is $\{(x, y) \in \mathbf{R}^2 \mid x > 0$ and $y > 0\}$. But $\{(x, y) \mid x \geq 0, y \geq 0\}$ is not open. Why? As another illustration consider $X = \{(x, y) \mid x^2 + y^2 \leq 1\}$. It is not hard to see that $\mathscr{I}(X) = \{(x, y) \mid x^2 + y^2 < 1\}$. What about the points in X *not* in the interior of X—the set $\{(x, y) \mid x^2 + y^2 = 1\}$? This set is called the *boundary* of X (sometimes the word "frontier" is used), according to the following definition.

Definition 8. *A point* **a** *is a **boundary point** of a set* $X \subset \mathbf{R}^n \Leftrightarrow$ *every* $N(\mathbf{a})$ *contains a point of* X *and a point not in* X. *The set of all boundary points of* X *is called the **boundary of** X,* $\mathscr{B}(X)$.

Note that the circle $\{(x, y) \mid x^2 + y^2 = 1\}$ consists only of boundary points: $X = \mathscr{B}(X)$. For $X = \{(x, y) \mid x \geq 0$ and $y \geq 0\}$, $\mathscr{B}(X)$ consists of the origin and the positive half of each axis.

Definition 9. *A set* $X \subset \mathbf{R}^n$ *is **closed** ⟺ X contains all its boundary points. In symbols,*
$$X \text{ closed} \Leftrightarrow \mathscr{B}(X) \subset X.$$

The terms "open" and "closed" can be misleading. Some sets are both open and closed (Examples: $\varnothing$ and $\mathbf{R}^n$) and some sets are neither open nor closed (Example: $\{(x, y) \mid x \geq 0, y > 0\}$).

Finally, we need the idea of a *connected set*; intuitively, this simply means the set is in only one piece. Curiously, making a precise definition of the concept becomes a tricky matter. For sets in $\mathbf{R}^n$ we can partially sidestep the difficulty in the following way.

Definition 10. *An open set $X \subset \mathbf{R}^n$ is **connected** $\Leftrightarrow$ any two points of X can be joined by a continuous curve all points of which lie in X.*

Thus, if $X = \{(x, y) \mid x > 0$ and $y > 0\}$, then X is connected; but if $X = \{(x, y) \mid xy > 0\}$, then X is not connected (why?).

Now, we can introduce the type of set toward which we were heading.

Definition 11. *An **open region** in $\mathbf{R}^n$ is an open connected set.*

As examples of open regions in $\mathbf{R}^3$, we have $\{(x, y, z) \mid x > 0, y > 0, z > 0\}$, or $X = \{(x, y, z) \mid x^2 + y^2 + z^2 < 1\}$, the interior of the *unit ball*.

If a function f defined on an open region X is continuous at every point of X, then we say f is *continuous on X*.

EXERCISES

1. Find the domain $X \subset \mathbf{R}^2$ for each of the functions described below.

(a) $f(x, y) = \dfrac{x^2 - y^2}{xy}$.

(b) $f(x, y) = x \log y$.

(c) $f(x, y) = |x| + |y|$.

(d) $f(x, y) = [x] + [y]$.

(e) $f(x, y) = \dfrac{e^{-x} \sin y}{(x - 1)(y - 2)}$.

(f) $f(x, y) = \log (xy - 1)$.

(g) $f(x, y) = \log \sqrt{\dfrac{x^2 - y^2}{x^2 + y^2}}$.

(h) $f(x, y) = \dfrac{x^2 y}{\sqrt{4 - x^2 - y^2}}$.

2. Find the domain $X \subset \mathbf{R}^3$ of the functions described below:

(a) $f(x, y, z) = \sqrt{1 - x^2 - y^2 - z^2}$.

(b) $f(x, y, z) = \dfrac{y^2}{x^2 - z^2}$.

(c) $f(x, y, z) = z \log xy$.

(d) $f(x, y, z) = e^{x/y} \sin z$.

3. For each of the following sets $X \subset \mathbf{R}^2$ find the set X' (cluster points), $\mathscr{I}(X)$ (interior points), and $\mathscr{B}(X)$ (boundary points). Draw a sketch.

(a) $X = \{(x, y) \mid 0 \le x \le 1, 0 \le y \le 1\}$.

(b) $X = \{(x, y) \mid -1 < x \le 1, y = \sqrt{1 - x^2}\}$.

(c) $X = \{(x, y) \mid y = x\}$.

(d) $X = \{(x, y) \mid x > 0, 0 \le y \le x\}$.

(e) $X = \{(x, y) \mid x > 0, y > x^2\}$.

(f) $X = \{(x, y) \mid xy < 0\}$.

4. (a) Which of the sets in Exercise 3 are open?

   (b) Which of the sets in Exercise 3 are closed?

   (c) Which of the sets in Exercise 3 are open and connected?

5. Let $f(x, y) = \dfrac{x^2 - y^2}{x^2 + y^2}$, $(x, y) \neq (0, 0)$. What can be said about $\lim\limits_{(x,y)\to(0,0)} f(x, y)$? Why?

6. Let $f(x, y) = \dfrac{x^2 y^2}{x^2 + y^2}$, $(x, y) \neq (0, 0)$. What can be said about $\lim\limits_{(x,y)\to(0,0)} f(x, y)$? Why?

7. For each of the functions of Exercise 1, give the subset of the domain at which the function is continuous.

8. Consider the function of Example 1,

$$f(x, y) = \frac{xy}{x^2 + y^2}, \qquad (x, y) \neq (0, 0).$$

For each of the following values of c find $\{(x, y) \mid f(x, y) = c\}$. These sets are called *contour curves* for f.

   (a) $c = 0$.   (b) $c = \frac{1}{2}$.   (c) $c = \frac{1}{4}$.

9. See Exercise 8. Describe, in general, the nature of the contour curves for each of the following functions:

   (a) $f(x, y) = x^2 + y^2$.
   (b) $f(x, y) = x^2 - y^2$.   (d) $f(x, y) = \dfrac{x - y}{x + y}$.
   (c) $f(x, y) = x^2 - y$.

10. We have defined a closed set to be one which contains all its boundary points. We could just as well have defined it to be a set which contains all its cluster points. Prove this; i.e., prove

$$\mathscr{B}(X) \subset X \Leftrightarrow X' \subset X. \tag{*}$$

[*Hints.* (1) For $\Rightarrow$. Suppose $x_0 \in X'$, but $x_0 \notin X$. Since every $N^*(x_0)$ contains a point of X, every $N(x_0)$ contains a point of X and a point not in X. Why? Now use the hypothesis.

(2) For $\Leftarrow$. Suppose $x_0 \in \mathscr{B}(X)$, but $x_0 \notin X$. Every $N(x_0)$ must contain a point of X, and if $x_0 \notin X$ this cannot be x_0; thus every $N^*(x_0)$ also contains a point of X. This says $x_0 \in X'$. Why? Now use the hypothesis.]

11. Does it follow from the assertion (*) of Exercise 10 that $\mathscr{B}(X) = X'$? Example.

12. Can you find a set X in $\mathbf{R}$ such that $X' = X$? A set with this property is said to be *perfect*. Find a perfect set in $\mathbf{R}^2$.

13. Prove the assertion about cluster points made immediately after Definition 3. [*Hint.* See Theorem 3.2 and its proof.]

13.2   Partial Derivatives

An attempt to parallel the definition of derivative for a function of a single variable would go something like this for a function f of two variables. Consider two points in the domain of f: (x_0, y_0) and a "nearby" point $(x_0 + h, y_0 + k)$; divide the difference in the functional values at these points by the distance between the points, and consider the limit of this ratio as the distance goes to 0 (see Figure 3). The expression would be

$$\lim_{(h, k) \to (0, 0)} \frac{f(x_0 + h, y_0 + k) - f(x_0, y_0)}{\sqrt{h^2 + k^2}}.$$

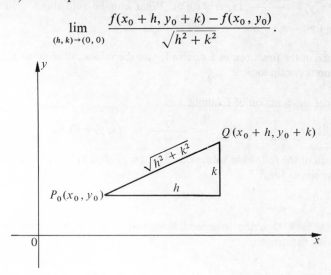

Figure 3

Unfortunately, this limit usually fails to exist, even for the simplest functions. Consider, for example,

$$f(x, y) = xy,$$

a polynomial of degree two in x and y—surely a well-behaved function. The procedure just described, applied to this f, would lead to

$$\frac{f(x_0 + h, y_0 + k) - f(x_0, y_0)}{\sqrt{h^2 + k^2}} = \frac{(x_0 + h)(y_0 + k) - x_0 y_0}{\sqrt{h^2 + k^2}}$$

$$= \frac{y_0 h + x_0 k + hk}{\sqrt{h^2 + k^2}} = r(h, k).$$

We show that r fails to have a limit by considering various ways in which $(h, k) \to (0, 0)$ (see Figure 4).

(i) Let $h > 0$, $k = 0$. Then

$$r(h, k) = r(h, 0) = \frac{y_0 h}{\sqrt{h^2}} = \frac{y_0 h}{h} = y_0 \to y_0.$$

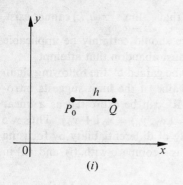

(i)

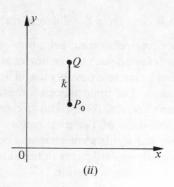

(ii)

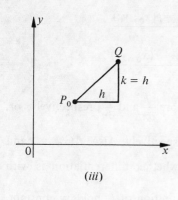

(iii)

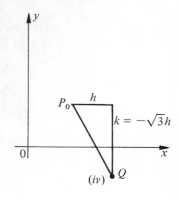

(iv)

Figure 4

(ii) If $h = 0$, $k > 0$, then

$$r(h, k) = r(0, k) = \frac{x_0 k}{\sqrt{k^2}} = x_0 \to x_0.$$

(iii) If $h = k > 0$, then

$$r(h, k) = r(h, h) = \frac{y_0 h + x_0 h + h^2}{\sqrt{2h^2}} = \frac{y_0 + x_0 + h}{\sqrt{2}} \to \frac{y_0 + x_0}{\sqrt{2}}.$$

(iv) If $k = -\sqrt{3}h$, $h > 0$, then

$$r(h, k) = r(h, -\sqrt{3}h) = \frac{y_0 h - \sqrt{3}\, h x_0 - \sqrt{3}\, h^2}{\sqrt{h^2 + 3h^2}}$$

$$= \frac{y_0 - \sqrt{3}\, x_0 + \sqrt{3}\, h}{2}$$

$$\to \frac{y_0 - \sqrt{3}\, x_0}{2}.$$

It is clear from the different results obtained that $\lim\limits_{(h,\,k)\to(0,\,0)} r(h,k)$ cannot exist. Since any reasonable definition of a derivative should certainly be applicable to a function such as the one considered, we must abandon that attempt.

But a clue to a possibly useful approach may be gained by the following chain of ideas. The importance of *direction* on the value of the limit suggests introducing *vectors*. As we know, every vector in $\mathbf{R}^2$ can be expressed as a linear combination of the unit vectors $\mathbf{i}$ and $\mathbf{j}: \mathbf{v} = (x_0, y_0) = x_0\mathbf{i} + y_0\mathbf{j}$. Thus we lower our sights somewhat and begin our study of differentiability by focusing attention on derivatives in the $\mathbf{i}$ and $\mathbf{j}$ directions—compare with (i) and (ii) in the preceding discussion.

Definition 12. *Let f be defined on $X \subset \mathbf{R}^2$ and let $(x_0, y_0) \in X$. The **partial derivatives** with respect to x and y, respectively, are defined by*

$$f_x(x_0, y_0) = \lim_{h\to 0} \frac{f(x_0 + h, y_0) - f(x_0, y_0)}{h},$$

$$f_y(x_0, y_0) = \lim_{k\to 0} \frac{f(x_0, y_0 + k) - f(x_0, y_0)}{k}.$$

Other notations for $f_x(x_0, y_0)$ and $f_y(x_0, y_0)$ are $\dfrac{\partial f}{\partial x}$ and $\dfrac{\partial f}{\partial y}$, respectively, or, more completely, $\dfrac{\partial f(x_0, y_0)}{\partial x}$ and $\dfrac{\partial f(x_0, y_0)}{\partial y}$, respectively. Also, $f_1(x_0, y_0)$ and $f_2(x_0, y_0)$ are used, the subscripts indicating whether differentiation is with respect to the first or second variable.

One advantage of these forms is this: the definition of f_x holds y constant, and this means that the calculation of f_x can be made by means of the differentiation theorems already found for a function of a single variable. Thus, if f is defined by the formula

$$f(x, y) = x^2 y + \sin(x + y) + e^{xy^2}, \tag{9}$$

then

$$f_x(x, y) = 2xy + \cos(x + y) + y^2 e^{xy^2}. \tag{10}$$

Similarly, the definition of f_y involves holding x fixed or constant. We have, then,

$$f_y(x, y) = x^2 + \cos(x + y) + 2xy\, e^{xy^2}. \tag{11}$$

The partial derivatives for functions of 3 or more variables are defined and calculated in a similar way. Thus, if f is defined on a set $X \subset \mathbf{R}^3$, and $(x_0, y_0, z_0) \in X$, then

$$f_1(x_0, y_0, z_0) = \frac{\partial f}{\partial x} = f_x(x_0, y_0, z_0) = \lim_{h\to 0} \frac{f(x_0 + h, y_0, z_0) - f(x_0, y_0, z_0)}{h}$$

$$f_2(x_0, y_0, z_0) = \frac{\partial f}{\partial y} = f_y(x_0, y_0, z_0) = \lim_{k\to 0} \frac{f(x_0, y_0 + k, z_0) - f(x_0, y_0, z_0)}{k}$$

$$f_3(x_0, y_0, z_0) = \frac{\partial f}{\partial z} = f_z(x_0, y_0, z_0) = \lim_{l\to 0} \frac{f(x_0, y_0, z_0 + l) - f(x_0, y_0, z_0)}{l}.$$

Consider, for example, the function f defined by

$$f(x, y, z) = x^2 z + \log (y^2 - z) - x \, e^{yz}. \tag{12}$$

We can easily calculate that

$$f_x(x, y, z) = 2xz - e^{yz}, \tag{13}$$

$$f_y(x, y, z) = \frac{2y}{y^2 - z} - xz \, e^{yz}, \tag{14}$$

$$f_z(x, y, z) = x^2 - \frac{1}{y^2 - z} - xy \, e^{yz}. \tag{15}$$

Implicit differentiation was introduced in Chapter 4 for a function of a single variable. The need for it can arise in the present context; there is no essential difference in the technique.

Example 2. The equation of the unit sphere in three space, $x^2 + y^2 + z^2 = 1$ can be used to define z as a function of x and y (there are, in fact, two such functions—one for the northern hemisphere, $z \geq 0$, and one for the southern). If we let $z = f(x, y)$, then we can calculate $\dfrac{\partial f}{\partial x}$ as follows:

$$x^2 + y^2 + (f(x, y))^2 = 1;$$

differentiating with respect to x,

$$2x + 2f(x, y) \frac{\partial f}{\partial x} = 0,$$

and solving for $\dfrac{\partial f}{\partial x}$:

$$\frac{\partial f}{\partial x} = \frac{-x}{f(x, y)} = \frac{-x}{z}.$$

In a similar way one finds

$$\frac{\partial f}{\partial y} = \frac{-y}{z}.$$

Of course, in this simple example, one could easily solve for z and find $\dfrac{\partial z}{\partial x}$ directly. But that procedure is not always available.

Example 3. Assuming

$$\sin (x + z) - x \, e^{yz} = 0$$

defines z as a function f of x and y, we find $\dfrac{\partial z}{\partial x} = f_x$.

In practice, one does not usually replace z by $f(x, y)$ as we did in Example 2.

Thus, the usual technique is as follows: we differentiate with respect to x, treating z as a function of x and y, holding y fixed;

$$\cos(x+z)\left[1+\frac{\partial z}{\partial x}\right] - \left[x\,e^{yz}\left(y\frac{\partial z}{\partial x}\right) + e^{yz}\cdot 1\right] = 0.$$

Solving for $\dfrac{\partial z}{\partial x}$ is now a matter of algebra:

$$\frac{\partial z}{\partial x} = \frac{\cos(x+z) - e^{yz}}{xy\,e^{yz} - \cos(x+z)}.$$

Of course $\dfrac{\partial z}{\partial y}$ can be found in a similar way. We leave this as an exercise.

Because of the rather special formulation of the definitions of the partial derivatives, interpretations of them are immediately available. First of all, the essential fact about *every* derivative is that it is a *measure of rate of change*. The derivatives f_x and f_y both measure the rate of change of the function f; specifically, $f_x(x_0, y_0)$ is a measure of the rate of change of f in the x-direction at (x_0, y_0) and $f_y(x_0, y_0)$ is a measure of the rate of change of f in the y-direction at (x_0, y_0). (See Section 13.5 where this concept is generalized.)

Secondly, we consider the geometric interpretation as follows. The graph of f is the set of points

$$\{(x, y, z)\,|\,z = f(x, y), (x,y) \in \text{domain of } f\},$$

ordinarily a surface $\mathscr{S}$ in three space. Let (x_0, y_0) be a point at which f_x and f_y exist and let $(x_0, y_0, z_0 = f(x_0, y_0))$ be a point P_0 on $\mathscr{S}$. In calculating $f_x(x_0, y_0)$, y is held fixed at y_0. Now the equation $y = y_0$ is a plane (parallel to the zx-plane) which will cut $\mathscr{S}$ in a curve $\mathscr{C}_1$. The number $f_x(x_0, y_0)$ is the slope of the tangent line to this curve at P_0. Similarly, in calculating $f_y(x_0, y_0)$ x is held fixed at x_0. The plane $x = x_0$ will cut $\mathscr{S}$ in a curve $\mathscr{C}_2$; the slope of the tangent line to $\mathscr{C}_2$ at P_0 is $f_y(x_0, y_0)$ (see Figure 5).

In general, of course, these two tangent lines at P_0 will determine a tangent plane. But this is not always the case, and because of this fact we must defer our discussion of the tangent plane until after the important theorem of the next section.

We conclude this section with two words of caution.

The first concerns the notation $\dfrac{\partial f}{\partial x}$, an obvious modification of the Leibniz notation $\dfrac{dy}{dx}$ used extensively for a function of a single variable. The cautionary remark concerns the fact that, by suitably defining differentials dy and dx, we could think of $\dfrac{dy}{dx}$ as a ratio of these differentials; although we shall later define a differential for functions of several variables, *we shall not be able to consider* $\dfrac{\partial f}{\partial x}$ *and* $\dfrac{\partial f}{\partial y}$ *as fractions*, as the notation might suggest.

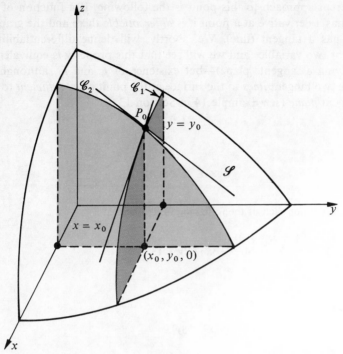

Figure 5

The second point is a reminder that the definitions of partial derivatives involved, in a way, a retrenchment, a lowering of our aims. As a consequence, existence of the partial derivatives is not as strong a condition as existence of the derivative for a function of a single variable. For example, it is a basic theorem that $f'(x_0)$ exists $\Rightarrow f$ continuous at x_0. The analogous proposition for a function of two variables would be

$$\left.\begin{array}{c} f_x(x_0, y_0) \\[2mm] \text{exist} \\[2mm] f_y(x_0, y_0) \end{array}\right\} \Rightarrow f \text{ continuous at } (x_0, y_0).$$

This proposition is false. As a counterexample, we use a slightly modified version of the function of Example 1,

$$\left\{\begin{array}{ll} f(x, y) = \dfrac{xy}{x^2 + y^2}, & (x, y) \neq (0, 0) \\[3mm] f(0, 0) = 0 \end{array}\right\}.$$

It is easy to see that $f(x, 0) = 0$ for every x, and $f(0, y) = 0$ for every y. From this remark it readily follows that

$$f_x(0, 0) = f_y(0, 0) = 0.$$

But we already know (Example 1) that f is not continuous at $(0, 0)$.

A different approach to this point is the following. If a function of a single variable has a derivative at a point it is *differentiable* there and the graph of the function has a tangent (line). We, shortly, will define differentiability for a function of two variables and we will see that this property is equivalent to the graph having a tangent (plane)—but existence of f_x and f_y, although it does guarantee two tangent *lines* to the surface at the point is *not sufficient* to guarantee a tangent *plane* (see Example 14 in Section 13.6).

EXERCISES

1. Find f_x and f_y for each of the following functions.

   (a) $f(x, y) = x^2 y - 3xy + 4y^3$.

   (b) $f(x, y) = x^2 - 2xy + 4y^2 - 3x + 2y - 13$.

   (c) $f(x, y) = \tan^{-1} \dfrac{y}{x} + e^{x^2 + y^2}$.

   (d) $f(x, y) = \dfrac{x - 2y}{3x + y^2}$.

   (e) $f(x, y) = \sin(2x - y) + \log(x^2 + 3y)$.

   (f) $f(x, y) = e^{xy} + \sin^{-1} \dfrac{x}{y}$.

2. Find f_1, f_2, and f_3 for each of the following functions.

   (a) $f(x, y, z) = x^2 yz - 3xy^2 z + 7xyz^2 + xyz - 2z^3$.

   (b) $f(x, y, z) = x^2 + 3xy + 2y^2$.

   (c) $f(x, y, z) = z$.

   (d) $f(x, y, z) = \cos x \cos y + \sin x \sin z - e^{xyz}$.

   (e) $f(x, y, z) = \log \sqrt{x^2 + y^2 + z^2} - \tan\left(\dfrac{xy}{z}\right)$.

3. Find $\dfrac{\partial z}{\partial x}$ and $\dfrac{\partial z}{\partial y}$, assuming each of the following relations defines z as a function of x and y.

   (a) $x^2 + y^2 + z^2 = 4$.

   (b) $xy - z^2 = 1$.

   (c) $\tan^{-1} \dfrac{y}{x} + x^2 \sin yz - e^{yz} = 0$.

   (d) $x^2 + y^2 - z^2 = 1$.

   (e) $\dfrac{z - y}{x} + \dfrac{x - z}{y} + \dfrac{y - x}{z} = 2$.

   (f) $\sin \dfrac{x^2 + y^2}{y^2 + z^2} + \log(x^2 + y^2 + z^2) = 3$.

4. Find $\dfrac{\partial w}{\partial x}, \dfrac{\partial w}{\partial y}, \dfrac{\partial w}{\partial z}$, assuming the following relations define w as functions of x, y, and z.

   (a) $w^2xy^2z + 2wx^2yz^3 - 5wxyz^3 = 1$.
   (b) $\sin wx + \log(w^2 + z) - e^{wy} = 0$.

5. Calculate $\dfrac{\partial z}{\partial y}$ from the relation defined in Example 3.

13.3 The Fundamental Increment Theorem

As we pointed out in the last paragraph of the preceding section, mere existence of the partial derivatives is not as strong a condition as existence of *the* derivative for a function of a single variable. In this section we prove a theorem which gives us the extra power needed to develop the theory further. As a careful reading of the remainder of this chapter will show, the theorem of this chapter is basic to almost everything that follows. Consequently, it cannot be too strongly stressed how essential it is for the student to have a good comprehension of this proposition.

Our procedure will depart from the usual in developing the main theorem. Instead of stating the assertion formally, we will indicate the conclusion we would like to obtain, then work toward this, keeping a record of the assumptions necessary to continue on our path. When we have achieved the desired conclusion we will make a complete statement of the theorem.

As an indication of the result we have in mind, we recall that at the beginning of Section 4.2 we made the following assertion:

$$f'(x_0) \text{ exists} \Rightarrow f(x_0 + h) - f(x_0) = f'(x_0)h + \varepsilon h, \lim_{h \to 0} \varepsilon = 0. \qquad (16)$$

This says that if f is differentiable at x_0 (i.e., $f'(x_0)$ exists), then the increment in f, $f(x_0 + h) - f(x_0)$, can be expressed as the sum of two terms, one involving $f'(x_0)$ and the other being very small if h is small. Thus, for small h, $f'(x_0)h$ is an approximation to the increment in f.

Our aim now is the following. We have a function f of two variables, points $P_0(x_0, y_0)$ and $Q(x_0 + h, y_0 + k)$ in the domain of f. We define the *increment* in f to be

$$\Delta f = f(x_0 + h, y_0 + k) - f(x_0, y_0). \qquad (17)$$

We want to obtain a statement for f analogous to that in (16). In particular, we would like to approximate f by terms involving $f_x(x_0, y_0)$ and $f_y(x_0, y_0)$. As the natural starting point, Eq. (17), does not give any clue about introducing either f_x or f_y, we create the needed opportunity by bringing in the value of f at either of the points $P_2(x_0, y_0 + k)$ or $P_1(x_0 + h, y_0)$ (see Figure 6).

Thus, choosing P_2, we have

$$\Delta f = [f(x_0 + h, y_0 + k) - f(x_0, y_0 + k)] + [f(x_0, y_0 + k) - f(x_0, y_0)]. \qquad (18)$$

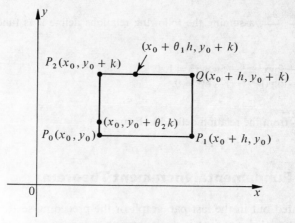

(This is not an obvious step; on the other hand, it is not new—similar tricks have been used frequently in the past).

We now observe that the ordinate, $y_0 + k$, is the same at both points in the first brackets on the right of (18). In order to exploit this we temporarily introduce a new function: let

$$g(x) = f(x, y_0 + k) \quad \text{for} \quad x_0 \le x \le x_0 + h.$$

(We see, in fact, that g is simply f restricted to the line segment $P_2\,Q$ in Figure 6.) Notice that $g'(x) = f_x(x, y_0 + k) = f_1(x, y_0 + k)$. Now if we assume that f_x exists on $x_0 \le x \le x_0 + h$, then we can conclude that g is continuous and g' exists on that interval, enabling us to apply the Mean Value Theorem. Actually, we make our first assumption stronger than necessary.

Hypothesis 1. *The derivative f_x exists at every point on and within the rectangle* $P_0 P_1 Q P_2$, *which we shall denote by* $\boxed{P_0\,Q}$.

The Mean Value Theorem now gives

$$g(x_0 + h) - g(x_0) = g'(x_0 + \theta_1 h)h, \qquad 0 < \theta_1 < 1,$$

or

$$f(x_0 + h, y_0 + k) - f(x_0, y_0 + k) = f_x(x_0 + \theta_1 h, y_0 + k)h, \qquad (19)$$

where $0 < \theta_1 < 1$ (see Figure 6).

In a precisely similar fashion, by defining

$$G(y) = f(x_0, y) \quad \text{for} \quad y_0 \le y \le y_0 + k,$$

and noting that $G'(y) = f_y(x_0, y)$, we can apply the Mean Value Theorem to G, providing that we assume that f is suitably continuous. We assume more than is necessary.

Hypothesis 2. f_y *exists on* $\boxed{P_0\,G}$.

We can then write

$$G(y_0 + k) - G(y_0) = G'(y_0 + \theta_2 k)k, \qquad 0 < \theta_2 < 1,$$

or

$$f(x_0, y_0 + k) - f(x_0, y_0) = f_y(x_0, y_0 + \theta_2 k)k, \qquad 0 < \theta_2 < 1; \qquad (20)$$

(see Figure 6).

Substituting from (19) and (20) into (18) gives us, then,

$$\Delta f = f_x(x_0 + \theta_1 h, y_0 + k)h + f_y(x_0, y_0 + \theta_2 k)k, \qquad (21)$$

where $0 < \theta_i < 1$, $i = 1, 2$.

This equation does express Δf in terms of f_x and f_y, but it was our stated aim to have these derivatives evaluated at P_0. Now, if h and k are small, then all points in $\boxed{P_0\,Q}$ are close to P_0. This means we can call on continuity of f_x and f_y to justify saying

$$
\begin{aligned}
f_x(x_0 + \theta_1 h, y_0 + k) &= f_x(x_0, y_0) + \varepsilon_1 \\
f_y(x_0, y_0 + \theta_2 k) &= f_y(x_0, y_0) + \varepsilon_2, \qquad \lim_{(h,\,k)\to(0,\,0)} \varepsilon_i = 0.
\end{aligned}
\qquad (22)
$$

These statements can almost be made if we simply assume that f_x and f_y are continuous at (x_0, y_0). However, we would then not be able to choose Q with complete freedom. Thus we again make a somewhat stronger hypothesis than is required.

Hypothesis 3. f_x *and* f_y *are continuous on* $\boxed{P_0\,Q}$.

If we substitute from (22) into (21) we obtain

$$\Delta f = f_x(x_0, y_0)h + f_y(x_0, y_0)k + \varepsilon_1 h + \varepsilon_2 k, \qquad \lim_{(h,\,k)\to(0,\,0)} \varepsilon_i = 0.$$

We see that this is completely equivalent to the expression for Δf in (16), and we can now state our theorem.

Theorem 1 (*The Fundamental Increment Theorem*). *Let* $f: X \to \mathbf{R}$, $X \subset \mathbf{R}^2$, *and let* $\boxed{P_0\,Q}$ *denote the closed rectangle with vertices* $P_0(x_0, y_0)$, $P_1(x_0 + h, y_0)$, $P_2(x_0, y_0 + k)$, $Q(x_0 + h, y_0 + k)$. *We assume that* f_x *and* f_y *exist and are continuous on* $\boxed{P_0\,Q}$. *Then, letting* $\Delta f = f(x_0 + h, y_0 + k) - f(x_0, y_0)$, *we have*

$$\Delta f = f_x(x_0, y_0)h + f_y(x_0, y_0)k + \varepsilon_1 h + \varepsilon_2 k, \qquad \lim_{(h,\,k)\to(0,\,0)} \varepsilon_i = 0. \qquad (23)$$

It is fairly obvious that the hypotheses of Theorem 1 are stronger than required, but the fact is they are usually satisfied by the functions with which we shall be working.

Before illustrating Theorem 1, we note an immediate corollary: existence *and continuity of* f_x *and* f_y $\Rightarrow$ *continuity of* f (cf. the discussion at the end of the preceding section). More precisely this assertion is as follows.

Theorem 2. *If* $X \subset \mathbf{R}^2$, $f: X \to \mathbf{R}$, f_x *and* f_y *are continuous on an open region* $G \subset X$, *then* f *is continuous on* G.

Proof. We take $P_0 \in G$ and choose h, k so that $\boxed{P_0\,Q} \subset G$. Then, by Theorem 1,

$$f(x_0 + h, y_0 + k) - f(x_0, y_0) = f_x(x_0, y_0)h + f_y(x_0, y_0)k + \varepsilon_1 h + \varepsilon_2 k,$$

where $\lim_{(h,k)\to(0,0)} \varepsilon_i = 0$, $i = 1, 2$. From this we easily see that

$$\lim_{(h,k)\to(0,0)} [f(x_0 + h, y_0 + k) - f(x_0, y_0)] = 0,$$

i.e., f is continuous at (x_0, y_0). Since this was an arbitrary point in G, f is continuous on G. ∎

Example 4. Let f be defined by

$$f(x, y) = x^2 + 2xy - 3y^2.$$

Then

$$f(x + h, y + k) = (x + h)^2 + 2(x + h)(y + k) - 3(y + k)^2$$

and

$$\Delta f = 2hx + h^2 + 2hy + 2kx + 2hk - 6yk - 3k^2;$$

rearranging, we have

$$\Delta f = (2x + 2y)h + (2x - 6y)k + h^2 + 2hk - 3k^2.$$

The decomposition of the final three terms into $\varepsilon_1 h + \varepsilon_2 k$ can be made in various ways, one of which is

$$\Delta f = f_x(x, y)h + f_y(x, y)k + \underbrace{(h + k)}_{\varepsilon_1}h + \underbrace{(h - 3k)}_{\varepsilon_2}k.$$

It should be clear that statements analogous to Theorems 1 and 2 hold for functions of more than two variables. For future reference we state the three variable version of Theorem 1.

Theorem 1[3]. *Let* $X \subset \mathbf{R}^3$, $f: X \to \mathbf{R}$, *and let* $\boxed{P_0\,Q}$ *denote the closed rectangular parallelpiped with sides parallel to the axes and with* $P_0\,Q$ *as one diagonal, where* $P_0(x_0, y_0, z_0)$ *and* $Q(x_0 + h, y_0 + k, z_0 + l)$. *Assume* f_x, f_y, *and* f_z *are continuous on* $\boxed{P_0\,Q}$. *Then, letting*

$$\Delta f = f(x_0 + h, y_0 + k, z_0 + l) - f(x_0, y_0, z_0),$$

we can write

$$\Delta f = f_x(x_0, y_0, z_0)h + f_y(x_0, y_0, z_0)k + f_z(x_0, y_0, z_0)l$$
$$+ \varepsilon_1 h + \varepsilon_2 k + \varepsilon_3 l, \tag{24}$$

where $\lim_{(h,k,l)\to(0,0,0)} \varepsilon_i = 0$, $i = 1, 2, 3$.

An immediate application of Theorem 1 is the use of the first two terms of (23) as an approximation of Δf. For if h and k are " small," then the expression $\varepsilon_1 h + \varepsilon_2 k$ will be " very small " and the major or *principal part* of Δf is contained in the first two terms. In this context it is perhaps more suggestive to replace h and k by Δx and Δy, respectively, interpreted as increments in x and y, respectively. In addition, we write

$$\Delta f_L = f_x(x_0, y_0)\, \Delta x + f_y(x_0, y_0)\, \Delta y, \tag{25}$$

the subscript "L" denoting the fact (as we shall see later) that this is the *linear* part of Δf. Thus we have, for "small" Δx and Δy.

$$\Delta f \approx \Delta f_L. \tag{26}$$

Clearly, similar comments, *mutatis mutandis*, apply to Theorem 1[3].
We give a few illustrations of this application.

Example 5. The dimensions of a room are measured as $20 \times 15 \times 8$ feet, the measurements being correct to 0.01 foot. If the volume is calculated from these measurements, what is the maximum possible error in the volume?
We use the function

$$V = V(x, y, z) = xyz.$$

The *exact* value of the maximum possible error is ΔV (which, in this case, would be very easy to find—see Exercise 2), but we shall settle for the approximation ΔV_L. This is

$$\Delta V_L = V_x\, \Delta x + V_y\, \Delta y + V_z\, \Delta z$$

$$= yz\, \Delta x + xz\, \Delta y + xy\, \Delta z.$$

From the information given above, we conclude that

$$|\Delta x| \leq 0.01,\ |\Delta y| \leq 0.01,\ |\Delta z| \leq 0.01;$$

thus

$$|\Delta V_L| \leq (yz + xz + xy)(0.01)$$

$$= (120 + 160 + 300)(0.01)$$

$$= 5.80 \text{ cubic feet}$$

Frequently the *relative error* is more informative than the possible error. This is defined to be the ratio of the possible error to the measurement itself.
In the present case the numerical value is easily found, but we take time to show the *form* the expression for the relative error takes:

$$\frac{\Delta V_L}{V} = \frac{yz\, \Delta x + xz\, \Delta y + xy\, \Delta z}{xyz} = \frac{\Delta x}{x} + \frac{\Delta y}{y} + \frac{\Delta z}{z}.$$

In other words, *the relative error in the product is the sum of the relative errors.*

Example 6. The area K of a triangle can be found from the formula

$$K = \tfrac{1}{2}bc \sin A,$$

b and c representing the lengths of the sides adjacent to angle A. If $b = 5$ feet, $c = 3$ feet, $A = 45°$, and if b and c are measured to the nearest 0.1 foot, A is measured to the nearest degree, find the maximum possible error in the area K.

Again the value sought would be given by ΔK, but in this case it is not trivial to find this exactly. Thus the use of ΔK_L as an approximation makes good sense; for ΔK_L is easily found:

$$\Delta K_L = \tfrac{1}{2}bc \cos A \; \Delta A + \tfrac{1}{2}c \sin A \; \Delta b + \tfrac{1}{2}b \sin A \; \Delta c.$$

Of course we must translate the values for A and ΔA to radians. We have, then,

$$|\Delta b| \le 0.1, \qquad |\Delta c| \le 0.1, \qquad |\Delta A| \le \frac{\pi}{180},$$

$$\sin A = \cos A = \frac{\sqrt{2}}{2}.$$

Consequently,

$$\Delta K \approx \Delta K_L = \frac{1}{2} \cdot \frac{\sqrt{2}}{2}\left(15 \cdot \frac{\pi}{180} + 3(0.1) + 5(0.1)\right)$$

$$= \frac{\sqrt{2}}{4}\left(\frac{\pi}{12} + 0.8\right) \approx 0.375 \text{ sq ft.}$$

EXERCISES

1. Illustrate Theorem 1 (1^3) as was done in Example 4—for each of the following functions

   (a) $f(x, y) = xy$.   (b) $f(x, y) = 2x^2 + 3xy - 5y^2$.   (c) $f(x, y, z) = 3yz^2 - 2xz$.

2. This refers to Example 5. Calculate the maximum value of $|\Delta V|$ and compare with the maximum value of $|\Delta V_L|$ found in the example.

3. This refers to Example 6. Show that the relative error in K can be expressed as

$$\frac{\Delta K_L}{K} = \left(\frac{A}{\tan A}\right)\frac{\Delta A}{A} + \frac{\Delta b}{b} + \frac{\Delta c}{c}.$$

4. The outside measurements of a wooden box are $2 \times 2 \times 6$ feet. If the lumber used is $\tfrac{1}{2}$ inch thick, what is the volume of the interior?

   (a) Approximately.   (b) Exactly.

5. The radius and height of a right circular cylinder are measured as 5 and 20 feet, respectively, the measurements being correct to the nearest 0.1 foot. Find (approximately) the maximum possible error in computing the volume of the cylinder. What is the relative error?

6. Ohm's law can be written as

$$I = \frac{E}{R},$$

where I is the current in amperes, E is the electromotive force in volts, and R is the resistance in ohms.

(a) If at first $E = 120$ volts, $R = 30$ ohms, but then the voltage drops to 115 and the resistance increases to 32 ohms, by how much does the current change?

(b) Find an expression for the relative error in I.

7. If two resistances R_1 and R_2 (in ohms) are hooked up in parallel, the resistance of the circuit is R, where

$$\frac{1}{R} = \frac{1}{R_1} + \frac{1}{R_2}.$$

Find the relative error in R if the maximum relative error in R_1 and R_2 is 0.01.

8. Let f be a first degree polynomial in x and y: $f(x, y) = ax + by + c$. Prove that

$$\Delta f = \Delta f_L.$$

9. The conclusion [Eq. (23)] of Theorem 1 can be obtained with the following hypotheses:
(1) f_x and f_y exist in $N(x_0, y_0)$.
(2) f_x is continuous at (x_0, y_0).

(a) Compare these hypotheses with those of Theorem 1.

(b) Prove the assertion.

[*Hints.* (1) First, $Q(x + h, y + k)$ must be chosen "sufficiently close" to $P_0(x_0, y_0)$—this restriction is because f_x is assumed continuous only at (x_0, y_0).

(2) Second, use the equivalent of (16), for partial derivatives, on (18), once for f_x, once for f_y. This gives

$$\Delta f = f_x(x_0, y_0 + k)h + \varepsilon_1' h + f_y(x_0, y_0)k + \varepsilon_2 k.$$

(3) Now, use the continuity of f_x at (x_0, y_0).]

13.4 Differentiability

We begin this section by recalling that a function of a single variable is *differentiable* at a point provided that the derivative exists there. We also remark that the implication expressed in (16) at the beginning of the preceding section does, in fact, go both ways. Thus, in symbols, we have

$$f \text{ differentiable at } x_0 \Leftrightarrow f'(x_0) \text{ exists,}$$

$$f'(x_0) \text{ exists} \Leftrightarrow f(x_0 + h) - f(x_0) = f'(x_0)h + \varepsilon h, \qquad \lim_{h \to 0} \varepsilon = 0.\} \tag{27}$$

Now we have already made it clear that, for a function of two or more variables, mere existence of the partial derivatives is not as strong a condition as is existence of the derivative for a function of a single variable, and thus we have delayed defining differentiability for such functions. But consideration of (27) and (23) suggests how to make this definition.

Definition 13. *Let* $X \subset \mathbf{R}^2$, $f: X \to \mathbf{R}$, $(x_0, y_0) \in X$. *Then* f *is* **differentiable** *at* $(x_0, y_0) \Leftrightarrow$ *there exist numbers* a *and* b, *and there exists* $N(x_0, y_0)$ *such that for all* h, k *with* $(x_0 + h, y_0 + k) \in N(x_0, y_0)$ *it is true that*

$$f(x_0 + h, y_0 + k) - f(x_0, y_0) = ah + bk + \varepsilon_1 h + \varepsilon_2 k, \tag{28}$$

where $\lim_{(h, k) \to (0, 0)} \varepsilon_i = 0, \ i = 1, 2.$

To be perfectly explicit, we remark that a and b are independent of h and k (see Theorem 3 below) but that ε_1 and ε_2 *do* depend upon h and k.

The relation between Theorem 1 and Definition 13 will now be made clear.

Theorem 3. *If* f *is differentiable at* (x_0, y_0) *then the partial derivatives exist there and*

$$a = f_x(x_0, y_0), \qquad b = f_y(x_0, y_0).$$

Proof. We begin with (28), but we take $k = 0$;

$$f(x_0 + h, y_0) - f(x_0, y_0) = ah + \varepsilon_1 h, \qquad \lim_{h \to 0} \varepsilon_1 = 0.$$

If, now, we divide by h and then take the limit as $h \to 0$, we find

$$f_x(x_0, y_0) = \lim_{h \to 0} \frac{f(x_0 + h, y_0) - f(x_0, y_0)}{h} = a.$$

Similarly, by taking $h = 0$, we can show that

$$f_y(x_0, y_0) = \lim_{k \to 0} \frac{f(x, y_0 + k) - f(x_0, y_0)}{k} = b. \quad \blacksquare$$

It takes only a glance at the proof of Theorem 2 to see that it remains valid if the hypothesis there is replaced by the hypothesis of differentiability at (x_0, y_0). Thus we have the following assertion.

Theorem 4. *If* $X \subset \mathbf{R}^2$, $f: X \to \mathbf{R}$, $(x_0, y_0) \in X$, *then*

$$f \text{ differentiable at } (x_0, y_0) \Rightarrow f \text{ continuous at } (x_0, y_0).$$

Moreover, a comparison of Theorem 1 and Definition 13 gives us immediately the following proposition.

Theorem 5. *If* $f: X \to \mathbf{R}$, $X \subset \mathbf{R}^2$; *if* $(x_0, y_0) \in X$, *and if* $\exists N(x_0, y_0)$ *within which* f_x *and* f_y *are continuous, then* f *is differentiable at* (x_0, y_0).

Fom now on we make the blanket assumption that, *unless otherwise specified, all functions will have continuous partial derivatives*. The purpose, of course, of this assumption is to assure differentiability.

It may be well to point out that the two properties mentioned in the preceding paragraph are not equivalent. If a function *f* has continuous derivatives then *f* is differentiable; but not conversely. This is not, however, the time to go into that.

We now look at the statement of differentiability from a slightly different point of view. We have

$$f \text{ differentiable} \atop \text{at } (x_0, y_0) \Bigg\} \Rightarrow$$

$$f(x_0 + h, y_0 + k) - f(x_0, y_0) = [f_x(x_0, y_0)h + f_y(x_0, y_0)k] + [\varepsilon_1 h + \varepsilon_2 k],$$

$$\text{where} \quad \lim_{(h, k) \to (0, 0)} \varepsilon_i = 0. \quad (29)$$

Now the terms in the brackets on the right are clearly in the form of inner products:

$$f_x(x_0, y_0)h + f_y(x_0, y_0)k = (f_x(x_0, y_0)\mathbf{i} + f_y(x_0, y_0)\mathbf{j}) \cdot (h\mathbf{i} + k\mathbf{j}),$$

and

$$\varepsilon_1 h + \varepsilon_2 k = (\varepsilon_1 \mathbf{i} + \varepsilon_2 \mathbf{j}) \cdot (h\mathbf{i} + k\mathbf{j}).$$

In order to exploit this observation we make the following definition.

Definition 14

(i) *If f is a function of two variables, if* (x_0, y_0) *is in the domain of f, then the* **gradient** *of f at* (x_0, y_0) *is the vector*

$$\nabla f(x_0, y_0) = f_x(x_0, y_0)\mathbf{i} + f_x(x_0, y_0)\mathbf{j}.$$

(ii) *If* $f: X \to \mathbf{R}$, $X \subset \mathbf{R}^n$, $\mathbf{x}_0 \in X$, *then the gradient of f at* $\mathbf{x}_0$ *is the vector*

$$\nabla f(\mathbf{x}_0) = (f_1(\mathbf{x}_0), \ldots, f_n(\mathbf{x}_0)).$$

(We use subscripts here to represent partial differentiation.)

The symbol ∇ used for the gradient vector is called either *nabla* or *del*, the latter being more popular. Also ∇f is sometimes written as **grad** *f*.

It is now an easy matter to write, succinctly, an extension of (29).

Consider an open region $X \subset \mathbf{R}^n$, let $\mathbf{x}_0 \in X$, let $\mathbf{h} \in \mathbf{R}^n$ be such that $\mathbf{x}_0 + \mathbf{h} \in X$, let $f: X \to \mathbf{R}$. Then

$$f \text{ differentiable at } \mathbf{x}_0 \Rightarrow f(\mathbf{x}_0 + \mathbf{h}) - f(\mathbf{x}_0) = \nabla f(\mathbf{x}_0) \cdot \mathbf{h} + \varepsilon \cdot \mathbf{h},$$

$$\text{where} \lim_{|\mathbf{h}| \to 0} |\varepsilon| = 0. \quad (30)$$

It is instructive to compare (30) with (16).

If we interpret the vector $\mathbf{h}$ as an "increment vector" and if we recall that the inner product is linear (i.e., $\nabla f(\mathbf{x}_0) \cdot (\mathbf{h}_1 + \mathbf{h}_2) = \nabla f(\mathbf{x}_0) \cdot \mathbf{h}_1 + \nabla f(\mathbf{x}_0) \cdot \mathbf{h}_2$ and

$\nabla f(x_0) \cdot (ch) = c\nabla f(x_0) \cdot h)$, then we can interpret differentiability of f at x_0, as expressed by (30), as saying that f can be approximated in a nbd. of x_0 by the *linear function* $\nabla f(x_0) \cdot h$, i.e.,

$$f(x_0 + h) \approx f(x_0) + \nabla f(x_0) \cdot h,$$

the quality of the approximation depending, among other things, upon $|h|$.

We return to the case of two variables and look at the expression in the first pair of brackets on the right of Eq. (29),

$$f_x(x_0, y_0)h + f_y(x_0, y_0)k = f_x(x_0, y_0)\,\Delta x + f_y(x_0, y_0)\,\Delta y, \tag{31}$$

replacing h and k by Δx and Δy respectively.

This is usually defined to be the differential of f and denoted by df. It is, of course, precisely what we call Δf_L, the linear part of f, in Section 13.3. However, it will be recalled that we defined the differential of a function of a single variable to be a *function* (cf. Definition 4.1). We should be consistent here. The fact is that the differential of a function of several variables is the *linear function* $\nabla f(x_0)$, its method of operating on the increment vector h being precisely by means of the inner product.

Definition 15. *Let* $X \subset \mathbf{R}^n, f : X \to \mathbf{R}, x_0 \in X$. *Then the **differential** of f at x_0 is the linear function* $\nabla f(x_0) : N(0) \to \mathbf{R}$, *defined by*

$$\nabla f(x_0)(h) = \nabla f(x_0) \cdot h, \tag{32}$$

where $h \in N(0) \subset \mathbf{R}^n$.

It would be unwise for us to run counter to usage as firmly established as is that for the notation of the differential. The "increment" vector h is usually indicated by $(dx_1, \ldots, dx_n)$ or even by $(\Delta x_1, \ldots, \Delta x_n)$, and the *value* of the differential at dx is ambiguously indicated by df. Thus the standard notation for the expression in (32) is

$$df = f_1(x_0)\,dx_1 + \cdots + f_n(x_0)\,dx_n. \tag{33}$$

Looking again at (31), we see that it is the value of the differential at (h, k), the two-dimensional version of (33).

Note, by the way, that if we take the increment vector $h = dx$ to be e_i, the unit vector in the direction of the ith coordinate axis, we find the value of the differential to be

$$df = \nabla f(x_0) \cdot e_i = f_i(x_0).$$

Finally, we point out (for those familiar with matrices) that we can represent the differential of f at x_0 by the $1 \times n$ matrix $[f_1(x_0) \ldots f_n(x_0).]$ Then the value of the differential at dx is

$$df = [f_1(x_0) \cdots f_n(x_0)] \begin{bmatrix} dx_1 \\ \vdots \\ dx_n \end{bmatrix} = \sum_{i=1}^{n} f_i(x_0)\,dx_i.$$

Example 7. Let $f(x, y, z) = xyz^2 + 2x^2z - yz$, let $P_0(1, 3, 2)$. We find df at P_0. First

$$f_1(x, y, z) = yz^2 + 4xz \Rightarrow f_1(1, 3, 2) = 12 + 8 = 20$$

$$f_2(x, y, z) = xz^2 - z \Rightarrow f_2(1, 3, 2) = 2$$

$$f_3(x, y, z) = 2xyz + 2x^2 - y \Rightarrow f_3(1, 3, 2) = 12 + 2 - 3 = 11.$$

Consequently,

$$df = 20\, dx + 2\, dy + 11\, dz.$$

Example 8. Let $f(x, y, z) = x^2 + y^2 - z$. Then we readily see that at $P_0(x_0, y_0, z_0)$ the value of the differential is

$$df = 2x_0\, dx + 2y_0\, dy - dz.$$

To show another way of writing the value of the differential, let the increment vector $(dx, dy, dz) = (x - x_0, y - y_0, z - z_0)$. Then

$$df = 2x_0(x - x_0) + 2y_0(y - y_0) - (z - z_0). \tag{34}$$

If we apply (30), we can write the value of f at points $(x, y, z) \in N(x_0, y_0, z_0)$ in the form

$$f(x, y, z) = f(x_0, y_0, z_0) + 2x_0(x - x_0) + 2y_0(y - y_0) - (z - z_0) + ls,$$

where $\tag{35}$

$$ls \text{ (little stuff)} = (x - x_0)\varepsilon_1 + (y - y_0)\varepsilon_2 + (z - z_0)\varepsilon_3, \qquad \lim_{P \to P_0} |\varepsilon| = 0.$$

E X E R C I S E S

1. Find the value of the differential of each of the following functions at the point indicated.

   (a) $f(x, y) = 2x^2y - 3xy^3$ at $(2, 1)$

   (b) $f(x, y) = x \cos xy$ at $\left(2, \dfrac{\pi}{4}\right)$

   (c) $f(x, y) = xe^y + y \sin x$ at $\left(\dfrac{\pi}{2}, 2\right)$.

2. Find the value of the differential of each of the following functions at the point indicated.

   (a) $f(x, y, z) = x^2yz - 2xy^2z + 4yz^3$ at $(1, 2, 1)$

   (b) $f(x, y, z) = xy \sin z - y^2 e^{xz}$ at $\left(2, 1, \dfrac{\pi}{4}\right)$

   (c) $f(x, y, z) = \log \dfrac{x^2 + y^2}{z} + z \tan^{-1} \dfrac{y}{x}$ at $(1, 1, 2)$.

3. This exercise discusses a function which has partial derivatives at a point, but which is not differentiable there.

   We begin by dividing the plane into two regions, determined by the lines $y = \pm x$:

   $$\text{region I} = \{(x, y) \mid y^2 \geq x^2\},$$
   $$\text{region II} = \{(x, y) \mid y^2 < x^2\}.$$

   Next we define f at (x, y) as follows:

   (i) if $(x, y) \in$ region I, then $f(x, y) = |x|$,
   (ii) if $(x, y) \in$ region II, then $f(x, y) = |y|$;

   or, alternatively,

   $$f(x, y) = \begin{cases} |x|, & \text{if } y^2 \geq x^2 \\ |y|, & \text{if } y^2 < x^2 \end{cases}.$$

   (a) Sketch the two regions I and II in the plane.

   (b) Verify that $f(x, 0) = f(0, y) = 0$, all x and all y; in other words, f is zero at every point on both axes. In particular, $f(0, 0) = 0$.

   (c) Prove that $f_x(0, 0) = f_y(0, 0) = 0$. Thus, both partial derivatives do exist at the origin.

   (d) Now show f is not differentiable at $P_0(0, 0)$. [*Hints.* Take points Q_1 and Q_2 in region II in the following way. Let $Q_1(h, k)$, where $0 < k < h$. Then $f(Q_1) = k$. Let $Q_2(h, k)$, where $0 < -k < h$. Then $f(Q_2) = -k$. Now consider the corresponding values of Δf:

   $$\Delta_1 f = f(Q_1) - f(P_0) = k - 0 = k = 0 \cdot h + 1 \cdot k + 0 \cdot h + 0 \cdot k,$$

   and

   $$\Delta_2 f = f(Q_2) - f(P_0) = -k - 0 = -k = 0 \cdot h + (-1)k + 0 \cdot h + 0 \cdot k.$$

   Compare these statements with (28), recall that the a and b of that equation must be independent of h and k, and conclude that f is not differentiable at $(0, 0)$.]

   (e) What can be said about f_x and f_y at the origin? Why?

4. This refers to the preceding exercise. Consider points in region I as follows:

   (i) $P_1(x, y)$, where $0 < x < y$.
   (ii) $P_2(x, y)$, where $0 < -x < y$.
   (iii) $P_3(0, y)$, where $0 < y$.

   (a) Find $f_x(P_1)$.

   (b) Find $f_x(P_2)$.

   (c) What can be said about $f_x(P_3)$? Compare this situation with that of Example 4 in Section 2.2.

5. Find ∇f for each of the following functions f:

   (a) $f(x, y) \quad = x^2 + 3\,xy + 2y^2$
   (b) $f(x, y) \quad = y\,e^x + x \log y$
   (c) $f(x, y) \quad = 2x \cos y + \sin y$
   (d) $f(x, y, z) = 3x^2 + 4y^2 - 5z^2$
   (e) $f(x, y, z) = xy \sin z + zy\,e^x$

6. Find the gradient vector of each of the following functions at the point P_0:

(a) $f(x, y) = x^2 - 3y^2, P_0(2, 1)$

(b) $f(x, y) = x \sin y + y e^x, P_0\left(1, \dfrac{\pi}{2}\right)$

(c) $f(x, y, z) = 4x^2 - y^2 + 9z^2, P_0(2, 1, 1)$.

13.5 Directional Derivatives

We now begin reaping some of the benefits resulting from the preceding theory. We shall be concerned in this section entirely with functions of either two or three variables.

It will be recalled that the partial derivatives of a function f measure the rate of change of f in the direction of the coordinate axes. It is now an easy matter to obtain a measure of a rate of change of f in an arbitrary direction.

To be specific, suppose $X \subset \mathbf{R}^3, f : X \to \mathbf{R}, \mathbf{x}_0 \in X, \mathbf{u}$ is a unit vector, and $s \in \mathbf{R}$ (usually we shall be interested in $s > 0$).

Definition 16. *The **directional derivative** of the function f at $\mathbf{x}_0$ in the direction $\mathbf{u} \Leftrightarrow$*

$$D_{\mathbf{u}} f(\mathbf{x}_0) = \lim_{s \to 0} \frac{f(\mathbf{x}_0 + s\mathbf{u}) - f(\mathbf{x}_0)}{s}, \qquad (36)$$

provided the limit exists.

See Figure 7, where $\mathbf{x}_0$ is shown at the origin.

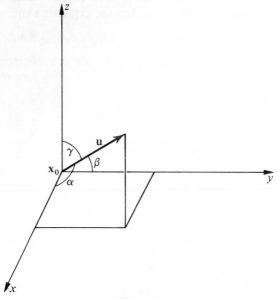

Figure 7

Both a criterion for existence of $D_u f(\mathbf{x}_0)$ and an explicit formula therefor are immediately obtainable.

Theorem 6. *If f is differentiable at $\mathbf{x}_0$ then $D_u f(\mathbf{x}_0)$ exists, and*

$$D_u f(\mathbf{x}_0) = \nabla f(\mathbf{x}_0) \cdot \mathbf{u}. \tag{37}$$

More explicitly, if $\mathbf{u} = \cos \alpha \mathbf{i} + \cos \beta \mathbf{j} + \cos \gamma \mathbf{k}$, then

$$D_u f(\mathbf{x}_0) = f_1(x_0, y_0, z_0) \cos \alpha + f_2(x_0, y_0, z_0) \cos \beta + f_3(x_0, y_0, z_0) \cos \gamma. \tag{38}$$

Proof. By Eq. (30),

$$f(\mathbf{x}_0 + s\mathbf{u}) - f(\mathbf{x}_0) = \nabla f(\mathbf{x}_0) \cdot (s\mathbf{u}) + (s\mathbf{u}) \cdot \boldsymbol{\varepsilon}, \qquad \lim_{s \to 0} |\boldsymbol{\varepsilon}| = 0.$$

Thus,

$$D_u f(\mathbf{x}_0) = \lim_{s \to 0} \frac{f(\mathbf{x}_0 + s\mathbf{u}) - f(\mathbf{x}_0)}{s}$$

$$= \lim_{s \to 0} \frac{\nabla f(\mathbf{x}_0) \cdot (s\mathbf{u}) + (s\mathbf{u}) \cdot \boldsymbol{\varepsilon}}{s}$$

$$= \lim_{s \to 0} [\nabla f(\mathbf{x}_0) \cdot \mathbf{u} + \mathbf{u} \cdot \boldsymbol{\varepsilon}]$$

$$= \nabla f(\mathbf{x}_0) \cdot \mathbf{u},$$

which is Eq. (37). The expression in (38) follows from the definition of the gradient and the description of the unit vector $\mathbf{u} = \cos \alpha \mathbf{i} + \cos \beta \mathbf{j} + \cos \gamma \mathbf{k}$. ∎

Clearly, the preceding discussion is applicable to functions of two variables, the only modification necessary being in formula (38). If f is differentiable on a region of the plane containing (x_0, y_0), then the expression equivalent to (38) is

$$D_u f(x_0, y_0) = f_1(x_0, y_0) \cos \alpha + f_2(x_0, y_0) \cos \beta.$$

In two dimensions it is customary to use only one angle in describing a direction (see Figure 8). Thus we can write the preceding formula as

$$D_\alpha f(x_0, y_0) = f_1(x_0, y_0) \cos \alpha + f_2(x_0, y_0) \sin \alpha. \tag{39}$$

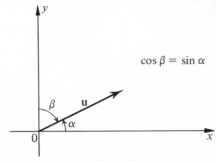

Figure 8

Example 9. Let f be defined by

$$f(x, y) = x^2 + 3xy - y^2.$$

We find the directional derivative of f at $P_0(2, 1)$ in the direction of $(5, -3)$ (see Figure 9).

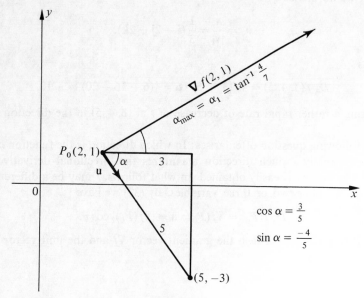

$$\cos \alpha = \frac{3}{5}$$

$$\sin \alpha = \frac{-4}{5}$$

Figure 9

In general, i.e., at (x, y),

$$\nabla f(x, y) = (2x + 3y)\mathbf{i} + (3x - 2y)\mathbf{j}.$$

Thus, at $P_0(2, 1)$, $\nabla f(2, 1) = 7\mathbf{i} + 4\mathbf{j}$. If α is the angle determining the direction from $(2, 1)$ to $(5, -3)$, then $\cos \alpha = \dfrac{3}{5}$, $\sin \alpha = \dfrac{-4}{5}$. Thus,

$$D_\alpha f(2, 1) = 7\left(\frac{3}{5}\right) + 4\left(\frac{-4}{5}\right) = 1.$$

Note that, for arbitrary α,

$$D_\alpha f(2, 1) = 7 \cos \alpha + 4 \sin \alpha. \tag{40}$$

Example 10. Let f be defined by

$$f(x, y, z) = x^2 + y^2 - z^2.$$

We find $D_{\mathbf{u}} f(P_0)$, where $P_0(3, 4, 5)$, and the direction is determined by $\mathbf{v} = \mathbf{i} - 2\mathbf{j} + 2\mathbf{k}$.

We first find the gradient:

$$\nabla f(x, y, z) = 2x\mathbf{i} + 2y\mathbf{j} - 2z\mathbf{k};$$

thus

$$\nabla f(3, 4, 5) = 6\mathbf{i} + 8\mathbf{j} - 10\mathbf{k}.$$

Next we normalize **v**:

$$\mathbf{u_v} = \frac{\mathbf{v}}{|\mathbf{v}|} = \frac{1}{3}(\mathbf{i} - 2\mathbf{j} + 2\mathbf{k}).$$

Thus

$$D_{\mathbf{u}} f(3, 4, 5) = \nabla f(3, 4, 5) \cdot \mathbf{u} = \tfrac{1}{3}(6 - 16 - 20) = -10,$$

indicating a rather rapid rate of decrease of f at $(3, 4, 5)$ in the direction of **v**.

The following question often arises: In which direction is the function changing most rapidly—which direction maximizes the directional derivative at a point? The answer is easily obtained. In what follows, f may be a differentiable function of either two or three variables. By (37) we have

$$D_{\mathbf{u}} f(P_0) = \nabla f(P_0) \cdot \mathbf{u} = |\nabla f(P_0)| \cos \theta, \tag{41}$$

where θ is the angle between the gradient vector ∇f and the unit vector **u** (see Figure 10).

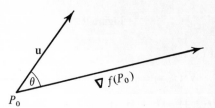

Figure 10

Given f and P_0, $\nabla f(P_0)$ is a fixed vector; **u** is a unit vector with variable direction. Since $-1 \leq \cos \theta \leq 1$, it is clear from (41) that $D_{\mathbf{u}} f(P_0)$ is a maximum when $\cos \theta = 1$, i.e., when $\theta = 0$, or **u** is in the direction of the gradient vector. Similarly, the maximum negative value of $D_{\mathbf{u}} f(P_0)$ occurs when $\theta = \pi$, i.e., when **u** and $\nabla f(P_0)$ have diametrically opposite directions. In summary, we have the following:

The direction of $\nabla f(P_0)$ is the direction in which $D_{\mathbf{u}} f(P_0)$ is a maximum, and this maximum value of the directional derivative is $|\nabla f(P_0)|$. Similarly, the maximum rate of *decrease* of f at P_0 is in the direction diametrically opposite to that of the gradient vector at P_0, this maximum rate of *decrease* being the magnitude of the gradient vector.

This property is one of the reasons why the gradient vector is important in this part of calculus.

EXERCISES

1. Find $D_u f(P_0)$ for each f described below at the P_0 given and in the direction indicated.

(a) $f(x, y, z) = xe^y + y \cos z$, $P_0(1, 1, 0)$, $\quad$ $\mathbf{v} = \mathbf{i} + \mathbf{j} + \mathbf{k}$.

(b) $f(x, y, z) = x^2 yz - 3xyz + 2yz^2$, $P_0(1, 2, 1)$, $\quad$ $\mathbf{v} = 2\mathbf{i} - 2\mathbf{j} - \mathbf{k}$.

(c) $f(x, y, z) = z \log (x^2 + y^2) - xe^y + z$, $P_0(3, 4, 1)$, in the direction of $P_1(5, 2, 0)$.

(d) $f(x, y, z) = \log \sqrt{x^2 + y^2 + z^2} + xyz$, $P_0(1, 3, 4)$, $\quad$ $\mathbf{v} = 3\mathbf{i} - 12\mathbf{j} + 4\mathbf{k}$.

2. For each function described below find $D_\alpha f(P_0)$ at the point P_0 in the direction indicated.

(a) $f(x, y) = xy^2 - y^3$, $P_0(2, 1)$, $\alpha = \dfrac{\pi}{4}$.

(b) $f(x, y) = x \cos y - ye^x$, $P_0\left(1, \dfrac{\pi}{3}\right)$, $\alpha = \dfrac{5\pi}{6}$.

(c) $f(x, y) = x^2 - 3xy + 4y^2$, $P_0(1, -1)$, in the direction of $P_1(2, 2)$.

(d) $f(x, y) = \dfrac{x^2 - y^2}{x^2 + y^2}$, $P_0(-2, 3)$, in the direction of $P_1(1, -1)$.

3. For each function and P_0 in Exercise 2 find the value of α which maximizes $D_\alpha f(P_0)$.

4. Let f be a function which is differentiable at (x_0, y_0). Show:

(a) $D_0 f(P_0) = f_1(x_0, y_0)$. $\qquad$ (c) $D_\pi f(P_0) = -f_1(x_0, y_0)$.

(b) $D_{\pi/2} f(P_0) = f_2(x_0, y_0)$. $\qquad$ (d) $D_{3\pi/2} f(P_0) = -f_2(x_0, y_0)$.

5. Let $f(x, y, z) = yz + zx + xy$, $P_0(1, -2, 3)$. Find the rate of change of f at P_0:

(a) In the direction of the origin.

(b) In the direction in which f is changing most rapidly.

(c) In the direction of $P_1(2, 0, 4)$.

13.6 Geometric Applications

In this section we shall be concerned with the geometry of three space. For this reason the functions considered will usually be those defined in $\mathbf{R}^2$ or $\mathbf{R}^3$.

We take up first the problem of finding the tangent plane to a surface S at a point P_0 on S.

The approach roughly analogous to that used in discussing the tangent line to a curve in two space is as follows (we give only an outline here, because we plan to develop the ideas from a different point of view). We consider a surface S as the graph of a function f of two variables—$\{(x, y, z) \mid z = f(x, y)\}$. We define the tangent plane to S at a point $P_0(x_0, y_0, z_0 = f(x_0, y_0))$ by a limiting process: consider an approximating plane determined by three noncollinear points

P_0, P_1, P_2 on S; if as $P_1 \to P_0$ and $P_2 \to P_0$ (always such that P_0, P_1, P_2 are not collinear) the approximating planes approach a (unique) limiting plane, then this limiting plane is defined to be the tangent plane to S at P_0.

The next step would be to prove the following result.

Theorem. *If f is differentiable at (x_0, y_0) then S has a tangent plane at P_0 and its equation is*

$$f_x(x_0, y_0)(x - x_0) + f_y(x_0, y_0)(y - y_0) + (-1)(z - z_0) = 0. \tag{42}$$

Moreover, the line normal to S at P_0 is

$$\frac{x - x_0}{f_x(x_0, y_0)} = \frac{y - y_0}{f_y(x_0, y_0)} = \frac{z - z_0}{-1}. \tag{43}$$

The theorem is true and its proof is not hard—although it is messy in the final stages. However, we prefer to follow a different path, partly because it is more general and partly because it enables us to apply some of the ideas developed in the preceding sections.

We begin with a function F of three variables defined on a subset of $\mathbf{R}^3$ and we consider a surface S to be a *contour* or *level* surface for F, i.e., the set of points in $\mathbf{R}^3$ determined by

$$\{(x, y, z) \,|\, F(x, y, z) = c\},$$

where c is in the range of F. (If, for example, F gave a temperature distribution for a portion of three space, then the level surface would be an isothermal surface; other similar physical interpretations are obviously possible.) As an illustration, if

$$F(x, y, z) = x^2 + y^2 - z^2,$$

then the level surfaces $F = c$ are

(i) hyperboloids of one sheet, if $c > 0$;
(ii) a right circular cone, if $c = 0$;
(iii) hyperboloids of two sheets, if $c < 0$.

We can, for the sake of simplicity assume that $c = 0$ (for if $F(x, y, z) = c, c \neq 0$, we could define $G = F - c$ and work with $G(x, y, z) = 0$). Note that the case outlined at the beginning of this section is included in this discussion; for if

$$z = f(x, y), \quad \text{define} \quad F(x, y, z) = f(x, y) - z. \tag{44}$$

We shall return to this point later.

Now we assume a surface S determined by $F(x, y, z) = 0$, and we consider a point $P_0(x_0, y_0, z_0)$ on S. If F is differentiable at P_0 (our blanket assumption about functions), then (Theorem 6) $D_{\mathbf{u}} F(P_0)$ exists in every direction through P_0. To be specific, consider a curve C through P_0 on S; we are interested in $DF(P_0)$ in a direction along C. But C on S and S a *level* surface for $F \Rightarrow$ that

$F(x, y, z) = 0$ on S—and hence on C. Thus F is *constant* on C, and $DF(P_0)$ in a direction of C must be zero. This must be true for *every* curve C on S through P_0. From Eq. (37), then, we have

$$D_{\mathbf{u}} F(P_0) = \nabla F(P_0) \cdot \mathbf{u} = 0 \tag{45}$$

for every unit vector $\mathbf{u}$ at P_0 which is in the direction of a curve on S through P_0. The conclusion of this discussion is important enough to state formally.

Theorem 7. *If F is differentiable at a point $P_0(x_0, y_0, z_0)$, then the gradient vector at P_0,*

$$\nabla F(P_0) = F_1(x_0, y_0, z_0)\mathbf{i} + F_2(x_0, y_0, z_0)\mathbf{j} + F_3(x_0, y_0, z_0)\mathbf{k}$$

is perpendicular to every curve on S, the level surface for F, through P_0.

Motivated by this result, we make the following definition.

Definition 17. *The normal line to a surface S at a point P_0 on S is the line through P_0 which is perpendicular to every curve on S through P_0, provided such a line exists.*

Theorem 8. *If F is differentiable at a point $P_0(x_0, y, z)$, then the level surface for F through P_0 has a normal, and its direction is that of the gradient vector $\nabla F(P_0)$. Thus the symmetric form of the equations of the normal line is*

$$\frac{x - x_0}{F_1(P_0)} = \frac{y - y_0}{F_2(P_0)} = \frac{z - z_0}{F_3(P_0)}. \tag{46}$$

It is now a straightforward matter to define and obtain the essential results about the tangent plane to a surface.

Definition 18. *If a surface has a normal line at a point P_0 on it then the tangent plane to the surface at P_0 is the plane through P_0 with normal vector in the direction of the normal line at P_0.*

The next step is a natural one.

Theorem 9. *If F is differentiable at a point $P_0(x_0, y_0, z_0)$, then the level surface for F at P_0 has a tangent plane, the equation of which is*

$$F_1(x_0, y_0, z_0)(x - x_0) + F_2(x_0, y_0, z_0)(y - y_0) + F_3(x_0, y_0, z_0)(z - z_0) = 0. \tag{47}$$

Proof. Since the tangent plane goes through P_0, its equation must be of the form

$$a(x - x_0) + b(y - y_0) + c(z - z_0) = 0,$$

where $\mathbf{n} = a\mathbf{i} + b\mathbf{j} + c\mathbf{k}$ is normal to the plane. By Theorem 8 the normal vector is the gradient vector

$$\nabla F(P_0) = F_1(P_0)\mathbf{i} + F_2(P_0)\mathbf{j} + F_3(P_0)\mathbf{k}.$$

Using the components of this vector for a, b, c, respectively, gives us (47). ∎

We point out that if S is obtained as the graph of a function f defined on a region of $\mathbf{R}^2$, so that Eq. (44) is applicable

$$F(x, y, z) = f(x, y) - z,$$

then

$$F_1(x, y, z) = f_x(x, y), \qquad F_2(x, y, z) = f_y(x, y), \qquad F_3(x, y, z) = -1.$$

Using these expressions in Eqs. (47) and (46) give (42) and (43), respectively. In other words, our present discussion is in agreement with the alternative approach to the special case outlined earlier. It is time for some illustrations.

Example 11. We consider the point $P_0\left(1, 2, \dfrac{\sqrt{11}}{3}\right)$ on the ellipsoid

$$\frac{x^2}{4} + \frac{y^2}{9} + \frac{z^2}{4} = 1.$$

If we define

$$F(x, y, z) = \tfrac{1}{36}[9x^2 + 4y^2 + 9z^2 - 36],$$

then the ellipsoid is the level surface $F = 0$. It is routine to calculate that

$$F_1 = \tfrac{1}{2}x, \; F_2 = \tfrac{2}{9}y, \; F_3 = \tfrac{1}{2}z.$$

Thus the gradient vector at $P_0\left(1, 2, \dfrac{\sqrt{11}}{3}\right)$ is

$$\nabla F(P_0) = \frac{1}{2}\mathbf{i} + \frac{4}{9}\mathbf{j} + \frac{\sqrt{11}}{6}\mathbf{k}.$$

Using Eqs. (46) and (47), we can write the equations of the normal line and tangent plane to the ellipsoid at P_0.

Normal line:
$$\frac{x-1}{\frac{1}{2}} = \frac{y-2}{\frac{4}{9}} = \frac{z - \frac{\sqrt{11}}{3}}{\frac{\sqrt{11}}{6}}.$$

Tangent plane:
$$\frac{1}{2}(x-1) + \frac{4}{9}(y-2) + \frac{\sqrt{11}}{6}\left(z - \frac{\sqrt{11}}{3}\right) = 0.$$

Of course, each of these can be written in different forms. For example, the equation of the tangent plane can be modified to

$$9x + 8y + 3\sqrt{11}z = 36$$

(see Figure 11).

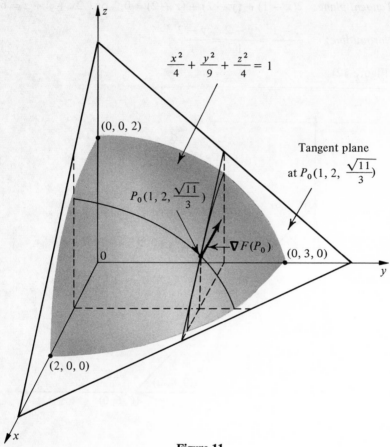

Figure 11

Example 12. We consider the graph of

$$z = 4 - x^2 - \tfrac{1}{4}y^2,$$

an elliptic paraboloid, at $P_0(1, 2, 2)$.

If we define F by

$$F(x, y, z) = x^2 + \tfrac{1}{4}y^2 - 4 + z,$$

then $F(1, 2, 2) = 0$, and the surface is the level surface for $F = 0$.

At a general point (x, y, z) the gradient vector is

$$\nabla F(x, y, z) = 2x\mathbf{i} + \tfrac{1}{2}y\mathbf{j} + \mathbf{k};$$

thus,

$$\nabla F(P_0) = 2\mathbf{i} + \mathbf{j} + \mathbf{k}.$$

The equations of the tangent plane and normal line are

Tangent plane: $2(x - 1) + (y - 2) + (z - 2) = 0,$ or $2x + y + z = 6,$

Normal line: $\dfrac{x - 1}{2} = \dfrac{y - 2}{1} = \dfrac{y - 2}{1}$

(see Figure 12).

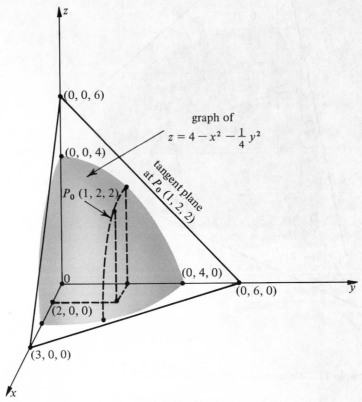

Figure 12

We return to the case where the surface is the graph of a function $f: S = \{(x, y, z) \mid z = f(x, y)\}$. We assume, as usual, that f is differentiable at a point (x_0, y_0) in its domain, and we consider a nearby point (x, y). Because of the differentiability of f, we can write

$$\Delta z = \Delta f = \nabla f(x_0, y_0) \cdot [(x - x_0)\mathbf{i} + (y - y_0)\mathbf{j}] + \varepsilon\text{-terms.}$$

If we drop the ε-terms and replace Δz by $z - z_0$, the preceding equation becomes

$$z - z_0 = f_x(x_0, y_0)(x - x_0) + f_y(x_0, y_0)(y - y_0),$$

the tangent plane to the surface at (x_0, y_0, z_0). Note that the right-hand side of this equation is precisely what we referred to in Section 13.3 as Δf_L, the *linear part* of Δf. Geometrically, dropping the ε-terms is equivalent to throwing a switch at P_0 on the surface and transferring from the surface to the tangent plane to S at P_0 (see Figure 13).

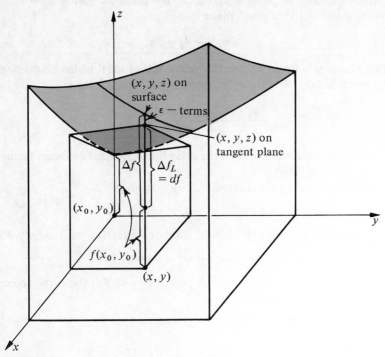

Figure 13

Example 13. We consider the hyperboloid H of two sheets $x^2 - 4y^2 - z^2 = 4$, and find first the equation of the tangent plane at an arbitrary point $P_0(x_0, y_0, z_0)$ on H.

We let $F(x, y, z) = x^2 - 4y^2 - z^2 - 4$. Then H is the level surface $F = 0$. Since the gradient of F at P_0 is

$$\nabla F(P_0) = 2x_0\,\mathbf{i} - 8y_0\,\mathbf{j} - 2z_0\,\mathbf{k}, \tag{48}$$

the equation of the tangent plane to H at P_0 is

$$2x_0(x - x_0) - 8y_0(y - y_0) - 2z_0(z - z_0) = 0. \tag{49}$$

[We insert a word of caution. In this equation x, y, z are the *running* coordinates of a point on the plane; x_0, y_0, z_0 are the coordinates of an arbitrary (but *fixed*, as far as any particular tangent plane is concerned) point on the surface.

Carelessness sometimes causes students to forget that the components of the gradient vector (48) must be evaluated at P_0—and, hence, are numbers. As a result of this sort of carelessness the equation of the tangent plane is likely to be written *incorrectly* as

$$\frac{2x_0}{1}(x + \frac{1}{1}) + \frac{1}{1}(y + \frac{1}{1}) + \frac{1}{1}(z + \frac{1}{1}) \neq 0$$

not linear, and thus *not* a plane.]

We next raise the following question. Are there any points on the hyperboloid H at which the tangent plane is parallel to the plane $3x - 4y + 2z = 5$?

A normal vector to the given plane is

$$\mathbf{n} = 3\mathbf{i} - 4\mathbf{j} + 2\mathbf{k}.$$

The two planes will be parallel $\Leftrightarrow$ the vector $\mathbf{n}$ is parallel to the gradient vector $\nabla F(P_0)$ given in (48). And these two vectors will be parallel $\Leftrightarrow$

$$\frac{2x_0}{3} = \frac{-8y_0}{-4} = \frac{-2z_0}{2} = 2t,$$

(we use $2t$ as the common value of the ratio because of the common factor 2 in the components of $\nabla F(P_0)$).

Solving the preceding equations for x_0, y_0, z_0 gives

$$x_0 = 3t, \ y_0 = t, \ z_0 = -2t.$$

Since P_0 must be on the hyperboloid, these coordinates must satisfy $F = 0$:

$$9t^2 - 4t^2 - 4t^2 - 4 = 0,$$

whence $t = \pm 2$. We thus get two such points P_1 and P_2; these and the corresponding tangent planes are

$$P_1(6, 2, -4), \quad 3x - 4y + 2z = 2,$$
$$P_2(-6, -2, 4), \quad 3x - 4y + 2z = -2.$$

Example 14. For a function of one variable, differentiability of a function f at a point is equivalent, geometrically, to existence of a tangent line to the graph of f at the corresponding point. An analogous statement holds for a function of two variables, with tangent plane replacing tangent line. We have proven only part of this assertion: differentiability $\Rightarrow$ existence of tangent plane. We now show an example of a function which is not differentiable at a point P_0, and which does not have a tangent plane at P_0.

The example is the one discussed in Exercise 3 after Section 13.4:

$$f(x, y) = \begin{cases} |x|, & y^2 \geq y^2 \\ |y|, & y^2 < x^2 \end{cases}.$$

the point P_0 being the origin. The fact that there is no tangent plane at the origin follows from the failure of a normal to exist there. In turn, this is shown by indicating some of the curves which lie on the surface and go through the origin:

both x- and y-axes,

$$x = y = z, \qquad \text{for } x \geq 0, \quad y \geq 0,$$
$$x = -y = z, \qquad \text{for } x \geq 0, \quad y \leq 0,$$
$$-x = y = z, \qquad \text{for } x \leq 0, \quad y \geq 0,$$
$$-x = -y = z, \qquad \text{for } x \leq 0, \quad y \leq 0.$$

Clearly—see Definition 17—this surface cannot have a normal line at the origin (see Figure 14, where a portion of the front half of the surface is shown).

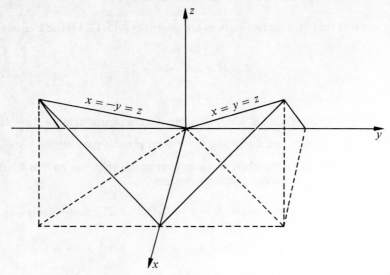

Figure 14

EXERCISES

In each of numbers 1–10 find the equations of the tangent plane and normal line to the surface at the point P_0.

1. $x^2 + y^2 + z^2 = 4$, $P_0(1, -1, \sqrt{2})$.   **2.** $z = x^2 + y^2$, $P_0(1, 2, 5)$.

3. $z = 10 - x^2 - y^2$, $P_0(1, 2, 5)$.   **4.** $x^2 + y^2 = z^2$, $P_0(0, 1, 1)$.

5. $x^2 + y^2 - z^2 = 1$, $P_0(0, 1, 0)$. Make a sketch.

6. $z = y^2 - x^2$, $P_0(0, 0, 0)$. Make a sketch.   **7.** $z = ye^x$, $P_0(1, 2, 2e)$.

8. $4z = y^2$, $P_0(x_0, 2, 1)$. What is the significance of the fact that x_0 does not appear in the equation of the tangent plane?

9. $z = e^{-x} \sin y$, $P_0\left(1, \dfrac{\pi}{4}, \dfrac{1}{e\sqrt{2}}\right)$.

10. $z = e^{-y}$, $P_0(x_0, -1, e)$. What is the meaning of the fact that the equation of the tangent plane does not involve x_0?

11. Consider the two surfaces $S_1 : x^2 + y^2 + z^2 = 9$ and $S_2 : 4z = 13 - x^2 - y^2$.

   (a) Find the curve of intersection of S_1 and S_2.

   (b) Verify that $P_0(1, 2, 2)$ is on the curve of (a).

   (c) Prove that the two surfaces share the same tangent plane at $P_0(1, 2, 2)$. Give a name to this relationship between two surfaces.

12. Prove that the following two surfaces are tangent at $P_0(5, 12, 13)$ (see Exercise 11c).

$$S_1 : 13z = x^2 + y^2.$$
$$S_2 : z^2 + 169 = 2x^2 + 2y^2.$$

13. Consider the ellipsoid $S : x^2 + 4y^2 + 9z^2 = 36$.

   (a) Find the point(s) on S at which the tangent plane is parallel to $x - 2y - 3z = 4$.

   (b) Find the point(s) on S at which the tangent plane is parallel to $x + y = 1$.

   (c) Show that, given any plane in space, there exist two points on S at which the tangent plane is parallel to the given plane.

14. Let S be the elliptic paraboloid $4z = x^2 + 2y^2$. Find all points—if any—on S at which the tangent plane is parallel to

   (a) $x - 2y - 2z = 4$.   (b) $2x + 4y + z = 3$.   (c) $x + y = 1$.

15. Consider the two surfaces $F = 0$ and $G = 0$, where $F(x, y, z) = x^2 + y^2 - z$, $G(x, y, z) = 16x^2 + 16y^2 - (z + 4)^2$. Show that at any point $(x_0, y_0, 4)$ common to the two surfaces they are tangent (see Exercise 11c).

16. We consider the two paraboloids $2z = x^2 + y^2$ and $2z = 2 - x^2 - y^2$.

   (a) Show that $P_0(0, 1, \tfrac{1}{2})$ is a point of intersection of these surfaces and that the two gradient vectors at P_0 are perpendicular. When this is the case the surfaces are said to be orthogonal at P_0.

   (b) Show that the two surfaces are orthogonal at every point of intersection.

17. Outline a theory of tangent line to a curve in two space analogous to the theory of the tangent plane to a surface as developed in this section.

   [*Hints.*

   (1) Consider a function F of two variables, and let a curve $\mathscr{C}$ be $\{(x, y) \mid F(x, y) = c\}$, for some number c in the range of F.

   (2) If $P_0(x_0, y_0)$ is a point on $\mathscr{C}$, show that the gradient vector at P_0, $\nabla F(P_0)$, is perpendicular to the curve.

(3) From (2) show that the slope of the normal line to the curve at P_0 is
$m_n = \dfrac{F_2(P_0)}{F_1(P_0)}$ if $F_1(P_0) \neq 0$. What happens if $F_1(P_0) = 0$?

(4) Define the tangent line to the curve at P_0 as the line through P_0 perpendicular to the normal. Show that the slope of the tangent is $m_t = \dfrac{-F_1(P_0)}{F_2(P_0)}$, if $F_2(P_0) \neq 0$. What if $F_2(P_0) = 0$?

(5) Show that if the curve is the graph of $y = f(x)$, then $f'(x_0) = \dfrac{-F_1(P_0)}{F_2(P_0)}$. Compare this with the method of implicit differentiation.]

13.7 Chain Rules

We have frequently stressed, in the work with functions of a single variable, the importance of the chain rule for finding the derivative of the composition of two differentiable functions. It is natural to anticipate that the theory of functions of several variables will include an analogous theorem. This is essentially correct, except that, as the section title implies, there are more than one. We shall prove two of the chain rules, giving a clear idea of the nature of proof, and then state without proof a general theorem which encompasses all useful possibilities.

The simplest case can be illustrated as follows: f is a function of two variables, say

$$u = f(x, y) = x^2 - 4xy - 2y^2; \tag{50}$$

in turn, each of x and y is a function of a single variable t (one could think of t as representing time)

$$x = x(t) = t^2 - 1, \, y = y(t) = 2t. \tag{51}$$

The composition of f with x and y produces a function F of the single variable t which, under suitable differentiability assumptions, should have a derivative— and this derivative should be expressible in terms of derivatives of the original functions f, x, and y. (Of course, in the preceding simple illustration one can easily substitute the x and y functions directly in the f function, obtaining $f(x(t), y(t)) = F(t)$ explicitly. If this were always possible and convenient we would have no need for chain rules.)

A more or less complete description of the appropriate conditions is as follows. We assume $G \subset \mathbf{R}^2, f: G \to \mathbf{R}; I \subset \mathbf{R}, x: I \to X \subset \mathbf{R}, y: I \to Y \subset \mathbf{R}$, and $X \times Y \subset G$. (These conditions assure that the composition function has nonempty domain—see Figure 15.) We further assume that f has continuous partial derivatives on G and that x' and y' exist on I.

Now we can state the first chain rule.

Theorem 10. *Under the conditions just specified, the function F defined on I by $F(t) = f(x(t), y(t))$ has a derivative F' and*

$$F'(t) = f_x(x, y)x'(t) + f_y(x, y)y'(t). \tag{52}$$

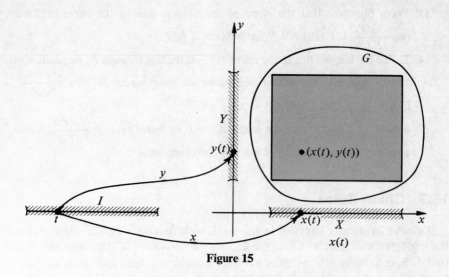

Figure 15

Proof. By definition

$$F'(t) = \lim_{h \to 0} \frac{F(t+h) - F(t)}{h}.$$

Now

$$F(t+h) - F(t) = f(x(t+h), y(t+h)) - f(x(t), y(t))$$
$$= f(x + \Delta x, y + \Delta y) - f(x, y),$$

where we have written $x + \Delta x$ for $x(t+h)$, and correspondingly for y.

By the assumption that f has continuous partial derivatives and Theorem 1,

$$\Delta f = f(x + \Delta x, y + \Delta y) - f(x, y) = f_1(x, y)\,\Delta x + f_2(x, y)\,\Delta y + \varepsilon_1\,\Delta x + \varepsilon_2\,\Delta y,$$

$$\text{where} \quad \lim_{(\Delta x, \Delta y) \to (0, 0)} \varepsilon_i = 0. \qquad (53)$$

But x and y are differentiable, so

$$\Delta x = x(t+h) - x(t) = x'(t)h + \varepsilon_3\,h, \qquad \lim_{h \to 0} \varepsilon_3 = 0, \qquad (54)$$

$$\Delta y = y(t+h) - y(t) = y'(t)h + \varepsilon_4\,h, \qquad \lim_{h \to 0} \varepsilon_4 = 0. \qquad (55)$$

Substituting Eq. (54) and (55) into (53) gives

$$\Delta f = f_1(x, y)[x'(t)h + \varepsilon_3\,h] + f_2(x, y)[y'(t)h + \varepsilon_4 h]$$
$$+ \varepsilon_1[x'(t)h + \varepsilon_3\,h] + \varepsilon_2[y'(t)h + \varepsilon_4 h].$$

Notice that every term has a factor h. It is easy to see now that, as a result of the statements about the ε_i, if we divide by h and take the limit:

$$F'(t) = \lim_{h \to 0} \frac{F(t+h) - F(t)}{h} = \lim_{h \to 0} \frac{\Delta f}{h}$$

$$= f_1(x, y)x'(t) + f_2(x, y)y'(t). \quad \blacksquare$$

The statement (52) can also be written as

$$\frac{dF(t)}{dt} = \frac{\partial f}{\partial x}\frac{dx}{dt} + \frac{\partial f}{\partial y}\frac{dy}{dt},$$ (56)

in some ways more suggestive, but also more ambiguous, than (52).

To complete the illustration given at the beginning,

$$u = f(x, y) = x^2 + 4xy - 2y^2$$
$$x = x(t) = t^2 - 1, \qquad y = y(t) = 2t,$$

we have, using (52),

$$\frac{du}{dt} = F'(t) = (2x + 4y)(2t) + (4x - 4y)2.$$

The fact that this result is in terms of all three variables x, y, and t is to be expected—see the parenthetical comment at the end of the second paragraph of this section.

The next general case would again involve a function f of two variables x and y, each of which is now itself a function of two variables, say, r and s. In this case, the composition of f with x and y would produce a function F of r and s:

$$F(r, s) = f(x(r, s), y(r, s)).$$

We assume—without spelling out all the details—that the product $X \times Y$ of the ranges of x and y is a subset of the domain of f, thus guaranteeing the existence of the composition function F.

Theorem 11. *Let* $u = f(x, y)$ *have continuous derivatives, let* $x(r, s)$, $y(r, s)$ *have continuous derivatives on a common domain of* $\mathbf{R}^2$. *Then the composition function*

$$F(r, s) = f(x(r, s), y(r, s))$$

has partial derivatives and

$$\left.\begin{aligned} F_r(r, s) &= f_x(x, y)x_r(r, s) + f_y(x, y)y_r(r, s), \\ F_s(r, s) &= f_x(x, y)x_s(r, s) + f_y(x, y)y_s(r, s). \end{aligned}\right\}$$ (57)

Proof. We remark first that we shall prove only the result about F_r, since the proof for F_s is essentially the same. Second, we note that the general outline is very similar to the proof of Theorem 10, so we shall be briefer than in that proof. Since

$$\frac{\partial u}{\partial r} = F_r(r, s) = \lim_{h \to 0} \frac{F(r + h, s) - F(r, s)}{h},$$

we consider

$$F(r + h, s) - F(r, s) = f(x(r + h, s), y(r + h, s)) - f(x(r, s), y(r, s))$$
$$= f(x + \Delta x, y + \Delta y) - f(x, y) = \Delta f,$$

where $x + \Delta x = x(r + h, s)$, $y + \Delta y = y(r + h, s)$. Now, since f is differentiable, Eq. (53) holds, as before. We also have

$$\left. \begin{array}{l} \Delta x = x(r + h, s) - x(r, s) = x_r(r, s)h + \varepsilon_3 h, \quad \lim_{h \to 0} \varepsilon_3 = 0, \\[2mm] \Delta y = y(r + h, s) - y(r, s) = y_r(r, s)h + \varepsilon_4 h, \quad \lim_{h \to 0} \varepsilon_4 = 0, \end{array} \right\} \quad (58)$$

since both x and y are assumed to have continuous derivatives.

If we substitute from (58) into (53) and divide by h, we have

$$\frac{F(r + h, s) - F(r, s)}{h} = f_1(x, y)x_r(r, s) + f_2(x, y)y_r(r, s)$$

$$+ f_1(x, y)\varepsilon_3 + f_2(x, y)\varepsilon_4 + x_r(r, s)\varepsilon_1$$

$$+ y_r(r, s)\varepsilon_2 + \varepsilon_1\varepsilon_3 + \varepsilon_2\varepsilon_4 .$$

As $h \to 0$, $\varepsilon_i \to 0$, $i = 1, 2, 3, 4$; thus

$$F_r(r, s) = f_x(x, y)x_r(r, s) + f_y(x, y)y_r(r, s). \quad \blacksquare$$

The curly d notation describes the formulas in (57) as follows:

$$\left. \begin{array}{l} \dfrac{\partial F}{\partial r} = \dfrac{\partial f}{\partial x}\dfrac{\partial x}{\partial r} + \dfrac{\partial f}{\partial y}\dfrac{\partial y}{\partial r}, \\[4mm] \dfrac{\partial F}{\partial s} = \dfrac{\partial f}{\partial x}\dfrac{\partial x}{\partial s} + \dfrac{\partial f}{\partial y}\dfrac{\partial y}{\partial s}, \end{array} \right\} \quad (59)$$

As an illustration, consider the function f of the earlier example:

$$f(x, y) = x^2 + 4xy - 2y^2.$$

If we introduce polar coordinates,

$$x = r \cos \theta$$

$$y = r \sin \theta,$$

then we obtain a function F of r and θ, and by (57),

$$F_r(r, \theta) = (2x + 4y) \cos \theta + (4x - 4y) \sin \theta,$$

$$F_\theta(r, \theta) = (2x + 4y)(-r \sin \theta) + (4x - 4y)(r \cos \theta).$$

The statement of the most general theorem produces a minor problem because of the way we have been using subscripts to indicate partial differentiation. We can describe it as follows.

Theorem 12. *Let f be a function of m variables $f(x, y, z, \ldots, q)$, defined and having continuous derivatives on a region of $\mathbf{R}^m$. Let each of $x, y, \ldots, q$ in turn be a function of n variables having a common domain in $\mathbf{R}^n$:*

$$x = x(t_1, \ldots, t_n)$$
$$y = y(t_1, \ldots, t_n)$$
$$\cdot$$
$$\cdot$$
$$\cdot$$
$$q = q(t_1, \ldots, t_n).$$

We assume each of these functions has continuous derivatives on the common domain. Then the composite function

$$F(t_1, \ldots, t_n) = f(x(t_1, \ldots, t_n), \ldots, q(t_1, \ldots, t_n))$$

has derivatives and, for each $i = 1, \ldots, n$

$$
\begin{aligned}
F_i(t_1, \ldots, t_n) = {} & f_x(x, y, \ldots, q)x_i(t_1, \ldots, t_n) \\
& + f_y(x, y, \ldots, q)y_i(t_1, \ldots, t_n) + \cdots \qquad (60) \\
& + f_q(x, y, \ldots, q)q_i(t_1, \ldots, t_n).
\end{aligned}
$$

In the Leibniz notation, the result in (60) looks like this:

$$\frac{\partial F}{\partial t_i} = \frac{\partial f}{\partial x}\frac{\partial x}{\partial t_i} + \frac{\partial f}{\partial y}\frac{\partial y}{\partial t_i} + \cdots + \frac{\partial f}{\partial q}\frac{\partial q}{\partial t_i},$$

somewhat less forbidding.

Example 15. Let f be defined by

$$f(x, y, z) = x^2 + 4y^2 + 9z^2;$$

suppose x, y, z are functions of ρ, θ, φ, as follows:

$$x = \rho \cos \theta \sin \varphi,$$
$$y = \rho \sin \theta \sin \varphi,$$
$$z = \rho \cos \varphi.$$

Then the composite function F is defined by

$$F(\rho, \theta, \varphi) = f(x(\rho, \theta, \varphi), y(\rho, \theta, \varphi), z(\rho, \theta, \varphi)).$$

As all functions involved have continuous derivatives, F has derivatives, and

$$
\begin{aligned}
F_\rho(\rho, \theta, \varphi) = {} & f_x(x, y, z)x_\rho(\rho, \theta, \varphi) + f_y(x, y, z)y_\rho(\rho, \theta, \varphi) \\
& + f_z(x, y, z)z_\rho(\rho, \theta, \varphi) \\
= {} & 2x \cos \theta \sin \varphi + 8y \sin \theta \sin \varphi + 18z \cos \varphi.
\end{aligned}
$$

We return now to the subject of the differential. To be specific, suppose f is a function of two variables. Then the differential of f at (x, y) is a linear function ∇f which operates on an increment vector. If we write the increment vector as $dx\mathbf{i} + dy\mathbf{j}$, as is frequently done, then

$$df = \nabla f(x, y) \cdot (dx\mathbf{i} + dy\mathbf{j}) = f_x(x, y)\, dx + f_y(x, y)\, dy. \qquad (61)$$

The implication in Section 13.4 was that the increment vector $dx\mathbf{i} + dy\mathbf{j}$ was an independent variable. Now suppose x and y are themselves functions: $x = x(r, s)$, $y = y(r, s)$. Then, of course, dx and dy are values of the differentials of the x and y functions. This, however, has no effect on the differential, as we now show.

From $x = x(r, s)$ and $y = y(r, s)$, we have

$$\left. \begin{aligned} dx &= \nabla x \cdot (dr\mathbf{i} + ds\mathbf{j}) = x_r(r, s)\, dr + x_s(r, s)\, ds \\ dy &= \nabla y \cdot (dr\mathbf{i} + ds\mathbf{j}) = y_r(r, s)\, dr + y_s(r, s)\, ds. \end{aligned} \right\} \tag{62}$$

We now substitute from (62) into the expression on the right-hand side in (61):

$$df = f_x(x, y)[x_r(r, s)\, dr + x_s(r, s)\, ds] + f_y(x, y)[y_r(r, s)\, dr + y_s(r, s)\, ds]$$

$$= [f_x(x, y)x_r(r, s) + f_y(x, y)y_r(r, s)]\, dr + [f_x(x, y)x_s(r, s) + f_y(x, y)y_s(r, s)]\, ds$$

$$= F_r(r, s)\, dr + F_s(r, s)\, ds \qquad \text{(by Theorem 11)}$$

$$= dF.$$

The significance of this equation should be clearly understood. The differential of a function at a point when applied to an increment vector gives a number. If the function is f, the point is (x_0, y_0), and the increment vector is $dx\mathbf{i} + dy\mathbf{j}$, then this number is

$$df = \nabla f(x_0, y_0) \cdot (dx\mathbf{i} + dy\mathbf{j}) = f_x(x_0, y_0)\, dx + f_y(x_0, y_0)\, dy. \tag{63}$$

Now if F is defined as the composite of f, and of new functions x and y in terms of the variables r and s, then the differential of F at (r_0, s_0) applied to an increment vector $dr\mathbf{i} + ds\mathbf{j}$ gives the number

$$dF = \nabla F(r_0, s_0) \cdot (dr\mathbf{i} + ds\mathbf{j}) = F_r(r_0, s_0)\, dr + F_s(r_0, s_0)\, ds. \tag{64}$$

If $x_0 = x(r_0, s_0)$, $y_0 = y(r_0, s_0)$ and if the relation between the increment vectors is as described in (62), then what we have shown above is that the number df of (63) and the number dF of (64) are in fact equal. Not only is the *form* preserved upon such a change of variable, but the *value* of the differential remains the same. See, in this regard, the discussion in Section 8.1, about a differential for a function of a single variable.

At the risk of belaboring this point we propose to take a look at the same relation from a different point of view, for the benefit of those familiar with matrices. As a differential is a linear function (transformation), it can be represented by a matrix—see the discussion preceding Example 7 in Section 13.4. Thus, using $d\mathbf{r}$ for the increment vector $dr\mathbf{i} + ds\mathbf{j}$, we can write

$$dF = \nabla F \cdot d\mathbf{r} = [F_r \; F_s]\begin{bmatrix} dr \\ ds \end{bmatrix}. \tag{65}$$

Assuming the conditions of Theorem 11 hold between F, f and x, y and r, s, we have, by the chain rule,

$$F_r = f_x x_r + f_y y_r, \qquad F_s = f_x x_s + f_y y_s.$$

Thus the matrix for ∇F can be written

$$[F_r \ F_s] = [f_x x_r + f_y \ y_r, \ f_x \ x_s + f_y y_s]$$

$$= [f_x \ f_y]\begin{bmatrix} x_r & x_s \\ y_r & y_s \end{bmatrix}.$$

Using this expression in (65), we see that

$$dF = [f_x \ f_y]\begin{bmatrix} x_r & x_s \\ y_r & y_s \end{bmatrix}\begin{bmatrix} dr \\ ds \end{bmatrix}$$

$$= [f_x \ f_y]\begin{bmatrix} x_r \, dr + x_s \, ds \\ y_r \, dr + y_s \, ds \end{bmatrix} = [f_x \ f_y]\begin{bmatrix} dx \\ dy \end{bmatrix}$$

$$= df.$$

EXERCISES

1. If $f(x, y, z) = x^2y + yz + 3zx$, and if $x = t$, $y = t^2$, $z = t^3$, find $\dfrac{dF}{dt}$, where $F(t) = f(x(t), y(t), z(t))$.

2. If $z = \ln \sqrt{x^2 + y^2}$, $x = u + v$, $y = u - v$, find $\dfrac{\partial z}{\partial v}$.

3. If $f(x, y) = \sin(x + y) - e^{xy}$, $x = 2r - s$, $y = r + 2s$, find F_r, where $F(r, s) = f(x(r, s), y(r, s))$.

4. Let $u = \sqrt{x^2 + y^2 + z^2}$, $x = \cos r \sin s$, $y = \sin r \sin s$, $z = \cos s$, find $\dfrac{\partial u}{\partial s}$.

5. If $w = \dfrac{zx}{x^2 + (y - 1)^2 + (z - 2)^2}$, if $x = u^2 + v^2$, $y = u^2 - v^2$, $z = 2uv$, find $\dfrac{\partial w}{\partial u}$.

6. If $u = yz + zx + xy$, and $x = \cos t$, $y = \sin t$, $z = t$, find $\dfrac{du}{dt}$.

7. Let $f(x, y) = x \log y + y \log x$, $x = r \cos \theta$, $y = r \sin \theta$; if $F(r, \theta) = f(r \cos \theta, r \sin \theta)$, find F_r and F_θ.

8. Let $u = xf\left(\dfrac{y}{x}\right)$, where f is differentiable. Show that u satisfies

$$x \frac{\partial u}{\partial x} + y \frac{\partial u}{\partial y} = u.$$

9. (a) Suppose f is a function of x and y and suppose these variables are replaced by polar coordinates $(x = r \cos \theta, \; y = r \sin \theta)$, giving a function F of r and θ. Find F_r and F_θ.

   (b) Solve the equations found in (a) for f_x and f_y.

   (c) With the results of (b), show that

$$f_x^2 + f_y^2 = F_r^2 + \frac{1}{r^2} F_\theta^2.$$

10. Let $r = (x^2 + y^2 + z^2)^{1/2}$.

   (a) Find ∇r.

   (b) Find ∇r^n.

11. A function f of two variables which satisfies

$$f(tx, ty) = t^n f(x, y) \qquad\qquad (*)$$

for all $t > 0$ is said to be *homogeneous of degree n*. For example, $f(x, y) = x^2 + y^2$ is homogeneous of degree 2, $f(x, y) = \dfrac{y}{x}$ is homogeneous of degree 0, and $g(x, y) = x^2 + xy + y$ is not homogeneous.

   Euler's theorem on homogeneous functions of degree n says that

$$x f_1(x, y) + y f_2(x, y) = n f(x, y).$$

Prove it.

[*Hint.* Start with the defining equation (*) and differentiate with respect to t. For the left-hand side, let $u = tx$, $v = ty$, and use a chain rule. You should come out with

$$f_1(u, v)x + f_2(u, v)y = nt^{n-1} f(x, y).$$

Now set $t = 1$.]

12. (a) Note that the right-hand side of the expression (52) is an inner product. What are the two vectors?

   (b) Same as (a) for both right-hand sides in (57).

13. Find F_θ and F_φ for the function F of Example 15.

13.8   Partial Derivatives of Higher Order

If f is a function of two variables, then so are both partial derivatives of f; each of these functions may, therefore, have two partial derivatives—second partial derivatives of f. Similarly, if g is a function of three variables, then each of the three partial derivatives may itself have three partial derivatives—the nine second partial derivatives of g. And so on.

Definition 19. *Let f be a function of two variables. Assume that each of these partial derivatives has derivatives. Then*

$$\frac{\partial^2 f}{\partial x^2} = \frac{\partial}{\partial x}\left(\frac{\partial f}{\partial x}\right) = f_{xx} = f_{11}$$

$$\frac{\partial^2 f}{\partial y\,\partial x} = \frac{\partial}{\partial y}\left(\frac{\partial f}{\partial x}\right) = f_{xy} = f_{12}$$

$$\frac{\partial^2 f}{\partial x\,\partial y} = \frac{\partial}{\partial x}\left(\frac{\partial f}{\partial y}\right) = f_{yx} = f_{21}$$

$$\frac{\partial^2 f}{\partial y^2} = \frac{\partial}{\partial y}\left(\frac{\partial f}{\partial y}\right) = f_{yy} = f_{22}.$$

More generally, if it exists,

$$\frac{\partial^{m+n+1} f}{\partial x^{m+1}\,\partial y^n} = \frac{\partial}{\partial x}\left(\frac{\partial^{m+n} f}{\partial x^m\,\partial y^n}\right) = f_{\underbrace{y\ldots y}_{n}\underbrace{x\ldots x\,x}_{m}}.$$

There is a kind of perversity about the different symbols for the second mixed partials,

$$\frac{\partial^2 f}{\partial x\,\partial y} = f_{yx} \quad \text{and} \quad \frac{\partial^2 f}{\partial y\,\partial x} = f_{xy}:$$

the order of the letters is different. In one way, things are worse than that, for books of some years ago used $\dfrac{\partial^2 f}{\partial y\,\partial x}$ for f_{yx} and $\dfrac{\partial^2 f}{\partial x\,\partial y}$ for f_{xy}. But in another way the situation is far better. Suppose we look at f, f_x, and f_y given in Eqs. (9), (10) and (11) in Section 13.2:

$$f(x, y) = x^2 y + \sin(x + y) + e^{xy^2}, \tag{9}$$

$$f_x(x, y) = 2xy + \cos(x + y) + y^2 e^{xy^2}, \tag{10}$$

$$f_y(x, y) = x^2 + \cos(x + y) + 2xy\, e^{xy^2}. \tag{11}$$

We calculate the four second derivatives:

$$f_{xx}(x, y) = 2y - \sin(x + y) + y^4 e^{xy^2}, \tag{66}$$

$$f_{xy}(x, y) = 2x - \sin(x + y) + 2xy^3 e^{xy^2} + 2y\, e^{xy^2}, \tag{67}$$

$$f_{yx}(x, y) = 2x - \sin(x + y) + 2xy^3 e^{xy^2} + 2y\, e^{xy^2}, \tag{68}$$

$$f_{yy}(x, y) = -\sin(x + y) + 4x^2 y^2 e^{xy^2} + 2x\, e^{xy^2}. \tag{69}$$

Our interest centers on (67) and (68): *the two second mixed partials are equal.* Coincidence, perhaps? The answer to that, for the functions with which one is usually concerned in elementary calculus, is No.

Theorem 13. *If f_{xy} and f_{yx} are continuous in an open region $X \subset \mathbf{R}^2$, then*

$$f_{xy}(x, y) = f_{yx}(x, y)$$

at all points $(x, y) \in X$.

Proof. Let $(a, b) \in X$, and suppose h and k are sufficiently small so that the rectangle with vertices (a, b), $(a + h, b)$, $(a, b + k)$, and $(a + h, b + k)$ lies in X (see Figure 16).

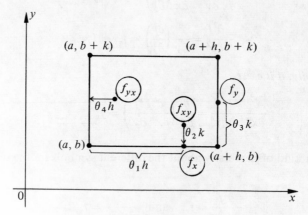

Figure 16

We consider the following combination, *the second difference of f*, of the values of the function at the vertices:

$$\Delta^2 f = f(a + h, b + k) - f(a + h, b) - f(a, b + k) + f(a, b)$$

$$= [f(a + h, b + k) - f(a + h, b)] - [f(a, b + k) - f(a, b)] \qquad \textbf{(70)}$$

$$= F(a + h) - F(a).$$

This last expression is obtained by introducing a function F of a single variable defined in terms of f:

$$F(x) = f(x, b + k) - f(x, b).$$

Now we apply the Mean Value Theorem to F on the interval $[a, a + h]$:

$$F(a + h) - F(a) = hF'(a + \theta_1 h), \qquad 0 < \theta_1 < 1.$$

In terms of f this becomes

$$\Delta^2 f = h[f_x(a + \theta_1 h, b + k) - f_x(a + \theta_1 h, b)].$$

But now we can apply the Mean Value Theorem a second time, treating f_x as a function of the second variable:

$$\Delta^2 f = hk[f_{xy}(a + \theta_1 h, b + \theta_2 k)], \qquad 0 < \theta_2 < 1. \qquad \textbf{(71)}$$

The next part of the proof is similar to the preceding part, involving an obvious variation in the order. We now write $\Delta^2 f$ as

$$\Delta^2 f = [f(a + h, b + k) - f(a, b + k)] - [f(a + h, b) - f(a, b)]$$
$$= G(b + k) - G(b),$$

where G is defined by $G(y) = f(a + h, y) - f(a, y)$.

A first application of the Mean Value Theorem to G on $[b, b + k]$ gives $G(b + k) - G(b) = kG'(b + \theta_3 k)$, $0 < \theta_3 < 1$, or

$$\Delta^2 f = k[f_y(a + h, b + \theta_3 k) - f_y(a, b + \theta_3 k)].$$

A final application of the Mean Value Theorem, now to f_y and in terms of the first variable gives

$$\Delta^2 f = hk[f_{yx}(a + \theta_4 h, b + \theta_3 k)]. \tag{72}$$

Equating the right-hand sides of (71) and (72) leads to

$$f_{xy}(a + \theta_1 h, b + \theta_2 k) = f_{yx}(a + \theta_4 h, b + \theta_3 k).$$

Now we draw on the continuity of f_{xy} and f_{yx} in X; as $(h, k) \to (0, 0)$ each expression in the preceding equation has as limit the value of its function at (a, b):

$$f_{xy}(a, b) = f_{yx}(a, b). \quad \blacksquare$$

Several comments are in order about this theorem. First, the hypotheses are stronger than they need be: one can weaken the hypotheses, but the proof is then more difficult.

Second, we see now that whenever Theorem 13 is valid, confusion about notation need create no problems. Moreover, although the statement of the theorem is for *second* derivatives of functions of *two* variables, it is easy to see that as long as all derivatives involved are continuous, the order in which they were calculated is irrelevant. This means, for example, that

$$f_{yxxyx} = f_{xxxyy} = \frac{\partial^5 f}{\partial x^3 \, \partial y^2},$$

or, if f is a function of three variables,

$$f_{xyzx} = f_{zyxx} = f_{xxyz} = \frac{\partial^4 f}{\partial x^2 \, \partial y \, \partial z},$$

assuming the derivatives involved are continuous.

Third, however, we must warn that equality of, for example, f_{xy} and f_{yx} need *not* hold (for example, see Exercise 5).

Example 16. Let f be defined by

$$f(x, y) = x^2 y + y e^x + x \sin y.$$

We show that $f_{112} = f_{121} = f_{211}$. We first calculate the first partials:

$$f_x(x, y) = 2xy + ye^x + \sin y, \quad f_y(x, y) = x^2 + e^x + x \cos y.$$

Then we can find the four second partial derivatives:

$$f_{xx}(x, y) = 2y + ye^x, \quad f_{yy}(x, y) = -x \sin y,$$
$$f_{xy}(x, y) = 2x + e^x + \cos y, \quad f_{yx}(x, y) = 2x + e^x + \cos y.$$

We now find three of the third derivatives:

$$f_{xxy}(x, y) = 2 + e^x, \quad f_{yxx}(x, y) = 2 + e^x.$$
$$f_{xyx}(x, y) = 2 + e^x,$$

From these, we see that $f_{112} = f_{121} = f_{211}$.

Calculation difficulties can arise when finding higher order derivatives of composite functions. Because this is one of the places where clarity is greater when working with general symbols rather than with symbols for specific functions, we begin our explication of the technique in general terms.

We consider a situation such as that for Theorem 11, i.e.,

$$u = f(x, y),$$
$$x = x(r, s),$$
$$y = y(r, s),$$

all functions being differentiable. Then, by Theorem 11,

$$u_r = f_x x_r + f_y y_r.$$

But now we want to find u_{rr}. We proceed as follows:

$$u_{rr} = \frac{\partial}{\partial r} u_r = \frac{\partial}{\partial r} (f_x x_r + f_y y_r)$$

$$= \frac{\partial}{\partial r} (f_x x_r) + \frac{\partial}{\partial r} (f_y y_r) \quad \text{(derivative of sum)}$$

$$= f_x \frac{\partial}{\partial r} x_r + x_r \frac{\partial}{\partial r} f_x + f_y \frac{\partial}{\partial r} y_r + y_r \frac{\partial}{\partial r} f_y \quad \text{(derivative of product)}.$$

Each term of this last expression requires a further differentiation; however, those in the first and third terms are easy, since $\frac{\partial}{\partial r} x_r = x_{rr}$ and $\frac{\partial}{\partial r} y_r = y_{rr}$. Moreover, *the differentiation in the second and fourth terms is simply a matter of applying Theorem 11 in each case: in the second term to f_x and in the fourth to f_y.*

Using these comments we can write

$$u_{rr} = f_x x_{rr} + x_r(f_{xx} x_r + f_{xy} y_r) + f_y y_{rr} + y_r(f_{yx} x_r + f_{yy} y_r).$$

This completes the differentiation. Rearranging terms and using $f_{yx} = f_{xy}$ gives

$$u_{rr} = f_{xx} x_r^2 + 2f_{xy} x_r y_r + f_{yy} y_r^2 + f_x x_{rr} + f_y y_{rr},$$

a formula which the student is urged *not* to try to remember.

To give emphasis to the procedure we also calculate u_{rs}, omitting some of the explanatory remarks. We have

$$u_{rs} = \frac{\partial}{\partial s} u_r = \frac{\partial}{\partial s} (f_x x_r + f_y y_r)$$

$$= \frac{\partial}{\partial s} (f_x x_r) + \frac{\partial}{\partial s} (f_y y_r)$$

$$= f_x x_{rs} + x_r \frac{\partial}{\partial s} f_x + f_y y_{rs} + y_r \frac{\partial}{\partial s} f_y$$

$$= f_x x_{rs} + x_r (f_{xx} x_s + f_{xy} y_s) + f_y y_{rs} + y_r (f_{yx} x_s + f_{yy} y_s)$$

$$= f_{xx} x_r x_s + f_{xy} (x_r y_s + x_s y_r) + f_{yy} y_r y_s + f_x x_{rs} + f_y y_{rs}.$$

Finally, we show how the technique works with a particular illustration.

Example 17. Let

$$u = x^2 + xy - 3y^2,$$

$$x = r \cos \theta,$$

$$y = r \sin \theta.$$

We find $u_{r\theta}$. First, of course, we write down u_r:

$$u_r = (2x + y) \cos \theta + (x - 6y) \sin \theta.$$

Now

$$u_{r\theta} = \frac{\partial}{\partial \theta} u_r = \frac{\partial}{\partial \theta} [(2x + y) \cos \theta + (x - 6y) \sin \theta]$$

$$= \frac{\partial}{\partial \theta} [(2x + y) \cos \theta] + \frac{\partial}{\partial \theta} [(x - 6y) \sin \theta]$$

$$= (2x + y)(-\sin \theta) + \cos \theta \frac{\partial}{\partial \theta} (2x + y)$$

$$+ (x - 6y) \cos \theta + \sin \theta \frac{\partial}{\partial \theta} (x - 6y)$$

$$= -(2x + y) \sin \theta + \cos \theta [2x_\theta + 1 y_\theta]$$
$$+ (x - 6y) \cos \theta + \sin \theta [1 x_\theta - 6 y_\theta]$$

$$= -(2x + y) \sin \theta + \cos \theta (-2r \sin \theta + r \cos \theta)$$
$$+ (x - 6y) \cos \theta + \sin \theta (-r \sin \theta - 6r \cos \theta)$$

$$= -(2x + y) \sin \theta + (x - 6y) \cos \theta + r(\cos 2\theta - 4 \sin 2\theta).$$

Of course, an equivalent answer could easily be found in this case by expressing u immediately in terms of r and θ; our interest here was in demonstrating a technique.

EXERCISES

1. For the function f of Example 16 verify each of the following:

   (a) $f_{yyx} = f_{xyy} = f_{yxy}$.

   (b) $f_{xxyy} = f_{yyxx} = f_{xyxy}$.

   (c) $f_{yyyx} = f_{xyyy} = f_{yxyy}$.

   (d) $f_{1112} = f_{1211} = f_{2111}$.

2. Find all second partial derivatives for each function described:

   (a) $f(x, y) = e^x \cos y + e^y \cos x$.

   (b) $f(x, y) = \tan^{-1} \dfrac{y}{x}$.

   (c) $f(x, y) = \log \sqrt{x^2 + y^2}$.

   (d) $f(x, y) = \log (x - \sqrt{x^2 - y^2})$.

   (e) $f(x, y) = x^2 e^y + y^2 \sin x$.

   (f) $f(x, y, z) = 2x^2 yz + 3xy^2 z - 4xyz^2 - x^2 y^2 z^2$.

   (g) $f(x, y, z) = \cos (xyz)$.

   (h) $f(x, y, z) = \dfrac{x^2 + y^2}{z} + z \sin (x^2 + y^2)$.

3. A function which satisfies $f_{xx} + f_{yy} = 0$ (the Laplace Differential Equation in two dimensions) is called a *harmonic function*. Show that each of the following functions is harmonic.

   (a) $f(x, y) = \log (x^2 + y^2)$.

   (b) $f(x, y) = e^x \cos y + e^y \cos x$.

   (c) $f(x, y) = \tan^{-1} \dfrac{y}{x}$.

   (d) $f(x, y) = e^x \sin y$.

   (e) $f(x, y) = x^2 - y^2$.

4. At a certain point (x_0, y_0) f_{xy} and f_{yx} both exist, but $f_{xy}(x_0, y_0) \neq f_{yx}(x_0, y_0)$. What can be said about f_{xy} and f_{yx} at (x_0, y_0)? Why?

5. Let f be defined on $\mathbf{R}^2$ by

$$\left\{ \begin{aligned} f(x, y) &= xy \frac{x^2 - y^2}{x^2 + y^2}, \qquad (x, y) \neq (0, 0) \\ f(0, 0) &= 0 \end{aligned} \right\}.$$

   (a) Find $f_x(0, y)$ and $f_y(x, 0)$.

   (b) Find $f_{xy}(0, y)$ and $f_{yx}(x, 0)$.

   (c) Find $f_{xy}(0, 0)$ and $f_{yx}(0, 0)$.

   (d) What can you conclude about f_{xy} and f_{yx} at $(0, 0)$?

6. For the function of Example 17 find:

   (a) u_{rr}.   (b) $u_{\theta r}$.   (c) $u_{\theta\theta}$.

7. Suppose we use $x^2 + y^2 + z^2 = 1$ to define z as a function f of x and y. Differentiate implicitly to find:

(a) $\dfrac{\partial z}{\partial x}$.

(c) $\dfrac{\partial^2 z}{\partial x^2} = \dfrac{\partial}{\partial x}\left(\dfrac{\partial z}{\partial x}\right)$.

(b) $\dfrac{\partial z}{\partial y}$.

(d) $\dfrac{\partial^2 z}{\partial x\,\partial y} = \dfrac{\partial}{\partial x}\left(\dfrac{\partial z}{\partial y}\right)$.

8. In each of the following suppose that z is defined implicitly as a function of x and y. Find the derivatives indicated.

(a) $x^2 + 4y^2 + 9z^2 = 36$; $\dfrac{\partial^2 z}{\partial x^2}$, $\dfrac{\partial^2 z}{\partial x\partial y}$.   (b) $2x + y^2 - (y - z)^2 = 1$; $\dfrac{\partial^2 z}{\partial y^2}$, $\dfrac{\partial^2 z}{\partial y\,\partial x}$.

(c) $x^2 + y^2 - z^2 = 4$; $\dfrac{\partial^2 z}{\partial x^2}$, $\dfrac{\partial^2 z}{\partial y^2}$.

9. If $u = f(x, y)$, $x = r \cos \theta$, $y = r \sin \theta$, show that

$$\frac{\partial^2 u}{\partial x^2} + \frac{\partial^2 u}{\partial y^2} = \frac{\partial^2 u}{\partial r^2} + \frac{1}{r}\frac{\partial u}{\partial r} + \frac{1}{r^2}\frac{\partial^2 u}{\partial \theta^2}$$

(see Exercise 3).

13.9 Maxima and Minima

One of the important applications of the derivative of a function of a single variable is to the location of extrema—maximum and minimum points. It is natural to expect the corresponding statement to hold for functions of several variables. This is so. Moreover, our experience in extending theory from functions of one to functions of several variables is sufficiently great to lead us to the following conclusions: (1) the theory will be very similar to, and perhaps a little more complicated than, that for the case studied earlier; and (2) the gradient vector of the function will play an essential role—*as it has in most of our work since the gradient was introduced.* We shall see that these expectations will be borne out.

We need, first of all, some definitions. These are, however, practically the same as those given in Chapter 2 (Definitions 2.8 and 2.9).

Definition 20. *Let f be defined on a region $X \subset \mathbf{R}^n$, let $\mathbf{x}_0 \in X$. Then*

f has a relative maximum [minimum] at $\mathbf{x}_0 \Leftrightarrow$

$\exists N(\mathbf{x}_0)$ *such that* $\forall \mathbf{x} \in N(\mathbf{x}_0) \Rightarrow f(\mathbf{x}) \le f(\mathbf{x}_0)[f(\mathbf{x}) \ge f(\mathbf{x}_0)]$.

Definition 21. *Let f be defined on a region $X \subset \mathbf{R}^n$, and let $\mathbf{x}_0 \in X$. Then*

f has an absolute maximum [minimum] at $\mathbf{x}_0 \Leftrightarrow$

$\forall \mathbf{x} \in X \Rightarrow f(\mathbf{x}) \le f(\mathbf{x}_0)[f(\mathbf{x}) \ge f(\mathbf{x}_0)]$.

If we wish to speak of a maximum or minimum without specifying which, we shall refer to an *extremum*.

For a function of a single variable the fact best known to calculus students about extrema is that if the derivative exists at the point it must then be zero there. The analogous theorem in the present case simply replaces the derivative f' with the gradient vector ∇f (see Theorem 2.8).

Theorem 14. *Suppose f has domain $X \subset \mathbf{R}^n$, $\mathbf{x}_0$ is an interior point of X, f is differentiable at $\mathbf{x}_0$, and f has a relative maximum or minimum at $\mathbf{x}_0$. Then $\nabla f(\mathbf{x}_0) = 0$. In symbols,*

$$\left.\begin{array}{l} f: X \to \mathbf{R},\ X \subset \mathbf{R}^n \\ \mathbf{x}_0 \in \mathscr{I}(X) \\ f\ differentiable\ at\ \mathbf{x}_0 \\ f\ has\ relative\ maximum \\ [minimum]\ at\ \mathbf{x}_0 \end{array}\right\} \Rightarrow \nabla f(\mathbf{x}_0) = 0.$$

Proof. We suppose, to the contrary, that $\nabla f(\mathbf{x}_0) \neq 0$ and we consider the value of f at a point near $\mathbf{x}_0$. In particular, we choose the nearby point to be $\mathbf{x}_0 + t\nabla f(\mathbf{x}_0)$, where $t \in \mathbf{R}$ (see Figure 17). By the definitions of differentiability and of gradient, we have then that

$$\Delta f = f(\mathbf{x}_0 + t\nabla f(\mathbf{x}_0)) - f(\mathbf{x}_0) = \nabla f(\mathbf{x}_0) \cdot (t\nabla f(\mathbf{x}_0)) + t\nabla f(\mathbf{x}_0) \cdot \boldsymbol{\varepsilon},$$

where $\lim_{t \to 0} |\boldsymbol{\varepsilon}| = 0$. We can write this as

$$\Delta f = t[|\nabla f(\mathbf{x}_0)|^2 + |\nabla f(\mathbf{x}_0)|\,|\boldsymbol{\varepsilon}|\cos\theta],$$

where θ is the angle between the gradient vector and $\boldsymbol{\varepsilon}$ (by Theorem 11.4). Because $\lim_{t \to 0} |\boldsymbol{\varepsilon}| = 0$, we can take t small enough so that the quantity in the brackets is

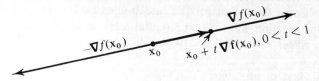

Figure 17

dominated by the first term and is, therefore, positive. But then $t > 0 \Rightarrow \Delta f > 0$, which means f could not have a maximum at $\mathbf{x}_0$; similarly, $t < 0 \Rightarrow \Delta f < 0$, which implies that f could not have a minimum at $\mathbf{x}_0$. It follows that for f to have either a maximum or a minimum at $\mathbf{x}_0$ it is *necessary* that $\nabla f(\mathbf{x}_0) = 0$. ∎

It is worth mentioning that

$$\nabla f(\mathbf{x}_0) = 0 \Rightarrow f_1(\mathbf{x}_0) = f_2(\mathbf{x}_0) = \cdots = f_n(\mathbf{x}_0) = 0. \tag{73}$$

(Is the converse true?) It is also worth emphasizing that the condition is only *necessary*.

Example 18. We consider the behavior of three functions at the origin.

(i) Let f be defined by $f(x, y) = x^2 + y^2$. Then $f_1(x, y) = 2x$, $f_2(x, y) = 2y$ and

$$\left.\begin{array}{l} f_1(x, y) = 0 \\ f_2(x, y) = 0 \end{array}\right\} \Rightarrow x = y = 0.$$

Thus the origin is the only candidate for an extremum. But $f(0, 0) = 0$ and $(x, y) \neq (0, 0) \Rightarrow f(x, y) > 0$. From this it is clear that f has a minimum—relative and absolute—at $(0, 0)$ (see Figure 18i).

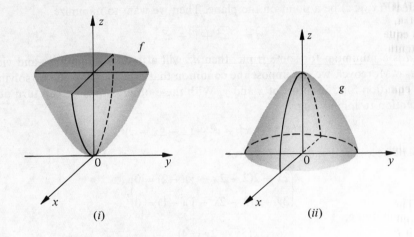

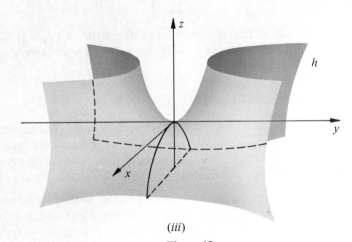

Figure 18

(ii) Let g be defined on $\mathbf{R}^2$ by $g(x, y) = 1 - x^2 - y^2$. Then $g_1(x, y) = -2x$, $g_2(x, y) = -2y$. Once again the condition of Theorem 14 [or Eq. (73)] leads to the origin as the only candidate for an extremum. But for this function, $g(0, 0) = 1$ and $(x, y) \neq (0, 0) \Rightarrow g(x, y) < 1$. We see then that g has a maximum at $(0, 0)$ (see Figure 18ii).

(iii) Finally, we consider a function h defined by $h(x, y) = y^2 - x^2$. For h we have $h_1(x, y) = -2x, h_2(x, y) = 2y$. Again $h_1(x, y) = h_2(x, y) = 0 \Rightarrow (x, y) = (0, 0)$. Now note that $h(0, 0) = 0$ and, if $\varepsilon > 0$, then $h(\varepsilon, 0) = -\varepsilon^2 < 0$, $h(0, \varepsilon) = \varepsilon^2 > 0$, from which it follows that $(0, 0)$ cannot be an extremum for h (see Figure 18iii).

As an illustration of a different sort we look at the following problem.

Example 19. We find the shortest distance from the origin to the plane $2x + y + z = 2$.

Let $P(x, y, z)$ be a point on the plane. Then we want to minimize

$$d = \sqrt{x^2 + y^2 + z^2}.$$

If d is a minimum for some triple, then d^2 will also be a minimum—and vice versa. Moreover, we can impose the condition that P be on the plane by solving its equation for z in terms of x and y. With these observations we can turn our attention to minimizing

$$f(x, y) = x^2 + y^2 + (2 - 2x - y)^2.$$

The necessary condition (73) gives

$$\begin{cases} 2x + 2(2 - 2x - y)(-2) = 0 \\ 2y + 2(2 - 2x - y)(-1) = 0 \end{cases},$$

or, simplifying,

$$\begin{cases} 5x + 2y = 4 \\ x + y = 1 \end{cases}. \qquad (74)$$

The unique solution of this system is easily found to be $(x_0 = \frac{2}{3}, y_0 = \frac{1}{3})$. From the equation of the plane we calculate that $z_0 = \frac{1}{3}$. The distance d_{min} from 0 to $P_0(\frac{2}{3}, \frac{1}{3}, \frac{1}{3})$ is

$$d_{min} = \frac{\sqrt{6}}{3}.$$

What is the justification for saying that f has a *minimum* at $(\frac{2}{3}, \frac{1}{3})$? The nonrigorous answer is that it is geometrically "obvious" that there should be a point on the plane closest to the origin, and the necessary conditions for an extremum of some sort produced only the candidate $(\frac{2}{3}, \frac{1}{3})$.

It is reasonably clear from the two preceding examples that we need a criterion so as to determine whether a candidate for an extremum *is* one, and, if so, which kind it is. For a function of a single variable, a useful criterion was expressible in terms of the second derivative. Now, a function of two variables has, assuming the usual continuity, three second derivatives. We shall see they all play a role in framing the desired condition.

We let f be a function of two variables and we assume f has continuous first and second partial derivatives at (x_0, y_0) in the domain of f. *The discriminant of f* is the function

$$\Delta = f_{xx}f_{yy} - f_{xy}^2. \qquad (75)$$

We shall, of course, be interested in the value of Δ at P_0. (The symbol Δ is, perhaps, being somewhat overworked, but then so is the other natural candidate, D.)

We state the following assertion without proof.

Theorem 15. *Let $f: X \to \mathbf{R}$, $X \subset \mathbf{R}^2$, and let $P_0(x_0, y_0) \in X$. Assume that all first and second derivatives of f are continuous at P_0, and assume that $f_1(x_0, y_0) = f_2(x_0, y_0) = 0$. Then*

(1) *If $\Delta(x_0, y_0) > 0$, f has an extremum at P_0, and*
    (a) *if $f_{11}(x_0, y_0) < 0$, the extremum is a maximum;*
    (b) *if $f_{11}(x_0, y_0) > 0$, the extremum is a minimum.*
(2) *If $\Delta(x_0, y_0) < 0$, f has no extremum at P_0.*
(3) *If $\Delta(x_0, y_0) = 0$, f may have either maximum or minimum at P_0, or neither.*

Several comments are in order about this theorem. First it is clear that if $\Delta(x_0, y_0) > 0$, then $f_{11}(x_0, y_0)$ and $f_{22}(x_0, y_0)$ must agree in sign—in particular, neither can be zero. Thus, in 1(a) and 1(b) in the theorem, f_{11} could be replaced by f_{22}. Second, assertion (3) is discussed in Exercise 9.

As an illustration of the use of Theorem 15, we return to the functions of Example 18. We have already seen that at the origin both first derivatives are zero for each of f, g, h. Moreover, at $(0, 0)$

$$\left.\begin{array}{l} f_{11} = f_{22} = 2 \\ f_{12} = 0, \quad \Delta = 4 \end{array}\right\} \Rightarrow f \text{ has minimum at } (0, 0);$$

$$\left.\begin{array}{l} g_{11} = g_{22} = -2 \\ g_{12} = 0, \quad \Delta = 4 \end{array}\right\} \Rightarrow g \text{ has maximum at } (0, 0)$$

and

$$\left.\begin{array}{l} h_{11} = -2, \quad h_{22} = 2 \\ h_{12} = 0, \quad \Delta = -4 \end{array}\right\} \Rightarrow h \text{ has no extremum at } (0, 0).$$

It is important to recall that an extremum might occur on the boundary of the region—and in this case Theorem 14 need not be applicable.

Example 20. We consider a disc, $x^2 + y^2 \le 1$, which has a temperature distribution described by $T(x, y) = 3x^2 + 2y^2 - 2x$. The problem is to find the maximum and minimum temperatures on the disc and the points where these occur.

Proceeding in the usual way, we find

$$T_1(x, y) = 6x - 2$$

$$T_2(x, y) = 4y.$$

Solving the system

$$\begin{pmatrix} 6x - 2 = 0 \\ 4y = 0 \end{pmatrix}$$

gives $(\frac{1}{3}, 0)$. Note that $T(\frac{1}{3}, 0) = \frac{1}{3} - \frac{2}{3} = -\frac{1}{3}$. It is easy to see, since $T(0, 0) = 0$, that if $(\frac{1}{3}, 0)$ is an extremum, it is a minimum. But at $(\frac{1}{3}, 0)$

$$\left.\begin{array}{ll} T_{11} = 6, & T_{22} = 4 \\ T_{12} = 0, & \Delta = 24 \end{array}\right\} \Rightarrow T(\tfrac{1}{3}, 0) = -\tfrac{1}{3} \text{ is a } \textit{minimum.}$$

In order to find the maximum value of T we must look on the boundary of the disc: $\{(x, y) \mid x^2 + y^2 = 1\}$. If we write T as

$$T(x, y) = 3x^2 + 2y^2 - 2x = x^2 + 2(x^2 + y^2) - 2x,$$

we see that *on the boundary,*

$$T_{\text{bdy}}(x) = x^2 + 2 - 2x, \quad -1 \le x \le 1.$$

Looking at the ends of this interval, we find

$$T_{\text{bdy}}(-1) = 5, \ T_{\text{bdy}}(1) = 1. \tag{76}$$

For any possible critical points on the interior of the interval we find

$$T'_{\text{bdy}}(x) = 2x - 2.$$

Since $T'_{\text{bdy}}(x) = 0 \Rightarrow x = 1$, we know from (76) that this gives a minimum on the boundary.

Our conclusion is that the hottest point on the disc is at $(-1, 0)$, where $T = 5$; the coldest point is $(\frac{1}{3}, 0)$, where $T = -\frac{1}{3}$. Would it be correct to say that for points (x, y) on the disc

$$-\tfrac{1}{3} \le T(x, y) \le 5,$$

and that for *every* T_0 between $-\frac{1}{3}$ and 5 there is (x_0, y_0) such that $T(x_0, y_0) = T_0$? Why?

EXERCISES

1. Show that the box (rectangular parallelpiped) of fixed volume and minimum surface area is a cube.

2. Show that the box (rectangular parallelpiped) of fixed surface area and maximum volume is a cube.

3. Find the dimensions of a topless box which encloses 108 cubic ft and has minimum surface area.

4. Consider the values of $F(x, y, z) = xyz^2$ as (x, y, z) travels on the surface of the unit sphere $x^2 + y^2 + z^2 = 1$. What are the maximum and minimum values of F and where do these occur?

5. Find the equation of the plane which goes through $(1, 2, 3)$ and which cuts off minimum volume from the first octant.

6. A metal plate occupies the position of the unit square and its interior, $\{(x, y)\mid 0 \leq x \leq 1, 0 \leq y \leq 1\}$. Find the maximum and minimum values of the temperature and the points where these extreme values occur, if the temperature distribution is given by

(a) $T(x, y) = x^2 + 2y^2 - x - 2y$.   (c) $T(x, y) = x^2 + 3y^2 - x - 2y$.

(b) $T(x, y) = 6 - 2x^2 - y^2 + x + 2y$.   (d) $T(x, y) = 4 - x^2 - 2y^2 + x + 2y$.

[*Hint.* Do not overlook the boundary points.]

7. A metal plate occupies the position of the unit circle and its interior, $\{(x, y)\mid x^2 + y^2 \leq 1\}$. Find the maximum and minimum values of the temperature and the points where these extrema occur if the temperature is given by

(a) $T(x, y) = x^2 + 2y^2 + x$.   (c) $T(x, y) = 4 - x^2 - 2y^2 + x$.

(b) $T(x, y) = x^2 + 2y^2 + y$.

8. Use vector techniques to find the minimum distance from the origin to the plane of Example 19.

9. Show that for each of the following functions $\Delta(0, 0) = 0$. Then show that at the origin f has a minimum, g has a maximum, and h has neither.

(i) $f(x, y) = x^4 + y^4$.   (ii) $g(x, y) = 1 - x^4 - y^4$.   (iii) $h(x, y) = x^3 + y^3$.

Chapter **14** Multiple Integration

In the preceding chapter we saw how some of the ideas of differential calculus of functions of a single variable (functions defined on **R**) could be extended to functions of several variables (functions defined on $\mathbf{R}^n$, $n \geq 2$). It will be our purpose in this chapter to carry out a similar program for integral calculus. We shall see that the extension of the integral is possible in a natural and useful way. Moreover, as was the case with partial derivatives, we shall find that the calculation techniques for functions of a single variable will enable us to evaluate most of the multiple integrals one usually encounters in elementary work.

14.1 The Double Integral

In order to achieve our first aim, defining an integral for a function defined on a subset of $\mathbf{R}^2$, we begin by reviewing briefly the definition of an integral of a function of a single variable.

We assume the function f is bounded on a closed interval $[a, b]$. Next we form a partition π of $[a, b]$:

$$\pi = \{a = x_0, x_1, x_2, \ldots, x_{i-1}, x_i, \ldots, x_{n-1}, x_n = b\},$$

where $x_{i-1} < x_i$ for $i = 1, \ldots, n$. We then choose, quite arbitrarily, a point in each of the subintervals of the partition: $x_{i-1} \leq z_i \leq x_i$ (see Figure 1.) By definition, the *norm* $|\pi|$ of the partition is $|\pi| = \max\limits_{i=1, \ldots, n} [x_i - x_{i-1}] = \max\limits_{i=1, \ldots, n} \Delta x_i$,

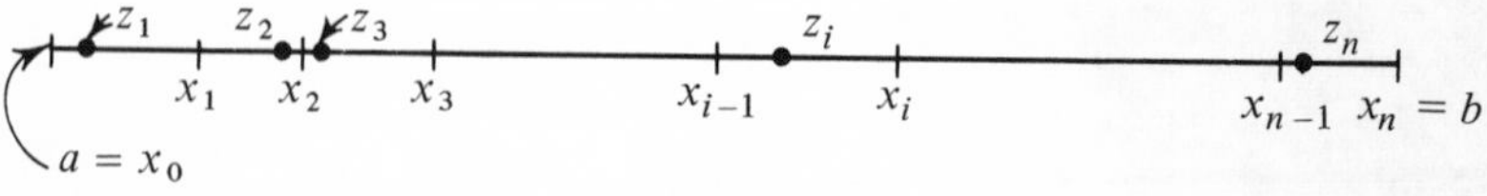

Figure 1

where $\Delta x_i = x_i - x_{i-1}$. The next step is to form the Riemann sum (also called an *approximating sum*)

$$\sum_{i=1}^{n} f(z_i) \, \Delta x_i,$$

and, finally, to inquire whether such sums approach a limit L in the following sense:

$$\lim_{|\pi| \to 0} \sum_{i=1}^{n} f(z_i) \, \Delta x_i = L \Leftrightarrow$$

for every $\varepsilon > 0 \Rightarrow \exists \delta_\varepsilon > 0$ such that for every partition π with

$$|\pi| < \delta \Rightarrow \left| \sum_{i=1}^{n} f(z_i) \, \Delta x_i - L \right| < \varepsilon,$$

for every possible choice of $z_i \in [x_{i-1}, x_i]$. When the preceding limit does exist we say f is integrable on $[a, b]$ and write, instead of L, $\int_a^b f$ or $\int_a^b f(x) \, dx$.

Now the obvious extension would involve a function f with domain $X \subset \mathbf{R}^2$; the analog of an interval would be the cartesian product of two intervals: $[a, b] \times [c, d]$, this being a rectangle S in the plane. We assume f is bounded on this rectangle. The partition of the rectangle can be achieved by a partition of each of the intervals $[a, b]$ and $[c, d]$:

$$\{a = x_0, x_1, \ldots, x_i, \ldots, x_{m-1}, x_m = b\},$$

$$\{c = y_0, y_1, \ldots, y_j, \ldots, y_{n-1}, y_n = d\}.$$

(For future reference we call attention to the fact that this partition makes use of some of the coordinate curves, $x = c$ and $y = c$.) Then in each subregion (subrectangle) determined by the partition we choose, quite arbitrarily, a point $(u_i, v_j) \in [x_{i-1}, x_i] \times [y_{j-1}, y_j]$. (There is a minor notational difficulty here. As just described, it would appear that, for a fixed i, the points (u_i, v_j) must all have the same abscissa u_i — and similarly, for a fixed j the points (u_i, v_j) would all have the same ordinate v_j. This need not be so; for every pair (i, j), (u_i, v_j) can be chosen as *any* point in $[x_{i-1}, x_i] \times [y_{j-1}, y_j]$.)

For the *norm* $|\pi|$ of the partition we use the *maximum diagonal of the sub-rectangles*:

$$|\pi| = \max\sqrt{\Delta x_i^2 + \Delta y_j^2},$$

where $\Delta x_i = x_i - x_{i-1}$, $\Delta y_j = y_j - y_{j-1}$, and (x_i, y_j) is a partition point (see Figure 2).

Continuing with our analogy to the one variable case, we next form a Riemann sum,

$$\sum_{i=1}^{m} \sum_{j=1}^{n} f(u_i, v_j) \, \Delta x_i \, \Delta y_j.$$

With these preliminaries we are now ready for a definition.

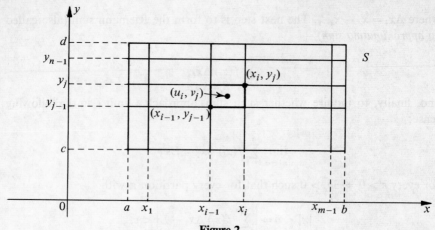

Figure 2

Definition 1. *Let the function f be bounded on the rectangle S, $[a, b] \times [c, d]$. Then f is **integrable** on $S \Leftrightarrow \lim\limits_{|\pi| \to 0} \sum_{i=1}^{m} \sum_{j=1}^{n} f(u_i, v_j) \Delta x_i \Delta y_j = L$, where the limit is to be interpreted in the following sense: $\forall \varepsilon > 0 \Rightarrow \exists \delta_\varepsilon > 0$ such that for all partitions π with $|\pi| < \delta$ and for all possible choices of $(u_i, v_j) \in [x_{i-1}, x_i] \times [y_{j-1}, y_j]$ it is true that*

$$\left| \sum_{i=1}^{m} \sum_{j=1}^{n} f(u_i, v_j) \Delta x_i \Delta y_j - L \right| < \varepsilon.$$

When the limit exists we use, rather than L, the symbol

$$\iint_S f \quad \text{or} \quad \iint_S f(x, y) \, dA,$$

*called the **double integral** of f over the rectangle S.*

In contrast to what we saw in the preceding chapter when we attempted to extend the idea of derivative to functions of two variables—and found that the "obvious" extension usually failed to exist—the foregoing generalization of integral to functions of two variables "works," in that the analogy to the one variable case is nearly complete.

An immediate question What functions *are* integrable? is answered by the following theorem, which we state without proof.

Theorem 1. *If f is bounded on a rectangle $S = [a, b] \times [c, d]$ and continuous there with the possible exception—as regards continuity—of a set of points of area zero, then f is integrable on S.*

We hasten to point out that we use the word "area" in the statement of this theorem in the intuitive sense. For example, the area of the boundary of S is zero, as is the area of the set of points on any of the curves we have encountered in our work thus far. On the other hand, the existence of exceedingly strange and pathological sets in $\mathbf{R}^2$ can be the source of major difficulties, however, we shall be concerned only with "well-behaved" subsets of $\mathbf{R}^2$.

We next consider the possibility of defining an integral over a region which is not a rectangle. In order to do this we need the following definition.

Definition 2. *A subset S of* $\mathbf{R}^2$ *is* **bounded** $\Leftrightarrow$ *S is contained entirely within a circle of finite radius M and center at the origin. In other words, S is bounded* $\Leftrightarrow$ $\forall (x, y) \in S \Rightarrow x^2 + y^2 < M^2$.

Now suppose we have a function f which is bounded on a bounded set $S \subset \mathbf{R}^2$, the boundary of S having zero area. We choose a rectangle S^* such that $S \subset S^*$ (see Figure 3) and we define an extension f^* of f to S^* as follows:

$$\left.\begin{cases} (x, y) \in S \Rightarrow f^*(x, y) = f(x, y) \\ (x, y) \in S^* - S \Rightarrow f^*(x, y) = 0 \end{cases}\right\}. \tag{1}$$

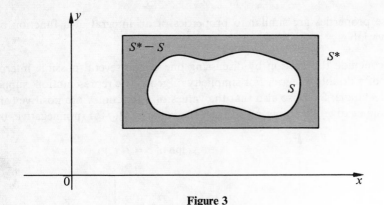

Figure 3

Definition 3. *If f is a bounded function on a bounded set S, if S* is a rectangle containing S in its interior, and if f* is defined on S* as in (1), then*

$$\iint\limits_{S} f(x, y)\, dA = \iint\limits_{S^*} f^*(x, y)\, dA,$$

provided the integral on the right exists.

Note that even if f is continuous on S, f^* is likely to be discontinuous on S^*, unless f has the value zero on the boundary of S.

We remark also that, as should be clear from the preceding statement, when we use the word "rectangle" in this chapter we mean a rectangle with sides parallel to the coordinate axes.

We postpone until the next section the question of how to evaluate a double integral if it exists, and report now on some of the properties of the double integral. In the following theorem, which we do not prove, all sets are assumed to be bounded.

Theorem 2

(1) *If the functions f and g are integrable on S, if a, b* $\in$ **R**, *then af + bg is integrable on S, and*

$$\iint_S [af(x, y) + bg(x, y)] \, dA = a \iint_S f(x, y) \, dA + b \iint_S g(x, y) \, dA.$$

(2) *If f is integrable on S and f(x, y)* $\geq$ 0, *all (x, y)* $\in$ *S, then* $\iint_S f(x, y) \, dA \geq 0$.

(3) *If f and g are integrable on S and if (x, y)* $\in$ *S* $\Rightarrow$ *f(x, y)* $\leq$ *g(x, y), then*

$$\iint_S f(x, y) \, dA \leq \iint_S g(x, y) \, dA.$$

(4) *If f is integrable on* S_1 *and on* S_2, *if* $S = S_1 \cup S_2$, *and if the area of* $S_1 \cap S_2$ *is zero, then f is integrable on S and*

$$\iint_S f(x, y) \, dA = \iint_{S_1} f(x, y) \, dA + \iint_{S_2} f(x, y) \, dA.$$

These properties are similar to properties of an integral of a function of a single variable.

We conclude this section by discussing one of the several possible interpretations of a double integral. For simplicity of geometric representation, suppose S is a rectangle. Suppose also that the values of a function f are positive (or at least nonnegative) at points of S. Then the value of $\iint_S f \, dA$ (nonnegative, by 2

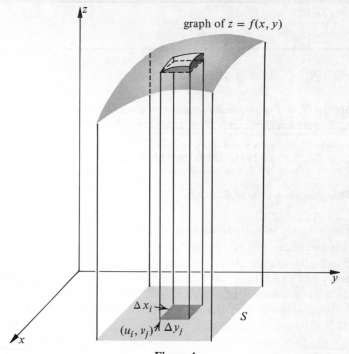

Figure 4

of Theorem 2) will represent the volume bounded above by the surface $z = f(x, y)$, below by S and on the sides by plane regions parallel to the zx- and yz-planes (see Figure 4).

For, just as the individual terms in the Riemann sum for the integral of a positive function of a single variable can be interpreted as areas of rectangles, so can the individual terms of the Riemann sum for the double integral of a positive function be interpreted as the measure of the volume of a column, of height $f(u_i, v_j)$, area of base $\Delta x_i \Delta y_j$. Thus the Riemann sum can be thought of as an approximating sum for the measure of the volume illustrated in Figure 4).

Example 1. We let S be the unit square, $\{(x, y) \mid 0 \le x \le 1, 0 \le y \le 1\}$ and we let f be defined on S by $f(x, y) = 1 - y$. By geometry, then, it is easy to see (cf. Figure 5) that $\iint_S f(x, y) \, dA = \frac{1}{2}$.

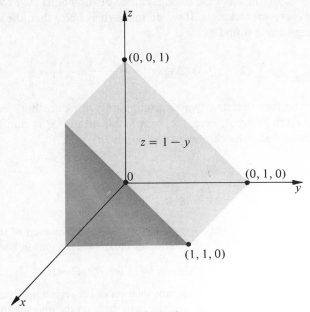

Figure 5

Even though the geometric interpretation of the double integral enables us, in this simple case, to find its exact value, we illustrate the definition by making a rather coarse partition and finding two approximating sums. The partition is illustrated in Figure 6: on both the x- and y-axes we use $\{0, \frac{1}{2}, 1\}$ as the linear partition; thus the area of each of the subrectangles is equal to $\frac{1}{4}$ square unit. If we use the midpoint of each subrectangle as the point (u, v) for our first approximating sum, then its value is

$$\sum_{i=1}^{2} \sum_{j=1}^{2} (1 - v_j) \Delta x_i \Delta y_j = \left(\frac{3}{4} + \frac{1}{4} + \frac{3}{4} + \frac{1}{4} \right) \cdot \frac{1}{4} = \frac{1}{2}.$$

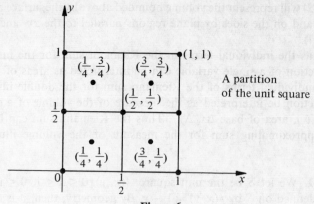

Figure 6

A second possibility in this case for the choice of the points (u, v) would be to use $(\frac{1}{2}, \frac{1}{2})$ for *every* subrectangle. If we do make this choice then the value of the approximating sum is found as

$$\sum_{i=1}^{2}\sum_{j=1}^{2}(1 - v_j)\,\Delta x_i\,\Delta y_j = \left(\frac{1}{2} + \frac{1}{2} + \frac{1}{2} + \frac{1}{2}\right)\frac{1}{4} = \frac{1}{2}.$$

Of course the fact that the two approximating sums are both equal to the exact value of the integral, even for such small m and n, is due to the very special nature of f and the choices of the points (u_i, v_j).

E X E R C I S E S

1. Let S be the unit square, $\{(x, y) \mid 0 \le x \le 1, 0 \le y \le 1\}$. For each of the following functions use the geometric interpretation of the double integral to find its value.

   (a) $f(x, y) = x$.   (b) $f(x, y) = \sqrt{1 - x^2}$.   (c) $f(x, y) = 1$.

   (d) $f(x, y) = x + y$. [*Hint.* Consider the relation of the region involved to the box (rectangular parallelepiped) of height 2, with base on the unit square.]

2. For each of the functions of Exercise 1 find approximating sums for the double integral by using the partition and the two different choices of (u_i, v_j) of Example 1.

3. Say whether or not each of the following functions is integrable over the region described. If the answer is negative, say why. Sketch S.

   (a) $f(x, y) = xy$, $S = \{(x, y) \mid x^2 + y^2 \le 1\}$.

   (b) $f(x, y) = \dfrac{1}{xy}$, $S = \{(x, y) \mid x^2 + y^2 \le 1\}$.

   (c) $f(x, y) = xy$, $S = \{(x, y) \mid x \ge 0, y \ge 0\}$.

(d) $f(x, y) = e^{-x-y}$, $S = \{(x, y)|\ 0 \le x \le 1, 0 \le y \le x\}$.

(e) $f(x, y) = e^{-x-y}$, $S = \{(x, y)|\ x \ge 0, y \ge 0\}$.

(f) $f(x, y) = \dfrac{1 + xy}{x^2 + y^2}$, $S = \{(x, y)|\ 0 \le x \le 1, 0 \le y \le 1\}$.

(g) $f(x, y) = \dfrac{1 + xy}{x^2 + y^2}$, $S = \{(x, y)|\ 1 \le x \le 3, 0 \le y \le x^2\}$.

(h) $f(x, y) = [x] + [y]$, $S = \{(x, y)|\ 0 \le x \le 2, 0 \le y \le 4\}$.

(i) $f(x, y) = \log(x^2 + y^2)$, $S = \{(x, y)|\ 0 \le x \le 1, 0 \le y \le 1\}$.

(j) $f(x, y) = \log(x^2 + y^2)$, $S = \{(x, y)|\ 1 \le x \le 4, 0 \le y \le \sqrt{x}\}$.

(k) $\begin{cases} \text{if } x^2 + y^2 \le 1, \text{ then } f(x, y) = 1 - x^2 - y^2 \\ \text{if } x^2 + y^2 > 1, \text{ then } f(x, y) = x^2 + y^2 - 1 \end{cases}$, $S = \{(x, y)|\ x^2 + y^2 \le 4\}$.

4. Justify assertion (2) of Theorem 2.

5. By using assertion (2) of Theorem 2, prove assertion (3).

6. Let f be defined by $f(x, y) = \sqrt{4 - x^2 - y^2}$; let $S = \{(x, y)|\ 0 \le x \le 2, 0 \le y \le \sqrt{4 - x^2}\}$.

(a) Use the geometric interpretation of the double integral to find

$$\iint\limits_{S} f(x, y)\, dA.$$

(b) Using the partition $\{0, 1, 2\}$ on both the x- and y-axes, find an approximating sum for the integral of part (a). *You* choose the (u_i, v_j).

14.2 Iterated Integrals

Our primary aim in this section is to obtain a reasonable method for evaluating a double integral of a function f over a region $S \subset \mathbf{R}^2$.

It turns out that the major tool is what amounts to a close analog of the second mixed partial derivative, namely, an *iterated integral*. The sense in which these concepts are analogous will be quite clear from Definition 4.

We shall work at first with rectangular regions. Later, by means of Definition 3, we can extend the ideas to regions of more general types.

Suppose we begin with an illustration.

Example 2. We consider

$$I_1 = \int_0^2 \left(\int_1^4 (x^2 y + 2xy^2)\, dy \right) dx,$$

the interpretation being as follows: one starts with the inner integral, integrating with respect to y—this is indicated by the presence of the dy—holding x fixed;

the result will be a function of x which is in turn integrated. Watch.

$$I_1 = \int_0^2 \left(\int_1^4 (x^2 y + 2xy^2) \, dy \right) dx = \int_0^2 \left(\frac{1}{2} x^2 y^2 + \frac{2}{3} xy^3 \Big|_1^4 \right) dx$$

$$= \int_0^2 \left[\left(\frac{1}{2} x^2 \cdot 4^2 + \frac{2}{3} x \cdot 4^3 \right) - \left(\frac{1}{2} x^2 + \frac{2}{3} x \right) \right] dx$$

$$= \int_0^2 \left(\frac{15}{2} x^2 + 42x \right) dx = \frac{5}{2} x^3 + 21x^2 \Big|_0^2$$

$$= 104.$$

We leave it for the student to verify that

$$I_2 = \int_1^4 \left(\int_0^2 (x^2 y + 2xy^2) \, dx \right) dy = 104.$$

Now the interesting fact is that if we let $f(x, y) = x^2 y + 2xy^2$ and let $S = \{(x, y) \mid 0 \leq x \leq 2, \ 1 \leq y \leq 4\}$, then

$$\iint_S f(x, y) \, dA = I_1 = I_2 = 104,$$

as we shall show.

First we define the iterated integrals.

Definition 4. *Let f be defined on $S = [a, b] \times [c, d]$, integrable with respect to y for every $x \in [a, b]$ and integrable with respect to x for every $y \in [c, d]$. Let, or $x \in [a, b]$, $y \in [c, d]$.*

$$\int_c^d f(x, y) \, dy = F(x) \qquad \int_a^b f(x, y) \, dx = G(y).$$

*Then the **iterated integrals** of f are*

$$\int_a^b \left(\int_c^d f(x, y) \, dy \right) dx = \int_a^b F(x) \, dx,$$

$$\int_c^d \left(\int_a^b f(x, y) \, dx \right) dy = \int_c^d G(y) \, dy.$$

Usually the parentheses separating the inner and outer integrals are not written; however, we shall continue to use them, at least for a while.

The assertion we made at the end of Example 2 can now be stated formally and demonstrated.

Theorem 3. *Let f be continuous on $S = [a, b] \times [c, d]$. Then*

$$\iint_S f \, dA = \int_a^b \left(\int_c^d f(x, y) \, dy \right) dx = \int_c^d \left(\int_a^b f(x, y) \, dx \right) dy. \qquad (2)$$

Before giving the proof we take time to describe a plausibility argument, for positive f, in terms of volumes. We refer to Figure 7. For $x_0 \in [a, b]$, the number

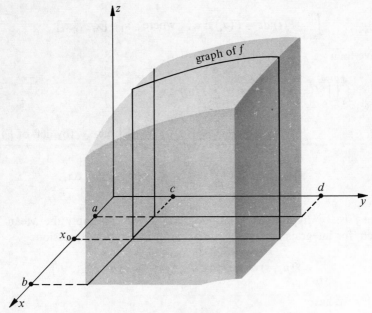

Figure 7

$F(x_0) = \int_c^d f(x_0, y)\, dy$ represents the area of the plane section cut from the solid by the plane $x = x_0$. As we saw in Section 2.10, the volume bounded above by the surface can then be found as

$$V = \int_a^b F(x)\, dx = \int_a^b \left(\int_c^d f(x, y)\, dy \right) dx.$$

Since we also know that

$$V = \iint_S f(x, y)\, dA,$$

we conclude that

$$\iint_S f(x, y)\, dA = \int_a^b \left(\int_c^d f(x, y)\, dy \right) dx.$$

A similar argument, with the plane $y = y_0$, $y_0 \in [c, d]$, makes the remainder of (2) reasonable.

Proof of Theorem 3. We consider a partition π of S as described before Definition 1 in the preceding section. Then

$$\int_a^b \left(\int_c^d f(x, y)\, dy \right) dx = \int_a^b F(x)\, dx = \sum_{i=1}^m \int_{x_{i-1}}^{x_i} F(t)\, dt.$$

Now f continuous on $S \Rightarrow F$ is continuous on $[a, b]$. Thus, by the Mean Value Theorem for integrals (Theorem 2.14) each of the m integrals in the preceding sum can be written as

$$\int_{x_{i-1}}^{x_i} F(t) \, dt = F(u_i) \, \Delta x_i, \quad \text{where} \quad u_i \in [x_{i-1}, x_i].$$

We have then

$$\int_a^b \left(\int_c^d f(x, y) \, dy \right) dx = \sum_{i=1}^m F(u_i) \, \Delta x_i$$

$$= \sum_{i=1}^m \left(\int_c^d f(u_i, y) \, dy \right) \Delta x_i \quad \text{(by def. of } F)$$

$$= \sum_{i=1}^m \left(\sum_{j=1}^n \int_{y_{j-1}}^{y_j} f(u_i, s) \, ds \right) \Delta x_i.$$

Since f is, by hypothesis, continuous on S, we can apply the Mean Value Theorem for integrals to each of the integrals in the last expression:

$$\int_{y_{j-1}}^{y_j} f(u_i, s) \, ds = f(u_i, v_j) \, \Delta y_j, \quad v_j \in [y_{j-1}, y_j].$$

With this we have

$$\int_a^b \left(\int_c^d f(x, y) \, dy \right) dx = \sum_{i=1}^m \sum_{j=1}^n f(u_i, v_j) \, \Delta x_i \, \Delta y_j, \tag{3}$$

an approximating sum for $\iint_S f(x, y) \, dA$. Since f, continuous on S, is integrable there, the expression on the right-hand side of (3) can be made as close as we please to $\iint_S f(x, y) \, dA$, by taking $|\pi|$ sufficiently small. But, by (3) the approximating sum is in every case equal to the iterated integral. It must follow that the double integral and the iterated integral are equal. In a similar way one can show that

$$\int_c^d \left(\int_a^b f(x, y) \, dx \right) dy = \iint_S f \, dA. \quad \blacksquare$$

Example 3. Let f be defined by $f(x, y) = xy\sqrt{1 - x^2 y}$, let $S = [0, \sqrt{2}] \times [0, \frac{1}{2}]$. We find

$$I = \iint_S f(x, y) \, dA.$$

By Theorem 3,

$$\iint_S f(x, y) \, dA = \int_0^{1/2} \left(\int_0^{\sqrt{2}} xy\sqrt{1 - x^2 y} \, dx \right) dy.$$

(We draw on the ever ready authorial omniscience for the decision to integrate first over x.) By suitably adjusting the inner integral, we have

$$I = \int_0^{1/2} \left(-\frac{1}{2} \int_0^{\sqrt{2}} (1 - x^2 y)^{1/2} (- 2xy \, dx) \right) dy$$

$$= \int_0^{1/2} \left(-\frac{1}{2} \cdot \frac{2}{3} (1 - x^2 y)^{3/2} \Big|_0^{\sqrt{2}} \right) dy = -\frac{1}{3} \int_0^{1/2} [(1 - 2y)^{3/2} - 1] \, dy$$

$$= -\frac{1}{3} \left[-\frac{1}{2} \cdot \frac{2}{5} (1 - 2y)^{5/2} - y \Big|_0^{1/2} \right] = \frac{1}{3} \left[\frac{1}{5} (0 - 1) + \frac{1}{2} \right]$$

$$= \frac{1}{10}.$$

The student should experiment briefly with the possibility of integrating first with respect to y.

Example 4. Suppose f is defined by $f(x, y) = xy \sin xy^2$; let S be the rectangle $\left[0, \frac{\pi}{2} \right] \times [0, 1]$. We seek the value of $I = \iint_S f \, dA$.

By Theorem 3, we can use an iterated integral:

$$I = \int_0^{\pi/2} \left(\int_0^1 xy \sin xy^2 \, dy \right) dx$$

$$= \int_0^{\pi/2} \left(\frac{1}{2} \int_0^1 \sin xy^2 (2xy \, dy) \right) dx = \int_0^{\pi/2} \left(-\frac{1}{2} \cos xy^2 \Big|_0^1 \right) dx$$

$$= \int_0^{\pi/2} \left(-\frac{1}{2} \cos x + \frac{1}{2} \right) dx = \frac{1}{2} \left[x - \sin x \Big|_0^{\pi/2} \right]$$

$$= \frac{1}{2} \left(\frac{\pi}{2} - 1 \right) \approx 0.285.$$

When S is not a rectangle it will often—*but not invariably*—be a region of one of the following types:

(i) $\{(x, y) \mid a \le x \le b, g_1(x) \le y \le g_2(x)\}$,

(ii) $\{(x, y) \mid h_1(y) \le x \le h_2(y), c \le y \le d\}$;

these could perhaps be called pseudorectangles (see Figure 8). It is to be understood here that g_1 and g_2 are functions whose graphs form part of the boundary of S [in (i)]; similarly for the functions h_1 and h_2 in (ii).

By means of the extension f^* of f, as described in (1), and Definition 3, we

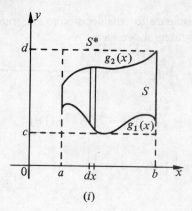
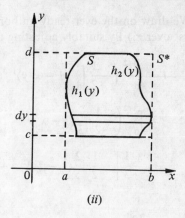

(i)   (ii)

Figure 8

can easily use iterated integrals to evaluate double integrals over regions of the types described. Thus, if f is continuous on a region such as (i), we have

$$\iint_S f \, dA = \iint_{S^*} f^* \, dA \qquad \text{(Definition 3)}$$

$$= \int_a^b \left(\int_c^d f^*(x, y) \, dy \right) dx. \qquad \text{(Theorem 3)}$$

or

$$\iint_S f \, dA = \int_a^b \left(\int_{g_1(x)}^{g_2(x)} f(x, y) \, dy \right) dx, \qquad (4)$$

since $(x, y) \in S^* - S \Rightarrow f^*(x, y) = 0$.

In a similar way, for a function f continuous over a region S such as (ii),

$$\iint_S f \, dA = \iint_{S^*} f^* \, dA$$

$$= \int_c^d \left(\int_a^b f^*(x, y) \, dx \right) dy,$$

or, since $(x, y) \in S^* - S \Rightarrow f^*(x, y) = 0$,

$$\iint_S f \, dA = \int_c^d \left(\int_{h_1(y)}^{h_2(y)} f(x, y) \, dx \right) dy. \qquad (5)$$

It is important to realize that for regions of these more general types one may be essentially restricted to just one choice for the order of integration in the iterated integral. Thus, in (i) we integrate first over y, whereas in (ii) we integrate first with respect to x. One can think intuitively of integration with respect to y as a summing in the y direction and of integration with respect to x as a summing in the x direction (positively, from left to right) (see the "elements" in Figure 8).

One further remark is in order at this point. Conceptually, double integrals and iterated integrals are quite different—see Definitions 1 and 4—and they should not be confused. Usually what is wanted is the value of the double integral; by Theorem 3 this number can be found by translating the double integral to a suitable iterated integral.

Example 5. Let f be defined by $f(x, y) = y \sin x$, let

$$S = \left\{ (x, y) \,\middle|\, 0 \le x \le \frac{\pi}{2}, 0 \le y \le x \right\}$$

(see Figure 9). We find

$$I = \iint_S f(x, y)\, dA.$$

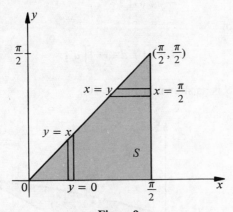

Figure 9

Although S is not rectangular it is possible to find I by integrating first in either direction. We illustrate by integrating over x first. Thus

$$I = \int_0^{\pi/2} \left(\int_y^{\pi/2} y \sin x\, dx \right) dy = \int_0^{\pi/2} \left(-y \cos x \,\bigg|_y^{\pi/2} \right) dy$$

$$= \int_0^{\pi/2} y \cos y\, dy = y \sin y + \cos y \,\bigg|_0^{\pi/2}$$

$$= \frac{\pi}{2} - 1.$$

The integration over y first would proceed as follows. The limits on the iterated integral are obtained best from the picture of S, *not* by some mechanical manipulation of the limits used in the last equation.

$$I = \int_0^{\pi/2} \left(\int_0^x y \sin x\, dy \right) dx = \int_0^{\pi/2} \left(\frac{1}{2} y^2 \sin x \,\bigg|_0^x \right) dx$$

$$= \frac{1}{2} \int_0^{\pi/2} x^2 \sin x\, dx = \frac{1}{2} \left(2x \sin x - (x^2 - 2) \cos x \,\bigg|_0^{\pi/2} \right)$$

$$= \frac{\pi}{2} - 1.$$

It will be noted that the antidifferentiation problem for the second method is slightly more involved than that for the first; of course, with a set of tables available there is essentially no difference.

Example 6. In this example our concern is with the mechanics of translating from the double integral to the iterated integrals. In order, therefore, not to get distracted by extraneous matters, we take f to be the constant function $f(x, y) = 1$, all (x, y). We take S as the region bounded by the curves

$$y^2 = x + 3.$$

$$y = \tfrac{1}{2}x.$$

We seek the value of

$$I = \iint_S f \, dA = \iint_S dA.$$

We discern that S is as shown in Figure 10.

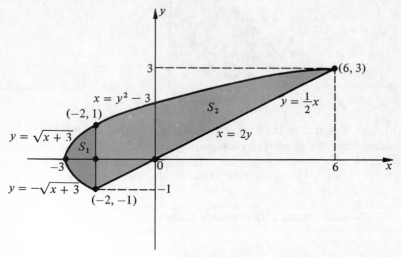

Figure 10

(a) Suppose we agree to use the iterated integral which integrates in the x direction first. We note that the left-hand boundary of S is everywhere, i.e., for all y involved, the parabola, whereas the right-hand boundary is everywhere the straight line. We must therefore express the equations of these curves as functions of y:

$$x = y^2 - 3,$$

$$x = 2y.$$

Then

$$I = \iint_S dA = \int_{-1}^{3} \left(\int_{y^2-3}^{2y} dx \right) dy.$$

Notice that the y interval is obtained by projecting S horizontally onto the y-axis. The evaluation of the preceding integral is quite straightforward:

$$I = \int_{-1}^{3} (2y - y^2 + 3)\, dy = y^2 - \frac{1}{3} y^3 + 3y \Big|_{-1}^{3} = \frac{32}{3}.$$

(b) If, however, we wish to integrate first in the y direction, we encounter a complication caused by the fact that the lower boundary of S is not the same throughout the x interval involved. For $-3 \le x \le -2$, the lower boundary is the lower half of the parabola, whereas for $-2 < x \le 6$, the straight line forms the lower boundary. A way around this difficulty is to divide S into two pieces, as shown in Figure 10; then $S = S_1 \cup S_2$ and (4) of Theorem 2 can be used.

$$I = \iint_S dA = \iint_{S_1} dA + \iint_{S_2} dA$$

$$= \int_{-3}^{-2} \left(\int_{-\sqrt{x+3}}^{\sqrt{x+3}} dy \right) dx + \int_{-2}^{6} \left(\int_{x/2}^{\sqrt{x+3}} dy \right) dx$$

$$= \int_{-3}^{-2} 2\sqrt{x + 3}\, dx + \int_{-2}^{6} \left(\sqrt{x + 3} - \frac{1}{2} x \right) dx$$

$$= \frac{4}{3}(x + 3)^{3/2} \Big|_{-3}^{-2} + \left[\frac{2}{3}(x + 3)^{3/2} - \frac{1}{4} x^2 \Big|_{-2}^{6} \right]$$

$$= \frac{4}{3} + \frac{28}{3}$$

$$= \frac{32}{3}.$$

What is the natural geometric interpretation of the value of $\iint_S dA$?

EXERCISES

1. For each of the following iterated integrals sketch the region S covered, reverse the order of integration, and integrate one of the two forms.

(a) $\displaystyle \int_0^4 \left(\int_0^{(1/2)x^2} x\, dy \right) dx.$

(e) $\displaystyle \int_0^6 \left(\int_{(1/4)y^2}^{9} (2xy - y^2)\, dx \right) dy.$

(b) $\displaystyle \int_0^3 \left(\int_{y^2}^{3y} x\, dx \right) dy.$

(f) $\displaystyle \int_1^{e^2} \left(\int_0^{\log x} 2x\, dy \right) dx.$

(c) $\displaystyle \int_0^4 \left(\int_{e^{-x}}^{1} y\, dy \right) dx.$

(g) $\displaystyle \int_0^1 \left(\int_y^{\sqrt{y}} y\, dx \right) dy.$

(d) $\displaystyle \int_0^1 \left(\int_{2-2x^2}^{2} xy\, dy \right) dx.$

(h) $\displaystyle \int_0^1 \left(\int_x^{1} e^x\, dy \right) dx.$

2. Find $\iint_S f\,dA$ for each pair f and S:

(a) $f(x, y) = x^2 + y^2,$ $S = \{(x, y)| \, 0 \leq x \leq 2, 0 \leq y \leq \frac{1}{2}x\}.$

(b) $f(x, y) = y,$ $S = \{(x, y)| \, 0 \leq x \leq \pi, 0 \leq y \leq \sin x\}.$

(c) $f(x, y) = ye^{-x},$ $S = \{(x, y)| \, 0 \leq x \leq 2y, 0 \leq y \leq 4\}.$

(d) $f(x, y) = x^2 + y^2,$ $S = \{(x, y)| \, x^2 + y^2 \leq 1\}.$

(e) $f(x, y) = \sin(x + y),$ $S = \{(x, y)| \, 0 \leq x \leq \pi, \pi - x \leq y \leq \pi\}.$

(f) $f(x, y) = y,$ $S = \{(x, y)| \, 0 \leq x \leq 2, 0 \leq y \leq e^x\}.$

(g) $f(x, y) = \sqrt{x^2 + y^2},$ $S = \{(x, y)| \, 0 \leq x \leq 1, \sqrt{1 - x^2} \leq y \leq 2(1 - x^2)\}.$

(h) $f(x, y) = e^{x+y},$ $S = \{(x, y)| \, 0 \leq x \leq 4, \frac{1}{2}x \leq y \leq 2x\}.$

(i) $f(x, y) = x^2 + y^2,$ $S = \{(x, y)| \, 0 \leq x \leq 4, \frac{1}{8}x^2 \leq y \leq \sqrt{x}\}.$

(j) $f(x, y) = 2xy,$ $S = \{(x, y)| \, 0 \leq x \leq \log y, 1 \leq y \leq 4\}.$

(k) $f(x, y) = x,$ $S = \{(x, y)| \, 2(y^2 - 1) \leq x \leq -\sqrt{1 - y^2}, -1 \leq y \leq 1\}.$

3. Assume f continuous over S. Set up one (two, if you can) iterated integral for finding $\iint_S f\,dA$ for each S described.

(a) The region bounded by $y = x^2$ and $y = x + 6$.

(b) The region in quadrants I and III bounded by $y = x^3$ and $y = 4x$.

(c) The region in quadrant I bounded by $y = \sin x$ and $y = \dfrac{2}{\pi}\, x$.

(d) The region in quadrants I and IV bounded below by $x^2 + y^2 = 4$ and above by $y = 2(1 - x^2)$.

(e) The region bounded by $x = y^4 - 10y^2 + 9$ and $x = 105$.

4. Describe how to set up iterated integrals for finding $\iint_S f\,dA$, where S is the region of Exercise 3(e) if the integration is to be performed first in the y direction. [*Hint.* The equation $y^4 - 10y^2 + 9 - x = 0$ is easily solved as a quadratic in y^2.]

5. There are times when changing the order of integration is not only a simplifying step—it may be essential to the completion of the problem. Consider briefly the problem of integrating each of the following as it is given; then reverse the order and carry out the integration.

(a) $\displaystyle\int_0^1 \left(\int_y^1 e^{x^2}\,dx \right) dy$

(b) $\displaystyle\int_0^1 \left(\int_y^1 \frac{\sin x}{x}\,dx \right) dy$

(c) $\displaystyle\int_0^1 \left(\int_y^1 \sin x^2\,dx \right) dy.$

6. Find the volume in the first octant bounded above by the plane $z = x + y$, below by the part of the xy-plane which is within the unit circle; and on the sides by the zx-plane, the yz-plane, and the cylinder $x^2 + y^2 = 1$. [*Hint.* Begin by expressing the volume as a double integral.]

14.3 Applications (1): Areas and Volumes

In this section we concern ourselves in some detail with two of the geometric applications of the double integral which we have already mentioned in passing in the preceding two sections. We refer, of course, to the measure of area and volume. We shall illustrate the ideas and techniques mainly by means of a series of examples.

AREA. It is clear from Definitions 1 and 3 that if f is the constant function 1 throughout the region S then the value of the double integral of f over S is precisely the area of S:

$$\iint_S dA = \text{area of } S. \tag{6}$$

For, in this case, the terms of an approximating sum are simply the measures of the area of the subregions, the value of the sum itself being the area of S.

The technique in using (6) to measure area is essentially as follows: one expresses the area as a double integral and then translates to whichever one of the two iterated integrals appears to be the more felicitous one with which to work (in some cases the advantage of one over the other may not become apparent until the problem of antidifferentiation is faced up to).

Before looking at an example or two we comment on a matter of terminology. The words "area" and "volume" are widely used to mean, on the one hand, a *region* of $\mathbf{R}^2$ and $\mathbf{R}^3$, respectively, and, on the other hand, to connote the *numerical measure* of these regions. We have already been guilty of this ambiguous use, and we shall not always be careful in the future. Usually the meaning is clear from the context.

Example 7. We find the area of the region S in the first quadrant bounded by

$$y = \sqrt{8x}, \qquad y = 2\sqrt{6 - x}, \qquad \text{and} \quad y = 0.$$

The first two equations represent portions of parabolas which are readily found to intersect at $(2, 4)$. It is straightforward to determine that S is as shown in Figure 11.

We have

$$\text{area of } S = \iint_S dA,$$

our first concern being whether, in translating to the iterated integral, to integrate first over x or in the y direction. If we choose the former, we note that the left boundary of S is everywhere the graph of $y = \sqrt{8x}$ and the right boundary is the graph of $y = 2\sqrt{6 - x}$. However, setting up the correct iterated integral involves expressing these equations as functions of y. These are, respectively,

$$x = \tfrac{1}{8}y^2 \quad \text{and} \quad x = 6 - \tfrac{1}{4}y^2.$$

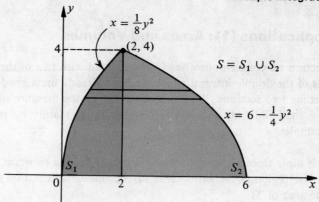

Figure 11

Thus

$$\iint_S dA = \int_0^4 \left(\int_{y^2/8}^{6-y^2/4} dx \right) dy$$

$$= \int_0^4 \left(6 - \frac{1}{4}y^2 - \frac{1}{8}y^2 \right) dy$$

$$= 16 \text{ square units.}$$

On the other hand, if we insist on integrating first in the y direction, then we must take into account the fact that the upper boundary of S is not the same curve throughout. This difficulty can be surmounted by decomposing S into the two subregions S_1 and S_2 as shown in Figure 11. Then $S = S_1 \cup S_2$ and

$$\iint_S dA = \iint_{S_1} dA + \iint_{S_2} dA$$

$$= \int_0^2 \left(\int_0^{\sqrt{8}x^{1/2}} dy \right) dx + \int_2^6 \left(\int_0^{2\sqrt{6-x}} dy \right) dx$$

$$= \int_0^2 \sqrt{8}x^{1/2} \, dx + \int_2^6 2\sqrt{6-x} \, dx$$

$$= \frac{16}{3} + \frac{32}{3}$$

$$= 16 \text{ square units.}$$

VOLUME. We have already described the use of a double integral to measure volume (see Figure 4 in Section 14.1 and the surrounding discussion). To summarize these remarks we assert the following:

If $(x, y) \in S \Rightarrow f(x, y) \geq 0$, then $\iint_S f(x, y) \, dA$ represents the volume of the region of $\mathbf{R}^3$ bounded above by the surface which is the graph of f, below by S—in the xy-plane— and on the sides by the cylinder whose base curve is the boundary of S, elements parallel to the z-axis (see Figure 12).

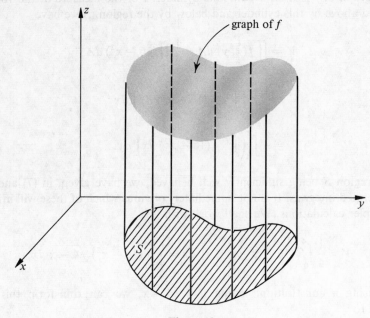

Figure 12

Example 8. Let f be defined by $f(x, y) = \frac{1}{4}(16 - x^2)$ and let S be the region in the first quadrant bounded by the axes and the parabola $y^2 = 4 - x$ (see Figure 13).

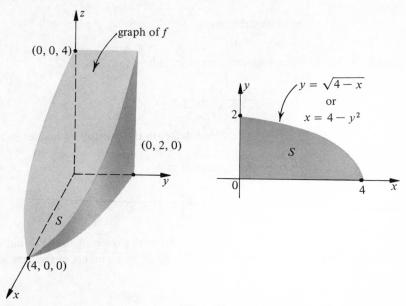

Figure 13

The graph of f is itself a parabolic cylinder. For the measure of the volume bounded above by this cylinder and below by the region, S we have

$$V = \iint_S f(x, y)\, dA = \frac{1}{4} \iint_S (16 - x^2)\, dA$$

$$= \frac{1}{4} \int_0^4 \left(\int_0^{\sqrt{4-x}} (16 - x^2)\, dy \right) dx \tag{7}$$

$$= \frac{1}{4} \int_0^2 \left(\int_0^{4-y^2} (16 - x^2)\, dx \right) dy. \tag{8}$$

The region S being sufficiently well behaved, we have given, in (7) and (8), both iterated integrals. It is not immediately obvious which of these will involve the simpler calculations. We shall work with (7):

$$V = \frac{1}{4} \int_0^4 \left((16 - x^2)y \Big|_0^{\sqrt{4-x}} \right) dx = \frac{1}{4} \int_0^4 (16 - x^2)\sqrt{4 - x}\, dx.$$

By using a substitution, letting $u = \sqrt{4 - x}$, we can transform this last integral to

$$V = \frac{1}{2} \int_0^2 (8u^4 - u^6)\, du = \frac{1}{2} \left[\frac{8u^5}{5} - \frac{u^7}{7} \Big|_0^2 \right]$$

$$= \frac{576}{35}$$

$$\approx 16.46 \text{ cubic units.}$$

Example 9. We find the volume of an ellipsoid

$$\frac{x^2}{a^2} + \frac{y^2}{b^2} + \frac{z^2}{c^2} = 1. \tag{9}$$

Because of the symmetry we can concentrate on the portion which lies in the first octant (see Figure 14).

We first solve (9) for the positive value of z:

$$z = c\sqrt{1 - \frac{x^2}{a^2} - \frac{y^2}{b^2}} = f(x, y).$$

The region S in the xy-plane is the region within the trace of the ellipsoid on the xy-plane. Thus, the boundary curve of S is given by segments of the axes and

$$y = b\sqrt{1 - \frac{x^2}{a^2}}, \qquad 0 \le x \le a.$$

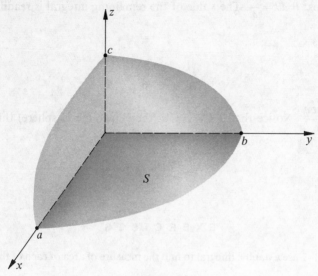

Figure 14

With these preliminaries we can write the double and iterated integrals for finding V:

$$\frac{1}{8} V = \iint_S z \, dA = c \iint_S \sqrt{1 - \frac{x^2}{a^2} - \frac{y^2}{b^2}} \, dA$$

$$= c \int_0^a \left(\int_0^{b\sqrt{1-x^2/a^2}} \sqrt{1 - \frac{x^2}{a^2} - \frac{y^2}{b^2}} \, dy \right) dx.$$

The antidifferentiation may be simplified if we temporarily let $\sqrt{1 - \frac{x^2}{a^2}} = k$. The last integral then becomes

$$\frac{1}{8} V = c \int_0^a \left(\int_0^{bk} \sqrt{k^2 - \frac{y^2}{b^2}} \, dy \right) dx.$$

We now let $y = bk \sin \theta$; then $\sqrt{k^2 - \frac{y^2}{b^2}} = k \cos \theta$, and the y-integral is transformed to a θ-integral:

$$\frac{1}{8} V = c \int_0^a \left(\int_0^{\pi/2} bk^2 \cos^2 \theta \, d\theta \right) dx$$

$$= \frac{\pi bc}{4} \int_0^a k^2 \, dx = \frac{\pi bc}{4} \int_0^a \left(1 - \frac{x^2}{a^2} \right) dx,$$

since $\int_0^{\pi/2} \cos^2 \theta \, d\theta = \dfrac{\pi}{4}$. The value of the remaining integral is readily found to

be $\dfrac{2a}{3}$. Thus

$$\frac{1}{8} V = \frac{\pi abc}{6},$$

or $V = \dfrac{4\pi abc}{3}$. Notice that if $b = c = a$ (the ellipsoid is a sphere) this becomes

$V = \dfrac{4}{3}\pi a^3$.

E X E R C I S E S

In numbers 1–7 use a double integral to find the measure of area of each of the following regions.

1. Bounded by the curves $y = x^2$ and $y = 8 - x^2$.

2. Bounded by the curves $y = \dfrac{1}{81} x^3$ and $y^2 - 6y - 3x = 0$. [*Hint.* One point of intersection is $(9, 9)$.]

3. In the first quadrant, bounded by $y = x^{1/2}$ and $y = x^{3/2}$.

4. Bounded by the curves $y^2 = 2x$ and $x^2 + y^2 = 4y$.

5. In the first quadrant, bounded by $4x = 8 - y^2$ and $4x = y^2$.

6. Bounded by the curves $x + y = 1$ and $y^2 = x + 1$.

7. In the first quadrant, bounded on the right by $x^2 + y^2 = 32$ and on the left by $y^2 = 4x$.

In numbers 8–15 find the volume of each of the regions described.

8. Bounded above by $z = x^2 + y^2 + 3$;
$$S = \{(x, y) \mid x^2 + y^2 \le 1\}.$$

9. Bounded above by the plane $z = x + y + 4$;
$$S = \{(x, y) \mid x^2 + y^2 \le 4\}.$$

10. Bounded above by the paraboloid $az = a^2 - x^2 - y^2$, bounded below by $z = 0$.

11. Bounded by the cylinder $y^2 = 4 - z$ and the planes $y = x$, $x = 0$, and $z = 0$.

12. Bounded above by $z = y$, below by $z = y^2$;

$$S = \{(x, y)|\ 0 \le x \le 1, 0 \le y \le \sqrt{1 - x^2}\}.$$

13. Bounded by $z = xy$, $x = 0$, $x = 2$, $y = 0$, $y = 2$, $z = 0$.

14. Bounded by $z = \log y$, $y = x + 1$, $x = 0$, $z = 0$, and $y = e$.

15. Bounded by $z = e^{-x}$, $y = 0$, $y = \frac{1}{2}x$, $z = 0$, and $x = 4$.

16. Find the volume of the region in the first octant under the paraboloid $z = 4 - x^2 - y^2$ and outside the cylinder $x^2 + y^2 = 2$.

17. Let $f(x, y) = \frac{1}{4}x^2 + \frac{1}{9}y^2 + 4$. Find the volume of the region bounded above by the graph of f and below by the set S, where:

(a) $S = \{(x, y)|\ 0 \le x \le 1, 0 \le y \le 1\}$.
(b) $S = \{(x, y)|\ x^2 + y^2 \le 1\}$.
(c) $S = \{(x, y)|\ 0 \le x \le 2, 0 \le y \le \sqrt{4 - x^2}\}$.
(d) $S = \{(x, y)|\ 0 \le x \le a, 0 \le y \le b\}$.
(e) $S = \{(x, y)|\ 0 \le x \le 4, 0 \le y \le \frac{1}{2}x\}$.
(f) $S = \{(x, y)|\ 0 \le x \le 2y, 0 \le y \le 2\}$.

18. Find the volume V in Example 8 by using the iterated integral (8).

19. Find the volume in the first octant common to the two cylinders $x^2 + y^2 = a^2$ and $x^2 + z^2 = a^2$.

14.4 Applications (2): Moments and Centroids

As we have remarked once or twice before, we have largely limited our applications to the realm of mathematics itself—and to geometry in particular—because it is safe to assume a common background of knowledge there. Except for the most superficial—and therefore largely meaningless—applications to other fields of knowledge, it would be necessary for us to embark on a digression in order to lay the essential foundations each time an application to a different subject was introduced. The body of mathematical ideas involved in a modern calculus course is so large that one must usually dispense with the luxury of bringing in ideas from other fields which use mathematics.

Usually. We are, in fact, at a place where it seems advisable to make an exception to our general procedure. The reason is that double and triple integrals are convenient tools for measuring *moments*, in the branch of physics known as mechanics. This use of integrals will at least suggest why their importance is far greater than it would be if they were of value for finding only areas and volumes.

Consequently, we give here a brief and very elementary discussion of the concept of and means of measuring a *moment*.

Intuitively, a moment describes the turning effect of a force about a point or line or plane. Because of one of Newton's laws, $\mathbf{F} = m\mathbf{a}$, where m stands for mass, we can also speak of "moment of mass," and this is what we shall be concerned with. If a mass m is a horizontal distance x from a point 0, then the moment M of the mass about 0 is, by definition, $M = mx$ (see Figure 15).

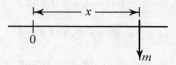

Figure 15

Moments combine in an additive fashion; by this we mean if, instead of a single mass, one has a finite system of masses $m_1, \ldots, m_n$ at distances $x_1, \ldots, x_n$ from 0, then the moment for the system is the sum of the moments:

$$M = \sum_{i=1}^{n} m_i x_i = M_1 + \cdots + M_n, \quad \text{where} \quad M_i = m_i x_i.$$

The distance x used in defining a moment is a directed distance. If some of the masses of a system are on one side of 0 and some on the other, the turning effects tend to offset one another: This can be taken into account by the sign of x. Consider, for example, a system of three masses, $m_1 = 3$ lb, $m_2 = 2$ lb, $m_3 = 3$ lb at distances $x_1 = 4$ ft, $x_2 = 7$ ft, and $x_3 = -9$ ft, respectively (Figure 16). The

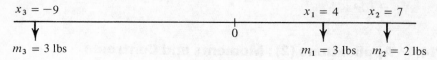

Figure 16

total moment of the system is then

$$M = \sum_{i=1}^{3} m_i x_i = (3)(4) + (2)(7) + (3)(-9) = -1 \text{ ft lb.,}$$

indicating that the small turning effect is in the negative direction—to the left. If $M = 0$, there would be no turning effect, the system would be in equilibrium.

Given a system of masses, it is often of interest to find the point about which the moment is zero; such a point is called the *centroid* or *center of gravity*. For the system described above, after Figure 15, the centroid is easily found as follows.

If the coordinate of the centroid C is $\bar{x}$, then the moment M_c of the system about C is

$$M_c = \sum_{i=1}^{n} m_i(x_i - \bar{x}) = \sum_{i=1}^{n} m_i x_i - \bar{x} \sum_{i=1}^{n} m_i.$$

If we let the total mass of the system be $m = \sum_{i=1}^{n} m_i$, and recall that C is the balancing point of the system ($M_c = 0$), we find from the preceding equation that

$$M_0 = m\bar{x}, \tag{10}$$

or $\bar{x} = \dfrac{M_0}{m}$, where M_0 is the moment about 0.

Note that if we write the equation for $\bar{x}$ as

$$\bar{x} = \frac{\sum\limits_{i=1}^{n} x_i m_i}{\sum\limits_{i=1}^{n} m_i},$$

we see that $\bar{x}$ is simply an arithmetic mean. In particular, if instead of masses m_i, we have frequencies f_i, then $\bar{x}$ is the arithmetic mean of elementary statistics.

Another comment about (10) is in order. It can be interpreted as saying that the centroid C is the point with the property that concentrating the total mass of the system there will produce the same moment about 0 as does the original system of masses.

We remark that, as is true with "area" and "volume," the word "moment" is made to do double duty; we use the same word for the physical concept, the turning effect, and for its measure, the number of footpounds, say. The practice is widespread.

Now, in practice one is more likely to be concerned with a continuous distribution of mass rather than with a discrete system of mass "particles." At this time we restrict ourselves to two-dimensional distributions; one could think of a thin sheet of metal, for example, in the shape of a region S of two-space. If we introduce a coordinate system into $\mathbf{R}^2$ we might be interested in finding moments with respect to (about) the x- and y-axes. First, of course, the concept of moment must be generalized to include such a case. The definition of the double (*double*, not iterated) integral fits our needs perfectly. If we take a partition π of the region S (in Figure 17 we show only one subregion), then, approximately, the

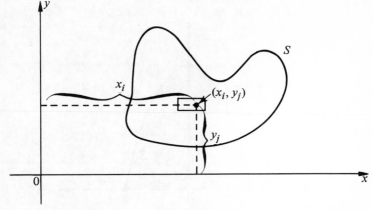

Figure 17

moment of the mass Δm_{ij} in a small subregion about the y-axis, is $x_i \Delta m_{ij}$. Thus, approximately, the moment of the mass of S about the y-axis is

$$M_y \approx \sum_{i=1}^{n} \sum_{j=1}^{k} x_i \Delta m_{ij}$$

$$= \sum_{i=1}^{n} \sum_{j=1}^{k} x_i \delta \Delta x_i \Delta y_j,$$

where δ represents the *density* or *mass per unit area*. (If the metal in the sheet is uniformly distributed, then δ will be constant; however, δ might be a function of $(x, y) \in S$.) It is natural, then to *define* the moment about the y-axis to be

$$M_y = \iint_S \delta x \, dA = \iint_S x(\delta \, dA) = \iint_S x \, dm. \tag{11}$$

In a similar fashion we define the moment of mass of S about the x-axis to be

$$M_x = \iint_S \delta y \, dA = \iint_S y \, dm. \tag{12}$$

(One must be cautious in the use of these formulas because of the mixup of x's and y's.)

If, further, we define the mass m as

$$m = \iint_S \delta \, dA = \iint_S dm, \tag{13}$$

then we can define the centroid $C(\bar{x}, \bar{y})$ by

$$\begin{cases} m\bar{x} = M_y \\ m\bar{y} = M_x \end{cases}$$

(see Eq. (10) and a comment made thereafter).

Example 10. A thin metal plate occupies the region $S = \{(x, y) \mid -2 \le x \le 2, 0 \le y \le 4 - x^2\}$. We find the centroid $C(\bar{x}, \bar{y})$ (see Figure 18).

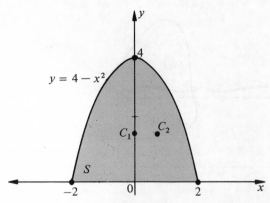

Figure 18

(i) We first assume a homogeneous distribution of mass, i.e., $\delta = \text{const.}$ Then

$$m = \iint\limits_{S} \delta \, dA = \delta \int_{-2}^{2} \left(\int_{0}^{4-x^2} dy \right) dx$$

$$= \delta \int_{-2}^{2} (4 - x^2) \, dx = 2\delta \int_{0}^{2} (4 - x^2) \, dx \qquad \text{(since } 4 - x^2 \text{ is even)}$$

$$= \frac{2^5 \delta}{3}.$$

Also,

$$M_x = \iint\limits_{S} y\delta \, dA = \delta \int_{-2}^{2} \left(\int_{0}^{4-x^2} y \, dy \right) dx = \delta \int_{-2}^{2} \left(\frac{1}{2} y^2 \Big|_{0}^{4-x^2} \right) dx$$

$$= \frac{1}{2} \delta \int_{-2}^{2} (4 - x^2)^2 \, dx = \delta \int_{0}^{2} (4 - x^2)^2 \, dx \qquad \text{(since } (4 - x^2)^2 \text{ is even)}$$

$$= \frac{2^8 \delta}{15}.$$

Now we assert that, because of the symmetry of S with respect to the y-axis, $M_y = 0$. This would quickly show if one began to evaluate the integral for M_y: the x-integrand would be an odd function, the interval would be $[-2, 2]$. We leave it as an exercise to check this assertion. In general, symmetry of the region with respect to an axis and homogeneity of the mass distribution can be taken advantage of to reduce calculations.

It follows, then, that for this case

$$\bar{x} = \frac{M_y}{m} = 0, \qquad \bar{y} = \frac{M_x}{m} = \frac{2^8 \delta}{15} \cdot \frac{3}{2^5 \delta} = \frac{8}{5},$$

so the centroid is $C_1 \left(0, \dfrac{8}{5} \right)$.

(ii) Suppose, however, the density function is $\delta(x, y) = x + 2$. We find then that

$$m = \iint\limits_{S} \delta \, dA = \int_{-2}^{2} \left(\int_{0}^{4-x^2} (x + 2) \, dy \right) dx$$

$$= \int_{-2}^{2} (x + 2)(4 - x^2) \, dx = \int_{-2}^{2} (4x - x^3 + 8 - 2x^2) \, dx$$

$$= 2 \int_{0}^{2} (8 - 2x^2) \, dx \qquad (4x - x^3 \text{ is odd, } 8 - 2x^2 \text{ even})$$

$$= \frac{2^6}{3}.$$

Neither moment is zero:

$$M_y = \iint_S x\delta \, dA = \iint_S (x^2 + 2x) \, dA = \int_{-2}^{2} \left(\int_0^{4-x^2} (x^2 + 2x) \, dy \right) dx$$

$$= \int_{-2}^{2} (x^2 + 2x)(4 - x^2) \, dx = \int_{-2}^{2} (4x^2 - x^4 + 8x - 2x^3) \, dx$$

$$= 2 \int_0^2 (4x^2 - x^4) \, dx \qquad (4x^2 - x^4 \text{ is even, } 8x - 2x^3 \text{ odd})$$

$$= \frac{2^7}{15};$$

similarly,

$$M_x = \iint_S y\delta \, dA = \int_{-2}^{2} \left(\int_0^{4-x^2} (x + 2)y \, dy \right) dx$$

$$M_x = \int_{-2}^{2} \left(\frac{1}{2}(x + 2)y^2 \bigg|_0^{4-x^2} \right) dx$$

$$= \frac{1}{2} \int_{-2}^{2} (x + 2)(4 - x^2)^2 \, dx = 2 \int_0^2 (4 - x^2)^2 \, dx \qquad (\text{why?})$$

$$= 2 \int_0^2 (16 - 8x^2 + x^4) \, dx$$

$$= \frac{2^9}{15}.$$

For the coordinates of the centroid we find

$$\bar{x} = \frac{M_y}{m} = \frac{2^7}{15} \cdot \frac{3}{2^6} = \frac{2}{5}, \qquad \bar{y} = \frac{M_x}{m} = \frac{2^9}{15} \cdot \frac{3}{2^6} = \frac{8}{5};$$

thus $C_2\left(\dfrac{2}{5}, \dfrac{8}{5}\right)$.

Note that $\bar{y}$ is the same for both cases; this was to be expected, since in (ii) the density function is independent of y.

The *second moments* for a continuous distribution of mass have definitions similar to those of the (first) moments in (11) and (12), except that the *square* of the distance is used. The second moment, useful in problems involving rotational motion, is also called the *moment of inertia*. The definitions are

$$I_x = \iint_S y^2\delta \, dA, \qquad I_y = \iint_S x^2\delta \, dA, \qquad I_0 = \iint_S (x^2 + y^2)\delta \, dA. \qquad (14)$$

The last of these expressions, the moment of inertia about the origin, is often called the *polar moment of inertia*.

Example 10 (continued). We use the region S of Example 10 and assume δ is constant, as in (i) there. Then

$$I_x = \iint_S y^2 \delta \, dA = \delta \int_{-2}^{2} \left(\int_0^{4-x^2} y^2 \, dy \right) dx$$

$$= \delta \int_{-2}^{2} \left(\frac{1}{3} y^3 \Big|_0^{4-x^2} \right) dx = \frac{1}{3} \delta \int_{-2}^{2} (4 - x^2)^3 \, dx$$

$$= \frac{2}{3} \delta \int_0^{2} (4^3 - 3 \cdot 4^2 x^2 + 3 \cdot 4 x^4 - x^6) \, dx$$

$$= \frac{2^{12} \delta}{105}.$$

Also

$$I_y = \iint_S x^2 \delta \, dA = \delta \int_{-2}^{2} \left(\int_0^{4-x^2} x^2 \, dy \right) dx$$

$$= \delta \int_{-2}^{2} (4x^2 - x^4) \, dx = 2\delta \int_0^{2} (4x^2 - x^4) \, dx$$

$$= 2\delta \left[\frac{4x^3}{3} - \frac{x^5}{5} \Big|_0^2 \right]$$

$$= \frac{2^7 \delta}{15}.$$

It is obvious from (14) that $I_0 = I_x + I_y$; consequently, for this region S we have

$$I_0 = \frac{2^{12} \delta}{105} + \frac{2^7 \delta}{15} = \frac{2^7 \delta}{105} (32 + 7) = \frac{2^7 \cdot 13 \delta}{35}.$$

The analog of the centroidal distances $\bar{x}$ and $\bar{y}$ for a moment of inertia is the *radius of gyration R*, defined by

$$mR^2 = I.$$

For instance, in the preceding example,

$$R_x^2 = \frac{I_y}{m} = \frac{2^7 \delta}{15} \cdot \frac{3}{2^5 \delta} = \frac{4}{5},$$

or $R_x = \dfrac{2}{\sqrt{5}}$. (Again the notation might be confusing; R_x is a *horizontal* distance from the y-axis.) If the entire mass were concentrated at a point R_x units from the y-axis, the resulting moment of inertia would equal that for the continuous distribution of mass.

E X E R C I S E S

In numbers 1–10 find the coordinates of the centroid of the region S described assuming the density is constant. Note that this allows you to take advantage of any symmetry.

1. $S = \{(x, y)| -1 \leq x \leq 1, 0 \leq y \leq \sqrt{1 - x^2}\}.$

2. $S = \{(x, y)| -1 \leq x \leq 1, 0 \leq y \leq 1 - x^2\}.$

3. $S = \left\{(x, y)| -1 \leq x \leq 1, 0 \leq y \leq \cos\frac{\pi}{2}x\right\}.$

4. $S = \{(x, y)| 1 \leq x \leq e, 0 \leq y \leq \log x\}.$

5. S is the region bounded by $y^2 = x$ and $x = 4$.

6. S is the region bounded by $y = \frac{1}{4}x^2$ and $y = \frac{1}{8}x^2 + 1$. Note the position of the centroid with respect to S.

7. S is the region bounded by $x^2 = 4y + 4$ and $x^2 = -2y + 4$.

8. S is the loop of the curve $y^2 = 4x^2 - x^3$.

9. S is the smaller area bounded by $x^2 + y^2 = a^2$ and $x + y = a$. [*Hint.* There is symmetry with respect to the line $y = x$.]

10. S is bounded by $x^2 + y^2 = 1$, $x = 1$, and $y = 1$. See the hint for Exercise 9.

11–13. Same as numbers 1–3, only use as density $\delta(x, y) = x + 1$.

14. Same as number 4, only let the density function be defined by $\delta(x, y) = 1 - y$.

15. Same as number 5, only use $\delta(x, y) = y + 2$.

16. Same as number 6, only use $\delta(x, y) = y$. *Now* notice the position of the centroid with respect to S.

17. Same as number 7, only use $\delta(x, y) = 2 - y$.

18. Same as number 8, only use $\delta(x, y) = \sqrt{4 - x}$.

19. Same as number 9, only use $\delta(x, y) = xy$.

20. Same as number 10, only use $\delta(x, y) = xy$.

21–30. For each of the regions S of numbers 1–10, find I_y, assuming the density function δ is constant.

14.5 Polar Coordinates

We begin this section by calling attention to a fact that up to this point we have deliberately suppressed. We are referring to the following notational matter. When we translate from a double integral to one of the corresponding iterated integrals (for evaluation purposes) the symbol dA goes into $dy\,dx$ or $dx\,dy$. Essentially this can be thought of as a consequence of our use of the coordinate curves $x = $ const. and $y = $ const. in setting up a partition of the region S. We have not heretofore made explicit mention of this point because of our desire to stress the distinction between double and iterated integrals.

And we *do* bring up the subject at this time because it must be directly faced when we consider, as we now wish to, the problem of working with a different coordinate system in the plane: namely, polar coordinates.

One approach to the problem is as follows. The polar coordinate analog of the rectangular region of cartesian coordinates is

$$S = \{(r, \theta) \mid \alpha \le \theta \le \beta, c \le r \le d\}.$$

We can obtain a partition π of S by means of a partition of the intervals $[\alpha, \beta]$ and $[c, d]$:

$$\{\alpha = \theta_0, \theta_1, \ldots, \theta_{i-1}, \theta_i, \ldots, \theta_n = \beta\}$$

$$\{c = r_0, r_1, \ldots, r_{j-1}, r_j, \ldots, r_m = d\}.$$

Let f be a function of (r, θ), bounded on S. Then, choosing a point (r_j^*, θ_i^*) in each subregion of the partition, we can form a Riemann sum

$$\sum_{i=1}^{n} \sum_{j=1}^{m} f(r_j^*, \theta_i^*)\, \Delta A_{ij},$$

where ΔA_{ij} is the area of the ijth region (see Figure 19.) If, as the maximum

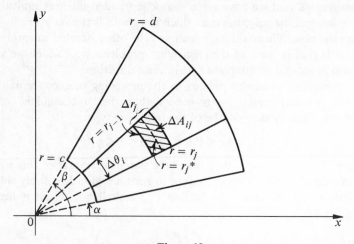

Figure 19

diagonal of the subregions gets arbitrarily small, the Riemann sum approaches a limit (in the same sense as for Definition 1), then we denote the limit by

$$\iint\limits_{S} f(r, \theta) \, dA,$$

and say that f is integrable over S.

As we found in Section 1, continuity of f except on a set of area zero in S is sufficient for f to be integrable. And if f is continuous on S then we can evaluate the double integral by means of iterated integrals. But to see how to effect the translation, we take a close look at the area ΔA_{ij}. Using the formula for the area of a sector of a circle, we have

$$\begin{aligned}
\Delta A_{ij} &= \tfrac{1}{2} r_j^2 \, \Delta\theta_i - \tfrac{1}{2} r_{j-1}^2 \, \Delta\theta_i \\
&= \tfrac{1}{2}(r_j^2 - r_{j-1}^2) \, \Delta\theta_i \\
&= \tfrac{1}{2}(r_j + r_{j-1})(r_j - r_{j-1}) \, \Delta\theta_i \\
&= \tfrac{1}{2}(r_j + r_{j-1}) \, \Delta r_j \, \Delta\theta_i \qquad (\Delta r_j = r_j - r_{j-1}) \\
&= r_j^* \, \Delta r_j \, \Delta\theta_i,
\end{aligned}$$

where $r_j^* = \tfrac{1}{2}(r_j + r_{j-1})$. From this we reach, heuristically, the conclusion that the polar coordinate equivalent of dA is $r \, dr \, d\theta$.

As a consequence, the polar coordinate version of Theorem 3 is the assertion that if f is continuous on $S = [\alpha, \beta] \times [c, d]$, then

$$\iint\limits_{S} f(r, \theta) \, dA = \int_\alpha^\beta \left(\int_c^d f(r, \theta) r \, dr \right) d\theta. \tag{15}$$

It will have been noticed that the preceding discussion was quite informal. The assertion of Eq. (15) is correct, but we cannot claim to have given it a formal demonstration.

We also remark that we have given only one iterated integral equivalent for the double integral, namely, the one which integrates first over r—radially outward from the pole. We could have included the other iterated integral in (15), but the fact is that in most of the elementary problems with which we shall be concerned it is natural to integrate first in the r direction.

A final comment, somewhat related to the preceding one, concerns the fact that we can consider regions more general than the "rectangular" ones described above. Usually they will be of the following type:

$$S = \{(r, \theta) \mid \alpha \le \theta \le \beta, g_1(\theta) \le r \le g_2(\theta)\}$$

(see Figure 20); or, at worst, they may be a union of several of this sort. The method of extending the integral concept to such a region is entirely similar to that described in Definition 3 in Section 1; we shall not repeat it here. The analog of Eq. (4) is

$$\iint\limits_{S} f(r, \theta) \, dA = \int_\alpha^\beta \left(\int_{g_1(\theta)}^{g_2(\theta)} f(r, \theta) r \, dr \right) d\theta. \tag{16}$$

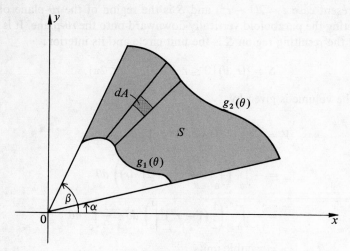

Figure 20

Example 11. We use polar coordinates to find the volume of the region bounded above by the paraboloid $z = 2 - 2r^2$, below by the $r\theta$-plane (see Figure 21).

As in Section 3, we have

$$V = \iint\limits_S z \, dA.$$

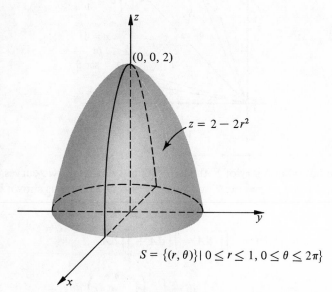

$$S = \{(r, \theta)\} \mid 0 \le r \le 1, 0 \le \theta \le 2\pi\}$$

Figure 21

In the present case $z = 2(1 - r^2)$ and S is the region of the $r\theta$-plane obtained by projecting the paraboloid vertically downward onto the $r\theta$-plane. It is readily seen that the resulting region S is the unit circle and its interior:

$$S = \{(r, \theta) \,|\, 0 \le r \le 1, 0 \le \theta \le 2\pi\}.$$

Thus the volume is given by

$$V = \int_0^{2\pi} \left(\int_0^1 2(1 - r^2) r\, dr \right) d\theta$$

$$= -\int_0^{2\pi} \left(\int_0^1 (1 - r^2)(-2r\, dr) \right) d\theta$$

$$= -\int_0^{2\pi} \left(\frac{1}{2}(1 - r^2)^2 \Big|_0^1 \right) d\theta = \frac{1}{2} \int_0^{2\pi} d\theta$$

$$= \pi \text{ cubic units.}$$

Example 12. In this example we carry off the tremendous feat of proving that the area of the unit square is one square unit (see Figure 22).

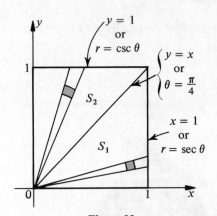

Figure 22

Since the outer boundary of S, the unit square, consists of two curves, $x = 1$ or $r = \sec\theta$ and $y = 1$ or $r = \csc\theta$, we divide S into two pieces as shown in Figure 22, $S = S_1 \cup S_2$. Then

$$A = \iint_S dA = \iint_{S_1 \cup S_2} dA = \iint_{S_1} dA + \iint_{S_2} dA$$

$$= \int_0^{\pi/4} \left(\int_0^{\sec\theta} r\, dr \right) d\theta + \int_{\pi/4}^{\pi/2} \left(\int_0^{\csc\theta} r\, dr \right) d\theta$$

$$= \int_0^{\pi/4} \frac{1}{2} \sec^2 \theta \, d\theta + \int_{\pi/4}^{\pi/2} \frac{1}{2} \csc^2 \theta \, d\theta$$

$$= \frac{1}{2} \tan \theta \bigg|_0^{\pi/4} - \frac{1}{2} \cot \theta \bigg|_{\pi/4}^{\pi/2} = \frac{1}{2}(1 - 0) - \frac{1}{2}(0 - 1)$$

$$= 1 \text{ square unit,}$$

as promised.

There is, however, another approach which can be taken toward double integrals in polar coordinates. We illustrate this approach before giving a general description.

Example 13. We want to find the value of

$$I = \iint_S f(x, y) \, dA,$$

where $f(x, y) = x^2 + y^2$, and S is the region on and within the circle $x^2 + y^2 = 2x$ (see Figure 23).

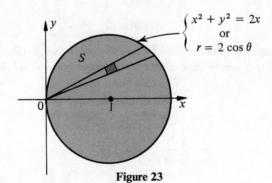

$$\begin{cases} x^2 + y^2 = 2x \\ \quad \text{or} \\ r = 2 \cos \theta \end{cases}$$

Figure 23

Working with rectangular coordinates would lead to

$$I = \int_0^2 \left(\int_{-\sqrt{2x-x^2}}^{\sqrt{2x-x^2}} (x^2 + y^2) \, dy \right) dx.$$

The evaluation of this iterated integral becomes a bit messy.

Suppose, though, we transform the problem to polar coordinates. The formula for the function f then becomes simply r^2 and the equation of the boundary curve for S is $r = 2 \cos \theta$. The iterated integral suggested by (16) is

$$I = \int_0^\pi \left(\int_0^{2 \cos \theta} r^2 \cdot r \, dr \right) d\theta$$

$$= \int_0^\pi \left(\frac{1}{4} 2^4 \cos^4 \theta \right) d\theta = 4 \int_0^\pi \cos^4 \theta \, d\theta$$

$$= 2^3 \int_0^{\pi/2} \cos^4 \theta \, d\theta \qquad \left(\cos^4 \theta \text{ is symmetric with respect to } \theta = \frac{\pi}{2} \right)$$

$$= 2^3 \frac{3 \cdot 1}{4 \cdot 2} \frac{\pi}{2} \qquad \text{(Wallis' formula)}$$

$$= \frac{3\pi}{2}.$$

The technique used here is quite analogous to the substitution technique introduced and greatly exploited in Chapter 8. In fact, the justification theorem which we are about to state is precisely the two-dimensional generalization of the corollary to Theorem 8.2 (q.v.). We omit the proof of this theorem.

Theorem 4. *Let S be a closed region of the xy-plane, and let the functions*

$$x = \varphi(u, v)$$

$$y = \psi(u, v)$$

provide a 1–1 mapping between S and a region $\bar{S}$ of the uv-plane.

We assume that φ and ψ have continuous first derivatives and that the Jacobian

$$J = \begin{vmatrix} \dfrac{\partial x}{\partial u} & \dfrac{\partial x}{\partial v} \\[2mm] \dfrac{\partial y}{\partial u} & \dfrac{\partial y}{\partial v} \end{vmatrix} = \begin{vmatrix} \varphi_u & \varphi_v \\ \psi_u & \psi_v \end{vmatrix} \tag{17}$$

has the same sign throughout S, with the possible exception of a finite number of points where J may equal 0. If f is continuous on S, then

$$\iint\limits_S (f(x, y) \, dx \, dy = \iint\limits_{\bar{S}} f(\varphi(u, v), \psi(u, v)) |J| \, du \, dv. \tag{18}$$

A point of the theorem is that when changing variables in a double integral, the differential of area dA, which in rectangular coordinates is $dx \, dy$ becomes $|J| \, du \, dv$, where J is the determinant in (17). A comparison of this theorem with Theorem 8.2 and its corollary would be extremely helpful at this time.

Note that, by (18), one must use the *absolute value* of J; this fact is often over-looked in the statement of this theorem.

Suppose we calculate J for the transformation from rectangular to polar coordinates. We have

$$\begin{cases} x = r \cos \theta \\ y = r \sin \theta \end{cases}$$

Thus

$$J = \begin{vmatrix} x_r & x_\theta \\ y_r & y_\theta \end{vmatrix} = \begin{vmatrix} \cos \theta & -r \sin \theta \\ \sin \theta & r \cos \theta \end{vmatrix} = r.$$

By (18), then, one transforms a double integral from rectangular to polar coordinates as follows:

$$\iint\limits_{S} f(x, y) \, dx \, dy = \iint\limits_{\bar{S}} f(r \cos \theta, r \sin \theta) \, r \, dr \, d\theta, \tag{19}$$

where $\bar{S}$ is the $r\theta$-region which corresponds to S. This is exactly the technique we used in Example 13.

Example 14. As a further illustration suppose we want to find the volume of the sphere of radius a, center at the origin. The equation of the surface of the sphere is $x^2 + y^2 + z^2 = a^2$. If we concentrate on the portion in the first octant, we can write

$$\frac{1}{8} V = \iint\limits_{S} \sqrt{a^2 - x^2 - y^2} \, dA = \int_0^a \left(\int_0^{\sqrt{a^2 - x^2}} \sqrt{a^2 - x^2 - y^2} \, dy \right) dx,$$

where S is the set of points in quadrant I bounded by the axes and the circle $x^2 + y^2 = a^2$ (see Figure 24).

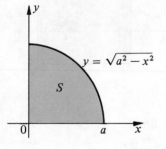
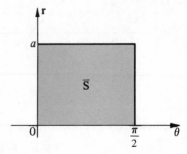

Figure 24

The above integration, not unlike that in Example 9, becomes rather tedious. Suppose, however, we transform to polar coordinates, using (19):

$$\frac{1}{8} V = \iint_S \sqrt{a^2 - r^2}\, r\, dr\, d\theta = \int_0^{\pi/2} \left(\int_0^a \sqrt{a^2 - r^2}\, r\, dr \right) d\theta$$

$$= -\frac{1}{2} \int_0^{\pi/2} \left(\int_0^a \sqrt{a^2 - r^2}\,(-2r\, dr) \right) d\theta = -\frac{1}{2} \int_0^{\pi/2} \frac{2}{3}(a^2 - r^2)^{3/2} \Big|_0^a d\theta$$

$$= \frac{\pi a^3}{6}.$$

Thus $V = \dfrac{4\pi}{3}\, a^3$.

It is useful to know that Theorem 4 has applicability far wider than the transformation from rectangular to polar coordinates. We give an indication of its utility.

Example 15. We wish to find the value of the integral

$$I = \iint_S f(x, y)\, dA,$$

where $f(x, y) = (x + y)^4$ and S is the parallelogram with vertices $(1, 0)$, $(2, 2)$, $(1, 3)$, and $(0, 1)$ (see Figure 25).

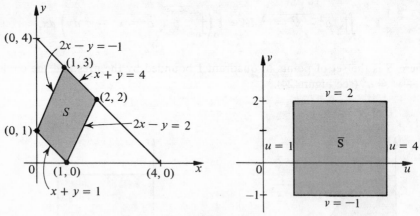

Figure 25

The boundary of S consists of segments of the lines

$$x + y = 1, \qquad x + y = 4,$$
$$2x - y = -1, \qquad 2x - y = 2.$$

Thus we introduce new variables by letting

$$\begin{cases} x + y = u \\ 2x - y = v \end{cases}.$$

It is a simple matter to solve for x and y:

$$\begin{cases} x = \tfrac{1}{3}u + \tfrac{1}{3}v \\ y = u - \tfrac{1}{2}v \end{cases}.$$

We see, then, that the boundary of S maps into

$$u = 1, \qquad u = 4$$
$$v = -1, \qquad v = 2$$

and that the value of the Jacobian is

$$J = \begin{vmatrix} \tfrac{1}{3} & \tfrac{1}{3} \\ 1 & -\tfrac{1}{2} \end{vmatrix} = -\tfrac{1}{6} - \tfrac{1}{3} = -\tfrac{1}{2},$$

a nonzero constant. It is not hard to discern that the image of S in the uv-plane is the square $\bar{S} = \{(u, v) \mid 1 \le u \le 4,\ -1 \le v \le 2\}$. (The significance of the minus sign in the value of J is that a change of orientation has occurred: as the boundary of S is traversed in the counterclockwise direction, the boundary of $\bar{S}$ will be traversed in the clockwise direction. But we need not concern ourselves with this now.)

By Theorem 4, we can find the value of I as

$$I = \iint_{S} u^4 \, |J| \, dv \, du \qquad \text{(the formula for } f \text{ becomes } u^4\text{)}$$

$$= \frac{1}{2} \int_{1}^{4} \left(\int_{-1}^{2} u^4 \, dv \right) du = \frac{1}{2} \int_{1}^{4} 3u^4 \, du$$

$$= \frac{3}{10} u^5 \Big|_{1}^{4} = \frac{3}{10} (4^5 - 1)$$

$$= \frac{3069}{10}.$$

The reader should satisfy himself that the evaluation of I in its original form would have been exceedingly cumbersome.

EXERCISES

In numbers 1–10 translate to polar coordinates and integrate. One way of thinking of the problem is to translate first to the double integral in rectangular coordinates and then use (19).

1. $\displaystyle\int_0^1 \left(\int_{\sqrt{3}y}^{\sqrt{4-y^2}} \cos(x^2+y^2)\, dx \right) dy.$

2. $\displaystyle\int_0^1 \int_0^x \sqrt{x^2+y^2}\, dy\, dx.$

3. $\displaystyle\int_0^2 \int_0^{\sqrt{2y-y^2}} (x^2+y^2)\, dx\, dy.$

4. $\displaystyle\int_0^1 \int_x^1 (1+x^2+y^2)\, dy\, dx.$

5. $\displaystyle\int_0^{\sqrt{2}} \int_y^{\sqrt{4-y^2}} x^2\, dx\, dy.$

6. $\displaystyle\int_0^1 \int_{\sqrt{3}x}^{\sqrt{4-x^2}} y\, dy\, dx.$

7. $\displaystyle\int_0^{2a} \int_{-\sqrt{2ay-y^2}}^0 (-x)\, dx\, dy.$

8. $\displaystyle\int_0^2 \int_{\sqrt{3}x}^{\sqrt{16-x^2}} y\, dy\, dx.$

9. $\displaystyle\int_0^{2\sqrt{3}} \int_{y/\sqrt{3}}^{\sqrt{16-y^2}} x^2\, dx\, dy.$

10. $\displaystyle\int_0^2 \int_{2x}^4 x\, dy\, dx.$

11–16. Give a physical interpretation for the *double integral* equivalent of each of the integrals in numbers 5–10.

In numbers 17–20 find the centroid of each of the following regions, assuming the density function is constant. [*Hint.* $x = r\cos\theta$, $y = r\sin\theta$.]

17. S is the region enclosed by the cardioid $r = a(1+\cos\theta)$.

18. S is the region enclosed by the inner loop of the limaçon $r = 1 - 2\cos\theta$.

19. S is the region enclosed by the leaf in the first quadrant of $r = \sin 2\theta$. [*Hint.* There is symmetry with respect to $y = x$.]

20. S is the region enclosed by the bifolium $r = a\sin\theta\cos^2\theta$. [*Hint.* Use Wallis' formula for the evaluation of the integral.]

In numbers 21–24 use polar coordinates to find the volume of each of the regions described.

21. S is bounded by $z = 4 - x^2 - y^2$, $z = 0$, and $x^2 + y^2 = 2x$.

22. S is bounded by $z = x^2 + y^2$, $z = 0$, and $x^2 + y^2 = 4$.

23. S is the region cut out of the sphere $x^2 + y^2 + z^2 = 4$ by the cylinder $x^2 + y^2 = 1$.

24. S is the region in the first octant bounded above by $z = y$, below by $z = 0$, and on the side by the cardioidal cylinder $r = 1 + \sin\theta$.

25. We consider the integral

$$I(b) = \iint_{S(b)} e^{-x^2-y^2}\, dA,$$

where $S(b) = \{(x,y)\mid 0 \le x \le b,\ 0 \le y \le \sqrt{b^2-x^2}\}$, i.e., $S(b)$ is the region in the first quadrant enclosed by the circle of radius b, center at the origin.

(a) Transform to polar coordinates and show that $I(b) = \dfrac{\pi}{4}(1 - e^{-b^2})$. Note how the polar coordinate version of dA aids in the antidifferentiation.

(b) Show that $\lim\limits_{b \to \infty} I(b) = \dfrac{\pi}{4}$. Say what $S(b)$ becomes as $b \to \infty$, (i.e., give the geo-metric interpretation of $S(\infty)$.

(c) Let $I(\infty) = \iint_{S(\infty)} e^{-x^2 - y^2}\, dA$. Show that

$$I(\infty) = \int_0^\infty \int_0^\infty e^{-x^2 - y^2}\, dx\, dy = \int_0^\infty e^{-x^2}\, dx \int_0^\infty e^{-y^2}\, dy = \left(\int_0^\infty e^{-x^2} dx\right)^2.$$

(d) Conclude from (b) and (c) that

$$\int_0^\infty e^{-x^2}\, dx = \frac{\sqrt{\pi}}{2}.$$

Two remarks are in order about this problem. The first is to the effect that the function $f(x) = e^{-x^2}$ is closely related to the function which describes the normal distribution in probability. Consequently, the result of (d) is an essential one for probability theory.

The second comment concerns the antiderivative of e^{-x^2}: it is not an elementary function. Because of this fact the usual technique for finding $\int_0^b e^{-x^2}\, dx$ would fail. To obtain the result of (d) one must resort to some sort of trick.

26. Evaluate each of the following integrals by making the indicated substitution.

(a) $\iint_S (x^2 - y^2)^2\, dA$, where S is the square with vertices $(1, 0)$, $(2, 1)$, $(1, 2)$, and $(0, 1)$. Let $x + y = u$, $x - y = v$.

(b) $\iint_S (x - 2y) \sin^2 (x + y)\, dA$, where S is the parallelogram with vertices $(\pi, 0)$, $(3\pi, \pi)$, $(2\pi, 2\pi)$, $(0, \pi)$. Let $x + y = u$, $x - 2y = v$.

27. (a) Suppose the region S is described as

$$S = \{(r, \theta)\,|\, c \leq r \leq d,\, h_1(r) \leq \theta \leq h_2(r)\}.$$

Show that

$$\iint_S f(r, \theta)\, dA = \int_c^d \left(\int_{h_1(r)}^{h_2(r)} f(r, \theta) r\, d\theta\right) dr. \tag{20}$$

(b) Let S be the annular region

$$S = \{(r, \theta)\,|\, c \leq r \leq d,\, 0 \leq \theta \leq 2\pi\}.$$

Find the polar moment of inertia of S, assuming constant density.

14.6 Triple Integrals

Once the concept of the double integral has been mastered the extension to a triple integral for a function of three variables is perfectly straightforward. Because of this our description below will be brief.

　　We begin with a function f whose domain in $\mathbf{R}^3$ includes a rectangular parallel-epiped

$$S = [a_1, a_2] \times [b_1, b_2] \times [c_1, c_2]$$
$$= \{(x, y, z) \mid a_1 \le x \le a_2, b_1 \le y \le b_2, c_1 \le z \le c_2\}.$$

By means of partitions of each of the intervals $[a_1, a_2]$, $[b_1, b_2]$, $[c_1, c_2]$ we form a partition π of S (thereby dividing the big box S into little boxes). A typical subregion of S determined by π would be

$$[x_{i-1}, x_i] \times [y_{j-1}, y_j] \times [z_{k-1}, z_k].$$

We let $\Delta x_i = x_i - x_{i-1}$, $\Delta y_j = y_j - y_{j-1}$, $\Delta z_k = z_k - z_{k-1}$, define the norm of the partition to be the maximum diagonal of any of the subregions:

$$|\pi| = \max \sqrt{\Delta x_i^2 + \Delta y_j^2 + \Delta z_k^2},$$

where (x_i, y_j, z_k) is a partition point. In each subregion we pick, quite arbitrarily, a point (x_i^*, y_j^*, z_k^*). Then we form the Riemann sum

$$\sum_{i=1}^m \sum_{j=1}^n \sum_{k=1}^q f(x_i^*, y_j^*, z_k^*) \, \Delta x_i \, \Delta y_j \, \Delta z_k,$$

noting that $\Delta x_i \Delta y_j \Delta z_k = \Delta V_{ijk}$ is the volume of subregion ijk. If the set of sums has a limit as $|\pi| \to 0$, for arbitrary choice of $x_i^* \in [x_{i-1}, x_i]$, $y_j^* \in [y_{j-1}, y_j]$, $z_k^* \in [z_{k-1}, z_k]$, then we say f is *integrable over* S and denote the value of the limit by

$$\iiint\limits_S f(x, y, z) \, dV,$$

called the *triple integral of f over S*. That is,

$$\iiint\limits_S f(x, y, z) \, dV = \lim_{|\pi| \to 0} \sum_{i=1}^m \sum_{j=1}^n \sum_{k=1}^q f(x_i^*, y_j^*, z_k^*) \, \Delta x_i \, \Delta y_j \, \Delta z_k, \qquad (21)$$

the limit on the right being taken in the same sense as explained for Definition 1.

　　Moreover, the results of Theorems 1 and 2 carry over directly. Briefly, the integral operates linearly on functions; if f is positive on S, then so is $\iiint_S f$; if $f \le g$ on S, then $\iiint_S f \le \iiint_S g$; and the integral is additive on regions whose intersection has zero volume. A sufficient condition for f to be integrable on S is that f be continuous on S except for a subset of zero volume.

　　If f is continuous on S then the triple integral of f over S can be evaluated by means of iterated integrals:

$$\iiint\limits_S f(x, y, z) \, dV = \int_{a_1}^{a_2} \int_{b_1}^{b_2} \int_{c_1}^{c_2} f(x, y, z) \, dz \, dy \, dx. \qquad (22)$$

When S is a rectangular region there would be, in all, six iterated integrals, any one of which could be used to find the value of the triple integral.

Example 16. Let f be defined by $f(x, y, z) = x^3 y^2 z$, let S be the box of dimensions 1, 2, 3, respectively, with one vertex at the origin. We find the integral of f over S. We have, by (22),

$$\iiint_S f(x, y, z)\, dV = \int_0^1 \int_0^2 \int_0^3 x^3 y^2 z\, dz\, dy\, dx$$

$$= \int_0^1 \int_0^2 \left(\frac{1}{2} x^3 y^2 z^2 \Big|_0^3 \right) dy\, dx$$

$$= \frac{9}{2} \int_0^1 \int_0^2 x^3 y^2\, dy\, dx = \frac{9}{2} \int_0^1 \left(\frac{1}{3} x^3 y^3 \Big|_0^2 \right) dx$$

$$= 12 \int_0^1 x^3\, dx$$

$$= 3.$$

(A natural question might concern the utility of this result. What interpretation can we give to the number 3 obtained as answer? We do not plan to go into this point now, but a possible answer is that if f represented a density function then the value of the integral would be the mass of the box.)

We next remark that one can integrate over regions more general than rectangular parallelepipeds, provided these more general regions are suitably well-behaved. Given a function f continuous on such a suitable region S, the method of integrating f over S is similar to that already described: enclose S in a box S^*, define f^* to be the same as f on S, and zero on $S^* - S$; etc.

A more important subject for our consideration is the nature of the "suitably well-behaved" S. Many of the regions we shall encounter will be of the following type. We have, to begin with, a closed region S_2 in the xy-plane (of course, S_2 might lie in some other coordinate plane—we shall restrict our discussion to this case, however) and two functions g_1 and g_2 defined on S_2 and such that $(x, y) \in S_2 \Rightarrow g_1(x, y) \le g_2(x, y)$. Then the region S is

$$S = \{(x, y, z) \mid (x, y) \in S_2, g_1(x, y) \le z \le g_2(x, y)\}$$

(see Figure 26).

Note in the figure that the graphs of g_1 and g_2 share a common boundary curve (in the "back" of S). When this does not happen, the sides of S will be portions of cylinders, the base curves of which are the boundaries of S_2. Of course, S may be like a sphere or like a potato, and then g_1 and g_2 would share the boundary curve throughout (the equator, if S is a sphere).

A final, technical point about these regions, a point often inadequately understood by calculus students: When a triple integral over such a region is translated to an iterated integral, the limits on the inner (z) integral are easily determined as $g_1(x, y)$ (lower) and $g_2(x, y)$ (upper). The point we want to make here is that the limits on the x- and y-integrals must be determined so as to cover the region S_2 in the xy-plane, the *projection of S on the xy-plane.*

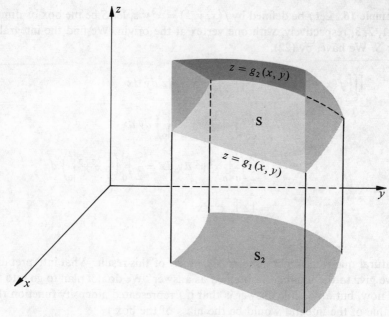

Figure 26

Example 17. We consider the region S which is bounded above by the plane $z = 1 + x + y$, below by the paraboloid $z = x^2 + y^2$, and on the sides by cylinders—vertical planes in this case—whose base curves are the boundaries of the unit square in the xy-plane; i.e., $S_2 = \{(x, y) \mid 0 \le x \le 1, 0 \le y \le 1\}$ (see Figure 27). We assume the density function is $\delta(x, y, z) = xy$, and we find the mass m of the region.

We have

$$m = \iiint_S \delta \, dV = \iiint_S xy \, dV$$

$$= \int_0^1 \int_0^1 \int_{x^2+y^2}^{1+x+y} xy \, dz \, dy \, dx$$

$$= \int_0^1 \int_0^1 xy(1 + x + y - x^2 - y^2) \, dy \, dx$$

$$= \int_0^1 \left(\frac{1}{2} xy^2 + \frac{1}{2} x^2 y^2 + \frac{1}{3} xy^3 - \frac{1}{2} x^3 y^2 - \frac{1}{4} xy^4 \Big|_0^1 \right) dx$$

$$= \int_0^1 \left(\frac{1}{2} x + \frac{1}{2} x^2 + \frac{1}{3} x - \frac{1}{2} x^3 - \frac{1}{4} x \right) dx = \int_0^1 \left(-\frac{1}{2} x^3 + \frac{1}{2} x^2 + \frac{7}{12} x \right) dx$$

$$= -\frac{1}{8} + \frac{1}{6} + \frac{7}{24}$$

$$= \frac{1}{3} \text{ mass units.}$$

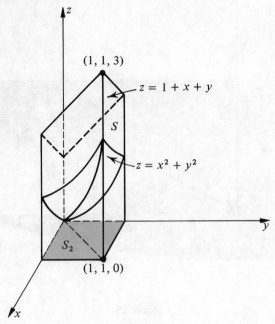

Figure 27

We leave as an exercise the problem of showing that the volume of S is $\dfrac{4}{3}$ cubic units.

Example 18. Let S be the region in the first octant bounded above by the parabolic cylinder $z = 4 - x^2$, below by the plane $z = \frac{1}{2}y$, and on the sides by portions of the yz- and zx-planes (see Figure 28). Initially we shall not specify the nature of the function f to be integrated over S; our concern will be with the translation of the triple integral to an iterated integral. The fact is that S is of a sufficiently simple nature that all six of the theoretically possible iterated integrals are actually possible, as we shall show.

If we choose to integrate first over z, then the z-limits present no problem; our interest centers on the region S_{xy} in the xy-plane which must be covered. To determine S_{xy} we solve simultaneously the equations of the two surfaces:

$$\left.\begin{cases} z = 4 - x^2 \\ z = \frac{1}{2}y \end{cases}\right\} \Rightarrow x = \sqrt{4 - \tfrac{1}{2}y} \qquad \text{or} \quad y = 2(4 - x^2). \tag{23}$$

As an equation in three space, either of these represents a surface, in this case a parabolic cylinder on which the curve of intersection of the two given surfaces lies. We show this curve as $\mathscr{C}$ in Figure 28. Its projection on the xy-plane gives us the curved portion of the boundary of S_{xy}. We show this in the figure as $\mathscr{C}_{xy}$; of course, as a curve in the xy-plane $\mathscr{C}_{xy}$ can be represented by either of the

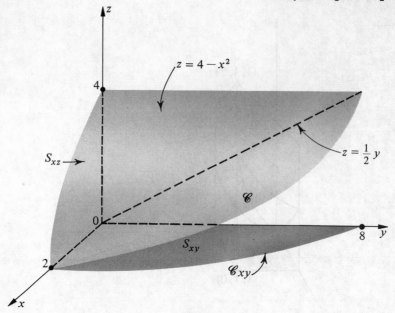

Figure 28

equations on the right in (23). With this discussion it is a simple matter to write two of the desired iterated integrals:

$$\iiint_S f(x, y, z) \, dV = \int_0^2 \int_0^{2(4-x^2)} \int_{y/2}^{4-x^2} f(x, y, z) \, dz \, dy \, dx, \qquad (24)$$

and

$$\iiint_S f(x, y, z) \, dV = \int_0^8 \int_0^{\sqrt{4-y/2}} \int_{y/2}^{4-x^2} f(x, y, z) \, dz \, dx \, dy. \qquad (25)$$

If we prefer to integrate first over x, then we can see that the outer boundary of S is the parabolic cylinder $z = 4 - x^2$, or $x = \sqrt{4 - z}$—since $x \geq 0$. The "back" boundary is simply a portion of the yz-plane, $x = 0$, and the projection of S onto the yz-plane produces the triangular region S_{yz} which we show in Figure 29. Thus two more iterated integrals are

$$\iiint_S f(x, y, z) \, dV = \int_0^8 \int_{y/2}^4 \int_0^{\sqrt{4-z}} f(x, y, z) \, dx \, dz \, dy, \qquad (26)$$

and

$$\iiint_S f(x, y, z) \, dV = \int_0^4 \int_0^{2z} \int_0^{\sqrt{4-z}} f(x, y, z) \, dx \, dy \, dz. \qquad (27)$$

Finally, if the first integration is in the y-direction, then the right boundary is the plane $y = 2z$, the left boundary is a portion of the zx-plane, and the projection of S onto the zx-plane is the region S_{xz}, shown in Figure 28, its bounding curve being

$$z = 4 - x^2 \text{ or } x = \sqrt{4 - z}.$$

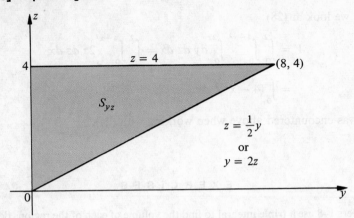

Figure 29

Consequently, we can write the remaining two iterated integrals:

$$\iiint_S f(x, y, z)\, dV = \int_0^2 \int_0^{4-x^2} \int_0^{2z} f(x, y, z)\, dy\, dz\, dx \tag{28}$$

and

$$\iiint_S f(x, y, z)\, dV = \int_0^4 \int_0^{\sqrt{4-z}} \int_0^{2z} f(x, y, z)\, dy\, dx\, dz. \tag{29}$$

We conclude this example—and section—by letting $f(x, y, z) = 1$ on S and evaluating three of the preceding integrals. Beginning with (24), we have

$$V = \iiint_S dV = \int_0^2 \int_0^{2(4-x^2)} \int_{y/2}^{4-x^2} dz\, dy\, dx$$

$$= \int_0^2 \int_0^{2(4-x^2)} (4 - x^2 - \tfrac{1}{2}y)\, dy\, dx = \int_0^2 \left((4 - x^2)y - \tfrac{1}{4}y^2 \Big|_0^{2(4-x^2)} \right) dx$$

$$= \int_0^2 (4 - x^2)^2\, dx$$

$$= \frac{2^8}{15} \approx 17.07 \text{ cubic units.}$$

From (27) we have

$$V = \int_0^4 \int_0^{2z} \int_0^{\sqrt{4-z}} dx\, dy\, dz = \int_0^4 \int_0^{2z} \sqrt{4-z}\, dy\, dz$$

$$= \int_0^4 2z\sqrt{4-z}\, dz.$$

By letting $\sqrt{4-z} = t$, one can transform this integral to

$$V = 4 \int_0^2 (4t^2 - t^4)\, dt = \frac{2^8}{15} \text{ cubic units.}$$

Last, we look at (28):

$$V = \int_0^2 \int_0^{4-x^2} \int_0^{2z} dy\, dz\, dx = \int_0^2 \int_0^{4-x^2} 2z\, dz\, dx$$

$$= \int_0^2 (4 - x^2)^2\, dx,$$

which was encountered above when working with (24).

E X E R C I S E S

In numbers 1–8 use a triple integral to find the volume of each of the regions described.

1. In the first octant; bounded by $x = 0$, $y = 0$, $z = 0$, $x + 4y + 9z = 36$.

2. In the first octant; bounded by $x = 0$, $y = 0$, $z = 0$, $x^2 + 4y^2 + 9z^2 = 36$.

3. In the first octant; bounded by $x = 0$, $y = 0$, $z = 0$, $x^2 + 4y^2 + 9z = 36$.

4. In the first octant; bounded by $z = e^x$, $z = 0$, $y = 0$, $x = 1$, $y = x$.

5. In the first octant; bounded above by $2z = 2 + y$, below by $2z = y^2$, on the sides by $x = 0$, $y = 0$, $x = 2$.

6. In the first octant; bounded by $z = 4 - x^2 - y^2$, $x^2 + y^2 = 2y$, $x = 0$, and $z = 0$.

7. In the first octant; bounded by the cylinders $x^2 + z^2 = a^2$ and $x^2 + y^2 = a^2$.

8. In the first octant; bounded above by $z = \log y$; the region

$$S_2 = S_{xy} = \{(x, y)|\ 0 \le x \le 2,\ x + 1 \le y \le 3\}.$$

9. Show that the volume of the region S described in Example 17 is $\dfrac{4}{3}$ cubic units.

10. Set up (you need not evaluate) the iterated integral for the triple integral of Exercise 7 with the differentials in the order:

   (a) $dy\, dz\, dx$.
   (b) $dx\, dy\, dz$.

11. *Set up* the iterated integral for the triple integral of Exercise 8 with the differentials in the order $dx\, dz\, dy$.

12. For each of the following iterated integrals describe the region S which is specified.

   (a) $\displaystyle\int_0^1 \int_x^1 \int_0^x f(x, y, z)\, dz\, dy\, dx$.   (b) $\displaystyle\int_0^1 \int_0^y \int_0^x f(x, y, z)\, dz\, dx\, dy$.

(c) $\displaystyle\int_0^1 \int_0^{1-x^2} \int_0^{\sqrt{2-x^2-y^2}} f(x, y, z)\, dz\, dy\, dx.$

(d) $\displaystyle\int_0^2 \int_0^{\sqrt{2x-x^2}} \int_0^{\sqrt{4-x^2-y^2}} f(x, y, z)\, dz\, dy\, dx.$

(e) $\displaystyle\int_{-2}^2 \int_0^{\sqrt{4-y^2}} \int_0^{2-x} dz\, dx\, dy.$

13. Let S be the region bounded above by the plane $z = 2x + 2y$ and below by the paraboloid $z = x^2 + y^2$. Find the volume of S.
[*Hints.*
(1) The intersection of the two surfaces lies on the cylinder $(x - 1)^2 + (y - 1)^2 = 2$.
(2) For integration purposes it may help to note that

$$2x + 2y - x^2 - y^2 = 2 - (x - 1)^2 - (y - 1)^2.$$

14. Let S be a rectangle in $\mathbf{R}^n$, i.e.,

$$S = [a_1', a_1''] \times [a_2', a_2''] \times \cdots \times [a_n', a_n''];$$

and let f be a function with a domain in $\mathbf{R}^n$ which includes S. Suppose f is bounded on S. Describe how to define an n-fold multiple integral of f over S, i.e., give a definition for

$$\iint \cdots \int_S f(\mathbf{x})\, dV_n,$$

where $\mathbf{x} = (x_1, \ldots, x_n)$.

14.7 Cylindrical and Spherical Coordinates

A question naturally arises about the extension of polar coordinates to $\mathbf{R}^3$. There are, in fact, two such extensions, *cylindrical* and *spherical* coordinates, which we now study, along with their use in triple integrals.

CYLINDRICAL COORDINATES. The most obvious and least subtle extension of polar coordinates to three dimensions is to retain the r, θ coordinates in the xy-plane and use as the third coordinate the z of rectangular coordinates. This is known as the *cylindrical coordinate system*; the reason for the name will be apparent presently (see Figure 30).

As usual when encountering a new coordinate system, we should look at the coordinate surfaces. If we set $r = c$, the set of points in space determined by this condition is a right circular cylinder (hence the name of the system), symmetric with respect to the z-axis, radius equal to c. The surface determined by $\theta = c$ is a plane through the z-axis (like a page in a book, the spine of which is along the z-axis). And the surface $z = c$ is a plane parallel to the xy-plane, its distance from the xy-plane being $|c|$. A portion of one of each of these surfaces is shown in Figure 30.

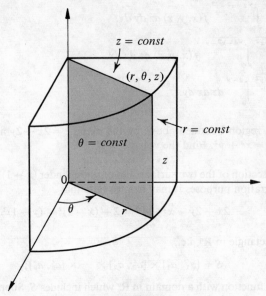

Figure 30

It is fairly evident from the nature of cylindrical coordinates and from the work in Section 14.5 that, when translating either from a triple integral in cylindrical coordinates or from an iterated integral in rectangular coordinates to an iterated integral in cylindrical coordinates, the volume differential is

$$dV = r\, dz\, dr\, d\theta. \tag{30}$$

To show that this is indeed so, we draw on the obvious generalization of Theorem 4 from two to three dimensions and calculate J. First we note the relation between rectangular and cylindrical coordinates:

$$\left\{ \begin{array}{l} x = r\cos\theta \\ y = r\sin\theta \\ z = z \end{array} \right\}. \tag{31}$$

From these equations we can set up the Jacobian determinant:

$$J = \begin{vmatrix} \cos\theta & -r\sin\theta & 0 \\ \sin\theta & r\cos\theta & 0 \\ 0 & 0 & 1 \end{vmatrix} = r.$$

The three-dimensional version of Theorem 4 then tells us that (30) is valid.

In particular, then, the translation from a triple integral in rectangular coordinates to the corresponding triple integral in cylindrical coordinates is achieved by the following formula:

$$\iiint\limits_{S} f(x, y, z)\, dV = \iiint\limits_{S} f(r\cos\theta, r\sin\theta, z)\, r\, dz\, dr\, d\theta. \tag{32}$$

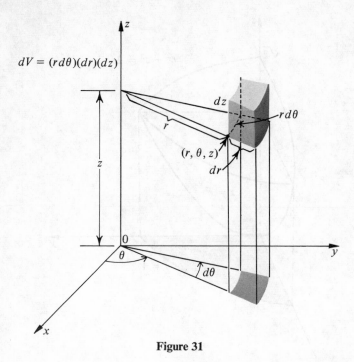

$$dV = (r\,d\theta)(dr)(dz)$$

Figure 31

In Figure 31 we show an intuitive geometric interpretation for the expression in Eq. (30).

Usually, when an iterated integral is set up in cylindrical coordinates the order of integration is $dz\,dr\,d\theta$. Geometrically this can be thought of as vertically upward, then radially outward but horizontally, and finally rotationally about the z-axis.

The question about when cylindrical coordinates are preferable to rectangular coordinates cannot be given a neat answer. Roughly, if the region S over which the integration is to be performed is symmetric with respect to the z-axis, or if a boundary surface is a right circular cylinder, or perhaps a portion of a plane $\theta = $ const., then one should consider using cylindrical coordinates.

Example 19. We find the volume V of the region S which is bounded above by the sphere $x^2 + y^2 + z^2 = 2$ and below by the paraboloid $z = x^2 + y^2$.

In cylindrical coordinates the equations of these surfaces are $r^2 + z^2 = 2$ and $z = r^2$, respectively. Note that substituting from the second into the first gives $z + z^2 = 2$ for the intersection of the two surfaces. The only meaningful solution to this equation is $z = 1$, the plane one unit above the $r\theta$-plane. From either of the original equations it is easy to see that the curve of intersection in this plane $z = 1$ is the circle $r = 1$. We show in Figure 32 that part of S which lies in the first octant.

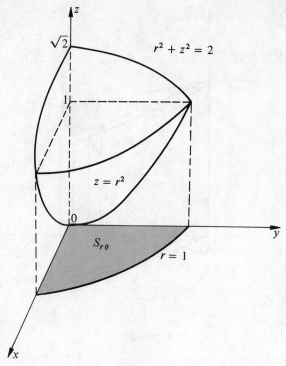

Figure 32

The calculation of V is now quite easy; using the symmetry with respect to the z-axis, we have

$$\frac{1}{4} V = \iiint_{S_1} dV \qquad (S_1 \text{ is the part of } S \text{ in octant I})$$

$$= \int_0^{\pi/2} \int_0^1 \int_{r^2}^{\sqrt{2-r^2}} r \, dz \, dr \, d\theta$$

$$= \int_0^{\pi/2} \int_0^1 r(\sqrt{2-r^2} - r^2) \, dr \, d\theta$$

$$= \int_0^{\pi/2} \left(-\frac{1}{2} \cdot \frac{2}{3} (2-r^2)^{3/2} - \frac{1}{4} r^4 \Big|_0^1 \right) d\theta$$

$$= \int_0^{\pi/2} \left(\frac{2\sqrt{2}}{3} - \frac{1}{3} - \frac{1}{4} \right) d\theta$$

$$= \frac{\pi}{24} (8\sqrt{2} - 7).$$

Thus $V = \frac{\pi}{6} (8\sqrt{2} - 7) \approx 2.258$ cubic units.

The calculation of V by means of rectangular coordinates is somewhat troublesome.

SPHERICAL COORDINATES. The triple of numbers used in rectangular coordinates all represent distances, whereas in cylindrical coordinates one of the three is an angular measure, the other two being measures of distance. In spherical coordinates, the other generalization to three dimensions of polar coordinates in the plane, two of the numbers are angular measures and only one is a linear distance. We describe the system by superimposing it on a rectangular system. The illustration is in Figure 33.

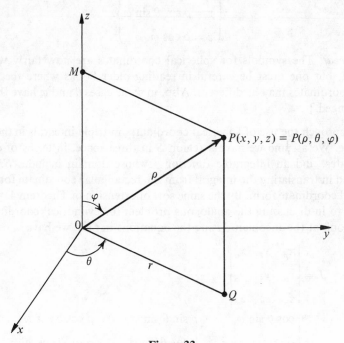

Figure 33

We let $P(x, y, z)$ be an arbitrary point in $\mathbf{R}^3$. The first of the three numbers used in spherical coordinates is described by $\rho = |\mathbf{OP}|$. Unlike the r of polar coordinates, ρ is usually taken as nonnegative. The second spherical coordinate is the same angle θ as is used in cylindrical coordinates; to be explicit, we can define it as the angle between the positive x-axis and $\mathbf{OQ}$, where $\mathbf{OQ}$ is the projection of $\mathbf{OP}$ on the xy-plane. The third coordinate of this system is the angle φ measured from the positive z-axis to $\mathbf{OP}$. The range of φ is the interval $0 \le \varphi \le \pi$.

The coordinate surfaces for this system are as follows. If we consider the set of points determined by $\rho = $ const., we have exactly the points on a sphere centered at the origin, radius equal to the value of the constant (hence the name of the system). The surfaces $\theta = $ const. are planes through the z-axis, as in cylindrical coordinates. Finally, except for the special cases of $0, \dfrac{\pi}{2}$, and π (see Exercise 10) the surfaces $\varphi = $ const. are half cones, vertex at the origin, axis of symmetry the z-axis.

The relations between spherical and rectangular coordinates can be easily obtained by noting first (see Figure 33) that the distance r of cylindrical coordinates is given by

$$r = \rho \sin \varphi.$$

Then, since $x = r \cos \theta$, $y = r \sin \theta$, we have

$$\begin{cases} x = \rho \cos \theta \sin \varphi \\ y = \rho \sin \theta \sin \varphi \\ z = \rho \cos \varphi \end{cases}. \tag{33}$$

[*A caveat.* The symbols for spherical coordinates are now fairly well standardized, but one must be careful in reading older books where the order of listing coordinates may be different. Also, in some cases θ and φ have their roles interchanged.]

We approach the use of spherical coordinates in triple integrals in the following sense. We assume we have a region S in three space, in terms of cartesian coordinates, and an integrable function f whose domain includes S. We are interested in translating the integral from the rectangular coordinate form to the spherical coordinate form. By the same sort of extension of Theorem 4, which we referred to in discussing the analogous problem for cylindrical coordinates, we should look at the Jacobian. Using the equations in (33), we have

$$J = \begin{vmatrix} x_\rho & x_\theta & x_\varphi \\ y_\rho & y_\theta & y_\varphi \\ z_\rho & z_\theta & z_\varphi \end{vmatrix}$$

$$= \begin{vmatrix} \cos \theta \sin \varphi & -\rho \sin \theta \sin \varphi & \rho \cos \theta \cos \varphi \\ \sin \theta \sin \varphi & \rho \cos \theta \sin \varphi & \rho \sin \theta \cos \varphi \\ \cos \varphi & 0 & -\rho \sin \varphi \end{vmatrix}$$

$$= \rho^2 [\cos \varphi (-\sin \varphi \cos \varphi) - \sin \varphi (\sin^2 \varphi)]$$

$$= -\rho^2 \sin \varphi.$$

(The determinant was expanded by using the cofactors of the bottom row.) Since $|J| = \rho^2 \sin \varphi$ (recall that $0 \le \varphi \le \pi \Rightarrow \sin \varphi \ge 0$), we have

$$dV = \rho^2 \sin \varphi \, d\rho \, d\varphi \, d\theta. \tag{34}$$

Thus the translation formula analogous to (32) is

$$\iiint\limits_S f(x, y, z) \, dV = \iiint\limits_S f(\rho \cos \theta \sin \varphi, \rho \sin \theta \sin \varphi, \rho \cos \varphi)\rho^2 \sin \varphi \, d\rho \, d\varphi \, d\theta.$$

$$\tag{35}$$

Of course, when the triple integral on the right is itself translated to an iterated integral, the limits must be chosen so as to cover the region S.

We can give an intuitive geometric interpretation of the expression in (34) by thinking of an element of volume as a box (see Figure 34). If we think of the

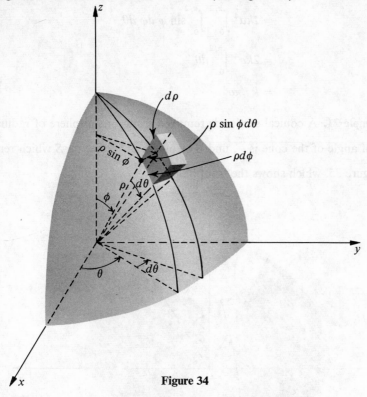

Figure 34

volume of the box as the product of the three dimensions, then we have

$$dV = (\rho \sin \varphi \, d\theta)(\rho \, d\varphi)(d\rho)$$
$$= \rho^2 \sin \varphi \, d\rho \, d\varphi \, d\theta.$$

It is not possible to lay down a hard and fast rule about the "best" order for setting up an iterated integral in spherical coordinates; to a great extent it depends upon the region S. Frequently, though, the order indicated in (34) is satisfactory.

Example 20. The density of a sphere is proportional to the distance from the center. If the radius is a, find the mass.

Working directly in spherical coordinates, we can take the equation of the sphere as $\rho = a$, the density function as $\delta(\rho, \theta, \varphi) = k\rho$. Thus, using the symmetry, we have

$$\frac{1}{8} m = \iiint\limits_S \delta \, dV = \iiint\limits_S k\rho \rho^2 \sin \varphi \, d\rho \, d\varphi \, d\theta,$$

where S is the part of the sphere in the first octant. Consequently,

$$m = 8 \int_0^{\pi/2} \int_0^{\pi/2} \int_0^a k\rho^3 \sin \varphi \, d\rho \, d\varphi \, d\theta$$

$$= 2ka^4 \int_0^{\pi/2} \int_0^{\pi/2} \sin \varphi \, d\varphi \, d\theta$$

$$= 2ka^4 \int_0^{\pi/2} d\theta$$

$$= k \cdot \pi a^4.$$

Example 21. A conical section is removed from a hemisphere of radius a. If the half angle of the cone is $\dfrac{\pi}{6}$, find the volume of the region S which remains. See Figure 35, which shows the front half of S.

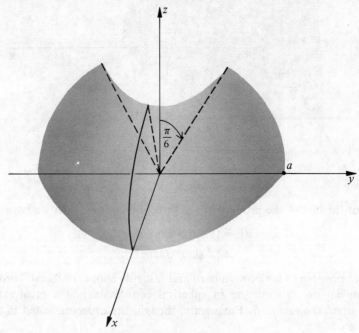

Figure 35

The spherical coordinate equation of the hemisphere is $\rho = a$, for $0 \le \varphi \le \dfrac{\pi}{2}$, $0 \le \theta < 2\pi$; the equation of the cone is $\varphi = \dfrac{\pi}{6}$, $0 \le \theta < 2\pi$. Thus the volume V of the region S in question is

$$V = \iiint_S dV = \iiint_S \rho^2 \sin \varphi \, d\rho \, d\varphi \, d\theta.$$

Because of the symmetry of S with respect to the z-axis we concentrate on the portion in the first quadrant:

$$V = 4 \int_0^{\pi/2} \int_{\pi/6}^{\pi/2} \int_0^a \rho^2 \sin \varphi \, d\rho \, d\varphi \, d\theta$$

$$= \frac{4a^3}{3} \int_0^{\pi/2} \int_{\pi/6}^{\pi/2} \sin \varphi \, d\varphi \, d\theta$$

$$= \frac{4a^3}{3} \int_0^{\pi/2} \left(- \cos \varphi \Big|_{\pi/6}^{\pi/2} \right) d\theta = \frac{2a^3 \sqrt{3}}{3} \int_0^{\pi/2} d\theta$$

$$= \frac{\pi a^3 \sqrt{3}}{3} \text{ cubic units.}$$

EXERCISES

In numbers 1–8 set up iterated integrals in both cylindrical and spherical coordinates for finding $\iiint_S f \, dV$ for the specified S. In each case take $f = 1$ and evaluate one of the two iterated integrals. Take advantage of symmetry wherever possible.

1. S is the region common to the sphere $x^2 + y^2 + z^2 = 4$ and the cylinder $x^2 + y^2 = 1$.

2. S is bounded above by $x^2 + y^2 + z^2 = 5$, below by $x^2 + y^2 - 4z = 0$.

3. S is bounded above by $z = \sqrt{4 - x^2 - y^2}$, below by $z = \dfrac{1}{\sqrt{3}} \sqrt{x^2 + y^2}$.

4. S is bounded by $z = x^2 + y^2$, $z = 0$, and $x^2 + y^2 = 4$.

5. S is bounded by $z = 1$, $z = 0$, $y = 0$, $y = x$, $x = 1$. [*Hint.* For spherical coordinates express S as $S = S_1 \cup S_2$ where S_1 and S_2 are determined by $0 \le \varphi \le \tan^{-1}(\sec \theta)$ and $\tan^{-1}(\sec \theta) \le \varphi \le \dfrac{\pi}{2}$. Also, for this region set up iterated integrals in rectangular coordinates and compare with the other two integrals set up.]

6. S is the region inside the sphere $x^2 + y^2 + z^2 = 4$ and outside the cylinder $x^2 + y^2 = 2$.

7. S is the region inside the paraboloid $z = x^2 + y^2$ and outside the cone $z^2 = x^2 + y^2$.

8. S is the region bounded above by $x^2 + y^2 + z^2 = 4z$, below by $x^2 + y^2 = z^2$.

9. Use cylindrical coordinates to find the volume of the region bounded above by the paraboloid $2x^2 + 2y^2 + z = 8$ and bounded below by the hemisphere $z = \sqrt{4 - x^2 - y^2}$. Can you set up the iterated integral in spherical coordinates?

10. Describe the coordinate surfaces $\varphi = 0$, $\varphi = \dfrac{\pi}{2}$, and $\varphi = \pi$.

11. Show that if Eqs. (33) are solved for ρ, φ, θ, the result is

$$\begin{cases} \rho = \sqrt{x^2 + y^2 + z^2} \\[2mm] \cos \varphi = \dfrac{z}{\sqrt{x^2 + y^2 + z^2}} \\[2mm] \tan \theta = \dfrac{y}{x} \end{cases}.$$

14.8 Applications of Triple Integrals

We have already illustrated, in Examples 17 and 20, how a triple integral can be used to find the mass of a nonhomogeneous (density not constant) region. In this section we extend to three-dimensional regions the concepts of moments and centroids introduced in Section 4 for two-dimensional regions.

The first point we make is that one is usually interested in *first* moments of mass with respect to *planes*, whereas second moments (moments of inertia) are usually found with respect to lines.

The motivation for the definition we shall give below for the moment of mass about the xy-plane, say, is briefly as follows. We partition the region S occupied by the mass in the usual way (i.e., as described at the beginning of Section 6) and, choosing arbitrarily a point (x_i^*, y_j^*, z_k^*) in each subregion determined by the partition, we form the sum

$$\sum_{i=1}^{m} \sum_{j=1}^{n} \sum_{k=1}^{q} z_k^* \, \delta(x_i^*, y_j^*, z_k^*) \, \Delta x_i \, \Delta y_j \, \Delta z_k.$$

This sum clearly serves as an approximation to the value of the (first) moment with respect to the xy-plane; this is so because a typical term represents, approximately, the product of the distance z_k^* between the subregion and the xy-plane and the mass ($\delta(x_i^*, y_j^*, z_k^*) \, \Delta V_{ijk}$) of the subregion. This sum is, of course, an approximating sum for the integral over S of the function f, where $f = z\delta$.

Similarly, one can set up approximating sums for moments with respect to the other coordinate planes.

The definitions themselves are as follows: Let a mass occupy a region S of three space; let the density function be δ, defined on S. Then, the measure m of the mass and the moments with respect to the xy-, yz-, and zx-planes are defined by, respectively,

$$m = \iiint_S \delta(x, y, z) \, dV, \tag{36}$$

$$M_{xy} = \iiint_S z\delta(x, y, z) \, dV, \tag{37}$$

$$M_{yz} = \iiint\limits_{S} x\delta(x, y, z) \, dV, \tag{38}$$

$$M_{zx} = \iiint\limits_{S} y\delta(x, y, z) \, dV. \tag{39}$$

The centroid, or *center of mass*, C is the point with coordinates $(\bar{x}, \bar{y}, \bar{z})$, defined by

$$\begin{cases} m\bar{x} = M_{yz} \\ m\bar{y} = M_{zx} \\ m\bar{z} = M_{xy} \end{cases}. \tag{40}$$

The *moments of inertia* with respect to the coordinate axes are defined by, respectively,

$$I_x = \iiint\limits_{S} (y^2 + z^2)\delta(x, y, z) \, dV \tag{41}$$

$$I_y = \iiint\limits_{S} (z^2 + x^2)\delta(x, y, z) \, dV \tag{42}$$

$$I_z = \iiint\limits_{S} (x^2 + y^2)\delta(x, y, z) \, dV. \tag{43}$$

Example 22. We return to the region described in Example 16—a box of dimensions 1, 2, 3, with a vertex at the origin. Interpreting the function $(x^3 y^2 z)$ used in Example 16 as a density function, we know the mass of the region is three units. It is now an easy matter to find the three first moments:

$$M_{yz} = \int_0^1 \int_0^2 \int_0^3 x(x^3 y^2 z) \, dz \, dy \, dx = \frac{12}{5};$$

$$M_{zx} = \int_0^1 \int_0^2 \int_0^3 y(x^3 y^2 z) \, dz \, dy \, dx = \frac{9}{2};$$

$$M_{xy} = \int_0^1 \int_0^2 \int_0^3 z(x^3 y^2 z) \, dz \, dy \, dx = 6.$$

With these numbers and the mass $m = 3$ already found we can compute the coordinates of the centroid:

$$\bar{x} = \frac{12}{5} \cdot \frac{1}{3} = \frac{4}{5}, \qquad \bar{y} = \frac{9}{2} \cdot \frac{1}{3} = \frac{3}{2}, \qquad \bar{z} = \frac{6}{3} = 2.$$

The presence of the distance function in the triple integrals for finding moments can sometimes ease and sometimes complicate the integration problem.

Example 23. We consider the region discussed in Example 19—bounded above by the sphere $x^2 + y^2 + z^2 = 2$, below by the paraboloid $z = x^2 + y^2$.

If we assume constant density δ, then the mass $m = \delta V = \dfrac{\pi\delta}{6}(8\sqrt{2} - 7)$ mass units. Because of symmetry and homogeneity, the centroid is on the z-axis, i.e., $\bar{x} = \bar{y} = 0$. To find $\bar{z}$ we calculate (refer to Example 19 for notation)

$$M_{xy} = 4 \iiint_{S_1} z\delta \, dV$$

$$= 4\delta \int_0^{\pi/2} \int_0^1 \int_{r^2}^{\sqrt{2-r^2}} rz \, dz \, dr \, d\theta$$

$$= 2\delta \int_0^{\pi/2} \int_0^1 rz^2 \Big|_{r^2}^{\sqrt{2-r^2}} dr \, d\theta$$

$$= 2\delta \int_0^{\pi/2} \int_0^1 (2r - r^3 - r^5) \, dr \, d\theta$$

$$= \frac{7\pi\delta}{12}.$$

(The factor z in the integrand made the integration simpler than it was for finding V.)

From this result we can find $\bar{z}$:

$$\bar{z} = \frac{M_{xy}}{m} = \frac{7\pi\delta}{12} \cdot \frac{6}{\pi\delta(8\sqrt{2} - 7)} \approx 0.81.$$

If, however, we calculate the moment of inertia about the z-axis for this region we find

$$I_z = 4 \iiint_{S_1} r^2 \delta \, dV \qquad \text{(since } x^2 + y^2 = r^2\text{)}$$

$$= 4\delta \int_0^{\pi/2} \int_0^1 \int_{r^2}^{\sqrt{2-r^2}} r^3 \, dz \, dr \, d\theta$$

$$= 4\delta \int_0^{\pi/2} \int_0^1 (r^3\sqrt{2-r^2} - r^5) \, dr \, d\theta.$$

This integral is a bit more troublesome than the others encountered for this region. It can be evaluated by a trigonometric substitution, which leads to

$$I_z = \frac{\pi\delta}{15}(16\sqrt{2} - 19).$$

If it is natural to set up the integral in terms of cylindrical or spherical coordinates one must remember to express the rectangular coordinate distances in terms of the particular system being used.

Example 24. This time we draw on Example 21 from the end of the previous section. If we assume constant density and use the symmetry with respect to the z-axis, we can conclude that $\bar{x} = \bar{y} = 0$. To find $\bar{z}$ we calculate M_{xy}:

$$M_{xy} = 4\delta \int_0^{\pi/2} \int_{\pi/6}^{\pi/2} \int_0^a z\rho^2 \sin\varphi \, d\rho \, d\varphi \, d\theta$$

$$= 4\delta \int_0^{\pi/2} \int_{\pi/6}^{\pi/2} \int_0^a \rho^3 \sin\varphi \cos\varphi \, d\rho \, d\varphi \, d\theta \quad (z = \rho\cos\varphi)$$

$$= \delta a^4 \int_0^{\pi/2} \int_{\pi/6}^{\pi/2} \sin\varphi \cos\varphi \, d\varphi \, d\theta$$

$$= \frac{3\pi\delta a^4}{16}.$$

From Example 21 and the assumption of constant density we have

$$m = \delta V = \frac{\sqrt{3}\,\pi\delta a^3}{3};$$

thus

$$\bar{z} = \frac{M_{xy}}{m} = \frac{3\sqrt{3}\,a}{16} \approx 0.325a.$$

Note that the centroid does not lie within S.

We also calculate the moment of inertia with respect to the z-axis for this mass. This is found by

$$I_z = 4\delta \int_0^{\pi/2} \int_{\pi/6}^{\pi/2} \int_0^a (x^2 + y^2)\rho^2 \sin\varphi \, d\rho \, d\varphi \, d\theta.$$

Since $x^2 + y^2 = \rho^2 \sin^2\varphi$, from Eqs. (33), this becomes

$$I_z = 4\delta \int_0^{\pi/2} \int_{\pi/6}^{\pi/2} \int_0^a \rho^4 \sin^3\varphi \, d\rho \, d\varphi \, d\theta$$

$$= \frac{3\sqrt{3}\,\pi\delta a^5}{20},$$

after routine integration.

If we define the *radius of gyration* R_z by the equation

$$mR_z^2 = I_z \tag{44}$$

we find

$$R_z^2 = \frac{I_z}{m} = \frac{9a^2}{20},$$

or $R_z = \dfrac{3a}{2\sqrt{5}}$. If the entire mass were concentrated at a point R_z units from the z-axis, the resulting moment of inertia would equal that found above; this is what (44) guarantees.

E X E R C I S E S

Use the coordinate system which you deem best suited to the problem. All references are to the exercises after Section 14.7.

1. S is the region described in Exercise 1.

    (a) If $\delta(x, y, z) = z + 2$, find the centroid.   (b) If δ is constant, find I_z.

2. S is the region of Exercise 2.

    (a) Assuming constant density, find the centroid.

    (b) Assuming constant density, find I_z.

3. For the region S of Exercise 3, find

    (a) The centroid, assuming $\delta(x, y, z) = x^2 + y^2 + z^2$.

    (b) I_z, assuming $\delta(x, y, z) = \sqrt{x^2 + y^2 + z^2}$.

4. For the region of Exercise 4, assume $\delta(x, y, z) = \sqrt{x^2 + y^2}$. Find

    (a) The centroid.   (b) I_z.

5. The region S is that described in Exercise 5. Let $\delta(x, y, z) = z$. Find

    (a) The centroid.   (b) I_x.

6. S is the region of Exercise 6. Assume $\delta(x, y, z) = z + 2$. Find

    (a) The mass m.   (b) I_z.   (c) R_z.

7. The region is that of Exercise 7. Assume constant density. Find

    (a) The centroid.   (b) I_z.   (c) R_z.

8. The region is that of Exercise 8. Assume constant density. Find

    (a) The centroid.   (b) I_z.   (c) R_z.

14.9 Line Integrals

The subject of this section does not properly come under the heading of "multiple integral." However, a line integral is a generalization of a simple integral and does involve functions of several variables. This fact, along with the importance of line integrals, both for applications and for theoretical mathematical considerations, justifies the inclusion of a brief discussion of line integrals in a chapter on integral calculus for functions of several variables.

We have already seen that a natural physical interpretation of a simple integral

$$\int_a^b f(x)\, dx$$

is the measure of work done when a particle is moved from a to b *along the x-axis* by a force of magnitude $f(x)$ at point x, acting in the direction of the x-axis (if the force is not directed along the x-axis we consider $f(x)$ to be the component, at x, of the force in the direction of the x-axis).

The generalization we are interested in here is simply to lift the restriction that the motion be in a straight line. We shall concern ourselves with motion in a plane, but as will be seen, the further generalization to three dimensions (or, for that matter, the generalization of the abstract concept of line integral to $\mathbf{R}^n$) is perfectly straighforward and easy.

We begin by developing, by standard integral calculus techniques, a solution to the physical problem mentioned above. This will lead, in a natural way, to the definition of the abstract concept, the line integral.

Suppose we have a curve $\mathscr{C}$ in the xy-plane which is defined analytically (see Section 11.4) by a vector function $\mathbf{r}$ defined on a t-interval, say $a \le t \le b$. Thus a point P on $\mathscr{C}$ is given by

$$\mathbf{r}(t) = x(t)\mathbf{i} + y(t)\mathbf{j},$$

where x and y are scalar functions defined on $[a, b]$; indeed, we assume x and y have continuous derivatives x' and y' on $[a, b]$. We let the points A and B be determined by $\mathbf{r}(a)$ and $\mathbf{r}(b)$, respectively (see Figure 36).

We next assume that the force, or *force field* as it is called in this case, is defined by a vector valued function $\mathbf{F}$ which is defined on a region S which includes the curve $\mathscr{C}$ in its interior. The values of $\mathbf{F}$ being vectors in $\mathbf{R}^2$, we can represent $\mathbf{F}$ more explicitly by

$$\mathbf{F}(\mathbf{x}) = f(\mathbf{x})\mathbf{i} + g(\mathbf{x})\mathbf{j},$$

or, letting $\mathbf{x} = (x, y) \in S$,

$$\mathbf{F}(x, y) = f(x, y)\mathbf{i} + g(x, y)\mathbf{j}.$$

With our ultimate goal (defining an integral) in mind, we assume the functions f and g are continuous on S.

Now we set up, using elementary considerations, an approximation to the work done by $\mathbf{F}$ in moving a particle along $\mathscr{C}$ from A to B. Thus we take a partition π of $[a, b]$,

$$\pi = \{a = t_0, t_1, \ldots, t_{k-1}, t_k, \ldots, t_n = b\}.$$

This partition induces a partition of $\mathscr{C}$:

$$\{A = P_0, P_1, \ldots, P_{k-1}, P_k, \ldots, P_n = B\}$$

where $\mathbf{OP}_k = \mathbf{r}(t_k)$. We next pick, quite arbitrarily, points $t_k^* \in [t_{k-1}, t_k]$, thereby obtaining points P_k^* on $\mathscr{C}$, by the relation $\mathbf{OP}_k^* = \mathbf{r}(t_k^*)$. We evaluate the force function $\mathbf{F}$ at these points P_k^*.

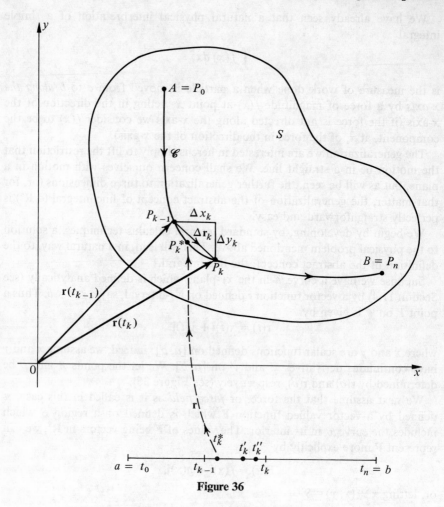

Figure 36

Because of the interpretation of the inner product $\mathbf{F} \cdot \mathbf{r}$ as a measure of work done (see Section 11.3) when a *constant* force $\mathbf{F}$ displaces a particle *linearly* by a vector $\mathbf{r}$, we can begin our approximation by expressing the work done by the constant force $\mathbf{F}(x_k^*, y_k^*)$ moving a particle from P_{k-1} to P_k along the straight line determined by $\Delta \mathbf{r}_k = \mathbf{r}(t_k) - \mathbf{r}(t_{k-1})$. This gives

$$\mathbf{F}(x_k^*, y_k^*) \cdot \Delta \mathbf{r}_k,$$

and adding up all such terms we can say about the work W that

$$W \approx \sum_{k=1}^{n} \mathbf{F}(x(t_k^*), y(t_k^*)) \cdot \Delta \mathbf{r}_k. \tag{45}$$

Since $\mathbf{F} = f\mathbf{i} + g\mathbf{j}$ and $\mathbf{r} = x\mathbf{i} + y\mathbf{j}$, which implies that $\Delta \mathbf{r}_k = \Delta x_k \mathbf{i} + \Delta y_k \mathbf{j}$, we can write (45) more explicitly as

$$W \approx \sum_{k=1}^{n} [f(x(t_k^*), y(t_k^*)) \, \Delta x_k + g(x(t_k^*), y(t_k^*)) \, \Delta y_k]. \tag{46}$$

We now look at Δx_k and Δy_k. Since we have assumed that x and y are differentiable functions of t on $[a, b]$, we know that we can apply the Mean Value Theorem to each of these functions on each of the subintervals of the partition π. Thus for $k = 1, \ldots, n$ we have

$$\Delta x_k = x(t_k) - x(t_{k-1}) = x'(t_k') \Delta t_k, \ t_k' \in [t_{k-1}, t_k],$$
$$\Delta y_k = y(t_k) - y(t_{k-1}) = y'(t_k'') \Delta t_k, \ t_k'' \in [t_{k-1}, t_k].$$

where $\Delta t_k = t_k - t_{k-1}$. With these results we can express the right side of (46) entirely in terms of t:

$$W \approx \sum_{k=1}^{n} [f(x(t_k^*), y(t_k^*))x'(t_k') + g(x(t_k^*), y(t_k^*))y'(t_k'')] \Delta t_k. \tag{47}$$

The expression on the right-hand side, complicated as it is, is nevertheless very close to a Riemann sum for an integral involving the single variable t and the interval $[a, b]$. The reason we must say "very close" is the fact that the various functions which appear within the brackets in the sum are not all evaluated at the same point within each subinterval. We have, in fact, the points t_k^*, t_k', and t_k'' (see Figure 36), and although we have control over the choice of the t_k^* we do not have control over the t_k' and t_k'' obtained by applying the Mean Value Theorem. The position we find ourselves in is exactly like that which developed in the proof of Theorem 11.8 (expressing length of arc of a curve in terms of an integral), and is covered by the discussion after the Corollary to Theorem 9.7.

We summarize the preceding discussion as follows.

Theorem 5. *Under the conditions just prescribed on* $\mathbf{F}, f, g, \mathbf{r}, x, y, x'$, *and* y' *the limit*

$$\lim_{|\pi| \to 0} \sum_{k=1}^{n} [f(x(t_k^*), y(t_k^*))x'(t_k') + g(x(t_k^*), y(t_k^*))y'(t_k'')] \Delta t_k \tag{48}$$

exists and is equal to

$$\int_a^b [f(x(t), y(t))x'(t) + g(x(t), y(t))y'(t)] \, dt. \tag{49}$$

The customary terminology and symbols for this integral are as follows:

Definition 5. *Let* $\mathscr{C}$ *be a curve defined by a vector function* $\mathbf{r} = x\mathbf{i} + y\mathbf{j}$, *where* x, y, x', *and* y' *are assumed to be continuous for* $a \le t \le b$. *Suppose* $\mathscr{C}$ *is in a region* $S \subset \mathbf{R}^2$; *let* $\mathbf{F} = f\mathbf{i} + g\mathbf{j}$ *be a vector function defined and continuous on* S. *Then the* **line integral** *of* $\mathbf{F}$ *over* $\mathscr{C}$ *is*

$$\int_{\mathscr{C}} f \, dx + g \, dy = \int_{\mathscr{C}} \mathbf{F} \cdot d\mathbf{r}$$
$$= \int_a^b [f(x(t), y(t))x'(t) + g(x(t), y(t))y'(t)] \, dt. \tag{50}$$

The notation $\int_{\mathscr{C}} \mathbf{F} \cdot d\mathbf{r}$ is justified by the fact that

$$\mathbf{r}(t) = x(t)\mathbf{i} + y(t)\mathbf{j} \Rightarrow$$
$$d\mathbf{r} = (x'(t) \, dt)\mathbf{i} + (y'(t) \, dt)\mathbf{j} = dx\mathbf{i} + dy\mathbf{j}.$$

Since $\mathbf{F} = f\mathbf{i} + g\mathbf{j}$, $\mathbf{F} \cdot d\mathbf{r} = f\,dx + g\,dy$.

Before discussing the properties of line integrals we consider an illustration.

Example 25. Let $\mathbf{r}$ be defined on $\frac{1}{2} \le t \le 2$ by

$$\mathbf{r}(t) = t\mathbf{i} + \frac{1}{t}\mathbf{j}.$$

i.e., $x(t) = t$, $y(t) = \dfrac{1}{t}$. Then

$$A = \mathbf{r}\left(\frac{1}{2}\right) = \left(\frac{1}{2}, 2\right), \qquad B = \mathbf{r}(2) = \left(2, \frac{1}{2}\right), \qquad x'(t) = 1, \qquad y'(t) = -\frac{1}{t^2}.$$

Figure 37 shows $\mathscr{C}$.

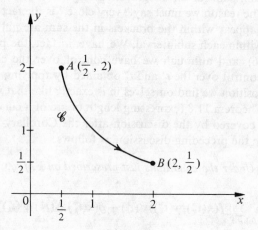

Figure 37

We let $\mathbf{F}$ be defined by

$$\mathbf{F}(x, y) = (x^2 - y^2)\mathbf{i} + (2xy)\mathbf{j};$$

thus, $f(x, y) = x^2 - y^2$, $g(x, y) = 2xy$, and these functions are continuous everywhere in $\mathbf{R}^2$.

By (50), then, we have

$$\int_{\mathscr{C}} \mathbf{F} \cdot d\mathbf{r} = \int_{\mathscr{C}} f\,dx + g\,dy = \int_{\mathscr{C}} (x^2 - y^2)\,dx + (2xy)\,dy$$

$$= \int_{1/2}^{2} \left[\left(t^2 - \frac{1}{t^2}\right) \cdot 1 + \left(2t \cdot \frac{1}{t}\right)\left(-\frac{1}{t^2}\right)\right] dt$$

$$= \int_{1/2}^{2} (t^2 - 3t^{-2})\,dt$$

$$= -\frac{15}{8}.$$

Before we lose sight of our original motivating goal, we remark that if, under the conditions of Definition 5, we interpret the vector function **F** as a force field, then we *define* the work done by **F** in moving a particle from A to B along $\mathscr{C}$ to be the value of the line integral (50).

This definition raises a question about the interpretation, in the context of work, of the negative sign in the answer in Example 25. Rather than provide an answer at this time we suggest that the reader calculate and draw a few values for **F** for points on $\mathscr{C}$. Also, it might help if he considers the value of $\int_{\mathscr{C}^-} \mathbf{F} \cdot d\mathbf{r}$, where $\mathscr{C}^-$ stands for $\mathscr{C}$ traversed in the opposite direction.

We now state—without proof—some of the properties of line integrals.

1. Linearity. If $\mathbf{F}_1$ and $\mathbf{F}_2$ both satisfy the conditions of Theorem 5, if $a_1, a_2 \in \mathbf{R}$, then

$$\int_{\mathscr{C}} (a_1\mathbf{F}_1 + a_2\mathbf{F}_2) \cdot d\mathbf{r} = a_1 \int_{\mathscr{C}} \mathbf{F}_1 \cdot d\mathbf{r} + a_2 \int_{\mathscr{C}} \mathbf{F}_2 \cdot d\mathbf{r}. \tag{51}$$

2. If the curve $\mathscr{C}$ is traversed in the opposite sense the value of the line integral is multiplied by (-1). In symbols, if we let $\mathscr{C}^-$ represent $\mathscr{C}$ with the reverse sense or orientation, then

$$\int_{\mathscr{C}^-} \mathbf{F} \cdot d\mathbf{r} = -\int_{\mathscr{C}} \mathbf{F} \cdot d\mathbf{r}. \tag{52}$$

3. The value of the line integral is independent of the parametrization used for $\mathscr{C}$ (chain rule).

4. Additivity along curves. To be explicit, suppose $\mathscr{C}_1$ is a curve from A to B, $\mathscr{C}_2$ is a curve from B to C. If we denote by $\mathscr{C} = \mathscr{C}_1 + \mathscr{C}_2$ the curve from A to C obtained by joining $\mathscr{C}_1$ to $\mathscr{C}_2$ then

$$\int_{\mathscr{C}} f\, dx + g\, dy = \int_{\mathscr{C}_1} f\, dx + g\, dy + \int_{\mathscr{C}_2} f\, dx + g\, dy. \tag{53}$$

It is assumed here that $\mathscr{C}$ lies in the region S where **F** is defined and continuous (see Figure 38).

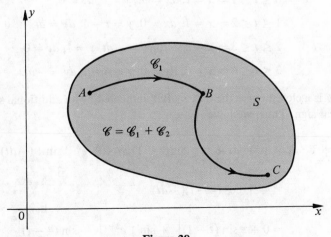

Figure 38

We now use a particular illustration to bring out several points.

Example 26. We let $\mathscr{C}$ be the boundary of the unit square (a *closed* path, in the sense that $B = A$) and we let **F** be defined by

$$\mathbf{F}(x, y) = e^x \sin y\mathbf{i} + e^x \cos y\mathbf{j},$$

i.e., $f(x, y) = e^x \sin y$, $g(x, y) = e^x \cos y$.

We can describe $\mathscr{C}$ analytically as follows (see Figure 39)

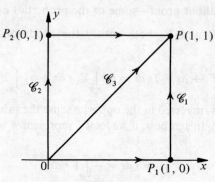

Figure 39

$$\mathbf{r}(t) = t\mathbf{i}, \qquad 0 \le t \le 1,$$
$$= \mathbf{i} + (t - 1)\mathbf{j}, \qquad 1 \le t \le 2,$$
$$= (3 - t)\mathbf{i} + \mathbf{j}, \qquad 2 \le t \le 3,$$
$$= (4 - t)\mathbf{j}, \qquad 3 \le t \le 4.$$

Put another way, the description of $\mathscr{C}$ is

$$0 \le t \le 1 \Rightarrow x = t, dx = dt, y = 0, dy = 0,$$
$$1 \le t \le 2 \Rightarrow x = 1, dx = 0, y = t - 1, dy = dt,$$
$$2 \le t \le 3 \Rightarrow x = 3 - t, dx = -dt, y = 1, dy = 0,$$
$$3 \le t \le 4 \Rightarrow x = 0, dx = 0, y = 4 - t, dy = -dt.$$

When $\mathscr{C}$ is a closed curve the fact is often indicated by an additional symbol on the integral sign. Thus, we have

$$\oint_{\mathscr{C}} \mathbf{F} \cdot d\mathbf{r} = \int_0^1 0 \cdot dt + \int_1^2 e \cos (t - 1) \, dt + \int_2^3 e^{3-t} \sin 1 \, (-dt)$$

$$+ \int_3^4 \cos (4 - t)(-dt)$$

$$= 0 + e \sin (t - 1) \Big|_1^2 + \sin 1 \, e^{3-t} \Big|_2^3 + \sin (4 - t) \Big|_3^4$$

$$= [0 + e \sin 1] + [\sin 1 - e \sin 1 - \sin 1]$$

$$= [e \sin 1] - [e \sin 1]$$

$$= 0.$$

(All that work for nothing. Or, to put it differently, the force pushes the object all the way round the block and does not get credit for having done any work.)

One result then is that the integral of **F** round the closed curve $\mathscr{C}$ is zero. But there is more. Notice from the use of the brackets in the preceding evaluation that the integral for $2 \le t \le 4$ is the negative of that for $0 \le t \le 2$. Now if we recall that reversing the direction along the curve changes the sign of the integral, we can make the following observation:

$$\int_{\mathscr{C}_1} \mathbf{F} \cdot d\mathbf{r} = \int_{\mathscr{C}_2} \mathbf{F} \cdot d\mathbf{r} = e \sin 1,$$

where

$$\mathscr{C}_1 = OP_1 + P_1 P,$$

$$\mathscr{C}_2 = OP_2 + P_2 P$$

(see Figure 39).

To drive home this point even more, let $\mathscr{C}_3$ be the curve from O to $P(1, 1)$ defined by

$$\mathbf{r}(t) = t\mathbf{i} + t\mathbf{j}, \qquad 0 \le t \le 1.$$

Then

$$x(t) = y(t) = t, \qquad dx = dy = dt,$$

and

$$\int_{\mathscr{C}_3} \mathbf{F} \cdot d\mathbf{r} = \int_0^1 (e^t \sin t + e^t \cos t)\, dt$$

$$= e^t \sin t \bigg|_0^1$$

$$= e \sin 1.$$

$$= \int_{\mathscr{C}_1} \mathbf{F} \cdot d\mathbf{r} = \int_{\mathscr{C}_2} \mathbf{F} \cdot d\mathbf{r}.$$

The conclusion we can be led to by these observations is that in at least some cases the value of a line integral is independent of the path. Moreover, as we shall ask you to show in Exercise 9, the integral is independent of the path if and only if $\oint_{\mathscr{C}} \mathbf{F} \cdot d\mathbf{r} = 0$.

If the guessed conclusion of the preceding paragraph has any validity—and it does—it would be useful to have some conditions which assure that a line integral is independent of the curve connecting the end points. We now state, without proof, two theorems of this sort.

Theorem 6. *A necessary and sufficient condition for the line integral $\int_{\mathscr{C}} f\,dx + g\,dy$ to be independent of the curve $\mathscr{C}$ joining the points A and B is that there exist a scalar function Φ such that $\mathbf{F} = \mathbf{grad}\,\Phi = \nabla\Phi$. When this condition holds*

$$\int_{\mathscr{C}} \mathbf{F} \cdot d\mathbf{r} = \int_{\mathscr{C}} f\,dx + g\,dy = \Phi(B) - \Phi(A),$$

$$= \Phi(\mathbf{r}(b)) - \Phi(\mathbf{r}(a)).$$

This theorem is a very close analog, for line integrals, of the fundamental theorem of calculus. Since, as we saw throughout Chapter 13, the gradient of a function of two or more variables plays a role very like that of a derivative for a function of a single variable, the condition of this theorem amounts to finding an "antiderivative" Φ for $\mathbf{F}$. Then the value of the integral of $\mathbf{F}$ is obtained by evaluating Φ at the endpoints.

Note, by the way, that for the $\mathbf{F}$ of Example 26, $\Phi(x, y) = e^x \sin y$. For

$$\left.\begin{array}{l} \Phi_x(x, y) = e^x \sin y \\ \Phi_y(x, y) = e^x \cos y \end{array}\right\} \Rightarrow \nabla\Phi = e^x \sin y\,\mathbf{i} + e^x \cos y\,\mathbf{j} = \mathbf{F}(x, y).$$

When the function Φ exists such that $\mathbf{grad}\,\Phi = \mathbf{F}$, Φ is called the *potential function* for $\mathbf{F}$. If $\mathbf{F}$ does represent a force field, and if $\mathbf{F}$ has a potential function, then $\mathbf{F}$ is said to be *conservative*.

Also, when $\mathbf{F}$ has a potential function Φ, the expression $f\,dx + g\,dy$ is called an *exact differential*; for, in fact, $f\,dx + g\,dy = d\Phi$.

The problem of determining whether or not a vector function $\mathbf{F}$ has a potential function Φ, analogous to finding an antiderivative, might be difficult. There is, however, a simpler criterion for determining whether or not an integral is independent of the path, provided we restrict the region S sufficiently.

The condition we must impose on S is that it be *simply connected*. This means, roughly, that S can have no holes in it. A slightly better formulation of the idea is this: a simply-connected region is one with the property that every simple closed curve (i.e., a closed curve which does not cross itself) in the region can be shrunk to a point without going outside the region (see Figure 40).

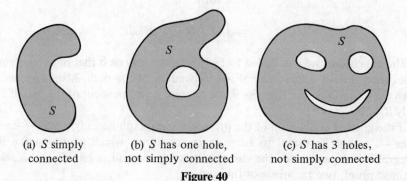

(a) S simply   (b) S has one hole,   (c) S has 3 holes,
connected   not simply connected   not simply connected

Figure 40

We can now state the "second fundamental theorem" for line integrals.

Theorem 7. *Let S be a simply-connected open region. A necessary and sufficient condition that*

$$\int_{\mathscr{C}} \mathbf{F} \cdot d\mathbf{r} = \int_{\mathscr{C}} f \, dx + g \, dy$$

$(\mathbf{F} = f\mathbf{i} + g\mathbf{j})$ *be independent of the curve $\mathscr{C}$ joining the points A and B is that*

$$f_y(x, y) = g_x(x, y) \tag{54}$$

hold for all $(x, y) \in S$.

When (54) holds, if $A(a, b)$ is a fixed point of S and $P(x, y)$ a variable point and if $\mathscr{C}$ joins A and P, then

$$\int_{\mathscr{C}} f \, dx + g \, dy = \Phi(x, y) - \Phi(a, b)$$

and $\nabla\Phi = \mathbf{F} = f\mathbf{i} + g\mathbf{j}$.

Again we look at the function $\mathbf{F} = f\mathbf{i} + g\mathbf{j}$ of Example 26:

$$f(x, y) = e^x \sin y, \quad g(x, y) = e^x \cos y.$$

It is easy to see that

$$f_y(x, y) = e^x \cos y = g_x(x, y).$$

EXERCISES

1. Let $\mathbf{F}$ be defined by $\mathbf{F}(x, y) = 2x^2 y\mathbf{i} + (x - 2y)\mathbf{j}$. Find $\int_{\mathscr{C}} \mathbf{F} \cdot d\mathbf{r}$ for each $\mathscr{C}$ described below. Note that every $\mathscr{C}$ has the same A and B.

   (a) $\mathscr{C} : \begin{cases} \mathbf{r}(t) = t\mathbf{i}, & 0 \le t \le 1 \\ \quad = \mathbf{i} + (t-1)\mathbf{j}, & 1 \le t \le 2 \end{cases}$.

   (b) $\mathscr{C} : \mathbf{r}(t) = t\mathbf{i} + t\mathbf{j}, \quad 0 \le t \le 1$.

   (c) $\mathscr{C} : \mathbf{r}(t) = t\mathbf{i} + t^2\mathbf{j}, \quad 0 \le t \le 1$.

   (d) $\mathscr{C} : \begin{cases} \mathbf{r}(t) = t\mathbf{j}, & 0 \le t \le 1 \\ \quad = (t-1)\mathbf{i} + \mathbf{j}, & 1 \le t \le 2 \end{cases}$.

   (e) $\mathscr{C} : \mathbf{r}(t) = t\mathbf{i} + t^3\mathbf{j}, \quad 0 \le t \le 1$.

   (f) $\mathscr{C} : \begin{cases} \mathbf{r}(t) = t\mathbf{i} + 8t\mathbf{j}, & 0 \le t \le \frac{1}{2} \\ \quad = t\mathbf{i} + (7 - 6t)\mathbf{j}, & \frac{1}{2} \le t \le 1 \end{cases}$.

2. Find the value of each of the following line integrals.

   (a) $\int_{\mathscr{C}} y^2 \, dx + (y - x) \, dy$, $\mathbf{r}(t) = t\mathbf{i} + t^2\mathbf{j}$, $-1 \le t \le 0$.

   (b) $\int_{\mathscr{C}} (x + y) \, dx + (x - y) \, dy$, $\mathbf{r}(t) = t\mathbf{i} + (4 - t)\mathbf{j}$, $0 \le t \le 4$.

3. Find $\int_{\mathscr{C}} y^2 \, dx + x^2 \, dy$ for each of the following curves joining $(0, 0)$ and $(1, 1)$. Sketch each curve.

   (a) $\mathbf{r}(t) = t\mathbf{i} + t^2\mathbf{j}$.   (b) $\mathbf{r}(t) = t^2\mathbf{i} + t^4\mathbf{j}$.   (c) $\mathbf{r}(t) = t^3\mathbf{i} + t^6\mathbf{j}$.

4. (a) Show that **F** defined by $\mathbf{F}(x, y) = (x^2 + y^2)\mathbf{i} + (2xy)\mathbf{j}$ is a conservative force.

   (b) Let $\mathscr{C}$ be a (any) curve joining the origin to (x, y). Find

   $$\int_{\mathscr{C}} \mathbf{F} \cdot d\mathbf{r}.$$

   [*Hint.* *You* pick the curve, the straight line, if you wish.]

   (c) Find a potential function Φ for **F**. Are there several such?

   (d) Find the work done by **F** in moving a particle from $A(2, 1)$ to $B(8, 5)$. From B to A.

   (e) Find the work done by **F** in moving a particle from $A(a_1, a_2)$ to $B(b_1, b_2)$.

5. Find $\int_{\mathscr{C}} (y - x)\, dx + (x^2 y)\, dy$, where $\mathscr{C}$ joins $(1, -1)$ and $(1, 1)$ as described. Note that you must provide the parametrization.

   (a) $\mathscr{C}$: The line $y = -x$ from $(1, -1)$ to $(0, 0)$; the line $y = x$ from $(0, 0)$ to $(1, 1)$.
   [*Hint.* Let

   $$x = 1 - t, \quad 0 \le t \le 1$$
   $$x = t - 1, \quad 1 \le t \le 2.]$$

   (b) $\mathscr{C}$ is the curve $y^2 = x^3$. [*Hint.* Let $x = t^2$.]

   (c) $\mathscr{C}$ is the left half of the circle $x^2 + y^2 = 2x$. [*Hint.* Let $y = t$. Alternatively, let $y = \sin t$.]

   (d) $\mathscr{C}$ is the parabola $y^2 = x$.

   (e) $\mathscr{C}$ is the straight line joining $(1, -1)$ and $(1, 1)$.

6. Find $\oint_{\mathscr{C}} \mathbf{F} \cdot d\mathbf{r}$ for each **F** described below, where in every case $\mathscr{C}$ is the unit square traversed in a counterclockwise direction (see Example 26).

   (a) $\mathbf{F}(x, y) = y\mathbf{i} + (-x)\mathbf{j}$.   (d) $\mathbf{F}(x, y) = 2xy\mathbf{i} + x^2\mathbf{j}$.
   (b) $\mathbf{F}(x, y) = y\mathbf{i} + x\mathbf{j}$.   (e) $\mathbf{F}(x, y) = (x^2 - y^2)\mathbf{i} + 2xy\mathbf{j}$.
   (c) $\mathbf{F}(x, y) = y^2\mathbf{i} + xy\mathbf{j}$.

7. Find the work done when each of the following forces **F** moves a particle from $A(a, b)$ to $P(x, y)$.

   (a) $\mathbf{F}(x, y) = y^3\mathbf{i} + 3xy^2\mathbf{j}$.   (c) $\mathbf{F}(x, y) = 2xy^2\mathbf{i} + 2x^2y\mathbf{j}$.
   (b) $\mathbf{F}(x, y) = 2xe^y\mathbf{i} + x^2e^y\mathbf{j}$.   (d) $\mathbf{F}(x, y) = (-y \sin x)\mathbf{i} + \cos x\mathbf{j}$.

8. The two-dimensional model for gravitational attraction is described by

   $$\mathbf{F}(x, y) = \frac{-x}{(x^2 + y^2)^{3/2}}\mathbf{i} + \frac{-y}{(x^2 + y^2)^{3/2}}\mathbf{j}.$$

   More specifically, a particle of mass at the origin will attract a particle of unit mass at (x, y) with a force **F** defined by the above equation.

   (a) Show that if the region S does not contain the origin, **F** is conservative in S.

   (b) Find a potential function Φ for **F**.

   (c) Find the work done by **F** when a particle is moved from $(-3, 4)$ to $(12, 5)$.

9. Prove the following result.

Theorem. *If* F *is continuous on S, then*

$$\left.\begin{array}{l}\displaystyle\int_{\mathscr{C}} \mathbf{F} \cdot d\mathbf{r} \text{ is independent} \\ \text{of the curve } \mathscr{C}\end{array}\right\} \Leftrightarrow \left\{\begin{array}{l}\displaystyle\oint_{\mathscr{C}} \mathbf{F} \cdot d\mathbf{r} = 0 \text{ for every} \\ \text{closed curve } \mathscr{C} \text{ in } S.\end{array}\right.$$

Hints.
(1) For ⇒, let $\mathscr{C}$ be a closed curve in S; pick distinct points A and B on $\mathscr{C}$, let $\mathscr{C}_1$ be the part of $\mathscr{C}$ from A to B in one direction, $\mathscr{C}_2$ the part of $\mathscr{C}$ from A to B in the other.
(2) For ⇐, let $\mathscr{C}_1$ and $\mathscr{C}_2$ be two curves joining A and B in S; Let $\mathscr{C} = \mathscr{C}_1 + \mathscr{C}_{\bar{2}}$.

10. Outline *briefly* the theory of line integrals in three space. Use vector notation as much as possible.

Chapter **15** Taylor's Theorem, Sequences, and Series

On several occasions in Chapter 7 we developed polynomial expressions which could be interpreted as approximating polynomials for functions which are not polynomials. To be explicit, in Section 7.2, by a combined use of the Mean Value Theorem and integration, we obtained, in Eq. (22),

$$e^x = 1 + \frac{x}{1!} + \frac{x^2}{2!} + \frac{x^3}{3!} + \cdots + \frac{x^n}{n!} + \frac{x^{n+1}}{(n+1)!} e^{x_0}, \qquad 0 < x_0 < x.$$

And in Example 13 in Section 7.6 we found, by similar methods, a corresponding expression for cosh x and sinh x.

Careful consideration of these representations raises several questions. Can polynomial approximations be obtained for other functions? If so, is there a general method? If these expressions are valid for all $n \in \mathbf{N}$, what happens if we consider letting n get big beyond all bounds?

The answers to these and related questions form an important part of analysis, which we investigate in this chapter.

15.1 Taylor's Theorem

Consideration of the problem of finding a polynomial function to serve as an approximation to a given function forces one to answer a number of other questions. For example, what may constitute a good approximation near one point may be an exceedingly poor one near some other point, so the question arises: approximation where? Indeed, a more basic question is: What constitutes a "good" approximation? It is not hard to see that different sets of criteria can be applied; as these can—and do—give different results, which should be used?

In order to reach our present goal within a reasonable time we provide the following answers to these questions. We shall be interested in an approximation to a function f within a nbd. of a point, say $x = a$. And, if we are going to work with polynomials of degree n, our primary criterion will be that the derivatives of the polynomial at $x = a$ equal the derivatives of f at $x = a$ (notice that this criterion assumes that the function f *have* derivatives at $x = a$).

Suppose we consider a simple but instructive example. We have a function f which has at least four derivatives at a point $x = a$, and we wish to approximate f by a polynomial p of degree four. It turns out to be convenient to assume p has the form

$$p(x) = c_0 + c_1(x - a) + c_2(x - a)^2 + c_3(x - a)^3 + c_4(x - a)^4. \qquad (1)$$

The condition we impose is that

$$p^{(k)}(a) = f^{(k)}(a), \qquad k = 0, 1, 2, 3, 4, \qquad (2)$$

where by $f^{(0)}$ we mean f itself. We begin by calculating the derivatives of p:

$$p'(x) = c_1 + 2c_2(x - a) + 3c_3(x - a)^2 + 4c_4(x - a)^3,$$

$$p''(x) = 2c_2 + 3 \cdot 2c_3(x - a) + 4 \cdot 3c_4(x - a)^2,$$

$$p'''(x) = 3 \cdot 2c_3 + 4 \cdot 3 \cdot 2c_4(x - a),$$

and

$$p^{iv}(x) = 4!c_4.$$

Evaluating p and its derivatives at $x = a$, we find

$$p(a) = c_0, \qquad p'(a) = c_1, \qquad p''(a) = 2c_2, \qquad p'''(a) = 3!c_3, \qquad p^{iv}(a) = 4!c_4.$$

With these values and condition (2) we solve for the c_k:

$$c_k = \frac{f^{(k)}(a)}{k!}, \qquad k = 0, 1, 2, 3, 4$$

(recall that $0! = 1$). Thus, this criterion for an approximating polynomial p to a function with four derivatives gives

$$p(x) = f(a) + f'(a)(x - a) + \frac{f''(a)}{2!}(x - a)^2 + \frac{f'''(a)}{3!}(x - a)^3 + \frac{f^{iv}(a)}{4!}(x - a)^4. \qquad (3)$$

It is a straightforward matter to show that, if one assumes f has n derivatives at $x = a$ and uses a polynomial p_n of degree n, condition (2) produces for p_n the following:

$$p_n(x) = f(a) + f'(a)(x - a) + \frac{f''(a)}{2!}(x - a)^2 + \cdots + \frac{f^{(n)}(x - a)}{n!}(x - a)^n. \qquad (4)$$

As a result of (4), we *could* write, for $x \in N(a)$, that $f(x) \approx p_n(x)$. But we have no knowledge of how *good* an approximation p_n provides for f. A preferable way would be to strive for an expression such as

$$f(x) = f(a) + f'(a)(x - a) + \frac{f''(a)}{2!}(x - a)^2 + \cdots + \frac{f^{(n)}(a)}{n!}(x - a)^n + R_n(x),$$

where $R_n(x)$, *the remainder after n terms*, has some *known* form.

As it happens, this can be done—with suitable hypotheses on f—in several ways, producing several forms for R_n. The following result is in terms of the Lagrange form for R_n.

Theorem 1 (*Taylor's Theorem*). *Let f and its first n derivatives be continuous on* $[a, b]$, *and let* $f^{(n+1)}$ *exist on* (a, b). *Then there exists* $x_0 \in (a, b)$ *such that*

$$f(b) = f(a) + f'(a)(b - a) + \frac{f''(a)}{2!}(b - a)^2$$

$$+ \cdots + \frac{f^{(n)}(a)}{n!}(b - a)^n + \frac{f^{(n+1)}(x_0)}{(n+1)!}(b - a)^{n+1}. \quad (5)$$

Proof. [The proof we give is quite easy, but it has the defect of being entirely unmotivated.]

The theorem follows directly from Theorem 4.9, Cauchy's extension of the Mean Value Theorem. All we need do is select appropriate functions F and G to which we apply the Cauchy Theorem.

We let

$$F(x) = f(x) + \sum_{k=1}^{n} \frac{1}{k!} f^{(k)}(x)(b - x)^k,$$

$$G(x) = (b - x)^{n+1},$$

noting that certainly F and G are continuous on $[a, b]$.

Next we find F' and G'. For G we observe that $G'(x) = -(n + 1)(b - x)^n$ and that $G'(x) \neq 0$ for $x \in (a, b)$, as required by Theorem 4.9. For F' we proceed as follows:

$$F'(x) = f'(x) + \sum_{k=1}^{n} \frac{1}{k!} [f^{(k)}(x)(-k)(b - x)^{k-1} + f^{(k+1)}(x)(b - x)^k]$$

$$= f'(x) + \sum_{k=1}^{n} \left[-\frac{1}{(k-1)!} f^{(k)}(x)(b - x)^{k-1} + \frac{1}{k!} f^{(k+1)}(x)(b - x)^k \right].$$

Now it is easy to see that the expression on the right is a telescoping sum: the second term in any bracket plus the first term in the succeeding bracket is zero, and the first term in the first bracket is annulled by $f'(x)$. Thus, all that remains is the second term in the last bracket:

$$F'(x) = \frac{1}{n!} f^{(n+1)}(x)(b - x)^n.$$

The hypotheses of the present theorem guarantee that all hypotheses of the Cauchy Theorem hold; thus $\exists x_0 \in (a, b)$ such that

$$\frac{F(b) - F(a)}{G(b) - G(a)} = \frac{F'(x_0)}{G'(x_0)};$$

i.e.,

$$\frac{f(b) - f(a) - \sum_{k=1}^{n} \frac{1}{k!} f^{(k)}(a)(b-a)^k}{0 - (b-a)^{n+1}} = \frac{\frac{1}{n!} f^{(n+1)}(x_0)(b-x_0)^n}{-(n+1)(b-x_0)^n}.$$

With a little algebra this becomes

$$f(b) = f(a) + \sum_{k=1}^{n} \frac{1}{k!} f^{(k)}(a)(b-a)^k + \frac{f^{(n+1)}(x_0)}{(n+1)!}(b-a)^{n+1}. \quad \blacksquare$$

It may be helpful to mention several different forms the assertion of Taylor's Theorem can take. If we replace b by x, then we have the assertion about polynomials mentioned earlier:

$$f(x) = f(a) + f'(a)(x-a) + \frac{f''(a)}{2!}(x-a)^2$$

$$+ \cdots + \frac{f^{(n)}(a)}{n}(x-a)^n + \frac{f^{n+1}(x_0)}{(n+1)!}(x-a)^{n+1}, \qquad a < x_0 < x. \quad (6)$$

We might also let $x = a + h$, $x - a = h$; then Eq. (6) becomes

$$f(a+h) = f(a) + f'(a)h + \frac{f''(a)}{2!}h^2$$

$$+ \cdots + \frac{f^{(n)}(a)}{n!}h^n + \frac{f^{(n+1)}(a+\theta h)}{(n+1)!}h^{n+1}, \qquad 0 < \theta < 1. \quad (7)$$

Note, by the way, that for $n = 0$ Eq. (7) reduces to

$$f(a+h) = f(a) + f'(a+\theta h)h,$$

the original Mean Value Theorem. Thus Taylor's Theorem is a generalization of the Mean Value Theorem, related to, but different from the Cauchy Theorem.

Next we note that if, in (6), we take $a = 0$, we have

$$f(x) = f(0) + f'(0)x + \frac{f''(0)}{2!}x^2 + \cdots + \frac{f^{(n)}(0)}{n!}x^n + \frac{f^{(n+1)}(x_0)}{(n+1)!}x^{n+1}, \quad (8)$$

where $0 < x_0 < x$. This result is often referred to as Maclaurin's Theorem; it is, of course, simply Taylor's Theorem, where f is *expanded about zero*.

In each of Eqs. (6), (7), and (8) the final term is denoted by R_n, *the remainder after n terms*.

Finally we observe that Eq. (6) is valid for $x < a$, provided that we then realize $x_0 \in (x, a)$. A similar comment applies to Eq. (8).

It is time for some illustrations.

Example 1. Let $f(x) = e^x$, let $a = 0$. Since for every $n = 1, 2, \ldots, f^{(n)}(x) = e^x$, so $f^{(n)}(0) = 1$, substitution in (8) gives

$$f(x) = e^x = 1 + x + \frac{x^2}{2!} + \cdots + \frac{x^n}{n!} + \frac{e^{x_0} x^{n+1}}{(n+1)!} \tag{9}$$

where $0 < x_0 < x$, precisely the expression found in Chapter 7 for e^x.

Example 2. Let f be the cosine function, take $a = 0$. Then

$$
\begin{aligned}
f(x) &= \cos x & f(0) &= 1 \\
f'(x) &= -\sin x & f'(0) &= 0 \\
f''(x) &= -\cos x & f''(0) &= -1 \\
f'''(x) &= \sin x & f'''(0) &= 0 \\
f^{iv}(x) &= \cos x & f^{iv}(0) &= 1 \\
f^v(x) &= -\sin x & f^v(0) &= 0.
\end{aligned}
$$

We see that the derivatives of f have a cycle of length four. In particular, every odd order derivative is zero at $x = 0$. Thus, using (8) we can write

$$\cos x = 1 - \frac{x^2}{2!} + \frac{x^4}{4!} - \frac{x^6}{6!} + \cdots + (-1)^n \frac{x^{2n}}{(2n)!} + (-1)^{n+1} \frac{\sin x_0}{(2n+1)!} x^{2n+1}, \tag{10}$$

which agrees with the result found in Exercise 4 [Eq. (77)] after Section 7.6.

Since $|\sin x_0| \le 1$, it follows from the expression in (10) that

$$|R_{2n}(x)| \le \frac{|x|^{2n+1}}{(2n+1)!}.$$

It is not too difficult (see Exercise 15) to show that, for every fixed x, $\lim_{n \to \infty} |R_{2n}(x)| = 0$. In other words, as n increases beyond bounds the polynomial approximation to cos given by Eq. (10) becomes increasingly better. In fact, this observation might lead one to modify (10) to read

$$\cos x = 1 - \frac{x^2}{2!} + \frac{x^4}{4!} - \frac{x^6}{6!} + \cdots, \tag{11}$$

where the three dots indicate that this expression continues indefinitely. As we shall see, this is a valid equation, but we must attach a meaning to the right-hand side. In order to make a study of these *infinite series* (such as in (11)), we first consider limits of sequences.

EXERCISES

In numbers 1–13 find the Taylor's Theorem expansion for f about the point a indicated for the specified n. If no n is prescribed find an expansion analogous to (10) in Example 2.

1. $f(x) = \log(1 + x)$, $a = 0$.

2. $f(x) = \log(1 + x)$, $a = 1$.

3. $f(x) = \tan x$, $a = 0$, $n = 3$.

4. $f(x) = \sin x$, $a = 0$.

5. $f(x) = \sin x$, $a = \dfrac{\pi}{2}$.

6. $f(x) = \cosh x$, $a = 0$.

7. $f(x) = \sinh x$, $a = 0$.

8. $f(x) = e^{-x^2}$, $a = 0$.

9. $f(x) = \arctan x$, $a = 0$, $n = 3$.

10. $f(x) = \dfrac{1}{1 - x}$, $a = 0$.

11. $f(x) = \log \cos x$, $a = 0$, $n = 3$.

12. $f(x) = \sin^2 x$, $a = 0$.   [*Hint.* $f'(x) = \sin 2x$.]

13. $f(x) = (1 + x)^q$,   where $x > -1$, $a = 0$.

14. (a) Expand $f(t) = (1 + t)^{-1}$ about $t = 0$, obtaining n terms.

(b) Replace t by x^2 in the result found in part (a), thus getting an expansion for
$$q(x) = \frac{1}{1 + x^2}.$$

(c) Integrate (i.e., find $\int_0^x q(t)\, dt$) both sides of the expression found in (b), thus deriving an expansion for $\tan^{-1} x$.

(d) Let $R_n(x)$ be the remainder for the expansion in (c). Show that $|x| \leq 1 \Rightarrow \lim_{n \to \infty} |R_n(x)| = 0$.

(e) Set $x = 1$ in the expansion in (c). Is it correct to conclude from the result that
$$\frac{\pi}{4} = 1 - \frac{1}{3} + \frac{1}{5} - \frac{1}{7} + \cdots \ ?$$

15. This exercise concerns the remainder $R_n(x)$ found in Example 2 in the expansion of $\cos x$. We found there that
$$|R_n(x)| \leq \frac{x^{n+1}}{(n + 1)!}.$$

We want to show here that, for arbitrary but fixed x, $\lim_{n \to \infty} |R_n(x)| = 0$.

Now the factorial is extremely difficult to handle algebraically. However, *Stirlings formula* says that for n large, one can use
$$n! \approx \sqrt{2\pi n}\ e^{-n} n^n. \tag{12}$$

In particular,

$$n! > \sqrt{2\pi n}\, e^{-n} n^n. \tag{13}$$

(a) Use (13) in the expression for $|R_n(x)|$ and show

$$|R_n(x)| < \frac{|ex|^{n+1}}{(n+1)^{n+1}} \cdot \frac{1}{\sqrt{2\pi(n+1)}} = \left(\frac{a}{t}\right)^t \frac{1}{\sqrt{2\pi(n+1)}},$$

where $a = |ex| > 0$ (if $x = 0$, the desired result is trivial) and $t = n + 1$.

(b) By using logarithms, show that

$$\lim_{t \to \infty} \left(\frac{a}{t}\right) = 0.$$

(c) Combine the results in (a) and (b) to conclude

$$\lim_{n \to \infty} |R_n(x)| = 0.$$

15.2 Sequences

An essential tool in the study of infinite series is the concept of limit of a sequence.

First of all we must say precisely what we mean by sequence.

Definition 1. *A **sequence** of real numbers is a function whose domain is the set* **N** *of positive integers, and whose range is in* **R**.

The notation used for sequences is different from that used generally for functions. In particular, the letter "n" is used for an element in the domain. Also, instead of writing $f(n)$ for the value of the sequence at n, it is customary to write a_n, or b_n, or s_n. We shall frequently describe the sequence itself as $\{a_n\}$. A few sequences with their defining formulas can be given as follows (we also list the first few sequential values, called the *terms of the sequence*):

$$a_n = n, \ \{1, 2, 3, \cdots\} \quad \text{(this is simply the identity function } j\text{),} \tag{14}$$

$$a_n = \frac{1}{n}, \ \left\{1, \frac{1}{2}, \frac{1}{3}, \cdots\right\} \tag{15}$$

$$c_n = 2, \ \{2, 2, 2, \ldots\} \quad \text{(a constant sequence),} \tag{16}$$

$$a_n = \frac{n}{n+1}, \ \left\{\frac{1}{2}, \frac{2}{3}, \frac{3}{4} \cdots\right\}, \tag{17}$$

$$b_n = \frac{(-1)^{n-1}}{n}, \quad \left\{1, -\frac{1}{2}, \frac{1}{3}, -\frac{1}{4}, \cdots\right\}, \tag{18}$$

$$a_n = \begin{Bmatrix} \dfrac{1}{n}, & n \text{ odd} \\[2mm] \dfrac{n-1}{n}, & n \text{ even} \end{Bmatrix}, \quad \left\{1, \dfrac{1}{2}, \dfrac{1}{3}, \dfrac{3}{4}, \dfrac{1}{5}, \dfrac{5}{6}, \ldots\right\}, \tag{19}$$

$$a_n = \begin{Bmatrix} \dfrac{1}{2^n}, & n = 1, 4, 7, \ldots \\[2mm] \dfrac{n-1}{n}, & n = 2, 5, 8, \ldots \\[2mm] 2, & n = 3, 6, 9, \ldots \end{Bmatrix}, \quad \left\{\dfrac{1}{2}, \dfrac{1}{2}, 2, \dfrac{1}{2^4}, \dfrac{4}{5}, 2, \dfrac{1}{2^7}, \dfrac{7}{8}, 2, \ldots\right\}. \tag{20}$$

It is fairly obvious that the attempt to graph in the usual way a function of this kind would not be very helpful. What may be done, instead, is to draw on an axis the points corresponding to terms of a sequence; as functional values, these points perhaps should be on a vertical axis, but in the interests of saving space the axis is usually drawn horizontally. Figures 1 to 3 illustrate a few of the examples just listed.

$$a_n = \frac{1}{n} \tag{15}$$

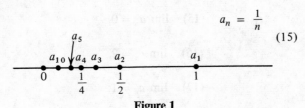

Figure 1

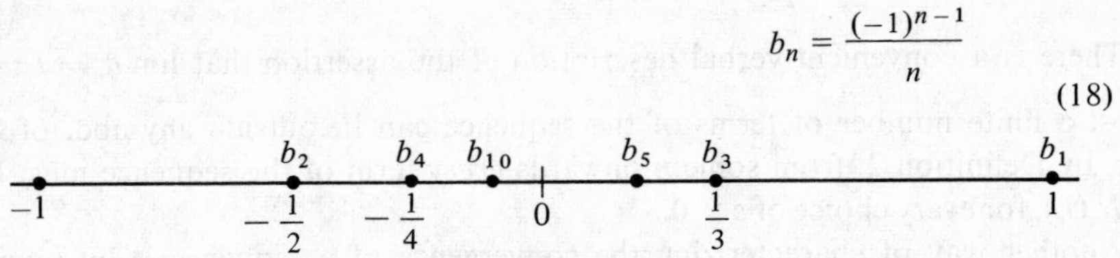

$$b_n = \frac{(-1)^{n-1}}{n} \tag{18}$$

Figure 2

$$a_n = \begin{cases} \dfrac{1}{2^n}, & n = 1, 4, 7, \ldots \\[2mm] \dfrac{n-1}{n}, & n = 2, 5, 8, \ldots \\[2mm] 2, & n = 3, 6, 9, \ldots \end{cases} \tag{20}$$

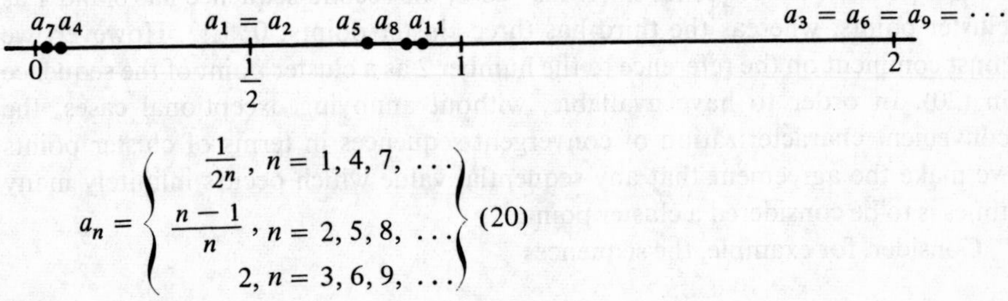

Figure 3

Now the set $\mathbf{N}$ of positive integers has only one cluster point, ∞. Consequently, the only limit we can consider for a sequence $\{a_n\}$ is that one symbolized as $\lim_{n\to\infty} a_n$. The following definition is simply a rephrasing of Definition 3.8.

Definition 2. $\lim_{n\to\infty} a_n = L \Leftrightarrow$ *for every* $N_\varepsilon(L)$ *there exists* $N_m(\infty)$ *such that* $n \in N_m(\infty) \Rightarrow a_n \in N_\varepsilon(L)$.

The version of Definition 2 which does not use nbds. would be as follows.

Definition 2a. $\lim_{n\to\infty} a_n = L \Leftrightarrow$ *for every* $\varepsilon > 0$ *there exists* n_ε *such that for all* $n > n_\varepsilon$ *it is true that* $|a_n - L| < \varepsilon$.

When a sequence has a limit (*necessarily finite*) the sequence is said to *converge*. Otherwise, the sequence *diverges*, or, *is divergent*. The following assertions can be made (verification left as exercise for the student) for the examples just given: numbers 14, 19 and 20 are divergent; 15, 16, 17, and 18 are convergent. For these last four, in fact,

$$(15) \qquad \lim_{n\to\infty} a_n = 0,$$

$$(16) \qquad \lim_{n\to\infty} c_n = 2,$$

$$(17) \qquad \lim_{n\to\infty} a_n = 1,$$

$$(18) \qquad \lim_{n\to\infty} b_n = 0.$$

There is a convenient verbal description of the assertion that $\lim_{n\to\infty} a_n = L$: at most a finite number of terms of the sequence can lie outside any nbd. of L; for, by Definition 2, from some n onwards *every* term of the sequence must lie in $N_\varepsilon(L)$, for every choice of $\varepsilon > 0$.

Another way of characterizing the convergence of a sequence is by saying that *the set of sequential values has exactly one finite cluster point*. This description shows clearly why the sequences in (14), (19) and (20) diverge: the single cluster point of the sequence in (14) is "∞"; the second sequence has 0 and 1 as cluster points, whereas the third has three cluster points: 0, 1, 2. However, we must comment on the reference to the number 2 as a cluster point of the sequence in (20). In order to have available, without annoying exceptional cases, the convenient characterization of convergent sequences in terms of cluster points we make the agreement that any sequential value which occurs infinitely many times is to be considered a cluster point.

Consider, for example, the sequences

$$a_n = \begin{cases} n, & 1 \le n \le 10^{10} \\ 1, & n > 10^{10} \end{cases} \qquad\qquad (21)$$

$$b_n = \begin{cases} 3, & n \text{ odd} \\ \dfrac{1}{n}, & n \text{ even} \end{cases} \tag{22}$$

$$c_n = \begin{cases} 2, & n \text{ odd} \\ \dfrac{2n+1}{n}, & n \text{ even} \end{cases}. \tag{23}$$

It is easy to see that $\{a_n\}$ has the single cluster point 1, $\{c_n\}$ has the single cluster point 2, whereas 0 and 3 are cluster points of $\{b_n\}$. Thus $\{a_n\}$ and $\{c_n\}$ converge, $\{b_n\}$ is divergent.

The theorems about limits carry over in a natural way to limits of sequences. We proceed to state some of the more useful ones.

Theorem 2. *A convergent sequence is bounded. In symbols,*

$$\lim_{n \to \infty} a_n = L \Rightarrow \exists M > 0 \text{ such that, for all } n, |a_n| < M.$$

Proof. We first use the *convergence* to get a bound M_1 for the "tail" of the sequence. Let $\varepsilon = 1$; then $\exists n_1$ such that $n > n_1 \Rightarrow |a_n - L| < 1$. It follows that, for $n > n_1$,

$$|a_n| = |a_n - L + L| \le |a_n - L| + |L| < 1 + |L|;$$

thus we can take $M_1 = 1 + |L|$. We know that $n > n_1 \Rightarrow |a_n| < M_1$.

Now we use the *finiteness* to obtain a bound M_2 for the first n_1 terms:

$$M_2 = 1 + \max_{n = 1, \ldots, n_1} |a_n|.$$

Then, $n = 1, \ldots, n_1 \Rightarrow |a_n| < M_2$.

Finally, if we define $M = \max(M_1, M_2)$ we can conclude that for *all* $n \in \mathbf{N}$, $|a_n| < M$. ∎

The next theorem is simply a restatement of Theorems 3.7, 3.8, and Corollary 2.

Theorem 3. *Suppose* $\lim\limits_{n \to \infty} a_n = L_1,\ \lim\limits_{n \to \infty} b_n = L_2$. *Then*

(a) $\lim\limits_{n \to \infty} (a_n \pm b_n) = L_1 \pm L_2$.

(b) $\lim\limits_{n \to \infty} (a_n b_n) = L_1 L_2$.

(c) $\lim\limits_{n \to \infty} \left(\dfrac{a_n}{b_n}\right) = \dfrac{L_1}{L_2}$.

(d) $\lim\limits_{n \to \infty} (c a_n) = c L_1$.

For (c) *we assume* $b_n \ne 0$, *all* n, *and* $L_2 \ne 0$.

The proofs of these results are quite analogous to the proofs given in Chapter 3, and we shall omit them.

We perhaps should comment on the arithmetic operations with sequences. Sequences being functions, these operations of adding, subtracting, multiplying, or dividing are carried out precisely as they are for functions; for example, if $\{a_n\}$ and $\{b_n\}$ are sequences, then by $\{a_n b_n\}$ we mean the sequence $\{c_n\}$ such that for every $n \in \mathbf{N}$, $c_n = a_n b_n$.

The following result might be referred to as a "squeezing theorem" (see Theorem 3.17).

Theorem 4

$$\left.\begin{array}{c} \lim_{n \to \infty} a_n = \lim_{n \to \infty} b_n = L \\ a_n \le c_n \le b_n, \text{ all } n \end{array}\right\} \Rightarrow \lim_{n \to \infty} c_n = L.$$

Proof. Let $\varepsilon > 0$ be arbitrary. Then $\exists n_1, n_2$ such that $n > n_1 \Rightarrow a_n \in N_\varepsilon(L)$, $n > n_2 \Rightarrow b_n \in N_\varepsilon(L)$. We define $n_\varepsilon = \max(n_1, n_2)$; then $n > n_\varepsilon \Rightarrow$

$$c_n \le b_n < L + \varepsilon$$

and

$$c_n \ge a_n > L - \varepsilon;$$

Thus, $n > n_\varepsilon \Rightarrow c_n \in N_\varepsilon(L)$, or $\lim_{n \to \infty} c_n = L$. ∎

Incidentally, we could weaken the hypothesis of Theorem 4, requiring that the inequalities

$$a_n \le c_n \le b_n$$

hold for all $n > n_3$, rather than for all n. Then we choose $n_\varepsilon = \max(n_1, n_2, n_3)$ and the result is as before. This remark illustrates the fact that with sequences "it is the tail that wags the dog."

The converse of Theorem 2 is not true, as the sequences in (19), (20), and (22) show very clearly; in other words, a bounded sequence need not converge. However, if one adds to boundedness a further hypothesis, then convergence will follow. The next theorem is one of the most fundamental and most important in analysis.

Theorem 5

(a) *Let* $\{a_n\}$ *be a sequence such that for all* n:

$$\text{(i)} \quad a_n < M,$$
$$\text{(ii)} \quad a_n \le a_{n+1}.$$

Then there is $A \le M$ *such that* $\lim_{n \to \infty} a_n = A$.

(b) *Let* $\{b_n\}$ *be a sequence such that for all* n:

$$\text{(i)} \quad b_n > Q,$$
$$\text{(ii)} \quad b_n \ge b_{n+1}.$$

Then there is $B \ge Q$ *such that* $\lim_{n \to \infty} b_n = B$.

In words, part (a) says that a sequence which is monotonic nondecreasing and bounded above is convergent; similarly, part (b) says that a sequence converges if it is monotonic nonincreasing and bounded below. Sometimes the two statements are loosely combined as " a bounded monotonic sequence converges."

Proof. Because of the similarity of the two parts, we shall prove only (a). By hypothesis (i) and the Axiom of Continuity we know the set $\{a_n\}$ has a least upper bound $A \le M$. We now show $\lim_{n \to \infty} a_n = A$. Consider any $N_\varepsilon(A)$. Since $A = \operatorname{lub} a_n$, we know $\exists a_{n_1}$ satisfying $a_{n_1} > A - \varepsilon$ (see Figure 4). But now, by the

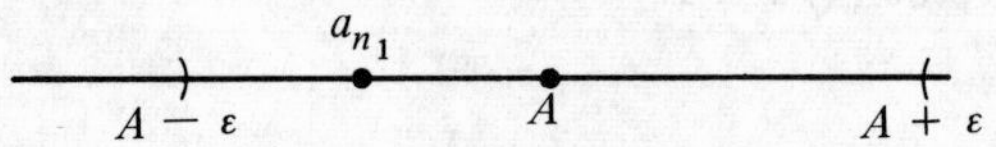

Figure 4

monotonic property of $\{a_n\}$, we know that $n > n_1 \Rightarrow A - \varepsilon < a_{n_1} \le a_n \le A$. Clearly, then, $n > n_1 \Rightarrow a_n \in N_\varepsilon(A)$, and $\lim_{n \to \infty} a_n = A$. ∎

Note that this theorem guarantees the convergence of the sequences in (15) $\left(a_n = \dfrac{1}{n}\right)$, (16) $(c_n = 2)$, and (17) $\left(a_n = \dfrac{n}{n + 1}\right)$; but the sequence in (18) is convergent without being monotonic.

The last theorem we state in this section is a famous one, partly because it gives a criterion for the convergence of a sequence, a criterion which does not involve prior knowledge of the limit L.

Theorem 6 (*The Cauchy Criterion of Convergence*). *A necessary and sufficient condition for the sequence $\{a_n\}$ to converge is that for every $\varepsilon > 0$ there exists n_ε such that for all $m, n > n_\varepsilon$ it is true that $|a_m - a_n| < \varepsilon$.*
Symbolically,

$$\lim_{n \to \infty} a_n = L \Leftrightarrow \begin{cases} \text{for every } \varepsilon > 0 \text{ there exists } n_\varepsilon \text{ such that} \\ m, n > n_\varepsilon \Rightarrow |a_m - a_n| < \varepsilon. \end{cases} \quad \text{(CCC)}$$

In Exercise 18 we outline a proof of this theorem. A verbal interpretation of the CCC may be helpful. It says that a sequence converges if and only if for sufficiently large n all terms of the sequence are arbitrarily close to one another. We now illustrate some of these ideas.

Example 3. Let a be any positive number. We assert that

$$\lim_{n \to \infty} \sqrt[n]{a} = 1. \quad (24)$$

(a) If $a = 1$, then $\sqrt[n]{a} = 1$, all n, so the assertion in (24) is trivially true.
(b) Let $a > 1$; then $\sqrt[n]{a} > 1$ (Why is this so?). If we let $\sqrt[n]{a} = 1 + x_n$, where

$x_n > 0$, then

$$a = (1 + x_n)^n > 1 + n \, x_n. \qquad \text{(Theorem 1.15)}$$

From this we find

$$0 < x_n < \frac{a - 1}{n}.$$

Now, $\lim\limits_{n \to \infty} \dfrac{a - 1}{n} = 0$ (why?), so by Theorem 4, $\lim\limits_{n \to \infty} x_n = 0$, which is equivalent to (24).

   (c) If $0 < a < 1$, then $\sqrt[n]{a} < 1$.

We let

$$\sqrt[n]{a} = \frac{1}{1 + x_n}, \qquad x_n > 0;$$

then

$$a = \frac{1}{(1 + x_n)^n} < \frac{1}{1 + nx_n}.$$

From this inequality we find

$$0 < x_n < \frac{\dfrac{1}{a} - 1}{n}.$$

As in (b), by the squeezing theorem we conclude that $\lim\limits_{n \to \infty} x_n = 0$, this being equivalent to (24).

Example 4. Prove by the definition that $\lim\limits_{n \to \infty} \dfrac{1}{n^2} = 0$. Using Definition 2a, with $L = 0$, we must find, for arbitrary $\varepsilon > 0$, n_ε such that $n > n_\varepsilon \Rightarrow \dfrac{1}{n^2} < \varepsilon$. But

$$\frac{1}{n^2} < \varepsilon \Leftrightarrow n^2 > \frac{1}{\varepsilon} \Leftrightarrow n > \sqrt{\frac{1}{\varepsilon}} = \frac{1}{\sqrt{\varepsilon}}.$$

From this it is clear that if we take n_ε as an integer $> \dfrac{1}{\sqrt{\varepsilon}}$ then Definition 2a will be satisfied.

Example 5. Prove that

$$\lim_{n \to \infty} \frac{2n^2 - 3n + 1}{n^2 + 10n + 25} = 2.$$

We have

$$\lim_{n \to \infty} \frac{2n^2 - 3n + 1}{n^2 + 10n + 25} = \lim_{n \to \infty} \frac{2 - \dfrac{3}{n} + \dfrac{1}{n^2}}{1 + \dfrac{10}{n} + \dfrac{25}{n^2}}$$

$$= \frac{\lim_{n \to \infty} \left[2 - \dfrac{3}{n} + \dfrac{1}{n^2} \right]}{\lim_{n \to \infty} \left[1 + \dfrac{10}{n} + \dfrac{25}{n^2} \right]} \quad \text{(why?)}$$

$$= \frac{2 - 0 + 0}{1 + 0 + 0} \quad \text{(why?)}$$

$$= 2.$$

Example 6. We prove that

$$|a| < 1 \Rightarrow \lim_{n \to \infty} a^n = 0. \tag{25}$$

By the result of Exercise 16 below $\left(\lim_{n \to \infty} a_n = 0 \Leftrightarrow \lim_{n \to \infty} |a_n| = 0 \right)$, we can assume

that $0 < a < 1$. Then $a = \dfrac{1}{1 + k}$, where $0 < k$, and

$$0 < a^n = \frac{1}{(1 + k)^n} < \frac{1}{1 + nk} < \frac{1}{nk}. \quad \text{(Theorem 1.15)}$$

Since $\lim_{n \to \infty} \dfrac{1}{nk} = 0$, we conclude, by the squeezing theorem, that $\lim_{n \to \infty} a^n = 0$.

EXERCISES

In numbers 1–12 write the first five terms of the sequence, determine whether the sequence converges or diverges, and if the former find the limit.

1. $a_n = \dfrac{n + (-1)^n}{n}$.

2. $a_n = \dfrac{3n - 1}{n + 2}$.

3. $a_n = \dfrac{n + 5}{2n + 1}$.

4. $a_n = \dfrac{n + 5}{2n^2 + 1}$.

5. $a_n = \dfrac{4n^2 - 8n + 100}{2n^2 - 11n - 1000}$.

6. $a_n = \dfrac{3n}{n^3 - 2}$.

7. $a_n = \dfrac{4n^3 - 7n^2 + 2}{2n^2 - 5n + 11}$.

8. $a_n = \dfrac{n^2 - 5n + 3}{3n^2 + 11n - 17}$.

9. $a_n = \dfrac{2n^2 + 6n + 31}{n + 100}$.

10. $a_n = \begin{cases} \dfrac{4n+2}{n+1}, & n \text{ odd} \\[2mm] \dfrac{4n-3}{n+5}, & n \text{ even.} \end{cases}$

11. $a_n = \begin{cases} \dfrac{n+1}{n}, & n \text{ odd} \\[2mm] \dfrac{n-2}{n}, & n \text{ even.} \end{cases}$

12. $a_n = \sqrt[n]{n}$ (l'Hospital's Rule)

13. How many cluster points does each of the following sequences have? Which sequences converge?

(a) $a_n = \cos \dfrac{n\pi}{2}$.

(b) $a_n = \cos^2 \dfrac{n\pi}{2}$.

(c) $a_n = \cos^2 n\pi$.

(d) $a_n = n\pi$.

14. Write out the details of the proof of part (b) of Theorem 3. [*Hint.* $a_n b_n - L_1 L_2 = a_n b_n - b_n L_1 + b_n L_1 - L_1 L_2$.]

15. Write out the proof of part (b) of Theorem 5.

16. Prove that $\lim\limits_{n \to \infty} a_n = 0 \Leftrightarrow \lim\limits_{n \to \infty} |a_n| = 0$. [*Hint.* Write out the defining expression for either limit and recall that $\|a\| = |a|$.]

17. (a) Let

$$a_n = \frac{1}{n+1} + \frac{1}{n+2} + \cdots + \frac{1}{2n}.$$

Show that the sequence $\{a_n\}$ converges. [*Hints.* (1) Show $a_{n+1} - a_n > 0$; and (2) show $a_n < \dfrac{n}{n+1} < 1$.]

(b) Let

$$b_n = \frac{1}{n} + \frac{1}{n+1} + \cdots + \frac{1}{2n}.$$

Show that the sequence $\{b_n\}$ converges. [*Hints.* (1) Evaluate b_1, b_2, b_3; and (2) see the hints for part (a).]

(c) Show that $\lim\limits_{n \to \infty} a_n = \lim\limits_{n \to \infty} b_n$. [*Hint.* Consider $b_n - a_n$.]

(d) By considering a_3 and b_3 give bounds for the limit of the sequences in parts (a) and (b).

(e) By considering a regular partition of the interval $[1, 2]$ and a lower sum for the integral of $f(x) = \dfrac{1}{x}$ on this interval, show that $\lim\limits_{n \to \infty} a_n = \log 2$ (see Example 3.2).

18. This exercise outlines a proof of Theorem 6, the Cauchy Criterion of Convergence Theorem.

(a) For the implication $\Rightarrow$ pick n_ε such that $n > n_\varepsilon \Rightarrow |a_n - L| < \dfrac{\varepsilon}{2}$. Then take $m, n > n_\varepsilon$ and use the fact that

$$a_m - a_n = a_m - L + L - a_n.$$

(b) The demonstration of the validity of the implication $\Leftarrow$ is more difficult than that of the reverse implication, chiefly because the limit L of the sequence must be produced. In brief, the method suggested is as follows:
   (i) Use the CCC to prove $\{a_n\}$ bounded.
   (ii) Use the Bolzano–Weierstrass Theorem (Section 3.8) to show the set $\{a_n\}$ has a cluster point L.
   (iii) Show $\lim\limits_{n \to \infty} a_n = L$.

(c) Show that a sequence $\{a_n\}$ which satisfies the CCC is bounded.
   Hints.
   (1) See the proof of Theorem 2.
   (2) Take $\varepsilon = 1$, apply the CCC to obtain n_1 such that $n, m > n_1 \Rightarrow |a_n - a_m| < 1$, i.e.,

$$-1 < a_n - a_m < 1.$$

   (3) Hold m fixed. Show that $M_1 = |a_m| + 1$ is a bound for the tail $(n > n_1)$ of the sequence.
   (4) Follow the proof of Theorem 2 to obtain a bound M for the entire sequence.

(d) To apply the Bolzano–Weierstrass Theorem to the set $\{a_n\}$ one must know it is not only bounded but infinite. Show that if $\{a_n\}$ is finite, then the CCC forces the sequence to be constant from some n onwards. Then this constant value is the value of L.
   [*Hint.* If a_j and a_k, $a_j \neq a_k$ both occur infinitely many times in the sequence, take $\varepsilon = \frac{1}{3}|a_j - a_k|$ and show that the CCC is violated.]

(e) If $\{a_n\}$ is not finite, then, being bounded, as shown in (c), $\{a_n\}$ has a cluster point L. Show $\lim\limits_{n \to \infty} a_n = L$.
   Hints.
   (1) For arbitrary $\varepsilon > 0$ use the CCC to show $\exists n_\varepsilon$ such that $m, n > n_\varepsilon \Rightarrow$
$$|a_m - a_n| < \dfrac{\varepsilon}{2}.$$
   (2) Use Theorem 3.2 to show that infinitely many of the a_n lie in $N_{\varepsilon/2}(L)$.
   (3) Pick $n_1 > n_\varepsilon$ such that $a_{n_1} \in N_{\varepsilon/2}(L)$.
   (4) Use

$$a_n - L = a_n - a_{n_1} + a_{n_1} - L$$

   to show that $n > n_\varepsilon \Rightarrow a_n \in N_\varepsilon(L)$.

15.3   Infinite Series: Preliminary Ideas

Intuitively, an infinite series is an "infinite sum," expressed symbolically as $\sum_{k=1}^{\infty} a_k$, where $\{a_k\}$ is a sequence. Since it is impossible to add a sum involving more than a finite number of terms, the symbol $\sum_{k=1}^{\infty} a_k$ is not in itself meaningful. However, it is a simple matter, by means of sequences, to assign a precise meaning to the vague concept of infinite sum or infinite series.

This is done by defining a second sequence $\{s_n\}$ by

$$s_n = \sum_{k=1}^{n} a_k. \tag{26}$$

The s_n are known as the *partial sums* of the series.

Essentially, the infinite series associated with the sequence $\{a_n\}$ is the sequence $\{s_n\}$ defined by (26); however, the symbol $\sum_{k=1}^{\infty} a_k$ (or even $\sum a_k$) is very useful and suggestive, as will be seen.

Definition 3. *The infinite series $\sum_{k=1}^{\infty} a_k$* **converges** $\Leftrightarrow$ *the sequence $\{s_n\}$ of partial sums defined by (26) converges. If $\lim\limits_{n \to \infty} s_n = s$, we write $\sum_{k=1}^{\infty} a_k = s$.*
If $\lim\limits_{n \to \infty} s_n$ does not exist, then the series $\sum_{k=1}^{\infty} a_k$ **diverges, or is divergent.**

The following illustration, the *geometric series*, is relatively simple but extremely valuable. Among other things, it shows some of the different possibilities occurring within the framework of Definition 3.

Example 7. We consider the series

$$\sum_{n=0}^{\infty} a^n = 1 + a + a^2 + \cdots + a^n + \cdots$$

(note that we begin this series with $n = 0$).

By elementary algebra we know

$$s_n = \sum_{k=0}^{n} a^k = \frac{1 - a^{n+1}}{1 - a}, \qquad \text{if} \quad a \neq 1.$$

(i) Suppose, first, that $|a| < 1$. Then

$$\lim_{n \to \infty} s_n = \lim_{n \to \infty} \frac{1 - a^{n+1}}{1 - a} = \lim_{n \to \infty} \frac{1}{1 - a} - \left(\frac{1}{1 - a}\right) \lim_{n \to \infty} a^{n+1}$$

$$= \frac{1}{1 - a},$$

since, by the result of Example 6 [Eq. (25)], $\lim\limits_{n \to \infty} a^{n+1} = 0$.

(ii) If $a = 1$, then clearly $s_n = n + 1$, and $\lim\limits_{n \to \infty} s_n = \infty$, so the series diverges.

(iii) if $a = -1$, then

$$s_n = \begin{cases} 0, & n \text{ odd} \\ 1, & n \text{ even} \end{cases}.$$

Since this sequence has two cluster points it is divergent, as is $\sum a^n$.
(iv) Finally, if $|a| > 1$, we can write

$$s_n = \frac{a^{n+1} - 1}{a - 1} = \frac{1}{a - 1} a^{n+1} - \frac{1}{a - 1}.$$

In this case (see Exercise 23 below) $\lim_{n \to \infty} s_n$ fails to exist, so the series diverges.

The result of this discussion is worth stating formally.

Theorem 7. *The geometric series $\sum_{k=0}^{\infty} x^k$ converges for all x such that $|x| < 1$ and diverges for all other $x \in \mathbf{R}$.*

Although it would be wrong to conclude that divergent series are unimportant, we shall be interested in this chapter in convergent series. One of the major problems is the development of conditions which enable one to conclude that a given series either converges or diverges. As we shall see, the number of such tests is rather large: there is, unfortunately, no simple all-embracing criterion, no universal touchstone, which can be applied to every series.

In the remainder of this section we develop a few general principles, and in the next section we enunciate some of the simpler tests for series of positive terms.

Theorem 8. *A necessary, but **not sufficient**, condition for the series $\sum_{k=1}^{\infty} a_k$ to converge is that $\lim_{n \to \infty} a_n = 0$.*

In symbols,

(i) $\displaystyle\sum_{k=1}^{\infty} a_k$ *converges* $\Rightarrow \lim_{n \to \infty} a_n = 0.$

(ii) $\lim_{n \to \infty} a_n = 0 \not\Rightarrow \sum a_k$ *converges.*

Proof. (i) Let $s_n = \sum_{k=1}^{n} a_k$, and let $\lim_{n \to \infty} s_n = s$. Then $a_n = s_n - s_{n-1}$, and

$$\lim_{n \to \infty} a_n = \lim_{n \to \infty} (s_n - s_{n-1}) = \lim_{n \to \infty} s_n - \lim_{n \to \infty} s_{n-1} = s - s = 0.$$

(ii) To demonstrate that the condition is not sufficient we provide a counterexample.

Let $a_n = \dfrac{1}{\sqrt{n}}$; then

$$\lim_{n \to \infty} a_n = \lim_{n \to \infty} \frac{1}{\sqrt{n}} = 0.$$

But

$$s_n = \sum_{k=1}^{n} a_k = \sum_{k=1}^{n} \frac{1}{\sqrt{k}} = \frac{1}{\sqrt{1}} + \frac{1}{\sqrt{2}} + \cdots + \frac{1}{\sqrt{n}} \geq \frac{1}{\sqrt{n}} + \frac{1}{\sqrt{n}} + \cdots + \frac{1}{\sqrt{n}}$$

$$= \frac{n}{\sqrt{n}} = \sqrt{n}.$$

Clearly, $\lim_{n \to \infty} s_n = \infty$, so the series $\sum a_k$ diverges. ∎

One must be constantly on guard against misusing the condition of Theorem 8 as being sufficient.

Convergent series combine linearly in a natural way, as the following assertion makes explicit.

Theorem 9. *Suppose* $\sum a_k$ *and* $\sum b_k$ *are convergent series with*

$$\sum_{k=1}^{\infty} a_k = s, \qquad \sum_{k=1}^{\infty} b_k = t.$$

Then the series

$$\sum_{k=1}^{\infty} (a_k + b_k), \qquad \sum_{k=1}^{\infty} (a_k - b_k), \qquad and \qquad \sum_{k=1}^{\infty} ca_k$$

all converge, and

$$\sum_{k=1}^{\infty} (a_k + b_k) = s + t, \qquad \sum_{k=1}^{\infty} (a_k - b_k) = s - t, \qquad \sum_{k=1}^{\infty} ca_k = cs.$$

Here, $c \in \mathbf{R}$.

This theorem is a direct consequence of Definition 3 and of the corresponding assertions for sequences (Theorem 3). We shall omit the details.

An important fact about series is that convergence or divergence is determined by the behavior of the tail. To put the matter differently, we make the following formal assertion.

Theorem 10

(i) *The addition or subtraction of any finite number of terms cannot make a convergent series divergent or a divergent series convergent.*

(ii) *The multiplication of every term of a series by a nonzero constant cannot change the convergence or divergence property of a series.*

Proof. For (i) we consider the series $\sum a_k$ and $\sum b_k$, where, for some fixed positive integer n_0,

$$b_1 = a_{n_0+1}$$
$$b_2 = a_{n_0+2}$$
$$\vdots$$
$$b_j = a_{n_0+j}, \qquad \text{etc.}$$

Let

$$s_n = \sum_{k=1}^{n} a_k, \qquad t_n = \sum_{k=1}^{n} b_k, \qquad q = \sum_{k=1}^{n_0} a_k.$$

Then, for $n > n_0$,

$$s_n = \sum_{k=1}^{n} a_k = \sum_{k=1}^{n_0} a_k + \sum_{k=n_0+1}^{n} a_k = q + \sum_{j=1}^{n-n_0} b_j = q + t_{n-n_0}.$$

From this equation we easily see that

$$\lim_{n \to \infty} s_n \text{ exists} \Leftrightarrow \lim_{n \to \infty} t_n \text{ exists},$$

and when either limit exists, $s = q + t$, where $s = \lim_{n \to \infty} s_n$, $t = \lim_{n \to \infty} t_n$.

(ii) The proof of the second assertion depends upon the fact (see Exercise 25 below) that, if $c \neq 0$, then

$$\lim_{n \to \infty} (cs_n) \text{ exists} \Leftrightarrow \lim_{n \to \infty} s_n \text{ exists};$$

if either limit exists, then, by Theorem 3d,

$$\lim_{n \to \infty} cs_n = c \lim_{n \to \infty} s_n. \quad \blacksquare$$

Example 8. Given a sequence $\{s_n\}$, if one treats the terms as the partial sums of a series, it is easy to recover a_n from s_n. For $a_n = s_n - s_{n-1}$. Thus, if $s_n = \dfrac{n}{2n+1}$, we can find

$$a_n = s_n - s_{n-1} = \frac{n}{2n+1} - \frac{n-1}{2n-1}$$

$$= \frac{1}{4n^2 - 1} = \frac{1}{(2n+1)(2n-1)}.$$

Thus, the series can be written as

$$\sum a_k = \tfrac{1}{3} \cdot \tfrac{1}{1} + \tfrac{1}{5} \cdot \tfrac{1}{3} + \tfrac{1}{7} \cdot \tfrac{1}{5} + \cdots.$$

Of course, as originally given,

$$s_n = \frac{n}{2n+1} \to \frac{1}{2} = s.$$

Example 9. Does the series $\sum a_n$, where

$$a_n = \frac{n - 10^{20}}{10^{10}n},$$

converge or diverge?

The series diverges, by Theorem 8, for

$$\lim_{n \to \infty} a_n = \lim_{n \to \infty} \frac{n - 10^{20}}{10^{10}n} = \frac{1}{10^{10}} \neq 0.$$

Example 10. In this example we consider a famous series, called the harmonic series:

$$\sum_{n=1}^{\infty} \frac{1}{n} = 1 + \frac{1}{2} + \frac{1}{3} + \frac{1}{4} + \cdots.$$

First of all, since $\lim_{n \to \infty} a_n = \lim_{n \to \infty} \frac{1}{n} = 0$, the series *might* converge—we could say it has passed the preliminary test. Moreover, if one is sufficiently industrious to calculate a few partial sums, he would find they increase very slowly. Intuitively, this would seem to be a convergent series. But it is not. To prove this we use Theorem 6 (the CCC) and consider two partial sums s_n and s_{2n}:

$$s_{2n} - s_n = \frac{1}{n+1} + \frac{1}{n+2} + \cdots + \frac{1}{2n}$$

$$\geq \frac{1}{2n} + \frac{1}{2n} + \cdots + \frac{1}{2n} = \frac{n}{2n} = \frac{1}{2}.$$

In other words, for *every* n, $s_{2n} - s_n \geq \frac{1}{2}$. But the CCC requires for $\{s_n\}$ to converge that, if n is sufficiently large, all terms of the sequence be arbitrarily close together. As this is impossible, by the above inequality, $\lim_{n=\infty} s_n = \infty$, and the harmonic series diverges.

EXERCISES

In numbers 1–8 find the sum of the series.

1. $\sum_{n=0}^{\infty} \frac{1}{2^n}.$

2. $\sum_{n=0}^{\infty} \frac{3}{4^n}.$

3. $\sum_{n=1}^{\infty} \frac{5}{(\sqrt{2})^n}.$ Note that the series begins with $n = 1$.

4. $\sum_{n=0}^{\infty} \frac{(-1)^n}{3^n}.$

5. $7 - \frac{7}{2} + \frac{7}{4} - \cdots + \frac{(-1)^n 7}{2^n} + \cdots.$

6. $\sum_{n=0}^{\infty} \frac{4}{10^n}.$

7. $3 - \dfrac{3}{10} + \dfrac{3}{10^2} - \cdots + \dfrac{3}{(-10)^n} + \cdots.$

8. $1 - \dfrac{1}{3} + \dfrac{1}{9} - \dfrac{1}{27} + \cdots.$

In each of numbers 9–18 an expression for the nth partial sum of a series is given. Find an expression for the nth term a_n, say whether or not the series converges, and if it does find its sum.

9. $s_n = n!$

10. $s_n = \dfrac{1}{n!}$

11. $s_n = \dfrac{2n}{3n+1}.$

12. $s_n = 1 + (-1)^n.$

13. $s_n = \dfrac{n^2}{2n^2 + 3}.$

14. $s_n = \dfrac{1 - \left(\dfrac{9}{10}\right)^{n+1}}{\dfrac{1}{10}}.$

15. $s_n = \dfrac{n^2}{n+1}.$

16. $s_n = \log \dfrac{n}{n+1}.$

17. $s_n = \sin n\pi x.$ Show $a_n = 2 \sin \tfrac{1}{2}\pi x \cos (n - \tfrac{1}{2})\pi x.$

18. $s_n = \tfrac{1}{2}[\log (n+3) + \log (n+4)].$

In numbers 19–22 each of the series is divergent. Why?

19. $\displaystyle\sum_{n=1}^{\infty} \dfrac{n}{n+3}.$

20. $2 - 2 + 2 + \cdots.$

21. $\displaystyle\sum_{n=0}^{\infty} \left(\dfrac{4}{3}\right)^n.$

22. $\displaystyle\sum_{n=1}^{\infty} \dfrac{n}{n^2 - \sqrt{3}}.$ $\left[Hint. \quad \dfrac{n}{n^2 - \sqrt{3}} > \dfrac{n}{n^2}. \text{ So } \dots ? \right]$

23. Prove that the geometric series $\sum_{n=0}^{\infty} a^n$ diverges if $|a| > 1$. [*Hint.* If $|a| > 1$, what can be said about $\lim_{n \to \infty} a^n$? (Theorem 8?)]

24. Prove Theorem 9.

25. For $\{s_n\}$ a sequence and $c \neq 0$, $c \in \mathbf{R}$, show that $\lim_{n \to \infty} cs_n$ exists $\Leftrightarrow$ $\lim_{n \to \infty} s_n$ exists.

15.4 Series of Positive Terms

The series which, in many ways, are easiest to work with are those which have only positive terms. In this section we limit ourselves to such series and develop several useful tests for convergence and divergence.

An immediate consequence of the assumption that $a_k > 0$, all $k \in \mathbf{N}$, is that the partial sums s_n of the series $\sum a_k$ form a monotonic increasing sequence. The following assertion is then an immediate consequence of Theorem 5.

Theorem 11. *If $a_n > 0$, all $n \in \mathbf{N}$, then*

$$\sum_{n=1}^{\infty} a_n \text{ converges} \Leftrightarrow \begin{cases} \text{the sequence } \{s_n\} \text{ of partial} \\ \text{sums is bounded.} \end{cases}$$

By means of this result we can quickly obtain a natural and widely applicable criterion.

Theorem 12 (*The Comparison Test*)

(i) *Let $\sum a_n$ and $\sum c_n$ be two series (of positive terms) with the properties that $\sum c_n$ converges and that for all $n \in \mathbf{N} \Rightarrow a_n \leq c_n$. Then $\sum a_n$ converges.*

(ii) *Let $\sum a_n$ and $\sum d_n$ be two series with the properties that $\sum d_n$ diverges and that for all $n \in \mathbf{N} \Rightarrow a_n \geq d_n$. Then $\sum a_n$ diverges.*
In symbols,

(i) $\left.\begin{array}{l} \sum c_n \text{ converges} \\ a_n \leq c_n, \text{ all } n \in \mathbf{N} \end{array}\right\} \Rightarrow \sum a_n \text{ converges.}$

(ii) $\left.\begin{array}{l} \sum d_n \text{ diverges} \\ a_n \geq d_n, \text{ all } n \in \mathbf{N} \end{array}\right\} \Rightarrow \sum a_n \text{ diverges.}$

Proof. (i) Let $s_n = \sum_{k=1}^{n} a_k$, $t_n = \sum_{k=1}^{n} c_k$. Then clearly $s_n \leq t_n$ for all n. Also, since $\sum c_n$ converges, $\lim_{n = \infty} t_n = t$, and $t_n \leq t$. But then t is an upper bound for the sequence $\{s_n\}$ and by Theorem 11 $\sum a_n$ converges.

(ii) Let $s_n = \sum_{k=1}^{n} a_k$, $u_n = \sum_{k=1}^{n} d_k$. The hypotheses for this portion of the theorem then say that

$$s_n \geq u_n, \quad \text{all } n \in \mathbf{N},$$

and that the sequence $\{u_n\}$ is unbounded (by Theorem 11). This means the sequence $\{s_n\}$ is unbounded, and (Theorem 11 again) $\sum a_n$ diverges. ∎

The fact is—and it is an important fact—that the inequalities in the hypotheses of Theorem 12 need hold only from a certain point onward in the series, not necessarily for *all* n. This observation is a consequence of Theorem 10. The formal, and more precise, statement follows.

Corollary. *Let $\sum a_n, \sum c_n, \sum d_n$ be series of positive terms.*

(i) $\left.\begin{array}{l} \sum c_n \text{ converges} \\ a_n \leq c_n \text{ for } n \geq n_1 \end{array}\right\} \Rightarrow \sum a_n \text{ converges.}$

(ii) $\left.\begin{array}{l} \sum d_n \text{ diverges} \\ a_n \geq d_n \text{ for } n \geq n_2 \end{array}\right\} \Rightarrow \sum a_n \text{ diverges.}$

From a practical point of view the comparison test is not of much use unless one has available a reasonable supply of series *of known behavior* to be used for comparison purposes. At this point it must be admitted that our supply is rather limited, consisting largely of the geometric series and the divergent harmonic

series, $\sum_{n=1}^{\infty} \dfrac{1}{n}$. We shall increase our stock shortly.

As an illustration of the use of the comparison test and as an indication of a possible difficulty in its application we look at a particular case.

Example 11. Test for convergence or divergence $\sum a_n$, where

$$a_n = \frac{n}{3n^2 - 2}.$$

We observe that a_n is *essentially* the same as $\dfrac{1}{3n} = \dfrac{1}{3} \cdot \dfrac{1}{n}$, suggesting that $\sum a_n$ diverges. In this case the formal verification is easy:

$$a_n = \frac{n}{3n^2 - 2} > \frac{n}{3n^2} = \frac{1}{3n} = d_n.$$

Since the harmonic series $\sum \dfrac{1}{n}$ diverges, so does (Theorem 10) the constant multiple $\sum d_n$. Thus by Theorem 12 $\sum a_n$ does indeed diverge.

Suppose, though, the formula for a_n had been

$$a_n = \frac{n}{3n^2 + 2}.$$

The heuristic argument for the divergence of $\sum a_n$ would be the same—and the conclusion would be correct—but the plus sign in the denominator creates an annoying difficulty in establishing the desired inequality. The following theorem provides a convenient way around this difficulty.

Theorem 13. *Let $\sum a_n$ and $\sum b_n$ be series (of positive terms) and suppose that*

$$\lim_{n \to \infty} \frac{a_n}{b_n} = q.$$

(i) *If q is a finite positive number $(0 < q < \infty)$, then the two series either both converge or both diverge.*

(ii) *If $q = 0$ and $\sum b_n$ converges then $\sum a_n$ converges.*

(iii) *If $\lim\limits_{n \to \infty} \dfrac{a_n}{b_n} = \infty$ and $\sum b_n$ diverges, then $\sum a_n$ diverges.*

Proof. (i) If $\lim\limits_{n \to \infty} \dfrac{a_n}{b_n} = q$, where $0 < q < \infty$, then $\exists n_0$ such that $n > n_0 \Rightarrow$

$$\frac{q}{2} < \frac{a_n}{b_n} < \frac{3q}{2}$$

(see Figure 5).

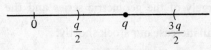

Figure 5

Suppose, now, that $\sum a_n$ converges. From the left-hand inequality we have, for $n > n_0$,

$$b_n < \frac{2}{q} a_n.$$

By Theorem 10, the convergence of $\sum a_n$ implies that of $\sum \frac{2}{q} a_n$; thus, by the Corollary to Theorem 12, $\sum b_n$ converges.

If we assume that $\sum b_n$ converges we can use a similar argument based on the right-hand inequality and

$$a_n < \frac{3q}{2} b_n, \qquad n > n_0,$$

obtained therefrom, to show that $\sum a_n$ also converges.

Next, if either $\sum a_n$ or $\sum b_n$ diverges, then so must the other; for, assuming not and using the preceding results would immediately produce a contradiction. The proofs of (ii) and (iii) are similar and we shall leave them as exercises. ∎

We point out that, since a_n and b_n are positive, $\lim\limits_{n \to \infty} \dfrac{a_n}{b_n}$, if it exists, cannot be negative. However, the limit might fail to exist in ways other than that mentioned in (iii) of the theorem. For example, let $a_n = n\,|\sin n|$, $b_n = n$.

Example 12. We return to the series, mentioned after Example 11, where

$$a_n = \frac{n}{3n^2 + 2};$$

as before, we intuit that $\sum a_n$, essentially like $\sum \dfrac{1}{n}$, diverges. Thus we let $b_n = \dfrac{1}{n}$ and calculate

$$\lim_{n \to \infty} \frac{a_n}{b_n} = \lim_{n \to \infty} \frac{n^2}{3n^2 + 2} = \frac{1}{3} > 0.$$

By Theorem 13, then, $\sum a_n$ does diverge.

Before looking at further examples of the comparison test (in either form) we discuss one more test.

Theorem 14 (The Integral Test). *Let the function f be nonnegative and nonincreasing on $[1, \infty)$. Let $a_n = f(n)$. Then the behavior of $\sum a_n$ is tied to that* of the improper integral $\int_1^\infty f(x)\, dx$; i.e., *the series and the improper integral either both converge or both diverge.*

Proof. We refer to the sketch in Figure 6. We assert that the following in-

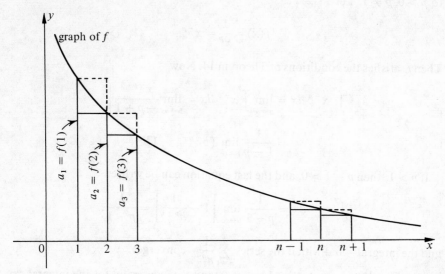

Figure 6

equalities hold for every n;

$$s_{n+1} - a_1 = \sum_{k=2}^{n+1} a_k \le \int_1^{n+1} f(x)\, dx \le \sum_{k=1}^{n} a_k = s_n;$$

for $\sum_{k=1}^{n} a_k$ is an upper sum for the integral, whereas $\sum_{k=2}^{n+1} a_k$ serves as a lower sum for the same integral.

If the improper integral converges, then, by the left-hand inequality,

$$\int_1^\infty f(x)\, dx = \lim_{n \to \infty} \int_1^{n+1} f(x)\, dx$$

serves as an upper bound for the sequence $\{s_n\}$ and, by Theorem 11, $\sum a_n$ converges. On the other hand, if the improper integral diverges then we use the right-hand inequality to assert that the sequence $\{s_n\}$ is unbounded and diverges. ∎

As an illustration of the integral test we prove the following result.

Theorem 15. *The series* $\sum\limits_{n=1}^{\infty} \dfrac{1}{n^p}$ *converges for all* $p > 1$ *and diverges for all* $p \le 1$.

This series is known as the *p-series*. Of course, we have a series for each value of p, so the assertion of the theorem provides us with a large and useful addition to our stock of series of known behavior.

Proof. The case $p = 1$ is simply the harmonic series which we have already proven is divergent. Thus we concern ourselves with $p \neq 1$. First of all, it is obvious that the series $\sum_{n=1}^{\infty} \frac{1}{n^p}$ diverges for $p \leq 0$, so we further restrict our attention to $p > 0, p \neq 1$. Let

$$f(x) = \frac{1}{x^p} = x^{-p}.$$

Then f satisfies the conditions of Theorem 14. Now

$$\int_1^{\infty} x^{-p}\, dx = \lim_{b \to \infty} \int_1^b x^{-p}\, dx = \lim_{b \to \infty} \frac{x^{-p+1}}{-p+1} \bigg|_1^b$$

$$= \frac{1}{1-p} \lim_{b \to \infty} [b^{-p+1} - 1].$$

If $p > 1$, then $p - 1 > 0$, and the last equation can be written

$$\int_1^{\infty} x^{-p}\, dx = \frac{1}{p-1} \lim_{b \to \infty} \left[1 - \frac{1}{b^{p-1}}\right] = \frac{1}{p-1},$$

and the integral—and with it the series $\sum_{n=1}^{\infty} \frac{1}{n^p}$—converges.

However, if $0 < p < 1$, then $1 - p > 0$, and the expression for the integral can be written

$$\int_1^{\infty} x^{-p}\, dx = \frac{1}{1-p} \lim_{b \to \infty} [b^{1-p} - 1] = \infty.$$

From this we conclude, by Theorem 14, that $\sum_{n=1}^{\infty} \frac{1}{n^p}$ diverges for $0 < p < 1$. ∎

Example 13. We consider $\sum_{n=1}^{\infty} a_n$, where

$$a_n = \frac{\log n}{n^3 + 3}.$$

Out preliminary reasoning proceeds like this: $\log n$ increases slowly, more slowly than n; the 3 in the denominator has little influence for large n and can be ignored. Thus, being generous as regards $\log n$, we say a_n is essentially like $\frac{1}{n^2}$ and we try that as the formula for b_n : $b_n = \frac{1}{n^2}$ (the preceding result, with $p = 2$,

tells us that $\sum b_n = \sum \frac{1}{n^2}$ converges).

Now we look at

$$\lim_{n \to \infty} \frac{a_n}{b_n} = \lim_{n \to \infty} \frac{n^2 \log n}{n^3 + 3}.$$

It is routine to use l'Hospital's Rule (Theorem 4.12) on this $\dfrac{\infty}{\infty}$ type limit, to

find that $\lim\limits_{n\to\infty} \dfrac{a_n}{b_n} = 0$. By Theorem 13(ii), $\sum a_n$ converges.

Example 14. We test the behavior of $\sum\limits_{n=1}^{\infty} \dfrac{n}{e^n}$. Suppose we try the integral test,

letting

$$f(x) = \frac{x}{e^x} = xe^{-x}.$$

The hypotheses of Theorem 14 are satisfied by f (as you should verify); by tables or by integration by parts we find

$$\int_1^b xe^{-x}\,dx = -e^{-x}(x+1)\Big|_1^b = \frac{2}{e} - \frac{b+1}{e^b}.$$

Now $\lim\limits_{b\to\infty} \dfrac{b+1}{e^b} = 0$ (l'Hospital's Rule), so $\int_1^\infty xe^{-x}\,dx = 2e^{-1}$. It follows that

the series $\sum\limits_{n=1}^{\infty} \dfrac{n}{e^n}$ converges. In a later section we prove this convergence in a

different way. (See Exercise 18 after Section 15.5.)

EXERCISES

In numbers 1–20 test the series for convergence or divergence.

1. $\sum\limits_{n=1}^{\infty} \dfrac{3}{n+4}$.

2. $\sum\limits_{n=1}^{\infty} \dfrac{3}{n^2+4}$.

3. $1 - \dfrac{1}{3} + \dfrac{1}{9} - \dfrac{1}{27} + \dfrac{1}{81} - \cdots$.

4. $\sum\limits_{n=1}^{\infty} \dfrac{1}{3^n}$.

5. $\sum\limits_{n=1}^{\infty} \dfrac{n}{3^n}$.   (See Example 14.)

6. $\sum\limits_{n=1}^{\infty} \dfrac{n+4}{n^2+4}$.

7. $\sum\limits_{n=1}^{\infty} \dfrac{2n^2-1}{n^3+8}$.

8. $\sum\limits_{n=1}^{\infty} \dfrac{3n-1}{n^3+4}$.

9. $\sum\limits_{n=1}^{\infty} \dfrac{\log n}{2n^3+5}$.

10. $\sum\limits_{n=1}^{\infty} \dfrac{n}{\log(n+1)}$.

11. $\sum\limits_{n=1}^{\infty} \dfrac{\sqrt{n}}{n^2+2}$.

12. $\sum\limits_{n=2}^{\infty} \dfrac{1}{n\log n}$.   (Note initial value for n.)

13. $\sum\limits_{n=2}^{\infty} \dfrac{\log n}{n^2}$.

14. $\sum\limits_{n=1}^{\infty} \dfrac{\cos n+1}{n^2}$.

15. $\sum\limits_{n=1}^{\infty} \dfrac{1}{\sqrt{n(n+1)}}$.

16. $\sum\limits_{n=1}^{\infty} \dfrac{\tan^{-1} n}{n^2+1}$.

17. $\sum_{n=1}^{\infty} \operatorname{csch} n.$ (See Exercise 14 after Section 7.5.)

18. $\sum_{n=1}^{\infty} \dfrac{n^2}{e^n}.$ **19.** $\sum_{n=1}^{\infty} \left(\dfrac{\pi}{2} - \tan^{-1} n\right).$ **20.** $\sum_{n=1}^{\infty} \operatorname{sech} n.$

21. Prove part (ii) of Theorem 13.   **22.** Prove part (iii) of Theorem 13.

23. Use part (iii) of Theorem 13, with $b_n = \dfrac{1}{n}$, to show that $\sum_{n=1}^{\infty} \dfrac{1}{n^p}$ diverges for $0 < p < 1.$

15.5   The Root and Ratio Tests

We have not yet made use of the geometric series, except in a trivial way, as a comparison series. In this section we show how a suitable combining of the comparison test with knowledge of the behavior of the geometric series leads to two tests, both due to Cauchy, which are probably the most widely used tests for convergence. We continue to assume that $a_n > 0$, all n.

Theorem 16 (*Root Test*). *Let $\sum a_n$ be a series of positive terms.*

(i) *If there exist n_0 and r, $0 < r < 1$, such that $n > n_0 \Rightarrow \sqrt[n]{a_n} \leq r$, then the series $\sum a_n$ converges.*

(ii) *If there exist n_0 and $r > 1$ such that $n > n_0 \Rightarrow \sqrt[n]{a_n} \geq r$, then the series $\sum a_n$ diverges.*

Proof. (i) By hypothesis $\sqrt[n]{a_n} \leq r < 1$, for $n > n_0$. This implies that $a_n \leq r^n$. Because $0 < r < 1$, the geometric series $\sum r^n$ converges, thus (Corollary to Theorem 12) $\sum a_n$ converges.

(ii) If, on the other hand, $n > n_0 \Rightarrow \sqrt[n]{a_n} \geq r > 1$, then $a_n \geq r^n > 1$ for $n > n_0$. In this case the condition necessary for convergence, $\lim_{n \to \infty} a_n = 0$, cannot be fulfilled and $\sum a_n$ diverges. ∎

It is important to keep in mind that in neither part of this theorem can $r = 1$.

For many applications the following slightly weaker version of the root test is easier to apply.

Theorem 17 (*Root Test, Limit Form*). *Let $\sum a_n$ be a series of positive terms. Suppose $\lim_{n \to \infty} \sqrt[n]{a_n} = k$.*

(i) *If $0 \leq k < 1$, $\sum a_n$ converges.*
(ii) *If $k > 1$, $\sum a_n$ diverges.*
(iii) *If $k = 1$, the test gives no information (the test fails).*

Proof. (i) Suppose $\lim\limits_{n\to\infty} \sqrt[n]{a_n} = k < 1$. We let $\varepsilon = \frac{1}{2}(1-k)$; then we know $\exists n_0$ such that $n > n_0 \Rightarrow \sqrt[n]{a_n} \in N_\varepsilon(k)$, i.e., $k - \varepsilon < \sqrt[n]{a_n} < k + \varepsilon$. If we let $k + \varepsilon = r$, then $r < 1$; for (see Figure 7)

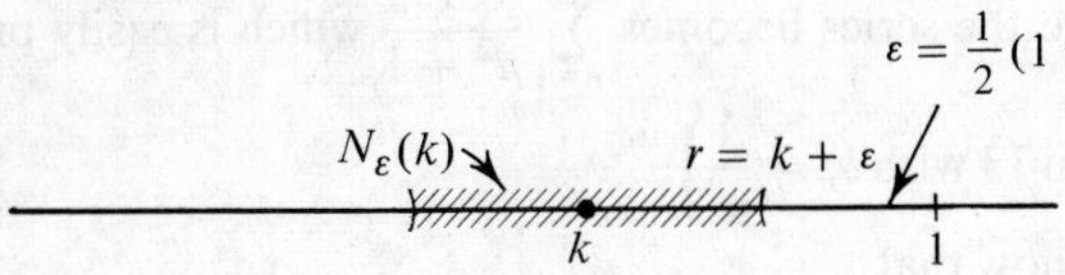

Figure 7

$$r = k + \varepsilon = k + \tfrac{1}{2}(1-k) = \tfrac{1}{2}(1+k) < 1, \qquad \text{since } k < 1.$$

Clearly, $\sqrt[n]{a_n} \in N_\varepsilon(k) \Rightarrow \sqrt[n]{a_n} < r < 1$. Thus, by (i) of Theorem 16, $\sum a_n$ converges.

(ii) In a similar way, if $\lim\limits_{n\to\infty} \sqrt[n]{a_n} = k > 1$, we take $\varepsilon = \frac{1}{2}(k-1)$; then $\exists n_0$ such that $n > n_0 \Rightarrow \sqrt[n]{a_n} \in N_\varepsilon(k)$, or $k - \varepsilon < \sqrt[n]{a_n} < k + \varepsilon$. In this case we define $r = k - \varepsilon = k - \frac{1}{2}(k-1) = \frac{1}{2}(k+1) > 1$ (see Figure 8). Clearly, $\sqrt[n]{a_n} \in N_\varepsilon(k) \Rightarrow$

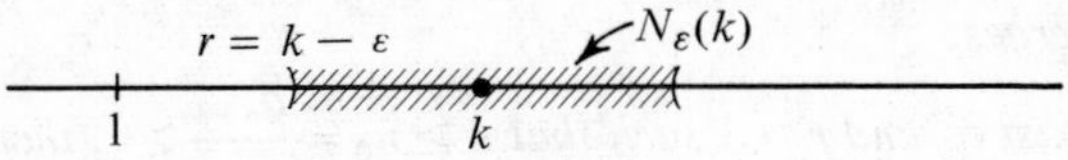

Figure 8

$\sqrt[n]{a_n} > r > 1$, and by (ii) of Theorem 16, $\sum a_n$ diverges.

(iii) To show that $\lim\limits_{n\to\infty} \sqrt[n]{a_n} = 1$ is inconclusive, let $a_n = \dfrac{1}{n^p}$. Then $\sqrt[n]{a_n} = \dfrac{1}{n^{p/n}}$. A straightforward application of l'Hospital's Rule shows that

$$\lim_{n\to\infty} \frac{1}{n^{p/n}} = 1,$$

independently of p. But we already know (Theorem 15) that $\sum \dfrac{1}{n^p}$ converges for $p > 1$ and diverges for $p \leq 1$. In other words, when $\lim\limits_{n\to\infty} \sqrt[n]{a_n} = 1$ "anything can happen." ∎

Example 15. Consider $\sum_{n=1}^{\infty} a_n$, where

$$a_n = \frac{a^n}{n^2 + 1}, \qquad a > 0.$$

To use Theorem 17, we calculate $\sqrt[n]{a_n} = \dfrac{a}{(n^2 + 1)^{1/n}}$. We can use l'Hospital's Rule

to show that $\lim\limits_{n \to \infty} (n^2 + 1)^{1/n} = 1$. Thus $\lim\limits_{n \to \infty} \sqrt[n]{a_n} = a$. It follows that for $0 < a < 1$,

$\sum a_n$ converges, and for $a > 1$, $\sum a_n$ diverges. Theorem 17 does not help if

$a = 1$; but in this case the series becomes $\sum\limits_{n=1}^{\infty} \dfrac{1}{n^2 + 1}$ which is easily proven con-

vergent $\left(\text{use Theorem 13 with } b_n = \dfrac{1}{n^2}\right)$.

In conclusion we know that

$$\sum_{n=1}^{\infty} \frac{a^n}{n^2 + 1}, \qquad a > 0$$

converges for $0 < a \le 1$, diverges for $a > 1$.

The second of the two Cauchy tests is called the *ratio test*. We first give it in the form analogous to the version of the root test given in Theorem 16.

Theorem 18 (Ratio Test). *Let $\sum a_n$ be a series of positive terms.*

(i) *If there exist n_0 and r, $0 < r < 1$, such that $n \ge n_0 \Rightarrow \dfrac{a_{n+1}}{a_n} \le r$, then the*

series $\sum a_n$ converges.

(ii) *If there exist n_0 and $r > 1$ such that $n \ge n_0 \Rightarrow \dfrac{a_{n+1}}{a_n} \ge r$, then the series $\sum a_n$*

diverges.

Proof. (i) From the hypothesis we can write

$$\frac{a_{n_0+1}}{a_{n_0}} \le r, \qquad \text{or} \quad a_{n_0+1} \le a_{n_0} r,$$

$$\frac{a_{n_0+2}}{a_{n_0+1}} \le r, \qquad \text{or} \quad a_{n_0+2} \le r a_{n_0+1} \le a_{n_0} r^2,$$

$$\frac{a_{n_0+3}}{a_{n_0+2}} \le r, \qquad \text{or} \quad a_{n_0+3} \le r a_{n_0+2} \le a_{n_0} r^3;$$

by induction, for all $k = 1, 2, \ldots,$

$$a_{n_0+k} \le a_{n_0} r^k.$$

Since $0 < r < 1$, the series $\sum r^k$ converges. Thus (Corollary to Theorem 12), $\sum a_n$ converges.

(ii) The proof of the second part is similar. From

$$\frac{a_{n+1}}{a_n} \ge r > 1 \qquad \text{for} \quad n \ge n_0$$

we conclude, in a similar manner that

$$a_{n_0+k} \geq a_{n_0} r^k.$$

But now $\sum r^k$ diverges, since $r > 1$, and hence so does $\sum a_n$. ∎

The weaker (but more applicable) version of the ratio test is proven in the same way as we proved Theorem 17. Consequently, we give only the formal statement.

Theorem 19 (*Ratio Test, Limit Form*). *Let $\sum a_n$ be a series of positive terms.*

Suppose $\lim\limits_{n \to \infty} \dfrac{a_{n+1}}{a_n} = k.$

(i) *If* $0 \leq k < 1$, $\sum a_n$ *converges.*
(ii) *If* $k > 1$, $\sum a_n$ *diverges.*
(iii) *If* $k = 1$, *the test gives no information (the test fails).*

Note, with regard to assertion (iii) of this series, that $a_n = \dfrac{1}{n^p}$ again supplies us with an example for which $k = 1$ and "anything can happen." For

$$\frac{a_{n+1}}{a_n} = \frac{n^p}{(n+1)^p} = \left(\frac{n}{n+1}\right)^p \to 1,$$

independent of the value of p.

Example 16. Consider $\sum a_n$, where

$$a_n = \frac{n^2 + 1}{2^n}.$$

Calculating the ratio, we have

$$\frac{a_{n+1}}{a_n} = \frac{(n+1)^2 + 1}{2^{n+1}} \cdot \frac{2^n}{n^2 + 1} = \frac{1}{2} \frac{n^2 + 2n + 2}{n^2 + 1} \to \frac{1}{2},$$

as $n \to \infty$. Thus by Theorem 19, $\sum a_n$ converges.

Example 17. Consider $\sum a_n$, where

$$a_n = \frac{1 \cdot 3 \cdot 5 \cdots (2n-1)}{n^3}.$$

The test ratio is

$$\frac{a_{n+1}}{a_n} = \frac{1 \cdot 3 \cdot 5 \cdots (2n-1)(2n+1)}{(n+1)^3} \frac{n^3}{1 \cdot 3 \cdot 5 \cdots (2n-1)}$$

$$= (2n+1)\left(\frac{n}{n+1}\right)^3 \to \infty,$$

as $n \to \infty$. The ratio test tells us the series $\sum a_n$ diverges.

Example 18. This example supports the assertion that Theorem 19 is weaker than Theorem 18. We consider $\sum a_n$, where

$$a_{2n-1} = \frac{3}{4^n}, \qquad a_{2n} = \frac{1}{4^n}.$$

There are, now, two different ratios:

$$\frac{a_{2n}}{a_{2n-1}} = \frac{1}{4^n} \cdot \frac{4^n}{3} = \frac{1}{3}$$

and

$$\frac{a_{2n+1}}{a_{2n}} = \frac{3}{4^{n+1}} \cdot \frac{4^n}{1} = \frac{3}{4}.$$

Clearly, the sequence $\left\{\dfrac{a_{n+1}}{a_n}\right\}$, having two cluster points, has no limit. As a consequence, Theorem 19 is not applicable. However, it is easy to see that, for every $n = 1, 2, 3, \ldots,$

$$\frac{a_{n+1}}{a_n} \leq \frac{3}{4} < 1.$$

By Theorem 18, then, the series converges.

EXERCISES

In numbers 1–24 test for convergence or divergence.

1. $\displaystyle\sum_{n=1}^{\infty} \frac{2^n}{(n^2+1)^n}.$

2. $\displaystyle\sum_{n=1}^{\infty} \frac{1}{n \cdot 2^n}.$

3. $\displaystyle\sum_{n=1}^{\infty} \frac{n^2}{n^3+1}.$

4. $\displaystyle\sum_{n=0}^{\infty} e^{-n^2}.$

5. $\displaystyle\sum_{n=0}^{\infty} \frac{\sin^2(2n+1)}{(2n+1)^2}.$

6. $\displaystyle\sum_{n=1}^{\infty} \frac{2 \cdot 4 \cdot 6 \cdots (2n)}{1 \cdot 3 \cdot 5 \cdots (2n-1)}.$

7. $\displaystyle\sum_{n=1}^{\infty} \frac{(n+2)(n+3)}{2 \cdot 4 \cdot 6 \cdots (2n)}.$

8. $\displaystyle\sum_{n=0}^{\infty} \frac{a^n}{n!}.$ (Does the size of a play a role?)

9. $\displaystyle\sum_{n=1}^{\infty} \frac{n!}{n^n}.$

10. $\displaystyle\sum_{n=1}^{\infty} \frac{n^{100}}{e^n}.$

11. $\displaystyle\sum_{n=0}^{\infty} \frac{4n+1}{3^n(2n+3)}.$

12. $\displaystyle\sum_{n=0}^{\infty} \frac{4n+1}{n!(2n+3)}.$

13. $\displaystyle\sum_{n=0}^{\infty} \frac{4n+1}{3^n \cdot n!(2n+3)}.$

14. $\displaystyle\sum_{n=0}^{\infty} \frac{(4n+1)2^n}{n!(2n+3)}.$

15. $\displaystyle\sum_{n=0}^{\infty} \frac{(4n+1)n!}{2^n(2n+3)}.$

16. $\displaystyle\sum_{n=0}^{\infty} \frac{4n+1}{2n+3}.$

17. $\displaystyle\sum_{n=0}^{\infty} \frac{4n+1}{(2n+3)^3}.$

18. $\displaystyle\sum_{n=1}^{\infty} \frac{n}{e^n}$.

19. $\displaystyle\sum_{n=1}^{\infty} e^{\sin n}$.

20. $\displaystyle\sum_{n=2}^{\infty} \frac{1}{(\log n)^n}$.

21. $\displaystyle\sum_{n=2}^{\infty} \frac{1}{(\log n)^{\log n}}$.

22. $\displaystyle\sum_{n=1}^{\infty} \frac{2^n}{n^2 \cdot 3^{n+1}}$.

23. $\displaystyle\sum_{n=1}^{\infty} \frac{n!}{10^{n+1}}$.

24. $\displaystyle\sum_{n=1}^{\infty} \frac{1 \cdot 3 \cdot 5 \cdots (2n-1)}{2 \cdot 4 \cdot 6 \cdots (2n)}$.

25. Test each of the following series for convergence or divergence.

(a) $\displaystyle\sum_{n=1}^{\infty} a_n$, where $a_{2n-1} = \dfrac{3}{5^n}$, $a_{2n} = \dfrac{2}{5^n}$.

(b) $\displaystyle\sum_{n=1}^{\infty} a_n$, where $a_{2n-1} = \dfrac{1}{3^n}$, $a_{2n} = \dfrac{1}{n}$.

26. Let $\sum a_n$ be a series shown to be convergent by the ratio test (Theorem 19). Show that $\sum_{n=1}^{\infty} n a_n$ is convergent.

27. There is a rather surprising theorem, due to Cauchy, which says that convergence or divergence of a series is determined by a relatively small proportion of the terms.

Cauchy's Condensation Theorem. *Let $\sum_{n=1}^{\infty} a_n$ be a series with the properties that, for all n, $a_n > 0$, $a_n \geq a_{n+1}$, and $\lim_{n \to \infty} a_n = 0$. Then $\sum_{n=1}^{\infty} a_n$ and*

$$\sum_{k=0}^{\infty} 2^k a_{2^k} = a_1 + 2a_2 + 4a_4 + 8a_8 + \cdots,$$

either both converge or both diverge.

Prove the theorem.

Hints.

(1) Let $s_n = \sum_{k=1}^{n} a_k$ and let t_k be the kth partial sum of the second series. Assume $n < 2^k$, write

$$s_n = a_1 + a_2 + a_3 + a_4 + a_5 + a_6 + a_7 + \cdots + a_n$$
$$< a_1 + (a_2 + a_3) + (a_4 + a_5 + a_6 + a_7) + \cdots + (a_{2^k} + \cdots + a_{2^{k+1}-1})$$
$$\leq a_1 + 2a_2 + 4a_4 + \cdots + 2^k a_{2^k}.$$

Thus, $n < 2^k \Rightarrow s_n < t_k$.

(2) Assume $n > 2^k$ and write

$$s_n = a_1 + a_2 + a_3 + a_4 + a_5 + \cdots + a_n$$
$$> a_1 + a_2 + (a_3 + a_4) + (a_5 + a_6 + a_7 + a_8) + \cdots + (a_{2^{k-1}+1} + \cdots + a_{2^k})$$
$$\geq \tfrac{1}{2}a_1 + \tfrac{1}{2}2a_2 + \tfrac{1}{4}4a_4 + \tfrac{1}{8}8a_8 \cdots + \tfrac{1}{2}2^k a_{2^k}.$$

Thus, if $n > 2^k$, then $2s_n > t_k$.

(3) From the result in (1), conclude that $\{t_k\}$ bounded $\Rightarrow \sum a_n$ converges. From the result in Hint (2) conclude that $\{s_n\}$ bounded $\Rightarrow \lim_{k \to \infty} t_k$ exists and the second series converges.

(4) Prove that if either series diverges so must the other diverge.

28. Use the Cauchy Condensation Theorem (Exercise 27) to show that each of the following series diverges.

(a) $\displaystyle\sum_{n=1}^{\infty} \frac{1}{n}$

(b) $\displaystyle\sum_{n=2}^{\infty} \frac{1}{n \log n}$.

15.6 Alternating Series

Next in simplicity after series all of whose terms are positive are those series which have alternately positive and negative terms.

Definition 4. *An **alternating series** is one which can be denoted by*

$$a_1 - a_2 + a_3 - a_4 + \cdots + (-1)^{n-1} a_n \pm \cdots,$$

where $a_n > 0$, all n.

There is a standard test, due to Leibniz, which provides a sufficient condition for the convergence of an alternating series.

Theorem 20. *If the alternating series*

$$a_1 - a_2 + a_3 - a_4 + \cdots + (-1)^n a_n + \cdots,$$

where $a_n > 0$, all n, satisfies

(i) $\lim_{n \to \infty} a_n = 0$

(ii) $a_n > a_{n+1}$

then the series converges.

Further, if we let the sum of the series be s, then $|s - s_n| < a_{n+1}$; i.e., the error in approximating s by the nth partial sum is less than the size of the first term not used.

Proof. We prove the convergence of the series by examining the even partial sums in two different ways. First of all,

$$\begin{aligned} s_{2n} &= a_1 - a_2 + a_3 - a_4 + \cdots + a_{2n-3} - a_{2n-2} + a_{2n-1} - a_{2n} \\ &= s_{2n-2} + (a_{2n-1} - a_{2n}) \\ &> s_{2n-2}, \end{aligned}$$

since $a_{2n-1} - a_{2n} > 0$, by hypothesis. In other words, the even partial sums form an increasing sequence.

Next,

$$s_{2n} = a_1 - (a_2 - a_3) - (a_4 - a_5) - \cdots - (a_{2n-2} - a_{2n-1}) - a_{2n}$$
$$< a_1,$$

since $(a_2 - a_3)$, $(a_4 - a_5)$, etc. are all positive. This says the increasing sequence of even partial sums is bounded. From Theorem 5 we conclude that the even partial sums form a convergent sequence. Let $\lim_{n \to \infty} s_{2n} = s$.

But the odd partial sums also converge to s; for

$$\lim_{n \to \infty} s_{2n+1} = \lim_{n \to \infty} (s_{2n} + a_{2n+1})$$

$$= \lim_{n \to \infty} s_{2n} + \lim_{n \to \infty} a_{2n+1}$$

$$= s + 0$$

$$= s,$$

by the result just obtained and by hypothesis (i). It follows, since the even and odd partial sums have the same limit s, that the series converges to s.

For the second assertion we observe that

$$|s - s_n| = a_{n+1} - a_{n+2} + a_{n+3} - \cdots$$
$$= a_{n+1} - (a_{n+2} - a_{n+3}) - (a_{n+4} - a_{n+5}) - \cdots$$
$$< a_{n+1},$$

since $(a_k - a_{k+1}) > 0$ for all k. ∎

(See Exercise 17 below for a slightly different approach to part of this proof.)

Example 19. As a simple illustration of an alternating series, consider

$$1 - \frac{1}{2} + \frac{1}{3} - \frac{1}{4} + \cdots + (-1)^{n-1} \frac{1}{n} + \cdots.$$

This is, of course, the harmonic series with the signs of the even-numbered terms changed. As $a_n = \frac{1}{n}$, we immediately see that $\lim_{n \to \infty} a_n = 0$ and that $a_n > a_{n+1}$. Thus, by Theorem 20, this series converges. As we shall see later, the sum $s = \log 2$. Also, still by the theorem,

$$\left| \log 2 - 1 + \frac{1}{2} - \frac{1}{3} + \cdots + (-1)^{n-1} \frac{1}{n} \right| < \frac{1}{n+1}.$$

Example 20. Test for convergence the series $\sum_{n=1}^{\infty} (-1)^{n-1} a_n$, where

$$a_n = \frac{n+1}{n^2 + 4n + 5}.$$

This is an alternating series, and it is obvious that $\lim_{n \to \infty} a_n = 0$. The verification of the monotonic property can be done either by showing that $a_n - a_{n+1} > 0$ or that $\dfrac{a_{n+1}}{a_n} < 1$— in the present case these amount to essentially the same algebraic steps. A third method, which often might be more efficient than the two just mentioned, is to choose f such that $f(n) = a_n$. In this case

$$f(x) = \frac{x+1}{x^2 + 4x + 5}.$$

If we can show that $x \geq 1 \Rightarrow f'(x) < 0$, then we know that f is decreasing, and $f(n) > f(n+1)$, or $a_n > a_{n+1}$, for all $n \in \mathbf{N}$.

For the function of this example, we immediately calculate that

$$f'(x) = \frac{-x^2 - 2x + 1}{(x^2 + 4x + 5)^2};$$

clearly $x \geq 1 \Rightarrow f'(x) < 0$. This shows that a_n is decreasing and $\sum_{n=1}^{\infty} (-1)^{n-1} a_n$ converges.

EXERCISES

In numbers 1–15 test the series for convergence or divergence.

1. $\displaystyle\sum_{n=1}^{\infty} \frac{(-1)^{n-1}}{3n+1}$.

2. $\displaystyle\sum_{n=1}^{\infty} \frac{(-1)^{n-1}}{\sqrt{n}}$.

3. $1 - \dfrac{1}{3} + \dfrac{1}{5} - \dfrac{1}{7} + \cdots$.

4. $\displaystyle\sum_{n=1}^{\infty} \frac{(-1)^{n+1}(n+2)}{n^2 + 3n + 8}$.

5. $\displaystyle\sum_{n=2}^{\infty} \frac{(-1)^n 3}{\log n}$.

6. $\displaystyle\sum_{n=0}^{\infty} \frac{(-1)^n}{n!}$.

7. $\displaystyle\sum_{n=1}^{\infty} \frac{(-1)^{n-1}(2n-1)}{4n+7}$.

8. $\displaystyle\sum_{n=2}^{\infty} \frac{(-1)^n \log n}{n}$.

9. $\displaystyle\sum_{n=1}^{\infty} \frac{(-1)^{n+1}(n+1)}{2n+7}$.

10. $\displaystyle\sum_{n=2}^{\infty} \frac{(-1)^n n}{\log n}$.

11. $\displaystyle\sum_{n=1}^{\infty} \frac{(-1)^{n-1} 10^n}{n!}$.

12. $\displaystyle\sum_{n=0}^{\infty} \frac{(-1)^n}{n+3^n}$.

13. $\displaystyle\sum_{n=0}^{\infty} \frac{(-1)^n}{n+(\frac{1}{3})^n}$.

14. $1 - \dfrac{1}{3!} + \dfrac{1}{5!} - \dfrac{1}{7!} + \cdots$.

15. $\displaystyle\sum_{n=1}^{\infty} \frac{(-1)^{n+1}\sqrt{n}}{n+3}$.

16. Consider the series $\sum_{n=1}^{\infty} (-1)^{n-1} a_n$, where

$$a_n = \frac{2 - \cos n\pi}{n}.$$

(a) Are the hypotheses of Theorem 20 satisfied?

(b) Is $\sum_{n=1}^{\infty} (-1)^n a_n$ convergent or divergent? Why?

17. This refers to the proof of Theorem 20.

(a) Show that, for all n, $s_{2n+1} < s_{2n-1}$; thus the odd partial sums form a decreasing sequence.

(b) Show that, for all n, $s_{2n+1} > s_2$.

(c) From the results of (a) and (b) show that $\lim_{n \to \infty} s_{2n+1}$ exists, $\lim_{n \to \infty} s_{2n+1} = t$, say.

(d) Show that $t = s$. [*Hint.* Use Hypothesis (i).]

(e) Show that all odd partial sums lie above s, all even partial sums lie below s.

(f) Show that, for any partial sum s_n, $|s - s_n| < |s_n - s_{n+1}| = a_{n+1}$.

15.7 Absolute and Conditional Convergence

In order to handle satisfactorily series which have negative terms but which are not alternating series we introduce the concept of *absolute convergence*.

Definition 5. *The series $\sum a_n$ converges absolutely, or is absolutely convergent $\Leftrightarrow$ the series $\sum |a_n|$ converges.*

It is a triviality that every convergent series of positive terms is absolutely convergent. One would also expect that an absolutely convergent series is convergent. This is true, but it is not trivial.

Theorem 21. *If $\sum a_n$ is absolutely convergent, then $\sum a_n$ is convergent. In symbols,*

$$\sum |a_n| \text{ converges} \Rightarrow \sum a_n \text{ converges}.$$

Moreover, if $\sum |a_n| = t$, $\sum a_n = s$, then $|s| \leq t$.

Proof. The first assertion can be proven in several ways. We shall draw on Theorem 6, the CCC, using it in both directions in the course of our argument.
  Let

$$s_n = \sum_{k=1}^{n} a_k, \qquad t_n = \sum_{k=1}^{n} |a_k|.$$

The hypothesis that $\sum |a_n|$ converges $\Rightarrow \lim_{n \to \infty} t_n = t$, say. By Theorem 6, then, if $\varepsilon > 0$ is arbitrary $\exists n_\varepsilon$ such that $n > m > n_\varepsilon \Rightarrow |t_n - t_m| < \varepsilon$, i.e.,

$$|a_{m+1}| + \cdots + |a_n| < \varepsilon.$$

But

$$|s_n - s_m| = |a_{m+1} + \cdots + a_n| \leq |a_{m+1}| + \cdots + |a_n|,$$

so $n > m > n_\varepsilon \Rightarrow$

$$|s_n - s_m| < \varepsilon.$$

Thus by Theorem 6, $\lim_{n \to \infty} s_n$ exists, $= s$, say, and $\sum a_n$ converges.

For the second assertion we note that

$$s_n \le t_n < t \Rightarrow s \le t.$$

Also, since $|a_k| = |-a_k|$,

$$-s_n = \sum_{k=1}^{n} (-a_k) \le t_n < t \Rightarrow -s \le t,$$

or $s \ge -t$. Thus s satisfies $-t \le s \le t$, or

$$|s| \le t. \quad \blacksquare$$

The converse of Theorem 21 is not true: a series can converge but not converge absolutely. The standard example is the alternating series

$$1 - \frac{1}{2} + \frac{1}{3} - \frac{1}{4} + \cdots + (-n)^{n+1} \frac{1}{n} + \cdots,$$

which we know converges; but its series of absolute values is the divergent harmonic series $\sum_{n=1}^{\infty} \frac{1}{n}$. This is an example of a *conditionally convergent series*.

Definition 6. *A series which converges but does not converge absolutely is* ***conditionally convergent***.

Roughly speaking, an absolutely convergent series converges because of the small size of the terms; for a conditionally convergent series, however, the size alone of the terms is not sufficient to guarantee convergence (even so, $\lim_{n \to \infty} a_n = 0$, by Theorem 8), which is due to a proper balance between the positive and negative terms of the series.

We shall try to make clear the fundamental distinction between absolutely convergent and conditionally convergent series in the following way. Let $\sum a_n$ be a series with both positive and negative terms. Define

$$\begin{cases} p_n = a_n, & \text{if } a_n \ge 0 \\ p_n = 0, & \text{if } a_n < 0 \end{cases}, \qquad \begin{cases} q_n = 0, & \text{if } a_n \ge 0 \\ q_n = -a_n, & \text{if } a_n < 0 \end{cases}.$$

(Note that $p_n \ge 0, q_n \ge 0$). Then

$$s_n = \sum_{k=1}^{n} a_k = \sum_{k=1}^{n} p_k - \sum_{k=1}^{n} q_k = u_n - v_n$$

(note that $\{u_n\}$ and $\{v_n\}$ are monotonic increasing sequences).

Now suppose $\sum a_n$ is absolutely convergent, i.e., suppose $\sum |a_k|$ converges to t, say. Then

$$t_n = \sum_{k=1}^{n} |a_k| = u_n + v_n < t.$$

It follows that the sequences $\{u_n\}$ and $\{v_n\}$ both converge, which is to say the two series

$$\sum p_k \quad \text{and} \quad \sum q_k,$$

the series of positive and negative terms, both converge: *If a_n converges absolutely then the series of positive terms and the series of negative terms both converge, to p and q, respectively, say, and $t = p + q$, $s = p - q$.* (Notice that this argument provides an alternate proof of Theorem 21.)

If, on the other hand, $\sum a_n$ converges conditionally, then both the sequences $\{u_n\}$ and $\{v_n\}$ must diverge. For, if they both converged, to p and q, respectively, say, then $\sum a_n$ would converge absolutely (to $p + q$); whereas, if $\{u_n\}$ converged and $\{v_n\}$ diverged, then

$$s_n = u_n - v_n \to -\infty$$

as $n \to \infty$, contrary to the assumption that $\sum a_n$ converges. Similarly, $s_n \to \infty$ if $\{u_n\}$ is assumed to diverge and $\{v_n\}$ converges. In summary, the positive and negative parts of a conditionally convergent series both consist of divergent series.

This distinction between the series of the two types can be made startlingly dramatic by mentioning the idea of a rearrangement of a series.

Definition 7. *The series $\sum b_k$ is a **rearrangement** of $\sum a_k \Leftrightarrow$ every a_n occurs exactly once as a b_m and every b_m occurs exactly once as an a_n.*

We now state, without proof, an important property of absolutely convergent series.

Theorem 22. *If $\sum a_n$ converges absolutely, $\sum a_n = s$, then every rearrangement of $\sum a_n$ also converges absolutely and has the same sum s.*

In contrast to this eminently satisfactory behavior of absolutely convergent series, consider the following assertion about conditionally convergent series. If $\sum a_n$ converges conditionally, then, by a suitable rearrangement, it can be made to converge to *any* preassigned number or to diverge to ∞ or to diverge to $-\infty$. The supporting argument is in part as follows; it uses the fact that the series of positive terms and of negative terms both diverge for a conditionally convergent series. Let $s_0 \in \mathbf{R}$ be arbitrary; to be definite, suppose $s_0 > 0$. Pick enough positive terms p_n from $\sum a_n$ so that the partial sum u_n just exceeds s_0 ; now, pick enough of the negative terms $-q_n$ so that the new partial sum $u_n - v_n$ is just less than s_0 ("just" means that including one less negative term would produce a partial sum greater than s_0). Proceeding in this way, one obtains a rearrangement of $\sum a_n$ which will indeed converge to s_0 (recall that $\sum a_n$ converges $\Rightarrow \lim_{n \to \infty} a_n = 0$).

It is worth remarking that absolutely convergent series combine linearly, as do convergent series. More exactly, we make the following assertion.

Theorem 23. *If $\sum a_n$ and $\sum b_n$ converge absolutely, then $\sum (a_n + b_n)$ and $\sum c a_n$ converge absolutely. Here $c \in \mathbf{R}$ is arbitrary.*

Proof. Exercise for student. ∎

Probably the most convenient test for absolute convergence is the ratio test, properly rephrased. Here it is.

Theorem 19a (***Ratio Test for Absolute Convergence***). *Let* $\sum a_n$ *be a series and let*

$$\lim_{n \to \infty} \left| \frac{a_{n+1}}{a_n} \right| = k.$$

(i) *If* $0 \le k < 1$, $\sum a_n$ *converges absolutely.*
(ii) *If* $k > 1$, $\sum a_n$ *diverges.*
(iii) *If* $k = 1$, *the test fails.*

Statement (i) follows from the definition of absolute convergence and the proof of Theorem 19 for series of positive terms. Statement (ii) results, as before, from the fact that when $k > 1$ it is not possible for $\lim_{n \to \infty} a_n = 0$. No further remarks about the proof are necessary. ∎

Example 21. We test the series

$$\sum_{n=1}^{\infty} \frac{(-1)^n n(n + 2)}{3^n}$$

for absolute convergence.
   Using the ratio test, we have

$$\left| \frac{a_{n+1}}{a_n} \right| = \frac{(n + 1)(n + 3)}{3^{n+1}} \cdot \frac{3^n}{n(n + 2)} = \frac{1}{3} \frac{(n + 1)(n + 3)}{n(n + 2)} \to \frac{1}{3}$$

as $n \to \infty$. By Theorem 19a, the series converges absolutely.

Example 22. Find the values of x for which the series

$$\sum_{n=1}^{\infty} \frac{(-1)^{n-1} x^n}{n}$$

converges absolutely.
   The ratio is

$$\left| \frac{a_{n+1}}{a_n} \right| = \left| \frac{x^{n+1}}{n + 1} \cdot \frac{n}{x^n} \right| = \frac{n}{n + 1} |x| \to |x|,$$

as $n \to \infty$. By Theorem 19a, the series converges absolutely for all x such that $|x| < 1$; the series diverges for x with $|x| > 1$; and the test gives no information for $x = 1$ and $x = -1$.
   However, considering these values separately, we find that for $x = 1$ the series becomes

$$1 - \tfrac{1}{2} + \tfrac{1}{3} - \tfrac{1}{4} + \cdots,$$

which we have already seen to be conditionally convergent. For $x = -1$, the series is

$$-1 - \tfrac{1}{2} - \tfrac{1}{3} - \tfrac{1}{4} - \cdots,$$

the negative of the divergent harmonic series—hence divergent.

In summary, the series converges absolutely for x such that $|x| < 1$, converges conditionally for $x = 1$, and diverges for all other x.

If the ratio test fails, then a suitable version of the comparison test may produce success.

Example 23. Test for absolute convergence the series

$$\sum_{n=1}^{\infty} \frac{(-1)^{n-1}(n+1)}{n^3 + 4}.$$

We try first the ratio test:

$$\left| \frac{a_{n+1}}{a_n} \right| = \frac{n+2}{(n+1)^3 + 4} \frac{n^3 + 4}{n+1} = \frac{n+2}{n+1} \cdot \frac{n^3 + 4}{(n+1)^3 + 1} \to 1,$$

as $n \to \infty$. The test fails.

We notice, however, that

$$|a_n| = \frac{n+1}{n^3 + 4},$$

which is essentially the same as $\dfrac{1}{n^2}$. Thus we let $b_n = \dfrac{1}{n^2}$ and use Theorem 13:

$$\frac{|a_n|}{b_n} = \frac{n^3 + n^2}{n^3 + 4} \to 1,$$

as $n \to \infty$. Since $\sum_{n=1}^{\infty} \dfrac{1}{n^2}$ converges ($p = 2 > 1$), Theorem 13 assures us that $\sum |a_n|$ converges, or $\sum a_n$ converges absolutely.

EXERCISES

In Exercises 1–18 test for absolute convergence.

1. $\displaystyle\sum_{n=1}^{\infty} \frac{(-1)^{n-1} n}{2^n}$.

2. $\displaystyle\sum_{n=1}^{\infty} \frac{(-1)^{n+1}(n^2 + 2)}{n^4 + 1}$.

3. $\displaystyle\sum_{n=1}^{\infty} \frac{(-1)^{3n-1}(3n - 1)}{n^2 + 1}$.

4. $\displaystyle\sum_{n=0}^{\infty} \frac{2 + 3(-1)^n}{n^2 + 4}$.

5. $\displaystyle\sum_{n=0}^{\infty} (-1)^n \frac{10^{2n+1}}{(2n+1)!}$.

6. $\displaystyle\sum_{n=0}^{\infty} \frac{(-100)^{2n+1}}{(2n+1)!}$.

7. $\sum\limits_{n=1}^{\infty} \dfrac{(-1)^{4n-3}(3n+1)}{n^3+7}$.

8. $\sum\limits_{n=1}^{\infty} \dfrac{(-1)^{4n-3}(3n+1)}{n^2+7}$.

9. $\sum\limits_{n=0}^{\infty} (-1) \dfrac{(20)^{2n}}{(2n)!}$.

10. $\sum\limits_{n=0}^{\infty} \dfrac{(-2000)^{2n}}{(2n)!}$.

11. $\sum\limits_{n=2}^{\infty} \dfrac{(-1)^n \log n}{n}$.

12. $\sum\limits_{n=2}^{\infty} \dfrac{(-1)^n \log n}{n^2}$.

13. $\sum\limits_{n=2}^{\infty} \dfrac{(-1)^n}{n \log n}$.

14. $\sum\limits_{n=0}^{\infty} \dfrac{(-1)^n(n+2)^2 2^n}{n!}$.

15. $\sum\limits_{n=0}^{\infty} (-1)^n e^{-2n}$.

16. $\sum\limits_{n=0}^{\infty} \dfrac{(-1)^n(n+1)3^n}{2^n n!}$.

17. $\sum\limits_{n=0}^{\infty} \dfrac{(-1)^{3n-2}n^2}{3^n}$.

18. $\sum\limits_{n=0}^{\infty} (-1)^n \dfrac{n^n}{n!}$.

In numbers 19–24 find the values of x for which each series converges absolutely.

19. $\sum\limits_{n=0}^{\infty} (-1)^n \dfrac{x^{2n+1}}{(2n+1)!}$.

20. $\sum\limits_{n=0}^{\infty} \dfrac{x^n}{n!}$.

21. $\sum\limits_{n=1}^{\infty} \dfrac{x^n}{2n-1}$.

22. $\sum\limits_{n=1}^{\infty} \dfrac{x^n}{2^n \cdot n}$.

23. $\sum\limits_{n=1}^{\infty} (-1)^{n-1} \dfrac{(2x)^n}{3n-2}$.

24. $\sum\limits_{n=0}^{\infty} (-1)^n \dfrac{x^{2n}}{(2n!)}$.

25. Prove Theorem 23.

26. Suppose $\sum_{n=1}^{\infty} a_n$ converges absolutely; let $\{c_n\}$ be a bounded sequence. Prove that $\sum_{n=1}^{\infty} c_n a_n$ converges absolutely.

15.8 Power Series

The next natural step after the study of series whose terms are constants would be the consideration of series whose terms are functions. Clearly, such a project could keep us occupied for an unduly long time unless we limit its scope in some way. We do this by restricting ourselves to the study of *power series*, which involve functions of an especially simple sort.

The general form of a power series is

$$\sum_{n=0}^{\infty} a_n(y-c)^n, \tag{27}$$

where $c \in \mathbf{R}$. This is called a series *about* c. It is easy to see that by a substitution such as $x = y - c$, we can transform the series (27) to

$$\sum_{n=0}^{\infty} a_n x^n, \tag{28}$$

a series about $x = 0$. As a consequence we shall limit ourselves to series such as in (28). From the form of either (27) or (28) we note that a power series is a generalization of a polynomial.

[Next in importance after power series in the general study of series of functions are the *trigonometric series*, whose terms involve the sine or cosine functions. These are especially important in applications. The theory, however, is somewhat more difficult than that of power series, and the study should properly be postponed a bit.]

The first problem which presents itself in connection with power series is the determination of the set of values of x for which the series converges. Obviously, every power series $\sum_{n=0}^{\infty} a_n x^n$ converges for $x = 0$—and there are some, $\sum_{n=0}^{\infty} n! \, x^n$ is one such, which converge for no other value of x. At the other extreme, there are series which converge for *every* value of x; example $\sum_{n=0}^{\infty} \dfrac{x^n}{n!}$. And, as would be anticipated, there are series which converge for more than one value of x, but not for all. The situation, as will be seen shortly, is an exceedingly well-behaved one. As our starting point, we have the following assertion.

Theorem 24. (i) *If a power series $\sum_{n=0}^{\infty} a_n x^n$ converges for $x = x_0$, then it also converges (absolutely) for every x satisfying $|x| < |x_0|$.*

(ii) *On the other hand, if $\sum_{n=0}^{\infty} a_n x^n$ diverges for $x = x_1$, then it diverges for every x such that $|x| > |x_1|$.*

Proof. To prove (i) we have as hypothesis that $\sum_{n=0}^{\infty} a_n x_0^n$ converges. From this we know (Theorem 8) that $\lim_{n \to \infty} a_n x_0^n = 0$. This, in turn, implies (Theorem 2) that the terms of the sequence $\{a_n x_0^n\}$ are bounded, i.e., $\exists M > 0$ such that, for all $n \in \mathbf{N}$, $|a_n x_0^n| < M$. Now let k be any number satisfying $0 < k < 1$ and let x be such that $|x| \leq k |x_0|$. Then, for all n,

$$|a_n x^n| \leq |a_n k^n x_0^n| < M k^n.$$

Since the geometric series $\sum_{n=0}^{\infty} M k^n$, $0 < k < 1$, converges, so does the series $\sum_{n=0}^{\infty} |a_n x^n|$; thus $\sum_{n=0}^{\infty} a_n x^n$ converges absolutely.

(ii) If x_1 is a number such that $\sum_{n=0}^{\infty} a_n x^n$ diverges and if x is such that $|x| > |x_1|$, then $\sum_{n=0}^{\infty} a_n x^n$ must also diverge. For otherwise, by part (i) of this theorem $\sum_{n=0}^{\infty} a_n x_1^n$ would converge. ∎

Now the import of Theorem 24 is this: if the power series $\sum_{n=0}^{\infty} a_n x^n$ converges for some $x_0 \neq 0$ then there must exist an *interval*, $|x| < r$, within which the series converges and outside of which ($|x| > r$) the series diverges. It is not possible to say in general how the series behaves at $x = \pm r$ (examples can easily be given illustrating all four possibilities).

The number r is called the *radius of convergence* (for power series involving complex numbers, the "interval" of convergence becomes the interior of a circle—hence "radius," the more general term being used in both the complex and real cases). Clearly $r = \text{lub } |x|$, taken over the set of values x for which the series converges. If $\sum_{n=0}^{\infty} a_n x^n$ converges for all $x \in \mathbf{R}$, we write $r = \infty$; if the series converges only for $x = 0$, we write $r = 0$.

The radius of convergence can usually be found quite easily by means of the ratio test (Theorem 19a). If the reader would consult Example 22 in the previous section he will see that what was done there, in fact, was to determine that for

$$\sum_{n=1}^{\infty} \frac{(-1)^{n-1} x^n}{n}$$

the radius of convergence is $r = 1$. And Exercises 19 through 24 were really asking for the radius of convergence of the given power series.

Example 24. Consider the series mentioned earlier,

$$\sum_{n=0}^{\infty} n! \, x^n,$$

The ratio test gives

$$\left| \frac{(n+1)! \, x^{n+1}}{n! \, x^n} \right| = (n+1)|x| \to \infty,$$

as $n \to \infty$, independently of x: this series converges only for $x = 0$. Thus $r = 0$.

Example 25. At the other extreme, we have

$$\sum_{n=0}^{\infty} \frac{x^n}{n!}.$$

Now the ratio test leads to

$$\left| \frac{x^{n+1}}{(n+1)!} \cdot \frac{n!}{x^n} \right| = \frac{|x|}{n+1} \to 0,$$

as $n \to \infty$, irrespective of the size of x. In this case $r = \infty$; this series converges for all $x \in \mathbf{R}$.

Example 26. Find the values for which the series

$$\sum_{n=0}^{\infty} \frac{(-1)^n x^n}{(2n+1)^2 2^n}$$

converges.

Applying the ratio test, we find

$$\left| \frac{x^{n+1}}{(2n+3)^2 2^{n+1}} \cdot \frac{(2n+1)^2 2^n}{x^n} \right| = \frac{1}{2} \left(\frac{2n+1}{2n+3} \right)^2 |x| \to \tfrac{1}{2} |x|,$$

as $n \to \infty$. Using Theorem 19a, we find that convergence occurs for $|x| < 2$, divergence for $|x| > 2$; thus $r = 2$. The points $x = \pm 2$ must be considered separately.

If $x = 2$, the series becomes

$$\sum_{n=0}^{\infty} \frac{(-1)^n}{(2n+1)^2}.$$

Using $b_n = \frac{1}{n^2}$ and Theorem 13 we easily see that this series converges absolutely

(or, one can obtain convergence by using the alternating series theorem).

For $x = -2$, we get

$$\sum_{n=0}^{\infty} \frac{1}{(2n+1)^2}$$

which, as explained in the preceding paragraph, can be shown to converge by Theorem 13 with $b_n = \frac{1}{n^2}$.

Power series can be combined arithmetically, provided we stay within the intervals of convergence. To be exact, suppose $\sum_{n=0}^{\infty} a_n x^n$ and $\sum_{n=0}^{\infty} b_n x^n$ are two power series with radii of convergence r_1 and r_2, respectively. Let $c \in \mathbf{R}$. Then we assert (without proof, however) that

$$\sum_{n=0}^{\infty} a_n x^n + \sum_{n=0}^{\infty} b_n x^n = \sum_{n=0}^{\infty} (a_n + b_n) x^n \tag{29}$$

$$c \sum_{n=0}^{\infty} a_n x^n = \sum_{n=0}^{\infty} (c a_n) x^n \tag{30}$$

$$\left(\sum_{n=0}^{\infty} a_n x^n \right) \left(\sum_{n=0}^{\infty} b_n x^n \right) = \sum_{n=0}^{\infty} c_n x^n, \tag{31}$$

where, in (31)

$$c_n = \sum_{k=0}^{n} a_k b_{n-k}. \tag{32}$$

In the case of the sum and the product the radius $r = \min(r_1, r_2)$.

It should be pointed out that the description in (32) of the coefficients of the product is the "natural" one; for if we assumed we could multiply the two series as though they were polynomials we would find

$b_0 + b_1 x + b_2 x^2 + b_3 x^3 + \cdots$
$a_0 + a_1 x + a_2 x^2 + a_3 x^3 + \cdots$

$a_0 b_0 + (a_0 b_1 + a_1 b_0)x + (a_0 b_2 + a_1 b_1 + a_2 b_0)x^2$
$\qquad\qquad + (a_0 b_3 + a_1 b_2 + a_2 b_1 + a_3 b_0)x^3 + \cdots,$

as prescribed in (32). This is usually called the *Cauchy product*.

Example 27. We illustrate the preceding technique for multiplying two power series:

$$\sum_{k=0}^{\infty} b_k x^{2k+1} = x - \frac{x^3}{3!} + \frac{x^5}{5!} - \frac{x^7}{7!} + \cdots$$

$$\sum_{k=0}^{\infty} a_k x^{2k} = 1 - \frac{x^2}{2!} + \frac{x^4}{4!} - \frac{x^6}{6!} + \cdots$$

$$x - \frac{x^3}{3!} + \frac{x^5}{5!} - \frac{x^7}{7!} + \cdots$$

$$\qquad - \frac{x^3}{2!} + \frac{x^5}{3!2!} - \frac{x^7}{5!2!} + \cdots$$

$$\qquad\qquad + \frac{x^5}{1!4!} - \frac{x^7}{3!4!} + \cdots$$

$$\qquad\qquad\qquad - \frac{x^7}{1!6!} + \cdots$$

$$= x - \left(\frac{1}{3!} + \frac{1}{1!2!} \right) x^3 + \left(\frac{1}{5!} + \frac{1}{3!2!} + \frac{1}{1!4!} \right) x^5$$

$$\qquad - \left(\frac{1}{7!} + \frac{1}{5!2!} + \frac{1}{3!4!} + \frac{1}{1!6!} \right) x^7 + \cdots$$

$$= x - 4\frac{x^3}{3!} + 16\frac{x^5}{5!} - 64\frac{x^7}{7!} + \cdots$$

$$= \frac{1}{2} \left[(2x) - \frac{(2x)^3}{3!} + \frac{(2x)^5}{5!} - \frac{(2x)^7}{7!} + \cdots \right].$$

Notice that, at least as far as written, the expression in the brackets is the same as the first of the two series but with $2x$ instead of x. We now show, using (32), that this relation does indeed hold throughout.

The coefficients of the kth ($k = 0, 1, 2, \ldots$) term of the two series can be written as

$$a_k = \frac{(-1)^k}{(2k)!} \quad \text{and} \quad b_k = \frac{(-1)^k}{(2k+1)!}.$$

Thus

$$a_k b_{n-k} = \frac{(-1)^k}{(2k)!} \frac{(-1)^{n-k}}{(2n-2k+1)!} = \frac{(-1)^n}{(2k)!(2n-2k+1)!}.$$

From (32), then, we have

$$c_n = \sum_{k=0}^{n} a_k b_{n-k} = (-1)^n \sum_{k=0}^{n} \frac{1}{(2k)!(2n-2k+1)!}.$$

We multiply this expression by $\dfrac{(2n+1)!}{(2n+1)!}$ to get

$$c_n = (-1)^n \frac{1}{(2n+1)!} \sum_{k=0}^{n} \frac{(2n+1)!}{(2k)!(2n+1-2k)!}.$$

Now every term in the summation is in the form of a binomial coefficient; in fact, the general term is the binomial coefficient $\dbinom{2n+1}{2k}$. This means

$$c_n = \frac{(-1)^n}{(2n+1)!} \sum_{k=0}^{n} \binom{2n+1}{2k}.$$

This sum can be evaluated by drawing on results from Exercise (7a) and 7(b) after Section 1.5. These say that

$$\sum_{k=0}^{m} \binom{m}{k} = 2^m,$$

$$\sum_{k=0}^{m} (-1)^k \binom{m}{k} = 0.$$

We use these identities with $m = 2n + 1$, writing out some of the terms,

$$\sum_{k=0}^{2n+1} \binom{2n+1}{k} = \binom{2n+1}{0} + \binom{2n+1}{1} + \binom{2n+1}{2}$$

$$+ \cdots + \binom{2n+1}{2n} + \binom{2n+1}{2n+1} = 2^{2n+1}$$

$$\sum_{k=0}^{2n+1} (-1)^k \binom{2n+1}{k} = \binom{2n+1}{0} - \binom{2n+1}{1}$$

$$+ \binom{2n+1}{2} - \cdots + \binom{2n+1}{2n} - \binom{2n+1}{2n+1} = 0.$$

It is clear that adding the two equations produces on the left twice the sum appearing in the above expression for c_n:

$$2\left[\binom{2n+1}{0} + \binom{2n+1}{2} + \cdots + \binom{2n+1}{2n} \right] = 2^{n+1}.$$

Thus

$$\sum_{k=0}^{n} \binom{2n+1}{2k} = 2^{2n},$$

from which it follows that

$$c_n = \frac{(-1)^n 2^{2n}}{(2n+1)!} = \frac{1}{2} \frac{(-1)^n 2^{2n+1}}{(2n+1)!}.$$

The previous assertion about the form of the product series has been shown to be valid for all n:

$$\left(\sum_{k=0}^{\infty} a_k x^{2k}\right)\left(\sum_{k=0}^{\infty} b_k x^{2k+1}\right)$$

$$= \frac{1}{2}\left[(2x) - \frac{(2x)^3}{3!} + \frac{(2x)^5}{5!} - \frac{(2x)^7}{7!} + \cdots\right] = \frac{1}{2}\sum_{n=0}^{\infty}(-1)^n \frac{(2x)^{2n+1}}{(2n+1)!}.$$

In Exercises 19 and 24 after the preceding section, we asked you to show that the two original series converge for all x; as a result, the product series also converges for all x. The fact is, as we shall soon see, that the series of odd powers represents $\sin x$, the series of even powers $\cos x$. This means that we have proved the identity $\sin x \cos x = \frac{1}{2}\sin 2x$.

EXERCISES

In each of numbers 1–24 find the interval of convergence. Be sure to determine the behavior of the series at the endpoints.

1. $\displaystyle\sum_{n=0}^{\infty} x^n.$

2. $\displaystyle\sum_{n=0}^{\infty} \frac{x^n}{(n+1)3^{n+1}}.$

3. $\displaystyle\sum_{n=0}^{\infty} \frac{(n+1)x^{2n+1}}{(n+2)^2}.$

4. $\displaystyle\sum_{n=1}^{\infty} \frac{(-1)^{n-1}x^n}{2n-1}.$

5. $\displaystyle\sum_{n=1}^{\infty} \frac{(-1)^{n-1}x^n}{(2n-1)(2n)(2n+1)}.$

6. $\displaystyle\sum_{n=0}^{\infty} \frac{n!\, x^n}{(2n+1)^2}.$

7. $\displaystyle\sum_{n=0}^{\infty} \frac{x^{2n}}{(2n)!}.$

8. $\displaystyle\sum_{n=1}^{\infty} \frac{n^2(x-2)^n}{n+1}.$

9. $\displaystyle\sum_{n=0}^{\infty} \frac{3^n x^n}{(2n+1)^2}.$

10. $\displaystyle\sum_{n=0}^{\infty} \frac{(-1)^n x^n}{2^{n+1}}.$

11. $\displaystyle\sum_{n=0}^{\infty} \frac{(-1)^n(2n+1)x^{2n}}{3^n}.$

12. $\displaystyle\sum_{n=0}^{\infty} \frac{(-1)^n(x+3)^n}{2^n(2n+1)^2}.$

13. $\displaystyle\sum_{n=2}^{\infty} \frac{x^n}{\log n}.$

14. $\displaystyle\sum_{n=0}^{\infty} \frac{nx^n}{(n+1)(n+2)3^n}.$

15. $\displaystyle\sum_{n=0}^{\infty} \frac{(2x-1)^n}{4^n}.$

16. $\displaystyle\sum_{n=0}^{\infty} \frac{x^n}{2^n\sqrt{n+2}}.$

17. $\displaystyle\sum_{n=2}^{\infty} \frac{(-1)^n x^n}{n \log n}.$

18. $\displaystyle\sum_{n=0}^{\infty} \frac{(-1)^n(x-2)^n}{(n+1)^2}.$

19. $\sum_{n=0}^{\infty} (-1)^n n^n x^n$.

20. $\sum_{n=0}^{\infty} \frac{(2x)^n}{3^{n+1}}$.

21. $\sum_{n=0}^{\infty} \frac{4^n x^n}{n!}$.

22. $\sum_{n=0}^{\infty} \frac{(n+1)(2n-1)x^n}{2^{n+1}}$.

23. $\sum_{n=0}^{\infty} \frac{(-1)^n x^{2n+1}}{n+1}$.

24. $\sum_{n=0}^{\infty} \frac{n(x+2)^n}{(2n+1)^2}$.

25. Suppose that for the power series $\sum_{n=0}^{\infty} a_n x^n$ it is true that $\lim_{n \to \infty} \sqrt[n]{|a_n|} = k$. Show that

the radius of convergence of the series is $r = \frac{1}{k}$.

26. (a) Find the radius of convergence of each of the series

$$\sum_{n=0}^{\infty} x^n \quad \text{and} \quad \sum_{n=0}^{\infty} (-1)^n x^n.$$

(b) Find the sum of the two series.

(c) Find the product of the two series.

(d) What is the radius of convergence of each of the series found in (b) and (c)?

27. Find the product of the two series

$$\sum_{n=0}^{\infty} \frac{x^n}{n!} \quad \text{and} \quad \sum_{n=0}^{\infty} (-1)^n \frac{x^n}{n!}.$$

[*Hint.* Use Exercise 7(b) after Section 1.5. Do not overlook c_0.]

15.9 Differentiation and Integration of Power Series

It is clear that every power series represents a function defined for all x in the interval of convergence.

$$\sum_{n=0}^{\infty} a_n x^n = f(x), \qquad x \in (-r, r).$$

This observation naturally raises questions about continuity, differentiability, and integrability of f. In particular, if we recall that polynomials (finite power series) are continuous, differentiable, and integrable everywhere in **R**, we might have some hope that the same is true of power series. And the same *is* true of power series, provided we stay within the interval of convergence. More precisely, we have the following assertions.

Theorem 25. *Suppose the power series* $\sum_{n=0}^{\infty} a_n x^n = f(x)$ *for x in the interval of convergence* $(-r, r)$. *Then f is continuous in* $(-r, r)$.

Theorem 26. *Let the power series $\sum_{n=0}^{\infty} a_n x^n = f(x)$ have radius of convergence r, and let $[a, x]$ be a closed interval contained within $(-r, r)$. Then the series is integrable term by term over $[a, x]$,* i.e.,

$$\int_a^x f(t)\, dt = \int_a^x \sum_{n=0}^{\infty} a_n t^n\, dt = \sum_{n=0}^{\infty} \int_a^x a_n t^n\, dt.$$

Theorem 27. *If the power series $\sum_{n=0}^{\infty} a_n x^n = f(x)$ has radius of convergence r, then for $x \in (-r, r)$,*

$$f'(x) = \sum_{n=1}^{\infty} n a_n x^{n-1};$$

in other words, the power series can be differentiated term by term within its radius of convergence, and the resulting series converges to the derivative of the function defined by the original series.

The proofs of these three theorems can be given strictly in terms of power series. However, the concept underlying all three assertions is that of *uniform convergence over the interval of convergence.* The basic idea of uniform convergence over an interval is this: Given a series of functions a_n, convergent to some function f on an interval $[a, b]$, it is required, to establish convergence at $x_0 \in [a, b]$, to show the existence of n_0 such that $n > n_0 \Rightarrow |f(x_0) - \sum_{k=0}^{n} a_k(x_0)| < \varepsilon$. In general the n_0 will depend upon *both* ε and x_0. *If*, however, an n_0 can be found, independent of x_0, such that $n > n_0 \Rightarrow$

$$\left| f(x) - \sum_{k=0}^{n} a_k(x) \right| < \varepsilon$$

holds for *every* $x \in [a, b]$, then the series converges *uniformly* on $[a, b]$. And, series, such as power series, which converge uniformly on an interval are well behaved there, i.e., they have the desired continuity and integrability properties, provided the terms of the series have these properties. Certainly the individual terms, $a_n x^n$, of power series are continuous and integrable within the interval of convergence; thus, from the preceding discussion we can conclude that the power series also have these properties. Differentiability poses a slightly more difficult problem; even so, Theorem 27 is valid.

At this point we shall content ourselves with this informal discussion of these three important theorems. In the exercises below, however, we give an outline of the theory leading to their proofs.

As a simple illustration of Theorem 27, consider the following.

Example 28. We have already seen (Example 25) that $\sum_{n=0}^{\infty} \dfrac{x^n}{n!}$ converges for all $x \in \mathbf{R}$. Let

$$f(x) = \sum_{n=0}^{\infty} \frac{x^n}{n!}. \tag{33}$$

By Theorem 27,

$$f'(x) = \sum_{n=1}^{\infty} \frac{nx^{n-1}}{n!} = \sum_{n=1}^{\infty} \frac{x^{n-1}}{(n-1)!} = \sum_{k=0}^{\infty} \frac{x^k}{k!} = f(x).$$

Using the Leibniz notation, letting $f'(x) = \dfrac{dy}{dx}$, $f(x) = y$, we can write this last equation as

$$\frac{dy}{dx} = y,$$

or

$$\frac{dy}{y} = dx.$$

An integration (antidifferentiation) gives

$$\log|y| = x + \log c,$$

or

$$|y| = ce^x.$$

From (33) we easily see that $f(0) = 1$; this implies $c = 1$, and $y = f(x) = e^x$: The series (33) represents the exponential function.

Example 29. In Example 7 we saw that the geometric series

$$\frac{1}{1-x} = 1 + x + x^2 + x^3 + \cdots \tag{34}$$

converges for $|x| < 1$.

We replace x by $-t$:

$$\frac{1}{1+t} = 1 - t + t^2 - t^3 + \cdots.$$

Now, we integrate between 0 and x, where $|x| < 1$:

$$\int_0^x \frac{dt}{1+t} = \log(1+x) = x - \frac{x^2}{2} + \frac{x^3}{3} - \frac{x^4}{4} + \cdots.$$

If we set $x = 1$ in this last equation we find

$$\log 2 = 1 - \tfrac{1}{2} + \tfrac{1}{3} - \tfrac{1}{4} + \cdots,$$

the alternating series of Example 19.

Example 30. In the geometric series (34) we replace x by $-t^2$:

$$\frac{1}{1+t^2} = 1 - t^2 + t^4 - t^6 + \cdots. \tag{35}$$

We integrate between 0 and x, where $|x| < 1$:

$$\int_0^x \frac{dt}{1+t^2} = x - \frac{x^3}{3} + \frac{x^5}{5} - \frac{x^7}{7} + \cdots,$$

or

$$\tan^{-1} x = x - \frac{x^3}{3} + \frac{x^5}{5} - \frac{x^7}{7} + \cdots. \tag{36}$$

Note that the series in (35) diverges for $t = 1$, whereas the one in (36) converges for $x = 1$. If we do set $x = 1$ in this expression we find a means for calculating $\frac{\pi}{4}$:

$$\frac{\pi}{4} = 1 - \frac{1}{3} + \frac{1}{5} - \frac{1}{7} + \cdots.$$

This series, known as Gregory's Series, converges too slowly to be of much practical use.

If, rather than placing primary emphasis on the power series, we consider first the function, a basic question which naturally arises is: What functions f have power series representations? As Theorems 25 and 27 clearly indicate, necessary conditions are that f be continuous and differentiable within the interval of convergence. But it is easy to see that far more than this is required of f; for if Theorem 27 is applied to f', we see that f must have a second derivative. And an application of Theorem 27 to f'' shows that f''' must exist within the interval of convergence. If we continue in this way we conclude that f must have derivatives of all orders in the interval of convergence in order that f be represented by a power series. This would seem to be a sufficiently strong requirement of f to assure a power series representation for f.

But our intuition leads us astray in this regard. There exist functions which do have derivatives of all orders but which fail to have an infinite series expansion about 0, say. An illustration of one such function will be given subsequently.

As an application of the existence of derivatives of all orders for a function with a power series we prove the following important theorem.

Theorem 28 (*Uniqueness Theorem*). *Suppose a function f has a power series representation $f(x) = \sum_{n=0}^{\infty} a_n x^n$, convergent in $(-r, r)$, and another power series representation $f(x) = \sum_{n=0}^{\infty} b_n x^n$ convergent in the same interval $(-r, r)$. Then for all $n = 0, 1, 2, \ldots, a_n = b_n$.*

Proof. We begin with

$$f(x) = \sum_{n=0}^{\infty} a_n x^n = \sum_{n=0}^{\infty} b_n x^n;$$

setting $x = 0$, we have

$$f(0) = a_0 = b_0.$$

Next we use Theorem 27 to differentiate f and the two series:

$$f'(x) = \sum_{n=1}^{\infty} na_n x^{n-1} = \sum_{n=1}^{\infty} nb_n x^{n-1}.$$

If we set $x = 0$ in these expressions we find

$$f'(0) = a_1 = b_1.$$

To continue, we use Theorem 27 again, this time on f'

$$f''(x) = \sum_{n=2}^{\infty} n(n-1)a_n x^{n-2} = \sum_{n=2}^{\infty} n(n-1)b_n x^{n-2}.$$

Evaluating at $x = 0$ gives

$$f''(0) = 2 \cdot 1 a_2 = 2 \cdot 1 b_2 \Rightarrow a_2 = b_2.$$

For f''' we find

$$f'''(x) = \sum_{n=3}^{\infty} n(n-1)(n-2)a_n x^{n-3} = \sum_{n=3}^{\infty} n(n-1)(n-2)b_n x^{n-3};$$

setting $x = 0$, we have

$$f'''(0) = 3 \cdot 2 \cdot 1 a_3 = 3 \cdot 2 \cdot 1 b_3 \Rightarrow a_3 = b_3.$$

Continuing in this way gives the assertion of the theorem: $a_n = b_n$, $n = 0, 1, 2, 3, \ldots$. ∎

One of the implications of Theorem 28 is this: it is sometimes possible to find the coefficients in the series expansion for a function by several different methods; since, by the above theorem, all methods must lead to the same result, one might as well pick the method which is simplest.

E X E R C I S E S

1. Let $f(x) = x - \dfrac{x^3}{3!} + \dfrac{x^5}{5!} - \dfrac{x^7}{7!} + \cdots$.

(a) Find $f'(x)$.   (b) Find $\int_0^x f(t)\, dt$.

(c) What is the relation between the answers in (a) and (b)?

2. Let $f(x) = 1 + \dfrac{x^2}{2!} + \dfrac{x^4}{4!} + \dfrac{x^6}{6!} + \cdots$.

(a) Find $f'(x)$.   (b) Find $\int_0^x f(t)\, dt$.

(c) What is the relation between the results in (a) and (b)?

3. Use the technique of Example 29 to show that

$$\log(1-x) = -x - \frac{x^2}{2} - \frac{x^3}{3} - \cdots,$$

convergent for $|x| < 1$.

4. (a) Combine the results of Example 29 and Exercise 3 to show that

$$\log\frac{1+x}{1-x} = 2\left(x + \frac{x^3}{3} + \frac{x^5}{5} + \cdots\right).$$

(b) Show that, given any $q > 0$, $\exists x \in (-1, 1)$ such that $q = \dfrac{1+x}{1-x}$. Thus the series in

(a) can be used to find the logarithm of any positive number.

5. Assume that the function **0** has a power series representation $\sum_{n=0}^{\infty} a_n x^n$. Show that $a_n = 0$, $n = 0, 1, 2, \ldots$.

6. Let f be defined by

$$f(x) = \sum_{n=2}^{\infty} (-1)^n \frac{x^n}{n(n-1)}$$

(a) What is the domain of f?

(b) Find f'. Can you identify f'?

(c) Find f''. Can you identify f''?

(d) Find $\int_0^x f(t)\, dt$, where x is in the domain of f.

7. Find a power series expansion for $\dfrac{1}{(1-x)^2}$. [*Hint.* Compute the derivative of the function defined by Eq. (34).]

8. Find a power series expansion for $\dfrac{1}{(1-x)^3}$. See the hint for Exercise 7.

The next few exercises contain a sketch of the theory leading to proofs of Theorems 25, 26, and 27.

9. Let $\{a_n\}$ be a sequence of functions whose domains include the interval $[a, b]$.

Definition. *The series $\sum_{n=0}^{\infty} a_n(x)$ converges uniformly on $[a, b]$ to the function $f \Leftrightarrow \forall \varepsilon > 0 \Rightarrow \exists n_\varepsilon$ such that for all $n > n_\varepsilon$ and for all $x \in [a, b]$ it is true that $\left|\sum_{k=0}^{n} a_k(x) - f(x)\right| < \varepsilon$.*

As was pointed out in the text, the essential thing about uniform convergence is that the n_ε depends only upon ε and not upon $x \in [a, b]$.

The following theorem gives a simple and widely applicable means of testing for uniform convergence.

Theorem (*Weierstrass M-Test*). *Let* $\sum_{n=0}^{\infty} a_n$ *be a series of functions whose domains include* $[a, b]$. *If there exists a sequence* $\{M_k\}$ *of positive numbers such that*

(i) $\sum_{k=0}^{\infty} M_k$ *converges*

(ii) *For all* $x \in [a, b] \Rightarrow |a_k(x)| < M_k$, $k = 0, 1, 2, \ldots$,
  then the series $\sum_{n=0}^{\infty} a_n(x)$ *converges uniformly on* $[a, b]$.

Prove this theorem.

Hints.

(1) Use Theorem 6 twice. First, since $\sum_{k=0}^{\infty} M_k$ converges, there exists, for arbitrary $\varepsilon > 0$, n_ε such that $n > m > n_\varepsilon \Rightarrow |M_{m+1} + \cdots + M_n| < \varepsilon$.
(2) If $s_n(x) = \sum_{k=0}^{n} a_k(x)$, show that

$$\left. \begin{array}{c} n > m > n_\varepsilon \\ x \in [a, b] \end{array} \right\} \Rightarrow |s_n(x) - s_m(x)| < \varepsilon.$$

Now use Theorem 6 the second time.

10. Suppose $\sum_{n=0}^{\infty} a_n(x) = f(x)$, where the domains of the a_n and f include the interval $[a, b]$. It is possible that the a_n are continuous on $[a, b]$, yet f is not. Example: $s_n(x) = x^n$; $0 \le x \le 1$; $f(x) = 0$, $0 \le x < 1$, $f(1) = 1$. However, the following assertion provides a sufficient condition for the function f to be continuous.

Theorem. *Suppose the functions* a_n *are continuous on* $[a, b]$ *and* $\sum_{n=0}^{\infty} a_n$ *converges uniformly to* f *on* $[a, b]$. *Then* f *is continuous on* $[a, b]$.

Prove this theorem.

Hints.

(1) Let $x_0 \in [a, b]$ be arbitrary; let $\varepsilon > 0$ be arbitrary. Continuity of f on $[a, b]$ will have been established if it is possible to show that $\exists \delta_\varepsilon > 0$ such that $|h| < \delta_\varepsilon \Rightarrow |f(x_0 + h) - f(x_0)| < \varepsilon$.
(2) Let $s_n = \sum_{k=0}^{n} a_k$. Write

$$|f(x_0 + h) - f(x_0)| = |f(x_0 + h) - s_n(x_0 + h) + s_n(x_0 + h) - s_n(x_0)$$
$$+ s_n(x_0) - f(x_0)|$$
$$\le |f(x_0 + h) - s_n(x_0 + h)| + |s_n(x_0 + h) - s_n(x_0)|$$
$$+ |s_n(x_0) - f(x_0)|.$$

(3) The first and third expressions on the right can be made less than $\dfrac{\varepsilon}{3}$ by using the uniform convergence and choosing n suitably large. The middle expression can be made less than $\dfrac{\varepsilon}{3}$ by using the continuity of the a_n on $[a, b]$. (Why does it follow that s_n is continuous if the a_n are continuous?)
(4) Use the results of Hints 3 and 1.

11. We next show that under the same hypotheses of the previous theorem (in Exercise 10) the series can be integrated term by term. More explicitly here is the assertion.

Theorem. *Suppose the functions a_n are continuous on $[a, b]$ and $\sum_{n=0}^{\infty} a_n$ converges uniformly on $[a, b]$ to f. Let $x \in [a, b]$. Then*

$$\int_a^x f(t) \, dt = \int_a^x \sum_{n=0}^{\infty} a_n(t) \, dt = \sum_{n=0}^{\infty} \int_a^x a_n(t) \, dt.$$

Prove this theorem.

Hints.

(1) Let $s_n = \sum_{k=0}^{n} a_k$. Let $\varepsilon > 0$ be arbitrary. Use the hypothesis of uniform convergence to obtain n_ε such that, for all $x \in [a, b]$, and for $n > n_\varepsilon \Rightarrow |s_n(x) - f(x)| < \varepsilon$.

(2) Write

$$\left| \int_a^x [s_n(t) - f(t)] \, dt \right| = \left| \int_a^x \left[\sum_{k=0}^{n} a_k(t) - f(t) \right] dt \right|$$

$$= \left| \sum_{k=0}^{n} \int_a^x a_k(t) \, dt - \int_a^x f(t) \, dt \right|.$$

Why is this last step possible? Why is f integrable on $[a, x]$?

(3) Beginning with the same expression as in Hint 2, we can also say that

$$\left| \int_a^x [s_n(t) - f(t)] \, dt \right| \le \int_a^x |s_n(t) - f(t)| \, dt \qquad \text{(why?)}$$

$$< \int_a^x \varepsilon \, dt = \varepsilon(x - a),$$

provided that $n > n_\varepsilon$.

(4) Combining the results of Hints 2 and 3 gives

$$\left| \sum_{k=0}^{n} \int_a^x a_k(t) \, dt - \int_a^x f(t) \, dt \right| < \varepsilon(x - a).$$

Conclude from this inequality, which holds for all $n > n_\varepsilon$, that

$$\int_a^x f(t) \, dt = \sum_{k=0}^{\infty} \int_a^x a_k(t) \, dt,$$

the assertion of the theorem.

12. When it comes to differentiating a series term by term one cannot get by simply by assuming that the series itself is well behaved (e.g., converges uniformly). Instead it is necessary to know that the series of derivatives is uniformly convergent.

(a) Show that the series

$$\sum_{n=1}^{\infty} \frac{\cos n^4 \frac{\pi}{2} x}{n^2}$$

converges uniformly on any interval $\left(M_n = \frac{1}{n^2} \right)$, but that the series of derivatives diverges at $x = 1$.

(b) Prove the following assertion.

Theorem *Suppose $\sum_{k=0}^{\infty} a_k(x) = f(x)$ and $\sum_{k=0}^{\infty} a_k'$ converges uniformly on $[a, b]$
to φ. Assume the functions a_k' are continuous on $[a, b]$. Then $\varphi = f'$.*

Hints.
(1) Use the theorem in Exercise 11.

$$\int_a^x \varphi(t)\, dt = \int_a^x \sum_{k=0}^{\infty} a_k'(t)\, dt = \sum_{k=0}^{\infty} \int_a^x a_k'(t)\, dt = f(x) - f(a). \qquad \text{(Why?)}$$

(2) Thus $\varphi(x) = f'(x)$. Why?

13. We now return to power series and observe first of all that the functions involved
in a power series, $a_n x^n$ (where by a_n we mean now a number), are continuous and
differentiable everywhere. The second observation is this: the proof of Theorem 24
does in fact guarantee that a power series converges *uniformly* for $x \in (-r, r)$,
where r is the radius of convergence.
   Verify that this is so. [*Hint.* $M_n = Mk^n$.]
   This assures us that, if $\sum_{n=0}^{\infty} a_n x^n = f(x)$, then f is continuous on $(-r, r)$ and the
series is integrable term-by-term; thus we obtain Theorems 25 and 26.

14. To prove Theorem 27, we must show that the series of derivatives converges
uniformly within the interval of convergence. Do this.

Hints.
(1) Consider $f(x) = \sum_{n=0}^{\infty} a_n x^n$ and $\sum_{n=1}^{\infty} n a_n x^{n-1}$. Let $x_0 \in (-r, r)$. As in the
proof of Theorem 24, $\exists M > 0$ such that $|a_n x_0^n| < M$, all n. But this implies that

$$|a_n x_0^{n-1}| < \frac{M}{x_0} = Q.$$

(2) Now let k be such that $0 < k < 1$, and let x be chosen so that $|x| \le k|x_0|$.
Then

$$|n a_n x^{n-1}| \le |n a_n k^{n-1} x_0^{n-1}| < n k^{n-1} Q.$$

(3) Use the ratio test to show that the series

$$\sum_{n=1}^{\infty} n k^{n-1} Q$$

converges. Recall that $0 < k < 1$.
(4) Now apply the theorem in Exercise 12b.

15.10 Taylor's Series

We return to the question discussed briefly in the last section: given a function
f, can it be represented by a power series? We saw that a necessary condition for
a power series representation about 0 is the existence at 0 of derivatives of all
orders. Similarly, if a power series representation for f about $x = c$ is desired,
then f must have derivatives of all orders at $x = c$. The fact is that most of the
functions of elementary calculus which do have derivatives of all orders at a
point have a power series representation about that point.

If we assume that a function f has a power series expansion about 0, $f(x) = \sum_{n=0}^{\infty} a_n x^n$, convergent in some interval $(-r, r)$, the question arises about the nature of the coefficients, a_n. We have, in truth, provided an answer to this question in the proof of the Uniqueness Theorem (Theorem 28) in the preceding section. There we saw that

$$a_0 = f(0), \qquad a_1 = \frac{f'(0)}{1!}, \qquad a_2 = \frac{f''(0)}{2!}, \qquad a_3 = \frac{f'''(0)}{3!}.$$

That this pattern holds in general is easily shown. For if

$$f(x) = \sum_{n=0}^{\infty} a_n x^n,$$

then

$$f^{(k)}(x) = \sum_{n=k}^{\infty} n(n-1) \cdots (n-k+1) a_n x^{n-k}.$$

Setting $x = 0$, we have

$$f^{(k)}(0) = k(k-1) \cdots 1 \cdot a_k,$$

or

$$a_k = \frac{f^{(k)}(0)}{k!}. \tag{37}$$

Similarly, if one wishes a power series expansion of f about $x = c$:

$$f(x) = a_0 + a_1(x - c) + a_2(x - c)^2 + \cdots,$$

then the same argument shows that

$$a_k = \frac{f^{(k)}(c)}{k!} \tag{38}$$

Definition 8. *If a function f has derivatives of all orders at a point $x = c$, then the **Taylor's series** for f about c is the series*

$$\sum_{k=0}^{\infty} \frac{f^{(k)}(c)}{k!} (x - c)^k \tag{39}$$

If $c = 0$, the series

$$\sum_{k=0}^{\infty} \frac{f^{(k)}(0)}{k!} x^k \tag{40}$$

*is also called **Maclaurin's series** for f.*

No definition, of course, *proves* anything. In particular, Definition 8 provides no assurance that a Taylor's series will converge at more than one point $(x = c)$, or that, if it does converge at points x other than c, it will converge to $f(x)$. With regard to the first of these possible difficulties we assert that for most of the functions of elementary calculus, if a Taylor's series exists at $x = c$ it will converge at points other than c.

An answer to the second point raised can be provided by calling attention to the obvious fact that a Taylor's series is simply a generalization of the approximation of a function by a polynomial, as discussed in Section 1. In fact, the approximating polynomial of degree n is precisely the nth partial sum s_n of the Taylor's series. Thus, using Taylor's Theorem (Theorem 1), we can write

$$f(x) = s_n(x) + R_n(x). \tag{41}$$

Now, as $n \to \infty$ the nth partial sum s_n approaches Taylor's series. *Consequently we see from* (41) *that Taylor's series converges to $f(x)$ if and only if* $\lim_{n \to \infty} R_n(x) = 0$.

Example 31. To illustrate the preceding discussion we return to the function $f = \cos$ and the polynomial approximation found in Example 2 [Eq. (10)]:

$$\cos x = 1 - \frac{x^2}{2!} + \frac{x^4}{4!} - \frac{x^6}{6!} + \cdots + (-1)^n \frac{x^{2n}}{(2n)!} + (-1)^{n+1} \frac{\sin x_0}{(2n+1)!} x^{2n+1}.$$

[There is a minor annoyance in the labeling or counting of terms in this case because the coefficients of odd powers of x are zero.]

Now

$$|R_{2n}(x)| = \frac{|x^{2n+1}|}{(2n+1)!} |\sin x_0| \le \frac{|x^{2n+1}|}{(2n+1)!}.$$

We can show that $\lim_{n \to \infty} |R_{2n}(x)| = 0$, for every $x \in \mathbf{R}$, by the following sneaky trick. In Examples 25 and 28 we showed that the series for e^x, $\sum_{n=0}^{\infty} \frac{x^n}{n!}$, converges for all $x \in \mathbf{R}$. By Theorem 8, it follows that

$$\lim_{n \to \infty} \frac{|x|^n}{n!} = 0, \tag{42}$$

for every $x \in \mathbf{R}$. Thus $\lim_{n \to \infty} |R_{2n}(x)| = 0$, and the Taylor's series for cos does converge to $\cos x$ for every $x \in \mathbf{R}$ [cf. Eq. (11) and the surrounding discussion after Example 2].

Example 32. It is important to keep in mind the implication of the Uniqueness Theorem (Theorem 28). To illustrate, suppose one wishes to find a Taylor's series (about 0) for the function f defined by

$$f(x) = \frac{\sin x}{x}.$$

Now one *could* calculate the coefficients by means of Eq. (37), but it would soon be apparent that this task becomes exceedingly involved. As an alternative, we can proceed as follows. We have already asserted (in Example 27) and we shall ask you to prove in Exercise 1 below that

$$\sin x = x - \frac{x^3}{3!} + \frac{x^5}{5!} - \frac{x^7}{7!} + \cdots,$$

convergent for all $x \in \mathbf{R}$. As we can write $f(x) = \dfrac{\sin x}{x} = \dfrac{1}{x} \sin x$, it follows that the Taylor's series for f is

$$f(x) = \frac{\sin x}{x} = 1 - \frac{x^2}{3!} + \frac{x^4}{5!} - \frac{x^6}{7!} + \cdots.$$

Example 33. We give another illustration of the use of the Uniqueness Theorem. We want the Taylor's series about 0 for f defined by $f(x) = \sin^2 x$. In this case the coefficients could be found from Eq. (37) with little difficulty, but an easier way is available to us. Recall that

$$\sin^2 x = \tfrac{1}{2}(1 - \cos 2x).$$

From the result of Example 31, we know that

$$\cos x = 1 - \frac{x^2}{2!} + \frac{x^4}{4!} - \frac{x^6}{6!} + \cdots.$$

Thus

$$1 - \cos 2x = \frac{(2x)^2}{2!} - \frac{(2x)^4}{4!} + \frac{(2x)^6}{6!} - \frac{(2x)^8}{8!} + \cdots,$$

and

$$\sin^2 x = \frac{1}{2}(1 - \cos 2x) = \frac{1}{2}\left[\frac{(2x)^2}{2!} - \frac{(2x)^4}{4!} + \frac{(2x)^6}{6!} - \frac{(2x)^8}{8!} + \cdots\right],$$

convergent for all $x \in \mathbf{R}$ (why?).

Example 34. One of the important applications of infinite series is to numerical calculations. For example, the function f defined by $f(x) = \exp(-\tfrac{1}{2}x^2)$ is important in probability and statistics [the *density function* for the standard normal distribution is $\varphi(x) = \dfrac{1}{\sqrt{2\pi}}\exp(-\tfrac{1}{2}x^2]$ and values of its integral over various intervals are essential. The antiderivative of this function, however, is not an elementary function, and the Fundamental Theorem of Calculus cannot be used in finding integrals. One of the useful approximation methods is by means of series.

Suppose we want to find $\int_0^1 \exp(-\tfrac{1}{2}x^2)\, dx$. We know that

$$e^y = \sum_{n=0}^{\infty} \frac{y^n}{n!}.$$

Thus

$$e^{-\frac{1}{2}x^2} = \sum_{n=0}^{\infty} \frac{(-\frac{1}{2}x^2)^n}{n!} = \sum_{n=0}^{\infty} (-1)^n \frac{x^{2n}}{2^n n!} = 1 - \frac{x^2}{2} + \frac{x^4}{2^2 \cdot 2!} - \frac{x^6}{2^3 \cdot 3!} + \cdots .$$

convergent for all $x \in \mathbf{R}$. By Theorem 26, then,

$$\int_0^1 e^{-\frac{1}{2}x^2}\, dx = x - \frac{x^3}{6} + \frac{x^5}{2^2 \cdot 2!5} - \frac{x^7}{2^3 \cdot 3!7} + \frac{x^9}{2^4 \cdot 4!9} - \cdots \Big|_0^1$$

$$\approx 1 - \frac{1}{6} + \frac{1}{40} - \frac{1}{336} + \frac{1}{3456}$$

$$\approx 0.8556.$$

THE BINOMIAL SERIES. We conclude this section by finding the Taylor's series for the function f, where

$$f(x) = (1 + x)^q, \qquad q \notin \mathbf{N}. \tag{43}$$

[The reason for the restriction on q should be obvious: if q is a positive integer the binomial theorem of Theorem 1.16 gives us a finite polynomial *equal* to—not approximating—f. As we shall see, the binomial series gives us a generalization of the binomial theorem.]

We begin by assuming that f *can* be represented by a series,

$$f(x) = a_0 + a_1 x + a_2 x^2 + a_3 x^3 + \cdots .$$

Now, if we differentiate both sides of (43), we find

$$f'(x) = q(1 + x)^{q-1},$$

or, multiplying by $1 + x$,

$$(1 + x)f'(x) = q(1 + x)^q = qf(x). \tag{44}$$

We can exploit this relation to obtain the coefficients a_n. For it is easy to calculate that

$$(1 + x)f'(x) = a_1 + (a_1 + 2a_2)x + (2a_2 + 3a_3)x^2 + \cdots$$
$$+ (na_n + \overline{n + 1}\, a_{n+1})x^n + \cdots . \tag{45}$$

Similarly, we quickly find that

$$qf(x) = qa_0 + qa_1 x + qa_2 x^2 + \cdots + qa_n x^n + \cdots . \tag{46}$$

From Eq. (44) and the Uniqueness Theorem we find

$$\begin{cases} a_1 = qa_0 \\ a_1 + 2a_2 = qa_1 \\ 2a_2 + 3a_3 = qa_2 \\ \quad \vdots \qquad \vdots \\ na_n + \overline{n + 1}a_{n+1} = qa_n \end{cases}. \tag{47}$$

We find $a_0 = f(0) = 1$ by using the two expressions for $f(x)$. From this and the equations in (47), we can calculate that

$$a_0 = 1$$

$$a_1 = q$$

$$a_2 = \frac{a_1(q-1)}{2} = \frac{q(q-1)}{2}$$

$$a_3 = \frac{a_2(q-2)}{3} = \frac{q(q-1)(q-2)}{3},$$

and, by mathematical induction,

$$a_n = \frac{q(q-1)(q-2)\cdots(q-n+1)}{n!}.$$

(Of course, these coefficients can be found by Eq. (40) of Definition 8, but we were interested in illustrating an alternative technique.)

The Taylor's series for f is, then,

$$1 + qx + \frac{q(q-1)}{2!}x^2 + \frac{q(q-1)(q-2)}{3!}x^3 + \cdots$$

$$+ \frac{q(q-1)(q-2)\cdots(q-n+1)}{n!}x^n + \cdots. \quad (48)$$

But we must find its interval of convergence and determine whether or not this series does converge to $f(x)$.

The ratio test quickly gives us an answer for the radius of convergence:

$$\left| \frac{a_{n+1}x^{n+1}}{a_n x^n} \right| = \left| \frac{q(q-1)\cdots(q-n+1)(q-n)x^{n+1}}{(n+1)!} \frac{n!}{q(q-1)\cdots(q-n+1)x^n} \right|$$

$$= \left| \frac{q-n}{n+1} \right| |x| \to |x|,$$

as $n \to \infty$. Thus the series in (48) converges for $x \in (-1, 1)$ and diverges if $|x| > 1$.

To show that this series does indeed represent f, we denote it by φ and let

$$h(x) = \frac{\varphi(x)}{f(x)} = \frac{\varphi(x)}{(1+x)^q}.$$

Our aim will clearly be achieved by showing that $h(x) = 1$ for $x \in (-1, 1)$. To this end, we find $h'(x)$:

$$h'(x) = \frac{(1+x)^q \varphi'(x) - \varphi(x)q(1+x)^{q-1}}{(1+x)^{2q}}$$

$$= \frac{(1+x)\varphi'(x) - q\varphi(x)}{(1+x)^{q+1}}$$

$$= 0,$$

since the coefficients a_n of the series $\varphi(x) = \sum_{n=0}^{\infty} a_n x^n$ were calculated by making the expression in the numerator equal to zero. This assures us that h is a constant function. And evaluating h at $x = 0$ gives

$$h(0) = \frac{\varphi(0)}{1} = 1;$$

thus h *is* the constant function **1** for $|x| < 1$, and

$$(1 + x)^q = 1 + qx + \frac{q(q-1)}{2!} x^2 + \frac{q(q-1)(q-2)}{3!} x^3 + \cdots. \qquad (49)$$

Example 35. Find the series for $\sqrt{1 + x}$. By Eq. (49), with $q = \frac{1}{2}$, we find

$$\sqrt{1 + x} = (1 + x)^{1/2} = 1 + \frac{1}{2} x + \frac{\frac{1}{2}(\frac{1}{2} - 1)}{2!} x^2 + \frac{\frac{1}{2}(\frac{1}{2} - 1)(\frac{1}{2} - 2)}{3!} x^3$$

$$+ \frac{\frac{1}{2}(\frac{1}{2} - 1)(\frac{1}{2} - 2)(\frac{1}{2} - 3)}{4!} x^4 + \cdots$$

$$= 1 + \frac{x}{2} - \frac{1}{2!} \left(\frac{x}{2}\right)^2 + \frac{1 \cdot 3}{3!} \left(\frac{x}{2}\right)^3 - \frac{1 \cdot 3 \cdot 5}{4!} \left(\frac{x}{2}\right)^4 + \cdots.$$

EXERCISES

1. Show that

$$\sin x = x - \frac{x^3}{3!} + \frac{x^5}{5!} - \frac{x^7}{7!} + \cdots,$$

convergent for all $x \in \mathbf{R}$.

In numbers 2–12 find Taylor's series for the functions given, about the point indicated. In each case find the interval of convergence.

2. $\sinh x$, about 0.

3. e^x, about $x = 1$.

4. $\sqrt{1 - x}$, about $x = 0$.

5. $\dfrac{1}{\sqrt{1 + x}}$, about $x = 0$.

6. $\cos x$, about $x = \dfrac{\pi}{4}$.

7. $\sin x$, about $x = \dfrac{\pi}{6}$.

8. $\dfrac{1}{\sqrt{1 - x^2}}$, about $x = 0$.

9. $\dfrac{1}{1 + 2x}$, about $x = 0$.

10. $\cos^2 x$, about $x = 0$.

11. $\log (1 - x)$, about $x = 0$.

12. $\log x$, about $x = 2$.

13. (a) Use Eq. (40) to find the Taylor's series for $\tan x$ about 0. Go as far as the term in x^5.

(b) Obtain the series for $\tan x$ by dividing the series for $\sin x$ (Exercise 1) by that for $\cos x$ [Eq. (11)].

In numbers 14–16 use the method of Example 34 to approximate the value of the expression given.

14. $\displaystyle\int_0^1 \cos \sqrt{x}\, dx$; to 3 significant digits.

15. $\displaystyle\int_0^1 \cos x^2\, dx$; to 3 significant digits.

16. $\displaystyle\int_0^1 \sqrt{1+x^3}$

17. Find a power series for $\sin^{-1} x$ by finding the series for

$$\frac{1}{\sqrt{1-x^2}}$$

and then integrating term by term. What is the radius of convergence?

18. Let f be defined by

$$f(x) = \begin{cases} e^{-\frac{1}{x^2}}, & x \neq 0 \\ 0, & x = 0 \end{cases}.$$

(a) Show that, for every $n = 0, 1, 2, \ldots$,

$$f^{(n)}(0) = 0.$$

(b) What does the result of part (a) indicate about the Taylor's series for f about 0?

Chapter **16** Differential Equations

We have already encountered, mainly in Chapter 8, examples of differential equations, i.e., equations involving an unknown function and one or more of its derivatives. The problem of immediate concern is to solve the equation for a function—or class of functions—which satisfies the equation. (Of course, every anti-derivative problem is a differential equation problem, for integrating $\int f(x)\,dx$ amounts to finding a function y such that $y' = f(x)$.) Clearly, a problem described in such wide generality can be of enormous magnitude. In this brief introduction we shall pass over most of the theoretical questions concerned with existence and uniqueness of solutions and content ourselves with discussing a few of the standard techniques for solving some of the simpler types of differential equations, along with several elementary applications to problems of geometry and physics.

16.1 Preliminary Ideas

One of the natural approaches to the systematic study of differential equations is to classify the set of all differential equations into various types. We begin our discussion by listing a few specific differential equations in order to suggest some of the categories used in this classification:

$$\frac{dy}{dx} = xy - x^2, \tag{1}$$

$$y'' + 3y' + 2y = 0, \tag{2}$$

$$\frac{dy}{dx} + \frac{1}{x}\,y = 3x, \tag{3}$$

$$\frac{\partial^2 u}{\partial x^2} + \frac{\partial^2 u}{\partial y^2} = 0, \tag{4}$$

$$\left(\frac{d^2 y}{dx^2}\right)^2 = \left[1 + \left(\frac{dy}{dx}\right)^2\right]^3, \tag{5}$$

$$y'' + 2y' + 2y = x + \sin x, \tag{6}$$

$$(2x - 3y)\, dx + (4x + y)\, dy = 0. \tag{7}$$

We first remark that Eq. (4) differs from all the others in that it involves a function u of two independent variables. If an equation is in terms of a function of a single variable it is called an *ordinary differential equation*; if functions of two or more variables are involved the equation is called a *partial differential equation*. Thus, all the preceding examples are ordinary differential equations, except for (4) which is one of the best-known partial differential equations: the Laplace differential equation, already encountered in Chapter 13. *In this chapter we shall consider only ordinary differential equations.*

The *order* of a differential equation is the order of the derivative of highest order. In the preceding list, Eqs. (1), (3), and (7) are first order, whereas (2), (5), and (6) are second-order equations.

As (7) shows, it is sometimes convenient to write an equation in terms of differentials. (The great utility of the Leibniz notation for derivatives and differentials will be clearly in evidence in this chapter.)

The *solution* of a differential equation is a function which satisfies the equation. In many cases the technique of solving will produce an explicit solution, but not always. For example, the standard method for solving (7) gives the result, as we shall see later,

$$\log(2x^2 + xy + y^2) + 2\sqrt{7}\, \tan^{-1}\frac{x + 2y}{\sqrt{7x}} = C. \tag{8}$$

This relation defines y as a function of x, but the explicit form of the function is certainly not apparent.

The solution displayed in (8) shows what we have already observed with antidifferentiations problems: the presence of a constant. The number of constants is, in fact, equal to the order of the equation. For example, the solution to the second-order equation (2) is

$$y = c_1 e^{-x} + c_2 e^{-2x}.$$

A solution to an equation of order n having n constants is called the *general solution*. In most applications the problem will specify, along with the differential equation, enough conditions to determine the constants, to find, in other words, a *particular solution*. These additional conditions are likely to be either *initial conditions* or *boundary conditions*. An *initial condition* is a condition at a single point. A *boundary condition* is a condition involving two or more points. For example, an initial condition for (2) could be

$$y(0) = 0, \qquad y'(0) = 1.$$

In this case the particular solution is easily found to be

$$y(x) = e^{-x} - e^{-2x}.$$

Or a boundary condition for the same equation would be

$$y(0) = e, \qquad y(1) = e^{-2}.$$

This would lead to the particular solution

$$y(x) = -e^{-x} + (e + 1)e^{-2x}.$$

One way of solving an initial value problem or a boundary value problem is to find the general solution and then impose the conditions so as to determine the values of the constants. This will be the main technique used in this chapter. However, in many important problems one cannot afford the luxury of finding first the general solution; in these cases it is necessary to go directly after the particular solution, or an approximation thereto satisfying the given condition.

The following remarks may be appropriate at this time. The approach to solving the more elementary differential equations is quite analogous to that used in the related problem of antidifferentiation. It has been found that certain types of equations are amenable to certain methods. One must, then, gain some familiarity with the different types of equations and with the methods which are applicable. This description may suggest that the primary consideration for the study of a given equation is the availability of a method of solution, regardless of the *utility* of the equation. In general, it is not wise to engage in discussions of relative utility of theories or techniques or special equations in mathematics, but it can be said in this regard that each type of equation we shall study meets the criterion of being solvable as well as that of including equations which do arise in various problems.

Example 1. Show that $xy = c(x + y)$ is the (general) solution of $x^2y' + y^2 = 0$.

As the differential equation involves y', we begin by differentiating the suggested solution:

$$xy' + y = c(1 + y').$$

We must now eliminate c; this can be done by solving the given relation for c and substituting into the equation just obtained. Thus

$$xy' + y = \frac{xy}{x + y}(1 + y').$$

Multiplying by $x + y$ and simplifying, we obtain $x^2y' + y^2 = 0$.

Example 2. Solve the boundary value problem

$$x''(t) = 6t + 2, \qquad 0 \le t \le 1, \qquad x(0) = 0, \qquad x(1) = 1.$$

Performing two antidifferentiations gives

$$x'(t) = 3t^2 + 2t + c_1,$$
$$x(t) = t^3 + t^2 + c_1 t + c_2.$$

Now the condition $x(0) = 0 \Rightarrow c_2 = 0$, or $x(t) = t^3 + t^2 + c_1 t$. Next, $x(1) = 1 \Rightarrow c_1 = -1$; thus the solution is

$$x(t) = t^3 + t^2 - t, \qquad 0 \leq t \leq 1.$$

E X E R C I S E S

1. Verify that the following functions are solutions of the accompanying differential equation.

   (a) $x \log xy + 1 = cx;$ $y\,dx = xy\,dx + x^2\,dy$

   (b) $y = ce^{y/x};$ $(xy - x^2)\dfrac{dy}{dx} = y^2$

   (c) $y = c_1 e^x \cos(3x + c_2);$ $\dfrac{d^2 y}{dx^2} - 2\dfrac{dy}{dx} + 10\,y = 0$

   (d) $x = c_1 + c_2\,e^{-2t} + c_3\,te^{-2t};$ $x'''(t) + 4x''(t) + 4x'(t) = 0$

   (e) $y = c_1 e^{-x} + c_2 + x + \frac{1}{3}x^3;$ $y'' + y' = (1 + x)^2$

   (f) $y = c_1 \cos 2x + c_2 \sin 2x - \frac{1}{5} \cos 3x;$ $y'' + 4y = \cos 3x$

   (g) $g(x) = c_1 \cos \omega x + c_2 \sin \omega x;$ $y'' + \omega^2 y = 0.$

2. Consider the equation $y' + 3y = 1$.

   (a) Show that the function g, where $g(x) = \frac{1}{3} + ce^{-3x}$ is a solution for every value of the constant c.

   (b) Find the particular solution for which $g(0) = 1$.

   (c) Show that for every pair $(a, b) \in \mathbf{R} \times \mathbf{R}$ there is a solution such that $g(a) = b$.

3. Verify that the function defined by Eq. (8) is a solution of the differential Equation (7).

4. (a) Find the general solution of

   $$x''(t) = -\omega^2 \cos \omega t, \qquad 0 \leq t \leq 2\pi.$$

   (b) Solve the initial-value problem consisting of the equation in (a) and

   $$x(0) = 1, \qquad x'(0) = 1.$$

   (c) Solve the boundary-value problem consisting of the equation in (a) and

   $$x(0) = 1, \qquad x(2\pi) = -1.$$

5. (a) Find the general solution of

   $$y'' = 2 + e^{-x} + \cos x.$$

   (b) Solve the initial-value problem consisting of the equation in (a) and

   $$y(0) = 6, \qquad y'(0) = 2.$$

(c) Solve the boundary-value problem consisting of the equation in (a) and

$$y(\pi) = e^{-\pi}, \quad y(2\pi) = e^{-2\pi}.$$

6. Verify that $x^2 + y^2 = 1$ is a solution of Eq. (5).

16.2 First-Order Equations (1)

In this section we begin a study of the first-order differential equations which can be described by the general form

$$y' = f(x, y). \tag{9}$$

As our primary concern is the development of methods of solution, we shall assume that the function f is well behaved in some region of $\mathbf{R}^2$; we also assume that the projection of this region onto the x-axis is an interval I, not necessarily finite.

(a) As a start we remark that if f is independent of y, so that (9) becomes

$$y' = f(x), \tag{10}$$

we have precisely the problem of antidifferentiation already discussed in detail in Chapter 8.

(b) Next suppose that f is independent of x:

$$y' = f(y). \tag{11}$$

We can rewrite this equation as $\dfrac{dy}{dx} = f(y)$, or assuming $f(y) \neq 0$,

$$\frac{dx}{dy} = \frac{1}{f(y)}.$$

Letting $g(y) = \dfrac{1}{f(y)}$ and $x' = \dfrac{dx}{dy}$, we see that this equation is $x' = g(y)$, the same as (10) with the roles of x and y interchanged.

Example 3. We solve $y' = y^2 + 1$. This can be rewritten as

$$\frac{dy}{y^2 + 1} = dx.$$

Integrating both sides, we have $\tan^{-1} y = x + c$, or

$$y = \tan(x + c).$$

Example 4. Consider

$$y' = \frac{y^2 + 1}{y}.$$

This can be written as

$$\frac{y\,dy}{y^2+1}=dx.$$

Now an integration of both sides gives

$$\tfrac{1}{2}\log{(y^2+1)}=x+\tfrac{1}{2}\log c,$$

or

$$y^2+1=ce^{2x}.$$

(As indicated in Example 4, it is often advantageous to introduce a constant in a special form. Knowledge of when and how this might be done comes with a little experience.)

(c) *Variables Separable.* Both of the simple types (a) and (b) are special cases of the following. Suppose the function f is the product of functions g and h, where g involves only x and h only $y: f(x, y) = g(x)h(y)$.

When this occurs (9) can be written as

$$\frac{dy}{h(y)}=g(x)\,dx,\qquad(12)$$

assuming $h(y)\neq 0$. As the heading indicates, this is referred to as the type where the variables are separable. An integration of both sides gives the solution.

Example 5. Consider

$$\frac{dy}{dx}=\frac{\cos^2 y}{\sin^2 x}.$$

We can separate the variables as

$$\sec^2 y\,dy=\csc^2 x\,dx.$$

Now integrating both sides, we have

$$\tan y=-\cot x+c.$$

Example 6. We solve

$$x^3\,dy-xy^2\,dx=2y^2\,dx.$$

By a little algebra we find the equation can be written as

$$x^3\,dy=(x+2)y^2\,dx,$$

or

$$y^{-2}\,dy=(x^{-2}+2x^{-3})\,dx.$$

Integrating, we obtain

$$-y^{-1} = -x^{-1} - x^{-2} - c,$$

whence

$$y = \frac{x^2}{cx^2 + x + 1}.$$

EXERCISES

Solve the differential equations in numbers 1–14.

1. $2xy\,dx + (x^2 + 1)\,dy = 0.$

2. $\dfrac{dy}{dx} = e^y.$ **3.** $x\,dy - 2y\,dx = 0.$

4. $\dfrac{dx}{dt} = tx^2.$ **5.** $\sqrt{1-x^2}\,dy = \sqrt{1-y^2}\,dx.$

6. $y' = \tan y.$ **7.** $y' = \dfrac{y^2 + 1}{x^2 + 1}.$

8. $y' = 4 - y^2.$ **9.** $\dfrac{dy}{dx} = x \tan y.$

10. $y + xy' = xy(y' - 1).$ **11.** $y' = \sqrt{1-y^2}.$

12. $\dfrac{dy}{dx} = \dfrac{xy + y}{x + xy}.$ **13.** $t\dfrac{dx}{dt} = x^2 - x.$

14. $(xy^2 + x)\,dx + (x^2 y - x)\,dy = 0.$

In numbers 15–20 solve the initial value problem.

15. $\dfrac{dx}{dt} = \dfrac{1-t}{x};\quad x = 3$ when $t = 5.$

16. $xy\,dx + \sqrt{1+x^2}\,dy = 0;\quad y = e^{-1}$ when $x = 0.$

17. $y' = x^2 y^2;\quad y = -1$ when $x = 0.$

18. $2\,xy\,dx + \sqrt{x^2 + 1}\,dy = 0;\quad y = e^{-1}$ when $x = 0.$

19. $\dfrac{dy}{dx} = y \cos x;\quad y = e$ when $x = \dfrac{\pi}{2}.$

20. $x^2\,dy + y^2\,dx = 0;\quad y = 1$ when $x = 1.$

16.3 First-Order Equations (2)

In this section we continue our study of the class of first-order differential equations described by $y' = f(x, y)$.

(d) *Homogeneous Coefficients.* Suppose, to begin, that f is expressible as the ratio of two functions, say,

$$f(x, y) = \frac{-M(x, y)}{N(x, y)}.$$

Then the differential equation can be written as

$$M(x, y) \, dx + N(x, y) \, dy = 0. \tag{13}$$

We further assume that M and N are both *homogeneous of the same degree.* Recall (see Exercise 11 after Section 13.7) that a function F is homogeneous of degree n if and only if $F(tx, ty) = t^n F(x, y)$.

The homogeneity of M and N suggests letting $\dfrac{y}{x}$ equal a new variable, say, v; equivalently, we let

$$y = vx.$$

Then

$$\frac{dy}{dx} = v + x \frac{dv}{dx} \quad \text{or} \quad dy = v \, dx + x \, dv,$$

and the equation

$$\frac{dy}{dx} = \frac{-M(x, y)}{N(x, y)}$$

becomes

$$v + x \frac{dv}{dx} = \frac{-M(x, vx)}{N(x, vx)},$$

or, since M and N are homogeneous,

$$v + x \frac{dv}{dx} = \frac{-x^n M(1, v)}{x^n N(1, v)}.$$

This can be written as

$$x \frac{dv}{dx} = -\frac{M(1, v)}{N(1, v)} - v = Q(v),$$

or, separating the variables,

$$\frac{1}{Q(v)} \, dv = \frac{dx}{x}.$$

Now the solution can be found in as the preceding section, and v can be replaced by $\dfrac{x}{y}$.

Example 7. We consider the equation

$$(3y - 4x)\, dx + x\, dy = 0,$$

the coefficients being homogeneous of degree 1.

If $y = vx$, then $dy = v\, dx + x\, dv$, and the equation is transformed to

$$(3vx - 4x)\, dx + x(v\, dx + x\, dv) = 0,$$

or

$$(4v - 4)\, dx + x\, dv = 0.$$

Clearly, the variables x and v are separable:

$$4\frac{dx}{x} = -\frac{dv}{(v - 1)}.$$

Integrating both sides, we have

$$\log x^4 = -\log|v - 1| + \log c,$$

or

$$\log x^4 |v - 1| = \log c.$$

It follows that $x^4 |v - 1| = c$, or, replacing v with $\dfrac{y}{x}$,

$$x^4 \left| \frac{y}{x} - 1 \right| = c,$$

or

$$x^3 (y - x) = c.$$

(Why can the absolute value sign be dropped?)

Example 8. Solve the equation

$$(x^3 + y^3)\, dx - xy^2\, dy = 0.$$

The coefficients of dx and dy are homogeneous of degree 3. We let $y = vx$, $dy = v\, dx + x\, dv$:

$$(x^3 + v^3 x^3)\, dx - x^3 v^2 (v\, dx + x\, dv) = 0,$$

which reduces to

$$dx - xv^2\, dv = 0,$$

or

$$v^2\, dv = \frac{dx}{x}.$$

Integrating, we have $\frac{1}{3}v^3 = \log|x| + \log c$, which can, after a few easy steps, be modified to

$$y^3 = 3x^3 \log|cx|.$$

(e) *Exact Differentials.* We again consider the equation in the form

$$M(x, y)\,dx + N(x, y)\,dy = 0 \tag{13}$$

and recall that for a differentiable function u of x and y the differential is

$$du = \frac{\partial u}{\partial x}\,dx + \frac{\partial u}{\partial y}\,dy.$$

For example, if $u = xy$, then $du = y\,dx + x\,dy$; or, if $u = x^2 \sin y$, $du = 2x \sin y\,dx + x^2 \cos y\,dy$.

Now the point is, first of all, that the left-hand side of (13) has the *form* to be a differential of a function u, and, secondly, if this were in fact the case, the solution of the equation would be simply

$$u(x, y) = c.$$

These remarks lead naturally to the questions:

(1) Is there a reasonably simple test for determining whether an expression $M\,dx + N\,dy$ is the differential of a function u—is, in other words, an *exact differential*?

(2) Assuming one can find that $M\,dx + N\,dy$ is an exact differential, can the function u be found?

Fortunately, both questions have affirmative answers. With regard to the first, a *necessary* condition for $M\,dx + N\,dy$ to be an exact differential is easily found. For, suppose u exists such that

$$du = \frac{\partial u}{\partial x}\,dx + \frac{\partial u}{\partial y}\,dy = M\,dx + N\,dy.$$

It follows that

$$M = \frac{\partial u}{\partial x} \quad\text{and}\quad N = \frac{\partial u}{\partial y}.$$

Now if we differentiate the first of these equations with respect to y and the second with respect to x and use Theorem 13.13 (recall the blanket assumption made earlier that the functions we work with are sufficiently well behaved, i.e., have sufficient differentiability and continuity properties), we find

$$\frac{\partial M}{\partial y} = \frac{\partial^2 u}{\partial x\,\partial y} = \frac{\partial N}{\partial x}.$$

Moreover, this necessary condition is also sufficient. The proof of the sufficiency is not difficult, but it is a bit lengthy, so we shall content ourselves with having proved only half of the following assertion (cf. Theorem 14.7).

Theorem 1. *Let M and N be differentiable functions in a region of $\mathbf{R}^2$. Then there exists a function u such that $du = M\,dx + N\,dy$ if and only if*

$$\frac{\partial M}{\partial y} = \frac{\partial N}{\partial x}. \tag{14}$$

The answer to question (2) above can be given most easily by means of several examples.

Example 9. Consider the equation

$$(3x^2y + 2x)\,dx + (x^3 - 4)\,dy = 0.$$

Since $M = 3x^2y + 2x$, $N = x^3 - 4$, we check that (14) holds:

$$\frac{\partial M}{\partial y} = 3x^2 = \frac{\partial N}{\partial x}.$$

Thus, Theorem 1 guarantees the existence of a potential function u such that $du = M\,dx + N\,dy$. It follows that $M = \dfrac{\partial u}{\partial x}$ and $N = \dfrac{\partial u}{\partial y}$. From the first of these we can write

$$u = \int M\,dx = \int (3x^2y + 2x)\,dx$$

$$= x^3y + x^2 + g(y).$$

(Since the integration was with respect to x, the "constant" of integration must be a function of y.) Now we use the fact that $N = \dfrac{\partial u}{\partial y}$ to determine g:

$$\frac{\partial u}{\partial y} = x^3 + g'(y) = N = x^3 - 4.$$

We conclude that $g'(y) = -4$, or $g(y) = -4y + c_1$. Thus

$$u(x, y) = x^3y + x^2 - 4y + c_1.$$

Since the solution of the equation is $u = $ const., we can, combining several constants into one, write the solution as

$$u(x, y) = x^3y + x^2 - 4y = c.$$

Example 10. Consider the equation

$$(2xy - y^2e^{-x})\,dx + (x^2 + 2ye^{-x} + \cos y)\,dy = 0.$$

Letting $M = 2xy - y^2e^{-x}$, $N = x^2 + 2ye^{-x} + \cos y$, we find that

$$\frac{\partial M}{\partial y} = 2x - 2ye^{-x} = \frac{\partial N}{\partial x}.$$

Thus the equation is exact. To find u, we use the fact that $M = \dfrac{\partial u}{\partial x}$; thus

$$u = \int M \, dx = \int (2xy - y^2 e^{-x}) \, dx$$

$$= x^2 y + y^2 e^{-x} + g(y).$$

We find $g(y)$ by exploiting $\dfrac{\partial u}{\partial y} = N$; thus

$$\frac{\partial u}{\partial y} = x^2 + 2ye^{-x} + g'(y) = N = x^2 + 2ye^{-x} + \cos y.$$

It follows that $g'(y) = \cos y$, $g(y) = \sin y + \text{const.}$, and the solution of the differential equation is

$$x^2 y + y^2 e^{-x} + \sin y = c.$$

EXERCISES

In numbers 1–15 solve the differential equation.

1. $x \, dy - y \, dx - \sqrt{x^2 + y^2} \, dx = 0.$ **2.** $(x - y) \, dx + y \, dy = 0.$

3. $x^3 - 4y^3 + 3xy^2 y' = 0.$ **4.** $2x \, dy + \sqrt{1 - y^2} \, dx = 0.$

5. $(3x^2 + y^2) \, dx = 2xy \, dy.$ **6.** $(2x^3 + 3x^2 y) \, dx + (x^3 + 3y^2) \, dy = 0.$

7. $e^{-x} \sin y \, dx - e^{-x} \cos y \, dy = 0.$ **8.** $y' = \dfrac{x - y}{x + y}.$

9. $x \dfrac{dy}{dx} = x e^{y/x} + y.$ **10.** $(3x^2 y + e^x) \, dx + x^3 \, dy = 0.$

11. $(x^2 + y^2) \, dx - 2xy \, dy = 0.$ **12.** $(x^3 + y^3) \, dx - 3xy^2 \, dy = 0.$

13. $3x^2 y \, dx + (x^3 + y^3) \, dy = 0.$ **14.** $(3x^2 + 2y^2) \, dx + 4xy \, dy = 0.$

15. $(2x - 3y) \, dx + (4x + y) \, dy = 0.$

16. It may happen that $M \, dx + N \, dy$ is not an exact differential but that there exists a function F such that $FM \, dx + FN \, dy$ *is* an exact differential. Such a function F is called an *integrating factor*. Moreover, often the integrating factor can be found by inspection (providing one is up on his differentiation formulas). For example, $y \, dx - x \, dy$ is certainly not exact, but

$$\frac{y \, dx - x \, dy}{y^2} = d\left(\frac{x}{y}\right).$$

Thus, $y\,dx - x\,dy$ has the integrating factor $\dfrac{1}{y^2}$.

Find an integrating factor for each of the following equations and then solve.

(a) $2xy\,dx - x^2\,dy = 0$.

(b) $\dfrac{y}{x}\,dx - \log x\,dy = 0$.

(c) $2\,e^y\,dx + x\,e^y\,dy = 0$.

(d) $y\,dx + (2x + 16y^2)\,dy = 0$.

In numbers 17–20 solve the initial value problem.

17. $(2x + y)\,dx + (x + 2y)\,dy = 0$; $y = 1$ when $x = 0$.

18. $\dfrac{dy}{dx} = \dfrac{x^2 + 4y^2}{xy}$; $y = 1$ when $x = 1$.

19. $-y\,\csc^2 x\,dx + \cot x\,dy = 0$; $y = 2$ when $x = \dfrac{\pi}{4}$.

20. $(8xy + 3y^2)\,dx + (4x^2 + 6xy)\,dy = 0$; $y = -1$ when $x = 1$.

21. At every point (x, y) of a curve the slope is

$$m = \frac{4x^2 + y^2}{2xy}.$$

The point $(1, 1)$ is on the curve. Find its equation. How many such curves are there?

16.4   Linear Equations of the First Order

If the dependent variable is y in a differential equation, then the equation is said to be *linear* if it is of the first degree in y and its derivatives. Thus the most general linear equation of the first order would be

$$p(x)y' + q(x)y = r(x).$$

If the domain of p, q, and r is an interval I, and if we assume that $p(x) \neq 0$ for $x \in I$, we can divide the last equation by p, obtaining what is the standard form of the first order linear equation:

$$\frac{dy}{dx} + P(x)y = Q(x). \tag{15}$$

In order to develop a method of solution, we first remark that the left-hand side of (15) bears *some* resemblance to the derivative of a product. Next we recall that in Exercise 16 after Section 16.3 we introduced the idea of an *integrating factor*, a function F such that $FM\,dx + FN\,dy$ is an exact differential when $M\,dx + N\,dy$ is not. To exploit these remarks, we look at the form of the derivative of a product:

$$\frac{d}{dx}(uy) = u\frac{dy}{dx} + y\frac{du}{dx}. \tag{16}$$

Now suppose there does exist an integrating factor F for the left side of (15). Then we can compare the right side of (16) with

$$F\frac{dy}{dx} + FPy. \tag{17}$$

If such a function F exists, we see that we must have

$$F = u \quad \text{and} \quad FP = \frac{du}{dx},$$

or

$$uP = \frac{du}{dx}.$$

We can separate the variables in this differential equation and solve for u:

$$\frac{du}{u} = P\,dx,$$

or $\log u = \int P\,dx$, or

$$u = e^{\int P\,dx} = F.$$

Moreover, it is easy to see that this function *is* the desired integrating factor:

$$e^{\int P\,dx}\,y' + e^{\int P\,dx}\,Py = \frac{d}{dx}\,(y\,e^{\int P\,dx}).$$

Consequently, if we multiply (15) by this integrating factor, we can write the result as

$$\frac{d}{dx}\,(y\,e^{\int P\,dx}) = Q\,e^{\int P\,dx}.$$

Integrating, we have

$$y\,e^{\int P\,dx} = \int Q(x)\,e^{\int P\,dx}\,dx + c,$$

or

$$y = e^{-\int P\,dx}\int Q(x)\,e^{\int P\,dx}\,dx + c\,e^{-\int P\,dx}. \tag{18}$$

The result expressed in (18) is unquestionably formidable in appearance. We offer the following two mollifying comments. First, by notational modifications we can present the solution in a more acceptable form. We write the equation as

$$y' + hy = k,$$

where h and k are functions continuous on some interval I. Next, let H be an antiderivative of h, i.e., $H' = h$, and multiply through the equation by e^H: $e^H y' + e^H hy = e^H k$, or

$$\frac{d}{dx}\,(ye^H) = ke^H.$$

Now, let K be an antiderivative of ke^H, i.e., $K' = ke^H$; then

$$ye^H = K + c,$$

or

$$y = e^{-H}K + ce^{-H}, \qquad c \text{ constant.} \tag{19}$$

The second comment is to the effect that the formulas of (18) or (19) should not be memorized. Instead, the *technique* leading to these formulas should be kept in mind and followed in solving a specific equation, as we now illustrate.

Example 11. Consider the equation

$$\frac{dy}{dx} + \frac{y}{x} = 4.$$

This can be written as

$$y' + \frac{1}{x}y = 4.$$

In the notation preceding (19) we have $h(x) = \dfrac{1}{x}$, $H(x) = \log x$, $e^{H(x)} = e^{\log x} = x$, the integrating factor. Multiplying by x, we have

$$xy' + y = 4x,$$

or

$$\frac{d}{dx}(xy) = 4x.$$

Thus

$$xy = 2x^2 + c,$$

or

$$y = 2x + cx^{-1}.$$

Example 12. Solve the equation

$$x\frac{dy}{dx} + y + xy - 2e^x = 0.$$

We begin by dividing by x and rearranging the terms:

$$\frac{dy}{dx} + \frac{x+1}{x}y = \frac{2}{x}e^x.$$

In the notation leading to equation (18) we have

$$P(x) = \frac{x+1}{x} = 1 + \frac{1}{x}.$$

Thus $\int P(x)\,dx = x + \log x$, and the integrating factor is $\exp[\int P\,dx] = e^{x+\log x}$ $= xe^x$. Multiplying by this factor, we can write the equation as

$$xe^x y' + (x+1)e^x y = 2e^{2x},$$

or

$$\frac{d}{dx}(xe^x y) = 2e^{2x}.$$

Thus,

$$xe^x y = e^{2x} + c,$$

or

$$y = x^{-1}e^x + cx^{-1}e^{-x}.$$

EXERCISES

In numbers 1–10 find the general solution of the equation.

1. $x\dfrac{dy}{dx} + y = \cos x.$

2. $x^2\dfrac{dy}{dx} - 2xy = 2.$

3. $\dfrac{dy}{dx} = \cos x + y.$

4. $xy' + 2y = x^2.$

5. $y' + (\cot x)y = e^{\cos x}.$

6. $x\,dy - 3y\,dx = x^2\,dx.$

7. $y' + e^x y = 2e^x.$

8. $\dfrac{dy}{dx} - 2y = xe^{2x}.$

9. $(4x + 4y - 1)\,dx = dy.$

10. $\dfrac{dy}{dx} - \dfrac{y}{x} = 4x^2.$

Solve the initial value problems described in exercises 11–15.

11. $xy' - y = 2x^2;\quad y = 4$ when $x = 2.$

12. $y' = \cos x - y;\quad y = 1$ when $x = 0.$

13. $\dfrac{dx}{dt} = \dfrac{2x - t}{t};\quad x = 2$ when $t = 1.$

14. $\dfrac{dy}{dx} = e^{2x} - y;\quad y = \tfrac{2}{3}$ when $x = 0.$

15. $\sin x\,\dfrac{dy}{dx} = \sin 2x - 2y\cos x;\quad y = \dfrac{5}{3}$ when $x = \dfrac{\pi}{6}.$

16. The equation

$$\frac{dy}{dx} + h(x)y = k(x)y^n$$

is known as *Bernoulli's equation*. The presence of the factor y^n on the right means this is not a linear first order equation, except for the trivial cases $n = 0$ and $n = 1$, which we exclude from this discussion.

(a) As a first attempt to transform the Bernoulli equation to something like that in (15) multiply both sides by y^{-n};

$$y^{-n}\frac{dy}{dx} + h(x)y^{1-n} = k(x).$$

(b) Now let $u = y^{1-n}$ and show that the resulting equation in u becomes

$$\frac{du}{dx} + (1-n)h(x)u = (1-n)k(x),$$

a linear equation of the first order.

(c) Find the complete solution of

$$\frac{dy}{dx} + 2xy = 2xy^3.$$

17. Consider the special case of (15) where $Q = 0$ and $P(x) = a$, a constant: $y' + ay = 0$. Show that the general solution is $y = ce^{-ax}$.

16.5 Homogeneous Linear Equations of Second Order

Many physical applications lead to linear differential equations of second or higher order, i.e., to equations such as

$$y^{(n)} + a_1 y^{(n-1)} + \cdots + a_{n-1}y' + a_n y = h, \tag{20}$$

where, in general, $a_1, \ldots, a_n$, and h are functions of x defined on some interval I. As might be expected, the solution and accompanying theory are simpler when the coefficients $a_1, \ldots, a_n$ are constants, and we shall restrict ourselves to this case. Moreover, it also happens that the underlying theory is essentially the same for all $n \geq 2$—although algebraic difficulties might occur for $n > 2$. Consequently, we shall focus our attention on the case $n = 2$. Finally, if the function h on the right is the zero function the equation is called *homogeneous*. Again, it would be anticipated that the solution of homogeneous linear equations presents fewer difficulties than does the solution of nonhomogeneous equations. Because this is so, and also because, as we shall see, the solution of the non-homogeneous equation depends upon that of the corresponding homogeneous equation, we begin our study by considering the *second order, linear, homogeneous* equation with *constant coefficients*:

$$y'' + ay' + by = 0, \tag{21}$$

where a, $b \in \mathbf{R}$.

It will be convenient to denote the left-hand side of (21) by $L(y)$, to be thought of as a linear operator on y. Thus, the Eq. (21) can also be represented as $L(y) = 0$.

Before looking for the specific form of a solution we note that, as a consequence of the linearity and homogeneity of (21), solutions combine linearly: if φ_1 and φ_2 are solutions of (21), then so is $c_1\varphi_1 + c_2\varphi_2$ for arbitrary constants c_1 and c_2. In symbols this assertion is

$$\left. \begin{array}{l} L(\varphi_1) = L(\varphi_2) = 0 \\ c_1, c_2 \in \mathbf{R} \end{array} \right\} \Rightarrow L(c_1\varphi_1 + c_2\varphi_2) = 0.$$

The proof is straightforward:

$$\begin{aligned} L(c_1\varphi_1 + c_2\varphi_2) &= (c_1\varphi_1 + c_2\varphi_2)'' + a(c_1\varphi_1 + c_2\varphi_2)' + b(c_1\varphi_1 + c_2\varphi_2) \\ &= c_1(\varphi_1'' + a\varphi_1' + b\varphi_1) + c_2(\varphi_2'' + a\varphi_2' + b\varphi_2) \\ &= c_1 L(\varphi_1) + c_2 L(\varphi_2) \\ &= 0. \end{aligned}$$

In order to reach a reasonable starting point in our search for a solution to (21) we indulge in the following reflections. For the analogous *first* order linear equation (see Exercise 17 after Section 16.4) the solution is in terms of the exponential function. Also, it is clear from the form of (21) that any solution function must have the property that its derivatives are "essentially the same" as the function. Thus, we are led to look for a solution in the form of $\varphi(x) = e^{mx}$. Now

$$L(e^{mx}) = (m^2 + am + b)e^{mx}.$$

Thus, since $e^{mx} > 0$, all m and all x, $L(e^{mx}) = 0 \Leftrightarrow$

$$q(m) = m^2 + am + b = 0. \tag{22}$$

We call q the *characteristic* or *auxiliary* polynomial for L and $q(m) = 0$ the *auxiliary equation*. It follows that if the roots of $q(m) = 0$ are r_1 and r_2, then

$$\varphi_1(x) = e^{r_1 x} \quad \text{and} \quad \varphi_2(x) = e^{r_2 x}$$

are solutions of (21). Moreover, by linearity,

$$\varphi(x) = c_1 e^{r_1 x} + c_2 e^{r_2 x} \tag{23}$$

will be a solution for all $c_1, c_2 \in \mathbf{R}$.

Example 13. We solve $y'' - 3y' + 2y = 0$. The characteristic equation is

$$q(m) = m^2 - 3m + 2 = (m - 1)(m - 2) = 0,$$

the roots of which are $r_1 = 1$, $r_2 = 2$. Thus we have as solutions $\varphi_1(x) = e^x$, $\varphi_2(x) = e^{2x}$, or, more generally

$$\varphi(x) = c_1 e^x + c_2 e^{2x}. \tag{24}$$

The fact is, although we shall not prove it, that *every* solution of this equation is contained in (24).

Example 14. Consider the equation $y'' - 4y' + 4y = 0$. The auxiliary equation is

$$q(m) = m^2 - 4m + 4 = (m - 2)^2 = 0,$$

the two roots being equal. Thus, we have found only one solution, $\varphi_1(x) = e^{2x}$. Should there be another?

As Example 14 illustrates, if the auxiliary equation has equal roots we are led to essentially only one solution; more exactly, we get the set of solutions $\{\varphi | \varphi(x) = c_1 e^{r_1 x}, c_1 \in \mathbf{R}\}$. But we have come to expect that the general solution to an equation of second order will have two constants. We can arrive at a second, independent, solution by the following limiting process.

Suppose r_1 and r_2, $r_1 \neq r_2$, are roots of the auxiliary equation for L. Then $e^{r_1 x}$ and $e^{r_2 x}$ are solutions of $L(y) = 0$, and, by linearity, so is $e^{r_2 x} - e^{r_1 x}$, To carry out the limiting process we have in mind, we divide by $r_2 - r_1$, the result also being a solution. Then we let $r_2 \to r_1$:

$$\lim_{r_2 \to r_1} \frac{e^{r_2 x} - e^{r_1 x}}{r_2 - r_1} = \lim_{h \to 0} \frac{e^{(r_1 + h)x} - e^{r_1 x}}{h} \qquad (r_2 = r_1 + h)$$

$$= e^{r_1 x} \lim_{h \to 0} \frac{e^{hx} - 1}{h}$$

$$= e^{r_1 x} \lim_{h \to 0} \frac{xe^{hx}}{1} \qquad \text{(l'Hospital's Rule)}$$

$$= xe^{r_1 x}.$$

The preceding is in the category of "intelligent guesswork," suggesting that $\varphi_2(x) = xe^{r_1 x}$ may be a solution of $L(y) = 0$. In order to verify that this is indeed so we first recall that we have been assuming that $q(m) = 0$ has r_1 as its two equal roots. This means that

$$q(m) = m^2 + am + b = (m - r_1)^2,$$

and

$$q'(m) = 2m + a = 2(m - r_1). \tag{25}$$

Since $q(r_1) = 0$, it follows from (25) that

$$q'(r_1) = 2r_1 + a = 0. \tag{26}$$

Now consider $L(\varphi_2)$, or

$$L(xe^{r_1 x}) = (xe^{r_1 x})'' + a(xe^{r_1 x})' + bxe^{r_1 x}$$

$$= e^{r_1 x}(r_1^2 x + 2r_1) + ae^{r_1 x}(r_1 x + 1) + bxe^{r_1 x}$$

$$= e^{r_1 x}[(r_1^2 + ar_1 + b)x + (2r_1 + a)]$$

$$= 0, \qquad \text{since } q(r_1) = q'(r_1) = 0.$$

Thus $\varphi_2(x) = xe^{r_1 x}$ is also a solution; we assert (without proof) that the complete solution of the equation $L(y) = 0$ whose auxiliary equation has both roots equal to r_1 is

$$\varphi(x) = c_1 e^{r_1 x} + c_2 x e^{r_1 x}. \tag{27}$$

Definition 1. *Two functions φ_1 and φ_2 defined on an interval I are **independent** $\Leftrightarrow c_1\varphi_1(x) + c_2\,\varphi_2(x) = 0$, all $x \in I \Rightarrow c_1 = c_2 = 0$.*

It is easy to show (left as an exercise) that $r_1 \neq r_2 \Rightarrow \varphi_1(x) = e^{r_1 x}$ and $\varphi_2(x) = e^{r_2(x)}$ are independent. Similarly, the functions $\psi_1(x) = e^{rx}$ and $\psi_2(x) = xe^{rx}$ are independent. Thus, the effect of (23) and (27) is to write the complete solution as a linear combination of two *independent* solutions.

(Note, by the way, that $\varphi_1(x) = 2e^x$ and $\varphi_2(x) = 3e^x$ are *dependent*, i.e., not independent. Prove this.)

There is more to the present story, as the following illustrates.

Example 15. Consider the equation

$$y'' + 2y' + 5y = 0.$$

The auxiliary equation is

$$q(m) = m^2 + 2m + 5 = 0,$$

the roots of which are

$$r_1 = -1 + 2i, \qquad r_2 = -1 - 2i.$$

Since $r_2 \neq r_1$, we can write the complete solution as in (23):

$$\varphi(x) = c_1' e^{r_1 x} + c_2' e^{r_2 x}$$
$$= c_1' e^{(-1+2i)x} + c_2' e^{(-1-2i)x}$$
$$= e^{-x}[c_1' e^{2ix} + c_2' e^{-2ix}].$$

An obvious difficulty here is that we have not defined the exponential function for complex numbers. In order not to get too deeply involved in functions of a complex variable, we extricate ourselves by calling on old faithful: Leonhard Euler. An identity referred to as *Euler's relation* says

$$e^{i\theta} = \cos\theta + i\sin\theta. \tag{28}$$

Note that it follows from (28) that

$$e^{-i\theta} = \cos(-\theta) + i\sin(-\theta)$$
$$= \cos\theta - i\sin\theta. \tag{29}$$

Using (28) and (29) on the last form for φ gives

$$\varphi(x) = e^{-x}[c_1'(\cos 2x + i\sin 2x) + c_2'(\cos 2x - i\sin 2x)]$$
$$= e^{-x}[(c_1' + c_2')\cos 2x + i(c_1' - c_2')\sin 2x]$$
$$= e^{-x}[c_1\cos 2x + c_2\sin 2x]$$
$$= c_1(e^{-x}\cos 2x) + c_2(e^{-x}\sin 2x).$$

It can be checked that the functions

$$\varphi_1(x) = e^{-x} \cos 2x, \qquad \varphi_2(x) = e^{-x} \sin 2x$$

are solutions of $y'' + 2y' + 5y = 0$; moreover, φ_1 and φ_2 are independent.

In general, if the roots r_1 and r_2 of the auxiliary equation

$$q(m) = m^2 + am + b = 0$$

are complex numbers,

$$r_1 = \alpha + i\beta, \qquad r_2 = \alpha - i\beta$$

(recall that a, $b \in \mathbf{R} \Rightarrow$ complex roots of $q(m) = 0$ are *conjugate* complex numbers), then we can show that

$$\varphi_1(x) = e^{\alpha x} \cos \beta x \quad \text{and} \quad \varphi_2(x) = e^{\alpha x} \sin \beta x$$

are solutions of $L(y) = 0$ and that φ_1 and φ_2 are independent. This enables us to write the complete solution as

$$\varphi(x) = e^{\alpha x}(c_1 \cos \beta x + c_2 \sin \beta x). \tag{30}$$

Consider, for example $\varphi_1(x) = e^{\alpha x} \cos \beta x$. Now

$$\varphi_1'(x) = e^{\alpha x}[-\beta \sin \beta x + \alpha \cos \beta x],$$

and

$$\varphi_1''(x) = e^{\alpha x}[(\alpha^2 - \beta^2) \cos \beta x - 2\alpha\beta \sin \beta x].$$

Thus

$$L(\varphi_1) = e^{\alpha x}\{\alpha^2 - \beta^2) \cos \beta x - 2\alpha\beta \sin \beta x - a\beta \sin \beta x + a\alpha \cos \beta x + b \cos \beta x\}$$

$$= e^{\alpha x}[\alpha^2 - \beta^2 + a\alpha + b) \cos \beta x - (2\alpha\beta + a\beta) \sin \beta x].$$

To show that $L(\varphi_1) = 0$, we recall that $\alpha + i\beta$ is a root r_1 of $q(m) = 0$; thus

$$q(r_1) = (\alpha + i\beta)^2 + a(\alpha + i\beta) + b$$

$$= (\alpha^2 - \beta^2 + a\alpha + b) + i(2\alpha\beta + a\beta) = 0.$$

Since the complex number $x + iy = 0 \Leftrightarrow x = y = 0$, it follows that

$$\alpha^2 - \beta^2 + a\alpha + b = 2\alpha\beta + a\beta = 0.$$

Thus $L(\varphi_1) = 0$. In a similar way we can show that $L(\varphi_2) = 0$. It will be left as an exercise to show that φ_1 and φ_2 are independent.

Example 16. (a) Consider $y'' + y = 0$. The auxiliary equation is $m^2 + 1 = 0$, its roots being $r_1 = i, r_2 = -i$. Thus the complete solution of the equation is

$$\varphi(x) = c_1 \cos x + c_2 \sin x.$$

(b) On the other hand, consider $y'' - y = 0$. Now the auxiliary equation $m^2 - 1 = 0$ has the real roots $r_1 = 1$, $r_2 = -1$. This enables us to write the solution as

$$\varphi(x) = c_1' e^x + c_2' e^{-x}.$$

But if we let $c_1' = \frac{1}{2}(c_1 + c_2)$, $c_2 = \frac{1}{2}(c_1 - c_2)$, then the preceding solution takes the form

$$\varphi(x) = c_1 \frac{e^x + e^{-x}}{2} + c_2 \frac{e^x - e^{-x}}{2}$$

$$= c_1 \cosh x + c_2 \sinh x.$$

EXERCISES

In numbers 1–14 find the complete solution of the equation.

1. $y'' - 4y' + 3y = 0.$

2. $y'' + y' - 2y = 0.$

3. $\dfrac{d^2y}{dx^2} + \omega^2 y = 0,$ ω constant.

4. $\dfrac{d^2y}{dx^2} - \omega^2 y = 0,$ ω constant.

5. $y'' + 6y' + 9y = 0.$

6. $y'' + y' + y = 0.$

7. $y'' - 2y' + y = 0.$

8. $y'' - 2y' + 10y = 0.$

9. $y'' - 2y' + 5y = 0.$

10. $y'' - 2y' - 15y = 0.$

11. $\dfrac{d^2x}{dt^2} - 2\dfrac{dx}{dt} - 8x = 0.$

12. $y'' - 2y' + 17y = 0.$

13. $x'' - 7x' + 10x = 0.$

14. $2y'' + 5y' - 3y = 0.$

In numbers 15–18 solve the initial value problem.

15. $x''(t) - 5x'(t) + 6x(t) = 0;$ $x'(0) = 0, x(0) = 1.$

16. $y'' - y' - 2y = 0;$ $\varphi'(0) = 1, \varphi(0) = 2.$

17. $y'' + 4y' + 4y = 0;$ $\varphi'(0) = 0, \varphi(0) = 2.$

18. $y'' + 4y' + 13y = 0;$ $\varphi'(0) = 4, \varphi(0) = 1.$

In numbers 19–21 solve the boundary value problem.

19. $y'' - 2y' + y = 0;$ $x = 0 \Rightarrow y = 0, x = 1 \Rightarrow y = 2.$

20. $y'' - 2y' + 2y = 0;$ $\varphi(0) = 2, \varphi\left(\dfrac{\pi}{2}\right) = e^{\pi/2}.$

21. $y'' - 2y' + 10y = 0;$ $\varphi(0) = 3, \varphi\left(\dfrac{\pi}{6}\right) = -e^{\pi/6}.$

22. Prove each of the following:

   (a) $r_1 \neq r_2 \Rightarrow \varphi_1(x) = e^{r_1 x}$, $\varphi_2(x) = e^{r_2 x}$ are independent.

   (b) $\varphi_1(x) = e^{rx}$, $\varphi_2(x) = xe^{rx}$ are independent.

   (c) $\varphi_1(x) = 2e^x$, $\varphi_2(x) = 3e^x$ are dependent.

23. Prove that $\varphi_1(x) = e^{ax} \cos \beta x$, $\varphi_2(x) = e^{ax} \sin \beta x$ are independent.

16.6 Nonhomogeneous Linear Equations of Second Order

In this section we give brief consideration to differential equations of the following type:

$$L(y) = y'' + ay' + by = h. \tag{31}$$

We continue to assume that the coefficients a and b are constants, but it is understood that h is a function of x. Thus we shall be studying *nonhomogeneous linear equations of second order with constant coefficients*.

Near the beginning of the preceding section we remarked that the solution of the nonhomogeneous linear equation can be made to depend upon the solution of the corresponding homogeneous equation. To see how this is so, suppose we have found (by guess or by hook or crook) *one* solution φ_p of the equation $L(y) = h$. (We refer to φ_p as a *particular* solution.) Next suppose φ is an arbitrary solution of $L(y) = h$. Then

$$L(\varphi - \varphi_p) = L(\varphi) - L(\varphi_p) \qquad (L \text{ is linear})$$
$$= h - h \qquad (\varphi \text{ and } \varphi_p \text{ are solutions of } L(y) = h)$$
$$= 0.$$

In other words, $\varphi - \varphi_p$ is a solution of the *homogeneous* equation $L(y) = 0$. Now, if φ_1 and φ_2 are two independent solutions of $L(y) = 0$, then, as we have asserted (but have not proven), every solution of $L(y) = 0$ can be expressed as a linear combination of φ_1 and φ_2. It follows that there exist constants c_1 and c_2 such that

$$\varphi - \varphi_p = c_1 \varphi_1 + c_2 \varphi_2, \quad \text{or}$$
$$\varphi = c_1 \varphi_1 + c_2 \varphi_2 + \varphi_p.$$

This result is sufficiently important to have a formal statement.

Theorem 2. Let $L(y) = y'' + ay' + b$, let φ_1 and φ_2 be independent solutions of $L(y) = 0$, and let φ_p be a particular solution of the nonhomogeneous equation $L(y) = h$. Then if φ is an arbitrary solution of $L(y) = h$, there exist constants c_1 and c_2 such that

$$\varphi = c_1 \varphi_1 + c_2 \varphi_2 + \varphi_p. \tag{32}$$

The import of Theorem 2 is, of course, that the solution of the nonhomogeneous equation (31) requires only the solution of the homogeneous equation $L(y) = 0$ and the finding of one particular solution to $L(y) = h$. As we have taken care of the first of these matters in Section 16.5, we need only concern ourselves with the second: the finding of a particular solution.

Only? It turns out that the problem might not be so simple. Various methods have been devised, some amounting essentially to intelligent guessing, others a little more systematic—but not at all intuitive.

In this section we shall discuss a method of the former type, called the *method of undetermined coefficients*. This method has the virtues of being intuitively natural and fairly simple *when it works*—its major drawback is that it does not apply to all choices of the function h.

To be specific, then, we remark that the following types of functions essentially reproduce themselves upon differentiation: polynomials, sine and cosine, and exponential. Thus, if the function h in (31) is any of these, or a finite combination of them, it is reasonable to assume that the particular solution φ_p of $L(y) = h$ is of the same type and to attempt to determine the explicit form of φ_p accordingly. We shall illustrate the technique—and a complication pertaining thereto—by a series of examples.

Example 17. Consider the equation

$$L(y) = y'' + y' - 2y = 4x^2 - 3.$$

First, we note that the general solution of $L(y) = 0$ is

$$\varphi_c(x) = c_1 e^x + c_2 e^{-2x}.$$

This is often called the *complementary function*.

Next, since h is a second degree polynomial, h together with h' and h'' would involve only a quadratic function. Thus we assume that the particular solution is

$$\varphi_p(x) = Ax^2 + Bx + C.$$

Then

$$\varphi_p'(x) = 2Ax + B, \qquad \varphi_p''(x) = 2A,$$

and

$$L(\varphi_p) = -2Ax^2 + 2(A - B)x + (2A + B - 2C).$$

Comparing with $h(x) = 4x^2 - 3$, we have

$$\left\{ \begin{array}{r} -2A = 4 \\ 2A - 2B = 0 \\ 2A + B - 2C = -3 \end{array} \right\}.$$

The solution of this system is readily found to be $A = B = -2$, $C = -\frac{3}{2}$. Thus

$$\varphi_p(x) = -2x^2 - 2x - \tfrac{3}{2},$$

and the general solution is

$$\varphi = \varphi_c + \varphi_p = c_1 e^x + c_2 e^{-2x} - 2x^2 - 2x - \tfrac{3}{2}.$$

Note that if the equation had been

$$y'' + y' = 4x^2 - 3$$

(y is missing), then assuming a quadratic function for φ_p would cause $L(\varphi_p)$ to be a *first degree* polynomial. Obviously, in this case the intelligent guess would be

$$\varphi_p(x) = Ax^3 + Bx^2 + Cx + D.$$

Example 18. We consider

$$L(y) = y'' + y' - 2y = 4e^{2x} + 10 \sin x.$$

This is the same L as in Example 17; thus φ_c is the same as before. We can concentrate on finding a particular solution φ_p. Because of the behavior of the derivatives of e^{2x} and $\sin x$ we assume

$$\varphi_p(x) = Ae^{2x} + B \sin x + C \cos x.$$

Then

$$\varphi_p'(x) = 2Ae^{2x} + B \cos x - C \sin x,$$

$$\varphi_p''(x) = 4Ae^{2x} - B \sin x - C \cos x,$$

and

$$L(\varphi_p) = 4Ae^{2x} - (3B + C) \sin x + (B - 3C) \cos x.$$

Comparing $L(\varphi_p)$ with $h(x) = 4e^{2x} + 10 \sin x$, we have

$$4A = 4, \quad \begin{cases} 3B + C = -10 \\ B - 3C = 0 \end{cases},$$

the solution being $A = 1$, $B = -3$, $C = -1$. Thus

$$\varphi_p(x) = e^{2x} - 3 \sin x - \cos x,$$

and the general solution is

$$\varphi(x) = c_1 e^x + c_2 e^{-2x} + e^{2x} - 3 \sin x - \cos x.$$

Example 19. Suppose we retain the same L, $L(y) = y'' + y' - 2y$, but modify h to be $h(x) = 4e^x + 10 \sin x$. The equation is, then,

$$y'' + y' - 2y = 4e^x + 10 \sin x.$$

If we proceed as before, letting

$$\varphi_p(x) = Ae^x + B \sin x + C \cos x,$$

we would find that

$$L(\varphi_p) = 0 \cdot e^x - (3B + C) \sin x + (B - 3C) \cos x.$$

The reason for this is, of course, that $\varphi_1(x) = e^x$ is one of the solutions of $L(y) = 0$. The way round this minor difficulty is to recall what we did in the case of a repeated root of the auxiliary equation: we use, rather than Ae^x,

Axe^x. Then the exponential part of $L(\varphi_p)$ becomes—note that the terms involving B and C remain the same—$3Ae^x$. Thus

$$A = \tfrac{4}{3} \quad \text{and}$$
$$\varphi_p(x) = \tfrac{4}{3} xe^x - 3 \sin x - \cos x.$$

Example 20. As a final illustration, suppose we have

$$L(y) = y'' + y' - 2y = e^{2x} \cos x. \tag{33}$$

Once again the successful method is reasonably obvious—especially after it has been pointed out: because h is a product involving e^{2x} we can temporarily eliminate this factor by letting

$$y = e^{2x}v$$

Then

$$y' = e^{2x}v' + 2e^{2x}v$$
$$y'' = e^{2x}v'' + 4e^{2x}v' + 4e^{2x}v.$$

The equation in terms of v becomes

$$v'' + 5v' + 4v = \cos x, \tag{34}$$

which has as complementary function

$$v_c(x) = c_1 e^{-x} + c_2 e^{-4x}.$$

We assume for a particular solution

$$v_p(x) = A \cos x + B \sin x.$$

Then

$$v_p'(x) = -A \sin x + B \cos x$$
$$v_p''(x) = -A \cos x - B \sin x.$$

The equations for A and B are

$$\begin{cases} 3A + 5B = 1 \\ -5A + 3B = 0 \end{cases},$$

the solution being $A = \dfrac{3}{34}$, $B = \dfrac{5}{34}$. Thus, the general solution of (34) is

$$v = c_1 e^{-x} + c_2 e^{-4x} + \frac{1}{34}(3 \cos x + 5 \sin x).$$

Since $y = e^{2x}v$, the solution of (33) is

$$y = c_1 e^x + c_2 e^{-2x} + \frac{e^{2x}}{34}(3 \cos x + 5 \sin x).$$

The preceding examples should indicate how one can find a particular integral in the cases when the nonhomogeneous member h is a combination of polynomial, exponential, and sine and cosine functions. One must remember not to attempt this method if, for example, $h(x) = \log x$, or $h(x) = \tan x$, or any other h whose derivatives are "nonreproducing." In such cases a more general method known as "variation of parameters," or—note well!—"variation of constants" can be used.

EXERCISES

In numbers 1–20 find the general solution.

1. $y'' + 3y' + 2y = 2x^2 + x + 1$.

2. $y'' + 3y' + 2y = x + 2e^x$.

3. $y'' + 3y' + 2y = e^{-x}$.

4. $y'' + 3y' + 2y = e^x \cos x$.

5. $y'' - 2y' + 2y = x^3 - 3x + 2$.

6. $y'' - 2y' = 4x^2 + 1$.

7. $y'' - 2y' = x + e^{2x}$.

8. $y'' - 5y' + 6y = x \cos x$.

9. $y'' - 5y' + 6y = 2e^x + \cos x - 3 \sin x$.

10. $y'' - 5y' + 6y = 2e^{2x} + \cos x - 3 \sin x$.

11. $y'' - y = e^x \cos x$.

12. $y'' + y = 4 \sin x \cos x$.

13. $2y'' - 3y' + y = 3 \cos x - e^{-2x} + 4$.

14. $y'' + 2y' + y = \sin x + \sin 2x$.

15. $y'' + 4y = \cos^2 x$.

16. $y'' + y' = e^x + 3x$.

17. $\dfrac{d^2x}{dt^2} - 4\dfrac{dx}{dt} + 3x = 2t - e^{2t} + \cos t$.

18. $y'' + 4y = \cos x$.

19. $y'' - 3y' - 4y = e^{-x} - \cos x$.

20. $y'' + y' - 6y = x^2 e^x$.

Solve the initial value problems in numbers 21–24.

21. $y'' + y = 4$; $\varphi(0) = \varphi'(0) = 0$.

22. $y'' - 3y' + 2y = 2e^{3x}$; $\varphi(0) = \varphi'(0) = 0$.

23. $y'' - 4y' + 3y = x$; $\varphi(0) = -2, \varphi'(0) = 1$.

24. $y'' + y' = 4x^2$; $\varphi(0) = \varphi'(0) = 0$.

16.7   A Few Applications

In this section we indicate, chiefly by means of a few examples, some of the ways in which differential equations occur in geometry and physics.

Example 21. The equation $xy = c$ represents a family of equilateral hyperbolas. (Note that if we count the coordinate axes—the asymptotes for every curve in the family—as one member, then exactly one curve in the family goes through each point (x, y) in the plane.) We seek, if it exists, a second family of curves with the property that each curve of the second family intersects the curves of the first family at right angles. This second family is then called the *orthogonal trajectory* of the first.

We begin our search by calculating the slopes of the curves in the given family: from $xy = c$ we find

$$xy' + y = 0,$$

or

$$\frac{dy}{dx} = -\frac{y}{x}.$$

It follows that for the curves in the second family the derivatives must satisfy

$$\frac{dy}{dx} = \frac{x}{y}.$$

The variables are separable: $y\, dy = x\, dx$, or

$$\tfrac{1}{2}y^2 = \tfrac{1}{2}x^2 + \tfrac{1}{2}c,$$

or

$$y^2 - x^2 = c,$$

a family of equilateral hyperbolas having as asymptotes the lines $y = \pm x$. See Figure 1.

Example 22. (A mixing problem.) A tank contains 100 gallons of salt solution, the initial concentration being 2 lbs of salt per gallon. Brine containing 3 lbs of salt/gallon runs into the tank at the rate of 4 gallons/min. The solution is kept uniform by thorough mixing, and the solution runs out at the same rate of 4 gallons/min. Find the amount of salt in the tank at any instant.

We let $s = s(t) =$ number of pounds of salt in the tank at time t. Then the rate of change of s is

$$\frac{ds}{dt} = 3(4) - 4\,\frac{s}{100},$$

since salt is coming into the tank at the rate of 12 lbs/min and leaving at the rate of $\dfrac{4s}{100}$ lbs/min. The variables are separable in the preceding equation; the solution is

$$\log\,(3 - 0.01s) = -0.04t + c.$$

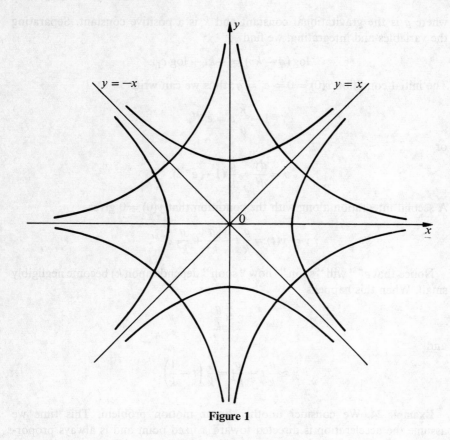

$y = -x$ $y = x$

Figure 1

The initial condition $s(0) = 200$ lbs $\Rightarrow c = 0$, enabling us to write

$$3 - 0.01s = e^{-0.04t},$$

or

$$s = 300 - 100e^{-0.04t}.$$

This shows that the amount of salt in the tank increases toward a least upper bound of 300 lbs.

Example 23. (Motion in a resisting medium.) We consider a body falling from rest subject to the force of gravity. The resistance of the air through which the body falls is assumed to be proportional to the velocity.

We use a vertical y-axis, directed positively *downward*, and assume the initial position of the body is at the origin. The velocity $v = \dfrac{dy}{dt}$ and the acceleration a are related by

$$a(t) = \frac{dv}{dt} = g - kv,$$

where g is the gravitational constant and k is a positive constant. Separating the variables and integrating, we find

$$\log(g - kv) = -kt + \log c_1.$$

The initial condition $v(0) = 0 \Rightarrow c_1 = g$; thus we can write

$$1 - \frac{k}{g}v = e^{-kt},$$

or

$$v = \frac{dy}{dt} = \frac{g}{k}(1 - e^{-kt}).$$

A second integration along with the condition that $y(0) = 0$ gives

$$y = y(t) = \frac{g}{k}t - \frac{g}{k^2} + \frac{g}{k^2}e^{-kt}.$$

Notice that e^{-kt} will "soon" (how "soon" depends upon k) become negligibly small. When this happens

$$v \approx \frac{g}{k}$$

and

$$y \approx \frac{g}{k}t - \frac{g}{k^2} = \frac{g}{k}\left(t - \frac{1}{k}\right).$$

Example 24. We consider another linear motion problem. This time we assume the acceleration is directed toward a fixed point and is always proportional to the (directed) distance the object is from the fixed point. We assume the object starts from rest at a point a units from the fixed point.

We take the x-axis as the line of motion and the fixed point as the origin. Then we have the initial value problem

$$\frac{d^2x}{dt^2} = -\omega^2 x, \qquad x'(0) = 0, \qquad x(0) = a,$$

where ω^2 is a constant.

The auxiliary equation $m^2 + \omega^2 = 0$ has complex roots $m = \pm i\omega$. Thus the general solution is

$$x(t) = c_1 \cos \omega t + c_2 \sin \omega t.$$

Applying the initial condition we find $c_1 = a$, $c_2 = 0$, and

$$x = x(t) = a \cos \omega t.$$

(Cf. Example 8.34.)

Example 25. Again we consider linear motion on the x-axis. We assume, as in Example 24, that the acceleration is proportional to x; moreover, we assume, as in Example 23, that there is a resistance proportional to the velocity. Thus the equation for the acceleration $\dfrac{d^2x}{dt^2}$ can be written

$$\frac{d^2x}{dt^2} = -\omega^2 x - 2kv = -\omega^2 x - 2k\frac{dx}{dt},$$

where ω and $k > 0$ are constants. Using primes for differentiation, we have

$$x''(t) + 2kx'(t) + \omega^2 x(t) = 0.$$

The auxiliary equation $m^2 + 2km + \omega^2 = 0$ has roots

$$r_1 = -k - \sqrt{k^2 - \omega^2},$$
$$r_2 = -k + \sqrt{k^2 - \omega^2}.$$

We consider three possible relationships between k and ω.

(i) $k = \omega$. Then $r_1 = r_2 = -k$ and the general solution is

$$x(t) = (c_1 + c_2 t)e^{-kt}.$$

(ii) $k^2 > \omega^2$. Then r_1 and r_2 are real and unequal. The general solution is

$$x(t) = c_1 e^{r_1 t} + c_2 e^{r_2 t}.$$

(iii) $k^2 < \omega^2$. In this case r_1 and r_2 are complex. If we let $\sqrt{k^2 - \omega^2} = \beta i$, the general solution can be written as

$$x(t) = e^{-kt}(c_1 \cos \beta t + c_2 \sin \beta t).$$

If the initial condition is $x(0) = 0$, $x'(0) = v_0$, then the three cases specified have as particular solutions:

(i) $x(t) = v_0 t e^{-kt}$.

(ii) $x(t) = \dfrac{v_0}{\sqrt{k^2 - \omega^2}} e^{-kt} \sinh \sqrt{k^2 - \omega^2}\, t$.

(iii) $x(t) = \dfrac{v_0}{\beta} e^{-kt} \sin \beta t$.

We leave it as an exercise to verify these particular solutions. With regard to case (iii), we point out that this is the damped vibration illustrated in Example 7.9 (Figure 7.8).

EXERCISES

1. Find the orthogonal trajectories of the following systems. In each case sketch a few curves of both systems.

(a) $x^2 + y^2 = 2ax$.

(b) $ax^2 + y^2 = 1$.

(c) $y = ax^2$.

(d) $y = x + ae^x$.

2. A tank contains (at the beginning) 200 gallons of brine with 100 lbs of salt. Then a solution containing 3 lbs of salt/gallon runs into the tank at the rate of 5 gallons/min; the solution is kept well mixed, and runs out at the same rate. How many pounds of salt are in the tank after 1 hour?

3. A body falls from rest through a medium which gives resistance proportional to the square of the velocity. Describe the motion.
   Hints.
   (1) Let the starting point be the origin on the y-axis directed positively downward. See Example 23.
   (2) Take the constant of proportionality as g/k^2, where g is the gravitational constant.
   (3) Consider what happens to the velocity as $t \to \infty$.

4. Verify the particular solutions given at the end of Example 25. Study the nature of the motion in cases (i) and (ii).

5. (a) Heat is lost by a body at a rate proportional to the difference in temperature between the body and the surrounding medium. If a thermometer reads T_0 degrees indoors and is taken outdoors where the temperature is T_1 degrees, show that the temperature at time t is

   $$T(t) = T_1 + (T_0 - T_1) e^{-k^2 t},$$

   where $-k^2$ is the constant of proportionality.

   (b) If $T_0 = 60°$, $T_1 = 0°$, and if 1 minute after the thermometer is carried outdoors the reading is $30°$, how long will it be until the reading is $10°$?

6. An elastic string of length l with one end fixed has a weighted particle attached to the other end. The equation of motion of the particle is

   $$\frac{d^2 s}{dt^2} = -\frac{g}{k}(s - l),$$

   where k (a constant) is the elongation due to the particle. If $v(0) = 0$ and $s(0) = s_0$, show that

   $$s(t) = (s_0 - l) \cos \sqrt{\frac{g}{k}}\, t + l.$$

Tables

TABLE 1. Common Logarithms

N	0	1	2	3	4	5	6	7	8	9
10	0000	0043	0086	0128	0170	0212	0253	0294	0334	0374
11	0414	0453	0492	0531	0569	0607	0645	0682	0719	0755
12	0792	0828	0864	0899	0934	0969	1004	1038	1072	1106
13	1139	1173	1206	1239	1271	1303	1335	1367	1399	1430
14	1461	1492	1523	1553	1584	1614	1644	1673	1703	1732
15	1761	1790	1818	1847	1875	1903	1931	1959	1987	2014
16	2041	2068	2095	2122	2148	2175	2201	2227	2253	2279
17	2304	2330	2355	2380	2405	2430	2455	2480	2504	2529
18	2553	2577	2601	2625	2648	2672	2695	2718	2742	2765
19	2788	2810	2833	2856	2878	2900	2923	2945	2967	2989
20	3010	3032	3054	3075	3096	3118	3139	3160	3181	3201
21	3222	3243	3263	3284	3304	3324	3345	3365	3385	3404
22	3424	3444	3464	3483	3502	3522	3541	3560	3579	3598
23	3617	3636	3655	3674	3692	3711	3729	3747	3766	3784
24	3802	3820	3838	3856	3874	3892	3909	3927	3945	3962
25	3979	3997	4014	4031	4048	4065	4082	4099	4116	4133
26	4150	4166	4183	4200	4216	4232	4249	4265	4281	4298
27	4314	4330	4346	4362	4378	4393	4409	4425	4440	4456
28	4472	4487	4502	4518	4533	4548	4564	4579	4594	4609
29	4624	4639	4654	4669	4683	4698	4713	4728	4742	4757
30	4771	4786	4800	4814	4829	4843	4857	4871	4886	4900
31	4914	4928	4942	4955	4969	4983	4997	5011	5024	5038
32	5051	5065	5079	5092	5105	5119	5132	5145	5159	5172
33	5185	5198	5211	5224	5237	5250	5263	5276	5289	5302
34	5315	5328	5340	5353	5366	5378	5391	5403	5416	5428
35	5441	5453	5465	5478	5490	5502	5514	5527	5539	5551
36	5563	5575	5587	5599	5611	5623	5635	5647	5658	5670
37	5682	5694	5705	5717	5729	5740	5752	5763	5775	5786
38	5798	5809	5821	5832	5843	5855	5866	5877	5888	5899
39	5911	5922	5933	5944	5955	5966	5977	5988	5999	6010
40	6021	6031	6042	6053	6064	6075	6085	6096	6107	6117
41	6128	6138	6149	6160	6170	6180	6191	6201	6212	6222
42	6232	6243	6253	6263	6274	6284	6294	6304	6314	6325
43	6335	6345	6355	6365	6375	6385	6395	6405	6415	6425
44	6435	6444	6454	6464	6474	6484	6493	6503	6513	6522
45	6532	6542	6551	6561	6571	6580	6590	6599	6609	6618
46	6628	6637	6646	6656	6665	6675	6684	6693	6702	6712
47	6721	6730	6739	6749	6758	6767	6776	6785	6794	6803
48	6812	6821	6830	6839	6848	6857	6866	6875	6884	6893
49	6902	6911	6920	6928	6937	6946	6955	6964	6972	6981
50	6990	6998	7007	7016	7024	7033	7042	7050	7059	7067
51	7076	7084	7093	7101	7110	7118	7126	7135	7143	7152
52	7160	7168	7177	7185	7193	7202	7210	7218	7226	7235
53	7243	7251	7259	7267	7275	7284	7292	7300	7308	7316
54	7324	7332	7340	7348	7356	7364	7372	7380	7388	7396
N	0	1	2	3	4	5	6	7	8	9

TABLE 1 [Contd.]

N	0	1	2	3	4	5	6	7	8	9
55	7404	7412	7419	7427	7435	7443	7451	7459	7466	7474
56	7482	7490	7497	7505	7513	7520	7528	7536	7543	7551
57	7559	7566	7574	7582	7589	7597	7604	7612	7619	7627
58	7634	7642	7649	7657	7664	7672	7679	7686	7694	7701
59	7709	7716	7723	7731	7738	7745	7752	7760	7767	7774
60	7782	7789	7796	7803	7810	7818	7825	7832	7839	7846
61	7853	7860	7868	7875	7882	7889	7896	7903	7910	7917
62	7924	7931	7938	7945	7952	7959	7966	7973	7980	7987
63	7993	8000	8007	8014	8021	8028	8035	8041	8048	8055
64	8062	8069	8075	8082	8089	8096	8102	8109	8116	8122
65	8129	8136	8142	8149	8156	8162	8169	8176	8182	8189
66	8195	8202	8209	8215	8222	8228	8235	8241	8248	8254
67	8261	8267	8274	8280	8287	8293	8299	8306	8312	8319
68	8325	8331	8338	8344	8351	8357	8363	8370	8376	8382
69	8388	8395	8401	8407	8414	8420	8426	8432	8439	8445
70	8451	8457	8463	8470	8476	8482	8488	8494	8500	8506
71	8513	8519	8525	8531	8537	8543	8549	8555	8561	8567
72	8573	8579	8585	8591	8597	8603	8609	8615	8621	8627
73	8633	8639	8645	8651	8657	8663	8669	8675	8681	8686
74	8692	8698	8704	8710	8716	8722	8727	8733	8739	8745
75	8751	8756	8762	8768	8774	8779	8785	8791	8797	8802
76	8808	8814	8820	8825	8831	8837	8842	8848	8854	8859
77	8865	8871	8876	8882	8887	8893	8899	8904	8910	8915
78	8921	8927	8932	8938	8943	8949	8954	8960	8965	8971
79	8976	8982	8987	8993	8998	9004	9009	9015	9020	9025
80	9031	9036	9042	9047	9053	9058	9063	9069	9074	9079
81	9085	9090	9096	9101	9106	9112	9117	9122	9128	9133
82	9138	9143	9149	9154	9159	9165	9170	9175	9180	9186
83	9191	9196	9201	9206	9212	9217	9222	9227	9232	9238
84	9243	9248	9253	9258	9263	9269	9274	9279	9284	9289
85	9294	9299	9304	9309	9315	9320	9325	9330	9335	9340
86	9345	9350	9355	9360	9365	9370	9375	9380	9385	9390
87	9395	9400	9405	9410	9415	9420	9425	9430	9435	9440
88	9445	9450	9455	9460	9465	9469	9474	9479	9484	9489
89	9494	9499	9504	9509	9513	9518	9523	9528	9533	9538
90	9542	9547	9552	9557	9562	9566	9571	9676	9581	9586
91	9590	9595	9600	9605	9609	9614	9619	9624	9628	9633
92	9638	9643	9647	9652	9657	9661	9666	9671	9675	9680
93	9685	9689	9694	9699	9703	9708	9713	9717	9722	9727
94	9731	9736	9741	9745	9750	9754	9859	9763	9768	9773
95	9777	9782	9786	9791	9795	9800	9805	9809	9814	9818
96	9823	9827	9832	9836	9841	9845	9850	9854	9859	9863
97	9868	9872	9877	9881	9886	9890	9894	9899	9903	9908
98	9912	9917	9921	9926	9930	9934	9939	9943	9948	9952
99	9956	9961	9965	9969	9974	9978	9983	9987	9991	9996
N	0	1	2	3	4	5	6	7	8	9

TABLE 2 Trigonometric Functions

↱↓	sin	cos	tan	cot	sec	csc	
0°	.0000	1.0000	.0000	......	1.000	......	90°
1°	.0175	.9998	.0175	57.29	1.000	57.30	89°
2°	.0349	.9994	.0349	28.64	1.001	28.65	88°
3°	.0523	.9986	.0524	19.08	1.001	19.11	87°
4°	.0698	.9976	.0699	14.30	1.002	14.34	86°
5°	.0872	.9962	.0875	11.43	1.004	11.47	85°
6°	.1045	.9945	.1051	9.514	1.006	9.567	84°
7°	.1219	.9925	.1228	8.144	1.008	8.206	83°
8°	.1392	.9903	.1405	7.115	1.010	7.185	82°
9°	.1564	.9877	.1584	6.314	1.012	6.392	81°
10°	.1736	.9848	.1763	5.671	1.015	5.759	80°
11°	.1908	.9816	.1944	5.145	1.019	5.241	79°
12°	.2079	.9781	.2126	4.705	1.022	4.810	78°
13°	.2250	.9744	.2309	4.331	1.026	4.445	77°
14°	.2419	.9703	.2493	4.011	1.031	4.134	76°
15°	.2588	.9659	.2679	3.732	1.035	3.864	75°
16°	.2756	.9613	.2867	3.487	1.040	3.628	74°
17°	.2924	.9563	.3057	3.271	1.046	3.420	73°
18°	.3090	.9511	.3249	3.078	1.051	3.236	72°
19°	.3256	.9455	.3443	2.904	1.058	3.072	71°
20°	.3420	.9397	.3640	2.747	1.064	2.924	70°
21°	.3584	.9336	.3839	2.605	1.071	2.790	69°
22°	.3746	.9272	.4040	2.475	1.079	2.669	68°
23°	.3907	.9205	.4245	2.356	1.086	2.559	67°
24°	.4067	.9135	.4452	2.246	1.095	2.459	66°
25°	.4226	.9063	.4663	2.145	1.103	2.366	65°
26°	.4384	.8988	.4877	2.050	1.113	2.281	64°
27°	.4540	.8910	.5095	1.963	1.122	2.203	63°
28°	.4695	.8829	.5317	1.881	1.133	2.130	62°
29°	.4848	.8746	.5543	1.804	1.143	2.063	61°
30°	.5000	.8660	.5774	1.732	1.155	2.000	60°
31°	.5150	.8572	.6009	1.664	1.167	1.942	59°
32°	.5299	.8480	.6249	1.600	1.179	1.887	58°
33°	.5446	.8387	.6494	1.540	1.192	1.836	57°
34°	.5592	.8290	.6745	1.483	1.206	1.788	56°
35°	.5736	.8192	.7002	1.428	1.221	1.743	55°
36°	.5878	.8090	.7265	1.376	1.236	1.701	54°
37°	.6018	.7986	.7536	1.327	1.252	1.662	53°
38°	.6157	.7880	.7813	1.280	1.269	1.624	52°
39°	.6293	.7771	.8098	1.235	1.287	1.589	51°
40°	.6428	.7660	.8391	1.192	1.305	1.556	50°
41°	.6561	.7547	.8693	1.150	1.325	1.524	49°
42°	.6691	.7431	.9004	1.111	1.346	1.494	48°
43°	.6820	.7314	.9325	1.072	1.367	1.466	47°
44°	.6947	.7193	.9657	1.036	1.390	1.440	46°
45°	.7071	.7071	1.000	1.000	1.414	1.414	45°
	cos	sin	cot	tan	csc	sec	↑↵

TABLE 3. Logarithms to base *e*

N	.0	.1	.2	.3	.4	.5	.6	.7	.8	.9
1	0.000	0.095	0.182	0.262	0.336	0.405	0.470	0.531	0.588	0.642
2	0.693	0.742	0.788	0.833	0.875	0.916	0.956	0.993	1.030	1.065
3	1.099	1.131	1.163	1.194	1.224	1.253	1.281	1.308	1.335	1.361
4	1.386	1.411	1.435	1.459	1.482	1.504	1.526	1.548	1.569	1.589
5	1.609	1.629	1.649	1.668	1.686	1.705	1.723	1.740	1.758	1.775
6	1.792	1.808	1.825	1.841	1.856	1.872	1.887	1.902	1.917	1.932
7	1.946	1.960	1.974	1.988	2.001	2.015	2.028	2.041	2.054	2.067
8	2.079	2.092	2.104	2.116	2.128	2.140	2.152	2.163	2.175	2.186
9	2.197	2.208	2.219	2.230	2.241	2.251	2.262	2.272	2.282	2.293
10	2.303	2.313	2.322	2.332	2.342	2.351	2.361	2.370	2.380	2.389

TABLE 4. e^x and e^{-x}

x	e^x	e^{-x}	x	e^x	e^{-x}
0.0	1.00	1.00	3.1	22.2	.045
0.1	1.11	.905	3.2	24.5	.041
0.2	1.22	.819	3.3	27.1	.037
0.3	1.35	.741	3.4	30.0	.033
0.4	1.49	.670	3.5	33.1	.030
0.5	1.65	.607	3.6	36.6	.027
0.6	1.82	.549	3.7	40.4	.025
0.7	2.01	.497	3.8	44.7	.022
0.8	2.23	.449	3.9	49.4	.020
0.9	2.46	.407	4.0	54.6	.018
1.0	2.72	.368	4.1	60.3	.017
1.1	3.00	.333	4.2	66.7	.015
1.2	3.32	.301	4.3	73.7	.014
1.3	3.67	.273	4.4	81.5	.012
1.4	4.06	.247	4.5	90.0	.011
1.5	4.48	.223	4.6	99.5	.010
1.6	4.95	.202	4.7	110	.0091
1.7	5.47	.183	4.8	122	.0082
1.8	6.05	.165	4.9	134	.0074
1.9	6.69	.150	5.0	148	.0067
2.0	7.39	.135	5.1	164	.0061
2.1	8.17	.122	5.2	181	.0055
2.2	9.02	.111	5.3	200	.0050
2.3	9.97	.100	5.4	221	.0045
2.4	11.0	.091	5.5	245	.0041
2.5	12.2	.082	5.6	270	.0037
2.6	13.5	.074	5.7	299	.0033
2.7	14.9	.067	5.8	330	.0030
2.8	16.4	.061	5.9	365	.0027
2.9	18.2	.055	6.0	403	.0025
3.0	20.1	.050			

Answers to
Odd-numbered Exercises

1.2, p. 4

1. (a) $A \cup B = \{1, 2, 3, 4, 5, 6, 7\}$. (b) $A \cup C = \{1, 2, 3, 4, 5, 7, 8\}$.
   (c) $B \cup C = \{1, 3, 4, 5, 6, 7, 8\}$. (d) $A \cap B = \{3, 4\}$. (e) $A \cap C = \{1, 3\}$.
   (f) $B \cap C = \{3, 5, 7\}$. (g) $(A \cup B) \cup C = \{1, 2, 3, 4, 5, 6, 7, 8\}$. (h) $A \cap (B \cap C) = \{3\}$.
   (i) $A \cap (B \cup C) = \{1, 3, 4\}$. (j) $(A \cap B) \cup (A \cap C) = \{1, 3, 4\}$.
   (k) $A \cup (B \cap C) = \{1, 2, 3, 4, 5, 7\}$. (l) $(A \cup B) \cap (A \cup C) = \{1, 2, 3, 4, 5, 7\}$.

3. (a) $A \cap B = B$. (b) $C \cap E = E$. (c) $B \cap C \cap D = D$. (d) $A \cup C \cup E = A$.
   (e) $A \cap B \cap C \cap D \cap E = E$.

7. (a) $A \cup B = \{x \mid 1 < x \leq 5\} = (1, 5]$. (c) $A \cap B = \varnothing$.

9. No. $A = \{1, 2\}$, $B = \{2, 3\}$, $C = \{3\}$.

11. (a) They are equal. (b) Yes; it equals the set of (a).

13. $A \cap B$ is either empty, a singleton, or an interval.

15. (a) $A \times B = \{(1, x), (1, y), (1, z), (2, x), (2, y), (2, z)\}$.
    (b) $B \times A = \{(x, 1), (x, 2), (y, 1), (y, 2), (z, 1), (z, 2)\}$, $B \times A \neq A \times B$.
    (c) $A \times A = \{(1, 1), (1, 2), (2, 1), 2, 2)\}$;
    $B \times B = \{(x, x), (x, y), (x, z), (y, x), (y, y), (y, z), (z, x), (z, y), (z, z)\}$ (d) $35; 35$.
    (e) $A \times \varnothing = \varnothing$ (f) Either $A = \varnothing$ or $B = \varnothing$ (g) $\mathbf{R} \times \mathbf{R}$ is the xy-plane.

1.3, p. 10

1. $\left. \begin{array}{r} ac = bc \\ c \neq 0 \end{array} \right\} \Rightarrow c^{-1}$ exists $\Rightarrow acc^{-1} = bcc^{-1} \Rightarrow a \cdot 1 = b \cdot 1 \Rightarrow a = b$.

7. b/a.

9. Since (a), *every* number is a solution of $0 \cdot x = 0$ and (b), *no* number is a solution of $0 \cdot x = b$, $b \neq 0$, division by 0 can never have a *unique* answer, and therefore is considered to be undefined.

1.4, p. 17

1. (a) $S = \{x \mid x < 3\}$.
 (b) $S = \{x \mid x > 2\}$.
 (c) $S = \{x \mid 0 < x < 3\}$.
 (d) $S = \{x \mid x < 0\} \cup \{x \mid x > 3\}$.
 (e) $S = \{x \mid x < -4\} \cup \{x \mid x > 2\}$.
 (f) $S = \{x \mid -2 < x < 5\}$.
 (g) $S = \{x \mid x < -6\} \cup \{x \mid x > -3\}$.
 (h) $S = \{x \mid 0 < x < 1\}$.
 (i) $S = \{x \mid 1 < x < 2\} \cup \{x \mid x > 3\}$.
 (j) $S = \mathbf{R}$.
 (k) $S = \varnothing$.
 (l) $S = \{x \mid -3 < x < 5\}$.
 (m) $S = \{x \mid -2 < x < 3\}$.
 (n) $S = \{x \mid x < -4\} \cup \{x \mid x > -2\}$.
 (o) $S = \mathbf{R}$.
 (p) $S = \varnothing$.
 (q) $S = \mathbf{R}$.
 (r) $S = \{x \mid x > 1\}$.

3. $a < b \Leftrightarrow b > a \Leftrightarrow b + (-a) > a + (-a) \Leftrightarrow b - a > 0$.

5. (a) $ab \in \mathbf{R}^+ \Rightarrow ab > 0$;

 (i) $a \in \mathbf{R}^+ \Rightarrow a > 0 \Rightarrow \dfrac{1}{a} > 0 \Rightarrow \dfrac{1}{a}(ab) > 0 \Rightarrow b > 0 \Rightarrow b \in \mathbf{R}^+$

 (ii) $a \in \mathbf{R}^- \Rightarrow a < 0 \Rightarrow \dfrac{1}{a} < 0 \Rightarrow \dfrac{1}{a}(ab) < 0 \Rightarrow b < 0 \Rightarrow b \in \mathbf{R}^-$.

 (b) $ab \in \mathbf{R}^- \Rightarrow ab < 0$;

 (i) $a \in \mathbf{R}^+ \Rightarrow a > 0 \Rightarrow \dfrac{1}{a} > 0 \Rightarrow \dfrac{1}{a}(ab) < 0 \Rightarrow b < 0 \Rightarrow b \in \mathbf{R}^-$

 (ii) $a \in \mathbf{R}^- \Rightarrow a < 0 \Rightarrow \dfrac{1}{a} < 0 \Rightarrow \dfrac{1}{a}(ab) > 0 \Rightarrow b > 0 \Rightarrow b \in \mathbf{R}^+$.

1.5, p. 24

3. $\dbinom{n}{n-k} = \dfrac{n!}{(n-k)![n-(n-k)]!} = \dfrac{n!}{(n-k)!\,k!} = \dbinom{n}{k}$.

5. The number of selections of $n - k$ objects from n objects is equal to the number of selections of k objects from n objects.

7. (c) *Hint.* Show

$$\sum_{k=1}^{n} \frac{k}{n}\binom{n}{k} = \sum_{k=1}^{n}\binom{n-1}{k-1} = \sum_{r=0}^{n-1}\binom{n-1}{r} = 2^{n-1}.$$

 (d) See Hint for (c).

1.6, p. 35

1. (a) $X = \mathbf{R}$.
 (b) $X = \{x \mid x \neq 0\}$.
 (c) $X = \{x \mid x \neq -1\}$.
 (d) $X = \{x \mid x^2 \geq 1\}$.
 (e) $X = \{x \mid x^2 \neq 1\}$.
 (f) $X = \mathbf{R}$.
 (g) $X = \{x \mid x \leq -1\} \cup \{x \mid x \geq 3\}$.
 (h) $X = \{x \mid -1 \leq x \leq 1\}$.

3. (a) $X = \mathbf{R}, f[X] = \{y \mid y \geq -9\}$ (b) $f(2) = -8$ (c) $\{-2, 4\}$ (d) $\{-1, 3\}$.
 (e) $\{x \mid -5 < f(x) < 0\} = \{x \mid -2 < x < -1\} \cup \{x \mid 3 < x < 4\}$.
 (f) $\{x \mid f(x) \geq 0\} = \{x \mid x \leq -2\} \cup \{x \mid x \geq 4\}$.

5. (a) $X_f \cap X_g = \{x \mid x \geq 0\}$.
 (b) $X_f \cap X_g = \{x \mid x \neq \pm 2, \pm 3\}$.
 (c) $X_f \cap X_g = \varnothing$.
 (d) $X_f \cap X_g = \{x \mid x \neq \pm 2\}$.

7. f and g of (a). f and g of (c). g of (d).

9. (a) $(f \circ g)(x) = \sqrt{x^2} = |x|,$ $X = \mathbf{R}.$
   $(g \circ f)(x) = (\sqrt{x})^2,$ $X = \{x \mid x \geq 0\}.$
   (b) $(f \circ g)(x) = (\sqrt{x-1})^2 + 1,$ $X = \{x \mid x \geq 1\}$
   $(g \circ f)(x) = \sqrt{x^2} = |x|,$ $X = \mathbf{R}.$
   (c) $(f \circ g)(x) = (g \circ f)(x) = x,$ $X = \mathbf{R}.$
   (d) $(f \circ g)(x) = (g \circ f)(x) = \dfrac{1}{1/x} = x, x \neq 0,$ $X = \{x \mid x \neq 0\}.$
   (e) $(f \circ g)(x) = -x^2 - 11,$ $X = \mathbf{R}.$
   $(g \circ f)(x) = \sqrt{x^4 + 14x^2 + 53},$ $X = \mathbf{R}.$
   (f) $(f \circ g)(x) = \dfrac{2x^2}{x^4 + 1},$ $X = \mathbf{R}$
   $(g \circ f)(x) = \dfrac{x^4 + 1}{-2x^2},$ $X = \{x \mid \neq 0\}.$
   (g) $(f \circ g)(x) = (g \circ f)(x) = x^2 - 2,$ $X = \mathbf{R}.$
   (h) $(f \circ g)(x) = (g \circ f)(x) = \dfrac{x^2 + 4}{x^2 - 7},$ $X = \{x \mid x^2 \neq 7\}.$
   (i) $(f \circ g)(x) = (g \circ f)(x) = g(x),$ $X = X_g.$

11. (a) $f.$ (e) 1.   (h) $(f \circ 0)(x) = f(0).$
    (b) $f.$ (f) $(f \circ 1)(x) = f(1).$ (i) $(f \circ \mathbf{c})(x) = f(c).$
    (c) $f.$ (g) $0 \circ f = 0.$ (j) $\mathbf{c} \circ f = \mathbf{c}.$
    (d) $f.$

1.7, p. 42

1. (a) Intercepts: $(\frac{1}{2}, 0),$ $(0, -1)$
      $x < \frac{1}{2} \Rightarrow f(x) < 0;$ $x > \frac{1}{2} \Rightarrow f(x) > 0.$
   (b) Intercepts: $(1, 0),$ $(-1, 0),$ $(0, -1).$
      $x^2 > 1 \Rightarrow f(x) > 0;$ $-1 < x < 1 \Rightarrow -1 < f(x) < 0.$
   (c) Intercepts: $(1, 0),$ $(0, 1)$ $f(x) \geq 0,$ all $x.$
   (d) Intercepts: $(-\frac{1}{2}, 0),$ $(0, -1).$
      $x < -\frac{1}{2} \Rightarrow f(x) > 0;$ $x > -\frac{1}{2} \Rightarrow f(x) < 0.$
   (e) Intercepts: $(1, 0),$ $(-1, 0),$ $(0, 0).$
      $-1 < x < 1 \Rightarrow f(x) < 0;$ $x^2 > 1 \Rightarrow f(x) > 0.$
   (f) Intercepts: $(-\frac{1}{2}, 0),$ $(0, 1)$
      $x < -\frac{1}{2} \Rightarrow f(x) < 0;$ $x > -\frac{1}{2} \Rightarrow f(x) > 0.$
   (g) No intercepts; $f(x) > 0,$ all $x \neq 0;$ $|x|$ small $\Rightarrow f(x)$ large, $|x|$ large $\Rightarrow f(x)$ small.
   (h) No intercepts; $f(x) > 0,$ all $x \neq 2.$ $|x - 2|$ small $\Rightarrow f(x)$ large, $|x - 2|$ large $\Rightarrow f(x)$ small.
   (i) Intercepts: $(1, 0),$ $(0, 1);$ $f(x) \geq 0,$ all $x.$ "Corner" at $(1, 0).$
   (j) No intercepts; $x < 0 \Rightarrow f(x) = -1;$ $x > 0 \Rightarrow f(x) = 1.$
   (k) Intercept: $(0, 0);$ $x < 0 \Rightarrow f(x) < 0; x > 0 \Rightarrow f(x) > 0.$
   (l) Intercepts: $(-1, 0),$ $(0, 0),$ $(1, 0);$ $x < -1 \Rightarrow f(x) < 0$
      $-1 < x < 0 \Rightarrow f(x) > 0, 0 < x < 1 \Rightarrow f(x) < 0, x > 1 \Rightarrow f(x) > 0.$
   (m) Intercepts: $(\frac{1}{2}, 0),$ $(0, 1);$ $f(x) \geq 0,$ all $x;$ corner at $(\frac{1}{2}, 0).$
   (n) Intercept: $(0, 1);$ $0 < f(x) \leq 1,$ all $x.$
   (o) Intercept: $(0, 0);$ $0 \leq f(x) < 1$ all $x.$
   (p) Intercepts: $(-2, 0),$ $(3, 0),$ $(0, -6);$ $-2 < x < 3 \Rightarrow f(x) < 0.$
   (q) Intercepts: $(-2, 0),$ $(3, 0),$ $(0, 6);$ $f(x) \geq 0,$ all $x.$

5. (1) $a = b = 0$: x-axis.
   (2) $a \neq 0,$ $b = 0$: line, neither horizontal nor vertical, through origin.
   (3) $a = 0,$ $b \neq 0$: horizontal line, $|b|$ units from x-axis, above if $b > 0,$ below if $b < 0.$
   (4) $a \neq 0,$ $b \neq 0$: line, neither horizontal nor vertical, not through origin—but through $(0, b).$

1.8, p. 53

1. (a) $m_{AB} = 3/7$, $m_{BC} = -7/3$;

$$\overline{AC}^2 = 116 = \overline{AB}^2 + \overline{BC}^2; \quad \overline{AB} = \overline{BC} \Rightarrow \text{angle } BAC = \text{angle BCA}.$$

(b) $m_{BC} = -5/2$, $m_{AC} = 2/5$; $\quad \overline{BC}^2 + \overline{AC}^2 = \overline{AB}^2 = 290$.

(c) $m_{AC}\, m_{BC} + 1 = 0$; $\quad \overline{AC}^2 + \overline{BC}^2 = \overline{AB}^2 = 225$.

3. (a) neither. (e) even. (h) even.
(b) odd. (f) even. (i) odd.
(c) odd. (g) even. (j) neither.
(d) odd.

5. (a) odd. (d) even. (g) even.
(b) neither. (e) odd. (h) odd.
(c) even. (f) even. (i) even.

7. $(x - h)^2 + (y - k)^2 = 1$.

1.9, p. 63

1. (a) $x + 3y = 0$. (b) $5x + 9y + 7 = 0$. (c) $2x - y = 4$. (d) $2x - y + 9 = 0$.
(e) $x + 2y - 5 = 0$.

3. (a) y-intercept $(0, -3/2)$. (b) x-intercept $(-3/4, 0)$. (c) slope $m = -2$.

7. The set of all points lying *below* the line $y = -2x + 3$.

11. (a) $(x - 3)^2 + (y - 4)^2 = 25$. (b) $(x + 2)^2 + (y - 4)^2 = 16$
(c) $2x^2 + 2y^2 + 12x + 8y - 23 = 0$.

2.1, p. 73

1. (a) $y = 4x - 4$. (d) $y = 2x - 1$. (g) $y = 3$.
(b) $y = 0$. (e) $y = mx + b$. (h) $y = x$.
(c) $y = 2ax - a^2$. (f) $y = 4$. (i) $y = -x$.

3. (a) The graph would appear to be the union of the x-axis and the line $y = 1$.
(b) The tangent line would not exist at any point.

5. (a) (i) 2, (ii) 3, (iii) 1/9. (b) (i) 2, (ii) 3, (iii) 1/9. (c) $h \neq 0$.

7. (a) $s = 4t$. (b) $v = 4$ ft/sec.

9. (a) $\delta(a) = 1$ mass unit/cm. (b) $\delta(a) = 2a$ mass units/cm.

2.2, p. 82

1. (a) $f'(x_0) = 2x_0$. (c) $f'(x_0) = -16x_0$.
(b) $f'(x_0) = 6x_0$. (d) $f'(x_0) = 2cx_0$.

3. (a) $f'(3) = 7$. (c) $f'(4) = -1/32$.
(b) $f'(2) = 12$. (d) $f'(5) = 1/4$.

5. (a) $X_f = \{x \mid x > 0\} = \mathbf{R}^+$. (b) $f'(x) = \dfrac{-1}{2x^{3/2}}$. (c) $X_{f'} = \mathbf{R}^+$.

7. (a) $f'(t) = 2at + b$. (b) $(f')'(t) = 2a$. (c) $(f')'$ is the instantaneous rate of change of f'.

1.3, p. 91

1. (a) $f'(x) = 6x^2 - 14x - 4$ (b) $f'(x) = 4x^3 + 12x^2 - 16x + 12$.

   (c) $f'(x) = -(x^2 + 1)\sin x + 2x\cos x$ (d) $f'(x) = \dfrac{4x}{(x^2 + 1)^2}$.

   (e) $f'(x) = \dfrac{-(3x^2 + x - 1)}{2\sqrt{x}(x^2 + x + 1)^2}$ (f) $f'(x) = \dfrac{-2x}{(x^2 - 1)^2}$ (g) $f'(x) = 2(\cos^2 x - \sin^2 x)$.

   (h) $f'(x) = \dfrac{-1}{\sqrt{x}(1 + \sqrt{x})^2}$ (i) $f'(x) = \dfrac{5x^2 - 26x + 22}{(x^2 + x - 7)^2}$ (j) $f'(x) = \dfrac{1 - \log x}{x^2}$.

   (k) $f'(x) = 2x + 3 - \dfrac{2}{x^2} + \dfrac{14}{x^3}$ (l) $f'(x) = 5x^{3/2} + 9/2\, x^{1/2} - \tfrac{1}{2}x^{-1/2}$.

3. (a) $f'(x) = \dfrac{1}{x^2}$ (b) $f'(x) = 1 - 7x^{-2} = 1 - \dfrac{7}{x^2}$ (c) $f'(x) = -2x^{-3} + 4x^{-2} = \dfrac{4x - 2}{x^3}$.

   (d) $f'(x) = \dfrac{-x^2 + 2x + 18}{x^4} = -x^{-2} + 2x^{-3} + 18\, x^{-4}$ (e) $f'(x) = \tfrac{1}{2}x$.

5. For the implication $\Rightarrow$ first use the second part of the hypothesis to write $D(af + bg) = D(af) + D(bg)$. Now use the first part of the hypothesis on each of these terms; thus

$$D(af + bg) = D(af) + D(bg) = a(Df) + b(Dg).$$

   For the implication $\Leftarrow$ the first assertion can be obtained from the hypothesis by setting $a = c$ and $b = 0$; the second assertion follows from $a = b = 1$.

7. Let

$$\left(\sum_{k=1}^{n} f_k\right)' = \sum_{k=1}^{n} f_k'$$

be denoted by (*). Let

$$S = \{n \in \mathbf{N} \,|\, (*) \text{ holds for } n\}.$$

   Clearly $1 \in S$, and, by Theorem 2a, $2 \in S$. Next, suppose $n \in S$ and consider $n + 1$ differentiable functions $f_1, \ldots, f_n, f_{n+1}$. Then

$$\left(\sum_{k=1}^{n+1} f_k\right)' = \left(\sum_{k=1}^{n} f_k + f_{n+1}\right)' = \left(\sum_{k=1}^{n} f_k\right)' + f_{n+1}' \qquad \text{(Theorem 2a)}$$

$$= \sum_{k=1}^{n} f_k' + f_{n+1}' \qquad \text{(since } n \in S)$$

$$= \sum_{k=1}^{n+1} f_k'.$$

   This says that $n \in S \Rightarrow n + 1 \in S$. Thus $S = \mathbf{N}$.

9. $D\left(\dfrac{f}{g}\right) = D\left(f \cdot \dfrac{1}{g}\right) = fD\left(\dfrac{1}{g}\right) + \dfrac{1}{g}\, Df \qquad \text{(Theorem 3)}$

$$= f\left(\dfrac{-g'}{g^2}\right) + \dfrac{1}{g}f' \qquad \text{(Theorem 4)}$$

$$= \dfrac{-fg'}{g^2} + \dfrac{f'}{g}$$

$$= \dfrac{gf' - fg'}{g^2}.$$

2.4, p. 96

1. $F'(x) = 21(3x + 1)^6$.

3. $F'(x) = 10x \cos (5x^2 + 3)$.

5. $F'(x) = -6x^2 \sin (2x^3 + 3)$.

7. $F'(x) = \dfrac{-8}{5} x(3 - 4x^2)^{-4/5}$.

9. $F'(x) = 4 \sin 2x \cos 2x = 2 \sin 4x$.

11. (a) $F(x) = f(g(x)) = f(c)$
(b) $F'(x) = 0$
(c) $F'(x) = f'(g(x))g'(x) = f'(c) \cdot 0 = 0$.

2.5, p. 101

1. (a) $y = -2x + 6$; $y + 1 = 0$; $y = 4x - 21$. (b) $y + 1 = 0$; $y = 12x - 17$.
(c) $y + 1 = 0$; $x + y + 1 = 0$ (d) $x - \sqrt{3}y - 4 = 0$ (e) $x + 2y + 4 = 0$.
(f) $y = x$; $y - \dfrac{1}{2} = \dfrac{\sqrt{3}}{2}\left(x - \dfrac{\pi}{6}\right)$; $y = 1$ (g) $x = 0$; $x - 4y + 4 = 0$ (h) $y = x - 1$.
(i) $x - 12y + 4 = 0$; $x = 0$ (j) $3x - y - 4 = 0$; $y = 0$.

3. (a) $v(t) = 2t - 8$ cm/sec, $a(t) = 2$ cm/sec^2
$s(0) = 7$ cm, $v(0) = -8$ cm/sec, $0 < t < 4 \Rightarrow v < 0$, $t > 4 \Rightarrow v > 0$.
(b) $v(t) = 2t + 1$ cm/sec, $a(t) = 2$ cm/sec^2
$s(0) = 1$ cm, $v(0) = 1$ cm/sec; $t \geq 0 \Rightarrow v > 0$.
(c) $v(t) = \cos t$ cm/sec, $a(t) = -\sin t$ cm/sec^2
$s(0) = 0$ cm, $v(0) = 1$ cm/sec
$v > 0$ for $2k\pi < t < (2k + 1)\pi$, $k = 0, 1, 2, \dots$.
(d) $v(t) = 3t^2 - 6t + 3$ cm/sec, $a(t) = 6t - 6$ cm/sec^2
$s(0) = 0$ cm, $s(1) = 1$ cm, $s(2) = 2$ cm, $v(0) = 3$ cm/sec
$0 \leq t < 1 \Rightarrow v > 0$, $v(1) = 0$, $t > 1 \Rightarrow v > 0$.
(e) $\begin{cases} 0 \leq t < 3, & v(t) = 2t \text{ cm/sec} \\ 3 < t, & v(t) = -3t^2 \text{ cm/sec} \end{cases}$, $\begin{cases} 0 \leq t < 3, & a(t) = 2 \text{ cm/sec}^2 \\ 3 < t, & a(t) = -6t \text{ cm/sec}^2 \end{cases}$.
$s(0) = 1$ cm, $v(0) = 0$ cm/sec, $v(3)$ does not exist.
The particle may have been given a shove backwards when $t = 3$ sec.
(f) $v(t) = \dfrac{1}{(t + 1)^2}$ cm/sec, $a(t) = \dfrac{-2}{(t + 1)}$ cm/sec^2
$s(0) = 0$ cm, $v(0) = 1$ cm/sec, $t \geq 0 \Rightarrow v(t) > 0$, $t \geq 0 \Rightarrow 0 \leq s < 1$ cm.
(g) $v(t) = \dfrac{t^2 + 2t}{(t + 1)^2} = \dfrac{t^2 + 2t + 1 - 1}{(t + 1)^2} = 1 - \dfrac{1}{(t + 1)^2}$ cm/sec
$a(t) = \dfrac{2}{(t + 1)^3}$ cm/sec^2
$s(0) = 0$ cm, $v(0) = 0$ cm/sec
$t \geq 0 \Rightarrow 0 \leq v < 1$ cm/sec.

5. (a) $f'(x) = 2ax + b$, $f''(x) = 2a$. (b) $f'(x) = \dfrac{1}{x}$, $f''(x) = \dfrac{-1}{x^2}$.
(c) $f'(x) = \cos x$, $f''(x) = -f(x)$. (d) $f'(x) = -\sin x$, $f''(x) = -f(x)$.
(e) $f' = f'' = f$. (f) $f'(x) = 3x^2 - 12x + 11$, $f''(x) = 6x - 12$.
(g) $f'(x) = 3x^2 - 6x + 3$, $f''(x) = 6x - 6$.
(h) $f'(x) = \dfrac{-(x + 1)}{2\sqrt{x}(x - 1)^2}$, $f''(x) = \dfrac{3x^2 + 6x - 1}{4x^{3/2}(x - 1)^3}$.
(i) $f'(x) = \dfrac{1 - x^2}{(1 + x^2)^2}$, $f''(x) = \dfrac{2x(x^2 - 3)}{(x^2 + 1)^3}$.

7. (a) $f'(x) = 3x^2 - 6x$; $f''(x) = 6x - 6$.

    (c) $f''(x) < 0 \Rightarrow$ tangent line lies above the curve,

        $f''(x) > 0 \Rightarrow$ tangent line lies below the curve.

2.6, p. 108

1. The function f is nondecreasing on:

    (a) $\mathbf{R}$.

    (b) $\{x \mid x \geq 0\}$.

    (c) $\mathbf{R}$.

    (d) $\mathbf{R}$.

    (e) $\{x \mid x \geq 0\}$.

    (f) $(-\infty, -3) \cup (5, \infty)$.

    (g) $\mathbf{R}$.

    (h) $(-\infty, 0)$.

    (i) $\mathbf{R}$.

    (j) $(-\infty, -1) \cup (-1, 0)$.

    (k) $(-\infty, -4) \cup (-4, 1.6) \cup (5.4, \infty)$.

3. (a) No.   **(b)** No.

7. (a) $v(t) = \dfrac{-1}{(t+1)^2}$ **(b)** $|v(0)| \geq |v(t)|$, $t \geq 0$. The maximum *speed* occurs when $t = 0$.

    (c) $v'(0) = 2$ **(d)** No. The maximum occurs at an *endpoint* of the interval.

9. (a) No absolute max or min on $(0, 1)$ **(b)** No absolute max or min on $(0, 1)$.

    (c) Absolute max at $(\frac{1}{2}, \frac{1}{2})$; no absolute min   **(d)** Absolute min at $(\frac{1}{2}, 0)$; no absolute max.

2.7, p. 116

1. (a) $\displaystyle\int_2^6 (1 - \tfrac{1}{2}x)\,dx = -4$. The region lies below the x-axis: $y < 0$.

    (b) $\displaystyle\int_0^4 (1 - \tfrac{1}{2}x)\,dx = 0$. The region lies half above and half below the x-axis.

3. (a) $z_i = x_{i-1} = 1 + (i-1)\dfrac{4}{n}$; $f(z_i) = \dfrac{5}{4} + \dfrac{i-1}{n}$.

5. Take a regular partition of $[0, b]$. Then $\Delta x = b/n$ and

$$x_k = k\,\frac{b}{n}, \, k = 0, 1, 2, \ldots, n; \, z_k = x_k = k\,\frac{b}{n}, \, k = 1, 2, \ldots, n.$$

Also

$$\sum_{k=1}^{n} f(z_k)\,\Delta x_k = \sum_{k=1}^{n} (z_k)^m\,\Delta x = \sum_{k=1}^{n} \left(k\,\frac{b}{n}\right)^m \frac{b}{n}$$

$$= \frac{b^{m+1}}{n^{m+1}} \sum_{k=1}^{n} k^m$$

$$= \frac{b^{m+1}}{n^{m+1}} \left[\frac{1}{m+1}\,n^{m+1} + c_m n^m + c_{m-1} n^{m-1} + \cdots \right]$$

$$= b^{m+1} \left[\frac{1}{m+1} + c_m \cdot \frac{1}{n} + c_{m-1}\,\frac{1}{n^2} + \cdots \right] \rightarrow \frac{b^{m+1}}{m+1} \text{ as } n \rightarrow \infty.$$

7. (a) $m = \dfrac{10^3}{3}$ mass units.   **(c)** $\dfrac{10^3}{3} - \dfrac{5^3}{3} = \dfrac{875}{3}$ mass units.

    (b) $\dfrac{5^3}{3}$ mass units.   **(d)** $\displaystyle\int_a^c f + \int_c^b f = \int_a^b f$.

2.8, p. 124

1. (a) $\int 1\,dx = x + c.$

(f) $\int x^n\,dx = \dfrac{1}{n+1}\,x^{n+1} + c.$

(b) $\int c\,dx = cx + c_1.$

(g) $\int cx^n\,dx = \dfrac{c}{n+1}\,x^{n+1} + c_1.$

(c) $\int x\,dx = \dfrac{1}{2}\,x^2 + c.$

(h) $\int (x + x^2)\,dx = \dfrac{1}{2}\,x^2 + \dfrac{1}{3}\,x^3 + c.$

(d) $\int x^2\,dx = \dfrac{1}{3}\,x^3 + c.$

(i) $\int (x^m + x^n)\,dx = \dfrac{1}{m+1}\,x^{m+1} + \dfrac{1}{n+1}\,x^{n+1} + c.$

(e) $\int x^3\,dx = x^4 + c.$

3. (a) $\int_2^6 \left(1 - \dfrac{1}{2}\,x\right) dx = x - \dfrac{1}{4}\,x^2 \Big|_2^6 = \left(6 - \dfrac{1}{4}\,6^2\right) - \left(2 - \dfrac{1}{4}\,2^2\right) = -4.$

(b) $\int_0^4 \left(1 - \dfrac{1}{2}\,x\right) dx = x - \dfrac{1}{4}\,x^2 \Big|_0^4 = 4 - 4 = 0.$

5. $A = 4$ square units.

7. $A = 1$ square unit.

9. Hint: $\displaystyle\sum_{i=1}^{n+1} f_i = \sum_{i=1}^{n} f_i + f_{n+1} = g + f_{n+1},$ where $g = \displaystyle\sum_{i=1}^{n} f_i.$

11. (a) Average $= 6.4.$
(b) no.

2.9, p. 129

1. (a) $x^2 - x + c.$

(d) $\dfrac{2}{5}\,x^5 - x^4 - \dfrac{1}{3}\,x^3 + 3x^2 + 4x + c.$

(b) $\dfrac{1}{3}\,x^3 + \dfrac{3}{2}\,x^2 - x + c.$

(e) $\dfrac{1}{3}\,x^3 - \dfrac{2}{x} + c.$

(c) $-3\cos x + 2e^x + c.$

(f) $\dfrac{1}{3}\,x^3 + \dfrac{3}{2}\,x^2 + 5x + \dfrac{2}{x} - \dfrac{7}{2x^2} + c.$

3. (a) $\frac{2}{3}x^{3/2} + c.$
(d) $\frac{2}{3}x^{3/2} + 2x^{1/2} + c.$
(b) $\frac{3}{4}x^{4/3} + c.$
(e) $\frac{6}{7}x^{7/2} - \frac{8}{5}x^{5/2} + \frac{14}{3}x^{3/2} + c.$
(c) $\frac{3}{5}x^{5/3} + c.$
(f) $\frac{16}{5}x^{5/2} - 2x^2 - 2x + 2x^{1/2} + c.$

5. $s(t) = t^2 - t^3.$

7. (a) $F(x) = nx + c_n,\ n \le x < n+1,\ n = 0, \pm 1, \pm 2, \dots, c_n$ arbitrary.
(b) The constants c_n can be chosen so that the graph is continuous. Arbitrary or random choice of the c_n will likely produce jumps in the graph.

9. (a) $f.$ **(b)** $f + c.$ **(c)** No. The arbitrary constant in (b). **(d)** $f(x).$ **(e)** $f(x) - f(a).$
(f) The difference is the number $f(a).$ The results are the same $\Leftrightarrow f(a) = 0.$

2.10, p. 141

1. (a) 36. **(c)** 1/4. **(e)** 1013/4.
(b) 148/3. **(d)** $1/(n+1).$ **(f)** 4.

3. (a) Area $\to 0.$
(b) The graph of f approaches as a limit the "curve" made up of the x-axis between 0 and 1, inclusive, and the portion of the line $x = 1$ between $y = 0$ and $y = 1.$

5. (a) 1024/3 units.   **(c)** 278 units.   **(e)** 52 units.
    (b) 1216/3 units.   **(d)** 776/3 units.   **(f)** 4.

9. (a) No.   **(b)** $\left|\int_a^b f\right| \le \int_a^b |f|$.

3.1, p. 149

1. (a) $B_n = \dfrac{1}{n} + \dfrac{1}{n+1} + \cdots + \dfrac{1}{2n-1}$.   **(b)** $B_n > \dfrac{1}{2n} + \dfrac{1}{2n} + \ldots + \dfrac{1}{2n}$.

3. (a) glb $S = 1$.   **(f)** lub $S = -1$.
    (b) glb $S = 1$,   lub $S = 2$.   **(g)** Neither lub S nor glb S exists.
    (c) glb $S = 1$,   lub $S = 2$.   **(h)** glb $S = 0$,   lub $S = 4$.
    (d) glb $S = 1$,   lub $S = 2$.   **(i)** glb $S = 0$,   lub $S = 6\sqrt{3}$. Working with **Q**,   glb $S = 0$,
    (e) glb $S = 0$,   lub $S = 8$.   lub S would not exist.

5. $y \in (-S) \Rightarrow -y \in S \Rightarrow -y \ge b \Rightarrow y \le -b$; etc.

3.2, p. 153

1. 14.   **9.** 7/8.   **13.** -2.

3. b.   **10.** 6/7.   **14.** $-7/2$.

5. 35.   **11.** 2.   **15.** Yes for all parts.

7. 8/3.   **12.** No limit.

3.3, p. 155

1. (a) Yes.   **(b)** No.   **(c)** Yes.   **(d)** Yes.

3. (b) $\{x \mid 3.999 < x < 4.001\}$.   **(f)** $\{x \mid 2 - \varepsilon < x < 2 + \varepsilon\}$.
    (c) $\{x \mid -\frac{1}{2} < x < \frac{1}{2}\}$.   **(g)** $\{x \mid -\frac{4}{3} < x < -\frac{2}{3}\}$.
    (d) $\{x \mid -1 < x < 1\}$.   **(h)** $\{x \mid a - \delta < x < a + \delta\}$.
    (e) $\{x \mid 7 - \delta < x < 7 + \delta\}$.   **(i)** $\{y \mid L - \varepsilon < y < L + \varepsilon\}$.

5. Take $\delta = 0.1 = \text{minimum} \ (0.1, 0.13)$.

7. Take $\delta = \text{minimum} \ (\delta_1, \delta_2)$.

3.4, p. 159

1. (a) $\delta = 1$.   **(b)** $\delta = 0.1$.   **(c)** $\delta = 0.01$.   **(d)** $\delta = 10^{-18}$.   **(e)** $\delta = \varepsilon$.

3. (a) $\delta = \frac{1}{2}$.   **(b)** $\delta = 0.05$.   **(c)** $\delta = 0.005$.   **(d)** $= = \frac{1}{2} 10^{-18}$.   **(e)** $\delta = \frac{1}{2}\varepsilon$.

5. (a) $\delta = \dfrac{0.1}{c}$.   **(b)** $\delta = \dfrac{0.001}{c}$.   **(c)** $\delta = \dfrac{10^{-9}}{c}$.   **(d)** $\delta = \dfrac{\varepsilon}{c}$.

3.5, p. 163

1. (b) $N^*_{0.01}(2) = \{x \mid 1.99 < x < 2.01, \ x \ne 2\}$.
    (c) $N^*_{0.001}(2) = \{x \mid 1.999 < x < 2.001, \ x \ne 2\}$.
    (d) $N^*_{0.1}(-1) = \{x \mid -1.1 < x < -0.9, \ x \ne -1\}$.
    (e) $N^*_{0.01}(0) = \{x \mid -0.01 < x < 0\} \cup \{x \mid 0 < x < 0.01\}$.
    (f) $N^*_{0.001}(-10) = \{x \mid -10.001 < x < -9.999, \ x \ne -10\}$.

3. (a) $\lim\limits_{x\to 4}\dfrac{x^2-16}{6x-24}=\lim\limits_{x=4}\dfrac{x+4}{6}\cdot\dfrac{x-4}{x-4}=\dfrac{4}{3}.$

$$\frac{4}{3}-\varepsilon<\frac{x+4}{6}<\frac{4}{3}+\varepsilon$$

$$8-6\varepsilon<x+4<8+6\varepsilon$$

$$4-6\varepsilon<x<4+6\varepsilon$$

Take $\delta=6\varepsilon.$

(b) $\lim\limits_{x\to 4}\dfrac{x^2-16}{12-3x}=\lim\limits_{x=4}\dfrac{x+4}{-3}\cdot\dfrac{x-4}{x-4}=-\dfrac{8}{3}$

$$-\frac{8}{3}-\varepsilon<\frac{x+4}{-3}<-\frac{8}{3}+\varepsilon$$

$$8+3\varepsilon>x+4>8-3\varepsilon$$

$$4+3\varepsilon>x>4-3\varepsilon$$

Take $\delta=3\varepsilon.$

(c) $L=-2.$ Any $\delta>0$ can be used. **(d)** $L=7/5.$ Take $\delta=5\varepsilon.$ **(e)** $L=1.$ Take $\delta=\varepsilon.$

4. (a) $L=27$; deleted nbd. unnecessary.   **(e)** $L=13$; deleted nbd. necessary.
(b) $L=7/5$; deleted nbd. unnecessary.   **(f)** $L=-2/5$; deleted nbd. unnecessary.
(c) $L=5/3$; deleted nbd. necessary.   **(g)** $L=0$; deleted nbd. unnecessary.
(d) $L=7$; deleted nbd. unnecessary.   **(h)** $L=-2/7$; deleted nbd. necessary.

3.6, p. 167

1. (a) $N_{100}(\infty)=\{x\,|\,x>100\}.$ **(b)** $N_{10,000}(\infty)=\{x\,|\,x>10,000\}.$
(c) $N_{-2}(-\infty)=\{x\,|\,x<-2\}.$ **(d)** $N_{-10,000,000}(-\infty)=\{x\,|\,x<-10,000,000\}.$

3. (a) ∞, **(b)** 0, **(c)** $\dfrac{1}{3}$, **(d)** $\dfrac{1}{3}$, **(e)** $-\dfrac{7}{13}$, **(f)** ∞, **(g)** $-\infty$, **(h)** 2, **(i)** 2, **(j)** ∞, **(k)** 2.

5. (a) ∞, **(b)** 0, **(c)** 0, **(d)** 4, **(e)** 4/81.

7. (a) The numbers $1/x^2$ get big beyond all bounds when x is close to 0.
(b) The numbers $2/(x-3)$ can be made arbitrarily large positively (if x is >3) and arbitrarily large negatively (if $x<3$) by taking x close to 3.
(c) The numbers x^2+4 get big beyond all bounds as x gets big.
(d) The numbers $(x^2-16)/(x^2-9)$ can be made arbitrarily large positively (if $x<3$) and arbitrarily large negatively (if $x>3$) by taking x close to 3.
(e) The numbers x^2 get big beyond all bounds as x gets big negatively.

9. (a) $\lim\limits_{x\to a}f(x)=-\infty\Leftrightarrow$ for every $N_Q(-\infty)$ there exists $N_\delta^*(a)$ such that $x\in N_\delta^*(a)\Rightarrow$ $f(x)\in N_Q(-\infty).$
(b) $\lim\limits_{x\to\infty}f(x)=-\infty\Leftrightarrow$ for every $N_Q(-\infty)$ there exists $N_K(\infty)$ such that $x\in N_K(\infty)\Rightarrow$ $f(x)\in N_Q(-\infty).$
(c) $\lim\limits_{x\to-\infty}f(x)=\infty\Leftrightarrow$ for every $N_M(\infty)$ there exists $N_Q(-\infty)$ such that $x\in N_Q(-\infty)\Rightarrow$ $f(x)\in N_M(\infty).$
(d) $\lim\limits_{x\to-\infty}f(x)=-\infty\Leftrightarrow$ for every $N_Q(-\infty)$ there exists $N_P(-\infty)$ such that $x\in N_P(-\infty)\Rightarrow$ $f(x)\in N_Q(-\infty).$

13. For x negative $-[2/(x-3)]$ is positive and hence is $>-\varepsilon.$

3.7, p. 171

1. (a) $N^-_{0.1}(0) = \{x \mid -0.1 < x < 0\}$. **(b)** $N^+_{0.05}(2) = \{x \mid 2 < x < 2.05\}$.
(c) $N^+_{0.01}(-8) = \{x \mid -8 < x < -7.99\}$. **(d)** $N^-_{0.14}(3) = \{x \mid 2.86 < x < 3\}$.
(e) $N^-_{0.26}(-5) = \{x \mid -5.26 < x < -5\}$. **(f)** $N^+_{0.017}(-0.01) = \{x \mid -0.01 < x < 0.007\}$.

2. (a) ∞, **(b)** $-\infty$, **(c)** ∞, **(d)** ∞, **(e)** 1, **(f)** 1, **(g)** 0, **(h)** 1, **(i)** 0, **(j)** 0, **(k)** 6, **(l)** 1.

3. The limits exist for the following parts of 2: (e), (f), (g), (h), (i), (j), (k), (l).

4. (a) $\displaystyle\lim_{x \to a^+} f(x) = \infty \Leftrightarrow$ for every $N_M(\infty)$ there exists $N^+_\delta(a)$ such that $x \in N^+_\delta(a) \Rightarrow$
$f(x) \in N_M(\infty)$.
(b) $\displaystyle\lim_{x \to a^+} f(x) = -\infty \Leftrightarrow$ for every $N_Q(-\infty)$ there exists $N^+_\delta(a)$ such that $x \in N^+_\delta(a) \Rightarrow$
$f(x) \in N_Q(-\infty)$.
(c) $\displaystyle\lim_{x \to a^-} f(x) = L \Leftrightarrow$ for every $N_\epsilon(L)$ there exists $N^-_\delta(a)$ such that $x \in N^-_\delta(a) \Rightarrow f(x) \in N_\epsilon(L)$.
(d) $\displaystyle\lim_{x \to a^-} f(x) = \infty \Leftrightarrow$ for every $N_M(\infty)$ there exists $N^-_\delta(a)$ such that $x \in N^-_\delta(a) \Rightarrow$
$f(x) \in N_M(\infty)$.

5. The limit in 4(c) exists.

3.8, p. 174

1. (b) $X' = [0, 1]$. **(c)** $X' = [1, 2] \cup [3, 4]$. **(d)** $X' = \varnothing$. **(e)** $X' = [2, 4] \cup [7, 10]$.
(g) $X' = \mathbf{R} \cup \{\infty\} \cup \{-\infty\}$. **(h)** $X' = \mathbf{R} \cup \{\infty\} \cup \{-\infty\}$. **(i)** $X' = \mathbf{R} \cup \{\infty\} \cup \{-\infty\}$.

3. (a) $\displaystyle\lim_{x \to 2} f(x)$ does not exist. **(b)** $\displaystyle\lim_{x \to 2} f(x) = 4$. **(c)** $\displaystyle\lim_{x \to 2} f(x) = \infty$.
5. (a) $X = [0, 1]$. **(b)** $X = (0, 1)$. **(c)** $X = (0, 1)$. **(d)** $X = [0, 1] \cup \{2\}$.
(e) $X = (0, 1) \cup \{2\}$. **(f)** $X = [0, 1]$. **(g)** $X = (0, 1]$.

3.9, p. 179

1. Deleted nbd. not necessary for the limits in parts (a), (b), (c), and (f).
3. (a) $\displaystyle\lim_{x \to 0} f(x)$ does not exist. **(b)** $f(2) \neq \displaystyle\lim_{x \to 2} f(x)$. **(c)** $\displaystyle\lim_{x \to 2} f(x)$ does not exist.

5. (a) f continuous at 0.   **(d)** Define $f(0) = 1$.
(b) f cannot be made continuous at 0.   **(e)** f cannot be made continuous at 0.
(c) f cannot be made continuous at 0.

7. (a) No point of discontinuity in the domain. **(c)** No discontinuities.
(d) No point of discontinuity in the domain. **(e)** Discontinuous at 2.
(f) No point of discontinuity in the domain.
(g) No point of discontinuity in the domain. **(h)** Discontinuous at $x = 0$.

3.10, p. 191

1. $\displaystyle\lim_{x \to 3}(4x^2 - 7x + 11) = \lim_{x \to 3} 4x^2 - \lim_{x \to 3} 7x + \lim_{x \to 3} 11$ (Theorem 7)

$$= 4 \lim_{x \to 3} x^2 - 7 \lim_{x \to 3} x + 11 \quad \text{(Corollary 2)}$$

$$= 4 \lim_{x \to 3} x \cdot \lim_{x \to 3} x - 7 \lim_{x \to 3} x + 11 \quad \text{(Theorem 8)}$$

$$= 4 \cdot 3 \cdot 3 - 7 \cdot 3 + 11$$

$$= 26.$$

Also, $\displaystyle\lim_{x \to 3}(4x^2 - 7x + 11) = 4 \cdot 3^2 - 7 \cdot 3 + 11 = 26$ (Theorem 9 and Definition 17a)

3. $L = 22/25$.   5. $L = 2a^2 - a + 13$

7. $L = 5/3$.   9. $L = \sin 4/5$ (Assumption, Cor. 4, Theorem 11, Def. 17a)

4.2, p. 203

1. (a) $df(x, h) = 3x^2 h$ (b) $\Delta f(x, h) = 3x^2 h + 3xh^2 + h^3$.
   (c) $\Delta f - df = 3xh^2 + h^3$; $\eta(h) = 3xh + h^2$.

3. $\dfrac{\overline{P_1 T}}{h} = m_{P_0 T} = f'(x_0)$; $\therefore \overline{P_1 T} = |f'(x_0)h|$.

5. (a) $\dfrac{\pi}{180} \cos x$;   (b) $\sin 31° \approx \dfrac{1}{2} + \dfrac{\pi\sqrt{3}}{360} \approx 0.5151$.

7. (a) $\Delta f(x, h) = mh$; (b) $df(x, h) = mh$.

9. (a) $df(x, h) = \dfrac{h}{(1 - x)^2}$.   (b) $df(0.1, 0.1) = \dfrac{10}{81} \approx 0.0123$; $df(0.8, 0.1) = 2.5$.

   (c) $\Delta f(x, h) = \dfrac{h}{(1 - x - h)(1 - x)}$.

4.3, p. 210

1. (a) $f'(x) = -12x + 36x^3 = -12x(1 - 3x^2)$. (b) $f'(x) = \dfrac{-24x^2}{(4x^3 + 1)^3}$.
   (c) $f'(x) = 6(3x + 1)(3x^2 + 2x - 7)^2$.

2. (a) $f'(x) = (2x - 1)^{-1/2}$.   (g) $f'(x) = \dfrac{-5x(x^2 + 2)}{3(1 - x^2)^{1/2}(4 + x^2)^{2/3}}$.
   (b) $f'(x) = 3x(x^2 + 1)^{1/2}$.
   (c) $f'(x) = 2x \cos x^2$.   (h) $f'(x) = \dfrac{a}{2}(e^{ax} - e^{-ax})$.
   (d) $f'(x) = 2\sin x \cos x$.
   (e) $f'(x) = (1 + x)^{-\frac{1}{4}}(1 - x)^{-\frac{3}{4}}$.   (i) $f'(x) = \dfrac{x - 8}{2(x - 4)^{3/2}}$.
                                             (j) $f'(x) = 35x^3(1 - x^2)^{3/2}$.
   (f) $f'(x) = \dfrac{x^2 + 3x - 1}{(x + 3)^2 \sqrt{x^2 - 1}}$.   (k) $f'(x) = \dfrac{x^3}{\sqrt{a^2 - x^2}}$.

3. $f'(x) = \dfrac{-2x}{(1 + x^2)^{3/2}(1 - x^2)^{1/2}}$.

5. (a) $y' = \dfrac{x}{y}$.   (c) $y' = \dfrac{-(2x + 3)y}{x^2 + 3x - 8y}$.

   (b) $y' = \dfrac{4x - 3y}{3x - 2y}$.   (d) $y' = \dfrac{6x - 4y}{4x - 3y^2}$.

4.4, p. 217

1. (a) $x_0 = 1/4$. (b) $x_0 = 9/4$. (c) $x_0 = \pm 2/\sqrt{3}$. (d) $x_0 = 1$. (e) $x_0 = 5/2$.

3. Yes. Consider f defined by $f(0) = 0$, $f(x) = 1$, $x \in (0, 1]$.

4.5, p. 221

1. (b) $\varphi(t) = t^3 - \frac{3}{2}t^2 + \frac{1}{2}$; $\varphi'(t) = 3t^2 - 3t = 3t(t-1)$
       $\varphi'(0) = 0$; $g'(0) = 0$.

3. (a) Curve is the unit circle. **(b)** $t_0 = \pi/2$ **(c)** $t_0 = -\pi/6$.
    (d) Yes; $g(-\pi/2) = g(\pi/2) = 0$; φ is not defined.

4.6, p. 226

1. $-\frac{1}{2}$ **9.** $-\frac{6}{5}$ **15.** No limit

3. 1   **11.** $\frac{1}{2}$ **17.** $\frac{1}{3}$

5. 5   **13.** $\frac{1}{6}$ **19.** No limit.

7. $-\frac{7}{12}$

5.1, p. 231

1. $40\,\pi$ cm²/sec.

3. (a) $\dfrac{169}{\sqrt{178}} \approx 12.67$ knots **(b)** 7.2 miles **(c)** $\dfrac{3(13 - \varepsilon)}{\sqrt{\varepsilon(26 - \varepsilon)}}$ miles **(d)** $31\,\dfrac{3}{7}$ miles.

5. $\dfrac{8}{5\pi}$ in./sec ≈ 0.51 in./sec.

7. $3\,\dfrac{3}{4}$ ft/sec

9. 10 psi/sec.

11. (a) $\dfrac{16}{3}$ in./sec **(b)** -14 in.²/sec **(c)** 0 in./sec.

5.2, p. 238

1. $x = 0$, $y = 1$.   **11.** $x = -4$, $x = 2$, $y = 1$.

3. $x = -2$, $x = 2$, $y = 0$.   **13.** $x = -5$, $x = 4$.

5. $x = 1$, $x = 2$, $y = 0$.   **15.** $x = -3$, $y = 1$.

7. $x = 0$, $y = x - 3$.   **17.** $y = 0$.

9. $y = 1$.

19. g has a maximum at $(1, \frac{1}{2})$. As g and f have different domains, $g \neq f$.

21. (1) Theorem 3.6   **(2)** Definition 3.17b.

5.3, p. 247

1. Maximum: $(-2, 18)$; minimum $(2, -14)$.

3. Maximum $(0, 0)$; minimum $(\frac{8}{5}, -108(\frac{4}{5})^5)$.

5. Minimum at $(2, -64)$.

7. No maxima or minima.

9. Minima at $x_1 = (5 - \sqrt{13})/3 \approx 0.5$ and $x_2 = (5 + \sqrt{13})/3 \approx 2.7$; maximum at $(2, 0)$.

11. Minima at $(4/3, -2^{13}/3^6)$ and $(4, 0)$; maximum at $(3, 27)$.

13. Minimum at $(0, -4/9)$.

15. Maximum $(2, 4)$; minimum $(0, 0)$ and $(4, 0)$.

17. Maximum $(-1, 1)$ and $(1, 1)$; minimum $(0, 0)$.

19. Maximum $(2, 1)$; minimum $(0, -1)$.   21. $\frac{1}{32}$.

5.4, p. 254

1. $f(x) = ax^2 + bx + c,\ a \neq 0 \Rightarrow f''(x) = 2a$, all x
   $a > 0 \Rightarrow$ graph concave upward everywhere,
   $a < 0 \Rightarrow$ graph concave downward everywhere.

3. Inflection points: $(\pm 1/\sqrt{3}, 3/4)$; $-1/\sqrt{3} < x < 1/\sqrt{3}$, graph concave downward.

5. Inflection points where $x = 2 \pm (2\sqrt{3}/3)$; $2 - 2(\sqrt{3}/3) < x < 2 + 2(\sqrt{3}/3)$, graph concave downward.

7. Inflection points where $x = 0$, $(12 \pm 2\sqrt{6})/5$; graph concave downward for $x < 0$ and $(12 - 2\sqrt{6})/5 < x < (12 + 2\sqrt{6})/5$.

9. No inflection points; graph concave downward for $x > 0$.

11. Inflection points where $x = \pm 1/\sqrt{3}$; curve concave upward for $-1/\sqrt{3} < x < 1/\sqrt{3}$.

13. Inflection points where $x = n\pi$, $n = 0,\ \pm 1,\ \pm 2,\ \ldots$; curve concave downward for $2n\pi < x < (2n + 1)\pi$.

15. Inflection point at $(-1, -6)$; curve concave downward for $x < -1$.

17. Neither concave upward nor concave downward.

19. Outline of proof. (1) Find tangent line to curve at (a, b), let $(x_1, 0)$ be x-intercept of this line.
    (2) Use Mean Value Theorem on $[a, x_1]$ to show $f(x_1) = b(1 - [f'(t)/f'(a)])$, where $a < t < x_1$.
    (3) Show $f(x_1) < 0$. One way: $f''(x) < 0$ for $x > a \Rightarrow f'(t) < f'(a)$. Second way: use Mean Value Theorem on f' over $[a, t]$.
    (4) Use Intermediate Value Theorem (Theorem 3.16).

5.5, p. 259

1. $10/3$, $20/3$; 3 and 7.

5. Maximum area $= 2\sqrt{12}$ square inches when triangle is equilateral.

7. Radius = height.   13. Height $= \sqrt{2}$ radius.

9. Width: length: height $= 1 : 4 : 8/5$.   15. $12\sqrt{5} \approx 26.8$ miles.

11. Depth $= \sqrt{2}$ breadth.   17. (a) $x_0 = (2\sqrt{3}/3)b \approx 1.155b$.

6.1, p. 273

1. (a) $\dfrac{1}{\sqrt{2}}$,   (b) $\dfrac{1}{\sqrt{2}}$,   (c) $\dfrac{-1}{\sqrt{2}}$,   (d) $\dfrac{1}{\sqrt{2}}$,   (e) $-\dfrac{1}{\sqrt{2}}$,   (f) $-\dfrac{1}{\sqrt{2}}$,   (g) $\dfrac{1}{\sqrt{2}}$,   (h) $\dfrac{-1}{\sqrt{2}}$.

3. (a) $\dfrac{\sqrt{3}}{2}$, (b) $-\dfrac{\sqrt{3}}{2}$, (c) $-\dfrac{\sqrt{3}}{2}$, (d) $-\dfrac{1}{2}$, (e) $-\dfrac{1}{2}$, (f) $\dfrac{1}{2}$, (g) 0, (h) 1,

(i) $\dfrac{1}{\sqrt{3}}$, (j) $\sqrt{3}$, (k) 1, (l) -1, (m) $\sqrt{3}$, (n) -2.

9. $2\pi/k$.

11. φ lies in either quadrant II or quadrant III; $\sin \varphi = \pm \frac{1}{2}$.

13. $\varphi = \pi/4 + n(\pi/2)$, $n = 0, \pm 1, \pm 2, \ldots$.

15. $\tan\left(\alpha \pm \dfrac{\pi}{2}\right) = \dfrac{\sin(\alpha \pm \pi/2)}{\cos(\alpha \pm \pi/2)} = \dfrac{\sin\alpha\cos\pi/2 \pm \cos\alpha\sin\pi/2}{\cos\alpha\cos\pi/2 \mp \sin\alpha\sin\pi/2} = \dfrac{\pm\cos\alpha}{\mp\sin\alpha} = -\cot\alpha.$

17. (17) $\tan(\varphi - \theta) = \tan(\varphi + (-\theta)) = \dfrac{\tan\varphi + \tan(-\theta)}{1 - \tan\varphi\tan(-\theta)} = \dfrac{\tan\varphi - \tan\theta}{1 + \tan\varphi\tan\theta}.$

(19) $\tan(\frac{1}{2})\varphi = \dfrac{\sin(\frac{1}{2})\varphi}{\cos(\frac{1}{2})\varphi} = \dfrac{\pm\sqrt{(1-\cos\varphi)/2}}{\pm\sqrt{(1+\cos\varphi)/2}}$

$$= \pm\sqrt{\dfrac{1-\cos\varphi}{1+\cos\varphi}} = \pm\sqrt{\dfrac{1-\cos\varphi}{1+\cos\varphi}} \cdot \sqrt{\dfrac{1+\cos\varphi}{1+\cos\varphi}}$$

$$= \dfrac{\sin\varphi}{1+\cos\varphi} \quad \left(\text{verify that } \tan(\tfrac{1}{2})\varphi \text{ and } \dfrac{\sin\varphi}{1+\cos\varphi} \text{ always agree in sign}\right).$$

6.2, p. 281

3. (a) $f'(x) = \cos x, f''(x) = -\sin x, f'''(x) = -\cos x, f^{iv}(x) = \sin x, f^{v}(x) = \cos x.$
   (b) $f^{(143)}(x) = f'''(x) = -\cos x.$
   $f^{(258)}(x) = f''(x) = -\sin x.$
   $f^{(600)}(x) = f(x) = \sin x.$

7. $D_x \sin x = \lim\limits_{h\to 0} \dfrac{\sin(x+h) - \sin x}{h} = \lim\limits_{h\to 0} \dfrac{2\cos(x + (\frac{1}{2})h)\sin(\frac{1}{2})h}{h}$

$$= \lim_{h\to 0}\cos(x + (\tfrac{1}{2})h)\lim_{h\to 0}\dfrac{\sin(\frac{1}{2})h}{(\frac{1}{2})h} = \lim_{h\to 0}\cos(x + (\tfrac{1}{2})h)\, 1$$

$$= \cos x, \quad \text{since } \cos \text{ is continuous for all } x, \text{ by Exercise 6.}$$

9. (a) $\dfrac{dy}{dx} = \dfrac{1}{\cos^2 x}$. (b) $\dfrac{dy}{dx} = -2\sin(2x+1)$. (c) $\dfrac{dy}{dx} = \dfrac{x\cos x - \sin x}{x^2}$.

(d) $\dfrac{dy}{dx} = -4\sin 3x\sin 4x + 3\cos 3x\cos 4x$. (e) $\dfrac{dy}{dx} = x^2\cos x + 2x\sin x$.

(f) $\dfrac{dy}{dx} = 4\sin^3 x\cos x$. (g) $\dfrac{dy}{dx} = \dfrac{2x(\sin x - x\cos x)}{\sin^3 x}$. (h) $\dfrac{dy}{dx} = \dfrac{\cos\sqrt{x}}{2\sqrt{x}}$.

(i) $\dfrac{dy}{dx} = \dfrac{\cos x}{2\sqrt{\sin x}}$. (j) $\dfrac{dy}{dx} = \dfrac{\sin x}{\cos^2 x}$.

6.3, p. 285

1. (a) $\sec x(\sec^2 x + \tan^2 x)$. (b) $2\tan x\sec^2 x$. (c) $-3\cot^2 x\csc^2 x$.

(d) $2\csc^2 x\cot x(\cot^2 x + \csc^2 x)$. (e) $\dfrac{4\tan x\sec^2 x}{(1-\tan^2 x)^2}$. (f) $|\sec x\tan x|$.

(g) $\dfrac{\csc^2 x\cot x}{|\cot x|}$. (h) $\cot^2 x$. (i) $\tan^2 x$. (j) $\sec^2 x(2x\tan x + 1)$.

3. (b) $D_x \cot x = D_x \dfrac{\cos x}{\sin x} = \dfrac{-\sin^2 x - \cos^2 x}{\sin^2 x} = -\csc^2 x.$ For $D_x \cot u$, where u is a differentiable function of x, use preceding and the chain rule.

(c) $D_x \sec x = D_x(\cos x)^{-1} = -(\cos x)^{-2}(-\sin x) = \dfrac{\sin x}{\cos^2 x} = \sec x \tan x.$

(d) $D_x \csc x = D_x(\sin x)^{-1} = -(\sin x)^{-2}(\cos x) = -\csc x \cot x.$

6.4, p. 287

1. (a) $\sin x - \frac{1}{2}x^2 + C.$ (b) $-\log|\cos x| - \cos x + C.$ (c) $\log|\sec^2 x + \sec x \tan x| + C.$
   (d) $2 \tan x - x + C.$ (e) $x + C.$ (f) $\log(1 - \cos x) + C.$

   (g) $\log|\sec x| - \log|\csc x + \cot x| + C = \log\left|\dfrac{\sin x}{\cos x(1 + \cos x)}\right| + C.$

3. $(\frac{1}{2}) \log 2 \approx 0.3466.$

5. (b) $\dfrac{\sqrt{3}}{2} \approx 0.866.$ (c) $\log(2 + \sqrt{3}) \approx 1.317.$ (d) $\log(2 + \sqrt{3}) - \dfrac{\sqrt{3}}{2} \approx 0.451.$

7. $-\log|\csc x + \cot x| = \log \dfrac{1}{|\csc x + \cot x|} = \log\left|\dfrac{\csc x - \cot x}{\csc^2 x - \cot^2 x}\right| = \log|\csc x - \cot x|.$

6.5, p. 297

1. Domain and range $= \mathbf{R}.$
   $f^{-1}(x) = (\frac{1}{2})(x + 3);$ $f'(x) = 2,$ $(f^{-1})'(x) = \frac{1}{2}.$

3. Domain and range $= \mathbf{R}.$
   $f^{-1}(x) = (1/m)(x - b);$ $f'(x) = m,$ $(f^{-1})'(x) = 1/m.$

5. Domain and range $= \mathbf{R}.$
   $f^{-1}(x) = x^{1/3};$ $f'(x) = 3x^2,$ $(f^{-1})'(x) = (\frac{1}{3})x^{-2/3}.$

7. Domain $= \mathbf{R};$ range $= \mathbf{R}^+ \cup \{0\}.$
   Domain of f restricted to $\mathbf{R}^+ \cup \{0\}: f^{-1}(x) = x^{1/4}; f'(x) = 4x^3, (f^{-1})'(x) = (\frac{1}{4})x^{-3/4}.$
   Domain of f restricted to $\mathbf{R}^-; f^{-1}(x) = -x^{1/4}, (f^{-1})'(x) = -(\frac{1}{4})x^{-3/4}.$

9. Domain and range $= \mathbf{R} - \{0\}.$
   $f^{-1}(x) = f(x) = \dfrac{1}{x}; f'(x) = \dfrac{-1}{x^2} = (f^{-1})'(x).$

11. Range $= [0, 1].$

   $f^{-1}(x) = f(x); f'(x) = \dfrac{-x}{\sqrt{1 - x^2}} = (f^{-1})'(x).$

13. $g^{-1}(x) = -\sqrt{x^2 + 1}.$

6.6, p. 306

1. (a) If $g(x) = \sin x, x \in [(\pi/2),(3\pi/2)],$ then $g'(x) = \cos x < 0, x \in \left(\dfrac{\pi}{2}, \dfrac{3\pi}{2}\right).$ g^{-1} exists,

   $g^{-1}: [-1, 1] \twoheadrightarrow [(\pi/2), (3\pi/2]; g^{-1}$ is continuous and monotonic decreasing. Also, $(g^{-1})'$ exists on $(-1, 1)$ and

   $$(g^{-1})'(x) = \dfrac{-1}{\sqrt{1 - x^2}}, \qquad -1 < x < 1.$$

(b) If $f(x) = \sin x$, $x \in [(3\pi/2), (5\pi/2)]$, then $f'(x) = \cos x > 0$, $x \in \left(\dfrac{3\pi}{2}, \dfrac{5\pi}{2}\right)$. f^{-1} exists, $f^{-1}: [-1, 1] \twoheadrightarrow [(3\pi/2), (5\pi/2)]$; f^{-1} is continuous and increasing. $(f^{-1})'$ exists on $(-1, 1)$ and

$$(f^{-1})'(x) = \frac{1}{\sqrt{1 - x^2}}, \qquad -1 < x < 1.$$

(c) If $g(x) = \sin x$, $x \in \left[-\dfrac{\pi}{2}, 0\right] \cup \left[\dfrac{\pi}{2}, \pi\right)$, then $g'(x) = \cos x$, where $g'(x) > 0$, $x \in (-\pi/2, 0)$; $g'(x) < 0$ for $x \in (\pi/2, \pi)$. g^{-1} exists,

$$g^{-1}: [-1, 0] \twoheadrightarrow [-\pi/2, 0]$$

$$g^{-1}: (0, 1] \twoheadrightarrow [\pi/2, \pi).$$

g^{-1} is neither continuous nor monotonic on $[-1, 1]$, but g^{-1} is continuous and increasing on $[-1, 0]$ and continuous and decreasing on $(0, 1]$.

$$(g^{-1})'(x) = \frac{1}{\sqrt{1 - x^2}}, \qquad x \in (-1, 0],$$

$$(g^{-1})'(x) = \frac{-1}{\sqrt{1 - x^2}}, \qquad x \in (0, 1).$$

3. If $f(x) = \cot x$, $x \in (0, \pi)$, then $f: (0, \pi) \twoheadrightarrow \mathbf{R}$; $f'(x) = -\csc^2 x < 0$, $x \in (0, \pi)$. Thus f^{-1} exists, is continuous and decreasing on $\mathbf{R}$, and

$$(f^{-1})'(x) = \frac{-1}{1 + x^2}.$$

5. (a) $\dfrac{1}{\sqrt{x - x^2}}$.

(b) $\dfrac{2x}{1 + x^4}$.

(c) $\dfrac{x^2}{\sqrt{2x - x^2}} + 2x \cos^{-1}(1 - x)$.

(d) $\dfrac{2}{x(1 + 4x^2)} - \dfrac{1}{x^2} \tan^{-1} 2x$.

(e) $\dfrac{-1}{\sqrt{1 - x^2}}$.

(f) $\dfrac{1}{\sqrt{1 - x^2 - 2x}}$.

(g) $\sin^{-1} x$

(h) $\dfrac{x^2}{(4 - x^2)^{3/2}}$.

(i) $2x \tan^{-1} x$.

(j) $\dfrac{-3}{(4 - 3x)\sqrt{(4 - 3x)^2 - 1}}$.

6.7, p. 310

1. $V_{max} = 4\pi a^3/3\sqrt{3} = 1/\sqrt{3}$ (volume of sphere).

5. Radius $= a/\sqrt{2}$, height $= a\sqrt{2}$, $S_{max} = \pi a^2$.

7. $-\frac{3}{16}$ radians/sec.

9. Let $g(\theta) = \tan \theta$, $f = g \circ \theta$, i.e., $f(x) = g(\theta(x)) = \tan \theta(x)$. Then

$$f'(x) = \sec^2 \theta(x) \theta'(x).$$

Since $\sec^2\theta(x) > 1$, all x,

$$\theta'(x) = 0 \Leftrightarrow f'(x) = 0,$$
$$\theta'(x) < 0 \Leftrightarrow f'(x) < 0,$$
$$\theta'(x) > 0 \Leftrightarrow f'(x) > 0.$$

7.1, p. 316

1. $\log a/b = \log a \cdot 1/b = \log a + \log 1/b = \log a - \log b$.

3. $f'(x) = \dfrac{-1}{1-x}$.

5. $f'(x) = \dfrac{4x}{x^4 - 1}$.

7. $f'(x) = \cot x$.

9. $f'(x) = \dfrac{-17}{6x^2 + x - 12}$.

11. $f'(x) = \sqrt{x^2 + a^2}$.

13. $f'(x) = \dfrac{1}{\sqrt{x^2 - a^2}}$.

15. $f'(x) = \log x$.

17. $f'(x) = \dfrac{1}{x \log x}$.

19. $f'(x) = \sin \log x$.

21. $\displaystyle\int \sqrt{x^2 + a^2}\, dx = \tfrac{1}{2}[x\sqrt{x^2 + a^2} + a^2 \log(x + \sqrt{x^2 + a^2})]$.

23. $\displaystyle\int \frac{dx}{\sqrt{x^2 - a^2}} = \log|x + \sqrt{x^2 - a^2}|$.　　**27.** $\displaystyle\int \frac{dx}{x \log x} = \log(\log x)$.

25. $\displaystyle\int \log x\, dx = x \log x - x$.　　**29.** $\displaystyle\int \sin \log x\, dx = \tfrac{1}{2}x \sin \log x - \tfrac{1}{2}x \cos \log x$.

33. (a) 0.4　　(d) 2.1　　(f) 2.5　　(h) 0.23
　　　(b) 1.4　　(e) 2.2　　(g) 3.2　　(i) 110.
　　　(c) 1.8

35. (a) $\tfrac{1}{2}$　　(d) 1　　(g) $\tfrac{1}{2}$　　(i) 0
　　　(b) 4　　(e) 0　　(h) 0　　(j) 0.
　　　(c) 0　　(f) 0

7.2, p. 324

2. (a) $f'(x) = 2x\, e^{x^2}$.
　　　(b) $f'(x) = \cos x\, e^{\sin x}$.
　　　(c) $f'(x) = 1$.
　　　(d) $f'(x) = 1$.
　　　(e) $f'(x) = (2x - \cos x)\, e^{x^2 - \sin x}$.
　　　(f) $f'(x) = e^x \cos e^x$.
　　　(g) $f'(x) = x e^{ax}$.
　　　(h) $f'(x) = e^x \sin x$.

　　　(i) $f'(x) = \dfrac{1}{1 + e^x}$.

　　　(j) $f'(x) = \dfrac{1}{a + be^x}$.

　　　(k) $f'(x) = -\dfrac{1}{x^2}\, e^{1/x}$.

　　　(l) $f'(x) = \dfrac{1}{2\sqrt{x}}\, e^{\sqrt{x}}$.

3. (g) $\displaystyle\int x e^{ax}\, dx = \frac{e^{ax}}{a^2}(ax - 1)$.　　(i) $\displaystyle\int \frac{dx}{1 + e^x} = \log \frac{e^x}{1 + e^x}$.

　　　(h) $\displaystyle\int e^x \sin x\, dx = \tfrac{1}{2}e^x(\sin x - \cos x)$.　　(j) $\displaystyle\int \frac{dx}{a + be^x} = \frac{x}{a} - \frac{1}{a} \log(a + be^x)$.

5. $\dfrac{1957}{720} < e < \dfrac{1960}{720}$ or $2.718 < e < 2.722$.

7. (a) 2. (d) 1. (f) 0. (h) 0.
   (b) 0. (e) 0. (g) $\frac{1}{2}$. (i) e.
   (c) $\frac{4}{3}$.

7.3, p. 331

1. (a) $\dfrac{x}{(x^2+1)\log 10}$. (d) $\dfrac{2x^2}{(x^2-4)\log a} + \log|x^2-4|$.

   (b) $\dfrac{x}{(x^2+1)\log 2}$. (e) $\dfrac{2\log_a x}{x\log a}$.

   (c) $\dfrac{4x}{(x^4-1)\log a}$. (f) $\dfrac{2x^2-\log a(x^2+1)\log_a(x^2+1)}{2\log ax^2(x^2+1)}$.

3. (a) 4.605170 (b) 6.907755 (c) 1.38629 (d) 1.79176.

7. $\dfrac{\log b}{\log a} = \log b \log_a e$ (by (30))

   $= \log_a b$ (by (29)).

9. Let $\log_a x = u$, $\log_a y = v$; then $a^u = x$, $a^v = y$.

   (a) $xy = a^u a^v = a^{u+v} \Rightarrow \log_a xy = u + v = \log_a x + \log_a y$.

   (b) $\dfrac{x}{y} = \dfrac{a^u}{a^v} = a^{u-v} \Rightarrow \log \dfrac{x}{y} = u - v = \log_a x - \log_a y$.

   (c) $x^q = (a^u)^q = a^{qu} \Rightarrow \log_a x^q = qu = q\log_a x$.

   (d) Use 28(b) with $x=1$.

11. (a) $f'(x) = f(x)\left[\dfrac{2}{x} + \dfrac{x}{x^2+1} - \dfrac{3}{x+1}\right]$.

    (b) $f'(x) = f(x)\left[\dfrac{3x}{3x^2+4} + \dfrac{x^2}{x^3-2} - \dfrac{4x}{x^2+4}\right]$.

    (c) $f'(x) = f(x)\left[\dfrac{x}{x^2+1} + \dfrac{2x}{3x^2-4} + \dfrac{8x^3}{5(2x^4+3)}\right]$.

    (d) $f'(x) = f(x)\left[\dfrac{3}{x} + \dfrac{1}{3(x-1)} - \dfrac{x}{2(x^2+2)}\right]$.

7.4, p. 340

1. Domain: $\mathbf{R}^+$; minimum at $x = e^{-1/2}$; inflection point at $x = e^{-3/2}$.

$$\lim_{x\to 0^+} y = 0, \quad \lim_{x\to 0^+} y' = 0.$$

3. Domain: $\mathbf{R}$. Symmetry with respect to origin.
   Horizontal asymptote: x-axis. Minimum at $x = -1/\sqrt{2}$, maximum at $x = 1/\sqrt{2}$.

5. Domain: $((4n-1)\pi/2, (4n+1)\pi/2)$, $n = 0, \pm 1, \pm 2, \ldots$.
   Range: $(-\infty, 0]$. Symmetry with respect to y-axis.
   Maxima: $x = 2n\pi$, $n = 0, \pm 1, \pm 2, \ldots$.
   Concave downward.

7. Domain: **R**. Maxima and minima: $x = (4n - 1)\pi/4$, $n = 0, \pm 1, \pm 2, \ldots$.
   Inflection points: $x = n\pi$, $n = 0, \pm 1, \pm 2, \ldots$ (where curve touches either $y = e^{-x}$ or $y = -e^{-x}$.

9. Domain: **R**. $0 \le y < 1$. Symmetry with respect to y-axis.
   Minimum: $x = 0$. Inflection points: $x = \pm \sqrt{\frac{2}{3}}$.

11. Domain: **R** $- \{0\}$. Vertical asymptote: y-axis.

$$x > 0 \Rightarrow y > 1; \quad x < 0 \Rightarrow y < 0.$$

$$\lim_{x \to \infty} y = 1; \quad \lim_{x \to -\infty} y = 0, \quad y' < 0.$$

13. Domain: **R** $- \{0\}$, $y' > 0$. $x < 0 \Rightarrow y < 0$, $x > 0 \Rightarrow y > 1$.

$$\lim_{x \to 0^+} y = 1; \quad \lim_{x \to 0^-} y = 0; \quad \lim_{x \to 0} y' = 0.$$

$$\lim_{x \to \infty} y = \infty; \quad \lim_{x \to -\infty} y = -\infty.$$

15. Domain: **R** $- \{0\}$. Range: $(\frac{1}{2}, 1)$.
   Symmetry to y-axis.
   Horizontal asymptote: $y = \frac{1}{2}$. $\lim_{x \to 0} y = 1$.

17. $A(b) = \frac{1}{2}(1 - e^{-b^2})$; $\lim_{b \to \infty} A(b) = \frac{1}{2}$.

19. $x(t) = e^{-t} + 3t$.   21. $y = y_0 e^{-kt}$.

7.5, p. 346

3. $f'(x) = \frac{1}{3}x^{-2/3} \operatorname{sech}^2 \sqrt[3]{x}$.

5. $f'(x) = \dfrac{-x}{\sqrt{x^2 - 1}} \operatorname{sech} \sqrt{x^2 - 1} \tanh \sqrt{x^2 - 1}$.   7. $f'(x) = \tanh x$.

9. $f'(x) = \operatorname{sech}^2 x \tanh x - 3 \operatorname{sech}^3 x \tanh^3 x$.

11. (a) $-1 < \tanh x < 1$; no maximum or minimum; symmetry to origin. $\lim_{x \to \infty} \tanh x = 1$;
    $\lim_{x \to -\infty} \tanh x = -1$.

   (b) $x > 0 \Rightarrow \coth x > 1$; $x < 0 \Rightarrow \coth x < -1$; no maxima or minima. Symmetry to
       origin. $\lim_{x \to 0^+} \coth x = \infty$; $\lim_{x \to \infty} \coth x = 1$.

   (c) $0 < \operatorname{sech} x \le 1$; symmetry to y-axis; maximum $(0, 1)$; asymptote: $y = 0$.

   (d) $x > \Rightarrow \operatorname{csch} x > 0$; $x < 0 \Rightarrow \operatorname{csch} x < 0$. Symmetry to origin. Asymptotes: $x = 0$, $y = 0$.
       No maxima or minima.

13. (a) $F_1(x) = 2 \tan^{-1} e^x$.   (b) $F_2(x) = \tan^{-1} (\sinh x)$.

8.1, p. 355

1. (a) -0.097 (b) -0.1644 (c) -0.470.

3. $df(x, a_1 h_1 + a_2 h_2) = f'(x)(a_1 h_1 + a_2 h_2) = a_1 f'(x) h_1 + a_2 f'(x) h_2$
   $\qquad\qquad\qquad\quad = a_1 df(x, h_1) + a_2 df(x, h_2)$.

8.2, p. 360

1. $\frac{1}{4}(x+1)^4$.

3. $\frac{1}{8}(x^2+1)^4$.

5. $\frac{1}{6}(x^4+1)^{3/2}$.

7. $x - \log|x+1|$.

9. $\frac{5}{3}x^3 + \frac{7}{2}x^2 - 3x + 4\log|x| + 2/x$.

11. $\frac{2}{5}x^{5/2}$.

13. $\frac{1}{5}\tan^5 x$.

15. $\frac{1}{9}\sin^3 3x$.

17. $2e^{\sqrt{x}}$.

19. $x - \tan^{-1} x$.

21. $\frac{1}{3}x^3 + \frac{3}{2}x^2 - 6x - 8\log|x|$.

23. $\log \dfrac{e^x}{1+e^x}$.

25. $\frac{1}{3}x^3$

27. $\log(x^2 + 4x + 7)$

29. $\frac{1}{2}(\log x)^2$.

31. $-2\cos\frac{1}{2}x$.

33. $(1)\ -\frac{1}{2}\cos 2x;\ (2)\ \sin^2 x;\ (3)\ -\cos^2 x$.

The answers differ from one another by a constant.

35. -1. No.

8.3, p. 369

1. $2\sqrt{x} - 2\log(\sqrt{x}+1)$.

3. $\frac{2}{3}(x+2)\sqrt{x-1}$.

5. $\dfrac{(3x+1)(2x-1)^{3/2}}{15}$.

7. $\frac{2}{3}\sqrt{x-4}(x+8)$.

9. $-\frac{2}{3}(\sin x)^{-3/2}$.

11. $-x\cos x + \sin x$.

13. $-\frac{1}{15}(3x^2+2)(1-x^2)^{3/2}$.

8.4, p. 374

1. $(x^2-2)\sin x + 2x\cos x$.

3. $\frac{1}{2}x^2\log x - \frac{1}{4}x^2$.

5. $x\tan^{-1} x - \frac{1}{2}\log(1+x^2)$.

7. $\dfrac{e^{ax}}{a^2+b^2}[a\sin bx - b\cos bx]$.

9. $-\frac{1}{3}(1-x^2)^{3/2}$.

11. $\frac{1}{2}(1+x^2)\tan^{-1} x - \dfrac{x}{2}$.

13. $\frac{1}{2}[\sec x\tan x + \log|\sec x + \tan x|]$.

15. $\frac{1}{3}x^3\tan^{-1} x - \frac{1}{6}x^2 + \frac{1}{6}\log(x^2+1)$.

17. $\dfrac{(x-4)^{13}}{1365}(91x^2 - 143x + 61)$.

8.5, p. 380

1. $\frac{1}{4}\sin^4 x - \frac{1}{6}\sin^6 x$.

3. $\frac{1}{3}\csc^3 x - \frac{1}{5}\csc^5 x$.

5. $-\frac{1}{10}\cos^5 2x$.

7. $\frac{1}{16}[x - \frac{1}{4}\sin 4x + \frac{1}{3}\sin^3 2x]$.

9. $\frac{1}{3}\tan^3 x + \frac{1}{5}\tan^5 x$.

11. $\frac{1}{2}[\sec x\tan x - \log|\sec x + \tan x|]$.

13. $\frac{1}{2}[\sec x + \tan x - \log|\sec x + \tan x|]$.

15. $\frac{1}{14}\sec^{14} x - \frac{1}{6}\sec^{12} x + \frac{1}{10}\sec^{10} x$.

17. $\tan x$.

19. $\csc x - \frac{1}{3}\csc^3 x$.

25. Let

$$F(m, n) = \int_0^{\pi/2} \sin^m x \cos^n x \, dx.$$

Then

(i) m odd $\Rightarrow$

$$F(m, n) = \frac{(m-1)(m-3) \cdots 4 \cdot 2}{(m+n)(m+n-2) \cdots (n+1)},$$

(ii) n odd $\Rightarrow$

$$F(m, n) = \frac{(n-1)(n-3) \cdots 4 \cdot 2}{(m+n)(m+n-2) \cdots (m+1)},$$

(iii) m and n even $\Rightarrow$

$$F(m, n) = \frac{(m-1)(m-3) \cdots 3 \cdot 1(n-1)(n-3) \cdots 3 \cdot 1}{(m+n)(m+n-2) \cdots 4 \cdot 2} \cdot \frac{\pi}{2}.$$

27. (a) $\frac{1}{2}x - \dfrac{1}{4m} \sin 2 mx.$ (b) $\frac{1}{2}x + \dfrac{1}{4m} \sin 2 mx.$ (c) $\dfrac{1}{2m} \sin^2 mx.$

8.6, p. 387

1. $\dfrac{-\sqrt{x^2+9}}{9x}.$

3. $\dfrac{x}{\sqrt{1-x^2}} - \dfrac{\sqrt{1-x^2}}{x}.$

5. $\dfrac{3x}{16}\sqrt{3-2x^2} + \dfrac{9\sqrt{2}}{32}\sin^{-1}\sqrt{\dfrac{2}{3}}\,x - \dfrac{x}{8}(\sqrt{3-2x^2})^3.$

7. $\sqrt{2+x^2}.$

9. $\sqrt{x^2+2x-2} - \log|(x+1)+\sqrt{x^2+2x-2}|.$

11. $-\dfrac{1}{a^2\sqrt{x^2-a^2}} - \dfrac{1}{a^3}\sec^{-1}\dfrac{x}{a}.$

13. $-\dfrac{\sqrt{x^2+a^2}}{2a^2x^2} + \dfrac{1}{2a^3}\log\left|\dfrac{a+\sqrt{x^2+a^2}}{x}\right|.$

15. $\sqrt{\dfrac{x-2}{x}}.$

17. $2\sin^{-1}\dfrac{x-2}{2} - \sqrt{4x-x^2}.$

19. $\dfrac{\pi a^4}{16}.$

21. $\dfrac{\pi}{3} - \dfrac{\sqrt{3}}{2}.$

23. $\dfrac{\pi + 4\sqrt{3} - 12}{96}.$

25. $\log\dfrac{2+\sqrt{3}}{\sqrt{2}+1}.$

27. $\dfrac{1}{2a}\log\left|\dfrac{x-a}{x+a}\right|.$

8.7, p. 399

1. $\log\dfrac{(x+5)^4}{|x-2|^3}.$ **3.** $\dfrac{1}{4}\log\left|\dfrac{x-2}{x+2}\right|.$ **5.** $\dfrac{1}{2a}\log\left|\dfrac{x-a}{x+a}\right|.$

7. $\dfrac{1}{4}\log\left|\dfrac{x}{x-2}\right| - \dfrac{1}{2}\dfrac{3x^2-x-2}{x^2(x-2)}.$

9. $\log(x+1)^4(\sqrt{x^2-x+1})^3 - \dfrac{1}{\sqrt{3}}\tan^{-1}\dfrac{2x-1}{\sqrt{3}}.$

11. $\log \dfrac{(x-1)^2}{\sqrt{x^2+x+1}} + \sqrt{3}\tan^{-1}\dfrac{2x+1}{\sqrt{3}} - \dfrac{2x+3}{x^2+x+1}.$

13. $\dfrac{1}{2}\log(x^2+1) + \dfrac{7}{8}\tan^{-1}x - \dfrac{x-4}{8(x^2+1)} + \dfrac{x-1}{4(x^2+1)^2}.$

15. (b) $\dfrac{1}{\sqrt{5}}\log\left|\dfrac{\tan\frac{\theta}{2}+2-\sqrt{5}}{\tan\frac{\theta}{2}+2+\sqrt{5}}\right|.$

(c) $\dfrac{1}{\sqrt{13}}\log\left|\dfrac{3-\sqrt{13}-\tan\frac{\theta}{2}}{3+\sqrt{13}-\tan\frac{\theta}{2}}\right|.$

(d) $\dfrac{1}{5}[2\theta + \log|\sin\theta + 2\cos\theta|].$

8.8, p. 404

1. $y = x^3 - 2x^2 + 2x - 42.$

3. $y = x\tan^{-1}x - \frac{1}{2}\log(x^2+1) + 3 + \log\sqrt{2} - \pi/4.$

5. $y = x\log x - x + 1.$

7. $y = \frac{1}{3}(x^2-1)^{3/2} + \sqrt{x^2-1} + 4 - 6\sqrt{15}.$

9. (a) $y = \begin{cases} -x^2 + C_1, & x<0, \\ x^3 + C_2, & x>0. \end{cases}$ **(b)** $C_1 = C_2 = y(0).$ **(c)** $y = \begin{cases} -x^2 - 5, & x<0, \\ x^3 - 17, & x>0. \end{cases}$

11. $y_1 - y_2 = x_1 - x_2 + e^{x_1} - e^{x_2}.$

9.1, p. 413

1. (b) $\underline{S}(\pi) = 6; \bar{S}(\pi) = 10.$ **(c)** $\underline{S}(\pi) = 6; \bar{S}(\pi) = 8.$

5. (b) $\underline{S}(\pi) = 0; \bar{S}(\pi) = 4.$ **(c)** $\underline{S}(\pi) = 0; \bar{S}(\pi) = 3$ **(d)** 2.

7. f continuous on $[a, b] \Rightarrow f$ assumes its glb and lub on each closed subinterval of $[a, b]$.

9.2, p. 424

1. (a) $S_{f+g}(\pi) = \sum_{i=1}^{n}(f+g)(z_i)\,\Delta x_i = \sum_{i=1}^{n}f_i(z)\,\Delta x_i + \sum_{i=1}^{n}g(z_i)\,\Delta x_i = S_f(\pi) + S_g(\pi).$

(b) $S_{cf}(\pi) = \sum_{i=1}^{n}(cf)(z_i)\,\Delta x_i = c\sum_{i=1}^{n}f(z_i)\,\Delta x_i = cS_f(\pi).$

3. If $c=0$, the assertion is trivially true. Assume $c \neq 0$, let $\varepsilon > 0$ be arbitrary. Then there exists δ such that $|\pi| < \delta \Rightarrow$

$$\left|S_f(\pi) - \int_a^b f\right| < \frac{\varepsilon}{|c|}.$$

Since $S_{cf}(\pi) = cS_f(\pi)$ (Exercise 1(b)), we have, for $|\pi| < \delta$,

$$\left| S_{cf}(\pi) - c \int_a^b f \right| = |c| \left| S_f(\pi) - \int_a^b f \right| < |c| \frac{\varepsilon}{|c|} = \varepsilon.$$

5. (a) Yes.   (b) Yes.

(d) Let f be defined on $[0, 1]$ as follows:

$$f(0) = 0,$$

$$\frac{1}{n+1} \le x < \frac{1}{n} \Rightarrow f(x) = \frac{1}{n+1},$$

$$f(1) = 1.$$

9.3, p. 430

1. 1.117.   **5.** 0.743.   **9.** 1.395.

3. 0.9261.   **7.** 0.927.

9.4, p. 436

1. 1.   **9.** $3^{4/3}$.   **17.** $1 - (\pi/4)$.

3. Diverges.   **11.** Diverges.   **19.** $\sqrt{3}$.

5. $\frac{1}{2} \log 2$.   **13.** Diverges.   **21.** (b) $1/(n-1)$.

7. π.   **15.** Diverges.

9.5, p. 442

1. $52\frac{1}{2}$ in. lbs.

3. No. The latter value of W is 3 times the former.

5. 8 in.   **9.** 3000 lbs.

7. 171,000 ft. lbs.   **11.** $1066\frac{2}{3}$ lbs.

10.1, p. 447

3. Circle of radius 2, center at the pole.

5. Vertical and horizontal lines, respectively.

10.2, p. 453

1. Circle, radius 1, center at $(1, \pi/2)$.

3. Cardioid, symmetric to $\theta = \pi/2$.

5. Limaçon.

7. Three-leaved rose.

11. Vertical line through $(2, 0)$.

17. $\left. \begin{array}{l} (r, \theta) \text{ on graph} \\ f \text{ odd} \end{array} \right\} \Rightarrow (-r, -\theta)$ on graph $\Rightarrow$ symmetry with respect to $\theta = \pi/2$.

10.3, p. 457

1. $x^2 + y^2 = 4y$.

3. $x = 2$.

5. $(x^2 + y^2)^3 = (x^2 - y^2)^2$.

7. $y = x + 2$.

9. $y^2 = 2x + 1$.

11. $r = 9 \csc \theta \cot \theta$.

13. $r = 2 \sin \theta$.

15. $r = \dfrac{4}{3 \sin \theta - 3 \cos \theta}$.

17. $r^2 = \cos 2\theta$.

19. $\theta = \dfrac{3\pi}{4}$.

25. Use law of cosines.

10.4, p. 463

1. $\tan \psi = \dfrac{2 + \cos \theta}{-\sin \theta}$; $\quad \dfrac{dy}{dx} = -\dfrac{2 \cos \theta + \cos 2\theta}{2 \sin \theta + \sin 2\theta}$;

$r = \dfrac{25}{2(\cos \theta + 3\sqrt{3} \sin \theta)}$.

3. $\tan \psi = -\cot 2\theta$; $\quad \dfrac{dy}{dx} = -\cot 3\theta$;

$r = \dfrac{1}{\sqrt{2}} \csc \theta$.

5. $\tan \psi = \cot \theta$; $\quad \dfrac{dy}{dx}$ does not exist (graph is a vertical line);

$r = \sec \theta$.

9. (i) $0 < b < a < 2b \Rightarrow \dfrac{dy}{dx} = 0$ for $\theta = \dfrac{\pi}{2}$, $\theta = \dfrac{3\pi}{2}$ and for the third and fourth quadrant

angles for which $\sin \theta = \dfrac{-a}{2b}$.

(ii) $a \geq 2b \Rightarrow \dfrac{dy}{dx} = 0$ only for $\theta = \dfrac{\pi}{2}$ and $\theta = \dfrac{3\pi}{2}$; in particular, $a > 2b \Rightarrow \dfrac{-a}{2b} < -1$.

10.5, p. 472

1. $a^2(\pi + 3\sqrt{3}) \approx 8.34 \, a^2$ sq. units.

3. a^2 sq. units.

5. $3 + \pi - \sqrt{3} \approx 4.41$ sq. units.

7. $4 - \pi \approx 0.86$ sq. units.

9. 4.75 sq. units.

11. $\frac{8}{3}$ sq. units.

13. $(2 - \pi/2)a^2$ sq. units.

10.6, p. 480

1. Ellipse.

3. Parabola.

5. Ellipse.

7. Ellipse.

9. Hyperbola.

11. Hyperbola.

17. $r = \dfrac{2}{2 - \cos \theta}$.

19. $r = \dfrac{4}{5 + 4 \cos \theta}$.

21. $r = \dfrac{14}{4 + 7 \sin \theta}$.

23. $r = \dfrac{10}{2 + 5 \cos \theta}$.

25. $A\left(\dfrac{2 ep}{1 - e}, 0\right), P\left(\dfrac{2 ep}{1 + e}, \pi\right)$.

10.7, p. 493

1. $x^2 = 4(1 - y)$; $x'^2 = -4y'$, $h = 0$, $k = 1$.

3. $16x^2 + 15y^2 - 16y = 64$; $\dfrac{y'^2}{(32/15)^2} + \dfrac{x'^2}{(8/\sqrt{15})^2} = 1$, $h = 0$, $k = \frac{8}{15}$.

5. $x^2 = 6(y + \frac{3}{2})$; $x'^2 = 6y'$, $h = 0$, $k = -\frac{3}{2}$.

7. $(x - 2)^2 = 4(y + 3)$; $V(2, -3)$; axis of symmetry: $x = 2$.

9. $(x - 5)^2 - (y + 3)^2 = 1$; $C(5, -3)$; axes of symmetry: $x = 5$, $y = -3$.

11. $(x - 4)^2 = -2y$; $V(4, 0)$; axis of symmetry: $x = 4$.

13. $y^2 - (x - 1)^2 = 4$; $C(1, 0)$; axes of symmetry: $x = 1$, $y = 0$.

15. $4(x - 3)^2 + 9(y + 1)^2 = 0$; locus is the point $(3, -1)$.

17. $(x + 3)^2 + y^2 = 9$; $C(-3, 0)$; locus is a circle, $\therefore$ every diameter is an axis of symmetry.

19. $2(x + 1)^2 + (y - 2)^2 = -2$; locus is the empty set.

21. $x^2 + 100y^2 = 100$; $C(0, 0)$; axes of symmetry: $x = 0$, $y = 0$.

23. $100y^2 - x^2 = 100$; $C(0, 0)$; axes of symmetry: $x = 0$, $y = 0$.

29. $y_1 y = 2p(x + x_1)$.

11.1, p. 500

3. The zero vector.

7. (a) The zero vector is the vector with magnitude zero. (b) Yes. (c) Yes.
   (d) Any (or every) direction.

9. (a) $\mathbf{v}_1$ is parallel to $\mathbf{v}_2 \Leftrightarrow \mathbf{v}_1 = c\mathbf{v}_2$, c a scalar.
   (b) $\mathbf{M}_3 \mathbf{M}_2 = \mathbf{M}_3 \mathbf{A} + \mathbf{AM}_2 = -\mathbf{AM}_3 + \mathbf{AM}_2 = \mathbf{a} - \frac{1}{2}\mathbf{b} + \frac{1}{2}\mathbf{b} - \frac{1}{2}\mathbf{a} = \frac{1}{2}\mathbf{a}$.
   (c) By the answer for (b), $|\mathbf{M}_3 \mathbf{M}_2| = \frac{1}{2}|\mathbf{a}|$.

11.2, p. 508

1. (a) $\mathbf{a} + \mathbf{b} = \mathbf{b} + \mathbf{a} = (2, 5)$ (b) $(\mathbf{a} + \mathbf{b}) + \mathbf{c} = \mathbf{a} + (\mathbf{b} + \mathbf{c}) = (5, 0)$ (c) $(-1)\mathbf{a} = (2, -3)$.
   (d) $\mathbf{a} - \mathbf{b} = (-6, 1)$; $\mathbf{b} - \mathbf{a} = (6, -1)$ (e) $2\mathbf{a} + 3\mathbf{b} = (8, 12)$ (f) $3\mathbf{a} - 4\mathbf{b} = (-22, 1)$.
   (g) $(0, 0)$ (h) $26\mathbf{a} + \mathbf{b} + 16\mathbf{c} = (0, 0)$ (i) $2(\mathbf{a} + \mathbf{b}) = 2\mathbf{a} + 2\mathbf{b} = (4, 10)$ (j) $(-14, 21)$
   (k) $(-2, 3) = \mathbf{a}$.

3. (a) $\mathbf{AB} = (6, 3)$, $\mathbf{BC} = (2, 6)$, $\mathbf{CD} = (-10, -5)$, $\mathbf{DA} = (2, -4)$.

   (b) $\mathbf{AB}$ and $\mathbf{CD}$ are parallel. (c) $|\mathbf{AD}| = 2\sqrt{5}$ (d) $\mathbf{u_{BC}} = \left(\dfrac{1}{\sqrt{10}}, \dfrac{3}{\sqrt{10}}\right)$.

5. (a) $c_1 = 2$, $c_2 = -1$. (b) $c_1 = \dfrac{-5}{3}$, $c_2 = \frac{7}{3}$. (c) $c_1 = 3$, $c_2 = 1$. (d) $c_1 = c_2 = -\frac{4}{3}$.
   (e) $c_1 = \frac{1}{3}(2a_1 + a_2)$, $c_2 = \frac{1}{3}(-a_1 + a_2)$.

7. $c_1 = 2$, $c_2 = 1$.

9. If $\mathbf{v}_1$ and $\mathbf{v}_2$ are not parallel, the scalars c_1 and c_2 can be found.

11. $(3, -6)$ and $(-9, 10)$.

13. (a) $(-2, 1)$ (b) $(0, -2)$ (c) $(4, 4)$ (d) $(-2, -3)$.

11.3, p. 517

1. $\cos\theta = \dfrac{-11}{\sqrt{290}}$; scalar proj. $= \dfrac{-11}{\sqrt{10}}$.

3. $\cos\theta = -1$; scalar proj. $= -2\sqrt{53}$.

5. $\cos\theta = \dfrac{-2}{\sqrt{13}}$; scalar proj. $= -2$.

7. $\cos\theta = 0$, scalar proj. $= 0$.

9. $\cos\theta = \dfrac{-4}{5}$; scalar proj. $= -20$.

11. $\cos A = \dfrac{58}{\sqrt{61}\sqrt{73}}$, $\cos B = \dfrac{5}{\sqrt{2}\sqrt{73}}$, $\cos C = \dfrac{1}{\sqrt{2}\sqrt{61}}$.

13. $180 + 102\sqrt{3}$.

15. $\mathbf{b} = \pm\frac{1}{5}(4\mathbf{i} + 3\mathbf{j})$.

17. $\mathbf{a} \cdot \mathbf{b} = |\mathbf{a}|\,|\mathbf{b}|\cos\theta \Rightarrow |\mathbf{a} \cdot \mathbf{b}| \le |\mathbf{a}|\,|\mathbf{b}| \Rightarrow (\mathbf{a} \cdot \mathbf{b})^2 \le |\mathbf{a}|^2\,|\mathbf{b}|^2$.

19. (a) $h = \dfrac{(\mathbf{v} \cdot \mathbf{a})(\mathbf{b} \cdot \mathbf{b}) - (\mathbf{v} \cdot \mathbf{b})(\mathbf{a} \cdot \mathbf{b})}{(\mathbf{a} \cdot \mathbf{a})(\mathbf{b} \cdot \mathbf{b}) - (\mathbf{a} \cdot \mathbf{b})^2}$, $\qquad k = \dfrac{(\mathbf{a} \cdot \mathbf{a})(\mathbf{v} \cdot \mathbf{b}) - (\mathbf{v} \cdot \mathbf{a})(\mathbf{a} \cdot \mathbf{b})}{(\mathbf{a} \cdot \mathbf{a})(\mathbf{b} \cdot \mathbf{b}) - (\mathbf{a} \cdot \mathbf{b})^2}$

   (c) $h = \dfrac{(\mathbf{v} \cdot \mathbf{a}) - (\mathbf{v} \cdot \mathbf{b})(\mathbf{a} \cdot \mathbf{b})}{1 - (\mathbf{a} \cdot \mathbf{b})^2}$, $\qquad k = \dfrac{(\mathbf{v} \cdot \mathbf{b}) - (\mathbf{v} \cdot \mathbf{a})(\mathbf{a} \cdot \mathbf{b})}{1 - (\mathbf{a} \cdot \mathbf{b})^2}$.

11.4, p. 522

1. Line segment from $(1, -1)$ to $(2, 0)$.

3. Entire line containing $(1, -1)$ and $2, 0)$, directed positively upward.

5. Lower half of circle of radius 2, center at origin; positive direction is from $(-2, 0)$ toward $(0, -2)$.

7. Line segment from $(1, 0)$ to $(0, 1)$.

9. Entire curve $y^2 = x^3$, directed positively upward.

11. Graph of $\sqrt{x} + \sqrt{y} = \sqrt{a}$ (a portion of a parabola), directed from $(a, 0)$ toward $(0, a)$.

13. The part of the hypocycloid of four cusps,

$$x^{2/3} + y^{2/3} = a^{2/3}$$

which lies in the first quadrant. Positive direction is from $(a, 0)$ toward $(0, a)$.

15. (a) Third quadrant (b) Fourth quadrant (c) First quadrant (d) Second quadrant.

17. The curves in (a), (b), and (c) are different representations of the parabola $y = x^2$, the positive direction being in every case the one from left to right. The curve in (d) is that portion of the same parabola which runs from $(1, 1)$ to $(0, 0)$ to $(-1, 1)$.

19. $\mathbf{r}(t) = (1 + t)\mathbf{i} + (1 + 2t)\mathbf{j}$.

21. $\mathbf{r}(t) = (a + ht)\mathbf{i} + (b + kt)\mathbf{j}$.

23. (a) $y = x - 2$. (d) $x^{2/3} + y^{2/3} = a^{2/3}$. (g) $x^2 y = 4a^2(2a - y)$.
   (b) $y = \sqrt{4 - x^2}$. (e) $y = x^2$.
   (c) $y^2 = x^3$. (f) $y = x^2$. (h) $y = \dfrac{abx}{x^2 + a^2}$.

11.5, p. 531

1. $\dfrac{dy}{dx} = -\dfrac{1}{3}; \dfrac{d^2y}{dx^2} = 0.$

3. $\dfrac{dy}{dx} = \dfrac{k}{h}; \dfrac{d^2y}{dx^2} = 0.$

5. $\dfrac{dy}{dx} = 2t^2; \dfrac{d^2y}{dx^2} = 2.$

7. $\dfrac{dy}{dx} = -\dfrac{1}{4}\csc t; \dfrac{d^2y}{dx^2} = -\dfrac{1}{16}\csc^3 t.$

9. $\dfrac{dy}{dx} = -2\sin^3\theta\cos\theta; \dfrac{d^2y}{dx^2} = \dfrac{1}{a}\sin^4\theta(3 - 4\sin^2\theta).$

17. $A = 3\pi a^2.$

11.6, p. 543

1. $\frac{1}{27}\left[13^{3/2} - 8\right].$ **5.** $\sinh 2.$

3. $\log(1 + \sqrt{2}).$ **7.** $8a.$

9. $\sqrt{e^4 + 1} + 2 - \sqrt{2} - \log(1 + \sqrt{e^4 + 1}) + \log(1 + \sqrt{2}).$

11. $\displaystyle\int_0^{\pi/2} \sqrt{1 + \cos^2 x}\,dx.$

13. $\displaystyle\int_0^{\pi/4} a\sqrt{\sec 2\theta}\,d\theta.$

15. $\displaystyle\int_0^1 \sqrt{1 + 9x^4}\,dx.$

11.7, p. 548

1. (a) Yes.   (b) No.   (c) Yes.   (d) No.   (e) Yes.

11.8, p. 559

3. $\mathbf{T} = \dfrac{1}{\sqrt{2}}(\mathbf{i} + \mathbf{j}); \mathbf{N} = \dfrac{1}{\sqrt{2}}(\mathbf{i} - \mathbf{j}); \kappa = \dfrac{3}{\sqrt{2}}.$

5. $\mathbf{T} = \operatorname{sech} 2\mathbf{i} + \tanh 2\mathbf{j}; \mathbf{N} = -\tanh 2\mathbf{i} + \operatorname{sech} 2\mathbf{j}; \kappa = \operatorname{sech}^2 2 \approx 0.071.$

7. $\mathbf{T} = \dfrac{1}{\sqrt{17}}(4\mathbf{i} - \mathbf{j}); \mathbf{N} = \dfrac{-1}{\sqrt{17}}(\mathbf{i} + 4\mathbf{j}); \kappa = \dfrac{2}{17^{3/2}}.$

9. $\mathbf{T} = \dfrac{1}{\sqrt{2}}(-\mathbf{i} + \mathbf{j}); \mathbf{N} = \dfrac{1}{\sqrt{2}}(\mathbf{i} + \mathbf{j}); \kappa = \dfrac{2}{3a}.$

11. $\mathbf{T} = \dfrac{1}{2}(\mathbf{i} - \sqrt{3}\mathbf{j}); \mathbf{N} = \dfrac{-1}{2}(\sqrt{3}\mathbf{i} + \mathbf{j}); \kappa = \dfrac{1}{2}.$

13. For $x > 0$, maximum y occurs for $x = \dfrac{2}{\sqrt{3}}$, maximum κ occurs for $x^2 = \dfrac{24 + 11\sqrt{11}}{45} \neq \dfrac{4}{3}.$

15. (a) $x^2 + y^2 = y$.

(b) $(x + 4\sqrt{2})^2 + (y + \frac{9}{4})^2 = (\frac{27}{4})^2$.

(c) $(x - 3)^2 + (y + 4)^2 = 36$.

17. For $y = \sin x$, $\kappa(x) = \dfrac{\sin x}{(1 + \cos^2 x)^{3/2}}$; κ increases from 0 to 1 on $\left[0, \dfrac{\pi}{2}\right]$.

For $y = \log x$, $\kappa(x) = \dfrac{x}{(1 + x^2)^{3/2}}$; κ is decreasing on $[1, e]$.

19. $x(t) = -4t^3$, $y(t) = \frac{1}{2}(1 + 6t^2)$.

11.9, p. 568

1. For $t_0 = 2$, $\mathbf{r} = 4\mathbf{i} + 2\mathbf{j}$, $\mathbf{v} = 2(\mathbf{i} + \mathbf{j})$, $v = 2\sqrt{2}$, $\mathbf{T} = \dfrac{1}{\sqrt{2}}(\mathbf{i} + \mathbf{j})$, $\mathbf{N} = \dfrac{1}{\sqrt{2}}(-\mathbf{i} + \mathbf{j})$,

$\kappa = \dfrac{1}{8\sqrt{2}}$, $\mathbf{a} = \dfrac{1}{\sqrt{2}}\mathbf{T} + \dfrac{1}{\sqrt{2}}\mathbf{N}$.

3. For $t_0 = \dfrac{\pi}{2}$, $\mathbf{r} = \left(\dfrac{\pi}{2} + 1\right)\mathbf{i} + \mathbf{j}$, $\mathbf{v} = \mathbf{i} + \mathbf{j}$, $v = \sqrt{2}$, $\mathbf{T} = \dfrac{1}{\sqrt{2}}(\mathbf{i} + \mathbf{j})$, $\mathbf{N} = \dfrac{1}{\sqrt{2}}(-\mathbf{i} + \mathbf{j})$,

$\kappa = \dfrac{1}{2\sqrt{2}}$, $\mathbf{a} = -\dfrac{1}{\sqrt{2}}\mathbf{T} + \dfrac{1}{\sqrt{2}}\mathbf{N}$.

5. For $t_0 = \dfrac{3\pi}{4}$, $\mathbf{r} = \dfrac{a}{2\sqrt{2}}(-\mathbf{i} + \mathbf{j})$, $\mathbf{v} = \dfrac{-3a}{2\sqrt{2}}(\mathbf{i} + \mathbf{j})$, $v = \dfrac{3a}{2}$, $\mathbf{T} = \dfrac{-1}{\sqrt{2}}(\mathbf{i} + \mathbf{j})$,

$\mathbf{N} = \dfrac{1}{\sqrt{2}}(-\mathbf{i} + \mathbf{j})$, $\kappa = \dfrac{2}{3a}$, $\mathbf{a} = \dfrac{3a}{2}\mathbf{N}$.

7. For $t_0 = \dfrac{\pi}{2}$, $\mathbf{r} = e^{\pi/2}\mathbf{j}$, $\mathbf{v} = -\mathbf{i} + e^{\pi/2}\mathbf{j}$, $v = \sqrt{1 + e^\pi}$, $\mathbf{T} = \dfrac{-\mathbf{i} + e^{\pi/2}\mathbf{j}}{\sqrt{1 + e^\pi}}$, $\mathbf{N} = \dfrac{e^{\pi/2}\mathbf{i} + \mathbf{j}}{\sqrt{1 + e^\pi}}$,

$\kappa = \dfrac{e^{\pi/2}}{(1 + e^\pi)^{3/2}}$, $\mathbf{a} = \dfrac{e^\pi}{\sqrt{1 + e^\pi}}\mathbf{T} + \dfrac{e^{\pi/2}}{\sqrt{1 + e^\pi}}\mathbf{N}$.

9. $\mathbf{v} = \mathbf{u}_\theta + (1 - \sqrt{3})\mathbf{u}_\theta'$, $\mathbf{a} = (2\sqrt{3} - 1)\mathbf{u}_\theta + 2\mathbf{u}_\theta'$, where $\mathbf{u}_\theta = -\frac{1}{2}(\sqrt{3}\mathbf{i} + \mathbf{j})$, $\mathbf{u}_\theta' = \frac{1}{2}(\mathbf{i} - \sqrt{3}\mathbf{j})$.

11. $\theta = \dfrac{\pi}{2}$: $\mathbf{v} = \mathbf{u}_\theta + \dfrac{\pi}{2}\mathbf{u}_\theta' = -\dfrac{\pi}{2}\mathbf{i} + \mathbf{j}$, $\mathbf{a} = -\dfrac{\pi}{2}\mathbf{u}_\theta + 2\mathbf{u}_\theta' = -2\mathbf{i} - \dfrac{\pi}{2}\mathbf{j}$.

$\theta = \dfrac{5\pi}{2}$: $\mathbf{v} = -\dfrac{5\pi}{2}\mathbf{i} + \mathbf{j}$, $\mathbf{a} = -2\mathbf{i} - \dfrac{5\pi}{2}\mathbf{j}$.

13. If κ is zero, then $\mathbf{a} = \dfrac{d^2 s}{dt^2}\mathbf{T}$.

12.1, p. 574

1. (a) $(a, b, -c)$ (c) $(a, -b, -c)$ (e) $(-a, b, -c)$.

(b) $(-a, b, c)$ (d) $(a, -b, c)$ (f) $(-a, -b, -c)$.

3. (a) All points above the xy-plane.

(b) The union of the following sets: the yz-plane, the zx-plane, the first octant and the octant below it, and the two octants symmetric to these with respect to the z-axis.

(c) The positive half of the x-axis.

(d) The z-axis.

(e) The circle of radius one, center on the z-axis, lying in the plane parallel to and one unit above the xy-plane.

(f) Straight line—intersection of the planes $y + z = 1$ and $x = 2$.

(g) The straight line parallel to the z-axis, through $(2, 1, 0)$.

5. $z = x$.

9. (a) Midpoint $P_0\left(\dfrac{x_1 + x_2}{2}, \dfrac{y_1 + y_2}{2}, \dfrac{z_1 + z_2}{2}\right)$.

   (b) $(3, 1, 1)$.

12.2, p. 578

1. $P_1 P_2 = i - 2j + 2k$; $\cos \alpha = \frac{1}{3}$, $\cos \beta = -\frac{2}{3}$, $\cos \gamma = \frac{2}{3}$.

3. $P_1 P_2 = i + j + k$; $\cos \alpha = \cos \beta = \cos \gamma = \dfrac{1}{\sqrt{3}}$.

5. $P_1 P_2 = i + k$; $\cos \alpha = \cos \gamma = \dfrac{1}{\sqrt{2}}$, $\cos \beta = 0$.

7. $P_1 P_2 = -3i - 4j - 5k$; $\cos \alpha = -\dfrac{3}{5\sqrt{2}}$, $\cos \beta = \dfrac{-4}{5\sqrt{2}}$, $\cos \gamma = \dfrac{-1}{\sqrt{2}}$.

9. $P_1 P_2 = -4j + 3k$; $\cos \alpha = 0$, $\cos \beta = \dfrac{-4}{5}$, $\cos \gamma = \dfrac{3}{5}$.

11. (a) $\cos \theta = \dfrac{-7}{15\sqrt{2}}$ (b) $\cos \theta = 0$ (c) $\cos \theta = \dfrac{-2}{3\sqrt{21}}$.

13. $P_1 P_2 = P_3 P_4 = 4i + 6j - 8k$, $P_1 P_3 = P_2 P_4 = 3i - 3j + 6k$; $P_1 P_2 \cdot P_1 P_3 = -54 \neq 0$.

15. (a) v is parallel to the xy-plane. (b) v is parallel to the x-axis.
   (c) v is parallel to the yz-plane. (d) v is parallel to the z-axis (e) $v = 0$.

12.3, p. 586

1. (a) $\dfrac{1}{\sqrt{3}}(-i + j + k)$ (b) $\dfrac{1}{\sqrt{14}}(3i - 2j - k)$ (c) $\dfrac{-1}{\sqrt{2}}(i + j)$.

3. (a) 3 cu. units   (b) 12 cu. units   (c) 0 cu. units.

5. (a) 0   (b) $\dfrac{12}{\sqrt{42}}$ (c) 0.

7. (a) $(a \times b) \times c = 14i - 2j - 8k$
   (b) $a \times (b \times c) = 7i - 3j - 11k$
   (c) Vector multiplication is not associative.

9. $w \cdot v_1 = w \cdot v_2 \Rightarrow w \cdot (v_1 - v_2) = 0$; if $w = v_1 - v_2$, this implies $(v_1 - v_2) \cdot (v_1 - v_2) = 0$, which in turn implies $v_1 = v_2$.

11. (a) $g > 0 \Rightarrow a \times b \cdot c > 0 \Rightarrow$ angle between $a \times b$ and c lies between 0 and $\pi/2$. Using the coordinate setup of Definition 3, $a \times b$ lies along the positive z-axis. By the first sentence, then, c and the positive z-axis lie on the same side of the xy-plane. By Definition 3, a, b, and c form a right-handed triple.

(b) Argument is similar to that in (a), except that $g < 0 \Rightarrow$ angle between $\mathbf{a} \times \mathbf{b}$ and $\mathbf{c}$ lies between $\pi/2$ and π. Hence $\mathbf{c}$ and the positive z-axis lie on opposite sides of the xy-plane.
(c) $g = 0 \Rightarrow \mathbf{a} \times \mathbf{b} \cdot \mathbf{c} = 0 \Rightarrow \mathbf{c} \perp \mathbf{a} \times \mathbf{b} \Rightarrow \mathbf{c}$ lies in the plane of $\mathbf{a}$ and $\mathbf{b}$.

17. $|\mathbf{a} \times \mathbf{b}|^2 \geq 0$ with equality holding $\Leftrightarrow$ $\mathbf{a}$ and $\mathbf{b}$ are parallel, i.e., $\mathbf{b} = c_1\mathbf{a}$ or $\mathbf{a} = c_2\mathbf{b}$. Thus the same must be true of $|\mathbf{a}|^2 |\mathbf{b}|^2 - (\mathbf{a} \cdot \mathbf{b})^2$.

12.4, p. 593

1. (a) $ax + by + cz = 0$. (b) $-2(x+1) + 4(y-3) - (z-7) = 0$, or $2x - 4y + z + 7 = 0$.
   (c) $x + y = 2$. (d) $z = 3$. (e) $x = 0$. (f) $y = z$.

3. $3x - 7y + z = 28$.

5. The plane $x + y + 3z = 7$.

7. $y + 4z = 28$.

9. $5x + 6z = 17$.

11. $\dfrac{x}{a} + \dfrac{y}{b} + \dfrac{z}{c} = 1$.

13. $3x + 7y + 5z = 21$.

12.5, p. 598

1. (a) $\begin{cases} x = 4 + 2t \\ y = -5 - 12t \\ z = 2 + 5t \end{cases}$, $\dfrac{x-4}{2} = \dfrac{y+5}{-12} = \dfrac{z-2}{5}$,
   $\mathbf{r}(t) = (4 + 2t)\mathbf{i} + (-5 - 12t)\mathbf{j} + (2 + 5t)\mathbf{k}$.

   (b) $\begin{cases} x = 3 + 2t \\ y = -3 \\ z = 6 - 4t \end{cases}$, $\dfrac{x-3}{2} = \dfrac{y+3}{0} = \dfrac{z-6}{-4}$,
   $\mathbf{r}(t) = (3 + 2t)\mathbf{i} - 3\mathbf{j} + (6 - 4t)\mathbf{k}$.

   (c) $\begin{cases} x = -1 + 3t \\ y = 5t \\ z = 8 - 12t \end{cases}$, $\dfrac{x+1}{3} = \dfrac{y}{5} = \dfrac{z-8}{-12}$,
   $\mathbf{r}(t) = (-1 + 3t)\mathbf{i} + 5t\mathbf{j} + (8 - 12t)\mathbf{k}$.

   (d) $\begin{cases} x = 3 + 3t \\ y = 5 \\ z = 2 \end{cases}$, $\dfrac{x-3}{3} = \dfrac{y-5}{0} = \dfrac{z-2}{0}$,
   $\mathbf{r}(t) = (3 + 3t)\mathbf{i} + 5\mathbf{j} + 2\mathbf{k}$.

   (e) $\begin{cases} x = 4 \\ y = -1 + 3t \\ z = 7 - 2t \end{cases}$, $\dfrac{x-4}{0} = \dfrac{y+1}{3} = \dfrac{z-7}{-2}$,
   $\mathbf{r}(t) = 4\mathbf{i} + (-1 + 3t)\mathbf{j} + (7 - 2t)\mathbf{k}$.

3. (a) $\begin{cases} x = -\frac{1}{8} + t \\ y = \frac{19}{8} - 11t \\ z = 8t \end{cases}$. (b) $\begin{cases} x = -2t \\ y = -22 - 19t \\ z = 6 + 5t \end{cases}$.

   (c) $\begin{cases} x = \frac{1}{5} + 14t \\ y = -\frac{1}{5} + 16t \\ z = 5t \end{cases}$. (d) $\begin{cases} x = \frac{9}{2} + t \\ y = 2t \\ z = \frac{1}{2} + t \end{cases}$.

7. (a) $\begin{cases} x = 5 + t \\ y = -4 - t \\ z = 2 - t \end{cases}$. (b) $\begin{cases} x = 1 + 4t \\ y = 1 + t \\ z = 1 - 3t \end{cases}$.

9. (a) $(-3, 1, 2)$. (b) No intersection.

12.6, p. 609

1. $T = \dfrac{1}{\sqrt{5}}(-\sqrt{3}i + j + k)$, $N = -\dfrac{1}{2}(i + \sqrt{3}j)$, $B = \dfrac{1}{2\sqrt{5}}(\sqrt{3}i - j + 4k)$, $\kappa = \dfrac{4}{5}$, $\tau = -\dfrac{2}{5}$.

3. $T = \dfrac{1}{e + e^{-1}}(ei - e^{-1}j + \sqrt{2}k)$, $N = \dfrac{1}{e + e^{-1}}(\sqrt{2}i + \sqrt{2}j - (e - e^{-1})k)$,

$B = \dfrac{1}{e + e^{-1}}(-e^{-1}i + ej + \sqrt{2}k)$; $\kappa = \tau = \dfrac{\sqrt{2}}{(e + e^{-1})^2}$.

5. $T = \dfrac{1}{\sqrt{2}}[\tanh 1 i + j + \operatorname{sech} 1 k]$, $N = \operatorname{sech} 1 i - \tanh 1 k$,

$B = \dfrac{1}{\sqrt{2}}[-\tanh 1 i + j - \operatorname{sech} 1 k]$, $\kappa = -\tau = \dfrac{1}{2 \cosh^2 1}$.

7. $2\pi\sqrt{a^2 + b^2}$.

12.7, p. 613

21. (a) The line segment $P_1 P_2$ is perpendicular to the xy-plane and the midpoint of $P_1 P_2$ is on the xy-plane
(b) $x_2 = x_1$, $y_2 = y_1$, $z_2 = -z_1$ (c) $(x, y, z) \in S \Rightarrow (x, y, -z) \in S$.

12.8, p. 619

11. $x^2 + y^2 = z$.   **17.** $y^2 + z^2 = e^{-2x}$.

13. $x^2 + y^2 = z^2$.   **19.** $1 - z = x^2 + y^2$.

15. $y^2 + z^2 = \tfrac{1}{4}x^2$.   **21.** Yes. The base curve is a line.

12.9, p. 625

1. Ellipsoid.   **15.** Hyperbolic paraboloid.

3. Hyperboloid of two sheets.   **17.** $x^2 - 4y^2 + z^2 = 0$.

5. Paraboloid of revolution.   **19.** $4x^2 + 4y^2 - z^2 = 4$.

7. Hyperbolic paraboloid.   **21.** $4x^2 + y^2 + 4z^2 = 4$.

9. Two planes.   **23.** $x^2 + y^2 + z^2 = 1$.

11. Cone.   **25.** $x^2 - 4y^2 + z^2 = 4$.

13. Paraboloid of revolution.

13.1, p. 632

1. (a) $X = \{(x, y) \mid xy \neq 0\}$.   (b) $X = \{(x, y) \mid y > 0\}$.   (c) $X = \mathbf{R}^2$.   (d) $X = \mathbf{R}^2$.
(e) $X = \{(x, y) \mid x \neq 1 \text{ and } y \neq 2\}$.   (f) $X = \{(x, y) \mid xy > 1\}$.   (g) $X = \{(x, y) \mid x^2 > y^2\}$.
(h) $X = \{(x, y) \mid x^2 + y^2 < 4\}$.

3. (a) $X' = X$, $\mathscr{I}(X) = \{(x, y) \mid 0 < x < 1, 0 < y < 1\}$,
$\mathscr{B}(X) = \{(x, y) \mid 0 \leq x \leq 1, y = 0\} \cup \{(x, y) \mid x = 1, 0 \leq y \leq 1\}$
$\cup \{(x, y) \mid 0 \leq x \leq 1, y = 1\} \cup \{(x, y) \mid x = 0, 0 \leq y \leq 1\}$.
(b) $X' = \mathscr{B}(X) = X$, $\mathscr{I}(X) = \varnothing$.   (c) $X' = \mathscr{B}(X) = X$, $\mathscr{I}(X) = \varnothing$.

(d) $X' = \{(x, y) \mid x \geq 0, 0 \leq y \leq x\}, \mathscr{I}(X) = \{(x, y) \mid x > 0, 0 < y < x\},$
$\mathscr{B}(X) = \{(x, y) \mid x \geq 0, y = 0\} \cup \{(x, y) \mid x \geq 0, y = x\}.$
(e) $X' = \{(x, y) \mid x \geq 0, y \geq x^2\}, \mathscr{I}(X) = X,$
$\mathscr{B}(X) = \{(x, y) \mid x = 0, y \geq 0\} \cup \{(x, y) \mid x \geq 0, y = x^2\}.$
(f) $X' = \{(x, y) \mid xy \leq 0\}, \mathscr{I}(X) = X, \mathscr{B}(X) = \{(x, y) \mid xy = 0\}.$

5. $\lim\limits_{(x,y) \to (0,0)} f(x, y)$ does not exist. $\lim\limits_{x \to 0} f(x, 0) = 1, \lim\limits_{y \to 0} f(0, y) = -1.$

7. f continuous:
(a) on X. (b) on X. (c) on X. (d) $\{(x, y) \mid x = m, y = n, m, n \in \mathbf{Z}\}$. (e) on X.
(f) on X. (g) on X. (h) on X.

9. (a) Circles, center at the origin. (b) Hyperbolas, asymptotes: $y^2 = x^2$.
(c) Parabolas, $y = x^2 - c$.
(d) Lines through the origin, $y = [(1 - c)/(1 + c)] x, c \neq -1$, and $x = 0$.

11. No. $X = \{(x, y) \mid x^2 + y^2 \leq 1\}. \mathscr{B}(X) = \{(x, y) \mid x^2 + y^2 = 1\}. X' = X.$

13.2, p. 640

1. (a) $f_x(x, y) = 2xy - 3y, f_y(x, y) = x^2 - 3x + 12y^2.$
(b) $f_x(x, y) = 2x - 2y - 3, f_y(x, y) = -2x + 8y + 2.$

(c) $f_x(x, y) = \dfrac{-y}{x^2 + y^2} + 2x\, e^{x^2 + y^2}, f_y(x, y) = \dfrac{x}{x^2 + y^2} + 2y\, e^{x^2 + y^2}.$

(d) $f_x(x, y) = \dfrac{y^2 + 6y}{(3x + y^2)^2}, f_y(x, y) = \dfrac{-6x + 2y^2 - 2xy}{(3x + y^2)^2}.$

(e) $f_x(x, y) = 2\cos(2x - y) + \dfrac{2x}{x^2 + 3y}, f_y(x, y) = -\cos(2x - y) + \dfrac{3}{x^2 + 3y}.$

(f) $f_x(x, y) = y\, e^{xy} + \dfrac{1}{\sqrt{y^2 - x^2}}, f_y(x, y) = x\, e^{xy} - \dfrac{x}{y\sqrt{y^2 - x^2}}.$

3. (a) $\dfrac{\partial z}{\partial x} = -\dfrac{x}{z}; \dfrac{\partial z}{\partial y} = \dfrac{-y}{z}.$

(b) $\dfrac{\partial z}{\partial x} = \dfrac{y}{2z}, \dfrac{\partial z}{\partial y} = \dfrac{-x}{2z}.$

(c) $\dfrac{\partial z}{\partial x} = \dfrac{\dfrac{y}{x^2 + y^2} - 2x \sin yz - z e^{xz}}{x^2 y \cos yz - x\, e^{xz}}, \dfrac{\partial z}{\partial y} = \dfrac{[x/(x^2 + y^2)] + x^2 z \cos yz}{x\, e^{xz} - x^2 y \cos yz}.$

(d) $\dfrac{\partial z}{\partial x} = \dfrac{x}{z}, \dfrac{\partial z}{\partial y} = \dfrac{y}{z}.$

(e) $\dfrac{\partial z}{\partial x} = \dfrac{2xy + 2yz - 2xz - y^2 + z^2}{2yz - 2xz - 2xy + x^2 - y^2}, \dfrac{\partial z}{\partial y} = \dfrac{2xz + 2yz - 2xy + x^2 - z^2}{2yz - 2xz - 2xy + x^2 - y^2}.$

5. $\dfrac{\partial z}{\partial y} = \dfrac{xz\, e^{yz}}{\cos(x + z) - xy\, e^{yz}}.$

13.3, p. 646

1. (a) $\Delta f = yh + xk + hk = f_x(x, y)h + f_y(x, y)k + (\frac{1}{2}k)h + (\frac{1}{2}h)k.$
(b) $\Delta f = (4x + 3y)h + (3x - 10y)k + \underbrace{2h^2 - 3hk - 5k^2}_{\varepsilon_1 h + \varepsilon_2 k}.$

(c) $\Delta f = -2zh + 3z^2 k + (6yz - 2x)l + 3yl^2 + 6zkl + 3kl^2 - 2hl.$

5. $\Delta V \leq 22.5\,\pi$ cu. ft ≈ 70.65 cu. ft. Relative error $= 0.045$.   **7.** 0.01.

13.4, p. 651

1. (a) $df(2, 1) = dx - 10\,dy$. (b) $df\left(2, \dfrac{\pi}{4}\right) = -\dfrac{\pi}{2}\,dx - 4\,dy$.

   (c) $df\left(\dfrac{\pi}{2}, 2\right) = e^2\,dx + \left(\dfrac{\pi}{2}e^2 + 1\right)dy$.

5. (a) $\nabla f(x, y) = (2x + 3y)\mathbf{i} + (3x + 4y)\mathbf{j}$.

   (b) $\nabla f(x, y) = (y\,e^x + \log y)\mathbf{i} + \left(e^x + \dfrac{x}{y}\right)\mathbf{j}$.

   (c) $\nabla f(x, y) = (2\cos y)\mathbf{i} + (-2\,x\sin y + \cos y)\mathbf{j}$.

   (d) $\nabla f(x, y, z) = 6x\mathbf{i} + 8y\mathbf{j} - 10z\mathbf{k}$.

   (e) $\nabla f(x, y, z) = (y\sin z + yz\,e^x)\mathbf{i} + (x\sin z + z\,e^x)\mathbf{j} + (xy\cos z + y\,e^x)\mathbf{k}$.

13.5, p. 657

1. (a) $D_{\mathbf{u}}f(P_0) = \dfrac{2e + 1}{\sqrt{3}}$. (c) $D_{\mathbf{u}}f(P_0) = \dfrac{4}{3}e^4 - \dfrac{2}{3}\log 5 + \dfrac{1}{25}$.

   (b) $D_{\mathbf{u}}f(P_0) = -\dfrac{8}{3}$. (d) $D_{\mathbf{u}}f(P_0) = \dfrac{-17}{338}$.

3. (a) $\alpha = \dfrac{\pi}{4}$ (b) $\nabla f\left(1, \dfrac{\pi}{3}\right) = \left(\dfrac{1}{2} - \dfrac{\pi e}{3}\right)\mathbf{i} + \left(-\dfrac{\sqrt{3}}{2} - e\right)\mathbf{j}$; α = angle in quadrant III with

   $\tan \alpha = \dfrac{6e + 3\sqrt{3}}{2\pi e - 3}$ or $\alpha = \pi + \tan^{-1}\dfrac{6e + 3\sqrt{3}}{2\pi e - 3}$.

   (c) $\alpha = \tan^{-1}\left(-\dfrac{11}{5}\right)$. (d) $\alpha = \pi + \tan^{-1}\dfrac{2}{3}$.

5. (a) $\tfrac{5}{7}\sqrt{14}$. (b) $3\sqrt{2}$. (c) $\tfrac{4}{3}\sqrt{6}$.

13.6, p. 665

1. $x - y + \sqrt{2}\,z = 4,\ \dfrac{x - 1}{1} = \dfrac{y + 1}{-1} = \dfrac{z - \sqrt{2}}{\sqrt{2}}$.

2. $2x + 4y + z = 15,\ \dfrac{x - 1}{2} = \dfrac{y - 2}{4} = \dfrac{z - 5}{1}$.

5. $y = 1,\ \{x = 0, y = 1 + t, z = 0\}$.

7. $2ex + ey - z = 2e,\ \dfrac{x - 1}{2e} = \dfrac{y - 2}{e} = \dfrac{z - 2e}{-1}$.

9. $x - y + e\sqrt{2}z = 2 - \dfrac{\pi}{4},\ e\sqrt{2}(x - 1) = -e\sqrt{2}\left(y - \dfrac{\pi}{4}\right) = z - \dfrac{1}{e\sqrt{2}}$.

11. (a) $z = 2,\ x^2 + y^2 = 5$.

    (c) $x + 2y + 2z = 9$ is the common tangent plane. The surfaces S_1 and S_2 are *tangent* at P_0.

13. (a) $P_1\left(2\sqrt{3}, -\sqrt{3}, -\dfrac{2}{3}\sqrt{3}\right),\ P_2\left(-2\sqrt{3}, \sqrt{3}, \dfrac{2}{3}\sqrt{3}\right)$.

    (b) $P_1\left(\dfrac{12}{\sqrt{5}}, \dfrac{3}{\sqrt{5}}, 0\right),\ P_2\left(\dfrac{-12}{\sqrt{5}}, \dfrac{-3}{\sqrt{5}}, 0\right)$.

15. At $(x_0, y_0, 4)$ (where $x_0^2 + y_0^2 = 4$) the common tangent plane is $2x_0 x + 2y_0 y - z = 4$.

13.7, p. 673

1. $\dfrac{dF}{dt} = (2xy + 3z) + (x^2 + z)2t + (y + 3x)3t^2.$

3. $F_r(r, s) = 3 \cos(x + y) - (x + 2y)\, e^{xy}.$

5. $\dfrac{\partial w}{\partial u} = 2\, \dfrac{uz[-x^2 + (y-1)^2 + (z-2)^2 - 2x(y-1)] + vx[x^2 + (y-1)^2 - z^2 + 4]}{[x^2 + (y-1)^2 + (z-2)^2]^2}.$

7. $\dfrac{\partial F}{\partial r} = \left(\log y + \dfrac{y}{x}\right)\cos\theta + \left(\dfrac{x}{y} + \log x\right)\sin\theta,$

$\dfrac{\partial F}{\partial \theta} = \left(\log y + \dfrac{y}{x}\right)(-r\sin\theta) + \left(\dfrac{x}{y} + \log x\right)\sin\theta.$

9. (a) $F_r = f_x \cos\theta + f_y \sin\theta,$ (b) $f_x = F_r \cos\theta - \dfrac{1}{r} F_\theta \sin\theta,$

     $F_\theta = f_x(-r\sin\theta)) + f_y r \cos\theta$ $f_y = F_r \sin\theta + \dfrac{1}{r} F_\theta \cos\theta.$

13. $F_\theta = 2\rho \sin\varphi(-x\sin\theta + 4y\cos\theta),$
$F_\varphi = 2x\rho \cos\theta \cos\varphi + 8y\rho \sin\theta \cos\varphi - 18z\rho \sin\varphi.$

13.8, p. 680

1. (a) Common value: $-\sin y.$ (b) Common value: $0.$ (c) Common value: $-\cos y.$
    (d) Common value: $e^x.$

5. (a) $f_x(0, y) = -y, f_y(x, 0) = x.$ (b) $f_{xy}(0, y) = -1, f_{yx}(x, 0) = 1.$
    (c) $f_{xy}(0, 0) = -1, f_{yx}(0, 0) = 1.$ (d) f_{xy} and f_{yx} are not continuous at $(0, 0).$

7. (a) $\dfrac{\partial z}{\partial x} = -\dfrac{x}{z}.$ (b) $\dfrac{\partial z}{\partial y} = -\dfrac{y}{z}.$ (c) $\dfrac{\partial^2 z}{\partial x^2} = -\dfrac{x^2 + z^2}{z^3}.$ (d) $\dfrac{\partial^2 z}{\partial x\, \partial y} = \dfrac{-xy}{z^3}.$

9. $\left[\text{\textit{Hint.}} \quad \text{Begin by calculating } \dfrac{\partial u}{\partial r}, \dfrac{\partial^2 u}{\partial r^2}, \dfrac{\partial^2 u}{\partial^2 \theta}\right].$

13.9, p. 686

3. length = width = 6 ft; height = 3 ft.

5. $6x + 3y + 2z = 18.$

7. (a) $T_{\max} = 2\tfrac{1}{4}$ at $\left(\tfrac{1}{2}, \pm\dfrac{\sqrt{3}}{2}\right)$; $T_{\min} = -\tfrac{1}{4}$ at $\left(\dfrac{-1}{2}, 0\right)$

   (b) $T_{\max} = 3$ at $(0, 1)$; $T_{\min} = -\tfrac{1}{8}$ at $\left(0, \dfrac{-1}{4}\right)$

   (c) $T_{\max} = 4\tfrac{1}{4}$ at $(\tfrac{1}{2}, 0)$; $T_{\min} = 1\tfrac{3}{4}$ at $\left(\dfrac{-1}{2}, \pm\dfrac{\sqrt{3}}{2}\right)$.

14.1, p. 694

1. (a) $\dfrac{1}{2}$, (b) $\dfrac{\pi}{4}$, (c) 1, (d) 1.

3. (a) yes, (b) no: f is unbounded, (c) no: S and f are unbounded, (d) yes, (e) no: S is
    unbounded, (f) no: f is unbounded, (g) yes, (h) yes, (i) no: f is unbounded, (j) yes,
    (k) yes.

5. [*Hint.* Let $F = g - f$; then $F(x, y) \geq 0.$]

14.2, p. 703

1. (a) $\int_0^8 \left(\int_{\sqrt{2y}}^4 x\, dx \right) dy$; 32.

(b) $\int_0^9 \left(\int_{\frac{1}{3}x}^{\sqrt{x}} x\, dy \right) dx$; $\dfrac{81}{5}$.

(c) $\int_{e^{-4}}^1 \left(\int_{-\log y}^4 y\, dx \right) dy$; $\dfrac{1}{4}(7 + e^{-8})$.

(d) $\int_0^2 \left(\int_{\sqrt{1-\frac{1}{2}y}}^1 xy\, dx \right) dy$; $\dfrac{2}{3}$.

(e) $\int_0^9 \left(\int_0^{2\sqrt{x}} (2xy - y^2)\, dy \right) dx$; $\dfrac{3564}{5}$.

(f) $\int_0^2 \left(\int_{e^y}^{e^2} 2x\, dx \right) dy$; $\dfrac{1}{2}(3e^4 + 1)$.

(g) $\int_0^1 \left(\int_{x^2}^x y\, dy \right) dx$; $\dfrac{1}{15}$.

(h) $\int_0^1 \left(\int_0^y e^x\, dx \right) dy$; $e - 2$.

3. (a) (i) $\int_{-2}^3 \left(\int_{x^2}^{x+6} f\, dy \right) dx$; (ii) $\int_0^4 \left(\int_{-\sqrt{y}}^{\sqrt{y}} f\, dx \right) dy + \int_4^9 \left(\int_{y-6}^{\sqrt{y}} f\, dx \right) dy$.

(b) (i) $\int_{-2}^0 \left(\int_{4x}^{x^3} f\, dy \right) dx + \int_0^2 \left(\int_{x^3}^{4x} f\, dy \right) dx$;

(ii) $\int_{-8}^0 \left(\int_{y^{1/3}}^{y/4} f\, dx \right) dy + \int_0^8 \left(\int_{y/4}^{y^{1/3}} f\, dx \right) dy$.

(c) (i) $\int_0^{\pi/2} \left(\int_{(2/\pi)x}^{\sin x} f\, dy \right) dx$; (ii) $\int_0^1 \left(\int_{\sin^{-1}y}^{(\pi/2)y} f\, dx \right) dy$.

(d) $\int_0^{(\sqrt{7}/2)} \left(\int_{-\sqrt{4-x^2}}^{2-2x^2} f\, dy \right) dx$.

(e) $\int_{-4}^4 \left(\int_{y^4 - 10y^2 + 9}^{105} f\, dx \right) dy$.

5. (a) $\frac{1}{2}(e - 1)$ (b) $1 - \cos 1$ (c) $\frac{1}{2}(1 - \cos 1)$.

14.3, p. 710

1. $\frac{64}{3}$ sq. units.   **9.** 16π cu. units.

3. $\frac{4}{15}$ sq. units.   **11.** 4 cu. units.

5. $\frac{8}{3}$ sq. units.   **13.** 4 cu. units.

7. $4\pi + \frac{8}{3}$ sq. units.   **15.** $\frac{1}{2}(1 - 5e^{-4})$ cu. units.

17. (a) $\dfrac{445}{108}$ cu. units (b) $\dfrac{589\pi}{144}$ cu. units (c) $\dfrac{157\pi}{36}$ cu. units

(d) $\dfrac{ab}{108}(9a^2 + 4b^2 + 432)$ cu. units (e) $\dfrac{656}{27}$ cu. units. (f) $\dfrac{176}{9}$ cu. units.

19. $\dfrac{2a^3}{3}$ cu. units.

14.4, p. 718

1. $\left(0, \dfrac{4}{3\pi}\right)$.

11. $\left(\dfrac{1}{4}, \dfrac{4}{3\pi}\right)$.

21. $\dfrac{\pi\delta}{8}$.

3. $\left(0, \dfrac{\pi}{8}\right)$.

13. $\left(1 - \dfrac{8}{\pi^2}, \dfrac{\pi}{8}\right)$.

23. $\dfrac{(4\pi^2 - 32)\delta}{\pi^3}$.

5. $\left(\dfrac{12}{5}, 0\right)$.

15. $\left(\dfrac{12}{5}, \dfrac{2}{5}\right)$.

25. $\dfrac{2^9\delta}{7}$.

7. $\left(0, \dfrac{2}{5}\right)$.

17. $\left(0, \dfrac{1}{14}\right)$.

27. $\dfrac{2^5\delta}{5}$.

9. $\left(\dfrac{2a}{3(\pi - 2)}, \dfrac{2a}{3(\pi - 2)}\right)$.

19. $\left(\dfrac{3a}{5}, \dfrac{3a}{5}\right)$.

29. $\dfrac{a^4\delta}{48}(3\pi - 4)$.

14.5, p. 727

1. $\dfrac{\pi}{12}\sin 4$.

17. $\left(\dfrac{5a}{6}, 0\right)$.

3. $\dfrac{3\pi}{4}$.

19. $\left(\dfrac{128}{105\pi}, \dfrac{128}{105\pi}\right)$.

5. $\dfrac{\pi}{2} + 1$.

21. $\dfrac{5\pi}{2}$.

7. $\dfrac{2}{3}a^3$.

23. $\pi\left(\dfrac{16}{3} - 2\sqrt{3}\right)$.

9. $\dfrac{32\pi}{3} + 8\sqrt{3}$.

27. (b) $\dfrac{\pi\delta}{2}(d^4 - c^4)$.

14.6, p. 736

1. 216 cu. units.

7. $\dfrac{2}{3}a^3$ cu. units.

3. 9π cu. units.

5. $\dfrac{10}{3}$ cu. units.

11. $\displaystyle\int_1^3 \left(\int_0^{\log y}\left(\int_0^{y-1} dx\right) dz\right) dy$.

13. 2π cu. units.

14.7, p. 745

1. $8\displaystyle\int_0^{\pi/2}\left(\int_0^1\left(\int_0^{\sqrt{4-r^2}} fr\, dz\right) dr\right) d\theta$;

$8\displaystyle\int_0^{\pi/2}\left(\int_0^{\pi/6}\left(\int_0^2 f\rho^2 \sin\varphi\, d\rho\right) d\varphi\right) d\theta + 8\int_0^{\pi/2}\left(\int_{\pi/6}^{\pi/2}\left(\int_0^{\csc\varphi} f\rho^2 \sin\varphi\, d\rho\right) d\varphi\right) d\theta$;

$$V = 4\pi\left(\dfrac{8}{3} - \sqrt{3}\right).$$

3. $4\displaystyle\int_0^{\pi/2}\left(\int_0^{\sqrt{3}}\left(\int_{r/\sqrt{3}}^{\sqrt{4-r^2}} fr\, dz\right) dr\right) d\theta$;

$4\displaystyle\int_0^{\pi/2}\left(\int_0^{\pi/3}\left(\int_0^2 f\rho^2 \sin\varphi\, d\rho\right) d\varphi\right) d\theta$; $V = \dfrac{8\pi}{3}$.

5. $\int_0^{\pi/4} \left(\int_0^{\sec\theta} \left(\int_0^1 fr \, dz \right) dr \right) d\theta$;

$\int_0^{\pi/4} \left(\int_0^{\tan^{-1}(\sec\theta)} \left(\int_0^{\sec\varphi} f\rho^2 \sin\varphi \, d\rho \right) d\varphi \right) d\theta$

$$+ \int_0^{\pi/4} \left(\int_{\tan^{-1}(\sec\theta)}^{\pi/2} \left(\int_0^{\sec\theta \csc\varphi} f\rho^2 \sin\varphi \, d\rho \right) d\varphi \right) d\theta; \quad V = \frac{1}{2};$$

$\int_0^1 \left(\int_0^x \left(\int_0^1 f \, dz \right) dy \right) dx$.

7. $4\int_0^{\pi/2} \left(\int_0^1 \left(\int_{r^2}^r fr \, dz \right) dr \right) d\theta$;

$4\int_0^{\pi/2} \left(\int_{\pi/4}^{\pi/2} \left(\int_0^{\csc\varphi \cot\varphi} f\rho^2 \sin\varphi \, d\rho \right) d\varphi \right) d\theta; \quad V = \frac{\pi}{6}$.

9. $\frac{32\pi}{3}$ cu. units.

14.8, p. 750

1. (a) $\left(0, 0, \frac{4(23 + 4\sqrt{3})}{185} \right) \approx (0, 0, 0.65)$, (b) $\frac{4\pi}{15} (64 - 33\sqrt{3})\delta$.

3. (a) $\left(0, 0, \frac{5}{4} \right)$, (b) $\frac{40\pi}{9}$.

5. (a) $(\frac{2}{3}, \frac{1}{3}, \frac{2}{3})$, (b) $\frac{1}{6}$.

7. (a) $(0, 0, \frac{1}{2})$, (b) $\pi\delta/15$, (c) $\frac{1}{6}\sqrt{10}$.

14.9, p. 759

1. (a) 0, (b) 0, (c) $\frac{1}{15}$, (d) $-\frac{1}{3}$, (e) $\frac{1}{12}$, (f) $-35/48$.

3. (a) $\frac{7}{10}$, (b) $\frac{7}{10}$, (c) $\frac{7}{10}$.

5. (a) 1, (b) $\frac{4}{5}$, (c) $\pi/2$, (d) $\frac{4}{3}$, (e) 0.

7. (a) $xy^3 - ab^3$, (b) $x^2e^y - a^2e^b$, (c) $x^2y^2 - a^2b^2$, (d) $y\cos x - b\cos a$.

15.1, p. 767

1. $\log(1 + x) = x - \frac{x^2}{2} + \frac{x^3}{3} - \frac{x^4}{4} + \cdots + (-1)^{n-1}\frac{x^n}{n} + (-1)^n \frac{x^{n+1}}{(n+1)(1+x_0)}$.

3. $\tan x = x + \frac{x^3}{3} + \frac{1}{3}\sec^2 x_0 \tan x_0(3\sec^2 x_0' - 1)x^4$.

5. $\sin x = 1 - \frac{1}{2!}\left(x - \frac{\pi}{2} \right)^2 + \frac{1}{4!}\left(x - \frac{\pi}{2} \right)^4 - \frac{1}{6!}\left(x - \frac{\pi}{2} \right)^6 + \cdots + (-1)^n \frac{1}{(2n)!}\left(x - \frac{\pi}{2} \right)^{2n}$

$$+ (-1)^{2n+1}\frac{\cos x_0}{(2n+1)!} x^{2n+1}.$$

7. $\sinh x = x + \frac{x^3}{3!} + \frac{x^5}{5!} + \cdots + \frac{x^{2n+1}}{(2n+1)!} + \frac{\cosh x_0}{(2n+2)!} x^{2n+2}$.

9. $\arctan x = x - \dfrac{x^3}{3} + \dfrac{x_0^2(1 - x_0^2)}{(1 + x_0^2)^4} x^4.$

11. $\log \cos x = -\tfrac{1}{2}x^2 - \tfrac{1}{12} \sec^2 x_0 (3 \sec^2 x_0 - 1)x^4.$

13. $(1 + x)^q = 1 + qx + \dfrac{q(q-1)}{2!} x^2 + \dfrac{q(q-1)(q-2)}{3!} x^3 + \cdots + \dfrac{q(q-1)\cdots(q-n+1)}{n!} x^n$

$\qquad + \dfrac{q(q-1)\cdots(q-n)}{(n+1)!} (1 + x_0)^{q-(n+1)} x^{n+1}.$

15.2, p. 775

1. $0, \dfrac{3}{2}, \dfrac{2}{3}, \dfrac{5}{4}, \dfrac{4}{5}, \ldots$; converges to 1.

3. $\dfrac{6}{3}, \dfrac{7}{5}, \dfrac{8}{7}, \dfrac{9}{9}, \dfrac{10}{11}, \ldots$; converges to $\dfrac{1}{2}$.

5. $\dfrac{96}{-1009}, \dfrac{100}{-1014}, \dfrac{112}{-1015}, \dfrac{132}{-1012}, \dfrac{160}{-1005}, \ldots$; converges to 2.

7. $-\dfrac{1}{8}, \dfrac{6}{9}, \dfrac{47}{14}, \dfrac{146}{23}, \dfrac{327}{36}, \ldots$; diverges.

9. $\dfrac{39}{101}, \dfrac{51}{102}, \dfrac{67}{103}, \dfrac{87}{104}, \dfrac{111}{105}, \ldots$; diverges.

11. $2, 0, \dfrac{4}{3}, \dfrac{1}{2}, \dfrac{6}{3}, \ldots$; converges to 1.

13. (a) $0, -1, 1$ are cluster points; sequence diverges.
(b) $0, 1$ are cluster points; sequence diverges.
(c) 1 is the only cluster point; sequence converges to 1.
(d) ∞ is the only cluster point; sequence diverges.

17. (d) $\dfrac{37}{60} < L < \dfrac{57}{60}.$

15.3, p. 782

1. 2.

3. $5(1 + \sqrt{2}).$

5. $\dfrac{14}{3}.$

7. $\dfrac{30}{11}.$

9. $a_n = (n-1)(n-1)!$ Diverges.

11. $a_n = \dfrac{2}{(3n+1)(3n-2)}.$ Converges to $\dfrac{2}{3}.$

13. $a_n = \dfrac{3(2n-1)}{(2n^2+3)(2n^2-4n+5)}.$ Converges to $\dfrac{1}{2}.$

15. $a_n = \dfrac{n^2 + n - 1}{n(n+1)}$. Diverges.

17. Series converges to 0 for $x = 0, \pm 1, \pm 2, \ldots$.

19. $\lim\limits_{n \to \infty} a_n = 1 \neq 0$.

21. $\lim\limits_{n \to \infty} a_n = 1 \neq 0$.

15.4, p. 789

1. Diverges.   **9.** Converges.   **15.** Diverges.

3. Converges.   **11.** Converges.   **17.** Converges.

5. Converges.   **13.** Converges.   **19.** Diverges.

7. Diverges.

15.5, p. 794

1. Converges.   **11.** Converges.   **21.** Diverges.

3. Diverges.   **13.** Converges.   **23.** Diverges.

5. Converges.   **15.** Diverges.   **25.** (a) Converges.

7. Converges.   **17.** Converges.   (b) Diverges.

9. Converges.   **19.** Diverges.

15.6, p. 798

1. Converges.   **7.** Diverges.   **13.** Converges.

3. Converges.   **9.** Diverges.   **15.** Converges.

5. Converges.   **11.** Converges.

15.7, p. 803

1. Converges absolutely.   **13.** Converges conditionally.

3. Converges conditionally.   **15.** Converges absolutely.

5. Converges absolutely.   **17.** Converges absolutely.

7. Converges absolutely.   **19.** All $x \in \mathbf{R}$.

9. Converges absolutely.   **21.** $|x| < 1$.

11. Converges conditionally.   **23.** $|x| < \frac{1}{2}$.

15.8, p. 810

1. $|x| < 1$.   **11.** $|x| < \sqrt{3}$.   **19.** $x = 0$.

3. $-1 \leq x < 1$.   **13.** $-1 \leq x < 1$.   **21.** $\mathbf{R}$.

5. $-1 \leq x \leq 1$.   **15.** $-\frac{3}{2} < x < \frac{5}{2}$.   **23.** $-1 < x \leq 1$.

7. $\mathbf{R}$.   **17.** $-1 < x \leq 1$.   **27.** 1.

9. $|x| \leq \frac{1}{3}$.

15.9, p. 815

1. (a) $f'(x) = 1 - \dfrac{x^2}{2!} + \dfrac{x^4}{4!} - \dfrac{x^6}{6!} + \cdots$.   7. $\dfrac{1}{(1-x)^2} = 1 + 2x + 3x^2 + \cdots, |x| < 1$.

   (b) $\displaystyle\int_0^x f(t)\, dt = \dfrac{x^2}{2!} - \dfrac{x^4}{4!} + \dfrac{x^6}{6!} - \cdots$.

   (c) $\displaystyle\int_0^x f(t)\, dt = 1 - f'(x)$.

15.10, p. 825

3. $e^x = e\left[1 + \dfrac{x-1}{1!} + \dfrac{(x-1)^2}{2!} + \dfrac{(x-1)^3}{3!} + \cdots\right]; \mathbf{R}$.

5. $\dfrac{1}{\sqrt{1+x}} = 1 - \dfrac{x}{2} + \dfrac{1\cdot 3}{2!}\left(\dfrac{x}{2}\right)^2 - \dfrac{1\cdot 3\cdot 5}{3!}\left(\dfrac{x}{2}\right)^3 + \cdots; -1 < x \leq 1$.

7. $\sin x = \dfrac{1}{2}\left[1 + \sqrt{3}\,\dfrac{(x-\pi/6)}{1!} - \dfrac{(x-\pi/6)^2}{2!} - \sqrt{3}\,\dfrac{(x-\pi/6)^3}{3!} + \dfrac{(x-\pi/6)^4}{4!} + \cdots\right]; \mathbf{R}$.

9. $\dfrac{1}{1+2x} = 1 - 2x + (2x)^2 - (2x)^3 + \cdots; |x| < \frac{1}{2}$.

11. $\log(1-x) = -\left[x + \dfrac{x^2}{2} + \dfrac{x^3}{3} + \cdots\right]; -1 \leq x < 1$.

13. (a) $\tan x = x + \dfrac{x^3}{3} + \dfrac{2x^5}{15} + \cdots$.

15. 0.9045.

17. $\sin^{-1} x = x + \dfrac{x^3}{2\cdot 3} + \dfrac{1\cdot 3}{2\cdot 4\cdot 5} x^5 + \dfrac{1\cdot 3\cdot 5}{2\cdot 4\cdot 6\cdot 7} x^7 + \cdots; |x| < 1$.

16.1, p. 830

5. (a) $y = x^2 + e^{-x} - \cos x + c_1 x + c_2$.   (b) $y = x^2 + e^{-x} - \cos x + 3x + 6$.
   (c) $y = x^2 + e^{-x} - \cos x + (2/\pi - 3\pi)x + 2\pi^2 - 3$.

16.2, p. 833

1. $y = \dfrac{c}{x^2+1}$.

3. $y = cx^2$.

5. $y = \sqrt{1-c^2}\,x + c\sqrt{1-x^2}$.

7. $y = \dfrac{x+c}{1-cx}$.

9. $\sin y = c \exp[(1/2)x^2]$.   15. $x^2 = 2t - t^2 + 24$.

11. $y = \sin(x+c)$.   17. $x^3 y + 3y + 3 = 0$.

13. $x = (1-ct)^{-1}$.   19. $y = e^{\sin x}$.

16.3, p. 838

1. $cx^2 = y + \sqrt{x^2 + y^2}$.   13. $y^4 + 4x^3 y = c$.

3. $y^3 = x^3 + cx^4$.

5. $y^2 = 3x^2 + cx$.

7. $e^x = c \sin y$.

9. $e^{y/x} \log cx + 1 = 0$.

11. $(x^2 - y^2) = cx$.

15. $\log c \sqrt{2x^2 + xy + y^2} + \sqrt{7} \tan^{-1} \dfrac{x + 2y}{\sqrt{7}x} = 0$.

17. $x^2 + xy + y^2 = 1$.

19. $y = \dfrac{2 \sin 2x}{1 + \cos 2x}$.

21. $4x^2 - y^2 - 3x = 0$.

16.4, p. 842

1. $xy = \sin x + c$.

3. $y = \frac{1}{2}(\sin x - \cos x) + ce^x$.

5. $y = \csc x(c - e^{\cos x})$.

7. $y = 2 + c \exp[(e^x)]$.

9. $y = -x + c\,e^{-4x}$.

11. $y = 2(x^2 - x)$.

13. $x = t^2 + t$.

15. $y = \frac{1}{3}(2 \sin x + \csc^2 x)$.

16.5, p. 848

1. $\varphi(x) = c_1 e^x + c_2 e^{3x}$.

3. $\varphi(x) = c_1 \cos \omega x + c_2 \sin \omega x$.

5. $\varphi(x) = c_1 e^{-3x} + c_2 x e^{-3x} = (c_1 + c_2 x)e^{-3x}$.

7. $\varphi(x) = (c_1 + c_2 x)e^x$.

9. $\varphi(x) = e^x(c_1 \cos 2x + c_2 \sin 2x)$.

11. $x(t) = c_1 e^{4t} + c_2 e^{-2t}$.

13. $x(t) = c_1 e^{2t} + c_2 e^{5t}$.

15. $x(t) = 3 e^{2t} - 2 e^{3t}$.

17. $\varphi(x) = (2 + 4x)\,e^{-2x}$.

19. $y = \dfrac{2}{e}\,x\,e^x$.

21. $\varphi(x) = e^x(3 \cos 3x - \sin 3x)$.

16.6, p. 853

1. $\varphi(x) = c_1 e^{-x} + c_2 e^{-2x} + x^2 - \frac{5}{2}x + \frac{13}{4}$.

3. $\varphi(x) = c_1 e^{-x} + c_2 e^{-2x} + x e^{-x}$.

5. $\varphi(x) = e^x(c_1 \cos x + c_2 \sin x) + \frac{1}{2}(x^3 + 3x^2 - 1)$.

7. $\varphi(x) = c_1 + c_2 e^{2x} + \frac{1}{4}(2x e^{2x} - x^2 - x)$.

9. $\varphi(x) = c_1 e^{2x} + c_2 e^{3x} + e^x - \frac{1}{5}(\cos x + 2 \sin x)$.

11. $\varphi(x) = c_1 e^x + c_2 e^{-x} + \frac{1}{5} e^x(-\cos x + 2 \sin x)$.

13. $\varphi(x) = c_1 e^{(1/2)x} + c_2 e^x + \frac{1}{30}(-9 \cos x - 27 \sin x - 2 e^{-2x} + 120)$.

15. $\varphi(x) = c_1 \cos 2x + c_2 \sin 2x + \frac{1}{8}(1 + x \sin 2x)$.

17. $x(t) = c_1 e^t + c_2 e^{3t} + \frac{2}{3}t + \frac{8}{9} + e^{2t} + \frac{1}{10} \cos t - \frac{1}{5} \sin t$.

19. $\varphi(t) = c_1 e^{-x} + c_2 e^{4x} - \frac{1}{5}x e^{-x} + \frac{1}{34}(5 \cos x + 3 \sin x)$.

21. $\varphi(x) = 4(1 - \cos x)$.

23. $\varphi(x) = -4e^x + \frac{14}{9} e^{3x} + \frac{1}{3}x + \frac{4}{9}$.

16.7, p. 857

1. (a) $x^2 + y^2 = 2cy$ (b) $y = c \exp[(1/2)(x^2 + y^2)]$ (c) $x^2 + 2y^2 = c$ (d) $x = y + 2 + c\,e^y$.

3. $y = \dfrac{k^2}{g} \log \cosh \dfrac{gt}{k}$. $\lim\limits_{t \to \infty} v = k$.   **5.** (b) $\dfrac{\log 6}{\log 2} \approx 2$ min, 35 sec.

Index

Symbols

$\Rightarrow$ implies (sometimes verbalized as "it is true that")

$\Leftrightarrow$ implies and is implied by, or if and only if, or necessary and sufficient condition for, or is logically equivalent to

$\Leftrightarrow$ means by definition

$\exists$ there exists (existential quantifier)

$\forall$ for all (universal quantifier)

$\in$ is an element of

$\notin$ is not an element of

$\subset$ is a subset of

$\cup$ union (for sets)

$\cap$ intersection (for sets)

N set of natural numbers $= \{1, 2, 3, \ldots\}$

Z set of all integers $= \{\ldots, -3, -2, -1, 0, 1, 2, 3, \ldots\}$

Q field of rational numbers

R field of real numbers

R$^+$ set of positive real numbers

Q$^-$ set of negative rational numbers

$n!$ n factorial $(n! = 1.2. \ldots n = n(n-1)!$, $0! = 1)$

$\binom{n}{r}$ binomial coefficient $=$ numbers of ways of selecting r objects from n objects
$$\binom{n}{r} = \frac{n!}{r!(n-r)!}$$

$[a, b]$ closed interval from a to $b = \{x \mid a \leq x \leq b\}$

(a, b) open interval from a to $b = \{x \mid a < x < b\}$

lub S least upper bound of set S (of numbers)

glb S greatest lower bound of set S (of numbers)

$f : X \to Y$ function f maps domain X into set Y

$f : X \twoheadrightarrow Y$ function f maps domain X onto set Y

$f[X]$ set of image points of function f with domain $X = \{y \mid y = f(x), x \in X\}$

j identity function; $j(x) = x$

$f \circ g$ composite function; $(f \circ g)(x) = f(g(x))$

f^{-1} function inverse to f $(f^{-1} \circ f = j)$

$|x|$ absolute value of x

$[x]$ greatest integer in x

$f' = Df$ derivative of f

$f'' = D^2f$ second derivative of f

$df(x_0, h)$ differential of f at x_0